Elementary and Intermediate Algebra

Mark D. Turner
Charles P. McKeague

2ND PRINTING — December 2017
    Miscellaneous corrections made
    Appendix: Synthetic Division added

Elementary and Intermediate Algebra

Mark D. Turner
Charles P. McKeague

Publisher: XYZ Textbooks

Project Manager: Katherine Heistand Shields

Composition: Katherine Heistand Shields,
    Matthew Hoy

Sales: Amy Jacobs, Richard Jones, Bruce Spears

Cover Design: Kyle Schoenberger,
    Katherine Heistand Shields

ISBN-13: 978-1-63098-065-8 / ISBN-10: 1-63098-065-X

For product information and technology assistance, contact us at
XYZ Textbooks, 1-877-745-3499

For permission to use material from this text or product,
e-mail: **info@mathtv.com**

XYZ Textbooks
1339 Marsh Street
San Luis Obispo, CA 93401
USA

Printed in the United States of America

For your course and learning solutions, visit www.xyztextbooks.com

Brief Contents

Contents

6 Factoring 383

7 Rational Expressions 445

8 Transitions 521

Preface: A Note to Instructors

Elementary and Intermediate Algebra
by Mark D. Turner and Charles P. McKeague

Description

Elementary and Intermediate Algebra fits the traditional, one-semester, combined elementary and intermediate algebra course. The prerequisite is Basic Mathematics or Prealgebra.

The normal sequence of topics is enriched with modeling applications, study skills, and other built-in features such as the "Spotlight on Success" (as detailed below). Encourage your students to make regular use of these features—you'll find that they will gradually build a foundation of successful studying practices that will benefit them in all their future courses.

This textbook is more than just the book itself. We built this book to be the hub of a math "toolbox" of sorts. While most students still prefer to use the printed book in their studies, the eBook extends the reach of the book, giving students and instructors access to a wide array of supporting tools:

- The eBook includes free access to the Elementary Algebra eBook, plus over 20 eBooks covering 8 math courses—great for remediation.
- It also includes free access to 10,000 MathTV videos, with 3-4 tutorials for every single example.
- Plus all of the accompanying worksheets and digital supplements for the book.
- Additionally, QR code technology connects the printed textbook directly to the digital resources through the students' smartphones and tablets.
- The associated Matched Problems Worksheets gives you the opportunity to flip your classroom, without the need to create new materials yourself.

Textbook Features

Every section has been written so that it can be discussed in a single class session. The clean layout and conversational style used by the authors make it easy for students to read, and important information, such as definitions and properties, are highlighted so that they can easily be located and referenced by students.

In addition, the following features provide both instructors and students a vast array of resources which can be used to enrich the learning environment and promote student success.

Chapter Introductions   We begin each chapter with a brief application that involves some of the concepts to be presented later in the chapter. These "glimpses" of what is to come help motivate students by showing them an interesting, real-world scenario that requires the knowledge and skills they will be attaining. Acting as a mini-theme for the chapter, students will encounter examples and problems in the following sections that directly relate to this application.

Learning Objectives   Every section now begins with a short set of learning objectives, listing the specific, measurable knowledge and skills students will be acquiring in that section. Objectives help students identify and focus on the important concepts in each section and increase the likelihood of their success by having established and clear goals. For instructors, the objectives can help in organizing class lessons and learning activities, and in creating student assessments.

Getting Ready for Class   It's always a challenge to get students to read, especially in math. To encourage them, we place four key questions at the end of every section, under the heading "Getting Ready for Class." If students have read the section, they should be able to answer each of these with ease. Even a minimal attempt to answer these questions can enhance the students' in-class experience.

We've heard some innovative strategies from early adopters of the textbook. Instructors in one department use these questions as a student's "ticket" to class. They collect the answers as students come in the door. A simple action that can start the class off right!

Getting Ready for the Next Section   When students finish a section, they can feel a great sense of accomplishment. We want to help maintain their momentum as much as possible, which is why we offer a brief preview of the next stop in their mathematical journey. A small set of "Getting Ready for the Next Section" problems appear near the end of every problem set. These are the exact same problems that students will see when they read through the next section of the text. Students who consistently work these problems will be much better prepared for class.

Learning Objectives Assessments   Every problem set concludes with a short section of multiple-choice questions that can be used by students or instructors to measure the extent to which students have met the learning objectives for that section. These questions can easily be adapted for use with clicker technology, or used as a quick exit quiz at the close of each class session, to verify that students understand the main points from the lesson.

Paying Attention to Instructions   Students tend to get stuck making the same mistakes over and over again, developing bad habits. The more time you spend teaching, the more you can start to anticipate these problems. For example, we know that students don't always pay attention to instructions when they are doing their homework, and it can get them into trouble on tests and quizzes.

The only way to fix this is to address it head-on. Our strategy was to build problems into the text itself, under the heading "Paying Attention to Instructions," that challenge students to carefully read the instructions for each problem. Small nuances make a big difference in mathematics, and we hope that this feature will help you demonstrate to your students just how important this is.

"How To" Segments   Many sections include a "How To" segment that outlines the steps in the method or process used to solve certain types of problems. These summaries help students internalize the particular problem solving strategy introduced in that section.

Spotlight on Success   Each student has a unique approach to learning. A one-size-fits-all strategy doesn't work, which is why our MathTV videos have always used multiple tutors for each example. We want to give every student the chance to succeed!

The "Spotlight on Success" feature is designed in the same spirit. Scattered throughout the text, this feature offers students a variety of strategies from many different sources. Some are from peers, others are from instructors. Many of the spotlights feature the same peer tutors that students will see on the MathTV videos that accompany the text.

Real-Data Application Problems   Students do better in math when they see its application to real-world problems. That's why we've included as many applied problems as we can. Many times the charts and graphics in the text look like the types of charts and graphics students see in the media.

Not only does this help them make the connection, but it can give these a greater mathematical "sense," and even make the concepts a little easier to understand.

Facts from Geometry   Anything we can do to help solidify abstract concepts is a good thing. Geometry can give students another view of the problem, and potentially, another avenue for understanding algebraic concepts. Students who are visual learners will love this feature.

Chapter Summaries and Tests   Every chapter concludes with a Chapter Summary and Chapter Test. The chapter summary lists the main properties and definitions found in the chapter, with examples given in the margin. The chapter test provides a representative sample of the various types of problems students have encountered in the chapter. These features are valuable assets to students in preparing for exams or refreshing their skills with previously learned concepts.

Connecting Print and Digital   We want students to get the most out of their course materials, which is why we think of the textbook as "toolbox" for students. QR codes are integrated throughout the textbook, to connect the printed version to the digital assets. As they read their printed book, support material is quickly and conveniently available via one scan of the accompanying QR code. No hunting and searching and scrolling—a direct link to additional support.

Supplements for the Instructor

Please contact your sales representative—or see xyztextbooks.com/instructors for more info.

MathTV.com   Every example in every XYZ Textbook is worked on video by multiple student instructors. Students benefit from seeing multiple approaches, and gain confidence in learning from their peers. The MathTV library contains over 10,000 videos, from basic math through calculus. It's great for learning the material at hand, and for remediation too.

Complete Solutions Manual   Available online, this manual contains complete solutions to all the exercises in the problem sets.

Printable Test Items   Choose from a bank of pre-created tests for most of our textbooks.

Supplements for the Student

MathTV.com   Students have access to math instruction 24 hours a day, seven days a week. Assistance with any problem or subject is never more than a few clicks away.

XYZ eBook   This textbook is available online for both instructors and students. Tightly integrated with MathTV.com, students can read the book and watch videos of the author and peer instructors explaining each example. Access to the online book is available free with the purchase of a new book.

QR Codes   QR Codes connect print to digital! Scan the QR codes located inside printed textbooks* with your mobile device, and it will take you directly to the accompanying MathTV video.

*QR codes are not available in every textbook.

Student Solutions Manual   Contains complete solutions to all the odd-numbered exercises in the text. Available for purchase separately.

A Note from Charles P. McKeague

I am extremely pleased to have Mark Turner as my co-author on this book. We have worked together for years—Mark is the co-author of the last four editions of my trigonometry book. He is an award-winning teacher and, as you will see, an excellent writer. He is an innovative instructor, bringing many new ideas into the classroom—and he gives regular presentations to share his knowledge and strategies with other instructors.

There are many things I like about working with Mark. First, and maybe most important, is that the integration of Mark's writing style with mine is seamless. When I read over our material, I often cannot tell which one of us wrote it. Mark also has an attention to detail and an eye for consistency that very few authors have. I know this is a better book because of Mark's contributions to it.

Preface: A Note to Students

We want you to succeed.

Welcome to the XYZ Textbooks/MathTV community. We want you to succeed in this course. As you will see as you progress through this book, and access the other tools we have for you, we are different that other publishers. Here's how:

Our Authors are Real Teachers The best textbooks are written by the best teachers, period. We select our authors based on one factor only: Can they teach? All of our authors have won awards for teaching. The result is the best instruction you can get in written form, produced by award-winning, experienced instructors.

Innovative Products The foundation of our products is the textbook, which is the hub for all the resources you will need to do well in your math course. These include eBooks, videos, worksheets, and a variety of ways to access these resources, from QR codes built into our books, to our MathTV Mobile site.

Peer Tutors Math can be difficult. Sometimes your class time and textbook are not enough. We understand that, which is why we created MathTV, providing you with a set of instructional videos by students just like you, who have found a way to master the material you are studying. You'll get to see how your peers solve each problem, sometimes offering a different view from how an instructor solves the problem, and other times, solving the problem in the same way your instructor does, giving you confidence that that is the way the problem should be solved. It also means that you can get help anytime (not just during office hours).

Fair Prices We're small, independently owned and independently run. Why does that matter to you? Because we do not have the overhead and expenses that the larger publishers have. Yes, we want to be a profitable business, but we believe that we can keep our prices reasonable and still give you everything you need to be successful. Also, we want you to use this book, and the best way to make sure that happens is to make it affordable.

Unlimited Access When you purchase one of our products, we give you access to all of our products. Why? Because everything you need to know about math is not contained in one book. Suppose you need to review a topic from a math course you completed previously? No problem. Suppose you want to see an alternate approach? It's all yours. As a member of our XYZ Textbooks/MathTV community, you have access to everything we produce, including all our eBooks.

We know you can do it.

We Believe in You We have seen students with all varieties of backgrounds and levels in mathematics do well in the courses we supply books and materials for. In fact, we have never run across a student that could not be successful in algebra. And that carries over to you: We believe in you; we believe you can be successful in whatever math class you are taking. Our job is to supply you with the tools you can use to attain success, you supply the drive and ambition.

We Know College can be Difficult It is not always the material you are studying that makes college difficult. We know that many of you are working, some part time, some full time. We know many of you have families to support, or look after. We understand that your time can be limited. We take all this to heart when we create the materials we think you will need. For example, we make our videos available on your smart phone, tablet, and on the Internet. That way, no matter where you are, you will have access to help when you get stuck on a problem.

We Believe in what We Do We know you will see the value in the things we have created. That's why the first chapter in every one of our eBooks is free, and so are all the resources that come with it. We want you to try us out for free. See what you think. We wouldn't do that if we didn't believe in what we do here.

Here are some strategies to help.

I often find my students getting frustrated and asking themselves the question, "Why can't I understand this stuff the first time through?" The answer is, "You're not expected to."

Learning a topic in mathematics isn't always accomplished the first time through the material. If you don't understand a topic the first time you see it, that's perfectly normal.

Stick with it. Understanding mathematics takes time. You may find that you need to read over new material a number of times before you can begin to work problems. The process of understanding requires reading the book, studying the examples, working problems, and getting your questions answered.

How to Be Successful in Mathematics

1. **If you are in a lecture class, be sure to attend all class sessions on time.** You simply will not know exactly what went on in class unless you were there. Missing class and then expecting to find out what went on from someone else is not a good strategy. Make the time to be there—and to be attentive.

2. **Read the book.** It is best to read the section that will be covered in class beforehand. It's OK if you don't fully understand everything you read! Reading in advance at least gives you a sense of what will be discussed, which puts you in a good position when you get to class.

3. **Work problems every day and check your answers.** The secret to success in mathematics is working problems. The more problems you work, the better you will perform. It's really that simple. The answers to the odd-numbered problems are given in the back of the book. When you have finished an assignment, be sure to compare your answers with those in the book. If you have made a mistake, find out what it is, and try to correct it.

4. **Do it on your own.** Having someone else show you how to work a problem is not the same as working the problem yourself. It is absolutely OK to get help when you are stuck. As a matter of fact, it is a good idea. Just be sure you do the work yourself. After all, when it's test time, it's all you! Get confident in every problem type, and you will do well.

5. **Review every day.** After you have finished the problems your instructor has assigned, take another 15 minutes and review a section you have already completed. This simple trick works wonders. The more you review, the longer you will retain the material you have learned. Since math topics build upon one another, this will help you throughout the term.

6. **Don't expect to understand every new topic the first time you see it.** Sometimes it will come easy and sometimes it won't. Don't beat yourself up over it—that's just the way things are in mathematics. It's perfectly normal. Expecting to understand each new topic the first time you see it can lead to disappointment and frustration. The process of understanding takes time and practice. It requires that you read the book, work problems, and get your questions answered.

7. **Spend as much time as it takes for you to master the material.** What's the exact amount of time you need to spend on mathematics to master it? There's no way to know except to do it. You will find out as you go what is or isn't enough time for you. Some sections may take less time, and some may take more. If you end up spending 2 or more hours on each section, OK. Then that's how much time it takes; trying to get by with less will not work.

8. **Relax.** It's probably not as difficult as you think. You might get stuck at points. That's OK, everyone does. Take a break if you need to. Seek some outside help. Watch a MathTV video of the problem. There is a solution, and you *will* find it—even if it takes a while.

The Basics

iStockphoto.com © Rawpixel Ltd

Much of what we do in mathematics is concerned with recognizing patterns. If you recognize the patterns in the following two sequences, then you can easily extend each sequence.

Sequence of odd numbers = 1, 3, 5, 7, 9,…

Sequence of squares = 1, 4, 9, 16, 25,…

Once we have classified groups of numbers as to the characteristics they share, we sometimes discover that a relationship exists between the groups. Although it may not be obvious at first, there is a relationship that exists between the two sequences shown. The introduction to *The Book of Squares*, written in 1225 by the mathematician known as Fibonacci, begins this way:

"I thought about the origin of all square numbers and discovered that they arise out of the increasing sequence of odd numbers."

The relationship that Fibonacci refers to is shown visually here.

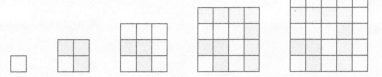

Many times we describe a relationship or pattern in a number of different ways. Here we have a visual description of a relationship. In this chapter we will work on describing relationships numerically and verbally (in writing).

Some of the students enrolled in our college algebra classes develop difficulties early in the course. Their difficulties are not associated with their ability to learn mathematics; they all have the potential to pass the course. Students who get off to a poor start do so because they have not developed the study skills necessary to be successful in algebra. Here is a list of things you can do to begin to develop effective study skills.

1. **Put Yourself on a Schedule** The general rule is that you spend 2 hours on homework for every hour you are in class. Make a schedule for yourself in which you set aside 2 hours each day to work on algebra. Once you make the schedule, stick to it. Don't just complete your assignments and stop. Use all the time you have set aside. If you complete an assignment and have time left over, read the next section in the book, and then work more problems.

2. **Find Your Mistakes and Correct Them** There is more to studying algebra than just working problems. You must always check your answers with the answers in the back of the book. When you have made a mistake, find out what it is and correct it. Making mistakes is part of the process of learning mathematics. In the prologue to *The Book of Squares*, Leonardo Fibonacci (ca. 1170–ca. 1250) had this to say about the content of his book:

   > I have come to request indulgence if in any place it contains something more or less than right or necessary; for to remember everything and be mistaken in nothing is divine rather than human . . .

   Fibonacci knew, as you know, that human beings make mistakes. You cannot learn algebra without making mistakes.

3. **Gather Information on Available Resources** You need to anticipate that you will need extra help sometime during the course. One resource is your instructor; you need to know your instructor's office hours and where the office is located. Another resource is the math lab or study center, if they are available at your school. It also helps to have the phone numbers of other students in the class, in case you miss class. You want to anticipate that you will need these resources, so now is the time to gather them together.

Learning Objectives

In this section, we will learn how to:

1. Translate a phrase into symbols.

2. Evaluate an exponent.

3. Simplify arithmetic expressions using the order of operations.

4. Interpret a bar chart.

5. Find the perimeter and area for squares, rectangles, and triangles.

Introduction

Suppose you have a checking account that costs you $15 a month, plus $0.05 for each check you write. If you write 10 checks in a month, then the monthly charge for your checking account will be

$$15 + 10(0.05)$$

Do you add 15 and 10 first and then multiply by 0.05? Or do you multiply 10 and 0.05 first and then add 15? If you don't know the answer to this question, you will after you have read through this section.

iStockphoto.com/©Jeffrey Smith

Variables

The difference between arithmetic and algebra is the use of variables in expressions. In algebra, we use a *variable* to represent an unknown number.

Consider our previous discussion regarding the monthly charge for a checking account. The expression

$$15 + 10(0.05)$$

is arithmetic because all of the values are known. However, the usefulness of this expression is very limited because it only gives us the monthly charge if ten checks were written. If we let the letter n represent the number of checks written, then the expression becomes

$$15 + n(0.05)$$

This is an algebraic expression, and it can be used to find the monthly charge for *any* number of checks we may write. The letter n is called a variable because the value it takes on may vary.

We use the variables a and b in the following lists so that the relationships shown there are true for all numbers that we will encounter in this book. By using variables, the following statements are general statements about all numbers, rather than specific statements about only a few numbers.

Symbols

First, we consider the symbols used to represent the four basic operations: addition, subtraction, multiplication, and division.

OPERATION SYMBOLS

Addition:	$a + b$	The *sum* of a and b
Subtraction:	$a - b$	The *difference* of a and b
Multiplication:	$a \cdot b, (a)(b), a(b), (a)b, ab$	The *product* of a and b
Division:	$a \div b, a/b, \dfrac{a}{b}, b\overline{)a}$	The *quotient* of a and b

Note In the past you may have used the notation 3×5 to denote multiplication. In algebra it is best to avoid this notation if possible, because the multiplication symbol $\times$ can be confused with the variable x when written by hand.

When we encounter the word *sum*, the implied operation is addition. To find the sum of two numbers, we simply add them. *Difference* implies subtraction, *product* implies multiplication, and *quotient* implies division. Notice also that there is more than one way to write the product or quotient of two numbers.

GROUPING SYMBOLS

Parentheses ( ) and brackets [ ] are the symbols used for grouping numbers together. Occasionally, braces { } are also used for grouping, although they are usually reserved for set notation, as we shall see.

The following examples illustrate the relationship between the operation symbols and grouping symbols and the English language.

VIDEO EXAMPLES

SECTION 1.1

EXAMPLES   For each phrase, write an equivalent expression in symbols.

Phrase	Equivalent Expression
1. The sum of 4 and 1	$4 + 1$
2. The difference of 8 and 1	$8 - 1$
3. Twice the sum of 3 and 4	$2(3 + 4)$
4. The difference of the product of 3 times x and 15	$3x - 15$
5. The product of 3 and the difference of x and 15	$3(x - 15)$
6. The quotient of y and 2	$\dfrac{y}{2}$

Exponents

The last type of notation we need to discuss is the notation that allows us to write repeated multiplications in a more compact form—*exponents*. In the expression 2^3, the 2 is called the *base* and the 3 is called the *exponent*. The exponent 3 tells us the number of times the base appears in the product; that is,

$$2^3 = 2 \cdot 2 \cdot 2 = 8$$

The expression 2^3 is said to be in exponential form, whereas $2 \cdot 2 \cdot 2$ is said to be in expanded form. Here are some additional examples of expressions involving exponents.

EXAMPLE 7   Evaluate each exponent.

a. 5^2 **b.** 2^5 **c.** 10^3

SOLUTION

a. $5^2 = 5 \cdot 5 = 25$ Base 5, exponent 2

b. $2^5 = 2 \cdot 2 \cdot 2 \cdot 2 \cdot 2 = 32$ Base 2, exponent 5

c. $10^3 = 10 \cdot 10 \cdot 10 = 1,000$ Base 10, exponent 3

Notation and Vocabulary Here is how we read expressions containing exponents.

Mathematical Expression	Written Equivalent
5^2	five to the second power
5^3	five to the third power
5^4	five to the fourth power
5^5	five to the fifth power
5^6	five to the sixth power

We have a shorthand vocabulary for second and third powers because the area of a square with a side of 5 is 5^2, and the volume of a cube with a side of 5 is 5^3.

5^2 can be read "five squared." 5^3 can be read "five cubed."

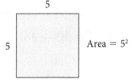

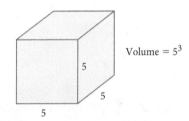

Order of Operations

The operation and grouping symbols are to mathematics what punctuation symbols are to English. Consider the following sentence:

Paul said John is tall.

It can have two different meanings, depending on how it is punctuated.

1. "Paul," said John, "is tall."

2. Paul said, "John is tall."

Let's take a look at a similar situation in mathematics. Consider the following mathematical statement:

$$5 + 2 \cdot 7$$

If we add the 5 and 2 first and then multiply by 7, we get an answer of 49. However, if we multiply the 2 and the 7 first and then add 5, we are left with 19. We have a problem that seems to have two different answers, depending on whether we add first or multiply first. We would like to avoid this type of situation. Every problem like $5 + 2 \cdot 7$ should have only one answer. Therefore, we will use the following rule for the order of operations.

RULE *Order of Operations*

When evaluating a mathematical expression, we will perform the operations in the following order, beginning with the expression in the innermost parentheses or brackets first and working our way out.

1. Simplify all numbers with exponents, working from left to right if more than one of these expressions is present.

2. Then do all multiplications and divisions left to right.

3. Perform all additions and subtractions left to right.

EXAMPLE 8   Simplify each expression following the order of operations.

a. $5 + 8 \cdot 2$ **b.** $12 \div 4 \cdot 2$

c. $2[5 + 2(6 + 3 \cdot 4)]$ **d.** $10 + 12 \div 4 + 2 \cdot 3$

e. $2^4 + 3^3 \div 9 - 4^2$

SOLUTION

a. $5 + 8 \cdot 2 = 5 + 16$ Multiply $8 \cdot 2$ first

$\qquad\qquad = 21$

b. $12 \div 4 \cdot 2 = 3 \cdot 2 = 6$ Work left to right

c. $2[5 + 2(6 + 3 \cdot 4)] = 2[5 + 2(6 + 12)]$ Simplify within the innermost grouping symbols first

$\qquad\qquad\qquad = 2[5 + 2(18)]$

$\qquad\qquad\qquad = 2[5 + 36]$ Next, simplify inside the brackets

$\qquad\qquad\qquad = 2[41]$

$\qquad\qquad\qquad = 82$ Multiply

d. $10 + 12 \div 4 + 2 \cdot 3 = 10 + 3 + 6$ Multiply and divide left to right

$\qquad\qquad\qquad = 19$ Add left to right

e. $2^4 + 3^3 \div 9 - 4^2 = 16 + 27 \div 9 - 16$ Simplify numbers with exponents

$\qquad\qquad\qquad = 16 + 3 - 16$ Then, divide

$\qquad\qquad\qquad = 19 - 16$ Finally, add and subtract left to right

$\qquad\qquad\qquad = 3$

Reading Tables and Bar Charts

The following table shows the average amount of caffeine in a number of beverages. The diagram in Figure 1 is a *bar chart*. It is a visual presentation of the information in the table. The table gives information in numerical form, whereas the chart gives the same information in a geometric way. In mathematics, it is important to be able to move back and forth between the two forms.

Caffeine Content of Hot Drinks	
Drink (6-ounce cup)	Caffeine (milligrams)
Brewed coffee	100
Instant coffee	70
Tea	50
Cocoa	5
Decaffeinated coffee	4

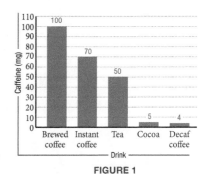

FIGURE 1

EXAMPLE 9 Referring to the table and Figure 1, suppose you have 3 cups of brewed coffee, 1 cup of tea, and 2 cups of decaf in one day. Write an expression that will give the total amount of caffeine in these six drinks, and then simplify the expression.

SOLUTION From the table or the bar chart, we find the number of milligrams of caffeine in each drink; then we write an expression for the total amount of caffeine:

$$3(100) + 50 + 2(4)$$

Using the rule for order of operations, we get 358 total milligrams of caffeine.

Geometry

We conclude this section by looking at some formulas for the area and perimeter of several geometric figures.

FACTS FROM GEOMETRY *Formulas for Area and Perimeter*

A square, rectangle, and triangle are shown in the following figures. Note that we have labeled the dimensions of each with variables. The formulas for the perimeter and area of each object are given in terms of its dimensions.

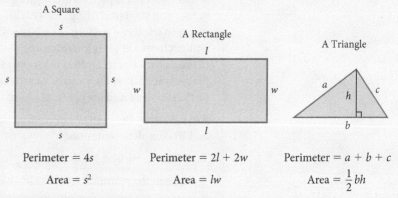

A Square

Perimeter = $4s$

Area = s^2

A Rectangle

Perimeter = $2l + 2w$

Area = lw

A Triangle

Perimeter = $a + b + c$

Area = $\frac{1}{2}bh$

Note The vertical line labeled h in the triangle is its height, or altitude. It extends from the top of the triangle down to the base, meeting the base at an angle of 90°. The altitude of a triangle is always perpendicular to the base. The small square shown where the altitude meets the base is used to indicate that the angle formed is 90°.

The formula for perimeter gives us the distance around the outside of the object along its sides, whereas the formula for area gives us a measure of the amount of surface the object has.

EXAMPLE 10   Find the perimeter and area of each figure.

a. 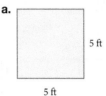   b. 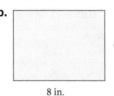   c.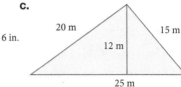

SOLUTION   We use the preceding formulas to find the perimeter and the area. In each case, the units for perimeter are linear units, whereas the units for area are square units.

a. Perimeter $= 4s = 4 \cdot 5$ feet $= 20$ feet

Area $= s^2 = (5 \text{ feet})^2 = 25$ square feet

b. Perimeter $= 2l + 2w = 2(8 \text{ inches}) + 2(6 \text{ inches}) = 28$ inches

Area $= lw = (8 \text{ inches})(6 \text{ inches}) = 48$ square inches

c. Perimeter $= a + b + c = (20 \text{ meters}) + (25 \text{ meters}) + (15 \text{ meters})$

$= 60$ meters

Area $= \dfrac{1}{2}bh = \dfrac{1}{2}(25 \text{ meters})(12 \text{ meters}) = 150$ square meters

Getting Ready for Class

Each section of the book will end with some problems and questions like the ones below. They are for you to answer after you have read through the section but before you go to class. All of them require that you give written responses in complete sentences. Writing about mathematics is a valuable exercise. If you write with the intention of explaining and communicating what you know to someone else, you will find that you understand the topic you are writing about even better than you did before you started writing. As with all problems in this course, you want to approach these writing exercises with a positive point of view. You will get better at giving written responses to questions as you progress through the course. Even if you never feel comfortable writing about mathematics, just the process of attempting to do so will increase your understanding and ability in mathematics.

After reading through the preceding section, respond in your own words and in complete sentences.

A. What is a variable?

B. Explain the relationship between an exponent and its base.

C. Write the first step in the order of operations.

D. How could you place grouping symbols in the expression $20 - 8 \cdot 2$ so that the value of the expression is 24 instead of 4?

For each phrase below, write an equivalent expression in symbols.

1. The sum of x and 5.   **2.** The difference of x and 4.

3. The product of 5 and y.   **4.** The product of 8 and y.

5. The product of 5 and the difference of y and 16.

6. The product of 3 and the sum of y and 6.

7. The quotient of x and 3.

8. The quotient of x and the difference of x and 4.

Evaluate each exponent.

9. 3^2 **10.** 4^2 **11.** 7^2 **12.** 9^2 **13.** 2^3 **14.** 3^3

15. 4^3 **16.** 5^3 **17.** 2^4 **18.** 3^4 **19.** 10^2 **20.** 10^4

21. 11^2 **22.** 111^2

Use the order of operations to simplify each expression as much as possible.

23. $2 \cdot 3 + 5$ **24.** $8 \cdot 7 + 1$ **25.** $2(3 + 5)$ **26.** $8(7 + 1)$

27. $5 + 2 \cdot 6$ **28.** $8 + 9 \cdot 4$ **29.** $(5 + 2) \cdot 6$ **30.** $(8 + 9) \cdot 4$

31. $5 \cdot 4 + 5 \cdot 2$ **32.** $6 \cdot 8 + 6 \cdot 3$ **33.** $5(4 + 2)$ **34.** $6(8 + 3)$

35. $8 + 2(5 + 3)$ **36.** $7 + 3(8 - 2)$ **37.** $(8 + 2)(5 + 3)$ **38.** $(7 + 3)(8 - 2)$

39. $20 + 2(8 - 5) + 1$ **40.** $10 + 3(7 + 1) + 2$

41. $5 + 2(3 \cdot 4 - 1) + 8$ **42.** $11 - 2(5 \cdot 3 - 10) + 2$

43. $8 + 10 \div 2$ **44.** $16 - 8 \div 4$

45. $4 + 8 \div 4 - 2$ **46.** $6 + 9 \div 3 + 2$

47. $3 + 12 \div 3 + 6 \cdot 5$ **48.** $18 + 6 \div 2 + 3 \cdot 4$

49. $3 \cdot 8 + 10 \div 2 + 4 \cdot 2$ **50.** $5 \cdot 9 + 10 \div 2 + 3 \cdot 3$

51. $(5 + 3)(5 - 3)$ **52.** $(7 + 2)(7 - 2)$ **53.** $5^2 - 3^2$ **54.** $7^2 - 2^2$

55. $(4 + 5)^2$ **56.** $(6 + 3)^2$ **57.** $4^2 + 5^2$ **58.** $6^2 + 3^2$

59. $3 \cdot 10^2 + 4 \cdot 10 + 5$ **60.** $6 \cdot 10^2 + 5 \cdot 10 + 4$

61. $2 \cdot 10^3 + 3 \cdot 10^2 + 4 \cdot 10 + 5$ **62.** $5 \cdot 10^3 + 6 \cdot 10^2 + 7 \cdot 10 + 8$

63. $10 - 2(4 \cdot 5 - 16)$ **64.** $15 - 5(3 \cdot 2 - 4)$

65. $4[7 + 3(2 \cdot 9 - 8)]$ **66.** $5[10 + 2(3 \cdot 6 - 10)]$

67. $5(7 - 3) + 8(6 - 4)$ **68.** $3(10 - 4) + 6(12 - 10)$

69. $3(4 \cdot 5 - 12) + 6(7 \cdot 6 - 40)$ **70.** $6(8 \cdot 3 - 4) + 5(7 \cdot 3 - 1)$

71. $3^4 + 4^2 \div 2^3 - 5^2$ **72.** $2^5 + 6^2 \div 2^2 - 3^2$

73. $5^2 + 3^4 \div 9^2 + 6^2$ **74.** $6^2 + 2^5 \div 4^2 + 7^2$

Simplify each expression.

75. $20 \div 2 \cdot 10$ **76.** $40 \div 4 \cdot 5$ **77.** $24 \div 8 \cdot 3$ **78.** $24 \div 4 \cdot 6$

79. $36 \div 6 \cdot 3$ **80.** $36 \div 9 \cdot 2$ **81.** $48 \div 12 \cdot 2$ **82.** $48 \div 8 \cdot 3$

83. $16 - 8 + 4$ **84.** $16 - 8 + 8$ **85.** $24 - 14 + 8$ **86.** $24 - 16 + 6$

87. $36 - 6 + 12$ **88.** $36 - 9 + 20$ **89.** $48 - 12 + 17$ **90.** $48 - 13 + 15$

Find the perimeter and area of each figure.

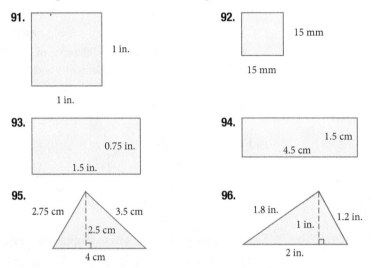

91. 1 in. 1 in.

92. 15 mm 15 mm

93. 0.75 in. 1.5 in.

94. 1.5 cm 4.5 cm

95. 2.75 cm 3.5 cm 2.5 cm 4 cm

96. 1.8 in. 1.2 in. 1 in. 2 in.

Applying the Concepts

Food Labels In 1993 the government standardized the way in which nutrition information was presented on the labels of most packaged food products. The standardized food label shown here is from a package of cookies. Use the information on the label to answer the following questions.

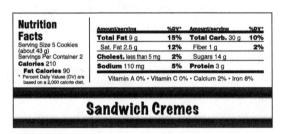

Nutrition Facts
Serving Size 5 Cookies (about 43 g)
Servings Per Container 2
Calories 210
    Fat Calories 90
* Percent Daily Values (DV) are based on a 2,000 calorie diet.

Amount/serving	%DV*	Amount/serving	%DV*
Total Fat 9 g	15%	**Total Carb.** 30 g	10%
Sat. Fat 2.5 g	12%	Fiber 1 g	2%
Cholest. less than 5 mg	2%	Sugars 14 g	
Sodium 110 mg	5%	**Protein** 3 g	

Vitamin A 0% • Vitamin C 0% • Calcium 2% • Iron 8%

Sandwich Cremes

97. How many cookies are in the package?

98. If you paid $2.25 for the package of cookies, how much did each cookie cost?

99. If the "calories" category stands for calories per serving, how many calories would you consume by eating the whole package of cookies?

100. Suppose that, while swimming, you burn 11 calories each minute. If you swim for 20 minutes, will you burn enough calories to cancel out the calories you added by eating 5 cookies?

Food Labels The food label shown here was taken from a bag of corn chips. Use the information to answer the following questions.

101. Approximately how many chips are in the bag?

102. If the bag of chips costs $1.69, approximately how much does one serving of chips cost?

103. The table toward the bottom of the label gives the recommended amount of total fat that should be consumed by a person eating 2,000 calories per day and by a person eating 2,500 calories per day. Use the numbers in the table to estimate the recommended fat intake for a person eating 3,000 calories per day.

104. Deidre burns 256 calories per hour by trotting on her horse at a constant rate. How long must she ride to burn the calories consumed by eating four servings of these chips?

Nutrition Facts

Serving Size 1 oz. (28 g/About 32 chips)
Servings Per Container 7

Amount Per Serving

Calories 160   Calories from Fat 90

	%?Daily Value*
Total Fat 10 g	**15%**
Saturated Fat 1.5 g	**8%**
Cholesterol 0 mg	**0%**
Sodium 160 mg	**7%**
Total Carbohydrate 15 g	**5%**
Dietary Fiber 1 g	**4%**
Sugars 0 g	
Protein 2 g	

Vitamin A 0%	•	Vitamin C 0%
Calcium 2%	•	Iron 0%

* Percent Daily Values are based on a 2,000 calorie diet. Your daily values may be higher or lower depending on your calorie needs:

	Calories:	2,000	2,500
Total Fat	Less than	65 g	80 g
Sat Fat	Less than	20 g	25 g
Cholesterol	Less than	300 mg	300 mg
Sodium	Less than	2,400 mg	2,400 mg
Total Carbohydrate		300 g	375 g
Dietary Fiber		25 g	30 g

Calories per gram:
Fat 9   •   Carbohydrate 4   •   Protein 4

105. **Reading Charts** The following bar chart gives the amount of caffeine in five different soft drinks. How much caffeine is in each of the following?

   a. A 6-pack of Jolt

   b. 2 Cokes plus 3 Tabs

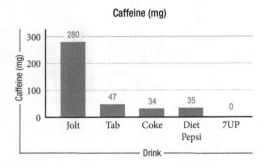

Caffeine (mg)

106. Reading Charts The following bar chart gives the amount of caffeine in five different nonprescription drugs. How much caffeine is in each of the following?

    a. A box of 12 Excedrin   **b.** 1 Dexatrim plus 4 Excedrin

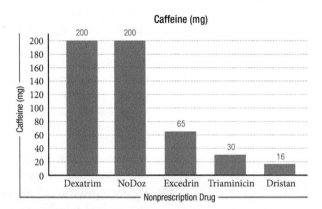

107. Reading Tables and Charts The following bar chart gives the number of calories burned by a 150-pound person during 1 hour of various exercises. The accompanying table should display the same information. Use the bar chart to complete the table.

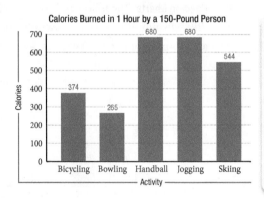

Calories Burned by 150-Pound Person	
Activity	Calories Burned in 1 Hour
Bicycling	374
Bowling	
Handball	
Jogging	
Skiing	

108. Reading Tables and Charts The following table and bar chart give the number of calories consumed by eating some popular fast foods. The accompanying table should display the same information. Use the bar chart to complete the table.

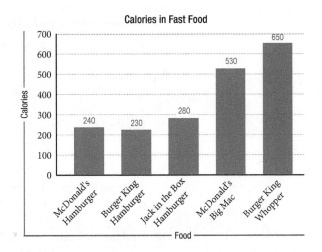

Calories In Fast Food

Food	Calories
McDonald's Hamburger	240
Burger King Hamburger	
Jack in the Box Hamburger	
McDonald's Big Mac	
Burger King Whopper	

109. Geometry Find the area and perimeter of an 8.5-by-11-inch piece of notebook paper.

110. Geometry Find the area and perimeter of an 8.5-by-5.5-inch piece of paper.

Learning Objectives Assessment

The following problems can be used to help assess if you have successfully met the learning objectives for this section.

111. Translate into symbols: The product of 4 and the difference of x and 9.

    a. $4(9 - x)$ **b.** $9 - 4x$ **c.** $4x - 9$ **d.** $4(x - 9)$

112. Evaluate: 8^2.

    a. 16   **b.** 256   **c.** 64   **d.** 512

113. Use the order of operations to simplify $6 + 4(3 \cdot 5 - 8) - 10$.

    a. 24   **b.** 60   **c.** 132   **d.** 7

114. Referring to Figure 1 of this section, how much more caffeine will you have by drinking a cup of instant coffee instead of a cup of tea?

    a. 70 mg   **b.** 50 mg   **c.** 120 mg   **d.** 20 mg

115. Find the perimeter of an 8x10 inch photo.

    a. 18 in.   **b.** 36 in.   **c.** 80 in^2 **d.** 40 in^2

Learning Objectives

In this section, we will learn how to:

1. Use the number line to represent real numbers.
2. Classify subsets of real numbers.
3. Find the absolute value of a number.
4. Find the opposite of a number.

Introduction

The bar chart shown here gives the record low temperature, in degrees Fahrenheit, for each month of the year in the city of Jackson, Wyoming. Notice that some of these temperatures are represented by negative numbers.

iStockPhoto.com/©Nicholas Belton

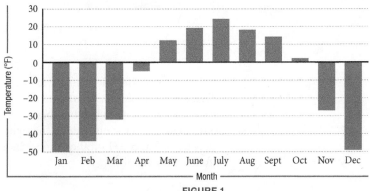

FIGURE 1

In this section we start our work with negative numbers. To represent negative numbers in algebra, we use what is called the *real number line*. Here is how we construct a real number line: We first draw a straight line and label a convenient point on the line with 0. Then we mark off equally spaced distances in both directions from 0. Label the points to the right of 0 with the numbers 1, 2, 3,…(the dots mean "and so on"). The points to the left of 0 we label in order, -1, -2, -3,…. Here is what it looks like.

Note If there is no sign (+ or −) in front of a number, the number is assumed to be positive (+).

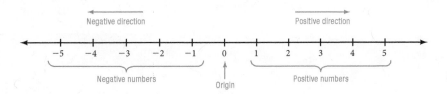

The numbers increase in value going from left to right. If we "move" to the right, we are moving in the positive direction. If we move to the left, we are moving in the negative direction.

15

EXAMPLE 1   Locate and label the points on the real number line associated with the numbers $-3.5, -1\frac{1}{4}, \frac{1}{2}, \frac{3}{4}, 2.5$.

SOLUTION   We draw a real number line from -4 to 4 and label the points in question.

Note There are other numbers on the number line that you may not be as familiar with. They are irrational numbers such as $\pi, \sqrt{2}, \sqrt{3}$. We will introduce these numbers later in the section.

(def) DEFINITION   *coordinate*

The number associated with a point on the real number line is called the *coordinate* of that point.

In the preceding example, the numbers $\frac{1}{2}, \frac{3}{4}, 2.5, -3.5$, and $-1\frac{1}{4}$ are the coordinates of the points they represent.

(def) DEFINITION   *real numbers*

The numbers that can be represented with points on the real number line are called *real numbers*.

Real numbers include whole numbers, fractions, decimals, and other numbers that are not as familiar to us as these.

When we compare two numbers on the number line, the number on the left is always less than the number on the right. For instance, -3 is less than -1 because it is to the left of -1 on the number line. When making comparisons, we use the following symbols.

[Δ≠Σ] COMPARISON SYMBOLS

Equality:	$a = b$	a is equal to b
	$a \neq b$	a is not equal to b
Inequality:	$a < b$	a is less than b (a lies to the left of b on the number line)
	$a > b$	a is greater than b (a lies to the right of b on the number line)
	$a \geq b$	a is greater than or equal to b
	$a \leq b$	a is less than or equal to b

Subsets of the Real Numbers

The numbers that make up the set of real numbers can be classified as *counting numbers, whole numbers, integers, rational numbers,* and *irrational numbers*; each is said to be a *subset* of the real numbers.

> **DEFINITION** *subset*
>
> Set A is called a *subset* of set B if set A is contained in set B; that is, if each and every element in set A is also a member of set B.

Here is a detailed description of the major subsets of the real numbers.

The *counting numbers* are the numbers with which we count. They are the numbers 1, 2, 3, and so on. The notation we use to specify a group of numbers like this is *set notation*. We use the symbols { and } to enclose the members of the set.

$$\text{Counting numbers} = \{1, 2, 3,...\}$$

Note In previous math classes, you may have seen the term "natural numbers." Natural numbers and counting numbers are the same subset of the real numbers.

EXAMPLE 2   Which of the numbers in the following set are not counting numbers?

$$\left\{ -3, 0, \frac{1}{2}, 1, 1.5, 3 \right\}$$

SOLUTION   The numbers $-3, 0, \frac{1}{2}$, and 1.5 are not counting numbers.

The *whole numbers* include the counting numbers and the number 0.

$$\text{Whole numbers} = \{0, 1, 2, \dots \}$$

The set of *integers* includes the whole numbers and the opposites of all the counting numbers. (Later in this section, we give a formal definition of the word *opposite* as it is used in mathematics.)

$$\text{Integers} = \{..., -3, -2, -1, 0, 1, 2, 3, \dots \}$$

When we refer to positive integers, we are referring to the numbers 1, 2, 3,.... Likewise, the negative integers are $-1, -2, -3, \dots$. The number 0 is neither positive nor negative.

EXAMPLE 3   Which of the numbers in the following set are not integers?

$$\left\{ -5, -1.75, 0, \frac{2}{3}, 1, \pi, 3 \right\}$$

SOLUTION   The only numbers in the set that are not integers are $-1.75, \frac{2}{3}$, and π.

The set of *rational numbers* is the set of numbers commonly called "fractions" together with the integers. The set of rational numbers is difficult to list in the same way we have listed the other sets, so we will use a different kind of notation:

$$\text{Rational numbers} = \left\{ \frac{a}{b} \mid a \text{ and } b \text{ are integers } (b \neq 0) \right\}$$

This notation is read "The set of elements $\frac{a}{b}$ such that a and b are integers (and b is not 0)." If a number can be put in the form $\frac{a}{b}$, where a and b are both from the set of integers, then it is called a rational number.

 EXAMPLE 4   Show why each of the numbers in the following set is a rational number.

$$\left\{-3, -\frac{2}{3}, 0, 0.333\ldots, 0.75\right\}$$

SOLUTION   The number -3 is a rational number because it can be written as the ratio of -3 to 1; that is,

$$-3 = \frac{-3}{1}$$

Similarly, the number $-\frac{2}{3}$ can be thought of as the ratio of -2 to 3, whereas the number 0 can be thought of as the ratio of 0 to 1.

Any repeating decimal, such as $0.333\ldots$ (the dots indicate that the 3s repeat forever), can be written as the ratio of two integers. In this case $0.333\ldots$ is the same as the fraction $\frac{1}{3}$.

Finally, any decimal that terminates after a certain number of digits can be written as the ratio of two integers. The number 0.75 is equal to the fraction $\frac{3}{4}$ and is therefore a rational number.

Still other numbers exist, each of which is associated with a point on the real number line, that cannot be written as the ratio of two integers. In decimal form they never terminate and never repeat a sequence of digits indefinitely. They are called *irrational numbers* (because they are not rational):

Irrational numbers $=$ {nonrational numbers; nonrepeating, nonterminating decimals}

One irrational number you have probably seen before is π. It is not 3.14. Rather, 3.14 is an approximation to π. It cannot be written as a terminating decimal number. Other representations for irrational numbers are $\sqrt{2}$, $\sqrt{3}$, $\sqrt{5}$, $\sqrt{6}$, and, in general, the square root of any number that is not itself a perfect square. (If you are not familiar with square roots, you will be after Chapter 8.)

To summarize, the set of real numbers is the set of numbers that are either rational or irrational; that is, a real number is either rational or irrational.

Real numbers $=$ {all rational numbers and all irrational numbers}

Fractions on the Number Line

As we mentioned previously, rational numbers can also be thought of as fractions. Here is the formal definition of a fraction.

> **DEFINITION**   *fraction*
>
> If a and b are real numbers, then the expression
>
> $$\frac{a}{b} \qquad b \neq 0$$
>
> is called a *fraction*. The top number a is called the *numerator*, and the bottom number b is called the *denominator*. The restriction $b \neq 0$ keeps us from writing an expression that is undefined. (As you will see, division by zero is not allowed.)

The number line can be used to visualize fractions. The denominator indicates the number of equal parts in the interval from 0 to 1 on the number line. The numerator indicates how many of those parts we have. If we take that part of the number line from 0 to 1 and divide it into three equal parts, we say that we have divided it into thirds (Figure 2). Each of the three segments is $\frac{1}{3}$ (one third) of the whole segment from 0 to 1.

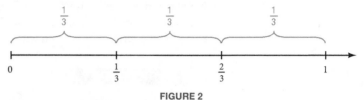

FIGURE 2

Two of these smaller segments together are $\frac{2}{3}$ (two thirds) of the whole segment. And three of them would be $\frac{3}{3}$ (three thirds), or the whole segment.

Let's do the same thing again with six equal divisions of the segment from 0 to 1 (Figure 3). In this case we say each of the smaller segments has a length of $\frac{1}{6}$ (one sixth).

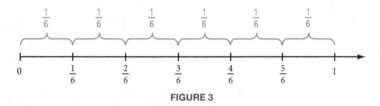

FIGURE 3

The same point we labeled with $\frac{1}{3}$ in Figure 2 is now labeled with $\frac{2}{6}$. Likewise, the point we labeled earlier with $\frac{2}{3}$ is now labeled $\frac{4}{6}$. It must be true then that

$$\frac{2}{6} = \frac{1}{3} \qquad \text{and} \qquad \frac{4}{6} = \frac{2}{3}$$

Actually, there are many fractions that name the same point as $\frac{1}{3}$. If we were to divide the segment between 0 and 1 into 12 equal parts, 4 of these 12 equal parts $\left(\frac{4}{12}\right)$ would be the same as $\frac{2}{6}$ or $\frac{1}{3}$; that is,

$$\frac{4}{12} = \frac{2}{6} = \frac{1}{3}$$

Even though these three fractions look different, each names the same point on the number line, as shown in Figure 4. All three fractions have the same value because they all represent the same number.

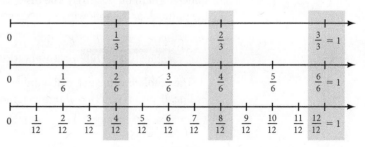

FIGURE 4

DEFINITION   *equivalent*

Fractions that represent the same number are said to be *equivalent*.
Equivalent fractions may look different, but they must have the same value.

It is apparent that every fraction has many different representations, each of which is equivalent to the original fraction. The next two properties give us a way of changing the terms of a fraction without changing its value.

PROPERTY 1

Multiplying the numerator and denominator of a fraction by the same nonzero number never changes the value of the fraction.

PROPERTY 2

Dividing the numerator and denominator of a fraction by the same nonzero number never changes the value of the fraction.

We can use Property 2 to reduce a fraction to *lowest terms* by dividing the largest common factor that appears in both the numerator and denominator.

EXAMPLE 5   Reduce $\dfrac{18}{30}$ to lowest terms.

SOLUTION The largest number that divides evenly into 18 and 30 is 6, so 6 is the largest common factor of the numerator and denominator.

$$\frac{18}{30} = \frac{6(3)}{6(5)}$$

$$= \frac{3}{5} \qquad \text{Divide the numerator and denominator by 6}$$

We say that $\frac{3}{5}$ is in lowest terms because 3 and 5 have no common factor other than 1.

Absolute Values and Opposites

Representing numbers on the number line lets us give each number two important properties: a direction from zero and a distance from zero. The direction from zero is represented by the sign in front of the number. (A number without a sign is understood to be positive.) The distance from zero is called the *absolute value* of the number, as the following definition indicates.

 DEFINITION   *absolute value*

The *absolute value* of a real number is its distance from zero on the number line. If x represents a real number, then the absolute value of x is written $|x|$.

EXAMPLE 6   Write each expression without absolute value symbols.

a. $|5|$ **b.** $|-5|$ **c.** $\left| -\dfrac{1}{2} \right|$

SOLUTION

a. $|5| = 5$ The number 5 is 5 units from zero

b. $|-5| = 5$ The number -5 is 5 units from zero

c. $\left| -\dfrac{1}{2} \right| = \dfrac{1}{2}$ The number $-\frac{1}{2}$ is $\frac{1}{2}$ units from zero

The absolute value of a number is never negative. It is the distance the number is from zero without regard to which direction it is from zero. When working with the absolute value of sums and differences, we must simplify the expression inside the absolute value symbols first and then find the absolute value of the simplified expression.

EXAMPLE 7   Simplify each expression.

a. $|8 - 3|$ **b.** $|3 \cdot 2^3 + 2 \cdot 3^2|$ **c.** $|9 - 2| - |8 - 6|$

SOLUTION

a. $|8 - 3| = |5| = 5$

b. $|3 \cdot 2^3 + 2 \cdot 3^2| = |3 \cdot 8 + 2 \cdot 9| = |24 + 18| = |42| = 42$

c. $|9 - 2| - |8 - 6| = |7| - |2| = 7 - 2 = 5$

Another important concept associated with numbers on the number line is that of opposites. Here is the definition.

DEFINITION   *opposites*

Numbers the same distance from zero but in opposite directions from zero are called *opposites*. If a is any real number, then we denote the opposite of a by $-a$.

EXAMPLE 8   Give the opposite of each number.

a. 5   **b.** -3 **c.** $\dfrac{1}{4}$ **d.** -2.3

SOLUTION

	Number	Opposite	
a.	5	$-(5) = 5$	5 and -5 are opposites ·
b.	-3	$-(-3) = 3$	-3 and 3 are opposites
c.	$\dfrac{1}{4}$	$-\left(\dfrac{1}{4} \right) = -\dfrac{1}{4}$	$\frac{1}{4}$ and $-\frac{1}{4}$ are opposites
d.	-2.3	$-(-2.3) = 2.3$	-2.3 and 2.3 are opposites

Each negative number is the opposite of some positive number, and each positive number is the opposite of some negative number. The opposite of a negative number is a positive number. In symbols, if a represents a positive number, then

$$-(-a) = a$$

Opposites always have the same absolute value. And, when you add any two opposites, the result is always zero:

$$a + (-a) = 0$$

Getting Ready for Class

After reading through the preceding section, respond in your own words and in complete sentences.

A. What is a real number?

B. What is a whole number?

C. Is every integer also a rational number? Explain.

D. How do you find the opposite of a number?

Draw a number line that extends from -5 to $+5$. Label the points with the following coordinates.

1. 5   **2.** -2 **3.** -4 **4.** -3

5. 1.5   **6.** -1.5 **7.** $\dfrac{9}{4}$ **8.** $\dfrac{8}{3}$

Given the numbers in the set $\{-3, -2.5, 0, 1, \dfrac{3}{2}, \sqrt{15}\}$:

9. List all the whole numbers.   **10.** List all the integers.

11. List all the rational numbers.   **12.** List all the irrational numbers.

13. List all the real numbers.

Given the numbers in the set $\{-10, -8, -0.333\ldots, -2, 9, \dfrac{25}{3}, \pi\}$:

14. List all the whole numbers.   **15.** List all the integers.

16. List all the rational numbers.   **17.** List all the irrational numbers.

18. List all the real numbers.

Identify the following statements as either true or false.

19. Every whole number is also an integer.

20. The set of whole numbers is a subset of the set of integers.

21. A number can be both rational and irrational.

22. The set of rational numbers and the set of irrational numbers have some elements in common.

23. Some whole numbers are also negative integers.

24. Every rational number is also a real number.

25. All integers are also rational numbers.

26. The set of integers is a subset of the set of rational numbers.

For each of the following numbers, give the opposite and the absolute value. (Assume all variables are nonzero.)

27. 10   **28.** 8   **29.** $\dfrac{3}{4}$ **30.** $\dfrac{5}{7}$ **31.** $\dfrac{11}{2}$ **32.** $\dfrac{16}{3}$

33. -3 **34.** -5 **35.** $-\dfrac{2}{5}$ **36.** $-\dfrac{3}{8}$ **37.** x **38.** a

Place one of the symbols $<$ or $>$ between each of the following to make the resulting statement true.

39. $-5 \,\square\, -3$ **40.** $-8 \,\square\, -1$ **41.** $-3 \,\square\, -7$ **42.** $-6 \,\square\, 5$

43. $|-4| \,\square\, -|-4|$ **44.** $3 \,\square\, -|-3|$ **45.** $7 \,\square\, -|-7|$ **46.** $-7 \,\square\, |-7|$

Simplify each expression.

47. $|8 - 2|$ **48.** $|6 - 1|$

49. $|5 \cdot 2^3 - 2 \cdot 3^2|$ **50.** $|2 \cdot 10^2 + 3 \cdot 10|$

51. $|7 - 2| - |4 - 2|$ **52.** $|10 - 3| - |4 - 1|$

53. $10 - |7 - 2(5 - 3)|$ **54.** $12 - |9 - 3(7 - 5)|$

55. $15 - |8 - 2(3 \cdot 4 - 9)| - 10$ **56.** $25 - |9 - 3(4 \cdot 5 - 18)| - 20$

Applying the Concepts

57. **Football Yardage** A football team gains 6 yards on one play and then loses 8 yards on the next play. To what number on the number line does a loss of 8 yards correspond? The total yards gained or lost on the two plays corresponds to what negative number?

58. **Checking Account Balance** A woman has a balance of $20 in her checking account. If she writes a check for $30, what negative number can be used to represent the new balance in her checking account?

Temperature In the United States, temperature is measured on the Fahrenheit temperature scale. On this scale, water boils at 212 degrees and freezes at 32 degrees. To denote a temperature of 32 degrees on the Fahrenheit scale, we write

32°F, which is read "32 degrees Fahrenheit"

Use this information for Problems 59 and 60.

59. **Temperature and Altitude** Marilyn is flying from Seattle to San Francisco on a Boeing 737 jet. When the plane reaches an altitude of 35,000 feet, the temperature outside the plane is 64 degrees below zero Fahrenheit. Represent the temperature with a negative number. If the temperature outside the plane gets warmer by 10 degrees, what will the new temperature be?

60. **Temperature Change** At 10:00 in the morning in White Bear Lake, Minnesota, John notices the temperature outside is 10 degrees below zero Fahrenheit. Write the temperature as a negative number. An hour later it has warmed up by 6 degrees. What is the temperature at 11:00 that morning?

Wind Chill The table below is a table of wind chill temperatures. The left column gives the air temperature, and the first row is wind speed in miles per hour. The numbers within the table indicate how cold the weather will feel. For example, if the thermometer reads 30°F and the wind is blowing at 15 miles per hour, the wind chill temperature is 9°F. Use Table 1 to answer Problems 61 and 62.

Wind Chill Temperatures

Air Temperature (°F)	Wind Speed (mph)				
	10	15	20	25	30
30°	16°	9°	4°	1°	−2°
25°	10°	2°	−3°	−7°	−10°
20°	3°	−5°	−10°	−15°	−18°
15°	−3°	−11°	−17°	−22°	−25°
10°	−9°	−18°	−24°	−29°	−33°
5°	−15°	−25°	−31°	−36°	−41°
0°	−22°	−31°	−39°	−44°	−49°
−5°	−27°	−38°	−46°	−51°	−56°

TABLE 1

61. **Reading Tables** Find the wind chill temperature if the thermometer reads 20°F and the wind is blowing at 25 miles per hour.

62. **Reading Tables** Which will feel colder: a day with an air temperature of 10°F with a 25-mile-per-hour wind, or a day with an air temperature of 25° F and a 10-mile-per-hour wind?

63. **Scuba Diving** Steve is scuba diving near his home in Maui. At one point he is 100 feet below the surface. Represent this number with a negative number. If he descends another 5 feet, what negative number will represent his new position?

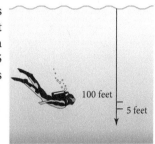

64. **Reading a Chart** The chart shows yields for certificates of deposit during one week in 2006. Write a mathematical statement using one of the symbols < or > to compare the following:

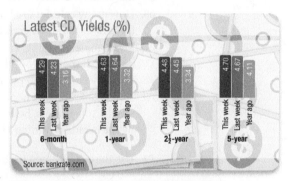

a. 6 month yield a year ago to 1 year yield last week

b. $2\frac{1}{2}$ year yield this week to 5 year yield a year ago

c. 5 year yield last week to 6 month yield this week

Calories and Exercise The table here gives the amount of energy expended per hour for various activities for a person weighing 120, 150, or 180 pounds. Use the table to answer questions 65–68.

Energy Expended from Exercising

Activity	Calories per Hour		
	120 lb	150 lb	180 lb
Bicycling	299	374	449
Bowling	212	265	318
Handball	544	680	816
Horseback trotting	278	347	416
Jazzercise	272	340	408
Jogging	544	680	816
Skiing (downhill)	435	544	653

65. Suppose you weigh 120 pounds. How many calories will you burn if you play handball for 2 hours and then ride your bicycle for an hour?

66. How many calories are burned by a person weighing 150 pounds who jogs for $\frac{1}{2}$ hour and then goes bicycling for 2 hours?

67. Two people go skiing. One weighs 180 pounds and the other weighs 120 pounds. If they ski for 3 hours, how many more calories are burned by the person weighing 180 pounds?

68. Two people spend 3 hours bowling. If one weighs 120 pounds and the other weighs 150 pounds, how many more calories are burned during the evening by the person weighing 150 pounds?

69. Use the chart shown here to answer the following questions.

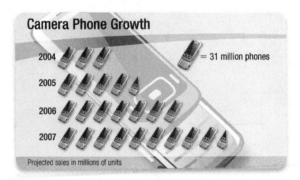

a. How many millions of camera phones were sold in 2004?

b. True or false? The chart shows sales in 2005 to be more than 155 million camera phones.

c. True or false? The chart shows sales in 2007 to be less than 310 million camera phones.

70. Improving Your Quantitative Literacy Quantitative literacy is a subject discussed by many people involved in teaching mathematics. The person they are concerned with when they discuss it is you. We are going to work at improving your quantitative literacy, but before we do that we should answer the question, What is quantitative literacy? Lynn Arthur Steen, a noted mathematics educator, has stated that quantitative literacy is "the capacity to deal effectively with the quantitative aspects of life."

a. Give a definition for the word *quantitative*.

b. Give a definition for the word *literacy*.

c. Are there situations that occur in your life that you find distasteful, or that you try to avoid, because they involve numbers and mathematics? If so, list some of them here. (For example, some people find the process of buying a car particularly difficult because they feel that the numbers and details of the financing are beyond them.)

Learning Objectives Assessment

The following problems can be used to help assess if you have successfully met the learning objectives for this section.

71. What is the coordinate of the point shown on the number line below?

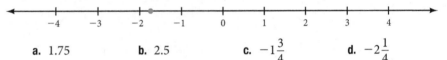

a. 1.75   **b.** 2.5   **c.** $-1\frac{3}{4}$ **d.** $-2\frac{1}{4}$

72. Given the numbers in the set $\left\{-4.5, 2, 0, 3\frac{1}{3}, -1, \sqrt{2}\right\}$ list all the integers.

a. 2, 0   **b.** 2, 0, −1

c. $-4.5, 2, 0, 3\frac{1}{3}, -1$ **d.** All of them

73. Find $|-9|$.

a. 9   **b.** −9   **c.** 0   **d.** $-\frac{1}{9}$

74. Find the opposite of −11.

a. 11   **b.** −11   **c.** 0   **d.** $-\frac{1}{11}$

Learning Objectives

In this section, we will learn how to:

1. Add real numbers.

2. Translate a phrase involving addition into a mathematical expression.

3. Find the next number in an arithmetic sequence.

Introduction

Suppose that you are playing a friendly game of poker with some friends, and you lose $3 on the first hand and $4 on the second hand. If you represent winning with positive numbers and losing with negative numbers, how can you translate this situation into symbols? Because you lost $3 and $4 for a total of $7, one way to represent this situation is with addition of negative numbers:

iStockPhoto.com/©Alexander Fairfull

$$(-\$3) + (-\$4) = -\$7$$

From this equation, we see that the sum of two negative numbers is a negative number. To generalize addition with positive and negative numbers, we use the number line.

Because real numbers have both a distance from zero (absolute value) and a direction from zero (sign), we can think of addition of two numbers in terms of distance and direction from zero.

Let's look at a problem for which we know the answer. Suppose we want to add the numbers 3 and 4. The problem is written $3 + 4$. To put it on the number line, we read the problem as follows:

1. The 3 tells us to "start at the origin and move 3 units in the positive direction."

2. The $+$ sign is read "and then move."

3. The 4 means "4 units in the positive direction."

To summarize, $3 + 4$ means to start at the origin, move 3 units in the positive direction, and then move 4 units in the positive direction.

We end up at 7, which is the answer to our problem: $3 + 4 = 7$.

Let's try other combinations of positive and negative 3 and 4 on the number line.

EXAMPLE 1　　Add $3 + (-4)$.

SOLUTION　Starting at the origin, move 3 units in the positive direction and then 4 units in the negative direction.

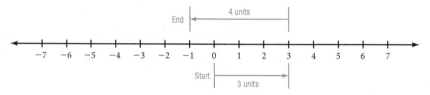

We end up at -1; therefore, $3 + (-4) = -1$.

EXAMPLE 2　　Add $-3 + 4$.

SOLUTION　Starting at the origin, move 3 units in the negative direction and then 4 units in the positive direction.

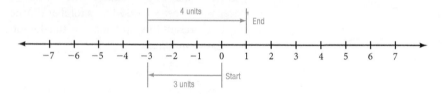

We end up at $+1$; therefore, $-3 + 4 = 1$.

EXAMPLE 3　　Add $-3 + (-4)$.

SOLUTION　Starting at the origin, move 3 units in the negative direction and then 4 units in the negative direction.

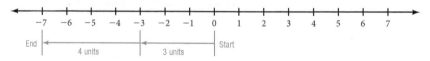

We end up at -7; therefore, $-3 + (-4) = -7$.

Here is a summary of what we have just completed:

$$3 + 4 = 7$$
$$3 + (-4) = -1$$
$$-3 + 4 = 1$$
$$-3 + (-4) = -7$$

Let's do four more problems on the number line and then summarize our results into a rule we can use to add any two real numbers.

EXAMPLE 4 Show that $5 + 7 = 12$.

SOLUTION

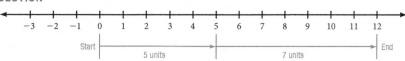

EXAMPLE 5 Show that $5 + (-7) = -2$.

SOLUTION

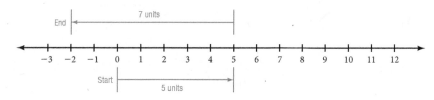

EXAMPLE 6 Show that $-5 + 7 = 2$.

SOLUTION

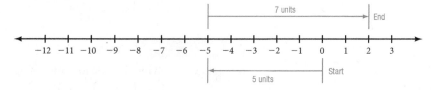

EXAMPLE 7 Show that $-5 + (-7) = -12$.

SOLUTION

If we look closely at the results of the preceding addition problems, we can see that they support (or justify) the following rule.

Note This rule is what we have been working towards. The rule is very important. Be sure that you understand it and can use it. The problems we have done up to this point have been done simply to justify this rule. Now that we have the rule, we no longer need to do our addition problems on the number line.

RULE

To add two real numbers with

1. The *same* sign: Simply add their absolute values and use the common sign. (If both numbers are positive, the answer is positive. If both numbers are negative, the answer is negative.)
2. *Different* signs: Subtract the smaller absolute value from the larger. The answer will have the sign of the number with the larger absolute value.

This rule covers all possible combinations of addition with real numbers. You must memorize it. After you have worked a number of problems, it will seem almost automatic.

EXAMPLE 8   Add all combinations of positive and negative 10 and 13.

SOLUTION   Rather than work these problems on the number line, we use the rule for adding positive and negative numbers to obtain our answers:

$$10 + 13 = 23$$
$$10 + (-13) = -3$$
$$-10 + 13 = 3$$
$$-10 + (-13) = -23$$

EXAMPLE 9   Add all possible combinations of positive and negative 12 and 17.

SOLUTION   Applying the rule for adding positive and negative numbers, we have

$$12 + 17 = 29$$
$$12 + (-17) = -5$$
$$-12 + 17 = 5$$
$$-12 + (-17) = -29$$

EXAMPLE 10   Add $-3 + 2 + (-4)$.

SOLUTION   Applying the rule for order of operations, we add left to right:

$$-3 + 2 + (-4) = -1 + (-4)$$
$$= -5$$

EXAMPLE 11   Add $-8 + [2 + (-5)] + (-1)$.

SOLUTION   Adding inside the brackets first and then left to right, we have

$$-8 + [2 + (-5)] + (-1) = -8 + (-3) + (-1)$$
$$= -11 + (-1)$$
$$= -12$$

EXAMPLE 12   Simplify $-10 + 2(-8 + 11) + (-4)$.

SOLUTION   First, we simplify inside the parentheses. Then, we multiply. Finally, we add left to right:

$$-10 + 2(-8 + 11) + (-4) = -10 + 2(3) + (-4)$$
$$= -10 + 6 + (-4)$$
$$= -4 + (-4)$$
$$= -8$$

Translating Words into Symbols

The following table shows a list of common phrases that are used to indicate a sum of two numbers, along with the corresponding mathematical expression.

Phrase	Equivalent Expression
the sum of a and b	$a + b$
a added to b	$b + a$
a increased by b	$a + b$
a plus b	$a + b$
a more than b	$b + a$
the total of a and b	$a + b$
a exceeded by b	$a + b$

EXAMPLE 13   Write the mathematical expression that is equivalent to the phrase, "5 more than the sum of -2 and x."

SOLUTION   This phrase involves two additions. We break the translation down into steps.

"5 more than" $\underline{\quad ? \quad} + 5$

"the sum of" $(\underline{\quad ? \quad} + \underline{\quad ? \quad}) + 5$

"-2 and x" $(-2 + x) + 5$

Arithmetic Sequences

A *sequence* is simply a list of numbers that have been placed in a particular order. In mathematics, most sequences follow some kind of pattern. When we notice a pattern to a sequence of numbers and then use the pattern to extend the sequence, we are using what is called *inductive reasoning*.

The pattern in a sequence of numbers is easy to identify when each number in the sequence comes from the preceding number by adding the same amount each time. This leads us to our next level of classification, in which we classify groups of sequences with a common characteristic.

> (déf) **DEFINITION**   *arithmetic sequence*
>
> An *arithmetic sequence* is a sequence of numbers in which each number (after the first number) comes from adding the same amount to the number before it.

Here is an example of an arithmetic sequence:

$$2, 5, 8, 11, \ldots$$

Each number is obtained by adding 3 to the number before it.

EXAMPLE 14   Each sequence below is an arithmetic sequence. Find the next two numbers in each sequence.

a. 7, 10, 13,...   **b.**   9.5, 10, 10.5,...   **c.** 5, 0, −5,...

SOLUTION   Because we know that each sequence is arithmetic, we know to look for the number that is added to each term to produce the next consecutive term.

a. 7, 10, 13,...: Each term is found by adding 3 to the term before it. Therefore, the next two terms will be 16 and 19.

b. 9.5, 10, 10.5,...: Each term comes from adding 0.5 to the term before it. Therefore, the next two terms will be 11 and 11.5.

c. 5, 0, −5,...: Each term comes from adding −5 to the term before it. Therefore, the next two terms will be $-5 + (-5) = -10$ and $-10 + (-5) = -15$.

Getting Ready for Class

After reading through the preceding section, respond in your own words and in complete sentences.

A. Explain how you would add 3 and −5 on the number line.

B. How do you add two negative numbers?

C. Give three different phrases that could be used to represent the expression $a + b$.

D. What is an arithmetic sequence?

1. Add all combinations of positive and negative 3 and 5. (Look back to Examples 8 and 9.)
2. Add all combinations of positive and negative 6 and 4.
3. Add all combinations of positive and negative 15 and 20.
4. Add all combinations of positive and negative 18 and 12.

Work the following problems. You may want to begin by doing a few on the number line.

5. $6 + (-3)$ 6. $7 + (-8)$ 7. $13 + (-20)$ 8. $15 + (-25)$

9. $18 + (-32)$ 10. $6 + (-9)$ 11. $-6 + 3$ 12. $-8 + 7$

13. $-30 + 5$ 14. $-18 + 6$ 15. $-6 + (-6)$ 16. $-5 + (-5)$

17. $-9 + (-10)$ 18. $-8 + (-6)$ 19. $-10 + (-15)$ 20. $-18 + (-30)$

Work the following problems using the rule for addition of real numbers. You may want to refer back to the rule for order of operations.

21. $5 + (-6) + (-7)$
22. $6 + (-8) + (-10)$

23. $-7 + 8 + (-5)$
24. $-6 + 9 + (-3)$

25. $5 + [6 + (-2)] + (-3)$
26. $10 + [8 + (-5)] + (-20)$

27. $[6 + (-2)] + [3 + (-1)]$
28. $[18 + (-5)] + [9 + (-10)]$

29. $20 + (-6) + [3 + (-9)]$
30. $18 + (-2) + [9 + (-13)]$

31. $-3 + (-2) + [5 + (-4)]$
32. $-6 + (-5) + [-4 + (-1)]$

33. $(-9 + 2) + [5 + (-8)] + (-4)$
34. $(-7 + 3) + [9 + (-6)] + (-5)$

35. $[-6 + (-4)] + [7 + (-5)] + (-9)$ 36. $[-8 + (-1)] + [8 + (-6)] + (-6)$

37. $(-6 + 9) + (-5) + (-4 + 3) + 7$ 38. $(-10 + 4) + (-3) + (-3 + 8) + 6$

The problems that follow involve some multiplication. Be sure that you work inside the parentheses first, then multiply, and finally, add left to right.

39. $-5 + 2(-3 + 7)$
40. $-3 + 4(-2 + 7)$

41. $9 + 3(-8 + 10)$
42. $4 + 5(-2 + 6)$

43. $-10 + 2(-6 + 8) + (-2)$
44. $-20 + 3(-7 + 10) + (-4)$

45. $2(-4 + 7) + 3(-6 + 8)$
46. $5(-2 + 5) + 7(-1 + 6)$

Recall that the word sum indicates addition. Write the numerical expression that is equivalent to each of the following phrases and then simplify.

47. The sum of 5 and 9

48. The sum of 6 and -3

49. Four added to the sum of -7 and -5

50. Six added to the sum of -9 and 1

51. The sum of -2 and -3 increased by 10

52. The sum of -4 and -12 increased by 2

Write the algebraic expression that is equivalent to each of the following phrases. Use *x* to represent the unknown number.

53. The sum of 4 and a number

54. Five more than a number

55. The total of −8 and a number

56. A number added to −6

57. The sum of a number and −2, increased by 3

58. Seven more than the sum of a number and −1

Answer the following questions.

59. What number do you add to −8 to get −5?

60. What number do you add to 10 to get 4?

61. The sum of what number and −6 is −9?

62. The sum of what number and −12 is 8?

Each sequence below is an arithmetic sequence. In each case, find the next two numbers in the sequence.

63. 3, 8, 13, 18, …   **64.** 1, 5, 9, 13, …   **65.** 10, 15, 20, 25, …

66. 10, 16, 22, 28, . . .   **67.** 20, 15, 10, 5, …   **68.** 24, 20, 16, 12, …

69. 6, 0, −6, …   **70.** 1, 0, −1, …   **71.** 8, 4, 0, …

72. 5, 2, −1, …

73. Is the sequence of odd numbers an arithmetic sequence?

74. Is the sequence of squares an arithmetic sequence?

Applying the Concepts

75. Temperature Change The temperature at noon is 12 degrees below 0 Fahrenheit. By 1:00 it has risen 4 degrees. Write an expression using the numbers −12 and 4 to describe this situation.

76. Stock Value On Monday a certain stock gains 2 points. On Tuesday it loses 3 points. Write an expression using positive and negative numbers with addition to describe this situation and then simplify.

77. Gambling On three consecutive hands of draw poker a gambler wins $10, loses $6, and then loses another $8. Write an expression using positive and negative numbers and addition to describe this situation and then simplify.

78. Number Problem You know from your past experience with numbers that subtracting 5 from 8 results in 3 (8 − 5 = 3). What addition problem that starts with the number 8 gives the same result?

79. Checkbook Balance Suppose that you balance your checkbook and find that you are overdrawn by $30; that is, your balance is −$30. Then you go to the bank and deposit $40. Translate this situation into an addition problem, the answer to which gives the new balance in your checkbook.

80. Checkbook Balance The balance in your checkbook is −$25. If you make a deposit of $75, and then write a check for $18, what is the new balance?

Profit, Revenue, and Costs In business, the difference of revenue and cost is profit, or $P = R - C$, where P is profit, R is revenue, and C is costs. The bar charts below show the costs and revenue for the Baby Steps Shoe Company for a recent 5-year period. Use this information to answer the questions below.

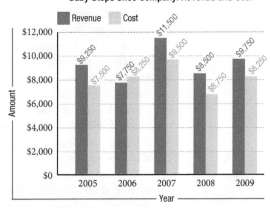

81. What was the profit for the year 2007?

82. In what year was the largest increase in costs from the previous year? How much was the increase?

83. What was the only year the company had a loss? (Profit is negative.) How much was the loss?

Learning Objectives Assessment

The following problems can be used to help assess if you have successfully met the learning objectives for this section.

84. Simplify: $12 + (-17)$.

    a. 5   **b.** -5 **c.** 29   **d.** -29

85. Translate the phrase "four more than -3" into an equivalent numerical expression.

    a. $4 > -3$ **b.** $4 - 3$ **c.** $(-3) + 4$ **d.** $4(-3)$

86. Find the next number in the arithmetic sequence 50, 44, 38, 32, ….

    a. 26   **b.** 28   **c.** 24   **d.** 22

SPOTLIGHT ON SUCCESS   *Student Instructor Cynthia*

Each time we face our fear, we gain strength,
courage, and confidence in the doing.
—Unknown

I must admit, when it comes to math, it takes me longer to learn the material compared to other students. Because of that, I was afraid to ask questions, especially when it seemed like everyone else understood what was going on. Because I wasn't getting my questions answered, my quiz and exam scores were only getting worse. I realized that I was already paying a lot to go to college and that I couldn't afford to keep doing poorly on my exams. I learned how to overcome my fear of asking questions by studying the material before class, and working on extra problem sets until I was confident enough that at least I understood the main concepts. By preparing myself beforehand, I would often end up answering the question myself. Even when that wasn't the case, the professor knew that I tried to answer the question on my own. If you want to be successful, but you are afraid to ask a question, try putting in a little extra time working on problems before you ask your instructor for help. I think you will find, like I did, that it's not as bad as you imagined it, and you will have overcome an obstacle that was in the way of your success.

Subtraction of Real Numbers

Learning Objectives

In this section, we will learn how to:

1. Subtract real numbers.

2. Translate a phrase involving subtraction into a mathematical expression.

Introduction

Suppose that the temperature at noon is 20° Fahrenheit and 12 hours later, at midnight, it has dropped to −15° Fahrenheit. What is the difference between the temperature at noon and the temperature at midnight? Intuitively, we know the difference in the two temperatures is 35°. We also know that the word difference indicates subtraction. The difference between 20 and −15 is written

$$20 - (-15)$$

It must be true that $20 - (-15) = 35$. In this section we will see how our definition for subtraction confirms that this last statement is in fact correct.

In the previous section we spent some time developing the rule for addition of real numbers. Because we want to make as few rules as possible, we can define subtraction in terms of addition. By doing so, we can then use the rule for addition to solve our subtraction problems.

⟦Δ≠Σ⟧ RULE

To subtract one real number from another, simply add its opposite.

Algebraically, the rule is written like this: If a and b represent two real numbers, then it is always true that

$$\underbrace{a - b}_{\text{To subtract } b} = \underbrace{a + (-b)}_{\text{add the opposite of } b}$$

This is how subtraction is defined in algebra. This definition of subtraction will not conflict with what you already know about subtraction, but it will allow you to do subtraction using negative numbers.

VIDEO EXAMPLES

SECTION 1.4

EXAMPLE 1 Subtract all possible combinations of positive and negative 7 and 2.

SOLUTION

$$
\begin{aligned}
7 - 2 &= 7 + (-2) = 5 \\
-7 - 2 &= -7 + (-2) = -9
\end{aligned}
\left.\right\} \quad \text{Subtracting 2 is the same as adding } -2
$$

$$
\begin{aligned}
7 - (-2) &= 7 + 2 = 9 \\
-7 - (-2) &= -7 + 2 = -5
\end{aligned}
\left.\right\} \quad \text{Subtracting } -2 \text{ is the same as adding 2}
$$

Notice that each subtraction problem is first changed to an addition problem. The rule for addition is then used to arrive at the answer.

We have defined subtraction in terms of addition, and we still obtain answers consistent with the answers we are used to getting with subtraction. Moreover, we now can do subtraction problems involving both positive and negative numbers.

As you proceed through the following examples and the problem set, you will begin to notice shortcuts you can use in working the problems. You will not always have to change subtraction to addition of the opposite to be able to get answers quickly. Use all the shortcuts you wish as long as you consistently get the correct answers.

EXAMPLE 2   Subtract all combinations of positive and negative 8 and 13.

SOLUTION

$$8 - 13 = 8 + (-13) = -5$$
$$-8 - 13 = -8 + (-13) = -21$$

Subtracting $+13$ is the same as adding -13

$$8 - (-13) = 8 + 13 = 21$$
$$-8 - (-13) = -8 + 13 = 5$$

Subtracting -13 is the same as adding $+13$

EXAMPLE 3   Simplify each expression as much as possible.

a. $7 + (-3) - 5$ **b.** $8 - (-2) - 6$ **c.** $-2 - (-3 + 1) - 5$

SOLUTION

a. $7 + (-3) - 5 = 7 + (-3) + (-5)$
$\qquad\qquad\qquad = 4 + (-5)$
$\qquad\qquad\qquad = -1$

Begin by changing all subtractions to additions

Then add left to right

b. $8 - (-2) - 6 = 8 + 2 + (-6)$
$\qquad\qquad\qquad = 10 + (-6)$
$\qquad\qquad\qquad = 4$

Begin by changing all subtractions to additions

Then add left to right

c. $-2 - (-3 + 1) - 5 = -2 - (-2) - 5$
$\qquad\qquad\qquad\qquad = -2 + 2 + (-5)$
$\qquad\qquad\qquad\qquad = -5$

Do what is in the parentheses first

The next two examples involve multiplication and exponents as well as subtraction. Remember, according to the order of operations, we evaluate the numbers containing exponents and multiply before we subtract.

EXAMPLE 4   Simplify $2 \cdot 5 - 3 \cdot 8 - 4 \cdot 9$.

SOLUTION   First, we multiply left to right, and then we subtract:

$$2 \cdot 5 - 3 \cdot 8 - 4 \cdot 9 = 10 - 24 - 36$$
$$= -14 - 36$$
$$= -50$$

EXAMPLE 5   Simplify $3 \cdot 2^3 - 2 \cdot 4^2$.

SOLUTION   We begin by evaluating each number that contains an exponent. Then we multiply before we subtract:

$$3 \cdot 2^3 - 2 \cdot 4^2 = 3 \cdot 8 - 2 \cdot 16$$
$$= 24 - 32$$
$$= -8$$

EXAMPLE 6   Subtract 7 from -3.

SOLUTION   First, we write the problem in terms of subtraction. We then change to addition of the opposite:

$$-3 - 7 = -3 + (-7)$$
$$= -10$$

EXAMPLE 7   Subtract -5 from 2.

SOLUTION   Subtracting -5 is the same as adding $+5$:

$$2 - (-5) = 2 + 5$$
$$= 7$$

EXAMPLE 8   Find the difference of 9 and 2.

SOLUTION   Written in symbols, the problem looks like this:

$$9 - 2 = 7$$

The difference of 9 and 2 is 7.

EXAMPLE 9   Find the difference of 3 and -5.

SOLUTION   Subtracting -5 from 3 we have

$$3 - (-5) = 3 + 5$$
$$= 8$$

Translating Words into Symbols

The following table shows a list of common phrases that are used to indicate a subtraction of two numbers, along with the corresponding mathematical expression.

Phrase	Equivalent Expression
the difference of a and b	$a - b$
a subtracted from b	$b - a$
a decreased by b	$a - b$
a minus b	$a - b$
a less than b	$b - a$
a reduced by b	$a - b$
a fewer than b	$b - a$

EXAMPLE 10   Write the mathematical expression that is equivalent to the phrase, "9 less than the difference of x and -4."

SOLUTION   This phrase involves two subtractions. Here is the translation, broken down into steps.

"9 less than"	$\underline{\quad ? \quad} - 9$
"the difference of"	$[\underline{\quad ? \quad} - \underline{\quad ? \quad}] - 9$
"x and -4"	$[x - (-4)] - 9$

Subtracting and Taking Away

For some people taking algebra for the first time, subtraction of positive and negative numbers can be a problem. These people may believe that $-5 - 9$ should be -4 or 4, not -14. If this is happening to you, you probably are thinking of subtraction in terms of taking one number away from another. Thinking of subtraction in this way works well with positive numbers if you always subtract the smaller number from the larger. In algebra, however, we encounter many situations other than this. The definition of subtraction, that $a - b = a + (-b)$, clearly indicates the correct way to use subtraction; that is, when working subtraction problems, you should think "addition of the opposite," not "take one number away from another." To be successful in algebra, you need to apply properties and definitions exactly as they are presented here.

Getting Ready for Class

After reading through the preceding section, respond in your own words and in complete sentences.

A. Why do we define subtraction in terms of addition?

B. Write the definition for $a - b$.

C. Explain in words how you would subtract 3 from -7.

D. Explain how it is possible to subtract two negative numbers and get a positive result.

The following problems are intended to give you practice with subtraction of positive and negative numbers. Remember, in algebra subtraction is not taking one number away from another. Instead, subtracting a number is equivalent to adding its opposite.

Subtract.

1. $5 - 8$ **2.** $6 - 7$ **3.** $3 - 9$ **4.** $2 - 7$

5. $5 - 5$ **6.** $8 - 8$ **7.** $-8 - 2$ **8.** $-6 - 3$

9. $-4 - 12$ **10.** $-3 - 15$ **11.** $-6 - 6$ **12.** $-3 - 3$

13. $-8 - (-1)$ **14.** $-6 - (-2)$ **15.** $15 - (-20)$ **16.** $20 - (-5)$

17. $-4 - (-4)$ **18.** $-5 - (-5)$

Simplify each expression by following the order of operations.

19. $3 - 2 - 5$ **20.** $4 - 8 - 6$ **21.** $9 - 2 - 3$

22. $8 - 7 - 12$ **23.** $-6 - 8 - 10$ **24.** $-5 - 7 - 9$

25. $-22 + 4 - 10$ **26.** $-13 + 6 - 5$ **27.** $10 - (-20) - 5$

28. $15 - (-3) - 20$ **29.** $8 - (2 - 3) - 5$ **30.** $10 - (4 - 6) - 8$

31. $7 - (3 - 9) - 6$ **32.** $4 - (3 - 7) - 8$ **33.** $5 - (-8 - 6) - 2$

34. $4 - (-3 - 2) - 1$ **35.** $-(5 - 7) - (2 - 8)$ **36.** $-(4 - 8) - (2 - 5)$

37. $-(3 - 10) - (6 - 3)$ **38.** $-(3 - 7) - (1 - 2)$ **39.** $16 - [(4 - 5) - 1]$

40. $15 - [(4 - 2) - 3]$ **41.** $5 - [(2 - 3) - 4]$ **42.** $6 - [(4 - 1) - 9]$

43. $21 - [-(3 - 4) - 2] - 5$ **44.** $30 - [-(10 - 5) - 15] - 25$

The following problems involve multiplication and exponents. Use the order of operations to simplify each expression as much as possible.

45. $2 \cdot 8 - 3 \cdot 5$ **46.** $3 \cdot 4 - 6 \cdot 7$ **47.** $3 \cdot 5 - 2 \cdot 7$

48. $6 \cdot 10 - 5 \cdot 20$ **49.** $5 \cdot 9 - 2 \cdot 3 - 6 \cdot 2$ **50.** $4 \cdot 3 - 7 \cdot 1 - 9 \cdot 4$

51. $3 \cdot 8 - 2 \cdot 4 - 6 \cdot 7$ **52.** $5 \cdot 9 - 3 \cdot 8 - 4 \cdot 5$ **53.** $2 \cdot 3^2 - 5 \cdot 2^2$

54. $3 \cdot 7^2 - 2 \cdot 8^2$ **55.** $4 \cdot 3^3 - 5 \cdot 2^3$ **56.** $3 \cdot 6^2 - 2 \cdot 3^2 - 8 \cdot 6^2$

Rewrite each of the following phrases as an equivalent expression in symbols, and then simplify.

57. Subtract 4 from -7.   **58.** Subtract 5 from -19.

59. Subtract -8 from 12.   **60.** Subtract -2 from 10.

61. Subtract -7 from -5.   **62.** Subtract -9 from -3.

63. Subtract 17 from the sum of 4 and -5.

64. Subtract -6 from the sum of 6 and -3.

Recall that the word *difference* indicates subtraction. The difference of a and b is $a - b$, in that order. Write a numerical expression that is equivalent to each of the following phrases, and then simplify.

65. The difference of 8 and 5.   **66.** The difference of 5 and 8.

67. The difference of -8 and 5.   **68.** The difference of -5 and 8.

69. The difference of 8 and -5.   **70.** The difference of 5 and -8.

Write the algebraic expression that is equivalent to each of the following phrases. Use x to represent the unknown number.

71. A number decreased by 6

72. A number minus -2

73. The difference of -4 and a number

74. Three fewer than a number

75. The sum of a number and 12, decreased by 5

76. The difference of a number and 8, increased by 1

Answer the following questions.

77. What number do you subtract from 8 to get -2?

78. What number do you subtract from 1 to get -5?

79. What number do you subtract from 8 to get 10?

80. What number do you subtract from 1 to get 5?

Applying the Concepts

81. Savings Account Balance A man with $1,500 in a savings account makes a withdrawal of $730. Write an expression using subtraction that describes this situation.

First Bank Account No. 12345			
Date	Withdrawals	Deposits	Balance
1/1/16			1,500
2/2/16	730		

82. Checkbook Balance Bob has $98 in his checking account when he writes a check for $65 and then another check for $53. Write a subtraction problem that gives the new balance in Bob's checkbook. What is his new balance?

83. Gambling A man who has lost $35 playing roulette in Las Vegas wins $15 playing blackjack. He then loses $20 playing the wheel of fortune. Write an expression using the numbers -35, 15, and 20 to describe this situation and then simplify it.

84. Altitude Change An airplane flying at 10,000 feet lowers its altitude by 1,500 feet to avoid other air traffic. Then it increases its altitude by 3,000 feet to clear a mountain range. Write an expression that describes this situation and then simplify it.

85. Temperature Change The temperature inside a weather probe is 73°F before reentry. During reentry the temperature inside the probe increases 10°. On landing it drops 8°F. Write an expression using the numbers 73, 10, and 8 to describe this situation. What is the temperature inside the probe on landing?

86. Temperature Change The temperature at noon is 23°F. Six hours later it has dropped 19°F, and by midnight it has dropped another 10°F. Write a subtraction problem that gives the temperature at midnight. What is the temperature at midnight?

87. **Depreciation** Stacey buys a used car for $4,500. With each year that passes, the car drops $550 in value. Write a sequence of numbers that gives the value of the car at the beginning of each of the first five years she owns it. Can this sequence be considered an arithmetic sequence?

88. **Depreciation** Wade buys a computer system for $6,575. Each year after that he finds that the system is worth $1,250 less than it was the year before. Write a sequence of numbers that gives the value of the computer system at the beginning of each of the first four years he owns it. Can this sequence be considered an arithmetic sequence?

89. **Grass Growth** The bar chart below shows the growth of a certain species of grass over a period of 10 days.

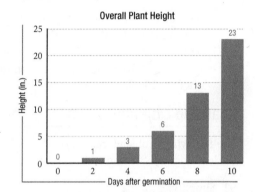

Day	Plant Height (inches)
0	0
2	
4	
6	
	13
10	

a. Use the chart to fill in the missing entries in the table.

b. How much higher is the grass after 8 days than after 2 days?

90. **Wireless Phone Costs** The bar chart below shows the cost of wireless phone use over a recent six-year period.

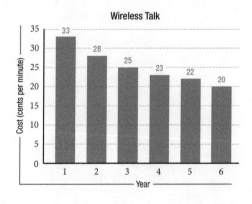

Year	Cents/Minute
1	33
2	
3	
	23
5	
6	

a. Use the chart to fill in the missing entries in the table.

b. What is the difference in cost between Year 1 and Year 2?

91. Triathlon Project Use the chart to answer the following questions.

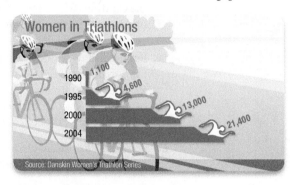

a. Do you think the numbers in the chart have been rounded? If so, to which place were they rounded?

b. How many more participants were there in 2004 than in 2000?

c. If the trend from 2000 to 2004 continued, how many participants were there in 2008?

Learning Objectives Assessment

The following problems can be used to help assess if you have successfully met the learning objectives for this section.

92. Simplify: $-12 - (-17)$.

    a. 29   b. -29 c. -5 d. 5

93. Translate the phrase "four less than -9" into an equivalent numerical expression.

    a. $-9 - 4$ b. $-9 + 4$ c. $4 < -9$ d. $4 - (-9)$

Multiplication and Division of Real Numbers

1.5

Learning Objectives

In this section, we will learn how to:

1. Multiply real numbers.

2. Divide real numbers.

3. Translate a phrase involving multiplication or division into a mathematical expression.

4. Find the next number in a geometric sequence.

Introduction

Suppose that you own 5 shares of a stock and the price per share drops $3. How much money have you lost? Intuitively, we know the loss is $15. Because it is a loss, we can express it as $-$15. To describe this situation with numbers, we would write

$$5(-3) = -15$$

Reasoning in this manner, we conclude that the product of a positive number with a negative number is a negative number. Let's look at multiplication in more detail.

Multiplication

From our experience with counting numbers, we know that multiplication is simply repeated addition; that is, $3(5) = 5 + 5 + 5$. We will use this fact, along with our knowledge of negative numbers, to develop the rule for multiplication of any two real numbers. The following example illustrates multiplication with all of the possible combinations of positive and negative numbers.

EXAMPLE 1   Multiply.

a. $3(5)$ **b.** $3(-5)$ **c.** $-3(5)$ **d.** $-3(-5)$

SOLUTION

a. Two positives: $3(5) = 5 + 5 + 5$

$\qquad\qquad\qquad\quad = 15$ Positive answer

b. One positive: $3(-5) = -5 + (-5) + (-5)$

$\qquad\qquad\qquad\quad = -15$ Negative answer

c. One negative: $-3(5) = 5(-3)$ Commutative property

$\qquad\qquad\qquad\quad = -3 + (-3) + (-3) + (-3) + (-3)$

$\qquad\qquad\qquad\quad = -15$ Negative answer

d. Two negatives: $-3(-5) = ?$

With two negatives, $-3(-5)$, it is not possible to work the problem in terms of repeated addition. (It doesn't "make sense" to write -5 down a -3 number of times.) The answer is probably $+15$ (that's just a guess), but we need some justification for saying so. We will solve a different problem and in doing so get the answer to the problem $(-3)(-5)$.

Note You may have to read the explanation for Example 1(d) several times before you understand it completely. The purpose of the explanation in Example 1(d) is simply to justify the fact that the product of two negative numbers is a positive number. If you have no trouble believing that, then it is not so important that you understand everything in the explanation.

Here is a problem to which we know the answer. We will work it two different ways.

$$-3[5 + (-5)] = -3(0) = 0$$

The answer is zero. We also can work the problem using the distributive property.

$$-3[5 + (-5)] = -3(5) + (-3)(-5) \quad \text{Distributive property}$$
$$= -15 + ?$$

Because the answer to the problem is 0, our ? must be $+15$. (What else could we add to -15 to get 0? Only $+15$.)

Here is a summary of the results we have obtained from the first four examples:

Original Numbers Have		The Answer is
the same sign	$3(5) = 15$	positive
different signs	$3(-5) = -15$	negative
different signs	$-3(5) = -15$	negative
the same sign	$-3(-5) = 15$	positive

By examining Example 1 and the preceding table, we can use the information there to write the following rule. This rule tells us how to multiply any two real numbers.

⟨Δ≠Σ RULE

To multiply any two real numbers, simply multiply their absolute values. The sign of the answer is

1. *Positive* if both numbers have the same sign (both + or both −).

2. *Negative* if the numbers have opposite signs (one +, the other −).

The following example illustrates how we use the preceding rule to multiply real numbers.

EXAMPLE 2   Multiply.

a. $-8(-3) = 24$

b. $-10(-5) = 50$ If the two numbers in the product have the same

c. $-4(-7) = 28$ sign, the answer is positive

d. $5(-7) = -35$

e. $-4(8) = -32$ If the two numbers in the product have different

f. $-6(10) = -60$ signs, the answer is negative

Note: Students have trouble with the expression $-8(-3)$ because they want to subtract rather than multiply. Because we are very precise with the notation we use in algebra, the expression $-8(-3)$ has only one meaning—multiplication. A subtraction problem that uses the same numbers is $-8 - 3$. Compare the two following lists.

All Multiplication	No Multiplication
$5(4)$	$5 + 4$
$-5(4)$	$-5 + 4$
$5(-4)$	$5 - 4$
$-5(-4)$	$-5 - 4$

In the following example, we combine the order of operations with the rule for multiplication to simplify expressions. Remember, the order of operations specifies that we are to work inside the parentheses first and then simplify numbers containing exponents. After this, we multiply and divide, left to right. The last step is to add and subtract, left to right.

EXAMPLE 3   Simplify as much as possible.

a. $-5(-3)(-4)$ **b.** $4(-3) + 6(-5) - 10$

c. $(-2)^3$ **d.** $-3(-2)^3 - 5(-4)^2$

e. $6 - 4(7 - 2)$

SOLUTION

a. $-5(-3)(-4) = 15(-4)$

$\qquad\qquad\qquad = -60$

b. $4(-3) + 6(-5) - 10 = -12 + (-30) - 10$ Multiply

$\qquad\qquad\qquad\qquad = -42 - 10$ Add

$\qquad\qquad\qquad\qquad = -52$ Subtract

c. $(-2)^3 = (-2)(-2)(-2)$ Definition of exponents

$\qquad\quad = -8$ Multiply, left to right

d. $-3(-2)^3 - 5(-4)^2 = -3(-8) - 5(16)$ Exponents first

$\qquad\qquad\qquad\quad = 24 - 80$ Multiply

$\qquad\qquad\qquad\quad = -56$ Subtract

e. $6 - 4(7 - 2) = 6 - 4(5)$ Inside parentheses first

$\qquad\qquad\qquad = 6 - 20$ Multiply

$\qquad\qquad\qquad = -14$ Subtract

Division

Suppose you and four friends bought equal shares of an investment for a total of $15,000 and then sold it later for only $13,000. How much did each person lose? Because the total amount of money lost can be represented by $-\$2,000$, and there are 5 people with equal shares, we can represent each person's loss with division:

$$\frac{-\$2,000}{5} = -\$400$$

From this discussion it seems reasonable to say that a negative number divided by a positive number is a negative number. Notice we can rephrase this result in terms of multiplication.

Because $\qquad -400(5) = -2000$

we have $\qquad -\dfrac{2000}{5} = -400$

Whether multiplying or dividing two numbers of unlike signs, the result is a negative number.

Following similar reasoning,

$$\text{Because} \qquad 400(-5) = -2000$$

$$\text{we have} \qquad \frac{-2000}{-5} = 400$$

The quotient of two negative numbers must be positive.

Because every division problem can be written as a multiplication problem, the rule for division of two real numbers is based upon the rule for multiplication.

> **RULE**
>
> To divide any two nonzero real numbers, simply divide their absolute values. The sign of the answer is
> 1. *Positive* if both numbers have the same sign (both + or both −).
> 2. *Negative* if the numbers have opposite signs (one +, the other −).

EXAMPLE 4   Divide.

a. $\dfrac{6}{2}$ **b.** $\dfrac{6}{-2}$ **c.** $\dfrac{-6}{2}$ **d.** $\dfrac{-6}{-2}$

SOLUTION

a. $\dfrac{6}{2} = 3$ \hspace{2cm} The quotient of two positives is positive

b. $\dfrac{6}{-2} = -3$

\hspace{3cm} The quotient of a positive and a negative is a negative

c. $\dfrac{-6}{2} = -3$

d. $\dfrac{-6}{-2} = 3$ \hspace{2cm} The quotient of two negatives is positive

Here are some more examples. If the original numbers have the same signs, the answer will be positive. If the original numbers have different signs, the answer will be negative.

EXAMPLE 5   Divide.

a. $\dfrac{12}{6} = 2$ \hspace{1cm} Like signs give a positive answer

b. $\dfrac{12}{-6} = -2$ \hspace{1cm} Unlike signs give a negative answer

c. $\dfrac{-12}{6} = -2$ \hspace{1cm} Unlike signs give a negative answer

d. $\dfrac{-12}{-6} = 2$ \hspace{1cm} Like signs give a positive answer

e. $\dfrac{15}{-3} = -5$ \hspace{1cm} Unlike signs give a negative answer

f. $\dfrac{-40}{-5} = 8$ \hspace{1cm} Like signs give a positive answer

g. $\dfrac{-14}{2} = -7$ \hspace{1cm} Unlike signs give a negative answer

Note It is important to remember that we cannot divide by 0. Dividing any number, positive or negative, by zero gives an *undefined* expression for an answer.

From the examples we have done so far, we can make the following generalization about quotients that contain negative signs:

If a and b are numbers and b is not equal to 0, then

$$\frac{-a}{b} = \frac{a}{-b} = -\frac{a}{b} \quad \text{and} \quad \frac{-a}{-b} = \frac{a}{b}$$

The last step in each of the following examples involves reducing a fraction to lowest terms. Recall that to reduce a fraction to lowest terms, we divide the numerator and denominator by the largest number that divides each of them exactly.

EXAMPLE 6   Simplify as much as possible.

a. $\dfrac{-4(5)}{6}$ **b.** $\dfrac{30}{-4 - 5}$

SOLUTION

Note When there is one negative sign in a fraction (either in the numerator or denominator, but not both), it is customary to write the final answer with the negative sign before the entire fraction. In other words,

$$\frac{-10}{3} = \frac{10}{-3} = -\frac{10}{3}$$

a. $\dfrac{-4(5)}{6} = \dfrac{-20}{6}$ Simplify numerator

$\qquad\quad = -\dfrac{10}{3}$ Reduce to lowest terms by dividing numerator and denominator by 2

b. $\dfrac{30}{-4 - 5} = \dfrac{30}{-9}$ Simplify denominator

$\qquad\qquad = -\dfrac{10}{3}$ Reduce to lowest terms by dividing numerator and denominator by 3

In the examples that follow, the numerators and denominators contain expressions that are somewhat more complicated than those we have seen thus far. To apply the rule for order of operations to these examples, we treat fraction bars the same way we treat grouping symbols; that is, fraction bars separate numerators and denominators so that each will be simplified separately.

EXAMPLE 7   Simplify.

a. $\dfrac{2(-3) + 4}{12}$ **b.** $\dfrac{5(-4) + 6(-1)}{2(3) - 4(1)}$

SOLUTION

a. $\dfrac{2(-3) + 4}{12} = \dfrac{-6 + 4}{12}$ In the numerator, we multiply before we add

$\qquad\qquad = \dfrac{-2}{12}$ Addition

$\qquad\qquad = -\dfrac{1}{6}$ Reduce to lowest terms by dividing the numerator and the denominator by 2

b. $\dfrac{5(-4) + 6(-1)}{2(3) - 4(1)} = \dfrac{-20 + (-6)}{6 - 4}$ Multiplication before addition

$\qquad\qquad\qquad = \dfrac{-26}{2}$ Simplify numerator and denominator

$\qquad\qquad\qquad = -13$ Divide -26 by 2

We must be careful when we are working with expressions such as $(-5)^2$ and -5^2 that we include the negative sign with the base only when parentheses indicate we are to do so.

Unless there are parentheses to indicate otherwise, we consider the base to be only the number directly below and to the left of the exponent. If we want to include a negative sign with the base, we must use parentheses.

To simplify a more complicated expression, we follow the same rule. For example,

$$-7^2 - 3^2 = -49 - 9$$

The bases are 7 and 3; the sign between the two terms is a subtraction sign ·

For another example,

$$5^3 - 3^4 = 125 - 81$$

We simplify exponents first, then subtract

EXAMPLE 8   Simplify.

a. $\dfrac{5^2 - 3^2}{-5 + 3}$ **b.** $\dfrac{(3 + 2)^2}{-3^2 - 2^2}$

SOLUTION

a. $\dfrac{5^2 - 3^2}{-5 + 3} = \dfrac{25 - 9}{-2}$ Simplify numerator and denominator separately

$$= \dfrac{16}{-2}$$

$$= -8$$

b. $\dfrac{(3 + 2)^2}{-3^2 - 2^2} = \dfrac{5^2}{-9 - 4}$ Simplify numerator and denominator separately

$$= \dfrac{25}{-13}$$

$$= -\dfrac{25}{13}$$

Translating Words into Symbols

The following table shows a list of common phrases that are used to indicate a product or quotient of two numbers, along with the corresponding mathematical expression.

Phrase	Equivalent Expression
the product of a and b	$a \cdot b$
a times b	$a \cdot b$
a multiplied by b	$a \cdot b$
twice b	$2b$
the quotient of a and b	$\dfrac{a}{b}$
the ratio of a to b	$\dfrac{a}{b}$
a divided by b	$\dfrac{a}{b}$
a into b	$\dfrac{b}{a}$

EXAMPLE 9   Write the mathematical expression that is equivalent to the phrase, "The quotient of two and one less than the product of x and y."

SOLUTION   This phrase involves a division, a multiplication and a subtraction. Here are the steps.

"The quotient of 2 and" $\dfrac{2}{?}$

"one less than" $\dfrac{2}{\underline{?}\ -\ 1}$

"the product of x and y" $\dfrac{2}{x \cdot y - 1}$

Division with the Number 0

As we discussed previously, for every division problem there is an associated multiplication problem involving the same numbers. We can use this relationship between division and multiplication to clarify division involving the number 0.

First, dividing 0 by a number other than 0 is allowed and always results in 0. To see this, consider dividing 0 by 5. We know the answer is 0 because of the relationship between multiplication and division. This is how we write it:

$$\frac{0}{5} = 0 \qquad \text{because} \qquad 0 = 0(5)$$

However, dividing a nonzero number by 0 is not allowed in the real numbers. Suppose we were attempting to divide 5 by 0. We don't know if there is an answer to this problem, but if there is, let's say the answer is a number that we can represent with the letter n. If 5 divided by 0 is a number n, then

$$\frac{5}{0} = n \qquad \text{and} \qquad 5 = n(0)$$

This is impossible, because no matter what number n is, when we multiply it by 0 the answer must be 0. It can never be 5. In algebra, we say expressions like $\frac{5}{0}$ are undefined because there is no answer to them; that is, division by 0 is not allowed in the real numbers.

The only other possibility for division involving the number 0 is 0 divided by 0. We will treat problems like $\frac{0}{0}$ as if they were undefined also.

Application

EXAMPLE 10   Figure 1 gives the calories that are burned in 1 hour for a variety of exercise by a person weighing 150 pounds. Figure 2 gives the calories that are consumed by eating some popular fast foods. Find the net change in calories for a 150-pound person playing handball for 2 hours and then eating a Whopper.

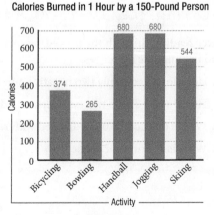

Calories Burned in 1 Hour by a 150-Pound Person

FIGURE 1

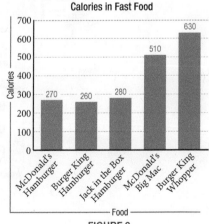

Calories in Fast Food

FIGURE 2

SOLUTION   The net change in calories will be the difference of the calories gained from eating and the calories lost from exercise.

$$\text{Net change in calories} = 630 - 2(680) = -730 \text{ calories}$$

Geometric Sequences

> ### DEFINITION   *geometric sequence*
>
> A *geometric sequence* is a sequence of numbers in which each number (after the first number) comes from the number before it by multiplying by the same amount each time.

For example, the sequence

$$2, 6, 18, 54,\ldots$$

is a geometric sequence because each number is obtained by multiplying the number before it by 3.

EXAMPLE 11   Each sequence below is a geometric sequence. Find the next number in each sequence.

a. $5, 10, 20,\ldots$ **b.** $3, -15, 75,\ldots$ **c.** $8, 4, 2,\ldots$

SOLUTION   Because each sequence is a geometric sequence, we know that each term is obtained from the previous term by multiplying by the same number each time.

a. $5, 10, 20,\ldots$: Starting with 5, each number is obtained from the previous number by multiplying by 2 each time. The next number will be $20 \cdot 2 = 40$.

b. $3, -15, 75,\ldots$: The sequence starts with 3. After that, each number is obtained by multiplying by -5 each time. The next number will be $75(-5) = -375$.

c. $8, 4, 2,\ldots$: This sequence starts with 8. Multiplying each number in the sequence by 0.5 produces the next number in the sequence. To extend the sequence, we multiply 2 by 0.5: $2(0.5) = 1$. The next number in the sequence is 1.

Getting Ready for Class

After reading through the preceding section, respond in your own words and in complete sentences.

A. How do you multiply two negative numbers?

B. How do you divide two numbers with different signs?

C. Why is division by 0 not allowed with real numbers?

D. What is a geometric sequence?

Use the rule for multiplying real numbers to find each of the following products.

1. $7(-6)$ **2.** $8(-4)$ **3.** $-8(2)$ **4.** $-16(3)$

5. $-3(-1)$ **6.** $-7(-1)$ **7.** $-11(-11)$ **8.** $-12(-12)$

9. $-3(2)(-1)$ **10.** $-2(3)(-4)$ **11.** $-3(-4)(-5)$ **12.** $-5(-6)(-7)$

13. $-2(-4)(-3)(-1)$ **14.** $-1(-3)(-2)(-1)$

15. $(-7)^2$ **16.** $(-8)^2$ **17.** $(-3)^3$ **18.** $(-2)^4$

Find the following quotients (divide).

19. $\dfrac{8}{-4}$ **20.** $\dfrac{10}{-5}$ **21.** $\dfrac{-48}{16}$ **22.** $\dfrac{-32}{4}$

23. $\dfrac{-7}{21}$ **24.** $\dfrac{-25}{100}$ **25.** $\dfrac{-39}{-13}$ **26.** $\dfrac{-18}{-6}$

27. $\dfrac{-6}{-42}$ **28.** $\dfrac{-4}{-28}$ **29.** $\dfrac{0}{-32}$ **30.** $\dfrac{0}{17}$

The following problems review all four operations with positive and negative numbers. Perform the indicated operations.

31. $-3 + 12$ **32.** $5 + (-10)$ **33.** $-3 - 12$ **34.** $5 - (-10)$

35. $-3(12)$ **36.** $5(-10)$ **37.** $-3 \div 12$ **38.** $5 \div (-10)$

The following problems involve more than one operation. Use the order of operations to simplify each expression as much as possible.

39. $\dfrac{3(-2)}{-10}$ **40.** $\dfrac{4(-3)}{24}$ **41.** $\dfrac{-5(-5)}{-15}$

42. $\dfrac{-7(-3)}{-35}$ **43.** $\dfrac{-8(-7)}{-28}$ **44.** $\dfrac{-3(-9)}{-6}$

45. $-2(2 - 5)$ **46.** $-3(3 - 7)$ **47.** $-5(8 - 10)$

48. $-4(6 - 12)$ **49.** $(4 - 7)(6 - 9)$ **50.** $(3 - 10)(2 - 6)$

51. $(-3 - 2)(-5 - 4)$ **52.** $(-3 - 6)(-2 - 8)$ **53.** $-3(-6) + 4(-1)$

54. $-4(-5) + 8(-2)$ **55.** $2(3) - 3(-4) + 4(-5)$ **56.** $5(4) - 2(-1) + 5(6)$

57. $\dfrac{27}{4 - 13}$ **58.** $\dfrac{27}{13 - 4}$ **59.** $\dfrac{20 - 6}{5 - 5}$

60. $\dfrac{10 - 12}{3 - 3}$ **61.** $\dfrac{-3 + 9}{2 \cdot 5 - 10}$ **62.** $\dfrac{2 + 8}{2 \cdot 4 - 8}$

63. $\dfrac{15(-5) - 25}{2(-10)}$ **64.** $\dfrac{10(-3) - 20}{5(-2)}$ **65.** $\dfrac{27 - 2(-4)}{-3(5)}$

66. $\dfrac{20 - 5(-3)}{10(-3)}$ **67.** $\dfrac{12 - 6(-2)}{12(-2)}$ **68.** $\dfrac{3(-4) + 5(-6)}{10 - 6}$

69. $4(-3)^2 + 5(-6)^2$

70. $2(-5)^2 + 4(-3)^2$

71. $7(-2)^3 - 2(-3)^3$

72. $10(-2)^3 - 5(-2)^4$

73. $6 - 4(8 - 2)$

74. $7 - 2(6 - 3)$

75. $9 - 4(3 - 8)$

76. $8 - 5(2 - 7)$

77. $-4(3 - 8) - 6(2 - 5)$

78. $-8(2 - 7) - 9(3 - 5)$

79. $\dfrac{5^2 - 2^2}{-5 + 2}$

80. $\dfrac{7^2 - 4^2}{-7 + 4}$

81. $\dfrac{8^2 - 2^2}{8^2 + 2^2}$

82. $\dfrac{4^2 - 6^2}{4^2 + 6^2}$

83. $\dfrac{(5 + 3)^2}{-5^2 - 3^2}$

84. $\dfrac{(7 + 2)^2}{-7^2 - 2^2}$

85. $\dfrac{(8 - 4)^2}{8^2 - 4^2}$

86. $\dfrac{(6 - 2)^2}{6^2 - 2^2}$

87. $7 - 2[-6 - 4(-3)]$

88. $6 - 3[-5 - 3(-1)]$

89. $7 - 3[2(-4 - 4) - 3(-1 - 1)]$

90. $5 - 3[7(-2 - 2) - 3(-3 + 1)]$

91. $8 - 6[-2(-3 - 1) + 4(-2 - 3)]$

92. $4 - 2[-3(-1 + 8) + 5(-5 + 7)]$

93. $\dfrac{-4 \cdot 3^2 - 5 \cdot 2^2}{-8(7)}$

94. $\dfrac{-2 \cdot 5^2 + 3 \cdot 2^3}{-3(13)}$

95. $\dfrac{3 \cdot 10^2 + 4 \cdot 10 + 5}{345}$

96. $\dfrac{5 \cdot 10^2 + 6 \cdot 10 + 7}{567}$

97. $\dfrac{7 - [(2 - 3) - 4]}{-1 - 2 - 3}$

98. $\dfrac{2 - [(3 - 5) - 8]}{-3 - 4 - 5}$

99. $\dfrac{6(-4) - 2(5 - 8)}{-6 - 3 - 5}$

100. $\dfrac{3(-4) - 5(9 - 11)}{-9 - 2 - 3}$

101. $\dfrac{3(-5 - 3) + 4(7 - 9)}{5(-2) + 3(-4)}$

102. $\dfrac{-2(6 - 10) - 3(8 - 5)}{6(-3) - 6(-2)}$

103. $\dfrac{|3 - 9|}{3 - 9}$

104. $\dfrac{|4 - 7|}{4 - 7}$

105. Simplify each expression.

    a. $20 \div 4 \cdot 5$ **b.** $-20 \div 4 \cdot 5$ **c.** $20 \div (-4) \cdot 5$

    d. $20 \div 4(-5)$ **e.** $-20 \div 4(-5)$

106. Simplify each expression.

    a. $32 \div 8 \cdot 4$ **b.** $-32 \div 8 \cdot 4$ **c.** $32 \div (-8) \cdot 4$

    d. $32 \div 8(-4)$ **e.** $-32 \div 8(-4)$

Answer the following questions.

107. Five added to the product of 3 and -10 is what number?

108. If the product of -8 and -2 is decreased by 4, what number results?

109. What number results if 8 is subtracted from the product of -9 and 2?

110. What number results if -8 is subtracted from the product of -9 and 2?

111. What is the quotient of -12 and -4?

112. The quotient of -4 and -12 is what number?

113. What number do we divide by -5 to get 2?

114. What number do we divide by -3 to get 4?

115. Twenty-seven divided by what number is -9?

116. Fifteen divided by what number is -3?

117. If the quotient of -20 and 4 is decreased by 3, what number results?

118. If -4 is added to the quotient of 24 and -8, what number results?

Here are some problems you will see later in the book. Simplify.

119. $3(x - 5) + 4$ **120.** $5(x - 3) + 2$

121. $2(3) - 4 - 3(-4)$ **122.** $2(3) + 4(5) - 5(2)$

Each of the following is a geometric sequence. In each case, find the next number in the sequence.

123. $1, 2, 4, \ldots$ **124.** $1, 5, 25, \ldots$ **125.** $10, -20, 40, \ldots$

126. $10, -30, 90, \ldots$ **127.** $3, -6, 12, \ldots$ **128.** $-3, 6, -12, \ldots$

Applying the Concepts

129. Temperature Change The temperature is 25°F at 5:00 in the afternoon. If the temperature drops 6°F every hour after that, what is the temperature at 9:00 in the evening?

130. Investment Value Suppose you purchase $500 worth of a mutual fund and find that the value of your purchase doubles every 2 years. Write a sequence of numbers that gives the value of your purchase every 2 years for the first 10 years you own it. Is this sequence a geometric sequence?

131. Investment Suppose that you and 3 friends bought equal shares of an investment for a total of $15,000 and then sold it later for only $13,600. How much did each person lose?

132. Investment If 8 people invest $500 each in a stamp collection and after a year the collection is worth $3,800, how much did each person lose?

133. Temperature Change Suppose that the temperature outside is dropping at a constant rate. If the temperature is 75°F at noon and drops to 61°F by 4:00 in the afternoon, by how much did the temperature change each hour?

134. Temperature Change In a chemistry class, a thermometer is placed in a beaker of hot water. The initial temperature of the water is 165°F. After 10 minutes the water has cooled to 72°F. If the water temperature drops at a constant rate, by how much does the water temperature change each minute?

135. Internet Mailing Lists A company sells products on the Internet through an email list. They predict that they sell one $50 product for every 25 people on their mailing list.

    a. What is their projected revenue if their list contains 10,000 email addresses?

    b. What is their projected revenue if their list contains 25,000 email addresses?

    c. They can purchase a list of 5,000 email addresses for $5,000. Is this a wise purchase?

136. Internet Mailing Lists A new band has a following on the Internet. They sell their CDs through an email list. They predict that they sell one $15 CD for every 10 people on their mailing list.

a. What is their projected revenue if their list contains 5,000 email addresses?

b. What is their projected revenue if their list contains 20,000 email addresses?

c. If they need to make $45,000, how many people do they need on their email list?

137. Reading Charts Refer to the bar charts below to find the net change in calories for a 150-pound person who bowls for 3 hours and then eats 2 Whoppers.

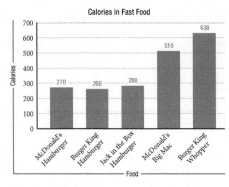

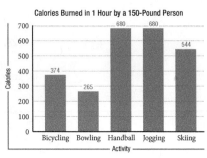

Learning Objectives Assessment

The following problems can be used to help assess if you have successfully met the learning objectives for this section.

138. Multiply: $-9(-5)$.

a. -45 b. 45 c. 14 d. -14

139. Divide: $\dfrac{-18}{0}$.

a. Undefined   b. 1 c. 0 d. -18

140. Translate into symbols: the quotient of 3 and the sum of x and 1.

a. $3(x + 1)$ b. $\dfrac{3}{x} + 1$ c. $\dfrac{3}{x + 1}$ d. $\dfrac{x + 1}{3}$

141. Find the next number in the geometric sequence $2, -6, 18, -54, \ldots$.

a. 108 b. 162 c. -162 d. -108

Fractions

Learning Objectives

In this section, we will learn how to:

1. Factor a number into a product of primes.
2. Reduce a fraction to lowest terms.
3. Find the reciprocal of a number.
4. Multiply and divide fractions.
5. Add and subtract fractions.

Introduction

In Section 1.2, we introduced the concept of a fraction, and learned how to obtain an equivalent fraction using multiplication or division. Now we will continue our study of fractions by learning how to multiply, divide, add, or subtract them. But before we do so, we need to consider some things involving prime numbers.

Prime Numbers and Factoring

The following diagram shows the relationship between multiplication and factoring:

Multiplication

$$\text{Factors} \longrightarrow 3 \cdot 4 = 12 \longleftarrow \text{Product}$$

Factoring

When we read the problem from left to right, we say the product of 3 and 4 is 12. Or we multiply 3 and 4 to get 12. When we read the problem in the other direction, from right to left, we say we have *factored* 12 into 3 times 4, or 3 and 4 are *factors* of 12.

The number 12 can be factored still further:

$$\begin{aligned} 12 &= 4 \cdot 3 \\ &= 2 \cdot 2 \cdot 3 \\ &= 2^2 \cdot 3 \end{aligned}$$

The numbers 2 and 3 are called *prime factors* of 12 because neither of them can be factored any further.

DEFINITION *factor*

If a and b represent integers, then a is said to be a *factor* (or divisor) of b if a divides b evenly; that is, if a divides b with no remainder.

DEFINITION *prime number*

A *prime number* is any positive integer larger than 1 whose only positive factors (divisors) are itself and 1.

VIDEO EXAMPLES

SECTION 1.6

Note It is customary to write the prime factors in order from smallest to largest.

Note There are some "tricks" to finding the divisors of a number. For instance, if a number ends in 0 or 5, then it is divisible by 5. If a number ends in an even number (0, 2, 4, 6, or 8), then it is divisible by 2. A number is divisible by 3 if the sum of its digits is divisible by 3. For example, 921 is divisible by 3 because the sum of its digits is $9 + 2 + 1 = 12$, which is divisible by 3.

Here is a list of the first few prime numbers.

$$\textbf{Prime numbers} = \{2, 3, 5, 7, 11, 13, 17, 19, 23, 29, 31, 37, 41, \dots\}$$

When a number is not prime, we can factor it into the product of prime numbers. To factor a number into the product of primes, we simply factor it until it cannot be factored further.

EXAMPLE 1   Factor the number 60 into the product of prime numbers.

SOLUTION   We begin by writing 60 as the product of any two positive integers whose product is 60, like 6 and 10:

$$60 = 6 \cdot 10$$

We then factor these numbers:

$$60 = 6 \cdot 10$$
$$= (2 \cdot 3) \cdot (2 \cdot 5)$$
$$= 2 \cdot 2 \cdot 3 \cdot 5$$
$$= 2^2 \cdot 3 \cdot 5$$

EXAMPLE 2   Factor the number 630 into the product of primes.

SOLUTION   Let's begin by writing 630 as the product of 63 and 10:

$$630 = 63 \cdot 10$$
$$= (7 \cdot 9) \cdot (2 \cdot 5)$$
$$= 7 \cdot 3 \cdot 3 \cdot 2 \cdot 5$$
$$= 2 \cdot 3^2 \cdot 5 \cdot 7$$

It makes no difference which two numbers we start with, as long as their product is 630. We will always get the same result because a number has only one set of prime factors.

$$630 = 18 \cdot 35$$
$$= 3 \cdot 6 \cdot 5 \cdot 7$$
$$= 3 \cdot 2 \cdot 3 \cdot 5 \cdot 7$$
$$= 2 \cdot 3^2 \cdot 5 \cdot 7$$

When we have factored a number into the product of its prime factors, we not only know what prime numbers divide the original number, but we also know all of the other numbers that divide it as well. For instance, if we were to factor 210 into its prime factors, we would have $210 = 2 \cdot 3 \cdot 5 \cdot 7$, which means that 2, 3, 5, and 7 divide 210, as well as any combination of products of 2, 3, 5, and 7. That is, because 3 and 7 divide 210, then so does their product 21. Because 3, 5, and 7 each divide 210, then so does their product 105.

$$21 \text{ divides } 210$$

$$210 = 2 \cdot 3 \cdot 5 \cdot 7$$

$$105 \text{ divides } 210$$

Reducing Fractions and Equivalent Fractions

Although there are many ways in which factoring is used in arithmetic and algebra, one simple application is in reducing fractions to lowest terms.

Recall that we reduce fractions to lowest terms by dividing the numerator and denominator by the same number. We can use the prime factorization of numbers to help us reduce fractions with large numerators and denominators.

EXAMPLE 3   Reduce $\dfrac{210}{231}$ to lowest terms.

SOLUTION   First we factor 210 and 231 into the product of prime factors. Then we reduce to lowest terms by dividing the numerator and denominator by any factors they have in common.

$$\frac{210}{231} = \frac{2 \cdot 3 \cdot 5 \cdot 7}{3 \cdot 7 \cdot 11} \qquad \text{Factor the numerator and denominator completely}$$

$$= \frac{2 \cdot 3 \cdot 5 \cdot 7}{3 \cdot 7 \cdot 11} \qquad \text{Divide the numerator and denominator by } 3 \cdot 7$$

$$= \frac{2 \cdot 5}{11}$$

$$= \frac{10}{11}$$

Note The small lines we have drawn through the factors that are common to the numerator and denominator are used to indicate that we have divided the numerator and denominator by those factors.

EXAMPLE 4   Write $\frac{3}{4}$ as an equivalent fraction with denominator 20.

SOLUTION   The denominator of the original fraction is 4. The fraction we are trying to find must have a denominator of 20. We know that if we multiply 4 by 5, we get 20. Property 1 for fractions indicates that we are free to multiply the denominator by 5 as long as we do the same to the numerator.

$$\frac{3}{4} = \frac{3 \cdot 5}{4 \cdot 5} = \frac{15}{20}$$

The fraction $\frac{15}{20}$ is equivalent to the fraction $\frac{3}{4}$. We can accomplish the same result by multiplying or original fraction by the number 1 in the form $\frac{5}{5}$.

$$\frac{3}{4} = \frac{3}{4} \cdot \frac{5}{5} = \frac{15}{20}$$

Reciprocals and Multiplication with Fractions

The next concept we want to cover in this section is the concept of reciprocals. Understanding reciprocals requires some knowledge of multiplication with fractions. To multiply two fractions, we simply multiply numerators and multiply denominators.

EXAMPLE 5 Multiply $\frac{3}{4} \cdot \frac{5}{7}$.

SOLUTION The product of the numerators is 15, and the product of the denominators is 28:

$$\frac{3}{4} \cdot \frac{5}{7} = \frac{3 \cdot 5}{4 \cdot 7} = \frac{15}{28}$$

EXAMPLE 6 Multiply $7\left(\frac{1}{3}\right)$.

SOLUTION The number 7 can be thought of as the fraction $\frac{7}{1}$:

$$7\left(\frac{1}{3}\right) = \frac{7}{1}\left(\frac{1}{3}\right) = \frac{7 \cdot 1}{1 \cdot 3} = \frac{7}{3}$$

EXAMPLE 7 Expand and multiply $\left(\frac{2}{3}\right)^3$.

SOLUTION Using the definition of exponents from the previous section, we have

$$\left(\frac{2}{3}\right)^3 = \frac{2}{3} \cdot \frac{2}{3} \cdot \frac{2}{3} = \frac{8}{27}$$

We can apply the rule for multiplication of positive and negative numbers to fractions in the same way we apply it to other numbers. We multiply absolute values: The product is positive if both fractions have the same sign and negative if they have different signs. Here is an example.

EXAMPLE 8 Multiply.

a. $-\frac{3}{4}\left(\frac{5}{7}\right)$ **b.** $-6\left(\frac{1}{2}\right)$ **c.** $-\frac{2}{3}\left(-\frac{3}{2}\right)$

SOLUTION

a. $-\frac{3}{4}\left(\frac{5}{7}\right) = -\frac{3 \cdot 5}{4 \cdot 7}$ Different signs give a negative answer

$$= -\frac{15}{28}$$

b. $-6\left(\frac{1}{2}\right) = -\frac{6}{1}\left(\frac{1}{2}\right)$ Different signs give a negative answer

$$= -\frac{6}{2}$$

$$= -3$$

c. $-\frac{2}{3}\left(-\frac{3}{2}\right) = \frac{2 \cdot 3}{3 \cdot 2}$ Same signs give a positive answer

$$= \frac{6}{6}$$

$$= 1$$

We are now ready for the definition of reciprocals.

> **def** **DEFINITION** *reciprocals*
>
> Two numbers whose product is 1 are called *reciprocals*.

EXAMPLE 9   Give the reciprocal of each number.

a. 5   **b.** -2 **c.** $\dfrac{1}{3}$ **d.** $-\dfrac{3}{4}$

SOLUTION

	Number	Reciprocal	
a.	5	$\dfrac{1}{5}$	Because $5\left(\frac{1}{5}\right) = \frac{5}{1}\left(\frac{1}{5}\right) = \frac{5}{5} = 1$
b.	-2	$-\dfrac{1}{2}$	Because $-2\left(-\frac{1}{2}\right) = -\frac{2}{1}\left(-\frac{1}{2}\right) = \frac{2}{2} = 1$
c.	$\dfrac{1}{3}$	3	Because $\frac{1}{3}(3) = \frac{1}{3}\left(\frac{3}{1}\right) = \frac{3}{3} = 1$
d.	$-\dfrac{3}{4}$	$-\dfrac{4}{3}$	Because $-\frac{3}{4}\left(-\frac{4}{3}\right) = \frac{12}{12} = 1$

We know that division by the number 2 is the same as multiplication by $\frac{1}{2}$; that is, 6 divided by 2 is 3, which is the same as 6 times $\frac{1}{2}$. Similarly, dividing a number by 5 gives the same result as multiplying by $\frac{1}{5}$. We can extend this idea to all real numbers with the following rule.

> **△≠∑** **RULE**
>
> If a and b represent any two real numbers (b cannot be 0), then it is always true that
>
> $$a \div b = \frac{a}{b} = a\left(\frac{1}{b}\right)$$

Division by a number is the same as multiplication by its reciprocal.

Division with Fractions

We can apply the definition of division to fractions. Because dividing by a fraction is equivalent to multiplying by its reciprocal, we can divide a number by the fraction $\frac{3}{4}$ by multiplying it by the reciprocal of $\frac{3}{4}$, which is $\frac{4}{3}$. For example,

$$\frac{2}{5} \div \frac{3}{4} = \frac{2}{5} \cdot \frac{4}{3} = \frac{8}{15}$$

You may have learned this rule in previous math classes. In some math classes, multiplication by the reciprocal is referred to as "inverting the divisor and multiplying." No matter how you say it, division by any number (except 0) is always equivalent to multiplication by its reciprocal. Here are additional examples that involve division by fractions.

EXAMPLE 10   Divide.

a. $\dfrac{2}{3} \div \dfrac{5}{7}$ **b.** $-\dfrac{3}{4} \div \dfrac{7}{9}$ **c.** $8 \div \left(-\dfrac{4}{5}\right)$

SOLUTION

a. $\dfrac{2}{3} \div \dfrac{5}{7} = \dfrac{2}{3} \cdot \dfrac{7}{5}$ Rewrite as multiplication by the reciprocal

$= \dfrac{14}{15}$ Multiply

b. $-\dfrac{3}{4} \div \dfrac{7}{9} = -\dfrac{3}{4} \cdot \dfrac{9}{7}$ Rewrite as multiplication by the reciprocal

$= -\dfrac{27}{28}$ Multiply

c. $8 \div \left(-\dfrac{4}{5}\right) = \dfrac{8}{1}\left(-\dfrac{5}{4}\right)$ Rewrite as multiplication by the reciprocal

$= -\dfrac{40}{4}$ Multiply

$= -10$ Divide 40 by 4

Adding and Subtracting Fractions

You may recall from previous math classes that to add two fractions with the same denominator, you simply add their numerators and put the result over the common denominator:

$$\frac{3}{4} + \frac{2}{4} = \frac{3+2}{4} = \frac{5}{4}$$

We will justify this process in the next section when we introduce the distributive property. For now, we simply state it as a fact. The reason we add numerators but do not add denominators is that we must follow the distributive property.

In symbols we have the following.

> **RULE**   *Addition and Subtraction with Fractions*
>
> If a, b, and c are integers and c is not equal to 0, then
> $$\frac{a}{c} + \frac{b}{c} = \frac{a+b}{c}$$
> This rule holds for subtraction as well; that is,
> $$\frac{a}{c} - \frac{b}{c} = \frac{a-b}{c}$$

EXAMPLE 11   Find the sum or difference. Reduce all answers to lowest terms. (Assume all variables represent nonzero numbers.)

a. $\dfrac{3}{8} + \dfrac{1}{8}$ **b.** $\dfrac{a+5}{8} - \dfrac{3}{8}$ **c.** $\dfrac{9}{x} - \dfrac{3}{x}$ **d.** $\dfrac{3}{7} + \dfrac{2}{7} - \dfrac{9}{7}$

SOLUTION

a. $\dfrac{3}{8} + \dfrac{1}{8} = \dfrac{3+1}{8}$ Add numerators; keep the same denominator

$= \dfrac{4}{8}$ The sum of 3 and 1 is 4

$= \dfrac{1}{2}$ Reduce to lowest terms

b. $\dfrac{a+5}{8} - \dfrac{3}{8} = \dfrac{a+5-3}{8}$ Combine numerators; keep the same denominator

$\qquad\qquad\quad = \dfrac{a+2}{8}$

c. $\dfrac{9}{x} - \dfrac{3}{x} = \dfrac{9-3}{x}$ Subtract numerators; keep the same denominator

$\qquad\qquad = \dfrac{6}{x}$ The difference of 9 and 3 is 6

d. $\dfrac{3}{7} + \dfrac{2}{7} - \dfrac{9}{7} = \dfrac{3+2-9}{7}$

$\qquad\qquad\quad = \dfrac{-4}{7}$

$\qquad\qquad\quad = -\dfrac{4}{7}$ Unlike signs give a negative answer

As Example 11 indicates, addition and subtraction are simple, straightforward processes when all the fractions have the same denominator. We will now turn our attention to the process of adding fractions that have different denominators. To get started, we need the following definition.

> **(def) DEFINITION** *least common denominator (LCD)*
>
> The *least common denominator (LCD)* for a set of denominators is the smallest number that is exactly divisible by each denominator. (Note that in some books the least common denominator is also called the least common multiple.)
>
> In other words, all the denominators of the fractions involved in a problem must divide into the least common denominator exactly; that is, they divide it without giving a remainder.

EXAMPLE 12   Find the LCD for the fractions $\dfrac{5}{12}$ and $\dfrac{7}{18}$.

Note The ability to find least common denominators is very important in mathematics. The discussion here is a detailed explanation of how to do it.

SOLUTION   The least common denominator for the denominators 12 and 18 must be the smallest number divisible by both 12 and 18. We can factor 12 and 18 completely and then build the LCD from these factors. Factoring 12 and 18 completely gives us

$$12 = 2 \cdot 2 \cdot 3 \qquad\qquad 18 = 2 \cdot 3 \cdot 3$$

Now, if 12 is going to divide the LCD exactly, then the LCD must have factors of $2 \cdot 2 \cdot 3$. If 18 is to divide it exactly, it must have factors of $2 \cdot 3 \cdot 3$. We don't need to repeat the factors that 12 and 18 have in common:

12 divides the LCD

$$12 = 2 \cdot 2 \cdot 3$$
$$18 = 2 \cdot 3 \cdot 3 \qquad \text{LCD} = 2 \cdot 2 \cdot 3 \cdot 3$$

18 divides the LCD

In other words, first we write down the factors of 12, then we attach the factors of 18 that do not already appear as factors of 12. We start with $2 \cdot 2 \cdot 3$ because those are the factors of 12. Then we look at the first factor of 18. It is 2. Because 2 already appears in the expression $2 \cdot 2 \cdot 3$, we don't need to attach another one. Next, we look at the factors $3 \cdot 3$. The expression $2 \cdot 2 \cdot 3$ has one 3. For it to contain the expression $3 \cdot 3$, we attach another 3. The final expression, our LCD, is $2 \cdot 2 \cdot 3 \cdot 3$.

The LCD for 12 and 18 is 36. It is the smallest number that is divisible by both 12 and 18; 12 divides it exactly three times, and 18 divides it exactly two times.

We can use the results of Example 12 to find the sum of the fractions $\frac{5}{12}$ and $\frac{7}{18}$.

EXAMPLE 13   Add $\frac{5}{12} + \frac{7}{18}$.

SOLUTION   We can add fractions only when they have the same denominators. In Example 12 we found the LCD for $\frac{5}{12}$ and $\frac{7}{18}$ to be 36. We change $\frac{5}{12}$ and $\frac{7}{18}$ to equivalent fractions that each have 36 for a denominator.

$$\frac{5}{12} = \frac{5}{12} \cdot \frac{3}{3} = \frac{15}{36}$$

$$\frac{7}{18} = \frac{7}{18} \cdot \frac{2}{2} = \frac{14}{36}$$

The fraction $\frac{15}{36}$ is equivalent to $\frac{5}{12}$, because it was obtained by multiplying both the numerator and denominator by 3. Likewise, $\frac{14}{36}$ is equivalent to $\frac{7}{18}$ because it was obtained by multiplying the numerator and denominator by 2. All we have left to do is to add numerators:

$$\frac{15}{36} + \frac{14}{36} = \frac{29}{36}$$

The sum of $\frac{5}{12}$ and $\frac{7}{18}$ is the fraction $\frac{29}{36}$. Let's write the complete problem again step-by-step.

$$\frac{5}{12} + \frac{7}{18} = \frac{5}{12} \cdot \frac{3}{3} + \frac{7}{18} \cdot \frac{2}{2} \qquad \text{Rewrite each fraction as an equivalent fraction with denominator 36}$$

$$= \frac{15}{36} + \frac{14}{36}$$

$$= \frac{29}{36} \qquad \text{Add numerators; keep the common denominator}$$

EXAMPLE 14   Find the LCD for $\frac{3}{4}$ and $\frac{1}{6}$.

SOLUTION   We factor 4 and 6 into products of prime factors and build the LCD from these factors:

$$\left. \begin{array}{l} 4 = 2 \cdot 2 \\ 6 = 2 \cdot 3 \end{array} \right\} \quad \text{LCD} = 2 \cdot 2 \cdot 3 = 12$$

The LCD is 12. Both denominators divide it exactly; 4 divides 12 exactly three times, and 6 divides 12 exactly two times.

EXAMPLE 15 Add $\frac{3}{4} + \frac{1}{6}$.

SOLUTION In Example 14 we found that the LCD for these two fractions is 12. We begin by changing $\frac{3}{4}$ and $\frac{1}{6}$ to equivalent fractions with denominator 12:

$$\frac{3}{4} = \frac{3}{4} \cdot \frac{3}{3} = \frac{9}{12}$$

$$\frac{1}{6} = \frac{1}{6} \cdot \frac{2}{2} = \frac{2}{12}$$

The fraction $\frac{9}{12}$ is equal to the fraction $\frac{3}{4}$ because it was obtained by multiplying the numerator and denominator of $\frac{3}{4}$ by 3. Likewise, $\frac{2}{12}$ is equivalent to $\frac{1}{6}$ because it was obtained by multiplying the numerator and denominator of $\frac{1}{6}$ by 2. To complete the problem, we add numerators:

$$\frac{9}{12} + \frac{2}{12} = \frac{11}{12}$$

The sum of $\frac{3}{4}$ and $\frac{1}{6}$ is $\frac{11}{12}$. Here is how the complete problem looks:

$$\frac{3}{4} + \frac{1}{6} = \frac{3}{4} \cdot \frac{3}{3} + \frac{1}{6} \cdot \frac{2}{2} \quad \text{Rewrite each fraction as an equivalent fraction with denominator 12}$$

$$= \frac{9}{12} + \frac{2}{12}$$

$$= \frac{11}{12} \quad \text{Add numerators; keep the same denominator}$$

EXAMPLE 16 Subtract $\frac{7}{15} - \frac{3}{10}$.

SOLUTION Let's factor 15 and 10 completely and use these factors to build the LCD:

$$\left. \begin{array}{l} 15 = 3 \cdot 5 \\ 10 = 2 \cdot 5 \end{array} \right\} \quad \text{LCD} = 2 \cdot 3 \cdot 5 = 30$$

15 divides the LCD

10 divides the LCD

Changing to equivalent fractions and subtracting, we have

$$\frac{7}{15} - \frac{3}{10} = \frac{7}{15} \cdot \frac{2}{2} - \frac{3}{10} \cdot \frac{3}{3} \quad \text{Rewrite as equivalent fractions with the LCD for denominator}$$

$$= \frac{14}{30} - \frac{9}{30}$$

$$= \frac{5}{30} \quad \text{Subtract numerators; keep the LCD}$$

$$= \frac{1}{6} \quad \text{Reduce to lowest terms}$$

As a summary of what we have done so far and as a guide to working other problems, we will now list the steps involved in adding and subtracting fractions with different denominators.

> **HOW TO**   *Add or Subtract Any Two Fractions*
>
> **Step 1:**   Factor each denominator completely and use the factors to build the LCD. (Remember, the LCD is the smallest number divisible by each of the denominators in the problem.)
> **Step 2:**   Rewrite each fraction as an equivalent fraction that has the LCD for its denominator.
> **Step 3:**   Add or subtract the numerators of the fractions produced in step 2. This is the numerator of the sum or difference. The denominator of the sum or difference is the LCD.
> **Step 4:**   Reduce the fraction produced in step 3 to lowest terms if it is not already in lowest terms.

The idea behind adding or subtracting fractions is really very simple. We can add or subtract only fractions that have the same denominators. If the fractions we are trying to add or subtract do not have the same denominators, we rewrite each of them as an equivalent fraction with the LCD for a denominator.

Here are some further examples of sums and differences of fractions.

EXAMPLE 17   Add $\dfrac{1}{6} + \dfrac{1}{8} + \dfrac{1}{4}$.

SOLUTION   We begin by factoring the denominators completely and building the LCD from the factors that result:

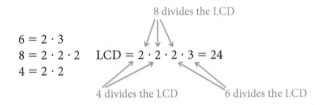

$$
\begin{aligned}
6 &= 2 \cdot 3 \\
8 &= 2 \cdot 2 \cdot 2 \qquad \text{LCD} = 2 \cdot 2 \cdot 2 \cdot 3 = 24 \\
4 &= 2 \cdot 2
\end{aligned}
$$

We then change to equivalent fractions and add as usual:

$$
\begin{aligned}
\frac{1}{6} + \frac{1}{8} + \frac{1}{4} &= \frac{1}{6} \cdot \frac{4}{4} + \frac{1}{8} \cdot \frac{3}{3} + \frac{1}{4} \cdot \frac{6}{6} \\
&= \frac{4}{24} + \frac{3}{24} + \frac{6}{24} \\
&= \frac{13}{24}
\end{aligned}
$$

EXAMPLE 18   Subtract $3 - \dfrac{5}{6}$.

SOLUTION   The denominators are 1 $\left(\text{because } 3 = \tfrac{3}{1}\right)$ and 6. The smallest number divisible by both 1 and 6 is 6.

$$3 - \frac{5}{6} = \frac{3}{1} - \frac{5}{6}$$

$$= \frac{3}{1} \cdot \frac{6}{6} - \frac{5}{6}$$

$$= \frac{18}{6} - \frac{5}{6}$$

$$= \frac{13}{6}$$

EXAMPLE 19   Find the next number in each sequence.

a. $\dfrac{1}{2}, 0, -\dfrac{1}{2}, \ldots$ **b.** $\dfrac{1}{2}, 1, \dfrac{3}{2}, \ldots$ **c.** $\dfrac{1}{2}, \dfrac{1}{4}, \dfrac{1}{8}, \ldots$

SOLUTION

a. $\frac{1}{2}, 0, -\frac{1}{2}, \ldots$: Adding $-\frac{1}{2}$ to each term produces the next term. The fourth term will be $-\frac{1}{2} + \left(-\frac{1}{2}\right) = -1$. This is an arithmetic sequence.

b. $\frac{1}{2}, 1, \frac{3}{2}, \ldots$: Each term comes from the term before it by adding $\frac{1}{2}$. The fourth term will be $\frac{3}{2} + \frac{1}{2} = 2$. This sequence is also an arithmetic sequence.

c. $\frac{1}{2}, \frac{1}{4}, \frac{1}{8}, \ldots$: This is a geometric sequence in which each term comes from the term before it by multiplying by $\frac{1}{2}$ each time. The next term will be $\frac{1}{8} \cdot \frac{1}{2} = \frac{1}{16}$.

Getting Ready for Class

After reading through the preceding section, respond in your own words and in complete sentences.

A. What is the reciprocal of a number?

B. How do we divide fractions?

C. What is a least common denominator?

D. What is the first step in adding two fractions that have different denominators?

Problem Set 1.6

Label each of the following numbers as prime or composite. If a number is composite, then factor it completely.

1. 48   **2.** 72   **3.** 37   **4.** 23

5. 1,023   **6.** 543

Factor the following into the product of primes. When the number has been factored completely, write its prime factors from smallest to largest.

7. 144   **8.** 288   **9.** 38   **10.** 63

11. 105   **12.** 210   **13.** 180   **14.** 900

15. 385   **16.** 1,925   **17.** 121   **18.** 546

19. 420   **20.** 598   **21.** 620   **22.** 2,310

Reduce each fraction to lowest terms by first factoring the numerator and denominator into the product of prime factors and then dividing out any factors they have in common.

23. $\dfrac{105}{165}$ **24.** $\dfrac{165}{385}$ **25.** $\dfrac{525}{735}$ **26.** $\dfrac{550}{735}$ **27.** $\dfrac{385}{455}$ **28.** $\dfrac{385}{735}$

29. $\dfrac{322}{345}$ **30.** $\dfrac{266}{285}$ **31.** $\dfrac{205}{369}$ **32.** $\dfrac{111}{185}$ **33.** $\dfrac{215}{344}$ **34.** $\dfrac{279}{310}$

35. Simplify the expression $3 \cdot 8 + 3 \cdot 7 + 3 \cdot 5$, and then factor the result into the product of primes. (Notice one of the factors of the answer is 3.)

36. Simplify the expression $5 \cdot 4 + 5 \cdot 9 + 5 \cdot 3$, and then factor the result into the product of primes.

Write each of the following fractions as an equivalent fraction with denominator 24.

37. $\dfrac{3}{4}$ **38.** $\dfrac{5}{6}$ **39.** $\dfrac{1}{2}$ **40.** $\dfrac{1}{8}$ **41.** $\dfrac{5}{8}$ **42.** $\dfrac{7}{12}$

Write each fraction as an equivalent fraction with denominator 60.

43. $\dfrac{3}{5}$ **44.** $\dfrac{5}{12}$ **45.** $\dfrac{11}{30}$ **46.** $\dfrac{9}{10}$

Place one of the symbols $<$ or $>$ between each of the following to make the resulting statement true.

47. $-\dfrac{3}{4} \ \square \ -\dfrac{1}{4}$ **48.** $-\dfrac{2}{3} \ \square \ -\dfrac{1}{3}$ **49.** $-\dfrac{3}{2} \ \square \ -\dfrac{3}{4}$ **50.** $-\dfrac{8}{3} \ \square \ -\dfrac{17}{3}$

Multiply the following.

51. $\dfrac{2}{3} \cdot \dfrac{4}{5}$ **52.** $\dfrac{1}{4} \cdot \dfrac{3}{5}$ **53.** $\dfrac{1}{2}(3)$ **54.** $\dfrac{1}{3}(2)$

55. $\dfrac{1}{4}(5)$ **56.** $\dfrac{1}{5}(4)$ **57.** $\dfrac{4}{3} \cdot \dfrac{3}{4}$ **58.** $\dfrac{5}{7} \cdot \dfrac{7}{5}$

59. $6\left(\dfrac{1}{6}\right)$ **60.** $8\left(\dfrac{1}{8}\right)$ **61.** $3 \cdot \dfrac{1}{3}$ **62.** $4 \cdot \dfrac{1}{4}$

Expand and multiply.

63. $\left(\dfrac{3}{4}\right)^2$ **64.** $\left(\dfrac{5}{6}\right)^2$ **65.** $\left(\dfrac{2}{3}\right)^3$ **66.** $\left(\dfrac{1}{2}\right)^3$ **67.** $\left(\dfrac{1}{10}\right)^4$ **68.** $\left(\dfrac{1}{10}\right)^5$

Multiply the following.

69. $-\dfrac{2}{3} \cdot \dfrac{5}{7}$ **70.** $-\dfrac{6}{5} \cdot \dfrac{2}{7}$ **71.** $-8\left(\dfrac{1}{2}\right)$ **72.** $-12\left(\dfrac{1}{3}\right)$

73. $-\dfrac{3}{4}\left(-\dfrac{4}{3}\right)$ **74.** $-\dfrac{5}{8}\left(-\dfrac{8}{5}\right)$ **75.** $\left(-\dfrac{3}{4}\right)^2$ **76.** $\left(-\dfrac{2}{5}\right)^2$

77. $-\dfrac{1}{3}(-3x)$ **78.** $-\dfrac{1}{5}(-5x)$

Divide and reduce all answers to lowest terms.

79. $\dfrac{4}{5} \div \dfrac{3}{4}$ **80.** $\dfrac{6}{8} \div \dfrac{3}{4}$ **81.** $-\dfrac{5}{6} \div \left(-\dfrac{5}{8}\right)$ **82.** $-\dfrac{7}{9} \div \left(-\dfrac{1}{6}\right)$

83. $\dfrac{10}{13} \div \left(-\dfrac{5}{4}\right)$ **84.** $\dfrac{5}{12} \div \left(-\dfrac{10}{3}\right)$ **85.** $-\dfrac{5}{6} \div \dfrac{5}{6}$ **86.** $-\dfrac{8}{9} \div \dfrac{8}{9}$

87. $-\dfrac{3}{4} \div \left(-\dfrac{3}{4}\right)$ **88.** $-\dfrac{6}{7} \div \left(-\dfrac{6}{7}\right)$

89. Simplify each expression.

  a. $8 \div \dfrac{4}{5}$ **b.** $8 \div \dfrac{4}{5} - 10$ **c.** $(-10)8 \div \dfrac{4}{5}$ **d.** $8 \div \left(-\dfrac{4}{5}\right) - 10$

90. Simplify each expression.

  a. $10 \div \dfrac{5}{6}$ **b.** $10 \div \dfrac{5}{6} - 12$ **c.** $(-12)10 \div \dfrac{5}{6}$ **d.** $10 \div \left(-\dfrac{5}{6}\right) - 12$

Find the following sums and differences, and reduce to lowest terms. Assume all variables represent nonzero numbers.

91. $\dfrac{3}{6} + \dfrac{1}{6}$ **92.** $\dfrac{2}{5} + \dfrac{3}{5}$ **93.** $\dfrac{3}{8} - \dfrac{5}{8}$ **94.** $\dfrac{1}{7} - \dfrac{6}{7}$

95. $-\dfrac{1}{4} + \dfrac{3}{4}$ **96.** $-\dfrac{4}{9} + \dfrac{7}{9}$ **97.** $\dfrac{x}{3} - \dfrac{1}{3}$ **98.** $\dfrac{x}{8} - \dfrac{1}{8}$

99. $\dfrac{1}{4} + \dfrac{2}{4} + \dfrac{3}{4}$ **100.** $\dfrac{2}{5} + \dfrac{3}{5} + \dfrac{4}{5}$ **101.** $\dfrac{x+7}{2} - \dfrac{1}{2}$ **102.** $\dfrac{x+5}{4} - \dfrac{3}{4}$

103. $\dfrac{1}{10} - \dfrac{3}{10} - \dfrac{4}{10}$ **104.** $\dfrac{3}{20} - \dfrac{1}{20} - \dfrac{4}{20}$ **105.** $\dfrac{1}{a} + \dfrac{4}{a} + \dfrac{5}{a}$ **106.** $\dfrac{5}{a} + \dfrac{4}{a} + \dfrac{3}{a}$

107.

First Number a	Second Number b	The Sum of a and b $a + b$
$\frac{1}{2}$	$\frac{1}{3}$	
$\frac{1}{3}$	$\frac{1}{4}$	
$\frac{1}{4}$	$\frac{1}{5}$	
$\frac{1}{5}$	$\frac{1}{6}$	

108.

First Number a	Second Number b	The Sum of a and b $a + b$
1	$\frac{1}{2}$	
1	$\frac{1}{3}$	
1	$\frac{1}{4}$	
1	$\frac{1}{5}$	

109.

First Number a	Second Number b	The Sum of a and b $a + b$
$\frac{1}{12}$	$\frac{1}{2}$	
$\frac{1}{12}$	$\frac{1}{3}$	
$\frac{1}{12}$	$\frac{1}{4}$	
$\frac{1}{12}$	$\frac{1}{6}$	

110.

First Number a	Second Number b	The Sum of a and b $a + b$
$\frac{1}{8}$	$\frac{1}{2}$	
$\frac{1}{8}$	$\frac{1}{4}$	
$\frac{1}{8}$	$\frac{1}{16}$	
$\frac{1}{8}$	$\frac{1}{24}$	

Find the LCD for each of the following; then use the methods developed in this section to add and subtract as indicated.

111. $\frac{4}{9} + \frac{1}{3}$ **112.** $\frac{1}{2} + \frac{1}{4}$ **113.** $2 + \frac{1}{3}$ **114.** $3 + \frac{1}{2}$

115. $-\frac{3}{4} + 1$ **116.** $-\frac{3}{4} + 2$ **117.** $\frac{1}{2} + \frac{2}{3}$ **118.** $\frac{2}{3} + \frac{1}{4}$

119. $\frac{5}{12} - \left(-\frac{3}{8}\right)$ **120.** $\frac{9}{16} - \left(-\frac{7}{12}\right)$ **121.** $-\frac{1}{20} + \frac{8}{30}$ **122.** $-\frac{1}{30} + \frac{9}{40}$

123. $\frac{17}{30} + \frac{11}{42}$ **124.** $\frac{19}{42} + \frac{13}{70}$ **125.** $\frac{25}{84} + \frac{41}{90}$ **126.** $\frac{23}{70} + \frac{29}{84}$

127. $\frac{13}{126} - \frac{13}{180}$ **128.** $\frac{17}{84} - \frac{17}{90}$ **129.** $\frac{3}{4} + \frac{1}{8} + \frac{5}{6}$ **130.** $\frac{3}{8} + \frac{2}{5} + \frac{1}{4}$

131. $\frac{1}{2} + \frac{1}{3} + \frac{1}{4} + \frac{1}{6}$ **132.** $\frac{1}{8} + \frac{1}{4} + \frac{1}{5} + \frac{1}{10}$

133. $1 - \frac{5}{2}$ **134.** $1 - \frac{5}{3}$ **135.** $1 + \frac{1}{2}$ **136.** $1 + \frac{2}{3}$

137. Find the sum of $\frac{3}{7}$, 2, and $\frac{1}{9}$. **138.** Find the sum of 6, $\frac{6}{11}$, and 11.

139. Give the difference of $\frac{7}{8}$ and $\frac{1}{4}$. **140.** Give the difference of $\frac{9}{10}$ and $\frac{1}{100}$.

Find the fourth term in each sequence.

141. $\frac{1}{3}, 0, -\frac{1}{3}, \dots$

142. $\frac{2}{3}, 0, -\frac{2}{3}, \dots$

143. $\frac{1}{3}, 1, \frac{5}{3}, \dots$

144. $1, \frac{3}{2}, 2, \dots$

145. $1, \frac{1}{5}, \frac{1}{25}, \dots$

146. $1, -\frac{1}{2}, \frac{1}{4}, \dots$

Find the perimeter of each figure.

147.
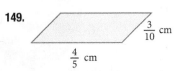
$\frac{3}{8}$ ft

$\frac{3}{8}$ ft

148.
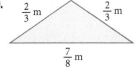
$\frac{4}{15}$ ft

$\frac{9}{20}$ ft

149.
$\frac{3}{10}$ cm

$\frac{4}{5}$ cm

150.
$\frac{2}{3}$ m $\frac{2}{3}$ m

$\frac{7}{8}$ m

Applying the Concepts

151. Sewing If $\frac{6}{7}$ yard of material is needed to make a blanket, how many blankets can be made from 12 yards of material?

152. Manufacturing A clothing manufacturer is making scarves that require $\frac{3}{8}$ yard for material each. How many can be made from 27 yards of material?

153. Capacity Suppose a bag of candy holds exactly $\frac{1}{4}$ pound of candy. How many of these bags can be filled from 12 pounds of candy?

154. Capacity A certain size bottle holds exactly $\frac{4}{5}$ pint of liquid. How many of these bottles can be filled from a 20-pint container?

155. Cooking A man is making cookies from a recipe that calls for $\frac{3}{4}$ teaspoon of oil. If the only measuring spoon he can find is a $\frac{1}{8}$ teaspoon, how many of these will he have to fill with oil in order to have a total of $\frac{3}{4}$ teaspoon of oil?

156. Cooking A cake recipe calls for $\frac{1}{2}$ cup of sugar. If the only measuring cup available is a $\frac{1}{8}$ cup, how many of these will have to be filled with sugar to make a total of $\frac{1}{2}$ cup of sugar?

157. Cartons of Milk If a small carton of milk holds exactly $\frac{1}{2}$ pint, how many of the $\frac{1}{2}$-pint cartons can be filled from a 14-pint container?

158. Pieces of Pipe How many pieces of pipe that are $\frac{2}{3}$ foot long must be laid together to make a pipe 16 feet long?

159. Capacity One carton of milk contains $\frac{1}{2}$ pint while another contains 4 pints. How much milk is contained in both cartons?

160. Baking A recipe calls for $\frac{2}{3}$ cup of flour and $\frac{3}{4}$ cup of sugar. What is the total amount of flour and sugar called for in the recipe?

161. Budget A family decides that they can spend $\frac{5}{8}$ of their monthly income on house payments. If their monthly income is $2,120, how much can they spend for house payments?

162. Savings A family saves $\frac{3}{16}$ of their income each month. If their monthly income is $1,264, how much do they save each month?

Reading a Pie Chart The pie chart below shows how the students at one of the universities in California are distributed among the different schools at the university. Use the information in the pie chart to answer questions 167 and 168.

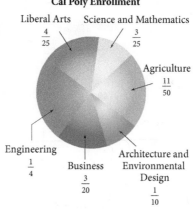

Cal Poly Enrollment

Liberal Arts $\frac{4}{25}$

Science and Mathematics $\frac{3}{25}$

Agriculture $\frac{11}{50}$

Engineering $\frac{1}{4}$

Business $\frac{3}{20}$

Architecture and Environmental Design $\frac{1}{10}$

163. If the students in the Schools of Engineering and Business are combined, what fraction results?

164. What fraction of the university's students are enrolled in the Schools of Agriculture, Engineering, and Business combined?

165. Final Exam Grades The table below gives the fraction of students in a class of 40 that received grades of A, B, or C on the final exam. Fill in all the missing parts of the table.

Grade	Number of Students	Fraction of Students
A		$\frac{1}{8}$
B		$\frac{1}{5}$
C		$\frac{1}{2}$
below C		
Total	40	1

166. Flu During a flu epidemic a company with 200 employees has $\frac{1}{10}$ of their employees call in sick on Monday and another $\frac{3}{10}$ call in sick on Tuesday. What is the total number of employees calling in sick during this 2-day period?

167. Subdivision A 6-acre piece of land is subdivided into $\frac{3}{5}$-acre lots. How many lots are there?

168. Cutting Wood A 12-foot piece of wood is cut into shelves. If each shelf is $\frac{3}{4}$ foot in length, how many shelves are there?

Learning Objectives Assessment

The following problems can be used to help assess if you have successfully met the learning objectives for this section.

169. Factor 132 into a product of primes.

    a. $2 \cdot 3^2 \cdot 7$ **b.** $2^2 \cdot 3 \cdot 11$ **c.** $2 \cdot 66$ **d.** $2 \cdot 3 \cdot 23$

170. Reduce $\frac{126}{168}$ to lowest terms.

    a. $\frac{21}{28}$ **b.** $\frac{63}{84}$ **c.** $\frac{4}{7}$ **d.** $\frac{3}{4}$

171. Find the reciprocal of $-\frac{6}{7}$.

    a. $\frac{6}{7}$ **b.** $-\frac{6}{7}$ **c.** $-\frac{7}{6}$ **d.** $\frac{7}{6}$

172. Divide: $\frac{2}{15} \div \left(-\frac{4}{3}\right)$.

    a. $-\frac{1}{10}$ **b.** $-\frac{8}{45}$ **c.** $\frac{1}{10}$ **d.** $-\frac{2}{5}$

173. Add: $\frac{2}{5} + \frac{4}{3}$.

    a. $\frac{26}{15}$ **b.** $\frac{8}{15}$ **c.** $\frac{3}{4}$ **d.** $\frac{22}{15}$

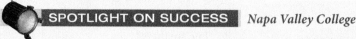 **SPOTLIGHT ON SUCCESS**   *Napa Valley College*

You may think that all your mathematics instructors started their college math sequence with precalculus or calculus, but that is not always the case. Diane Van Deusen, a full time mathematics instructor at Napa Valley College in Napa, California, started her career in mathematics in the same class you are taking. Here is part of her story from her website:

Dear Student,

Welcome to elementary algebra! Since we will be spending a significant amount of time together this semester, I thought I should introduce myself to you, and tell you how I ended up with a career in education.

I was not encouraged to attend college after high school, and in fact, had no interest in "more school". Consequently, I didn't end up taking a college class until I was 31 years old! Before returning to and while attending college, I worked locally in the restaurant business as a waitress and bartender and in catering. In fact, I sometimes wait tables a few nights a week during my summer breaks.

When I first came back to school, at Napa Valley College (NVC), I thought I might like to enter the nursing program but soon found out nursing was not for me. As I started working on general education requirements, I took elementary algebra and was surprised to learn that I really loved mathematics, even though I had failed 8th grade algebra! As I continued to appreciate and value my own education, I decided to become a teacher so that I could support other people seeking education goals. After earning my AA degree from NVC, I transferred to Sonoma State where I earned my bachelor's degree in mathematics with a concentration in statistics. Finally, I attended Cal State Hayward to earn my master's degree in applied statistics. It took me ten years in all to do this.

I feel that having been a returning student while a single, working parent, also an EOPS and Financial Aid recipient, I fully understand the complexity of the life of a community college student. If at any time you have questions about the college, the class or just need someone to talk to, my door is open.

I sincerely hope that my classroom will provide a positive and satisfying learning experience for you.

Diane Van Deusen

Elementary algebra is a great place to start your journey into college mathematics. You can start here and go as far as you want in mathematics. Who knows, you may end up teaching mathematics one day, just like Diane Van Deusen.

Learning Objectives

In this section, we will learn how to:

1. Rewrite expressions using the properties of real numbers.
2. Simplify expressions using the associative properties of addition and multiplication.
3. Simplify expressions using the distributive property.

Introduction

In this section we will list all the facts (properties) that you know from past experience are true about numbers in general. We will give each property a name so we can refer to it later in this book. Mathematics is very much like a game. The game involves numbers. The rules of the game are the properties and rules we are developing in this chapter. The goal of the game is to extend the basic rules to as many situations as possible.

You know from past experience with numbers that it makes no difference in which order you add two numbers; that is, $3 + 5$ is the same as $5 + 3$. This fact about numbers is called the *commutative property of addition*. We say addition is a commutative operation. Changing the order of the numbers does not change the answer.

There is one other basic operation that is commutative. Because $3(5)$ is the same as $5(3)$, we say multiplication is a commutative operation. Changing the order of the two numbers you are multiplying does not change the answer.

For all properties listed in this section, a, b, and c represent real numbers.

[Δ≠Σ] PROPERTY *Commutative Property of Addition*

In symbols: $a + b = b + a$
In words: Changing the **order** of the numbers in a sum will not change the result.

[Δ≠Σ] PROPERTY *Commutative Property of Multiplication*

In symbols: $a \cdot b = b \cdot a$
In words: Changing the **order** of the numbers in a product will not change the result.

VIDEO EXAMPLES

SECTION 1.7

Note At this point, some students are confused by the expression $x + 8$; they feel that there is more to do, but they don't know what. At this point, there isn't any more that can be done with $x + 8$ unless we know what x is. So $x + 8$ is as far as we can go with this problem.

For example, the statement $5 + 8 = 8 + 5$ is an example of the commutative property of addition and the statement $2 \cdot y = y \cdot 2$ is an example of the commutative property of multiplication.

EXAMPLE 1   Simplify: $5 + x + 3$.

SOLUTION   The expression $5 + x + 3$ can be simplified using the commutative property of addition:

$$5 + x + 3 = x + 5 + 3 \qquad \text{Commutative property of addition}$$
$$= x + 8 \qquad \text{Addition}$$

77

The other two basic operations, subtraction and division, are not commutative. The order in which we subtract or divide two numbers makes a difference in the answer.

Another property of numbers that you have used many times has to do with grouping. You know that when we add three numbers it makes no difference which two we add first. When adding $3 + 5 + 7$, we can add the 3 and 5 first and then the 7, or we can add the 5 and 7 first and then the 3. Mathematically, it looks like this: $(3 + 5) + 7 = 3 + (5 + 7)$. This property is true of multiplication as well. Operations that behave in this manner are called *associative* operations. The answer will not change when we change the association (or grouping) of the numbers.

[Δ≠Σ]   PROPERTY   *Associative Property of Addition*

In symbols: $a + (b + c) = (a + b) + c$
In words: Changing the **grouping** of the numbers in a sum will not change the result.

[Δ≠Σ]   PROPERTY   *Associative Property of Multiplication*

In symbols: $a(bc) = (ab)c$
In words: Changing the **grouping** of the numbers in a product will not change the result.

Note Subtraction and division are not associative operations. Using the numbers 24, 12, 2, can you show why they are not?

The following examples illustrate how the associative properties can be used to simplify expressions that involve both real numbers and variables.

EXAMPLE 2   Simplify.

a. $4 + (5 + x)$ **b.** $-5(2x)$ **c.** $6(-5y)$

SOLUTION

a. $4 + (5 + x) = (4 + 5) + x$ Associative property of addition

$= 9 + x$ Addition

b. $-5(2x) = (-5 \cdot 2)x$ Associative property of multiplication

$= -10x$ Multiplication

c. $6(-5y) = [6(-5)]y$ Associative property

$= -30y$ Multiplication

EXAMPLE 3   Simplify.

a. $\frac{1}{5}(5x)$ **b.** $-2\left(-\frac{1}{2}x\right)$ **c.** $12\left(\frac{2}{3}x\right)$

SOLUTION

a. $\frac{1}{5}(5x) = \left(\frac{1}{5} \cdot 5\right)x$ Associative property of multiplication

$= 1x$ Multiplication

$= x$

b.
$$-2\left(-\frac{1}{2}x\right) = \left[(-2)\left(-\frac{1}{2}\right)\right]x \qquad \text{Associative property of multiplication}$$
$$= 1x \qquad \text{Multiplication}$$
$$= x$$

c.
$$12\left(\frac{2}{3}x\right) = \left(12 \cdot \frac{2}{3}\right)x \qquad \text{Associative property of multiplication}$$
$$= 8x \qquad \text{Multiplication}$$

The associative and commutative properties apply to problems that are either all multiplication or all addition. There is a third basic property that involves both addition and multiplication. It is called the *distributive property* and looks like this.

> ⎰Δ≠Σ **PROPERTY** *Distributive Property*
>
> *In symbols:* $a(b + c) = ab + ac$
> *In words:* Multiplication **distributes** over addition.

Note Because subtraction is defined in terms of addition, it is also true that the distributive property applies to subtraction as well as addition; that is, $a(b - c) = ab - ac$ for any three real numbers a, b, and c.

You will see as we progress through the book that the distributive property is used very frequently in algebra. We can give a visual justification to the distributive property by finding the areas of rectangles. Figure 1 shows a large rectangle that is made up of two smaller rectangles. We can find the area of the large rectangle two different ways.

Method 1

We can calculate the area of the large rectangle directly by finding its length and width. The width is 5 inches, and the length is (3 + 4) inches.

$$\text{Area of large rectangle} = 5(3 + 4)$$
$$= 5(7)$$
$$= 35 \text{ square inches}$$

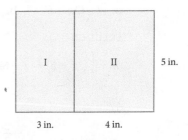

FIGURE 1

Method 2

Because the area of the large rectangle is the sum of the areas of the two smaller rectangles, we find the area of each small rectangle and then add to find the area of the large rectangle.

$$\text{Area of large rectangle} = \text{Area of rectangle I} + \text{Area of rectangle II}$$
$$= \qquad 5(3) \qquad + \qquad 5(4)$$
$$= \qquad 15 \qquad + \qquad 20$$
$$= \qquad 35 \text{ square inches}$$

In both cases the result is 35 square inches. Because the results are the same, the two original expressions must be equal. Stated mathematically, $5(3 + 4) = 5(3) + 5(4)$. We can either add the 3 and 4 first and then multiply that sum by 5, or we can multiply the 3 and the 4 separately by 5 and then add the products. In either case we get the same answer.

Here are some examples that illustrate how we use the distributive property.

EXAMPLE 4   Apply the distributive property to each expression, and then simplify the result.

a. $2(x + 3)$ **b.** $5(2x - 8)$ **c.** $-5(2x + 4y)$ **d.** $-4(3x - 5) - 8$

SOLUTION

a. $2(x + 3) = 2(x) + 2(3)$ Distributive property

             $= 2x + 6$ Multiplication

b. $5(2x - 8) = 5(2x) - 5(8)$ Distributive property

             $= 10x - 40$ Multiplication

Notice in part *b* that multiplication distributes over subtraction as well as addition.

c. $-5(2x + 4y) = -5(2x) + (-5)(4y)$ Distributive property

             $= -10x + (-20y)$ Multiplication

             $= -10x - 20y$

d. $-4(3x - 5) - 8 = -4(3x) - (-4)(5) - 8$ Distributive property

             $= -12x - (-20) - 8$ Multiplication

             $= -12x + 20 - 8$ Definition of subtraction

             $= -12x + 12$ Subtraction

Next we have some expressions to simplify that involve fractions.

EXAMPLE 5   Apply the distributive property to each expression, and then simplify the result.

a. $-\frac{1}{3}(2x - 6)$ **b.** $3\left(\frac{1}{3}x + 5\right)$ **c.** $a\left(1 + \frac{1}{a}\right)$ **d.** $12\left(\frac{2}{3}x + \frac{1}{2}y\right)$

SOLUTION

a. $-\frac{1}{3}(2x - 6) = -\frac{1}{3}(2x) - \left(-\frac{1}{3}\right)(6)$ Distributive property

             $= -\frac{2}{3}x - (-2)$ Multiplication

             $= -\frac{2}{3}x + 2$

b. $3\left(\frac{1}{3}x + 5\right) = 3 \cdot \frac{1}{3}x + 3 \cdot 5$ Distributive property

             $= x + 15$ Multiplication

c. $a\left(1 + \frac{1}{a}\right) = a \cdot 1 + a \cdot \frac{1}{a}$ Distributive property

             $= a + 1$ Multiplication

d. $12\left(\frac{2}{3}x + \frac{1}{2}y\right) = 12 \cdot \frac{2}{3}x + 12 \cdot \frac{1}{2}y$ Distributive property

             $= 8x + 6y$ Multiplication

In the next example, we use the rule for division, along with properties of real numbers, to simplify expressions.

EXAMPLE 6   Simplify each expression.

a. $10\left(\dfrac{x}{2}\right)$ **b.** $a\left(\dfrac{3}{a} - 4\right)$

SOLUTION

a. $10\left(\dfrac{x}{2}\right) = 10\left(\dfrac{1}{2}x\right)$ Rule for division

$\qquad\qquad = \left(10 \cdot \dfrac{1}{2}\right)x$ Associative property of multiplication

$\qquad\qquad = 5x$ Multiplication

b. $a\left(\dfrac{3}{a} - 4\right) = a \cdot \dfrac{3}{a} - a \cdot 4$ Distributive property

$\qquad\qquad\qquad = 3 - 4a$ Multiplication

If you recall from the previous section, to add two fractions with the same denominator, we add their numerators and put the result over the common denominator:

$$\frac{3}{4} + \frac{2}{4} = \frac{3+2}{4} = \frac{5}{4}$$

We can now justify why this process works. The reason we add numerators but do not add denominators is that we must follow the distributive property. To see this, you first have to recall that $\frac{3}{4}$ can be written as $3 \cdot \frac{1}{4}$, and $\frac{2}{4}$ can be written as $2 \cdot \frac{1}{4}$ (dividing by 4 is equivalent to multiplying by $\frac{1}{4}$). Here is the addition problem again, this time showing the use of the distributive property:

$$\frac{3}{4} + \frac{2}{4} = 3 \cdot \frac{1}{4} + 2 \cdot \frac{1}{4}$$

$$= (3 + 2) \cdot \frac{1}{4} \qquad \text{Distributive property}$$

$$= 5 \cdot \frac{1}{4}$$

$$= \frac{5}{4}$$

What we have here is the sum of the numerators placed over the *common denominator*.

Note Most people who have done any work with adding fractions know that you add fractions that have the same denominator by adding their numerators but not their denominators. However, most people don't know why this works. The reason why we add numerators but not denominators is because of the distributive property. That is what the discussion at the right is all about. If you really want to understand addition of fractions, pay close attention to this discussion.

Special Numbers

In addition to the three properties mentioned so far, we want to include in our list two special numbers that have unique properties. They are the numbers zero and one.

PROPERTY   *Additive Identity Property*

There exists a unique number 0 such that
In symbols: $a + 0 = a$ and $0 + a = a$

> **PROPERTY**   *Multiplicative Identity Property*
>
> There exists a unique number 1 such that
> *In symbols:* $a(1) = a$ and $(1)a = a$

> **PROPERTY**   *Additive Inverse Property*
>
> *In symbols:* $a + (-a) = 0$
> *In words:*   Opposites add to 0.

> **PROPERTY**   *Multiplicative Inverse Property*
>
> For every real number a, except 0, there exists a unique real number $\frac{1}{a}$ such that
>
> *In symbols:* $a\left(\frac{1}{a}\right) = 1$
>
> *In words:*   Reciprocals multiply to 1.

Of all the basic properties listed, the commutative, associative, and distributive properties are the ones we will use most often. They are important because they will be used as justifications or reasons for many of the things we will do.

The following example illustrates how we use the preceding properties. Each sub-example contains an algebraic expression that has been changed in some way. The property that justifies the change is written to the right.

EXAMPLE 7   State the property that justifies the given statement.

a. $x + 5 = 5 + x$ — Commutative property of addition

b. $(2 + x) + y = 2 + (x + y)$ — Associative property of addition

c. $6(x + 3) = 6x + 18$ — Distributive property

d. $2 + (-2) = 0$ — Additive inverse property

e. $3\left(\frac{1}{3}\right) = 1$ — Multiplicative inverse property

f. $(2 + 0) + 3 = 2 + 3$ — Additive identity property

g. $(2 + 3) + 4 = 3 + (2 + 4)$ — Commutative and associative properties of addition

h. $(x + 2) + y = (x + y) + 2$ — Commutative and associative properties of addition

As a final note on the properties of real numbers, we should mention that although some of the properties are stated for only two or three real numbers, they hold for as many numbers as needed. For example, the distributive property holds for expressions like $3(x + y + z + 5 + 2)$; that is,

$$3(x + y + z + 5 + 2) = 3x + 3y + 3z + 15 + 6$$

It is not important how many numbers are contained in the sum, only that it is a sum. Multiplication, you see, distributes over addition, whether there are two numbers in the sum or 200.

Getting Ready for Class

After reading through the preceding section, respond in your own words and in complete sentences.

A. What is the commutative property of addition?

B. Do you know from your experience with numbers that the commutative property of addition is true? Explain why.

C. Write the commutative property of multiplication in symbols and words.

D. How do you rewrite expressions using the distributive property?

Problem Set 1.7

State the property or properties that justify the following.

1. $3 + 2 = 2 + 3$ **2.** $5 + 0 = 5$ **3.** $4\left(\dfrac{1}{4}\right) = 1$

4. $10(0.1) = 1$ **5.** $4 + x = x + 4$ **6.** $3(x - 10) = 3x - 30$

7. $2(y + 8) = 2y + 16$ **8.** $3 + (4 + 5) = (3 + 4) + 5$

9. $(3 + 1) + 2 = 1 + (3 + 2)$ **10.** $(5 + 2) + 9 = (2 + 5) + 9$

11. $(8 + 9) + 10 = (8 + 10) + 9$ **12.** $(7 + 6) + 5 = (5 + 6) + 7$

13. $3(x + 2) = 3(2 + x)$ **14.** $2(7y) = (7 \cdot 2)y$ **15.** $x(3y) = 3(xy)$

16. $a(5b) = 5(ab)$ **17.** $4(xy) = 4(yx)$ **18.** $3[2 + (-2)] = 3(0)$

19. $8[7 + (-7)] = 8(0)$ **20.** $7(1) = 7$

Each of the following problems has a mistake in it. Correct the right-hand side.

21. $3(x + 2) = 3x + 2$ **22.** $5(4 + x) = 4 + 5x$ **23.** $9(a + b) = 9a + b$

24. $2(y + 1) = 2y + 1$ **25.** $3(0) = 3$ **26.** $5\left(\dfrac{1}{5}\right) = 5$

27. $3 + (-3) = 1$ **28.** $8(0) = 8$ **29.** $10(1) = 0$

30. $3 \cdot \dfrac{1}{3} = 0$

Use the associative property to rewrite each of the following expressions, and then simplify the result. (See Examples 2 and 3.)

31. $4 + (2 + x)$ **32.** $5 + (6 + x)$ **33.** $(x + 2) + 7$ **34.** $(x + 8) + 2$

35. $3(5x)$ **36.** $5(3x)$ **37.** $-9(6y)$ **38.** $-6(9y)$

39. $\dfrac{1}{2}(3a)$ **40.** $\dfrac{1}{3}(2a)$ **41.** $-\dfrac{1}{3}(3x)$ **42.** $-\dfrac{1}{4}(4x)$

43. $\dfrac{1}{2}(2y)$ **44.** $\dfrac{1}{7}(7y)$ **45.** $-\dfrac{3}{4}\left(\dfrac{4}{3}x\right)$ **46.** $-\dfrac{3}{2}\left(\dfrac{2}{3}x\right)$

47. $-\dfrac{6}{5}\left(-\dfrac{5}{6}a\right)$ **48.** $-\dfrac{2}{5}\left(-\dfrac{5}{2}a\right)$

Apply the distributive property to each of the following expressions. Simplify when possible.

49. $8(x + 2)$ **50.** $5(x + 3)$ **51.** $8(x - 2)$ **52.** $5(x - 3)$

53. $4(y + 1)$ **54.** $4(y - 1)$ **55.** $3(6x + 5)$ **56.** $3(5x + 6)$

57. $-2(3a + 7)$ **58.** $-5(3a + 2)$ **59.** $-9(6y - 8)$ **60.** $-2(7y - 4)$

61. $\dfrac{1}{3}(3x + 6)$ **62.** $\dfrac{1}{2}(2x + 4)$ **63.** $6(2x + 3y)$ **64.** $8(3x + 2y)$

65. $4(3a - 2b)$ **66.** $5(4a - 8b)$ **67.** $\dfrac{1}{2}(6x + 4y)$ **68.** $\dfrac{1}{3}(6x + 9y)$

69. $-4(a + 2)$ **70.** $-7(a + 6)$ **71.** $-\dfrac{1}{2}(3x - 6)$ **72.** $-\dfrac{1}{4}(2x - 4)$

73. $10\left(\dfrac{x}{2} + \dfrac{3}{5}\right)$ **74.** $6\left(\dfrac{x}{3} + \dfrac{5}{2}\right)$ **75.** $15\left(\dfrac{x}{5} - \dfrac{4}{3}\right)$ **76.** $6\left(\dfrac{x}{3} - \dfrac{1}{2}\right)$

77. $x\left(\dfrac{3}{x} + 1\right)$ **78.** $x\left(\dfrac{4}{x} + 3\right)$ **79.** $-21\left(\dfrac{x}{7} - \dfrac{y}{3}\right)$ **80.** $-36\left(\dfrac{x}{4} - \dfrac{y}{9}\right)$

81. $a\left(\dfrac{3}{a} - \dfrac{2}{a}\right)$ **82.** $a\left(\dfrac{7}{a} + \dfrac{1}{a}\right)$ **83.** $4(a + 4) + 9$ **84.** $6(a + 2) + 8$

85. $2(3x + 5) + 2$ **86.** $7(2x + 1) + 3$

87. $7(2x + 4) + 10$ **88.** $3(5x + 6) + 20$

89. $-3(2x - 5) - 7$ **90.** $-4(3x - 1) - 8$

91. $-5(3x + 4) - 10$ **92.** $-3(4x + 5) - 20$

Here are some problems you will see later in the book. Simplify.

93. $\left(\dfrac{1}{2} \cdot 18\right)^2$ **94.** $\left[\dfrac{1}{2}(-10)\right]^2$ **95.** $\left(\dfrac{1}{2} \cdot 3\right)^2$

96. $\left(\dfrac{1}{2} \cdot 5\right)^2$ **97.** $\dfrac{1}{2}(4x + 2)$ **98.** $\dfrac{1}{3}(6x + 3)$

99. $\dfrac{3}{4}(8x - 4)$ **100.** $\dfrac{2}{5}(5x + 10)$ **101.** $\dfrac{5}{6}(6x + 12)$

102. $\dfrac{2}{3}(9x - 3)$ **103.** $10\left(\dfrac{3}{5}x + \dfrac{1}{2}\right)$ **104.** $8\left(\dfrac{1}{4}x - \dfrac{5}{8}\right)$

105. $15\left(\dfrac{1}{3}x + \dfrac{2}{5}\right)$ **106.** $12\left(\dfrac{1}{12}m + \dfrac{1}{6}\right)$ **107.** $12\left(\dfrac{1}{2}m - \dfrac{5}{12}\right)$

108. $8\left(\dfrac{1}{8} + \dfrac{1}{2}m\right)$ **109.** $21\left(\dfrac{1}{3} + \dfrac{1}{7}x\right)$ **110.** $6\left(\dfrac{3}{2}y + \dfrac{1}{3}\right)$

111. $6\left(\dfrac{1}{2}x - \dfrac{1}{3}y\right)$ **112.** $12\left(\dfrac{1}{4}x + \dfrac{2}{3}y\right)$ **113.** $-\dfrac{1}{3}(-2x + 6)$

114. $-\dfrac{1}{2}(-2x + 6)$ **115.** $8\left(-\dfrac{1}{4}x + \dfrac{1}{8}y\right)$ **116.** $9\left(-\dfrac{1}{9}x + \dfrac{1}{3}y\right)$

117. $0.09(x + 2{,}000)$ **118.** $0.04(x + 7{,}000)$ **119.** $0.12(x + 500)$

120. $0.06(x + 800)$ **121.** $a\left(1 + \dfrac{1}{a}\right)$ **122.** $a\left(1 - \dfrac{1}{a}\right)$

123. $a\left(\dfrac{1}{a} - 1\right)$ **124.** $a\left(\dfrac{1}{a} + 1\right)$

Applying the Concepts

125. **Getting Dressed** While getting dressed for work, a man puts on his socks and puts on his shoes. Are the two statements "put on your socks" and "put on your shoes" commutative? That is, will changing the order of the events always produce the same result?

126. **Skydiving** A skydiver flying over the jump area is about to do two things: jump out of the plane and pull the rip cord. Are the two events "jump out of the plane" and "pull the rip cord" commutative?

127. Division Give an example that shows that division is not a commutative operation; that is, find two numbers for which changing the order of division gives two different answers.

128. Subtraction Simplify the expression $10 - (5 - 2)$ and the expression $(10 - 5) - 2$ to show that subtraction is not an associative operation.

129. Hours Worked Carlo works as a waiter. He works double shifts 4 days a week. The lunch shift is 2 hours and the dinner shift is 3 hours. Find the total number of hours he works per week using the numbers 2, 3, and 4. Do the calculation two different ways so that the results give further justification for the distributive property.

Learning Objectives Assessment

The following problems can be used to help assess if you have successfully met the learning objectives for this section.

130. Which property of real numbers justifies $(2 + x) + 5 = 5 + (2 + x)$?
    a. Associative property of addition   **b.** Commutative property of addition
    c. Distributive property   **d.** Additive inverse property

131. Use the associative property to simplify $-4(8x)$.
    a. $-32x$ **b.** $4x$ **c.** $-32 - 4x$ **d.** $8x - 4$

132. Simplify $-3(2x - 5)$ using the distributive property.
    a. $-6x - 5$ **b.** $-6x + 15$ **c.** $-6x - 15$ **d.** $2x - 8$

Chapter 1 Summary

The number(s) in brackets next to each heading indicates the section(s) in which that topic is discussed.

Exponents [1.1]

1. $2^5 = 2 \cdot 2 \cdot 2 \cdot 2 \cdot 2 = 32$
$5^2 = 5 \cdot 5 = 25$
$10^3 = 10 \cdot 10 \cdot 10 = 1{,}000$
$1^4 = 1 \cdot 1 \cdot 1 \cdot 1 = 1$

Exponents are notation used to indicate repeated multiplication. In the expression 3^4, 3 is the *base* and 4 is the *exponent*.

$$3^4 = 3 \cdot 3 \cdot 3 \cdot 3 = 81$$

Order of Operations [1.1]

2. $10 + (2 \cdot 3^2 - 4 \cdot 2)$
$= 10 + (2 \cdot 9 - 4 \cdot 2)$
$= 10 + (18 - 8)$
$= 10 + 10$
$= 20$

When evaluating a mathematical expression, we will perform the operations in the following order, beginning with the expression in the innermost parentheses or brackets and working our way out.

1. Simplify all numbers with exponents, working from left to right if more than one of these numbers is present.

2. Then do all multiplications and divisions left to right.

3. Finally, perform all additions and subtractions left to right.

Comparison Symbols [1.2]

$a = b$ a is equal to b.
$a \neq b$ a is not equal to b.
$a < b$ a is less than b.
$a \not< b$ a is not less than b.
$a > b$ a is greater than b.
$a \not> b$ a is not greater than b.
$a \geq b$ a is greater than or equal to b.
$a \leq b$ a is less than or equal to b.

Subsets of the Real Numbers [1.2]

3. a. 7 and 100 are counting numbers, but 0 and -2 are not.

b. 0 and 241 are whole numbers, but -4 and $\frac{1}{2}$ are not.

c. -15, 0, and 20 are integers.

d. -4, $-\frac{1}{2}$, 0.75, and 0.666 ... are rational numbers.

e. $-\pi$, $\sqrt{3}$, and π are irrational numbers.

f. All the numbers listed above are real numbers.

Counting numbers: $\{1, 2, 3, \dots\}$
Whole numbers: $\{0, 1, 2, 3, \dots\}$
Integers: $\{\dots, -3, -2, -1, 0, 1, 2, 3, \dots\}$
Rational numbers: {all numbers that can be expressed as the ratio of two integers}
Irrational numbers: {all numbers on the number line that cannot be expressed as the ratio of two integers}
Real numbers: {all numbers that are either rational or irrational}

Absolute Value [1.2]

4. $|5| = 5$
  $|-5| = 5$

The *absolute value* of a real number is its distance from zero on the real number line. Absolute value is never negative.

Opposites [1.2]

5. The numbers 3 and -3 are opposites; their sum is 0:
  $3 + (-3) = 0$

Any two real numbers the same distance from zero on the number line but in opposite directions from zero are called *opposites*. Opposites always add to zero.

Addition of Real Numbers [1.3]

6. Add all combinations of positive and negative 10 and 13.
  $10 + 13 = 23$
  $10 + (-13) = -3$
  $-10 + 13 = 3$
  $-10 + (-13) = -23$

To add two real numbers with

1. The same sign: Simply add their absolute values and use the common sign.

2. Different signs: Subtract the smaller absolute value from the larger absolute value. The answer has the same sign as the number with the larger absolute value.

Subtraction of Real Numbers [1.4]

7. Subtracting 2 is the same as adding -2:
  $7 - 2 = 7 + (-2) = 5$

To subtract one number from another, simply add the opposite of the number you are subtracting; that is, if a and b represent real numbers, then

$$a - b = a + (-b)$$

Multiplication of Real Numbers [1.5]

8. $3(5) = 15$
  $3(-5) = -15$
  $-3(5) = -15$
  $-3(-5) = 15$

To multiply two real numbers, simply multiply their absolute values. Like signs give a positive answer. Unlike signs give a negative answer.

Division of Real Numbers [1.5]

9. $-\dfrac{6}{2} = -3$

  $\dfrac{-6}{-2} = 3$

To divide two real numbers, simply divide their absolute values. Like signs give a positive answer. Unlike signs give a negative answer.

Factoring [1.6]

10. The number 150 can be factored into the product of prime numbers:
  $150 = 15 \cdot 10$
    $= (3 \cdot 5)(2 \cdot 5)$
    $= 2 \cdot 3 \cdot 5^2$

Factoring is the reverse of multiplication.

Multiplication

Factors$\rightarrow 3 \cdot 5 = 15 \leftarrow$ Product

Factoring

Least Common Denominator (LCD) [1.6]

11. The LCD for $\frac{5}{12}$ and $\frac{7}{18}$ is 36.

The *least common denominator* (LCD) for a set of denominators is the smallest number that is exactly divisible by each denominator.

Reciprocals [1.6]

12. The numbers 2 and $\frac{1}{2}$ are reciprocals; their product is 1:

$$2\left(\frac{1}{2}\right) = 1$$

Any two real numbers whose product is 1 are called *reciprocals*. Every real number has a reciprocal except 0.

Addition and Subtraction of Fractions [1.6]

13. $\frac{5}{12} + \frac{7}{18} = \frac{5}{12} \cdot \frac{3}{3} + \frac{7}{18} \cdot \frac{2}{2}$

$\quad = \frac{15}{36} + \frac{14}{36}$

$\quad = \frac{29}{36}$

To add (or subtract) two fractions with a common denominator, add (or subtract) numerators and use the common denominator.

$$\frac{a}{c} + \frac{b}{c} = \frac{a+b}{c} \qquad \text{and} \qquad \frac{a}{c} - \frac{b}{c} = \frac{a-b}{c}$$

Properties of Real Numbers [1.7]

	For Addition	*For Multiplication*
Commutative:	$a + b = b + a$	$a \cdot b = b \cdot a$
Associative:	$a + (b + c) = (a + b) + c$	$a \cdot (b \cdot c) = (a \cdot b) \cdot c$
Identity:	$a + 0 = a$	$a \cdot 1 = a$
Inverse:	$a + (-a) = 0$	$a\left(\frac{1}{a}\right) = 1$
Distributive:	$a(b + c) = ab + ac$	

⚠ COMMON MISTAKE

1. Interpreting absolute value as changing the sign of the number inside the absolute value symbols. $|-5| = +5, |+5| = -5$. (The first expression is correct; the second one is not.) To avoid this mistake, remember: Absolute value is a distance and distance is always measured in positive units.

2. Using the phrase "two negatives make a positive." This works only with multiplication and division. With addition, two negative numbers produce a negative answer. It is best not to use the phrase "two negatives make a positive" at all.

Chapter 1 Test

Evaluate each exponent. [1.1]

1. 12^2

2. 4^3

Simplify using the order of operations. [1.1, 1.3, 1.4, 1.5]

3. $10 + 2(7 - 3) - 4^2$

4. $15 + 24 \div 6 - 3^2$

From the set of numbers $\{-3, -\frac{1}{2}, 2, \sqrt{5}, \pi\}$ list all the elements that are in the following sets. [1.2]

5. Integers

6. Rational numbers

Write an expression in symbols that is equivalent to each English phrase, and then simplify it.

7. The sum of 6 and -9 [1.3]

8. The difference of -5 and -12 [1.4]

9. The product of 6 and -7 [1.5]

10. The quotient of 32 and -8 [1.5]

Find the next number in each sequence. [1.3, 1.5]

11. $-3, 1, 5, 9, \ldots$

12. $81, -27, 9, -3, \ldots$

Simplify the following: [1.5]

13. $-2(3) - 7$

14. $2(3)^3 - 4(-2)^4$

15. $9 + 4(2 - 6)$

16. $5 - 3[-2(1 + 4) + 3(-3)]$

17. $\dfrac{-4(3) + 5(-2)}{-5 - 6}$

18. $\dfrac{4(3 - 5) - 2(-6 + 8)}{4(-2) + 10}$

Factor into the product of primes. [1.6]

19. 660

20. 4,725

Combine. [1.6]

21. $\dfrac{5}{24} + \dfrac{9}{36}$

22. $\dfrac{5}{y} + \dfrac{6}{y}$

Match each expression below with the letter of the property that justifies it. [1.7]

23. $4(2y) = (4 \cdot 2)y$

24. $5(x - 3) = 5x - 15$

25. $4 + x = x + 4$

26. $(a + 5) - 2 = a + (5 - 2)$

    a. Commutative property of addition

    b. Commutative property of multiplication

    c. Associative property of addition

    d. Associative property of multiplication

    e. Distributive property

Apply the associative property, and then simplify. [1.7]

27. $5 + (7 + 3x)$

28. $3(-5y)$

Multiply by applying the distributive property. [1.7]

29. $-5(2x - 3)$

30. $\dfrac{1}{3}(6x + 12)$

Linear Equations and Inequalities

2

Chapter Outline

iStockphoto.com © Sergey Nivens

One year, I flew to Europe for vacation. From time to time, the video screens on the plane displayed statistics about the flight. At one point during the flight, the temperature outside the plane was −60°F. When I returned home, I did some research and found that the relationship between temperature T and altitude A can be described with the formula

$$T = -0.0035A + 70$$

when the temperature on the ground is 70°F.

To find the temperature at an altitude of 20,000 feet, we can evaluate the expression when $A = 20,000$:

$$\text{When} \qquad A = 20,000$$
$$\text{the formula} \qquad T = -0.0035A + 70$$
$$\text{becomes} \qquad T = -0.0035(20,000) + 70$$
$$= -70 + 70$$
$$= 0$$

At an altitude of 20,000 feet, the temperature is 0°F.

Given the temperature, we can find the altitude by solving the equation for A. For example, if the temperature is −60°F, we can solve

$$-60 = -0.0035A + 70$$

to obtain $A \approx 37,143$ feet.

In this chapter, we will learn how to evaluate formulas and solve equations similar to the one above.

If you have successfully completed Chapter 1, then you have made a good start at developing the study skills necessary to succeed in all math classes. Here is the list of study skills for this chapter.

1. **Imitate Success** Your work should look like the work you see in this book and the work your instructor shows. The steps shown in solving problems in this book were written by someone who has been successful in mathematics. The same is true of your instructor. Your work should imitate the work of people who have been successful in mathematics.

2. **List Difficult Problems** Begin to make lists of problems that give you the most difficulty. These are problems in which you are repeatedly making mistakes.

3. **Begin to Develop Confidence with Word Problems** It seems that the major difference between those people who are good at working word problems and those who are not is confidence. The people with confidence know that no matter how long it takes them, they eventually will be able to solve the problem. Those without confidence begin by saying to themselves, "I'll never be able to work this problem." Are you like that? If you are, what you need to do is put your old ideas about you and word problems aside for a while and make a decision to be successful. Sometimes that's all it takes. Instead of telling yourself that you can't do word problems, that you don't like them, or that they're not good for anything anyway, decide to do whatever it takes to master them.

Simplifying Expressions

Learning Objectives

In this section, we will learn how to:

1. Combine similar terms.
2. Simplify expressions containing parentheses.
3. Find the value of an expression.
4. Find the first few terms of a sequence.

Introduction

If a cellular phone company charges $35 per month plus $0.25 for each minute, or fraction of a minute, that you use one of their cellular phones, then the amount of your monthly bill is given by the expression $35 + 0.25t$. To find the amount you will pay for using that phone 30 minutes in one month, you substitute 30 for t and simplify the resulting expression. This process is one of the topics we will study in this section.

The expression $35 + 0.25t$ contains two terms. For our immediate purposes, a *term* is a number or a number and one or more variables multiplied together. For example, the number 5 is a term, as are the expressions $3x$, $-7y$, and $15xy$. The numerical factor in a term is called the *coefficient*. Here are some examples of terms and their coefficients.

Term	Coefficient	
$3x$	3	
$-7xy + 4$	-7	
$\dfrac{x}{2}$	$\dfrac{1}{2}$	Because $\dfrac{x}{2} = \dfrac{1}{2} \cdot x$
x^2	1	Because $x^2 = 1 \cdot x^2$
9	9	

If the term is a number only and does not contain any variables, then it is called a *constant term*, and the coefficient is the number itself. For instance, in the above examples, 9 is a constant term.

As you will see in the next few sections, the first step in solving an equation is to simplify both sides as much as possible. In the first part of this section, we will practice simplifying expressions by combining what are called *similar* (or like) terms.

> **def** **DEFINITION** *similar terms*
>
> Two or more terms with the same variable part are called *similar (or like) terms.*

The terms $3x$ and $4x$ are similar because their variable parts are identical. Likewise, the terms $18y$, $-10y$, and $6y$ are similar terms. Here are some more examples of like terms and unlike terms.

Like Terms	Unlike Terms
$x, -\dfrac{1}{2}x$	$x, -\dfrac{2}{x}$
$5x^2, -8x^2$	$5x, -8x^2$
$3xy, 11xy$	$3x^2y, 11xy^2$
$-\dfrac{1}{4}, \dfrac{5}{6}$	$-\dfrac{x}{4}, \dfrac{y}{6}$

Notice that similar terms can only differ in their coefficients.

To simplify an algebraic expression, we simply reduce the number of terms in the expression. We accomplish this by applying the distributive property along with our knowledge of addition and subtraction of positive and negative real numbers. The following examples illustrate the procedure.

VIDEO EXAMPLES

SECTION 2.1

EXAMPLE 1   Simplify by combining similar terms.

a. $3x + 4x$ **b.** $7a - 10a$ **c.** $18y - 10y + 6y$

SOLUTION   We combine similar terms by applying the distributive property.

a. $3x + 4x = (3 + 4)x$ Distributive property

$\qquad\qquad = 7x$ Add 3 and 4

b. $7a - 10a = (7 - 10)a$ Distributive property

$\qquad\qquad\ = -3a$ Add 7 and -10

c. $18y - 10y + 6y = (18 - 10 + 6)y$ Distributive property

$\qquad\qquad\qquad\quad = 14y$ Add 18, -10, and 6

When the expression we intend to simplify is more complicated, we use the commutative and associative properties first.

EXAMPLE 2   Simplify each expression.

a. $3x + 5 + 2x - 3$ **b.** $4a - 7 - 2a + 3$ **c.** $5x + 8 - x - 6$

SOLUTION   We combine similar terms by applying the commutative and associative properties first, and then the distributive property.

a. $3x + 5 + 2x - 3 = 3x + 2x + 5 - 3d$ Commutative property

$\qquad\qquad\qquad\quad = (3x + 2x) + (5 - 3)$ Associative property

$\qquad\qquad\qquad\quad = (3 + 2)x + (5 - 3)$ Distributive property

$\qquad\qquad\qquad\quad = 5x + 2$ Add

b. $4a - 7 - 2a + 3 = (4a - 2a) + (-7 + 3)$ Commutative and associative properties

$= (4 - 2)a + (-7 + 3)$ Distributive property

$= 2a - 4$ Add

c. $5x + 8 - x - 6 = (5x - x) + (8 - 6)$ Commutative and associative properties

$= (5 - 1)x + (8 - 6)$ Distributive property

$= 4x + 2$ Add

Notice that in each case the result has fewer terms than the original expression. Because there are fewer terms, the resulting expression is said to be simpler than the original expression.

Simplifying Expressions Containing Parentheses

If an expression contains parentheses, it is often necessary to apply the distributive property to remove the parentheses. This step will change the product in the expression into a sum or difference of individual terms, which will then allow us to combine any similar terms.

EXAMPLE 3   Simplify the expression: $5(2x - 8) - 3$.

SOLUTION   We begin by distributing the 5 across $2x - 8$. We then combine similar terms:

$$5(2x - 8) - 3 = 10x - 40 - 3 \qquad \text{Distributive property}$$
$$= 10x - 43$$

EXAMPLE 4   Simplify: $7 - 3(2y + 1)$.

SOLUTION   By the rule for order of operations, we must multiply before we add or subtract. For that reason, it would be incorrect to subtract 3 from 7 first. Instead, we multiply -3 and $2y + 1$ to remove the parentheses and then combine similar terms:

$$7 - 3(2y + 1) = 7 - 6y - 3 \qquad \text{Distributive property}$$
$$= -6y + 4$$

EXAMPLE 5   Simplify: $5(x - 2) - (3x + 4)$.

SOLUTION   We begin by applying the distributive property to remove the parentheses. The expression $-(3x + 4)$ can be thought of as $-1(3x + 4)$. Thinking of it in this way allows us to apply the distributive property:

$$-1(3x + 4) = -1(3x) + (-1)(4)$$
$$= -3x - 4$$

The complete solution looks like this:

$$5(x - 2) - (3x + 4) = 5x - 10 - 3x - 4 \qquad \text{Distributive property}$$
$$= 2x - 14 \qquad \text{Combine similar terms}$$

As you can see from the explanation in Example 5, we use the distributive property to simplify expressions in which parentheses are preceded by a negative sign. In general we can write

$$-(a + b) = -1(a + b)$$
$$= -a + (-b)$$
$$= -a - b$$

The negative sign outside the parentheses ends up changing the sign of each term within the parentheses. In words, we say "the opposite of a sum is the sum of the opposites."

The Value of an Expression

An expression like $3x + 2$ has a certain value depending on what number we assign to x. For instance, when x is 4, $3x + 2$ becomes $3(4) + 2$, or 14. When x is -8, $3x + 2$ becomes $3(-8) + 2$, or -22. The value of an expression is found by replacing the variable with a given number.

EXAMPLE 6   Find the value of the following expressions by replacing the variable with the given number.

Expression	The Variable	Value of the Expression
a. $3x - 1$	$x = 2$	$3(2) - 1 = 6 - 1$ $\qquad = 5$
b. $7a + 4$	$a = -3$	$7(-3) + 4 = -21 + 4$ $\qquad = -17$
c. $2x - 3 + 4x$	$x = -1$	$2(-1) - 3 + 4(-1) = -2 - 3 + (-4)$ $\qquad = -9$
d. $2x - 5 - 8x$	$x = 5$	$2(5) - 5 - 8(5) = 10 - 5 - 40$ $\qquad = -35$
e. $y^2 - 6y + 9$	$y = 4$	$4^2 - 6(4) + 9 = 16 - 24 + 9$ $\qquad = 1$

Simplifying an expression should not change its value; that is, if an expression has a certain value when x is 5, then it will always have that value no matter how much it has been simplified as long as x is 5. If we were to simplify the expression in Example 6d first, it would look like

$$2x - 5 - 8x = -6x - 5$$

When x is 5, the simplified expression $-6x - 5$ is

$$-6(5) - 5 = -30 - 5 = -35$$

It has the same value as the original expression when x is 5.

We also can find the value of an expression that contains two variables if we know the values for both variables.

EXAMPLE 7 Find the value of the expression $2x - 3y + 4$ when x is -5 and y is 6.

SOLUTION Substituting -5 for x and 6 for y, the expression becomes

$$2(-5) - 3(6) + 4 = -10 - 18 + 4$$
$$= -28 + 4$$
$$= -24$$

EXAMPLE 8 Find the value of the expression $x^2 - 2xy + y^2$ when x is 3 and y is -4.

SOLUTION Replacing each x in the expression with the number 3 and each y in the expression with the number -4 gives us

$$3^2 - 2(3)(-4) + (-4)^2 = 9 - 2(3)(-4) + 16$$
$$= 9 - (-24) + 16$$
$$= 33 + 16$$
$$= 49$$

Sequences

As the next example indicates, when we substitute the counting numbers, in order, into an algebraic expression, we form a sequence of numbers. To review, recall that the sequence of counting numbers (also called the sequence of positive integers) is

$$\text{Counting numbers} = 1, 2, 3, \ldots$$

EXAMPLE 9 Substitute 1, 2, 3, and 4 for n in the expression $2n - 1$.

SOLUTION Substituting as indicated, we have

When $n = 1, 2n - 1 = 2 \cdot 1 - 1 = 1$

When $n = 2, 2n - 1 = 2 \cdot 2 - 1 = 3$

When $n = 3, 2n - 1 = 2 \cdot 3 - 1 = 5$

When $n = 4, 2n - 1 = 2 \cdot 4 - 1 = 7$

As you can see, substituting the first four counting numbers into the expression $2n - 1$ produces the first four terms in the sequence of odd numbers.

The next example is similar to Example 9 but uses tables to display the information.

EXAMPLE 10   Fill in the tables below to find the sequences formed by substituting the first four counting numbers into the expressions $2n$ and n^2.

a.

n	1	2	3	4
$2n$				

b.

n	1	2	3	4
n^2				

SOLUTION Proceeding as we did in the previous example, we substitute the numbers 1, 2, 3, and 4 into the given expressions.

a. When $n = 1$, $2n = 2 \cdot 1 = 2$

When $n = 2$, $2n = 2 \cdot 2 = 4$

When $n = 3$, $2n = 2 \cdot 3 = 6$

When $n = 4$, $2n = 2 \cdot 4 = 8$

As you can see, the expression $2n$ produces the sequence of even numbers when n is replaced by the counting numbers. Placing these results into our first table gives us

n	1	2	3	4
$2n$	2	4	6	8

b. The expression n^2 produces the sequence of squares when n is replaced by 1, 2, 3, and 4. In table form we have

n	1	2	3	4
n^2	1	4	9	16

Getting Ready for Class

After reading through the preceding section, respond in your own words and in complete sentences.

A. What are similar terms?

B. Explain how the distributive property is used to combine similar terms.

C. What is wrong with writing $3x + 4x = 7x^2$?

D. Explain how you would find the value of $5x + 3$ when x is 6.

Simplify the following expressions.

1. $3x - 6x$ **2.** $7x - 5x$ **3.** $-2a + a$

4. $3a - a$ **5.** $7x + 3x + 2x$ **6.** $8x - 2x - x$

7. $3a - 2a + 5a$ **8.** $7a - a + 2a$ **9.** $4x - 3 + 2x$

10. $5x + 6 - 3x$ **11.** $3a + 4a + 5$ **12.** $6a + 7a + 8$

13. $2x - 3 + 3x - 2$ **14.** $6x + 5 - 2x + 3$ **15.** $3a - 1 + a + 3$

16. $-a + 2 + 8a - 7$ **17.** $-4x + 8 - 5x - 10$ **18.** $-9x - 1 + x - 4$

19. $7a + 3 + 2a + 3a$ **20.** $8a - 2 + a + 5a$ **21.** $5(2x - 1) + 4$

22. $2(4x - 3) + 2$ **23.** $7(3y + 2) - 8$ **24.** $6(4y + 2) - 7$

25. $-3(2x - 1) + 5$ **26.** $-4(3x - 2) - 6$ **27.** $5 - 2(a + 1)$

28. $7 - 8(2a + 3)$ **29.** $6 - 4(x - 5)$ **30.** $12 - 3(4x - 2)$

31. $-9 - 4(2 - y) + 1$ **32.** $-10 - 3(2 - y) + 3$ **33.** $-6 + 2(2 - 3x) + 1$

34. $-7 - 4(3 - x) + 1$ **35.** $(4x - 7) - (2x + 5)$ **36.** $(7x - 3) - (4x + 2)$

37. $8(2a + 4) - (6a - 1)$ **38.** $9(3a + 5) - (8a - 7)$ **39.** $3(x - 2) + (x - 3)$

40. $2(2x + 1) - (x + 4)$ **41.** $4(2y - 8) - (y + 7)$ **42.** $5(y - 3) - (y - 4)$

43. $-9(2x + 1) - (x + 5)$ **44.** $-3(3x - 2) - (2x + 3)$

Evaluate the following expressions when x is 2. (Find the value of the expressions if x is 2.)

45. $3x - 1$ **46.** $4x + 3$ **47.** $-2x - 5$ **48.** $-3x + 6$

49. $x^2 - 8x + 16$ **50.** $x^2 - 10x + 25$ **51.** $(x - 4)^2$ **52.** $(x - 5)^2$

Evaluate the following expressions when x is -5. Then simplify the expression, and check to see that it has the same value for $x = -5$.

53. $7x - 4 - x - 3$ **54.** $3x + 4 + 7x - 6$

55. $5(2x + 1) + 4$ **56.** $2(3x - 10) + 5$

Evaluate the following expressions when x is -3 and y is 5.

57. $x^2 - 2xy + y^2$ **58.** $x^2 + 2xy + y^2$ **59.** $(x - y)^2$

60. $(x + y)^2$ **61.** $x^2 + 6xy + 9y^2$ **62.** $x^2 + 10xy + 25y^2$

63. $(x + 3y)^2$ **64.** $(x + 5y)^2$

Find the value of $12x - 3$ for each of the following values of x.

65. $\dfrac{1}{2}$ **66.** $\dfrac{1}{3}$ **67.** $\dfrac{1}{4}$ **68.** $\dfrac{1}{6}$

69. $\dfrac{3}{2}$ **70.** $\dfrac{2}{3}$ **71.** $\dfrac{3}{4}$ **72.** $\dfrac{5}{6}$

73. Fill in the tables below to find the sequences formed by substituting the first four counting numbers into the expressions $3n$ and n^3.

a.

n	1	2	3	4
$3n$				

b.

n	1	2	3	4
n^3				

74. Fill in the tables below to find the sequences formed by substituting the first four counting numbers into the expressions $2n - 1$ and $2n + 1$.

a.

n	1	2	3	4
$2n - 1$				

b.

n	1	2	3	4
$2n + 1$				

Find the sequences formed by substituting the first four counting numbers, in order, into the following expressions.

75. $3n - 2$ **76.** $2n - 3$ **77.** $n^2 - 2n + 1$ **78.** $(n - 1)^2$

Here are some problems you will see later in the book. Simplify.

79. $7 - 3(2y + 1)$

80. $4(3x - 2) - (6x - 5)$

81. $0.08x + 0.09x$

82. $0.04x + 0.05x$

83. $(x + y) + (x - y)$

84. $(-12x - 20y) + (25x + 20y)$

85. $3x + 2(x - 2)$

86. $2(x - 2) + 3(5x)$

87. $4(x + 1) + 3(x - 3)$

88. $5(x + 1) + 3(x - 1)$

89. $x + (x + 3)(-3)$

90. $x - 2(x + 2)$

91. $3(4x - 2) - (5x - 8)$

92. $2(5x - 3) - (2x - 4)$

93. $-(3x + 1) - (4x - 7)$

94. $-(6x + 2) - (8x - 3)$

95. $(x + 3y) + 3(2x - y)$

96. $(2x - y) - 2(x + 3y)$

97. $3(2x + 3y) - 2(3x + 5y)$

98. $5(2x + 3y) - 3(3x + 5y)$

99. $-6\left(\dfrac{1}{2}x - \dfrac{1}{3}y\right) + 12\left(\dfrac{1}{4}x + \dfrac{2}{3}y\right)$

100. $6\left(\dfrac{1}{3}x + \dfrac{1}{2}y\right) - 4\left(x + \dfrac{3}{4}y\right)$

101. $0.08x + 0.09(x + 2{,}000)$

102. $0.06x + 0.04(x + 7{,}000)$

103. $0.10x + 0.12(x + 500)$

104. $0.08x + 0.06(x + 800)$

Find the value of $b^2 - 4ac$ for the given values of a, b, and c. (You will see these problems later in the book.)

105. $a = 1, b = -5, c = -6$

106. $a = 1, b = -6, c = 7$

107. $a = 2, b = 4, c = -3$

108. $a = 3, b = 4, c = -2$

Applying the Concepts

109. Temperature and Altitude If the temperature on the ground is 70°F, then the temperature at A feet above the ground can be found from the expression $-0.0035A + 70$. Find the temperature at the following altitudes.

a. 8,000 feet
b. 12,000 feet
c. 24,000 feet

110. Perimeter of a Rectangle The expression $2l + 2w$ gives the perimeter of a rectangle with length l and width w. Find the perimeter of the rectangles with the following lengths and widths.

a. Length = 8 meters
Width = 5 meters

b. Length = 10 feet
Width = 3 feet

5 m

3 ft

10 ft

8 m

111. Cellular Phone Rates A cellular phone company charges $35 per month plus $0.25 for each minute, or fraction of a minute, that you use one of their cellular phones. The expression $35 + 0.25t$ gives the amount of money you will pay for using one of their phones for t minutes a month. Find the monthly bill for using one of their phones.

a. 10 minutes in a month
b. 20 minutes in a month
c. 30 minutes in a month

112. Cost of Bottled Water A water bottling company charges $7.00 per month for their water dispenser and $1.10 for each gallon of water delivered. If you have g gallons of water delivered in a month, then the expression $7 + 1.1g$ gives the amount of your bill for that month. Find the monthly bill for each of the following deliveries.

a. 10 gallons
b. 20 gallons
c. 30 gallons

Learning Objectives Assessment

The following problems can be used to help assess if you have successfully met the learning objectives for this section.

113. Simplify: $7x + 4 - 2x - 1$.

    a. $8x$ **b.** $8 + x$ **c.** $5x + 3$ **d.** $9x + 5$

114. Simplify: $9 - 3(4 - x) + 2x$.

    a. $5x - 3$ **b.** $-x - 3$ **c.** $-4x + 24$ **d.** $x - 3$

115. Evaluate: $x^2 - 5x - 4$ when x is -2.

    a. 2 **b.** -10 **c.** 10 **d.** 18

116. Find the sequence formed by substituting the first three counting numbers into the expression $3n + 2$.

    a. $1, 2, 3$ **b.** $5, 8, 11$

    c. $5, 10, 15$ **d.** $33, 34, 35$

Getting Ready for the Next Section

These are problems that you must be able to work in order to understand the material in the next section. The problems below are exactly the type of problems you will see in the explanations and examples in the next section.

Simplify.

117. $17 - 5$ **118.** $12 + (-2)$

119. $2 - 5$ **120.** $25 - 20$

121. $-2.4 + (-7.3)$ **122.** $8.1 + 2.7$

123. $-\dfrac{1}{2} + \left(-\dfrac{3}{4}\right)$ **124.** $-\dfrac{1}{6} + \left(-\dfrac{2}{3}\right)$

125. $4(2 \cdot 9 - 3) - 7$ **126.** $5(3 \cdot 45 - 4) - 14 \cdot 45$

127. $4(2a - 3) - 7a$ **128.** $5(3a - 4) - 14a$

129. Find the value of $2x - 3$ when x is 5.

130. Find the value of $3x + 4$ when x is -2.

Addition Property of Equality

Learning Objectives

In this section, we will learn how to:

1. Identify a solution to an equation.

2. Use the addition property of equality to solve a linear equation.

3. Solve linear equations involving grouping symbols.

Introduction

When light comes into contact with any object, it is reflected, absorbed, and transmitted, as shown below.

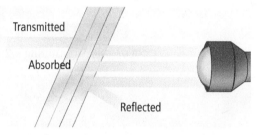

For a certain type of glass, 88% of the light hitting the glass is transmitted through to the other side, whereas 6% of the light is absorbed into the glass. To find the percent of light that is reflected by the glass, we can solve the equation

$$88 + R + 6 = 100$$

Solving equations of this type is what we study in this section.

Equations and Solutions

An *equation* is a mathematical statement that two quantities are the same, or equal. As comparisons, equations can be true or false. For instance, the equation $5 + 3 = 11$ is false, but the equation $5 + 6 = 11$ is true.

If the equation contains a variable, then the statement may be either true or false, depending on the value being used to replace the variable. For example, the equation

$$88 + R + 6 = 100$$

from the introduction to this section is true if $R = 6$, but will be false for any other value of R. To solve an equation we must find all replacements for the variable that make the equation a true statement.

> **def** **DEFINITION** *solution set*
>
> The **solution set** for an equation is the set of all numbers that when used in place of the variable make the equation a true statement.

For example, the equation $x + 2 = 5$ has the solution set $\{3\}$ because when x is 3 the equation becomes the true statement $3 + 2 = 5$, or $5 = 5$. We sometimes say that $x = 3$ *satisfies* the equation $x + 2 = 5$. When giving the solution to this equation, we can say the solution is $x = 3$, or we can say the solution set is $\{3\}$.

Note We can use a question mark over the equal signs to show that we don't know yet whether the two sides of the equation are equal.

EXAMPLE 1   Is 5 a solution to $2x - 3 = 7$?

SOLUTION   We substitute 5 for x in the equation, and then simplify to see if a true statement results. A true statement means we have a solution; a false statement indicates the number we are using is not a solution.

$$\begin{aligned} \text{When} && x &= 5 \\ \text{the equation} && 2x - 3 &= 7 \\ \text{becomes} && 2(5) - 3 &\stackrel{?}{=} 7 \\ && 10 - 3 &\stackrel{?}{=} 7 \\ && 7 &= 7 \quad \text{A true statement} \end{aligned}$$

Because $x = 5$ turns the equation into the true statement $7 = 7$, we know 5 is a solution to the equation.

EXAMPLE 2   Is -2 a solution to $8 = 3x + 4$?

SOLUTION   Substituting -2 for x in the equation, we have

$$\begin{aligned} 8 &\stackrel{?}{=} 3(-2) + 4 \\ 8 &\stackrel{?}{=} -6 + 4 \\ 8 &= -2 \quad \text{A false statement; } 8 \neq -2 \end{aligned}$$

Substituting -2 for x in the equation produces a false statement. Therefore, $x = -2$ is not a solution to the equation.

The important thing about an equation is its solution set. Therefore, we make the following definition to classify together all equations with the same solution set.

DEFINITION   *equivalent equations*

Two or more equations with the same solution set are said to be *equivalent equations*.

Equivalent equations may look different but must have the same solution set.

EXAMPLE 3

a. $x + 2 = 5$ and $x = 3$ are equivalent equations because both have solution set $\{3\}$.

b. $a - 4 = 3$, $a - 2 = 5$, and $a = 7$ are equivalent equations because they all have solution set $\{7\}$.

c. $y + 3 = 4$, $y - 8 = -7$, and $y = 1$ are equivalent equations because they all have solution set $\{1\}$.

The Addition Property of Equality

If two numbers are equal and we increase (or decrease) both of them by the same amount, the resulting quantities are also equal. We can apply this concept to equations. Adding the same amount to both sides of an equation always produces an equivalent equation—one with the same solution set. This fact about equations is called the *addition property of equality* and can be stated more formally as follows.

Note We will use this property many times in the future. Be sure you understand it completely by the time you finish this section.

⌊Δ≠Σ⌋ **PROPERTY** *Addition Property of Equality*
For any three algebraic expressions A, B, and C,
if $\qquad\qquad A = B$ then $\qquad A + C = B + C$
In words: Adding the same quantity to both sides of an equation will not change the solution set.

This property is just as simple as it seems. We can add any amount to both sides of an equation and always be sure we have not changed the solution set.

Consider the equation $x + 6 = 5$. We want to solve this equation for the value of x that makes it a true statement. We want to end up with x on one side of the equal sign and a number on the other. Because we want x by itself, we will add -6 to both sides:

Note Recall that the additive inverse property tells us that a number and its opposite add to zero. This is precisely why we chose to add -6 to both sides.

$$x + 6 + (-6) = 5 + (-6) \qquad \text{Addition property of equality}$$
$$x + 0 = -1 \qquad\qquad \text{Add}$$
$$x = -1$$

All three equations say the same thing about x. They all say that x is -1. All three equations are equivalent. The last one is just easier to read.

Here are some further examples of how the addition property of equality can be used to solve equations.

EXAMPLE 4 Solve the equation $x - 5 = 12$ for x.

SOLUTION Because we want x alone on the left side, we choose to add 5 to both sides:

$$x - 5 + 5 = 12 + 5 \qquad \text{Addition property of equality}$$
$$x + 0 = 17$$
$$x = 17$$

If we want to write our solution using set notation, we would write $\{17\}$ for the solution set.

To check our solution to Example 4, we substitute 17 for x in the original equation:

When $\qquad\qquad\qquad x = 17$

the equation $\qquad x - 5 = 12$

becomes $\qquad\qquad 17 - 5 \overset{?}{=} 12$

$$12 = 12 \qquad \text{A true statement}$$

As you can see, our solution checks. The purpose for checking a solution to an equation is to catch any mistakes we may have made in the process of solving the equation.

EXAMPLE 5   Solve for a: $a + \dfrac{3}{4} = -\dfrac{1}{2}$.

SOLUTION   Because we want a by itself on the left side of the equal sign, we add the opposite of $\frac{3}{4}$ to each side of the equation.

$$a + \frac{3}{4} + \left(-\frac{3}{4}\right) = -\frac{1}{2} + \left(-\frac{3}{4}\right) \qquad \text{Addition property of equality}$$

$$a + 0 = -\frac{1}{2} \cdot \frac{2}{2} + \left(-\frac{3}{4}\right) \qquad \text{LCD on the right side is 4}$$

$$a = -\frac{2}{4} + \left(-\frac{3}{4}\right) \qquad \tfrac{2}{4} \text{ is equivalent to } \tfrac{1}{2}$$

$$a = -\frac{5}{4} \qquad \text{Add fractions}$$

The solution is $a = -\frac{5}{4}$. To check our result, we replace a with $-\frac{5}{4}$ in the original equation. The left side then becomes $-\frac{5}{4} + \frac{3}{4}$, which reduces to $-\frac{1}{2}$, so our solution checks.

EXAMPLE 6   Solve for x: $7.3 + x = -2.4$.

SOLUTION   Again, we want to isolate x, so we add the opposite of 7.3 to both sides:

$$7.3 + (-7.3) + x = -2.4 + (-7.3) \qquad \text{Addition property of equality}$$

$$0 + x = -9.7$$

$$x = -9.7$$

The solution set is $\{-9.7\}$.

Sometimes it is necessary to simplify each side of an equation before using the addition property of equality. The reason we simplify both sides first is that we want as few terms as possible on each side of the equation before we use the addition property of equality. The following examples illustrate this procedure.

EXAMPLE 7   Solve for x: $-x + 2 + 2x = 7 + 5$.

SOLUTION   We begin by combining similar terms on each side of the equation. Then we use the addition property to solve the simplified equation.

$$x + 2 = 12 \qquad \text{Simplify both sides first}$$

$$x + 2 + (-2) = 12 + (-2) \qquad \text{Addition property of equality}$$

$$x + 0 = 10$$

$$x = 10$$

The next example illustrates how we solve an equation involving grouping symbols.

EXAMPLE 8   Solve: $4(2a - 3) - 7a = 2 - 5$.

SOLUTION   We must begin by applying the distributive property to separate terms on the left side of the equation. Following that, we combine similar terms and then apply the addition property of equality.

$$4(2a - 3) - 7a = 2 - 5 \qquad \text{Original equation}$$

$$8a - 12 - 7a = 2 - 5 \qquad \text{Distributive property}$$

$$a - 12 = -3 \qquad \text{Simplify each side}$$

$$a - 12 + 12 = -3 + 12 \qquad \text{Add 12 to each side}$$

$$a = 9 \qquad \text{Add}$$

To check our solution, we replace a with 9 in the original equation.

$$4(2 \cdot 9 - 3) - 7 \cdot 9 \stackrel{?}{=} 2 - 5$$
$$4(15) - 63 \stackrel{?}{=} -3$$
$$60 - 63 \stackrel{?}{=} -3$$
$$-3 = -3 \qquad \text{A true statement}$$

Note Again, we place a question mark over the equal sign because we don't know yet whether the expressions on the left and right side of the equal sign will be equal.

We can also add a term involving a variable to both sides of an equation.

EXAMPLE 9   Solve: $3x - 5 = 2x + 7$.

SOLUTION   We can solve this equation in two steps. First, we add $-2x$ to both sides of the equation. When this has been done, x appears on the left side only. Second, we add 5 to both sides:

$$3x + (-2x) - 5 = 2x + (-2x) + 7 \qquad \text{Add } -2x \text{ to both sides}$$
$$x - 5 = 7 \qquad \text{Simplify each side}$$
$$x - 5 + 5 = 7 + 5 \qquad \text{Add 5 to both sides}$$
$$x = 12 \qquad \text{Simplify each side}$$

Note In my experience teaching algebra, I find that students make fewer mistakes if they think in terms of addition rather than subtraction. So, you are probably better off if you continue to use the addition property just the way we have used it in the examples in this section. But, if you are curious as to whether you can subtract the same number from both sides of an equation, the answer is yes.

PROPERTY   *A Note on Subtraction*

Although the addition property of equality is stated for addition only, we can subtract the same number from both sides of an equation as well. Because subtraction is defined as addition of the opposite, subtracting the same quantity from both sides of an equation does not change the solution.

$$x + 2 = 12 \qquad \text{Original equation}$$
$$x + 2 - 2 = 12 - 2 \qquad \text{Subtract 2 from each side}$$
$$x = 10 \qquad \text{Subtract}$$

Getting Ready for Class

After reading through the preceding section, respond in your own words and in complete sentences.

A. What is a solution to an equation?

B. What are equivalent equations?

C. Explain in words the addition property of equality.

D. How do you check a solution to an equation?

Problem Set 2.2

1. Is $x = 4$ a solution to the equation $3x - 5 = 7$?
2. Is $x = -3$ a solution to the equation $2x + 1 = 5$?
3. Is $y = -2$ a solution to the equation $3y - 4(y + 6) + 2 = 8$?
4. Is $y = 6$ a solution to the equation $7y - 5(y - 1) - 3 = 14$?

For each of the following equations determine whether each given value is a solution to the equation.

5. $2m + 3 = m - 5$

   a. -1 **b.** -8

6. $3x + 7 = 4x - 6$

   a. 13 **b.** 1

7. $2x + \dfrac{5}{3} = x - \dfrac{1}{2}$

   a. $-\dfrac{13}{6}$ **b.** $\dfrac{7}{6}$

8. $5a - \dfrac{1}{2} = 4a + \dfrac{3}{4}$

   a. $-\dfrac{3}{2}$ **b.** $\dfrac{5}{4}$

Solve the following equations.

9. $x - 3 = 8$	**10.** $x - 2 = 7$	**11.** $x + 2 = 6$
12. $x + 5 = 4$	**13.** $a + \dfrac{1}{2} = -\dfrac{1}{4}$	**14.** $a + \dfrac{1}{3} = -\dfrac{5}{6}$
15. $x + 2.3 = -3.5$	**16.** $x + 7.9 = 23.4$	**17.** $y + 11 = -6$
18. $y - 3 = -1$	**19.** $x - \dfrac{5}{8} = -\dfrac{3}{4}$	**20.** $x - \dfrac{2}{5} = -\dfrac{1}{10}$
21. $m - 6 = -10$	**22.** $m - 10 = -6$	**23.** $6.9 + x = 3.3$
24. $7.5 + x = 2.2$	**25.** $5 = a + 4$	**26.** $12 = a - 3$
27. $-\dfrac{5}{9} = x - \dfrac{2}{5}$	**28.** $-\dfrac{7}{8} = x - \dfrac{4}{5}$	

Simplify both sides of the following equations as much as possible, and then solve.

29. $4x + 2 - 3x = 4 + 1$	**30.** $5x + 2 - 4x = 7 - 3$
31. $8a - \dfrac{1}{2} - 7a = \dfrac{3}{4} + \dfrac{1}{8}$	**32.** $9a - \dfrac{4}{5} - 8a = \dfrac{3}{10} - \dfrac{1}{5}$
33. $-3 - 4x + 5x = 18$	**34.** $10 - 3x + 4x = 20$
35. $-11x + 2 + 10x + 2x = 9$	**36.** $-10x + 5 - 4x + 15x = 0$
37. $-2.5 + 4.8 = 8x - 1.2 - 7x$	**38.** $-4.8 + 6.3 = 7x - 2.7 - 6x$
39. $2y - 10 + 3y - 4y = 18 - 6$	**40.** $15 - 21 = 8x + 3x - 10x$

The following equations contain parentheses. Apply the distributive property to remove the parentheses, then simplify each side before using the addition property of equality.

41. $2(x + 3) - x = 4$ **42.** $5(x + 1) - 4x = 2$

43. $-3(x - 4) + 4x = 3 - 7$ **44.** $-2(x - 5) + 3x = 4 - 9$

45. $5(2a + 1) - 9a = 8 - 6$ **46.** $4(2a - 1) - 7a = 9 - 5$

47. $-(x + 3) + 2x - 1 = 6$ **48.** $-(x - 7) + 2x - 8 = 4$

49. $4y - 3(y - 6) + 2 = 8$ **50.** $7y - 6(y - 1) + 3 = 9$

51. $-3(2m - 9) + 7(m - 4) = 12 - 9$ **52.** $-5(m - 3) + 2(3m + 1) = 15 - 8$

Solve the following equations by the method used in Example 9 in this section. Check each solution in the original equation.

53. $4x = 3x + 2$ **54.** $6x = 5x - 4$ **55.** $8a = 7a - 5$

56. $9a = 8a - 3$ **57.** $2x = 3x + 1$ **58.** $4x = 3x + 5$

59. $3y + 4 = 2y + 1$ **60.** $5y + 6 = 4y + 2$ **61.** $2m - 3 = m + 5$

62. $8m - 1 = 7m - 3$ **63.** $4x - 7 = 5x + 1$ **64.** $3x - 7 = 4x - 6$

65. $5x - \dfrac{2}{3} = 4x + \dfrac{4}{3}$ **66.** $3x - \dfrac{5}{4} = 2x + \dfrac{1}{4}$ **67.** $8a - 7.1 = 7a + 3.9$

68. $10a - 4.3 = 9a + 4.7$ **69.** $11y - 2.9 = 12y + 2.9$ **70.** $20y + 9.9 = 21y - 9.9$

Applying the Concepts

71. Light When light comes into contact with any object, it is reflected, absorbed, and transmitted, as shown in the following figure. If T represents the percent of light transmitted, R the percent of light reflected, and A the percent of light absorbed by a surface, then the equation $T + R + A = 100$ shows one way these quantities are related.

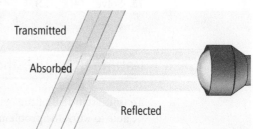

a. For glass, $T = 88$ and $A = 6$, meaning that 88% of the light hitting the glass is transmitted and 6% is absorbed. Substitute $T = 88$ and $A = 6$ into the equation $T + R + A = 100$ and solve for R to find the percent of light that is reflected.

b. For flat black paint, $A = 95$ and no light is transmitted, meaning that $T = 0$. What percent of light is reflected by flat black paint?

c. A pure white surface can reflect 98% of light, so $R = 98$. If no light is transmitted, what percent of light is absorbed by the pure white surface?

d. Typically, shiny gray metals reflect 70–80% of light. Suppose a thick sheet of aluminum absorbs 25% of light. What percent of light is reflected by this shiny gray metal? (Assume no light is transmitted.)

72. Geometry The three angles shown in the triangle at the front of the tent in the following figure add up to 180°. Use this fact to write an equation containing x, and then solve the equation to find the number of degrees in the angle at the top of the triangle.

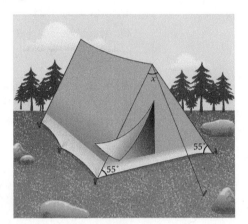

Learning Objectives Assessment

The following problems can be used to help assess if you have successfully met the learning objectives for this section.

73. Which of the following is a solution to the equation $5x - 6 = 4x + 3$?

   a. 9   **b.** -3 **c.** 3   **d.** -9

74. Solve: $9 + x = 27$.

   a. 36   **b.** 18   **c.** 3   **d.** -18

75. Solve: $-4(x - 2) + 5x = 3 - 9$.

   a. -4 **b.** 2   **c.** -14 **d.** 7

Getting Ready for the Next Section

To understand all of the explanations and examples in the next section you must be able to work the problems below.

Simplify.

76. $\dfrac{3}{2}\left(\dfrac{2}{3}y\right)$ **77.** $-\dfrac{5}{2}\left(-\dfrac{2}{5}y\right)$ **78.** $\dfrac{1}{5}(5x)$ **79.** $-\dfrac{1}{4}(-4a)$

80. $\dfrac{1}{5}(30)$ **81.** $-\dfrac{1}{4}(24)$ **82.** $\dfrac{3}{2}(4)$ **83.** $\dfrac{1}{26}(13)$

84. $12\left(-\dfrac{3}{4}\right)$ **85.** $12\left(\dfrac{1}{2}\right)$ **86.** $\dfrac{3}{2}\left(-\dfrac{5}{4}\right)$ **87.** $\dfrac{5}{3}\left(-\dfrac{6}{5}\right)$

88. $13 + (-5)$ **89.** $-13 + (-5)$ **90.** $-\dfrac{3}{4} + \left(-\dfrac{1}{2}\right)$ **91.** $-\dfrac{7}{10} + \left(-\dfrac{1}{2}\right)$

92. $7x + (-4x)$ **93.** $5x + (-2x)$

Learning Objectives

In this section, we will learn how to:

1. Use the multiplication property of equality to solve linear equations.

2. Solve linear equations using both the addition and multiplication properties of equality.

Introduction

We all have to pay taxes. According to Figure 1, people have been paying taxes for quite a long time.

FIGURE 1   *Collection of taxes, ca. 3000 B.C. Clerks and scribes appear at the right, with pen and papyrus, and officials and taxpayers appear at the left.*

Suppose 21% of your monthly pay is withheld for federal income taxes and another 8% is withheld for Social Security, state income tax, and other miscellaneous items, leaving you with $987.50 a month in take-home pay. The amount you earned before the deductions were removed from your check, your gross income G, is given by the equation

$$G - 0.21G - 0.08G = 987.5$$

In this section, we will learn how to solve equations of this type.

In the previous section, we found that adding the same number to both sides of an equation never changed the solution set. The same idea holds for multiplication by numbers other than zero. We can multiply both sides of an equation by the same nonzero number and always be sure we have not changed the solution set. (The reason we cannot multiply both sides by zero will become apparent later.) This fact about equations is called the *multiplication property of equality*, which can be stated formally as follows.

Note This property is also used many times throughout the book. Make every effort to understand it completely.

> **PROPERTY**   *Multiplication Property of Equality*
>
> For any three algebraic expressions A, B, and C, where $C \neq 0$,
>
> if $\qquad\qquad A = B$
> then $\qquad\quad AC = BC$
>
> *In words:*   Multiplying both sides of an equation by the same nonzero number will not change the solution set.

VIDEO EXAMPLES

SECTION 2.3

EXAMPLE 1   Solve: $5x = 30$.

SOLUTION   We have $5x$ on the left side but would like to have just x. To isolate the variable x, we need to change the coefficient from a 5 to a 1. The multiplicative inverse property gives us a way to do just that. We choose to multiply both sides by $\frac{1}{5}$ because it is the reciprocal of 5, and $\left(\frac{1}{5}\right)(5) = 1$. Here is the process:

$$5x = 30$$

$$\frac{1}{5}(5x) = \frac{1}{5}(30) \qquad \text{Multiplication property of equality}$$

$$\left(\frac{1}{5} \cdot 5\right)x = \frac{1}{5}(30) \qquad \text{Associative property of multiplication}$$

$$1x = 6 \qquad \text{Multiply}$$

$$x = 6$$

We can see from Example 1 that multiplication by any number except zero will not change the solution set. If, however, we were to multiply both sides by zero, we may get an equation that is not equivalent. Consider the equation

$$3 = -2$$

This equation is clearly false. However, if we multiply both sides by 0, we obtain

$$0(3) = 0(-2)$$

$$0 = 0$$

which is true. A false statement has been turned into a true one. The two are not equivalent. This is the only restriction of the multiplication property of equality. We are free to multiply both sides of an equation by any number except zero.

PROPERTY   *A Note on Division*

Because **division** is defined as multiplication by the reciprocal, multiplying both sides of an equation by the same number is equivalent to dividing both sides of the equation by the reciprocal of that number; that is, multiplying each side of an equation by $\frac{1}{5}$ and dividing each side of the equation by 5 are equivalent operations. If we were to solve the equation $5x = 30$ from Example 1 using division instead of multiplication, the steps would look like this:

$$5x = 30 \qquad \text{Original equation}$$

$$\frac{5x}{5} = \frac{30}{5} \qquad \text{Divide each side by 5}$$

$$x = 6$$

Using division instead of multiplication on a problem like this may save you some writing. However, with multiplication, it is easier to explain "why" we end up with just one x on the left side of the equation. (The "why" has to do with the associative property of multiplication.) My suggestion is that you continue to use multiplication to solve equations like this one until you understand the process completely. Then, if you find it more convenient, you can use division instead of multiplication.

Here are some more examples that use the multiplication property of equality. We use the multiplication property of equality to isolate the variable by changing the coefficient of the variable into a 1.

EXAMPLE 2   Solve for a: $-4a = 24$.

SOLUTION   Because we want a alone on the left side, we choose to multiply both sides by $-\frac{1}{4}$:

$$-\frac{1}{4}(-4a) = -\frac{1}{4}(24) \qquad \text{Multiplication property of equality}$$

$$\left[-\frac{1}{4}(-4)\right]a = -\frac{1}{4}(24) \qquad \text{Associative property}$$

$$a = -6 \qquad \text{Multiply}$$

> **Note** It is always a good idea to check your solution in the original equation. For Example 2, we would replace a with -6 and get $(-4)(-6) \overset{?}{=} 24$, or $24 = 24$, which is a true statement.

EXAMPLE 3   Solve for t: $-\frac{t}{3} = 5$.

SOLUTION   Because division by 3 is the same as multiplication by $\frac{1}{3}$, we can write $-\frac{t}{3}$ as $-\frac{1}{3}t$. To solve the equation, we multiply each side by the reciprocal of $-\frac{1}{3}$, which is -3.

$$-\frac{t}{3} = 5 \qquad \text{Original equation}$$

$$-\frac{1}{3}t = 5 \qquad \text{Dividing by 3 is equivalent to multiplying by } \tfrac{1}{3}$$

$$-3\left(-\frac{1}{3}t\right) = -3(5) \qquad \text{Multiply each side by } -3$$

$$t = -15 \qquad \text{Multiply}$$

We say the solution is $t = -15$ and the solution set is $\{-15\}$.

EXAMPLE 4   Solve: $\frac{2}{3}y = 4$.

SOLUTION   We can multiply both sides by $\frac{3}{2}$ and have $1y$ on the left side:

$$\frac{3}{2}\left(\frac{2}{3}y\right) = \frac{3}{2}(4) \qquad \text{Multiplication property of equality}$$

$$\left(\frac{3}{2} \cdot \frac{2}{3}\right)y = \frac{3}{2}(4) \qquad \text{Associative property}$$

$$y = 6 \qquad \text{Simplify } \tfrac{3}{2}(4) = \tfrac{3}{2}\left(\tfrac{4}{1}\right) = \tfrac{12}{2} = 6$$

> **Note** Notice in Examples 2 through 4 that if the variable is being multiplied by a number like -4 or $\frac{2}{3}$, we always multiply by the number's reciprocal, $-\frac{1}{4}$ or $\frac{3}{2}$, to end up with just the variable on one side of the equation.

EXAMPLE 5   Solve: $5 + 8 = 10x + 20x - 4x$.

SOLUTION   Our first step will be to simplify each side of the equation:

$$13 = 26x \qquad \text{Simplify both sides first}$$

$$\frac{1}{26}(13) = \frac{1}{26}(26x) \qquad \text{Multiplication property of equality}$$

$$\frac{13}{26} = x \qquad \text{Multiply}$$

$$\frac{1}{2} = x \qquad \text{Reduce to lowest terms}$$

> **Note** It makes no difference on which side of the equal sign x ends up. Most people prefer to have x on the left side because we read from left to right, and it seems to sound better to say x is 6 rather than 6 is x. Both expressions, however, have exactly the same meaning.

In the next four examples, we will use both the addition property of equality and the multiplication property of equality. We use the addition property of equality first in order to get a single term containing the variable on one side of the equation. Then we use the multiplication property of equality to isolate the variable itself by changing the coefficient into a 1.

EXAMPLE 6   Solve for x: $6x + 5 = -13$.

SOLUTION   We begin by adding -5 to both sides of the equation in order to isolate the term containing the variable:

$$6x + 5 + (-5) = -13 + (-5) \qquad \text{Add } -5 \text{ to both sides}$$
$$6x = -18 \qquad \text{Simplify}$$

Now we isolate x itself using the multiplication property of equality:

$$\frac{1}{6}(6x) = \frac{1}{6}(-18) \qquad \text{Multiply both sides by } \frac{1}{6}$$
$$x = -3$$

EXAMPLE 7   Solve for x: $5x = 2x + 12$.

SOLUTION   We begin by adding $-2x$ to both sides of the equation:

$$5x + (-2x) = 2x + (-2x) + 12 \qquad \text{Add } -2x \text{ to both sides}$$
$$3x = 12 \qquad \text{Simplify}$$
$$\frac{1}{3}(3x) = \frac{1}{3}(12) \qquad \text{Multiply both sides by } \frac{1}{3}$$
$$x = 4 \qquad \text{Simplify}$$

So $x = 4$ is the solution to our equation. Or we can write $\{4\}$ as the solution set.

> **Note**   Notice that in Example 7 we used the addition property of equality first to combine all the terms containing x on the left side of the equation. Once this had been done, we used the multiplication property to isolate x on the left side.

EXAMPLE 8   Solve for x: $3x - 4 = -2x + 6$.

SOLUTION   We begin by adding $2x$ to both sides:

$$3x + 2x - 4 = -2x + 2x + 6 \qquad \text{Add } 2x \text{ to both sides}$$
$$5x - 4 = 6 \qquad \text{Simplify}$$

Now we add 4 to both sides:

$$5x - 4 + 4 = 6 + 4 \qquad \text{Add 4 to both sides}$$
$$5x = 10 \qquad \text{Simplify}$$
$$\frac{1}{5}(5x) = \frac{1}{5}(10) \qquad \text{Multiply by } \frac{1}{5}$$
$$x = 2 \qquad \text{Simplify}$$

The next example involves fractions. You will see that the properties we use to solve equations containing fractions are the same as the properties we used to solve the previous equations.

EXAMPLE 9 Solve: $\dfrac{2}{3}x + \dfrac{1}{2} = -\dfrac{3}{4}$.

SOLUTION We can solve this equation by applying our properties and working with the fractions.

$$\dfrac{2}{3}x + \dfrac{1}{2} + \left(-\dfrac{1}{2}\right) = -\dfrac{3}{4} + \left(-\dfrac{1}{2}\right) \quad \text{Add } -\dfrac{1}{2} \text{ to each side}$$

$$\dfrac{2}{3}x = -\dfrac{5}{4} \quad \text{Note that } -\dfrac{3}{4} + \left(-\dfrac{1}{2}\right) = -\dfrac{3}{4} + \left(-\dfrac{2}{4}\right)$$

$$\dfrac{3}{2}\left(\dfrac{2}{3}x\right) = \dfrac{3}{2}\left(-\dfrac{5}{4}\right) \quad \text{Multiply each side by } \dfrac{3}{2}$$

$$x = -\dfrac{15}{8}$$

As we saw in the previous section, when grouping symbols appear in the equation, we use the distributive property to separate terms. Then we can proceed with the addition and multiplication properties of equality.

EXAMPLE 10 Solve: $2(x + 3) = 10$.

SOLUTION To begin, we apply the distributive property to the left side of the equation to separate terms:

$$2x + 6 = 10 \quad \text{Distributive property}$$

$$2x + 6 + (-6) = 10 + (-6) \quad \text{Addition property of equality}$$

$$2x = 4$$

$$\dfrac{1}{2}(2x) = \dfrac{1}{2}(4) \quad \text{Multiply each side by } \dfrac{1}{2}$$

$$x = 2 \quad \text{The solution is 2}$$

Getting Ready for Class

After reading through the preceding section, respond in your own words and in complete sentences.

A. Explain in words the multiplication property of equality.

B. Explain in words how you would solve the equation $3x = 7$ using the multiplication property of equality.

C. Why is it okay to divide both sides of an equation by the same nonzero number?

D. In solving the equation $2x + 5 = 9$, which property of equality do we use first? Why?

Problem Set 2.3

Solve the following equations. Be sure to show your work.

1. $5x = 10$ **2.** $6x = 12$ **3.** $7a = 28$ **4.** $4a = 36$

5. $-8x = 4$ **6.** $-6x = 2$ **7.** $8m = -16$ **8.** $5m = -25$

9. $-3x = -9$ **10.** $-9x = -36$ **11.** $-7y = -28$ **12.** $-15y = -30$

13. $2x = 0$ **14.** $7x = 0$ **15.** $-5x = 0$ **16.** $-3x = 0$

17. $\dfrac{x}{3} = 2$ **18.** $\dfrac{x}{4} = 3$ **19.** $-\dfrac{m}{5} = 10$ **20.** $-\dfrac{m}{7} = 1$

21. $-\dfrac{x}{2} = -\dfrac{3}{4}$ **22.** $-\dfrac{x}{3} = \dfrac{5}{6}$ **23.** $\dfrac{2}{3}a = 8$ **24.** $\dfrac{3}{4}a = 6$

25. $-\dfrac{3}{5}x = \dfrac{9}{5}$ **26.** $-\dfrac{2}{5}x = \dfrac{6}{15}$ **27.** $-\dfrac{5}{8}y = -20$ **28.** $-\dfrac{7}{2}y = -14$

Simplify both sides as much as possible, and then solve.

29. $-4x - 2x + 3x = 24$ **30.** $7x - 5x + 8x = 20$

31. $4x + 8x - 2x = 15 - 10$ **32.** $5x + 4x + 3x = 4 + 8$

33. $-3 - 5 = 3x + 5x - 10x$ **34.** $10 - 16 = 12x - 6x - 3x$

35. $18 - 13 = \dfrac{1}{2}a + \dfrac{3}{4}a - \dfrac{5}{8}a$ **36.** $20 - 14 = \dfrac{1}{3}a + \dfrac{5}{6}a - \dfrac{2}{3}a$

Solve the following equations by multiplying both sides by -1.

37. $-x = 4$ **38.** $-x = -3$ **39.** $-x = -4$ **40.** $-x = 3$

41. $15 = -a$ **42.** $-15 = -a$ **43.** $-y = \dfrac{1}{2}$ **44.** $-y = -\dfrac{3}{4}$

Solve each of the following equations using the method shown in Examples 6–9 in this section.

45. $3x - 2 = 7$ **46.** $2x - 3 = 9$ **47.** $2a + 1 = 3$

48. $5a - 3 = 7$ **49.** $\dfrac{1}{8} + \dfrac{1}{2}x = \dfrac{1}{4}$ **50.** $\dfrac{1}{3} + \dfrac{1}{7}x = -\dfrac{8}{21}$

51. $6x = 2x - 12$ **52.** $8x = 3x - 10$ **53.** $2y = -4y + 18$

54. $3y = -2y - 15$ **55.** $-7x = -3x - 8$ **56.** $-5x = -2x - 12$

57. $8x + 4 = 2x - 5$ **58.** $5x + 6 = 3x - 6$ **59.** $6m - 3 = m + 2$

60. $6m - 5 = m + 5$ **61.** $9y + 2 = 6y - 4$ **62.** $6y + 14 = 2y - 2$

Solve each of the following equations using the method shown in Example 10 in this section.

63. $2(x + 3) = 12$ **64.** $3(x - 2) = 6$ **65.** $6(x - 1) = -18$

66. $4(x + 5) = 16$ **67.** $2(4a + 1) = -6$ **68.** $3(2a - 4) = 12$

69. $14 = 2(5x - 3)$ **70.** $-25 = 5(3x + 4)$ **71.** $-2(3y + 5) = 14$

72. $-3(2y - 4) = -6$ **73.** $-5(2a + 4) = 0$ **74.** $-3(3a - 6) = 0$

75. $1 = \dfrac{1}{2}(4x + 2)$ **76.** $1 = \dfrac{1}{3}(6x + 3)$ **77.** $3(t - 4) + 5 = -4$

78. $5(t - 1) + 6 = -9$ **79.** $4(2x + 1) - 7 = 1$ **80.** $6(3y + 2) - 8 = -2$

81. Solve each equation.

    a. $2x = 3$ **b.** $2 + x = 3$ **c.** $2x + 3 = 0$

    d. $2x + 3 = -5$ **e.** $2x + 3 = 7x - 5$

82. Solve each equation.

    a. $5t = 10$ **b.** $5 + t = 10$ **c.** $5t + 10 = 0$

    d. $5t + 10 = 12$ **e.** $5t + 10 = 8t + 12$

Applying the Concepts

83. Break-Even Point Movie theaters pay a certain price for the movies that you and I see. Suppose a theater pays $1,500 for each showing of a popular movie. If they charge $7.50 for each ticket they sell, then the equation $7.5x = 1,500$ gives the number of tickets they must sell to equal the $1,500 cost of showing the movie. This number is called the break-even point. Solve the equation for x to find the break-even point.

84. Basketball Laura plays basketball for her community college. In one game she scored 13 points total, with a combination of free throws, field goals, and three-pointers. Each free throw is worth 1 point, each field goal is 2 points, and each three-pointer is worth 3 points. If she made 1 free throw and 3 field goals, then solving the equation

$$1 + 3(2) + 3x = 13$$

will give us the number of three-pointers she made. Solve the equation to find the number of three-point shots Laura made.

85. Taxes Suppose 21% of your monthly pay is withheld for federal income taxes and another 8% is withheld for Social Security, state income tax, and other miscellaneous items. If you are left with $987.50 a month in take-home pay, then the amount you earned before the deductions were removed from your check is given by the equation

$$G - 0.21G - 0.08G = 987.5$$

Solve this equation to find your gross income.

86. Rhind Papyrus The *Rhind Papyrus* is an ancient document that contains mathematical riddles. One problem asks the reader to find a quantity such that when it is added to one-fourth of itself the sum is 15. The equation that describes this situation is

$$x + \frac{1}{4}x = 15$$

Solve this equation.

Learning Objectives Assessment

The following problems can be used to help assess if you have successfully met the learning objectives for this section.

87. Solve: $3x - 8x = 20$.

    a. 15   **b.** 25   **c.** 4   **d.** -4

88. Solve: $4a - 5 = 8$.

    a. $\dfrac{13}{4}$ **b.** 7   **c.** $\dfrac{3}{4}$ **d.** -3

Getting Ready for the Next Section

To understand all of the explanations and examples in the next section you must be able to work the problems below.

Solve each equation.

89. $2x = 4$ **90.** $3x = 24$ **91.** $30 = 5x$

92. $0 = 5x$ **93.** $0.17x = 510$ **94.** $0.1x = 400$

Apply the distributive property and then simplify if possible.

95. $3(x - 5) + 4$ **96.** $5(x - 3) + 2$ **97.** $0.09(x + 2{,}000)$

98. $0.04(x + 7{,}000)$ **99.** $7 - 3(2y + 1)$ **100.** $4 - 2(3y + 1)$

101. $3(2x - 5) - (2x - 4)$ **102.** $4(3x - 2) - (6x - 5)$

Simplify.

103. $10x + (-5x)$ **104.** $12x + (-7x)$ **105.** $0.08x + 0.09x$ **106.** $0.06x + 0.04x$

Learning Objectives

In this section, we will learn how to:

1. Solve a linear equation containing grouping symbols.

2. Solve a linear equation containing fractions.

3. Identify an identity or a contradiction.

Introduction

We will now use the material we have developed in the first three sections of this chapter to build a method for solving any linear equation.

> **DEFINITION** *linear equation*
>
> A **linear equation** in one variable is any equation that can be put in the form $ax + b = 0$, where a and b are real numbers and a is not zero.

Each of the equations we will solve in this section is a *linear equation in one variable*. The general method of solving linear equations is actually very simple. It is based on the properties we developed in Chapter 1 and on two very simple properties we developed in Sections 2.3 and 2.4. We can add any number to both sides of the equation and multiply both sides by any nonzero number. The equation may change in form, but the solution set will not.

The steps we use to solve a linear equation in one variable are listed here. The overall goal is to isolate the variable on one side of the equation.

Note You may have some previous experience solving equations. Even so, you should solve the equations in this section using the method developed here. Your work should look like the examples in the text. If you have learned shortcuts or a different method of solving equations somewhere else, you can always go back to them later. What is important now is that you are able to solve equations by the methods shown here.

> **HOW TO** *Solve Linear Equations in One Variable*
>
> **Step 1a:** Use the distributive property to separate terms, if necessary.
> **1b:** If fractions are present, consider multiplying both sides by the LCD to eliminate the fractions. If decimals are present, consider multiplying both sides by a power of 10 to clear the equation of decimals.
> **1c:** Combine similar terms on each side of the equation.
> **Step 2:** Use the addition property of equality to get all variable terms on one side of the equation and all constant terms on the other side. A **variable term** is a term that contains the variable (for example, $5x$). A **constant term** is a term that does not contain the variable (the number 3, for example).
> **Step 3:** Use the multiplication property of equality to change the coefficient of the variable term into 1.
> **Step 4:** Check your solution in the original equation to be sure that you have not made a mistake in the solution process.

As you will see as you work through the examples in this section, it is not always necessary to use all four steps when solving equations. The number of steps used depends on the equation.

The examples that follow show a variety of equations and their solutions. When you have finished this section and worked the problems in the problem set, the steps in the solution process should be a description of how you operate when solving equations. That is, you want to work enough problems so that the Strategy for Solving Linear Equations is second nature to you.

Equations Containing Grouping Symbols

EXAMPLE 1   Solve for x: $3(x - 5) + 4 = 13$.

SOLUTION   Our first step will be to apply the distributive property to the left side of the equation:

Step 1a:	$3x - 15 + 4 = 13$	Distributive property
Step 1c:	$3x - 11 = 13$	Simplify the left side
Step 2:	$\begin{cases} 3x - 11 + 11 = 13 + 11 \\ 3x = 24 \end{cases}$	Add 11 to both sides
Step 3:	$\begin{cases} \frac{1}{3}(3x) = \frac{1}{3}(24) \\ x = 8 \end{cases}$	Multiply both sides by $\frac{1}{3}$ The solution is 8

Step 4:	When	$x = 8$
	the equation	$3(x - 5) + 4 = 13$
	becomes	$3(8 - 5) + 4 \stackrel{?}{=} 13$
		$3(3) + 4 \stackrel{?}{=} 13$
		$9 + 4 \stackrel{?}{=} 13$
		$13 = 13$ A true statement

EXAMPLE 2   Solve: $5(x - 3) + 2 = 5(2x - 8) - 3$.

SOLUTION   In this case, we apply the distributive property on each side of the equation:

Step 1a:	$5x - 15 + 2 = 10x - 40 - 3$	Distributive property
Step 1c:	$5x - 13 = 10x - 43$	Simplify each side
Step 2:	$\begin{cases} 5x + (-5x) - 13 = 10x + (-5x) - 43 \\ -13 = 5x - 43 \\ -13 + 43 = 5x - 43 + 43 \\ 30 = 5x \end{cases}$	Add $-5x$ to both sides Add 43 to both sides
Step 3:	$\begin{cases} \frac{1}{5}(30) = \frac{1}{5}(5x) \\ 6 = x \end{cases}$	Multiply both sides by $\frac{1}{5}$ The solution is 6

Step 4: Replacing x with 6 in the original equation, we have

$$5(6 - 3) + 2 \overset{?}{=} 5(2 \cdot 6 - 8) - 3$$

$$5(3) + 2 \overset{?}{=} 5(12 - 8) - 3$$

$$5(3) + 2 \overset{?}{=} 5(4) - 3$$

$$15 + 2 \overset{?}{=} 20 - 3$$

$$17 = 17 \qquad \text{A true statement}$$

EXAMPLE 3 Solve: $7 - 3(2y + 1) = 16$.

SOLUTION We begin by multiplying -3 times the sum of $2y$ and 1:

Step 1a: $\qquad 7 - 6y - 3 = 16 \qquad$ Distributive property

Step 1c: $\qquad -6y + 4 = 16 \qquad$ Simplify the left side

Step 2: $\qquad \begin{cases} -6y + 4 + (-4) = 16 + (-4) & \text{Add } -4 \text{ to both sides} \\ -6y = 12 \end{cases}$

Step 3: $\qquad \begin{cases} -\dfrac{1}{6}(-6y) = -\dfrac{1}{6}(12) & \text{Multiply both sides by } -\frac{1}{6} \\ y = -2 \end{cases}$

There are two things to notice about the example that follows: first, the distributive property is used to remove parentheses that are preceded by a negative sign, and second, the addition property and the multiplication property are not shown in as much detail as in the previous examples.

EXAMPLE 4 Solve: $3(2x - 5) - (2x - 4) = 6 - (4x + 5)$.

SOLUTION When we apply the distributive property to remove the grouping symbols and separate terms, we have to be careful with the signs. Remember, we can think of $-(2x - 4)$ as $-1(2x - 4)$, so that

$$-(2x - 4) = -1(2x - 4) = -2x + 4$$

It is not uncommon for students to make a mistake with this type of simplification and write the result as $-2x - 4$, which is incorrect. Here is the complete solution to our equation:

$$3(2x - 5) - (2x - 4) = 6 - (4x + 5) \qquad \text{Original equation}$$

$$6x - 15 - 2x + 4 = 6 - 4x - 5 \qquad \text{Distributive property}$$

$$4x - 11 = -4x + 1 \qquad \text{Simplify each side}$$

$$8x - 11 = 1 \qquad \text{Add } 4x \text{ to each side}$$

$$8x = 12 \qquad \text{Add 11 to each side}$$

$$x = \frac{12}{8} \qquad \text{Multiply each side by } \frac{1}{8}$$

$$x = \frac{3}{2} \qquad \text{Reduce to lowest terms}$$

The solution, $\dfrac{3}{2}$, checks when replacing x in the original equation.

Equations Containing Fractions

If the equation contains fractions, we can use the multiplication property of equality to clear fractions from the equation by multiplying both sides by the LCD. The next examples illustrate how this is done.

EXAMPLE 5   Solve: $\dfrac{2}{3}x + \dfrac{1}{2} = -\dfrac{3}{4}$.

SOLUTION   The LCD of all fractions in the equation is 12. We multiply both sides of the equation by 12 in order to eliminate fractions from the equation.

$$12\left(\frac{2}{3}x + \frac{1}{2}\right) = 12\left(-\frac{3}{4}\right) \qquad \text{Multiply each side by the LCD 12}$$

Step 1b:
$$12\left(\frac{2}{3}x\right) + 12\left(\frac{1}{2}\right) = 12\left(-\frac{3}{4}\right) \qquad \text{Distributive property on the left side}$$

$$8x + 6 = -9 \qquad \text{Multiply}$$

Step 2:
$$8x = -15 \qquad \text{Add } -6 \text{ to each side}$$

Step 3:
$$x = -\frac{15}{8} \qquad \text{Multiply each side by } \frac{1}{8}$$

As you can see, we obtain the same solution as we did in Example 9 of the previous section where we worked with fractions.

> *Note* Our original equation has denominators of 3, 2, and 4. The LCD for these three denominators is 12, and it has the property that all three denominators will divide it evenly. Therefore, if we multiply both sides of our equation by 12, each denominator will divide into 12 and we will be left with an equation that does not contain any denominators other than 1.

EXAMPLE 6   Solve: $\dfrac{1}{3}(x - 4) + 2x = \dfrac{3}{5}(4x + 1)$

SOLUTION   This equation contains both grouping symbols and fractions. Following our strategy for solving linear equations, we use the distributive property first to separate terms, and then use the LCD to eliminate fractions.

Step 1a:
$$\frac{1}{3}x - \frac{4}{3} + 2x = \frac{12}{5}x + \frac{3}{5} \qquad \begin{array}{l}\text{Distributive}\\\text{property}\end{array}$$

Step 1b:
$$15\left(\frac{1}{3}x - \frac{4}{3} + 2x\right) = 15\left(\frac{12}{5}x + \frac{3}{5}\right) \qquad \begin{array}{l}\text{Multiply both sides}\\\text{by the LCD 15}\end{array}$$

$$15\left(\frac{1}{3}x\right) - 15\left(\frac{4}{3}\right) + 15(2x) = 15\left(\frac{12}{5}x\right) + 15\left(\frac{3}{5}\right) \qquad \begin{array}{l}\text{Distributive}\\\text{property}\end{array}$$

$$5x - 20 + 30x = 36x + 9 \qquad \text{Multiply}$$

Step 1c:
$$35x - 20 = 36x + 9 \qquad \begin{array}{l}\text{Simplify the left}\\\text{side}\end{array}$$

$$35x + (-35x) - 20 = 36x + (-35x) + 9 \qquad \begin{array}{l}\text{Add } -35x \text{ to both}\\\text{sides}\end{array}$$

Step 2:
$$-20 = x + 9$$

$$-20 + (-9) = x + 9 + (-9) \qquad \begin{array}{l}\text{Add } -9 \text{ to both}\\\text{sides}\end{array}$$

$$-29 = x$$

If we substitute $x = -29$ into the original equation, we get $-69 = -69$, which is a true statement; so the solution set is $\{-29\}$.

Equations Containing Decimals

Now we will consider equations that contain one or more decimals.

EXAMPLE 7   Solve the equation $0.08x + 0.09(x + 2,000) = 690$.

SOLUTION   We can solve the equation in its original form by working with the decimals, or we can eliminate the decimals first by using the multiplication property of equality and solving the resulting equation. Both methods follow.

Method 1
Working with the decimals.

$$0.08x + 0.09(x + 2,000) = 690 \qquad \text{Original equation}$$

Step 1a: $\quad 0.08x + 0.09x + 0.09(2,000) = 690 \qquad$ Distributive property

Step 1c: $\qquad\qquad 0.17x + 180 = 690 \qquad$ Simplify the left side

Step 2:
$$\begin{cases} 0.17x + 180 + (-180) = 690 + (-180) & \text{Add } -180 \text{ to each side} \\ 0.17x = 510 \end{cases}$$

Step 3:
$$\begin{cases} \dfrac{0.17x}{0.17} = \dfrac{510}{0.17} & \text{Divide each side by } 0.17 \\ x = 3,000 \end{cases}$$

Note that we divided each side of the equation by 0.17 to obtain the solution. This is still an application of the multiplication property of equality because dividing by 0.17 is equivalent to multiplying by $\frac{1}{0.17}$.

Method 2
Eliminating the decimals in the beginning.

$$0.08x + 0.09(x + 2,000) = 690 \qquad \text{Original equation}$$

Step 1a: $\qquad\qquad 0.08x + 0.09x + 180 = 690 \qquad$ Distributive property

Step 1b:
$$\begin{cases} 100(0.08x + 0.09x + 180) = 100(690) & \text{Multiply both sides by 100} \\ 8x + 9x + 18,000 = 69,000 \end{cases}$$

Step 1c: $\qquad\qquad 17x + 18,000 = 69,000 \qquad$ Simplify the left side

Step 2: $\qquad\qquad\qquad 17x = 51,000 \qquad$ Add $-18,000$ to each side

Step 3:
$$\begin{cases} \dfrac{17x}{17} = \dfrac{51,000}{17} & \text{Divide each side by 17} \\ x = 3,000 \end{cases}$$

Substituting 3,000 for x in the original equation, we have

Step 4:
$$\begin{cases} 0.08(3,000) + 0.09(3,000 + 2,000) \overset{?}{=} 690 \\ 0.08(3,000) + 0.09(5,000) \overset{?}{=} 690 \\ 240 + 450 \overset{?}{=} 690 \\ 690 = 690 \qquad \text{A true statement} \end{cases}$$

Identities and Contradictions

We conclude this section by considering some special cases. First, we offer the following definitions.

> **(def) DEFINITION** *identity*
>
> An *identity* is an equation that is true when the variable is replaced by any real number for which the equation is defined.

With linear equations, the solution set for an identity will be the set of all real numbers. The opposite extreme is an equation that is false for any value of the variable.

> **(def) DEFINITION** *contradiction*
>
> A *contradiction* is an equation that has no solutions. It will be a false statement for any replacement of the variable.

The solution set for a contradiction is the empty set, { }, which can also be expressed using the null set symbol, $\varnothing$.

EXAMPLE 8   Solve: $9a - 2(3a + 5) = 3(a - 1) - 7$

SOLUTION   We begin by applying the distributive property to both sides of the equation.

Step 1a: $9a - 6a - 10 = 3a - 3 - 7$ Distributive property

Step 1c: $3a - 10 = 3a - 10$ Simplify

Notice that the left and right sides of the equation are identical. If we replace a with any real number, the result will be a true statement. For example,

$$\text{If } a = 0 \quad \text{we have} \quad 3(0) - 10 = 3(0) - 10$$
$$0 - 10 = 0 - 10$$
$$-10 = -10$$

$$\text{If } a = 5 \quad \text{we have} \quad 3(5) - 10 = 3(5) - 10$$
$$15 - 10 = 15 - 10$$
$$5 = 5$$

This equation is an identity. The solution set is the set of all real numbers.

EXAMPLE 9   Solve: $\frac{1}{6}(5x + 3) - \frac{1}{2}x = \frac{1}{3}(x - 5)$

SOLUTION   First we distribute, and then eliminate fractions.

Step 1a: $\frac{5}{6}x + \frac{1}{2} - \frac{1}{2}x = \frac{1}{3}x - \frac{5}{3}$ Distributive property

Step 1b: $\begin{cases} 12\left(\frac{5}{6}x + \frac{1}{2} - \frac{1}{2}x\right) = 12\left(\frac{1}{3}x - \frac{5}{3}\right) & \text{Multiply both sides by LCD 12} \\ \\ 10x + 6 - 6x = 4x - 20 \end{cases}$

Step 1c: $4x + 6 = 4x - 20$ Simplify

Step 2: $\begin{cases} 4x + (-4x) + 6 = 4x + (-4x) - 20 & \text{Add } -4x \text{ to both sides} \\ \\ 6 = -20 \end{cases}$

This statement will never be true. It will be false no matter what value we replace x with. The equation is a contradiction, and therefore has no solutions. The solution set is $\varnothing$.

Getting Ready for Class

After reading through the preceding section, respond in your own words and in complete sentences.

A. What is the first step in solving a linear equation containing parentheses?

B. If an equation contains fractions, what can you do to eliminate the fractions?

C. If an equation contains decimals, what can you do to eliminate the decimals?

D. What is an identity? How can you recognize if an equation is an identity?

Problem Set 2.4

Solve each equation.

1. $x + (2x - 1) = 2$ **2.** $x + (5x + 2) = 20$

3. $15 = 3(x - 1)$ **4.** $12 = 4(x - 5)$

5. $6 - 5(2a - 3) = 1$ **6.** $-8 - 2(3 - a) = 0$

7. $x - (3x + 5) = -3$ **8.** $x - (4x - 1) = 7$

9. $7(2y - 1) - 6y = -1$ **10.** $4(4y - 3) + 2y = 3$

11. $5x - 8(2x - 5) = 7$ **12.** $3x + 4(8x - 15) = 10$

13. $4x - (-4x + 1) = 5$ **14.** $-2x - (4x - 8) = -1$

15. $3(x - 3) + 2(2x) = 5$ **16.** $2(x - 2) + 3(5x) = 30$

17. $3x + 2(x - 2) = 6$ **18.** $5x - (x - 5) = 25$

19. $5x + 10(x + 8) = 245$ **20.** $5x + 10(x + 7) = 175$

21. $x + (x + 3)(-3) = x - 3$ **22.** $x - 2(x + 2) = x - 2$

23. $5(y + 2) = 4(y + 1)$ **24.** $3(y - 3) = 2(y - 2)$

25. $50(x - 5) = 30(x + 5)$ **26.** $34(x - 2) = 26(x + 2)$

27. $5(x + 2) + 3(x - 1) = -9$ **28.** $4(x + 1) + 3(x - 3) = 2$

29. $-2(3y + 1) = 3(1 - 6y) - 9$ **30.** $-5(4y - 3) = 2(1 - 8y) + 11$

31. $2(t - 3) + 3(t - 2) = 28$ **32.** $-3(t - 5) - 2(2t + 1) = -8$

33. $5x + 10(x + 3) + 25(x + 5) = 435$

34. $5(x + 3) + 10x + 25(x + 7) = 390$

35. $5(x - 2) - (3x + 4) = 3(6x - 8) + 10$

36. $3(x - 1) - (4x - 5) = 2(5x - 1) - 7$

37. $2(5x - 3) - (2x - 4) = 5 - (6x + 1)$

38. $3(4x - 2) - (5x - 8) = 8 - (2x + 3)$

39. $-(3x + 1) - (4x - 7) = 4 - (3x + 2)$

40. $-(6x + 2) - (8x - 3) = 8 - (5x + 1)$

41. $\dfrac{x}{2} + 4 = \dfrac{x}{5} - 1$ **42.** $\dfrac{x}{3} - 2 = \dfrac{x}{4} + 6$

43. $\dfrac{x}{7} - \dfrac{5}{21} = \dfrac{x}{3} + \dfrac{2}{7}$ **44.** $\dfrac{7}{6} - \dfrac{x}{2} = \dfrac{11}{12} + \dfrac{x}{3}$

45. $\dfrac{4}{9}x + \dfrac{5}{3} = 2 + \dfrac{2}{3}x$ **46.** $5 - \dfrac{3}{8}x = \dfrac{1}{2} + \dfrac{1}{4}x$

47. $\dfrac{1}{2}(x - 3) = \dfrac{1}{4}(x + 1)$ **48.** $\dfrac{1}{3}(x - 4) = \dfrac{1}{2}(x - 6)$

49. $\dfrac{3}{4}(8x - 4) + 3 = \dfrac{2}{5}(5x + 10) - 1$ **50.** $\dfrac{5}{6}(6x + 12) + 1 = \dfrac{2}{3}(9x - 3) + 5$

51. $0.5x + 0.2(18 - x) = 5.4$ **52.** $0.1x + 0.5(40 - x) = 32$

53. $0.06x + 0.08(100 - x) = 6.5$ **54.** $0.05x + 0.07(100 - x) = 6.2$

55. $0.2x - 0.5 = 0.5 - 0.2(2x - 13)$ **56.** $0.4x - 0.1 = 0.7 - 0.3(6 - 2x)$

57. $0.08x + 0.09(x + 2,000) = 860$ **58.** $0.11x + 0.12(x + 4,000) = 940$

59. $0.10x + 0.12(x + 500) = 214$ **60.** $0.08x + 0.06(x + 800) = 104$

61. $-0.7(2x - 7) = 0.3(11 - 4x)$ **62.** $-0.3(2x - 5) = 0.7(3 - x)$

63. $0.2x + 0.5(12 - x) = 3.6$ **64.** $0.3x + 0.6(25 - x) = 12$

Solve each equation and write the solution set. State if the equation is an identity or a contradiction.

65. $2x + 4 = 2x - 4$ **66.** $2x + 4 = 4 + 2x$

67. $3x - 5 = 5 - 3x$ **68.** $6x + 7 = 7 - 6x$

69. $4(3x + 2) - x = 7x + 2(2x + 4)$ **70.** $2(5x - 1) + 6 = 4(4x + 3) - 6x$

71. $\frac{4}{3} + \frac{1}{2}x - \frac{1}{6} = \frac{1}{3}x + 1 + \frac{1}{6}x$ **72.** $\frac{2}{3}x + \frac{1}{4} - \frac{1}{6}x = \frac{1}{3} + \frac{1}{2}x - \frac{1}{12}$

The next two problems are intended to give you practice reading, and paying attention to, the instructions that accompany the problems you are working. Working these problems is an excellent way to get ready for a test or a quiz.

73. Work each problem according to the instructions given.

    a. Solve: $4x - 5 = 0$.   **b.** Solve: $4x - 5 = 25$.

    c. Add: $(4x - 5) + (2x + 25)$.   **d.** Solve: $4x - 5 = 2x + 25$.

    e. Multiply: $4(x - 5)$.   **f.** Solve: $4(x - 5) = 2x + 25$.

74. Work each problem according to the instructions given.

    a. Solve: $3x + 6 = 0$.   **b.** Solve: $3x + 6 = 4$.

    c. Add: $(3x + 6) + (7x + 4)$.   **d.** Solve: $3x + 6 = 7x + 4$.

    e. Multiply: $3(x + 6)$.   **f.** Solve: $3(x + 6) = 7x + 4$.

Learning Objectives Assessment

The following problems can be used to help assess if you have successfully met the learning objectives for this section.

75. Solve: $4(2x - 1) + 9 = 7 - (5x + 3)$.

    a. $-\frac{1}{13}$ **b.** 0 **c.** -2 **d.** $-\frac{8}{13}$

76. Solve: $\frac{x}{8} + \frac{1}{3} - x = \frac{x}{12} + 2 - \frac{5}{6}$.

    a. $-\frac{10}{11}$ **b.** $\frac{13}{19}$ **c.** $-\frac{20}{23}$ **d.** $\varnothing$

77. Solve: $0.05x + 0.04(x - 300) = 312$.

    a. 373 **b.** $3,480$ **c.** $3,600$ **d.** 168

78. Solve: $3 + 9(x - 4) = 7x + 2(x - 15)$

    a. $\varnothing$ **b.** 0 **c.** $\frac{31}{6}$ **d.** All real numbers

Getting Ready for the Next Section

To understand all of the explanations and examples in the next section you must be able to work the problems below.

Solve each equation.

79. $40 = 2x + 12$ **80.** $80 = 2x + 12$ **81.** $12 + 2y = 6$ **82.** $3x + 18 = 6$

83. $24x = 6$ **84.** $45 = 0.75x$ **85.** $70 = x \cdot 210$ **86.** $15 = x \cdot 80$

Apply the distributive property.

87. $\frac{1}{2}(-3x + 6)$ **88.** $-\frac{1}{4}(-5x + 20)$

Learning Objectives

In this section, we will learn how to:

1. Solve a formula for a given variable.
2. Solve basic percent problems.

Introduction

In this section, we continue solving equations by working with formulas and percents. To begin, here is the definition of a *formula*.

> **DEFINITION** *formula*
>
> In mathematics, a **formula** is an equation that contains more than one variable.

The equation $P = 2l + 2w$, which tells us how to find the perimeter of a rectangle, is an example of a formula.

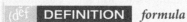

To begin our work with formulas, we will consider some examples in which we are given numerical replacements for all but one of the variables.

VIDEO EXAMPLES

SECTION 2.5

EXAMPLE 1   The perimeter P of a rectangular livestock pen is 40 feet. If the width w is 6 feet, find the length.

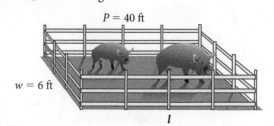

SOLUTION   First, we substitute 40 for P and 6 for w in the formula $P = 2l + 2w$. Then we solve for l:

$$\text{When} \qquad P = 40 \text{ and } w = 6$$

the formula $\qquad P = 2l + 2w$

becomes $\qquad 40 = 2l + 2(6)$

or $\qquad 40 = 2l + 12$ — Multiply 2 and 6

$\qquad\qquad 28 = 2l$ — Add -12 to each side

$\qquad\qquad 14 = l$ — Multiply each side by $\frac{1}{2}$

To summarize our results, if a rectangular pen has a perimeter of 40 feet and a width of 6 feet, then the length must be 14 feet.

EXAMPLE 2   Find y when $x = 4$ in the formula $3x + 2y = 6$.

SOLUTION   We substitute 4 for x in the formula and then solve for y :

When	$x = 4$	
the formula	$3x + 2y = 6$	
becomes	$3(4) + 2y = 6$	
or	$12 + 2y = 6$	Multiply 3 and 4
	$2y = -6$	Add -12 to each side
	$y = -3$	Multiply each side by $\frac{1}{2}$

In the next examples, we will solve a formula for one of its variables without being given numerical replacements for the other variables.

Consider the formula for the area of a triangle:

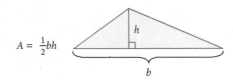

$$A = \tfrac{1}{2}bh$$

where A = area, b = length of the base, and h = height of the triangle.

Suppose we want to solve this formula for h. What we must do is isolate the variable h on one side of the equal sign. We begin by multiplying both sides by 2 to eliminate the fraction:

$$2 \cdot A = 2 \cdot \frac{1}{2}bh$$

$$2A = bh$$

Then we divide both sides by b:

$$\frac{2A}{b} = \frac{bh}{b}$$

$$h = \frac{2A}{b}$$

The original formula $A = \frac{1}{2}bh$ and the final formula $h = \frac{2A}{b}$ both give the same relationship among A, b, and h. The first one has been solved for A and the second one has been solved for h.

> **RULE**   *Solving a formula for a variable*
>
> To solve a formula for one of its variables, we must isolate that variable on either side of the equal sign. All other variables and constants will appear on the other side.

EXAMPLE 3   Solve $3x + 2y = 6$ for y.

SOLUTION To solve for y, we must isolate y on the left side of the equation. To begin, we use the addition property of equality to add $-3x$ to each side:

$$3x + 2y = 6 \qquad \text{Original formula}$$

$$3x + (-3x) + 2y = (-3x) + 6 \qquad \text{Add } -3x \text{ to each side}$$

$$2y = -3x + 6 \qquad \text{Simplify the left side}$$

$$\frac{1}{2}(2y) = \frac{1}{2}(-3x + 6) \qquad \text{Multiply each side by } \frac{1}{2}$$

$$y = -\frac{3}{2}x + 3 \qquad \text{Multiplication}$$

EXAMPLE 4   Solve $h = vt - 16t^2$ for v.

SOLUTION Let's begin by interchanging the left and right sides of the equation. That way, the variable we are solving for, v, will be on the left side.

$$vt - 16t^2 = h \qquad \text{Exchange sides}$$

$$vt - 16t^2 + 16t^2 = h + 16t^2 \qquad \text{Add } 16t^2 \text{ to each side}$$

$$vt = h + 16t^2$$

$$\frac{vt}{t} = \frac{h + 16t^2}{t} \qquad \text{Divide each side by } t$$

$$v = \frac{h + 16t^2}{t}$$

We know we are finished because we have isolated the variable we are solving for on the left side of the equation and it does not appear on the other side.

EXAMPLE 5   Solve for y: $\dfrac{y - 1}{x} = \dfrac{3}{2}$.

SOLUTION Although we will do more extensive work with formulas of this form later in the book, we need to know how to solve this particular formula for y in order to understand some things in the next chapter. We begin by multiplying each side of the formula by x. Doing so will simplify the left side of the equation, and make the rest of the solution process simple.

$$\frac{y - 1}{x} = \frac{3}{2} \qquad \text{Original formula}$$

$$x \cdot \frac{y - 1}{x} = \frac{3}{2} \cdot x \qquad \text{Multiply each side by } x$$

$$y - 1 = \frac{3}{2}x \qquad \text{Simplify each side}$$

$$y = \frac{3}{2}x + 1 \qquad \text{Add 1 to each side}$$

This is our solution. If we look back to the first step, we can justify our result on the left side of the equation this way: Dividing by x is equivalent to multiplying by its reciprocal $\frac{1}{x}$. Here is what it looks like when written out completely:

$$x \cdot \frac{y - 1}{x} = x\left(\frac{1}{x}\right)(y - 1) = 1(y - 1) = (y - 1)$$

Basic Percent Problems

The next examples in this section show how basic percent problems can be translated directly into equations. To understand these examples, you must recall that *percent* means "per hundred"; that is, 75% is the same as $\frac{75}{100}$, 0.75, and, in reduced fraction form, $\frac{3}{4}$. Likewise, the decimal 0.25 is equivalent to 25%. To change a decimal to a percent, we move the decimal point two places to the right and write the % symbol. To change from a percent to a decimal, we drop the % symbol and move the decimal point two places to the left. The table that follows gives some of the most commonly used fractions and decimals and their equivalent percents.

Fraction	Decimal	Percent
$\frac{1}{2}$	0.5	50%
$\frac{1}{4}$	0.25	25%
$\frac{3}{4}$	0.75	75%
$\frac{1}{3}$	$0.33\frac{1}{3}$	$33\frac{1}{3}\%$
$\frac{2}{3}$	$0.66\frac{2}{3}$	$66\frac{2}{3}\%$
$\frac{1}{5}$	0.2	20%
$\frac{2}{5}$	0.4	40%

Note You are probably familiar with the repeating decimals 0.333… and 0.666… for $\frac{1}{3}$ and $\frac{2}{3}$, respectively. The decimals we have written, $0.33\frac{1}{3}$ and $0.66\frac{2}{3}$, are equivalent to those repeating decimals, but are more helpful when converting to percents.

EXAMPLE 6   What number is 25% of 60?

SOLUTION   To solve a problem like this, we let x represent the number in question (that is, the number we are looking for). Then we translate the sentence directly into an equation by using an equal sign for the word "is" and multiplication for the word "of." Here is how it is done:

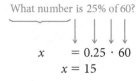

$$x \quad = 0.25 \cdot 60$$
$$x = 15$$

Notice that we must write 25% as a decimal in order to do the arithmetic in the problem.

   The number 15 is 25% of 60.

EXAMPLE 7   What percent of 24 is 6?

SOLUTION   Translating this sentence into an equation, as we did in Example 6, we have

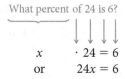

$$x \quad \cdot 24 = 6$$
$$\text{or} \quad 24x = 6$$

Next, we multiply each side by $\frac{1}{24}$. (This is the same as dividing each side by 24.)

$$\frac{1}{24}(24x) = \frac{1}{24}(6)$$

$$x = \frac{6}{24}$$

$$= \frac{1}{4}$$

$$= 0.25, \text{ or } 25\%$$

25% of 24 is 6, or in other words, the number 6 is 25% of 24.

EXAMPLE 8   45 is 75% of what number?

SOLUTION   Again, we translate the sentence directly:

45 is 75% of what number?

$$45 = 0.75 \cdot \qquad x$$

Next we multiply each side by $\frac{1}{0.75}$ (which is the same as dividing each side by 0.75):

$$\frac{1}{0.75}(45) = \frac{1}{0.75}(0.75x)$$

$$\frac{45}{0.75} = x$$

$$60 = x$$

The number 45 is 75% of 60.

EXAMPLE 9   At one time, the American Dietetic Association (ADA) recommended eating foods in which the calories from fat are less than 30% of the total calories. The nutrition labels from two kinds of granola bars are shown in Figure 1. For each bar, what percent of the total calories come from fat?

BAR I

Nutrition Facts	
Serving Size 2 bars (47g)	
Servings Per Container 6	
Amount Per Serving	
Calories	210
Calories from Fat	70
	% Daily Value*
Total Fat 8g	**12%**
Saturated Fat 1g	**5%**
Cholesterol 0mg	**0%**
Sodium 150mg	**6%**
Total Carbohydrate 32g	**11%**
Dietary Fiber 2g	**10%**
Sugars 12g	
Protein 4g	

* Percent Daily Values are based on a 2,000 calorie diet. Your daily values may be higher or lower depending on your calorie needs.

BAR II

Nutrition Facts	
Serving Size 1 bar (21g)	
Servings Per Container 8	
Amount Per Serving	
Calories	80
Calories from Fat	15
	% Daily Value*
Total Fat 1.5g	**2%**
Saturated Fat 0g	**0%**
Cholesterol 0mg	**0%**
Sodium 60mg	**3%**
Total Carbohydrate 16g	**5%**
Dietary Fiber 1g	**4%**
Sugars 5g	
Protein 2g	

* Percent Daily Values are based on a 2,000 calorie diet. Your daily values may be higher or lower depending on your calorie needs.

FIGURE 1

SOLUTION The information needed to solve this problem is located towards the top of each label. Each serving of Bar I contains 210 calories, of which 70 calories come from fat. To find the percent of total calories that come from fat, we must answer this question:

70 is what percent of 210?

For Bar II, one serving contains 80 calories, of which 15 calories come from fat. To find the percent of total calories that come from fat, we must answer this question:

15 is what percent of 80?

Translating each equation into symbols, we have

70 is what percent of 210?	15 is what percent of 80?
$70 = x \cdot 210$	$15 = x \cdot 80$
$x = \dfrac{70}{210}$	$x = \dfrac{15}{80}$
$x = 0.33$ to the nearest hundredth	$x = 0.19$ to the nearest hundredth
$x = 33\%$	$x = 19\%$

Comparing the two bars, 33% of the calories in Bar I are fat calories, whereas 19% of the calories in Bar II are fat calories. According to the ADA, Bar II is the healthier choice.

Applying the Concepts

As we mentioned in Chapter 1, in the U.S. system, temperature is measured on the Fahrenheit scale. In the metric system, temperature is measured on the Celsius scale. On the Celsius scale, water boils at 100 degrees and freezes at 0 degrees. To denote a temperature of 100 degrees on the Celsius scale, we write

100°C, which is read "100 degrees Celsius"

Table 1 is intended to give you an intuitive idea of the relationship between the two temperature scales. Table 2 gives the formulas, in both symbols and words, that are used to convert between the two scales.

TABLE 1

Situation	Temperature	
	Fahrenheit	Celsius
Water freezes	32°F	0°C
Room temperature	68°F	20°C
Normal body temperature	98.6°F	37°C
Water boils	212°F	100°C

TABLE 2

To Convert from	Formula in Symbols	Formula in Words
Fahrenheit to Celsius	$C = \dfrac{5}{9}(F - 32)$	Subtract 32, then multiply by $\dfrac{5}{9}$
Celsius to Fahrenheit	$F = \dfrac{9}{5}C + 32$	Multiply by $\dfrac{9}{5}$, then add 32

EXAMPLE 10 Mr. McKeague traveled to Buenos Aires with a group of friends. It was a hot day when they arrived. One of the bank kiosks indicated the temperature was 25°C. Someone asked what that would be on the Fahrenheit scale (the scale they were familiar with), and Budd, one of his friends said, "just multiply by 2 and add 30."

©Nikada/iStockPhoto.com

a. What was the temperature in °F according to Budd's approximation?

b. What is the actual temperature in °F?

c. Why does Budd's estimate work?

d. Write a formula for Budd's estimate.

SOLUTION

a. According to Budd, we multiply by 2 and add 30, so

$$2 \cdot 25 + 30 = 50 + 30 = 80°F$$

b. Using the formula $F = \frac{9}{5}C + 32$, with $C = 25$, we have

$$F = \frac{9}{5}(25) + 32 = 45 + 32 = 77°F$$

c. Budd's estimate works because $\frac{9}{5}$ is approximately 2 and 30 is close to 32.

d. In symbols, Budd's estimate is $F = 2 \cdot C + 30$.

Getting Ready for Class

After reading through the preceding section, respond in your own words and in complete sentences.

A. What is a solution to an equation?

B. What is a formula?

C. How do you solve a formula for one of its variables?

D. What does percent mean?

Problem Set 2.5

Use the formula $P = 2l + 2w$ to find the length l of a rectangular lot if

1. The width w is 50 feet and the perimeter P is 300 feet.
2. The width w is 75 feet and the perimeter P is 300 feet.

Use the formula $2x + 3y = 6$ to find y if

3. $x = 3$ **4.** $x = -2$ **5.** $x = 0$ **6.** $x = -3$

Use the formula $2x - 5y = 20$ to find x if

7. $y = 2$ **8.** $y = -4$ **9.** $y = 0$ **10.** $y = -6$

Use the equation $y = (x + 1)^2 - 3$ to find the value of y when

11. $x = -2$ **12.** $x = -1$ **13.** $x = 1$ **14.** $x = 2$

15. Use the formula $y = \dfrac{20}{x}$ to find y when

    a. $x = 10$ **b.** $x = 5$

16. Use the formula $y = 2x^2$ to find y when

    a. $x = 5$ **b.** $x = -6$

17. Use the formula $y = Kx$ to find K if

    a. $y = 15$ and $x = 3$ **b.** $y = 72$ and $x = 4$

18. Use the formula $y = Kx^2$ to find K if

    a. $y = 32$ and $x = 4$ **b.** $y = 45$ and $x = 3$

Solve each of the following formulas for the indicated variable.

19. $A = lw$ for l **20.** $d = rt$ for r

21. $V = lwh$ for h **22.** $PV = nRT$ for P

23. $P = a + b + c$ for a **24.** $P = a + b + c$ for b

25. $x - 3y = -1$ for x **26.** $x + 3y = 2$ for x

27. $-3x + y = 6$ for y **28.** $2x + y = -17$ for y

29. $2x + 3y = 6$ for y **30.** $4x + 5y = 20$ for y

31. $y - 3 = -2(x + 4)$ for y **32.** $y + 5 = 2(x + 2)$ for y

33. $y - 3 = -\dfrac{2}{3}(x + 3)$ for y **34.** $y - 1 = -\dfrac{1}{2}(x + 4)$ for y

35. $P = 2l + 2w$ for w **36.** $P = 2l + 2w$ for l

37. $h = vt + 16t^2$ for v **38.** $h = vt - 16t^2$ for v

39. $A = \pi r^2 + 2\pi rh$ for h **40.** $A = 2\pi r^2 + 2\pi rh$ for h

41. Solve for y.

    a. $\dfrac{y - 1}{x} = \dfrac{3}{5}$ **b.** $\dfrac{y - 2}{x} = \dfrac{1}{2}$ **c.** $\dfrac{y - 3}{x} = 4$

42. Solve for y.

a. $\dfrac{y+1}{x} = -\dfrac{3}{5}$ b. $\dfrac{y+2}{x} = -\dfrac{1}{2}$ c. $\dfrac{y+3}{x} = -4$

Solve each formula for y.

43. $\dfrac{x}{7} - \dfrac{y}{3} = 1$ **44.** $\dfrac{x}{5} - \dfrac{y}{9} = 1$

45. $-\dfrac{1}{4}x + \dfrac{1}{8}y = 1$ **46.** $-\dfrac{1}{9}x + \dfrac{1}{3}y = 1$

Translate each of the following questions into an equation, and then solve that equation.

47. What number is 25% of 40?   **48.** What number is 75% of 40?

49. What number is 12% of 2,000?   **50.** What number is 9% of 3,000?

51. What percent of 28 is 7?   **52.** What percent of 28 is 21?

53. What percent of 40 is 14?   **54.** What percent of 20 is 14?

55. 32 is 50% of what number?   **56.** 16 is 50% of what number?

57. 240 is 12% of what number?   **58.** 360 is 12% of what number?

Applications

In the introduction to this chapter, we discussed the formula

$$T = -0.0035A + 70$$

which describes the relationship between the temperature T and altitude A when the temperature on the ground is 70°F. Use this formula for Problems 59 through 64.

59. Evaluate the formula when $A = 10,000$. What is the practical meaning of your answer?

60. Evaluate the formula when $A = 30,000$. What is the practical meaning of your answer?

61. Find A if $T = 56$.

62. Find A if $T = -42$.

63. Solve the formula for the variable A.

64. Use your result from Problem 63 to find A if $T = -7$.

65. Let $F = 212$ in the formula $C = \frac{5}{9}(F - 32)$, and solve for C. Does the value of C agree with the information in Table 1?

66. Let $C = 100$ in the formula $F = \frac{9}{5}C + 32$, and solve for F. Does the value of F agree with the information in Table 1?

67. Let $F = 68$ in the formula $C = \frac{5}{9}(F - 32)$, and solve for C. Does the value of C agree with the information in Table 1?

68. Let $C = 37$ in the formula $F = \frac{9}{5}C + 32$, and solve for F. Does the value of F agree with the information in Table 1?

69. Solve the formula $F = \frac{9}{5}C + 32$ for C.

70. Solve the formula $C = \frac{5}{9}(F - 32)$ for F.

71. How far off is Budd's estimate when the temperature is 30°C? (See Example 10)

72. How far off is Budd's estimate when the temperature is 0°C? (See Example 10)

Circumference The circumference of a circle is given by the formula $C = 2\pi r$, where r is the radius of the circle.

73. Find the circumference if the radius is 7 meters and π is $\frac{22}{7}$.

74. Find the circumference if the radius is 28 meters and π is $\frac{22}{7}$.

75. Find the radius if the circumference is 9.42 inches and π is 3.14.

76. Find the radius if the circumference is 12.56 inches and π is 3.14.

Volume The volume of a cylinder is given by the formula $V = \pi r^2 h$, where r is the radius and h is the height of the cylinder.

77. Find the volume if the height is 2 centimeters, the radius is 3 centimeters, and π is 3.14.

78. Find the volume if the height is 3 centimeters, the radius is 2 centimeters, and π is 3.14.

79. Find the height if the volume is 42 cubic feet, the radius is $\frac{7}{22}$ feet, and π is $\frac{22}{7}$.

80. Find the height if the volume is 84 cubic inches, the radius is $\frac{7}{11}$ inches, and π is $\frac{22}{7}$.

Nutrition Labels The nutrition label in Figure 2 is from a quart of vanilla ice cream. The label in Figure 3 is from a pint of vanilla frozen yogurt. Use the information on these labels for problems 81–84. Round your answers to the nearest tenth of a percent.

Nutrition Facts	
Serving Size 1/2 cup (65g)	
Servings 8	
Amount/Serving	
Calories 150	Calories from Fat 90
	% Daily Value*
Total Fat 10g	**16%**
Saturated Fat 6g	**32%**
Cholesterol 35mg	**12%**
Sodium 30mg	**1%**
Total Carbohydrate 14g	**5%**
Dietary Fiber 0g	**0%**
Sugars 11g	
Protein 2g	
Vitamin A 6% • Vitamin C 0%	
Calcium 6% • Iron 0%	
* Percent Daily Values are based on a 2,000 calorie diet.	

FIGURE 2 *Vanilla ice cream*

Nutrition Facts	
Serving Size 1/2 cup (98g)	
Servings Per Container 4	
Amount Per Serving	
Calories 160	Calories from Fat 25
	% Daily Value*
Total Fat 2.5g	**4%**
Saturated Fat 1.5g	**7%**
Cholesterol 45mg	**15%**
Sodium 55mg	**2%**
Total Carbohydrate 26g	**9%**
Dietary Fiber 0g	**0%**
Sugars 19g	
Protein 8g	
Vitamin A 0% • Vitamin C 0%	
Calcium 25% • Iron 0%	
* Percent Daily Values are based on a 2,000 calorie diet.	

FIGURE 3 *Vanilla frozen yogurt*

81. What percent of the calories in one serving of the vanilla ice cream are fat calories?

82. What percent of the calories in one serving of the frozen yogurt are fat calories?

83. One serving of frozen yogurt is 98 grams, of which 26 grams are carbohydrates. What percent of one serving are carbohydrates?

84. One serving of vanilla ice cream is 65 grams. What percent of one serving is sugar?

Learning Objectives Assessment

The following problems can be used to help assess if you have successfully met the learning objectives for this section.

85. Solve the formula $2x - 3y = 6$ for y.

    a. $y = \dfrac{2}{3}x - 2$ **b.** $y = 2 - \dfrac{2}{3}x$

    c. $y = -2x - 2$ **d.** $y = 2x - 2$

86. 18 is what percent of 60?

    a. 0.3%   **b.** 30%   **c.** 3.3%   **d.** 10.8%

Getting Ready for the Next Section

To understand all of the explanations and examples in the next section, you must be able to work the problems below.

Write an equivalent expression in English. Include the words *sum* and *difference* when possible.

87. $4 + 1$ **88.** $7 + 3$ **89.** $6 - 2$ **90.** $8 - 1$

91. $x - 15$ **92.** $2x + 3$ **93.** $4(x - 3)$ **94.** $2(2x - 5)$

For each of the following phrases, write an equivalent mathematical expression.

95. Twice the sum of 6 and 3

96. Four added to the product of 5 and -1

97. The sum of twice 5 and 3

98. Twice the difference of 8 and 2

99. The sum of a number and five

100. The difference of ten and a number

101. Five times the sum of a number and seven

102. Five times the difference of twice a number and six

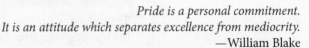 *University of North Alabama*

Pride is a personal commitment.
It is an attitude which separates excellence from mediocrity.
—William Blake

The University of North Alabama places its Pride Rock, a 60-pound granite stone engraved with a lion's paw print, behind the north end zone at all home football games. The rock reminds current Lion players of the proud athletic traditions that have been established at the school, and to take pride in their efforts on the field.

Photo courtesy UNA

The same idea holds true for your work in your math class. Take pride in it. When you turn in an assignment, it should be accurate and easy for the instructor to read. It shows that you care about your progress in the course and that you take pride in your work. The work that you turn in to your instructor is a reflection of you. As the quote from William Blake indicates, pride is a personal commitment; a decision that you make, yourself. And once you make that commitment to take pride in the work you do in your math class, you have directed yourself toward excellence, and away from mediocrity.

Learning Objectives

In this section, we will learn how to:

1. Solve number problems.
2. Solve age problems.
3. Solve geometry problems.
4. Solve coin problems.

Introduction

As you begin reading through the examples in this section, you may find yourself asking why some of these problems seem so contrived. The title of the section is "Applications," but many of the problems here don't seem to have much to do with "real life." You are right about that. Consider the following quote from *A Tour of the Calculus*, by David Berlinski:

> "The examples offered by elementary algebra are often uninspiring if only because no one wishes to really know which numbers correspond to the unknowns, the unknowns in word problems referring always to a strangely meditative farmer standing forlornly on that illustrated textbook hill of his, wondering in a way that suggests nothing of the power of mathematics how many turnips he might grow if he had two tons of fertilizer. ... But as always in any great art, the matter and the method need not necessarily be the same at first, the matter trivial (farmers and their fields), but the method, in the case of elementary algebra, suggesting in incremental steps the power of a system of equations adequate to nothing less than the description of the world."

The problems in this section may be contrived, but the strategy we will learn in solving these problems is very powerful, and it is easiest to master this strategy by beginning with some simple (if uninspiring) problems.

To begin this section, we list the steps used in solving application problems. We call this strategy the *Blueprint for Problem Solving*. It is an outline that will overlay the solution process we use on all application problems.

HOW TO *Use the Blueprint for Problem Solving*

Step 1: *Read* the problem, and then mentally *list* the items that are known and the items that are unknown.

Step 2: *Assign a variable* to one of the unknown items. (In most cases this will amount to letting x represent the item that is asked for in the problem.) Then *translate* the other *information* in the problem to expressions involving the variable.

Step 3: *Reread* the problem, and then *write an equation*, using the items and variables listed in steps 1 and 2, that describes the situation. We call this equation a *mathematical model* for the problem.

Step 4: *Solve the equation* found in step 3.

Step 5: *Write* your *answer* using a complete sentence.

Step 6: *Reread* the problem, and *check* your solution with the original words in the problem.

There are a number of substeps within each of the steps in our blueprint. For instance, with steps 1 and 2 it is always a good idea to draw a diagram or picture if it helps visualize the relationship between the items in the problem. In other cases, a table helps organize the information. As you gain more experience using the blueprint to solve application problems, you will find additional techniques that expand the blueprint.

To help with problems of the type shown next in Example 1, here are some additional common English words and phrases used to indicate equality.

English	Algebra
a is b	$a = b$
a was b	$a = b$
a is equal to b	$a = b$
a equals b	$a = b$
a represents b	$a = b$
a results in b	$a = b$

Number Problems

VIDEO EXAMPLES

SECTION 2.6

EXAMPLE 1   The sum of twice a number and three is seven. Find the number.

SOLUTION   Using the Blueprint for Problem Solving as an outline, we solve the problem as follows:

Step 1:   **Read** the problem, and then mentally **list** the items that are known and the items that are unknown.

     Known items: The numbers 3 and 7

     Unknown items: The number in question

Step 2:   **Assign a variable** to one of the unknown items. Then **translate** the other **information** in the problem to expressions involving the variable.

     Let x represent the number asked for in the problem, then "The sum of twice a number and three" translates to $2x + 3$.

Step 3:   **Reread** the problem, and then **write an equation,** using the items and variables listed in steps 1 and 2, that describes the situation. With all word problems, the word *is* translates to $=$.

$$\underbrace{\text{The sum of twice } x \text{ and 3}}_{2x + 3} \underbrace{\text{is}}_{=} \; 7$$

Step 4:   **Solve the equation** found in step 3.

$$2x + 3 = 7$$
$$2x + 3 + (-3) = 7 + (-3)$$
$$2x = 4$$
$$\frac{1}{2}(2x) = \frac{1}{2}(4)$$
$$x = 2$$

Step 5: *Write* your ***answer*** using a complete sentence.

The number is 2.

Step 6: ***Reread*** the problem, and ***check*** your solution with the original words in the problem.

The sum of twice 2 and 3 is 7; a true statement.

You may find some examples and problems in this section that you can solve without using algebra or our blueprint. It is very important that you solve these problems using the methods we are showing here. The purpose behind these problems is to give you experience using the blueprint as a guide to solving problems written in words. Your answers are much less important than the work that you show to obtain your answer. You will be able to condense the steps in the blueprint later in the course. For now, though, you need to show your work in the same detail that we are showing in the examples in this section.

EXAMPLE 2 One number is three more than twice another; their sum is eighteen. Find the numbers.

SOLUTION

Step 1: Read and list.
Known items: Two numbers that add to 18. One is 3 more than twice the other.
Unknown items: The numbers in question.

Step 2: Assign a variable, and translate information.
Let x be the first number. The other is $2x + 3$.

Step 3: Reread, and write an equation.

$$\underbrace{\text{Their sum}} \quad \text{is} \quad 18$$
$$x + (2x + 3) = 18$$

Step 4: Solve the equation.

$$x + (2x + 3) = 18$$
$$3x + 3 = 18$$
$$3x + 3 + (-3) = 18 + (-3)$$
$$3x = 15$$
$$x = 5$$

Step 5: Write the answer.
The first number is 5. The other is $2 \cdot 5 + 3 = 13$.

Step 6: Reread, and check.
The sum of 5 and 13 is 18, and 13 is 3 more than twice 5.

Age Problem

Remember as you read through the steps in the solutions to the examples in this section that step 1 is done mentally. Read the problem, and then mentally list the items that you know and the items that you don't know. The purpose of step 1 is to give you direction as you begin to work application problems. Finding the solution to an application problem is a process; it doesn't happen all at once. The first step is to read the problem with a purpose in mind. That purpose is to mentally note the items that are known and the items that are unknown.

EXAMPLE 3   Bill is 6 years older than Tom. Three years ago Bill's age was four times Tom's age. Find the age of each boy now.

SOLUTION   Applying the Blueprint for Problem Solving, we have

Step 1: Read and list.

> *Known items:* Bill is 6 years older than Tom. Three years ago Bill's age was four times Tom's age.
>
> *Unknown items:* Bill's age and Tom's age

Step 2: Assign a variable, and translate information.
Let x represent Tom's age now. That makes Bill $x + 6$ years old now. A table like the one shown here can help organize the information in an age problem. Notice how we placed the x in the box that corresponds to Tom's age now.

	Three Years Ago	Now
Bill		$x + 6$
Tom		x

If Tom is x years old now, 3 years ago he was $x - 3$ years old. If Bill is $x + 6$ years old now, 3 years ago he was $x + 6 - 3 = x + 3$ years old. We use this information to fill in the remaining blanks in the table.

	Three Years Ago	Now
Bill	$x + 3$	$x + 6$
Tom	$x - 3$	x

Step 3: Reread, and write an equation.
Reading the problem again, we see that

Three years ago Bill's age was four times Tom's age

$$x + 3 = 4 \cdot (x - 3)$$

Step 4: Solve the equation.

$$x + 3 = 4(x - 3)$$
$$x + 3 = 4x - 12$$
$$x + (-x) + 3 = 4x + (-x) - 12$$
$$3 = 3x - 12$$
$$3 + 12 = 3x - 12 + 12$$
$$15 = 3x$$
$$x = 5$$

Step 5: Write the answer.

Tom is 5 years old. Bill is 11 years old.

Step 6: Reread, and check.

If Tom is 5 and Bill is 11, then Bill is 6 years older than Tom. Three years ago Tom was 2 and Bill was 8. At that time, Bill's age was four times Tom's age. As you can see, the answers check with the original problem.

Geometry Problem

To understand Example 4 completely, you need to recall from Chapter 1 that the perimeter of a rectangle is the sum of the lengths of the sides. The formula for the perimeter is $P = 2l + 2w$.

EXAMPLE 4   The length of a rectangle is 5 inches more than twice the width. The perimeter is 34 inches. Find the length and width.

SOLUTION When working problems that involve geometric figures, a sketch of the figure helps organize and visualize the problem.

Step 1: Read and list.

Known items: The figure is a rectangle. The length is 5 inches more than twice the width. The perimeter is 34 inches.

Unknown items: The length and the width

Step 2: Assign a variable, and translate information.

Because the length is given in terms of the width (the length is 5 more than twice the width), we let x be the width of the rectangle. The length is 5 more than twice the width, so it must be $2x + 5$. The diagram below is a visual description of the relationships we have listed so far.

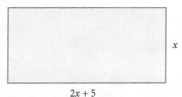

x

$2x + 5$

Step 3: **Reread, and write an equation.**
The equation that describes the situation is

$$2(\text{length}) \quad + \quad 2(\text{width}) \quad = \quad \text{perimeter}$$
$$2(2x + 5) \quad + \quad 2x \quad = \quad 34$$

Step 4: **Solve the equation.**

$2(2x + 5) + 2x = 34$	Original equation
$4x + 10 + 2x = 34$	Distributive property
$6x + 10 = 34$	Add $4x$ and $2x$
$6x = 24$	Add -10 to each side
$x = 4$	Divide each side by 6

Step 5: **Write the answer.**
The width x is 4 inches. The length is $2x + 5 = 2(4) + 5 = 13$ inches.

Step 6: **Reread, and check.**
If the length is 13 and the width is 4, then the perimeter must be $2(13) + 2(4) = 26 + 8 = 34$, which checks with the original problem.

Coin Problem

EXAMPLE 5 Jennifer has $2.45 in dimes and nickels. If she has 8 more dimes than nickels, how many of each coin does she have?

SOLUTION

Step 1: **Read and list.**
Known items: The type of coins, the total value of the coins, and that there are 8 more dimes than nickels.
Unknown items: The number of nickels and the number of dimes

Step 2: **Assign a variable, and translate information.**
If we let x be the number of nickels, then $x + 8$ is the number of dimes. Because the value of each nickel is 5 cents, the amount of money in nickels is $5x$. Similarly, because each dime is worth 10 cents, the amount of money in dimes is $10(x + 8)$. Here is a table that summarizes the information we have so far:

	Nickels	Dimes
Number	x	$x + 8$
Value (in cents)	$5x$	$10(x + 8)$

Step 3: **Reread, and write an equation.**
Because the total value of all the coins is 245 cents, the equation that describes this situation is

Amount of money in nickels	+	Amount of money in dimes	=	Total amount of money
$5x$	+	$10(x + 8)$	=	245

Step 4: Solve the equation.
To solve the equation, we apply the distributive property first.

$$5x + 10x + 80 = 245 \qquad \text{Distributive property}$$
$$15x + 80 = 245 \qquad \text{Add } 5x \text{ and } 10x$$
$$15x = 165 \qquad \text{Add } -80 \text{ to each side}$$
$$x = 11 \qquad \text{Divide each side by 15}$$

Step 5: Write the answer.
The number of nickels is $x = 11$.
The number of dimes is $x + 8 = 11 + 8 = 19$.

Step 6: Reread, and check.
To check our results

$$11 \text{ nickels are worth } 5(11) = \quad 55 \text{ cents}$$
$$\underline{19 \text{ dimes are worth } 10(19) = 190 \text{ cents}}$$

The total value is 245 cents = \$2.45

When you begin working the problems in the problem set that follows, there are a few things to remember. The first is that you may have to read the problems a number of times before you begin to see how to solve them. The second thing to remember is that word problems are not always solved correctly the first time you try them. Sometimes it takes a few attempts and some wrong answers before you can set up and solve these problems correctly.

Getting Ready for Class

After reading through the preceding section, respond in your own words and in complete sentences.

A. What good does it do you to solve application problems even when they don't have much to do with real life?

B. What is the first step in the Blueprint for Problem Solving?

C. What is the last thing you do when solving an application problem?

D. With coin problems, why do we multiply the number of coins by the value of each coin?

Problem Set 2.6

For Problems 1-8, translate each sentence into an equivalent equation in symbols.

1. The sum of x and 5 is 14.
2. The difference of x and 4 is 8.
3. The quotient of x and 3 is equal to the sum of x and 2.
4. The quotient of x and 2 is equal to the difference of x and 4.
5. Twice the difference of a number and nine, when increased by five, results in eleven.
6. Three times the sum of a number and six, when decreased by four, gives a result of twenty.
7. Half the sum of a number and 5 is three times the difference of the number and 5.
8. One-third a number added to one-half the number equals two less than the number.

Solve the following word problems. Follow the steps given in the Blueprint for Problem Solving.

Number Problems

9. The sum of a number and five is thirteen. Find the number.
10. The difference of ten and a number is negative eight. Find the number.
11. The sum of twice a number and four is fourteen. Find the number.
12. The difference of four times a number and eight is sixteen. Find the number.
13. Five times the sum of a number and seven is thirty. Find the number.
14. Five times the difference of twice a number and six is negative twenty. Find the number.
15. One number is two more than another. Their sum is eight. Find both numbers.
16. One number is three less than another. Their sum is fifteen. Find the numbers.
17. One number is four less than three times another. If their sum is increased by five, the result is twenty-five. Find the numbers.
18. One number is five more than twice another. If their sum is decreased by ten, the result is twenty-two. Find the numbers.

Age Problems

19. Shelly is 3 years older than Michele. Four years ago, the sum of their ages was 67. Find the age of each person now.

	Four Years Ago	Now
Shelly	$x - 1$	$x + 3$
Michele	$x - 4$	x

20. Cary is 9 years older than Dan. In 7 years, the sum of their ages will be 93. Find the age of each man now. (Begin by filling in the table.)

	Now	In Seven Years
Cary	$x + 9$	
Dan	x	$x + 7$

21. Cody is twice as old as Evan. Three years ago, the sum of their ages was 27. Find the age of each boy now.

	Three Years Ago	Now
Cody		
Evan	$x - 3$	x

22. Justin is 2 years older than Ethan. In 9 years, the sum of their ages will be 30. Find the age of each boy now.

	Now	In Nine Years
Justin		
Ethan	x	

23. Fred is 4 years older than Barney. Five years ago, the sum of their ages was 48. How old are they now?

	Five Years Ago	Now
Fred		
Barney		x

24. Tim is 5 years older than JoAnn. Six years from now, the sum of their ages will be 79. How old are they now?

	Now	Six Years From Now
Tim		
JoAnn	x	

25. Jack is twice as old as Lacy. In 3 years, the sum of their ages will be 54. How old are they now?

26. John is 4 times as old as Martha. Five years ago, the sum of their ages was 50. How old are they now?

27. Pat is 20 years older than his son Patrick. In 2 years, Pat will be twice as old as Patrick. How old are they now?

28. Diane is 23 years older than her daughter Amy. In 6 years, Diane will be twice as old as Amy. How old are they now?

Geometry Problems

29. The perimeter of a square is 36 inches. Find the length of one side.

30. The perimeter of a square is 44 centimeters. Find the length of one side.

31. The perimeter of a square is 60 feet. Find the length of one side.

32. The perimeter of a square is 84 meters. Find the length of one side.

33. One side of a triangle is three times the shortest side. The third side is 7 feet more than the shortest side. The perimeter is 62 feet. Find all three sides.

34. One side of a triangle is half the longest side. The third side is 10 meters less than the longest side. The perimeter is 45 meters. Find all three sides.

35. One side of a triangle is half the longest side. The third side is 12 feet less than the longest side. The perimeter is 53 feet. Find all three sides.

36. One side of a triangle is 6 meters more than twice the shortest side. The third side is 9 meters more than the shortest side. The perimeter is 75 meters. Find all three sides.

37. The length of a rectangle is 5 inches more than the width. The perimeter is 34 inches. Find the length and width.

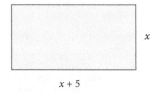

x

$x + 5$

38. The width of a rectangle is 3 feet less than the length. The perimeter is 10 feet. Find the length and width.

39. The length of a rectangle is 7 inches more than twice the width. The perimeter is 68 inches. Find the length and width.

40. The length of a rectangle is 4 inches more than three times the width. The perimeter is 72 inches. Find the length and width.

41. The length of a rectangle is 6 feet more than three times the width. The perimeter is 36 feet. Find the length and width.

42. The length of a rectangle is 3 feet less than twice the width. The perimeter is 54 feet. Find the length and width.

Coin Problems

43. Marissa has $4.40 in quarters and dimes. If she has 5 more quarters than dimes, how many of each coin does she have?

	Dimes	Quarters
Number	x	$x + 5$
Value (in cents)	$10(x)$	$25(x + 5)$

44. Kendra has $2.75 in dimes and nickels. If she has twice as many dimes as nickels, how many of each coin does she have?

	Nickels	Dimes
Number	x	$2x$
Value (in cents)	$5(x)$	

45. Tanner has $4.35 in nickels and quarters. If he has 15 more nickels than quarters, how many of each coin does he have?

	Nickels	Quarters
Number	$x + 15$	x
Value (in cents)		

46. Connor has $9.00 in dimes and quarters. If he has twice as many quarters as dimes, how many of each coin does he have?

	Dimes	Quarters
Number	x	$2x$
Value (in cents)		

47. Sue has $2.10 in dimes and nickels. If she has 9 more dimes than nickels, how many of each coin does she have?

48. Mike has $1.55 in dimes and nickels. If he has 7 more nickels than dimes, how many of each coin does he have?

49. Katie has a collection of nickels, dimes, and quarters with a total value of $4.35. There are 3 more dimes than nickels and 5 more quarters than nickels. How many of each coin is in her collection? (*Hint:* Let x be the number of nickels.)

	Nickels	Dimes	Quarters
Number	x		
Value			

50. Mary Jo has $3.90 worth of nickels, dimes, and quarters. The number of nickels is 3 more than the number of dimes. The number of quarters is 7 more than the number of dimes. How many of each coin does she have? (*Hint:* Let x be the number of dimes.)

	Nickels	Dimes	Quarters
Number		x	
Value			

51. Cory has a collection of nickels, dimes, and quarters with a total value of $2.55. There are 6 more dimes than nickels and twice as many quarters as nickels. How many of each coin is in her collection?

	Nickels	Dimes	Quarters
Number	x		
Value			

52. Kelly has a collection of nickels, dimes, and quarters with a total value of $7.40. There are four more nickels than dimes and twice as many quarters as nickels. How many of each coin is in her collection?

	Nickels	Dimes	Quarters
Number		x	
Value			

Learning Objectives Assessment

The following problems can be used to help assess if you have successfully met the learning objectives for this section.

For each of the following, which equation is an appropriate model for the given problem?

53. One number is three more than another. Their sum is twenty. Find both numbers.

    a. $x + 3 = 20$ **b.** $x + 3 = x + 20$

    c. $x + (x + 3) = 20$ **d.** $x = (x + 3) + 20$

54. Allison is 8 years older than Kaitlin. Five years ago, Allison was three times as old as Kaitlin. Find Kaitlin's age now.

    a. $x + 3 = 3(x - 5)$ **b.** $x + 8 = 3x - 5$

    c. $x - 5 = 3(x + 8)$ **d.** $3(x + 8) - 5 = x$

55. The length of a rectangle is 2 meters less than three times the width. The perimeter is 36 meters. Find the width.

    a. $3x - 2 = 36$ **b.** $(3x - 2) + x = 36$

    c. $3(x - 2) + x = 36$ **d.** $2(3x - 2) + 2x = 36$

56. Valerie has $2.75 in quarters and dimes. If she has four more quarters than dimes, how many dimes does she have?

    a. $10(x + 4) + 25x = 275$ **b.** $x + (x + 4) = 275$

    c. $10x + 25(x + 4) = 2.75$ **d.** $10x + 25(x + 4) = 275$

Getting Ready for the Next Section

To understand all of the explanations and examples in the next section you must be able to work the problems below.

Simplify the following expressions.

57. $x + 2x + 2x$ **58.** $x + 2x + 3x$ **59.** $x + 0.075x$ **60.** $x + 0.065x$

61. $0.09(x + 2,000)$ **62.** $0.06(x + 1,500)$

Solve the following equations.

63. $0.02x + 0.06(x + 1,500) = 570$ **64.** $0.08x + 0.09(x + 2,000) = 690$

65. $x + 2x + 3x = 180$ **66.** $2x + 3x + 5x = 180$

SPOTLIGHT ON SUCCESS   *Student Instructor Lauren*

There are a lot of word problems in algebra and many of them involve topics that I don't know much about. I am better off solving these problems if I know something about the subject. So, I try to find something I can relate to. For instance, an example may involve the amount of fuel used by a pilot in a jet airplane engine. In my mind, I'd change the subject to something more familiar, like the mileage I'd be getting in my car and the amount spent on fuel, driving from my hometown to my college. Changing these problems to more familiar topics makes math much more interesting and gives me a better chance of getting the problem right. It also helps me to understand how greatly math affects and influences me in my everyday life. We really do use math more than we would like to admit—budgeting our income, purchasing gasoline, planning a day of shopping with friends—almost everything we do is related to math. So the best advice I can give with word problems is to learn how to associate the problem with something familiar to you.

You should know that I have always enjoyed math. I like working out problems and love the challenges of solving equations like individual puzzles. Although there are more interesting subjects to me, and I don't plan on pursuing a career in math or teaching, I do think it's an important subject that will help you in any profession.

More Applications

Learning Objectives

In this section, we will learn how to:

1. Solve consecutive integer problems.

2. Solve interest problems.

3. Solve mixture problems.

4. Solve problems involving triangles.

Introduction

Now that you have worked through a number of application problems using our blueprint, you probably have noticed that step 3, in which we write an equation that describes the situation, is the key step. Anyone with experience solving application problems will tell you that there will be times when your first attempt at writing a model results in the wrong equation. Remember, mistakes are part of the process of learning to do things correctly. Many times the correct equation will become obvious after you have written an equation that is partially wrong. In any case it is better to write an equation that is partially wrong and be actively involved with the problem than to write nothing at all. Application problems, like other problems in algebra, are not always solved correctly the first time.

Consecutive Integers

Our first example involves *consecutive integers*. When we ask for consecutive integers, we mean integers that are next to each other on the number line, like

$$5 \text{ and } 6, \qquad 13 \text{ and } 14, \qquad \text{or } -4 \text{ and } -3$$

In the dictionary, consecutive is defined as following one another in uninterrupted order. If we ask for consecutive odd integers, then we mean odd integers that follow one another on the number line. For example,

$$3 \text{ and } 5, \qquad 11 \text{ and } 13, \qquad \text{and } -9 \text{ and } -7$$

are consecutive odd integers. As you can see, to get from one odd integer to the next consecutive odd integer we add 2.

If we are asked to find two consecutive integers and we let x equal the first integer, the next one must be $x + 1$, because consecutive integers always differ by 1. Likewise, if we are asked to find two consecutive odd or even integers, and we let x equal the first integer, then the next one will be $x + 2$ because consecutive even or odd integers always differ by 2. The following table summarizes this information.

In Words	Using Algebra	Example
Two consecutive integers	$x, x + 1$	The sum of two consecutive integers is 15. $x + (x + 1) = 15$ or $7 + 8 = 15$
Three consecutive integers	$x, x + 1, x + 2$	The sum of three consecutive integers is 24. $x + (x + 1) + (x + 2) = 24$ or $7 + 8 + 9 = 24$
Two consecutive odd integers	$x, x + 2$	The sum of two consecutive odd integers is 16. $x + (x + 2) = 16$ or $7 + 9 = 16$
Two consecutive even integers	$x, x + 2$	The sum of two consecutive even integers is 18. $x + (x + 2) = 18$ or $8 + 10 = 18$

VIDEO EXAMPLES

SECTION 2.7

EXAMPLE 1   The sum of two consecutive odd integers is 28. Find the two integers.

SOLUTION

Step 1:   Read and list.
Known items: Two consecutive odd integers. Their sum is equal to 28.
Unknown items: The numbers in question.

Step 2:   Assign a variable, and translate information.
If we let x be the first of the two consecutive odd integers, then $x + 2$ is the next consecutive one.

Step 3:   Reread, and write an equation.
Their sum is 28.

$$x + (x + 2) = 28$$

Step 4:   Solve the equation.

$2x + 2 = 28$	Simplify the left side
$2x = 26$	Add -2 to each side
$x = 13$	Multiply each side by $\frac{1}{2}$

Step 5:   Write the answer.
The first of the two integers is 13. The second of the two integers will be two more than the first, which is 15.

Step 6:   Reread, and check.
Suppose the first integer is 13. The next consecutive odd integer is 15. The sum of 15 and 13 is 28.

Interest

If a person invests an amount of money P, called the *principal*, in an account that has an *annual interest rate* r, then the *interest* the person earns after one year is given by the formula

$$\text{Interest} = \text{Rate}(\text{Principal})$$
$$I = rP$$

When using this formula, we must remember to express the interest rate r as a decimal.

EXAMPLE 2   Suppose you invest a certain amount of money in an account that earns 8% in annual interest. At the same time, you invest $2,000 more than that in an account that pays 9% in annual interest. If the total interest from both accounts at the end of the year is $690, how much is invested in each account?

SOLUTION

Step 1: Read and list.

Known items: The interest rates, the total interest earned, and how much more is invested at 9%

Unknown items: The amounts invested in each account

Step 2: Assign a variable, and translate information.

Let x be the amount of money invested at 8%. From this, $x + 2,000$ is the amount of money invested at 9%. The interest earned on x dollars invested at 8% is $0.08x$. The interest earned on $x + 2,000$ dollars invested at 9% is $0.09(x + 2,000)$.

Here is a table that summarizes this information:

	Dollars Invested at 8%	Dollars Invested at 9%
Number of	x	$x + 2,000$
Interest on	$0.08x$	$0.09(x + 2,000)$

Step 3: Reread, and write an equation.

Because the total amount of interest earned from both accounts is $690, the equation that describes the situation is

$$\begin{array}{ccccc} \text{Interest earned} & & \text{Interest earned} & & \text{Total interest} \\ \text{at 8\%} & + & \text{at 9\%} & = & \text{earned} \\ 0.08x & + & 0.09(x + 2,000) & = & 690 \end{array}$$

Step 4: Solve the equation.

$$0.08x + 0.09(x + 2,000) = 690$$

$$0.08x + 0.09x + 180 = 690 \qquad \text{Distributive property}$$

$$0.17x + 180 = 690 \qquad \text{Add } 0.08x \text{ and } 0.09x$$

$$0.17x = 510 \qquad \text{Add } -180 \text{ to each side}$$

$$x = 3,000 \qquad \text{Divide each side by } 0.17$$

Step 5: Write the answer:

The amount of money invested at 8% is $3,000, whereas the amount of money invested at 9% is $x + 2,000 = 3,000 + 2,000 = \$5,000$.

Step 6: Reread, and check.

The interest at 8% is 8% of 3,000 = $0.08(3,000) = \$240$
The interest at 9% is 9% of 5,000 = $0.09(5,000) = \$450$
The total interest is $690

Mixture Problem

Another type of application that involves working with percents is creating mixtures of various solutions. In this context, a solution is a liquid that contains two different substances.

For example, the liquid in the cooling system for most automobiles is a solution containing both water and antifreeze. If the cooling system holds 20 quarts of a 60% antifreeze solution, then

$$60\% \text{ of } 20 \text{ quarts} = 0.60(20 \text{ qt}) = 12 \text{ qt is antifreeze, and}$$
$$40\% \text{ of } 20 \text{ quarts} = 0.40(20 \text{ qt}) = 8 \text{ qt is water}$$

EXAMPLE 3   How much of a 30% alcohol solution and 60% alcohol solution must be mixed to get 15 gallons of 50% alcohol solution?

SOLUTION

Step 1:   **Read and list.**

Known items: There are two solutions that together must total 15 gallons. 30% of one of the solutions is alcohol and the rest is water, whereas the other solution is 60% alcohol and the other is 40% water. The mixture must be 50% alcohol.

Unknown items: The gallons of each individual solution we need.

Step 2:   **Assign a variable, and translate information.**

Let x represent the number of gallons of the 30% alcohol solution. Because a total of 15 gallons of solution is required, $15 - x$ is the number of gallons of 60% alcohol solution that must be used. The amount of alcohol in the 30% solution is $0.30x$. The amount of alcohol in the 60% solution is $0.60(15 - x)$. The amount of alcohol in the mixture will be $0.50(15) = 7.5$ gallons.

Here is a table that summarizes this information.

	30% Solution	60% Solution	Mixture
Number of Gallons	x	$15 - x$	15
Gallons of alcohol	$0.30x$	$0.60(15 - x)$	$0.50(15)$

Step 3:   **Reread, and write an equation.**

Because the total amount of alcohol from the two solutions must add up to the amount of alcohol in the mixture, the equation that describes the situation is

Gallons alcohol in 30% solution	+	Gallons alcohol in 60% solution	=	Gallons alcohol in mixture
$0.30x$	+	$0.60(15 - x)$	=	$0.50(15)$

Step 4:   **Solve the equation.**

$$0.30x + 0.60(15 - x) = 0.50(15)$$

$0.30x + 9 - 0.60x = 7.5$	Distributive property
$9 - 0.30x = 7.5$	Simplify left side
$-0.30x = -1.5$	Add -9 to each side
$x = 5$	Divide each side by -0.30

Step 5:   **Write the answer.**
5 gallons of the 30% alcohol solution should be mixed with $15 - 5 = 10$ gallons of the 60% alcohol solution.

Step 6:   **Reread, and check.**
$5 + 10 = 15$ gallons, and $0.30(5) + 0.60(10) = 1.5 + 6 = 7.5$ gallons, which is 50% of 15 gallons.

Triangles

FACTS FROM GEOMETRY   *Labeling Triangles and the Sum of the Angles in a Triangle*

One way to label the important parts of a triangle is to label the vertices with capital letters and the sides with small letters, as shown in Figure 1.

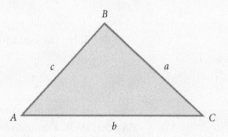

FIGURE 1

In Figure 1, notice that side a is opposite vertex A, side b is opposite vertex B, and side c is opposite vertex C. Also, because each vertex is the vertex of one of the angles of the triangle, we refer to the three interior angles as A, B, and C.

In any triangle, the sum of the interior angles is 180°. For the triangle shown in Figure 1, the relationship is written

$$A + B + C = 180°$$

EXAMPLE 4   The angles in a triangle are such that one angle is twice the smallest angle, whereas the third angle is three times as large as the smallest angle. Find the measure of all three angles.

SOLUTION

Step 1:   **Read and list.**
Known items: The sum of all three angles is 180°, one angle is twice the smallest angle, the largest angle is three times the smallest angle.
Unknown items: The measure of each angle

Step 2:   **Assign a variable, and translate information.**
Let x be the smallest angle, then $2x$ will be the measure of another angle and $3x$ will be the measure of the largest angle.

Step 3: **Reread, and write an equation.**

When working with geometric objects, drawing a generic diagram sometimes will help us visualize what it is that we are asked to find. In Figure 2, we draw a triangle with angles A, B, and C.

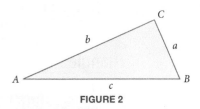

FIGURE 2

We can let the value of $A = x$, the value of $B = 2x$, and the value of $C = 3x$. We know that the sum of angles A, B, and C will be $180°$, so our equation becomes

$$x + 2x + 3x = 180°$$

Step 4: **Solve the equation.**

$$x + 2x + 3x = 180°$$
$$6x = 180°$$
$$x = 30°$$

Step 5: **Write the answer.**

The smallest angle A measures $30°$
Angle B measures $2x$, or $2(30°) = 60°$
Angle C measures $3x$, or $3(30°) = 90°$

Step 6: **Reread, and check.**

The angles must add to $180°$.

$$A + B + C = 180°$$
$$30° + 60° + 90° \overset{?}{=} 180°$$
$$180° = 180° \qquad \text{Our answers check}$$

Getting Ready for Class

After reading through the preceding section, respond in your own words and in complete sentences.

A. If x is an integer, what would the next smaller consecutive integer be?

B. In Example 3, explain why the equation contains the product $0.50(15)$.

C. How do we label triangles?

D. What rule is always true about the three angles in a triangle?

Consecutive Integer Problems

1. The sum of two consecutive integers is 11. Find the numbers.

2. The sum of two consecutive integers is 15. Find the numbers.

3. The sum of two consecutive integers is −9. Find the numbers.

4. The sum of two consecutive integers is −21. Find the numbers.

5. The sum of two consecutive odd integers is 28. Find the numbers.

6. The sum of two consecutive odd integers is 44. Find the numbers.

7. The sum of two consecutive even integers is 106. Find the numbers.

8. The sum of two consecutive even integers is 66. Find the numbers.

9. The sum of two consecutive even integers is −30. Find the numbers.

10. The sum of two consecutive odd integers is −76. Find the numbers.

11. The sum of three consecutive odd integers is 57. Find the numbers.

12. The sum of three consecutive odd integers is −51. Find the numbers.

13. The sum of three consecutive even integers is 132. Find the numbers.

14. The sum of three consecutive even integers is −108. Find the numbers.

Interest Problems

15. Suppose you invest money in two accounts. One of the accounts pays 8% annual interest, whereas the other pays 9% annual interest. If you have $2,000 more invested at 9% than you have invested at 8%, how much do you have invested in each account if the total amount of interest you earn in a year is $860? (Begin by completing the following table.)

	Dollars Invested at 8%	Dollars Invested at 9%
Number of	x	
Interest on		

16. Suppose you invest a certain amount of money in an account that pays 11% interest annually, and $4,000 more than that in an account that pays 12% annually. How much money do you have in each account if the total interest for a year is $940?

	Dollars Invested at 11%	Dollars Invested at 12%
Number of	x	
Interest on		

17. Tyler has two savings accounts that his grandparents opened for him. The two accounts pay 10% and 12% in annual interest; there is $500 more in the account that pays 12% than there is in the other account. If the total interest for a year is $214, how much money does he have in each account?

18. Travis has a savings account that his parents opened for him. It pays 6% annual interest. His uncle also opened an account for him, but it pays 8% annual interest. If there is $800 more in the account that pays 6%, and the total interest from both accounts is $104, how much money is in each of the accounts?

19. A stockbroker has money in three accounts. The interest rates on the three accounts are 8%, 9%, and 10%. If she has twice as much money invested at 9% as she has invested at 8%, three times as much at 10% as she has at 8%, and the total interest for the year is $280, how much is invested at each rate? (*Hint:* Let x = the amount invested at 8%.)

20. An accountant has money in three accounts that pay 9%, 10%, and 11% in annual interest. He has twice as much invested at 9% as he does at 10% and three times as much invested at 11% as he does at 10%. If the total interest from the three accounts is $610 for the year, how much is invested at each rate? (*Hint:* Let x = the amount invested at 10%.)

Mixture Problems

21. How many liters of 50% alcohol solution and 10% alcohol solution must be mixed to obtain 24 liters of 30% alcohol solution?

	50% Solution	10% Solution	Mixture
Number of Liters	x		24
Liters of Alcohol			

22. How many liters of 25% alcohol solution and 50% alcohol solution must be mixed to obtain 30 liters of 40% alcohol solution?

	25% Solution	50% Solution	Mixture
Number of Liters	x		30
Liters of Alcohol			

23. A mixture of 8% disinfectant solution is to be made from 10% and 5% disinfectant solutions. How much of each solution should be used if 25 gallons of 8% solution are needed?

24. How much 70% antifreeze solution and 40% antifreeze solution should be combined to give 30 gallons of 50% antifreeze solution?

25. Coffee beans worth $9.50 per pound are to be mixed with coffee beans worth $12.00 per pound to make 40 pounds of beans worth $10.00 per pound. How many pounds of each type of coffee bean should be used?

26. Peanuts worth $6.00 per pound are to be combined with cashews worth $11.00 per pound to make 60 pounds of a blend worth $8.00 per pound. How many pounds of each type of nut should be used?

Triangle Problems

27. Two angles in a triangle are equal and their sum is equal to the third angle in the triangle. What are the measures of each of the three interior angles?

28. One angle in a triangle measures twice the smallest angle, whereas the largest angle is six times the smallest angle. Find the measures of all three angles.

29. The smallest angle in a triangle is $\frac{1}{5}$ as large as the largest angle. The third angle is twice the smallest angle. Find the three angles.

30. One angle in a triangle is half the largest angle but three times the smallest. Find all three angles.

31. One angle of a triangle measures 20° more than the smallest, while a third angle is twice the smallest. Find the measure of each angle.

32. One angle of a triangle measures 50° more than the smallest, while a third angle is three times the smallest. Find the measure of each angle.

Miscellaneous Problems

33. **Ticket Prices** Miguel is selling tickets to a barbecue. Adult tickets cost $6.00 and children's tickets cost $4.00. He sells six more children's tickets than adult tickets. The total amount of money he collects is $184. How many adult tickets and how many children's tickets did he sell?

	Adult	Child
Number	x	$x + 6$
Income	$6(x)$	$4(x + 6)$

34. **Working Two Jobs** Maggie has a job working in an office for $10 an hour and another job driving a tractor for $12 an hour. One week she works in the office twice as long as she drives the tractor. Her total income for that week is $416. How many hours did she spend at each job?

Job	Office	Tractor
Hours Worked	$2x$	x
Wages Earned	$10(2x)$	$12x$

35. Phone Bill The cost of a long-distance phone call is $0.41 for the first minute and $0.32 for each additional minute. If the total charge for a long-distance call is $5.21, how many minutes was the call? Hint: Let $x =$ the number of additional minutes. After you solve for x, you will need to add 1 minute to your answer. Can you see why?

36. Phone Bill Danny, who is 1 year old, is playing with the telephone when he accidentally presses one of the buttons his mother has programmed to dial her friend Sue's number. Sue answers the phone and realizes Danny is on the other end. She talks to Danny, trying to get him to hang up. The cost for a call is $0.23 for the first minute and $0.14 for every minute after that. If the total charge for the call is $3.73, how long did it take Sue to convince Danny to hang up the phone?

37. Hourly Wages JoAnn works in the publicity office at the state university. She is paid $12 an hour for the first 35 hours she works each week and $18 an hour for every hour after that. If she makes $492 one week, how many hours did she work?

38. Hourly Wages Diane had a part-time job that paid her $6.50 an hour. During one week she worked 26 hours and was paid $178.10. She realized when she saw her check that she had been given a raise. How much per hour was that raise?

39. Office Numbers Professors Wong and Gil have offices in the mathematics building at Miami Dade College. Their office numbers are consecutive odd integers with a sum of 14,660. What are the office numbers of these two professors?

40. Cell Phone Numbers Diana and Tom buy two cell phones. The phone numbers assigned to each are consecutive integers with a sum of 11,109,295. If the smaller number is Diana's, what are their phone numbers?

41. Age Marissa and Kendra are 2 years apart in age. Their ages are two consecutive even integers. Kendra is the younger of the two. If Marissa's age is added to twice Kendra's age, the result is 26. How old is each girl?

42. Age Justin's and Ethan's ages form two consecutive odd integers. What is the difference of their ages?

43. Arrival Time Jeff and Carla Cole are driving separately from San Luis Obispo, California, to the north shore of Lake Tahoe, a distance of 425 miles. Jeff leaves San Luis Obispo at 11:00 a.m. and averages 55 miles per hour on the drive, Carla leaves later, at 1:00 p.m. but averages 65 miles per hour. Which person arrives in Lake Tahoe first?

44. Piano Lessons Tyler is taking piano lessons. Because he doesn't practice as often as his parents would like him to, he has to pay for part of the lessons himself. His parents pay him $0.50 to do the laundry and $1.25 to mow the lawn. In one month, he does the laundry 6 more times than he mows the lawn. If his parents pay him $13.50 that month, how many times did he mow the lawn?

At one time, the Texas Junior College Teachers Association annual conference was held in Austin. At that time a taxi ride in Austin was \$1.25 for the first $\frac{1}{5}$ of a mile and \$0.25 for each additional $\frac{1}{5}$ of a mile. Use this information for Problems 47 and 48.

45. Cost of a Taxi Ride If the distance from one of the convention hotels to the airport is 7.5 miles, how much will it cost to take a taxi from that hotel to the airport?

46. Cost of a Taxi Ride Suppose the distance from one of the hotels to one of the western dance clubs in Austin is 12.4 miles. If the fare meter in the taxi gives the charge for that trip as \$16.50, is the meter working correctly?

47. Geometry The width and length of a rectangle are consecutive even integers. The perimeter is 44 meters. Find the width and length.

48. Geometry The width and length of a rectangle are consecutive odd integers. The perimeter is 128 meters. Find the width and length.

49. Geometry The angles of a triangle are three consecutive integers. Find the measure of each angle.

50. Geometry The angles of a triangle are three consecutive even integers. Find the measure of each angle.

Ike and Nancy Lara give western dance lessons at the Elk's Lodge on Sunday nights. The lessons cost \$3.00 for members of the lodge and \$5.00 for nonmembers. Half of the money collected for the lesson is paid to Ike and Nancy. The Elk's Lodge keeps the other half. One Sunday night, Ike counts 36 people in the dance lesson. Use this information to work Problems 53 through 56.

51. Dance Lessons What is the least amount of money Ike and Nancy will make?

52. Dance Lessons What is the largest amount of money Ike and Nancy will make?

53. Dance Lessons At the end of the evening, the Elk's Lodge gives Ike and Nancy a check for \$80 to cover half of the receipts. Can this amount be correct?

54. Dance Lessons Besides the number of people in the dance lesson, what additional information does Ike need to know to always be sure he is being paid the correct amount?

Learning Objectives Assessment

The following problems can be used to help assess if you have successfully met the learning objectives for this section.

For each of the following, which equation is an appropriate model for the given problem?

55. The sum of two consecutive odd integers is 272. Find the numbers.

a. $x + (x + 2) = 272$ **b.** $2x = 272$

c. $x + (x + 1) = 272$ **d.** $x + (x - 1) = 272$

56. Suppose you invest some money in an account that pays 3% interest annually, and $600 more than that amount in another account that pays 4% annually. If the total interest for the year is $87, how much have you invested at 3%?

a. $3x + 4x + 600 = 87$ **b.** $0.03x + 0.04x + 600 = 87$

c. $3x + 4(x + 600) = 87$ **d.** $0.03x + 0.04(x + 600) = 87$

57. A mixture of 35% alcohol solution is to be made by combining 25% and 60% alcohol solutions. How much of the 25% solution should be used if 40 gallons of 35% solution are needed?

a. $0.25x + 0.60(40 - x) = 0.35(40)$ **b.** $0.25x + 0.60(40 - x) = 40$

c. $0.25x + 0.60x = 40$ **d.** $25x + 60x = 35(40)$

58. One angle in a triangle is 10° more than the smallest angle. A third angle is twice the smallest angle. Find all three angles.

a. $(x - 10) + 2x = 180$ **b.** $x + 2x - 10 = 90$

c. $x + (x + 10) + 2x = 180$ **d.** $x + (x + 10) + (x + 2) = 90$

Getting Ready for the Next Section

To understand all the explanations and examples in the next section you must be able to work the problems below.

Solve the following equations.

59. **a.** $x - 3 = 6$ **b.** $x + 3 = 6$ **c.** $-x - 3 = 6$ **d.** $-x + 3 = 6$

60. **a.** $x - 7 = 16$ **b.** $x + 7 = 16$ **c.** $-x - 7 = 16$ **d.** $-x + 7 = 16$

61. **a.** $\dfrac{x}{4} = -2$ **b.** $-\dfrac{x}{4} = -2$ **c.** $\dfrac{x}{4} = 2$ **d.** $-\dfrac{x}{4} = 2$

62. **a.** $3a = 15$ **b.** $3a = -15$ **c.** $-3a = 15$ **d.** $-3a = -15$

63. $2.5x - 3.48 = 4.9x + 2.07$ **64.** $2(1 - 3x) + 4 = 4x - 14$

65. $3(x - 4) = -2$ **66.** Solve for y: $2x - 3y = 6$

Learning Objectives

In this section, we will learn how to:

1. Solve a linear inequality.
2. Graph a solution set for a linear inequality on the number line.

Introduction

Linear inequalities are solved by a method similar to the one used in solving linear equations. The overall goal is to isolate the variable. The only real differences between the methods are in the multiplication property for inequalities and in expressing the solution set.

An *inequality* differs from an equation only with respect to the comparison symbol between the two quantities being compared. In place of the equal sign, we use $<$ (less than), $\leq$ (less than or equal to), $>$ (greater than), or $\geq$ (greater than or equal to).

Solution Sets and Notation

We can use *set-builder notation* to write the solution set, and then visually represent the solution set by graphing it on a number line. If the inequality symbol includes equality ($\leq$, $\geq$) then we use a solid point when graphing the solution set. If the inequality symbol does not include equality ($<$, $>$) then we use an open circle when graphing the solution set.

Here are some examples of equations and inequalities showing the notation used to write and graph the solution set.

Equation or Inequality	Set-Builder Notation	Number Line Graph
$x = 3$	$\{3\}$	
$x \geq 3$	$\{x \mid x \geq 3\}$	
$x > 3$	$\{x \mid x > 3\}$	
$x \leq 3$	$\{x \mid x \leq 3\}$	
$x < 3$	$\{x \mid x < 3\}$	

Solving Linear Inequalities

The addition property for inequalities is almost identical to the addition property for equality.

> **PROPERTY**   *Addition Property for Inequalities*
>
> For any three algebraic expressions A, B, and C,
> $$\text{if} \qquad A < B$$
> $$\text{then} \qquad A + C < B + C$$
>
> *In words*:   Adding the same quantity to both sides of an inequality will not change the solution set.

It makes no difference which inequality symbol we use to state the property. Adding the same amount to both sides always produces an inequality equivalent to the original inequality. Also, because subtraction can be thought of as addition of the opposite, this property holds for subtraction as well as addition.

VIDEO EXAMPLES

SECTION 2.8

EXAMPLE 1   Solve the inequality: $x + 5 < 7$.

SOLUTION   To isolate x, we add -5 to both sides of the inequality.

$$x + 5 < 7$$
$$x + 5 + (-5) < 7 + (-5) \qquad \text{Addition property for inequalities}$$
$$x < 2$$

Using set-builder notation we can write the solution set as $\{x \mid x < 2\}$. We can go one step further here and graph the solution set. The solution set is all real numbers less than 2. To graph this set, we simply draw a straight line and label a convenient point 0 (zero) for reference. Then we label the 2 on the right side of zero and extend an arrow beginning at 2 and pointing to the left. We use an open circle at 2 because it is not included in the solution set. Here is the graph:

EXAMPLE 2   Solve: $x - 6 \leq -3$.

SOLUTION   Adding 6 to each side will isolate x on the left side.

$$x - 6 \leq -3$$
$$x - 6 + 6 \leq -3 + 6 \qquad \text{Add 6 to both sides}$$
$$x \leq 3$$

The solution set is $\{x \mid x \leq 3\}$. The graph of the solution set is

Notice that the point at the 3 is solid because 3 is included in the solution set. We always will use open circles on the graphs of solution sets with $<$ or $>$ and solid points on the graphs of solution sets with $\leq$ or $\geq$.

To see the idea behind the multiplication property for inequalities, we will consider three true inequality statements and explore what happens when we multiply both sides by a positive number and then what happens when we multiply by a negative number.

Consider the following three true statements:

$$3 < 5 \qquad -3 < 5 \qquad -5 < -3$$

Now multiply both sides by the positive number 4:

$$4(3) < 4(5) \qquad 4(-3) < 4(5) \qquad 4(-5) < 4(-3)$$
$$12 < 20 \qquad\qquad -12 < 20 \qquad\qquad -20 < -12$$

In each case, the inequality symbol in the result points in the same direction it did in the original inequality. We say the "sense" of the inequality doesn't change when we multiply both sides by a positive quantity.

Notice what happens when we go through the same process but multiply both sides by -4 instead of 4:

$$3 < 5 \qquad\qquad\qquad -3 < 5 \qquad\qquad\qquad -5 < -3$$

$$-4(3) > -4(5) \qquad -4(-3) > -4(5) \qquad -4(-5) > -4(-3)$$
$$-12 > -20 \qquad\qquad 12 > -20 \qquad\qquad 20 > 12$$

In each case, we have to change the direction in which the inequality symbol points to keep each statement true. Multiplying both sides of an inequality by a negative quantity always reverses the sense of the inequality. Our results are summarized in the multiplication property for inequalities.

> *Note* This discussion is intended to show why the multiplication property for inequalities is written the way it is. You may want to look ahead to the property itself and then come back to this discussion if you are having trouble making sense out of it.

PROPERTY *Multiplication Property for Inequalities*

For any three algebraic expressions A, B, and C, where $C \neq 0$,

if	$A < B$	
then	$AC < BC$	when C is positive
and	$AC > BC$	when C is negative

In words: Multiplying both sides of an inequality by a positive number does not change the solution set. When multiplying both sides of an inequality by a negative number, it is necessary to reverse the inequality symbol to produce an equivalent inequality.

> *Note* Because division is defined in terms of multiplication, this property is also true for division. We can divide both sides of an inequality by any nonzero number we choose. If that number happens to be negative, we must also reverse the direction of the inequality symbol.

We can multiply both sides of an inequality by any nonzero number we choose. If that number happens to be negative, we must also reverse the sense of the inequality.

EXAMPLE 3   Solve $3a < 15$ and graph the solution set.

SOLUTION We begin by multiplying each side by $\frac{1}{3}$. Because $\frac{1}{3}$ is a positive number, we do not reverse the direction of the inequality symbol:

$$3a < 15$$

$$\frac{1}{3}(3a) < \frac{1}{3}(15) \qquad \text{Multiply each side by } \tfrac{1}{3}$$

$$a < 5$$

The solution set is $\{a \mid a < 5\}$, and its graph is

EXAMPLE 4   Solve $-3a \leq 18$, and graph the solution set.

SOLUTION   We begin by multiplying both sides by $-\frac{1}{3}$. Because $-\frac{1}{3}$ is a negative number, we must reverse the direction of the inequality symbol at the same time that we multiply by $-\frac{1}{3}$.

$$-3a \leq 18$$

$$-\frac{1}{3}(-3a) \geq -\frac{1}{3}(18) \qquad \text{Multiply both sides by } -\frac{1}{3} \text{ and reverse the direction of the inequality symbol}$$

$$a \geq -6$$

The solution set is $\{a \mid a \geq -6\}$, and the graph of the solution set is

EXAMPLE 5   Solve $-\frac{x}{4} > 2$ and graph the solution set.

SOLUTION   To isolate x, we multiply each side by -4. Because -4 is a negative number, we also must reverse the direction of the inequality symbol:

$$-\frac{x}{4} > 2$$

$$-4\left(-\frac{x}{4}\right) < -4(2) \qquad \text{Multiply each side by } -4, \text{ and reverse the direction of the inequality symbol}$$

$$x < -8$$

The solution set is $\{x \mid x < -8\}$, and its graph is

To solve more complicated inequalities, we use the following process.

HOW TO   *Solve Linear Inequalities in One Variable*

Step 1a: Use the distributive property to separate terms, if necessary.

1b: If fractions are present, consider multiplying both sides by the LCD to eliminate the fractions. If decimals are present, consider multiplying both sides by a power of 10 to clear the inequality of decimals.

1c: Combine similar terms on each side of the inequality.

Step 2:   Use the addition property for inequalities to get all variable terms on one side of the inequality and all constant terms on the other side.

Step 3:   Use the multiplication property for inequalities to get the variable by itself on one side of the inequality (change the coefficient of the variable term into 1).

Step 4:   Write and graph the solution set.

EXAMPLE 6   Solve: $2.5x - 3.48 < -4.9x + 2.07$.

SOLUTION   We have two methods we can use to solve this inequality. We can simply apply our properties to the inequality the way it is currently written and work with the decimal numbers, or we can eliminate the decimals to begin with and solve the resulting inequality.

Method 1 Working with the decimals.

$$2.5x - 3.48 < -4.9x + 2.07 \qquad \text{Original inequality}$$
$$2.5x + 4.9x - 3.48 < -4.9x + 4.9x + 2.07 \qquad \text{Add } 4.9x \text{ to each side}$$
$$7.4x - 3.48 < 2.07$$
$$7.4x - 3.48 + 3.48 < 2.07 + 3.48 \qquad \text{Add } 3.48 \text{ to each side}$$
$$7.4x < 5.55$$
$$\frac{7.4x}{7.4} < \frac{5.55}{7.4} \qquad \text{Divide each side by } 7.4$$
$$x < 0.75$$

Method 2 Eliminating the decimals in the beginning.

Because the greatest number of places to the right of the decimal point in any of the numbers is 2, we can multiply each side of the inequality by 100 and we will be left with an equivalent inequality that contains only integers.

$$2.5x - 3.48 < -4.9x + 2.07 \qquad \text{Original inequality}$$
$$100(2.5x - 3.48) < 100(-4.9x + 2.07) \qquad \text{Multiply each side by } 100$$
$$100(2.5x) - 100(3.48) < 100(-4.9x) + 100(2.07) \qquad \text{Distributive property}$$
$$250x - 348 < -490x + 207 \qquad \text{Multiplication}$$
$$740x - 348 < 207 \qquad \text{Add } 490x \text{ to each side}$$
$$740x < 555 \qquad \text{Add } 348 \text{ to each side}$$
$$\frac{740x}{740} < \frac{555}{740} \qquad \text{Divide each side by } 740$$
$$x < 0.75$$

The solution set by either method is $\{x \mid x < 0.75\}$. Here is the graph:

EXAMPLE 7   Solve: $3(x - 4) \geq -2$.

SOLUTION
$$3x - 12 \geq -2 \qquad \text{Distributive property}$$
$$3x - 12 + 12 \geq -2 + 12 \qquad \text{Add 12 to both sides}$$
$$3x \geq 10$$
$$\frac{1}{3}(3x) \geq \frac{1}{3}(10) \qquad \text{Multiply both sides by } \tfrac{1}{3}$$
$$x \geq \frac{10}{3}$$

The solution set is $\left\{ x \mid x \geq \dfrac{10}{3} \right\}$, and its graph is

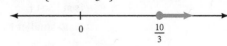

EXAMPLE 8   Solve $2(1 - 3x) + 4 < 4x - 14$ and graph the solution set.

SOLUTION

$2 - 6x + 4 < 4x - 14$	Distributive property
$-6x + 6 < 4x - 14$	Simplify
$-6x + 6 + (-6) < 4x - 14 + (-6)$	Add -6 to both sides
$-6x < 4x - 20$	
$-6x + (-4x) < 4x + (-4x) - 20$	Add $-4x$ to both sides
$-10x < -20$	
$\left(-\dfrac{1}{10}\right)(-10x) > \left(-\dfrac{1}{10}\right)(-20)$	Multiply by $-\dfrac{1}{10}$, reverse the direction of the inequality symbol
$x > 2$	

The solution set is $\{x \mid x > 2\}$. Here is the graph:

EXAMPLE 9   Solve $2x - 3y < 6$ for y.

SOLUTION   We can solve this formula for y by first adding $-2x$ to each side and then multiplying each side by $-\frac{1}{3}$. When we multiply by $-\frac{1}{3}$ we must reverse the direction of the inequality symbol. Because this is a formula, we will not graph the solution set.

$2x - 3y < 6$	Original formula
$2x + (-2x) - 3y < (-2x) + 6$	Add $-2x$ to each side
$-3y < -2x + 6$	
$-\dfrac{1}{3}(-3y) > -\dfrac{1}{3}(-2x + 6)$	Multiply each side by $-\frac{1}{3}$
$y > \dfrac{2}{3}x - 2$	Distributive property

Application

Here are some common phrases used when describing inequalities and their equivalent mathematical expressions.

Phrase	Equivalent Expression
a is less than b	$a < b$
a is more than b	$a > b$
a is greater than b	$a > b$
a is at most b	$a \leq b$
a is no larger than b	$a \leq b$
a does not exceed b	$a \leq b$
a is at least b	$a \geq b$
a is no smaller than b	$a \geq b$

Our last example is similar to an example done earlier in this chapter. This time it involves an inequality instead of an equation.

We can modify our Blueprint for Problem Solving to solve application problems whose solutions depend on writing and then solving inequalities.

EXAMPLE 10 The sum of two consecutive odd integers is at most 28. What are the possibilities for the first of the two integers?

SOLUTION When we use the phrase "their sum is at most 28," we mean that their sum is less than or equal to 28.

Step 1: Read and list.
Known items: Two consecutive odd integers. Their sum is less than or equal to 28.
Unknown items: The numbers in question.

Step 2: Assign a variable, and translate information.
If we let x be the first of the two consecutive odd integers, then $x + 2$ is the next consecutive one.

Step 3: Reread, and write an inequality.
Their sum is at most 28.

$$x + (x + 2) \leq 28$$

Step 4: Solve the inequality.

$$2x + 2 \leq 28 \qquad \text{Simplify the left side}$$

$$2x \leq 26 \qquad \text{Add } -2 \text{ to each side}$$

$$x \leq 13 \qquad \text{Multiply each side by } \tfrac{1}{2}$$

Step 5: Write the answer.
The first of the two integers must be an odd integer that is less than or equal to 13.

Step 6: Reread, and check.
Suppose the first integer is 13. The next consecutive odd integer is 15. The sum of 15 and 13 is 28. If the first odd integer is less than 13, the sum of it and the next consecutive odd integer will be less than 28.

Getting Ready for Class

After reading through the preceding section, respond in your own words and in complete sentences.

A. State the addition property for inequalities.

B. How is the multiplication property for inequalities different from the multiplication property of equality?

C. When do we reverse the direction of an inequality symbol?

D. Under what conditions do we not change the direction of the inequality symbol when we multiply both sides of an inequality by a number?

Problem Set 2.8

Solve the following inequalities using the addition property of inequalities. Graph each solution set.

1. $x - 5 < 7$ **2.** $x + 3 < -5$ **3.** $a - 4 \leq 8$ **4.** $a + 3 \leq 10$

5. $x - 4.3 > 8.7$ **6.** $x - 2.6 > 10.4$ **7.** $y + 6 \geq 10$ **8.** $y + 3 \geq 12$

9. $2 < x - 7$ **10.** $3 < x + 8$

Solve the following inequalities using the multiplication property of inequalities. If you multiply both sides by a negative number, be sure to reverse the direction of the inequality symbol. Graph the solution set.

11. $3x < 6$ **12.** $2x < 14$ **13.** $5a \leq 25$ **14.** $4a \leq 16$

15. $\dfrac{x}{3} > 5$ **16.** $\dfrac{x}{7} > 1$ **17.** $-2x > 6$ **18.** $-3x \geq 9$

19. $-3x \geq -18$ **20.** $-8x \geq -24$ **21.** $-\dfrac{x}{5} \leq 10$ **22.** $-\dfrac{x}{9} \geq -1$

23. $-\dfrac{2}{3}y > 4$ **24.** $-\dfrac{3}{4}y > 6$

Solve the following inequalities.

25. $2x - 3 < 9$ **26.** $3x - 4 < 17$ **27.** $-\dfrac{1}{5}y - \dfrac{1}{3} \leq \dfrac{2}{3}$

28. $-\dfrac{1}{6}y - \dfrac{1}{2} \leq \dfrac{2}{3}$ **29.** $-7.2x + 1.8 > -19.8$ **30.** $-7.8x - 1.3 > 22.1$

31. $\dfrac{2}{3}x - 5 \leq 7$ **32.** $\dfrac{3}{4}x - 8 \leq 1$ **33.** $-\dfrac{2}{5}a - 3 > 5$

34. $-\dfrac{4}{5}a - 2 > 10$ **35.** $5 - \dfrac{3}{5}y > -10$ **36.** $4 - \dfrac{5}{6}y > -11$

37. $0.3(a + 1) \leq 1.2$ **38.** $0.4(a - 2) \leq 0.4$ **39.** $2(5 - 2x) \leq -20$

40. $7(8 - 2x) > 28$ **41.** $3x - 5 > 8x$ **42.** $8x - 4 > 6x$

43. $\dfrac{1}{3}y - \dfrac{1}{2} \leq \dfrac{5}{6}y + \dfrac{1}{2}$ **44.** $\dfrac{7}{6}y + \dfrac{4}{3} \leq \dfrac{11}{6}y - \dfrac{7}{6}$

45. $-2.8x + 8.4 < -14x - 2.8$ **46.** $-7.2x - 2.4 < -2.4x + 12$

47. $3(m - 2) - 4 \geq 7m + 14$ **48.** $2(3m - 1) + 5 \geq 8m - 7$

49. $3 - 4(x - 2) \leq -5x + 6$ **50.** $8 - 6(x - 3) \leq -4x + 12$

Solve each of the following formulas for y.

51. $3x + 2y < 6$ **52.** $-3x + 2y < 6$ **53.** $2x - 5y > 10$

54. $-2x - 5y > 5$ **55.** $-3x + 7y \leq 21$ **56.** $-7x + 3y \leq 21$

57. $2x - 4y \geq -4$ **58.** $4x - 2y \geq -8$

The next two problems are intended to give you practice reading, and paying attention to, the instructions that accompany the problems you are working.

59. Work each problem according to the instructions given.

  a. Evaluate when $x = 0$: $-5x + 3$.   **b.** Solve: $-5x + 3 = -7$.

  c. Is 0 a solution to $-5x + 3 < -7$?   **d.** Solve: $-5x + 3 < -7$.

60. Work each problem according to the instructions given.

  a. Evaluate when $x = 0$: $-2x - 5$.   **b.** Solve: $-2x - 5 = 1$.

  c. Is 0 a solution to $-2x - 5 > 1$?   **d.** Solve: $-2x - 5 > 1$.

For each graph below, write an inequality whose solution is the graph.

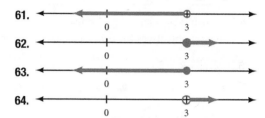

61.

    0   3

62.

    0   3

63.

    0   3

64.

    0   3

Applying the Concepts

65. Consecutive Integers The sum of two consecutive integers is at least 583. What are the possibilities for the first of the two integers?

66. Consecutive Integers The sum of two consecutive integers is at most 583. What are the possibilities for the first of the two integers?

67. Number Problems The sum of twice a number and six is less than ten. Find all solutions.

68. Number Problems Twice the difference of a number and three is greater than or equal to the number increased by five. Find all solutions.

69. Number Problems The product of a number and four is greater than the number minus eight. Find the solution set.

70. Number Problems The quotient of a number and five is less than the sum of seven and two. Find the solution set.

71. Geometry Problems The length of a rectangle is 3 times the width. If the perimeter is to be at least 48 meters, what are the possible values for the width? (If the perimeter is at least 48 meters, then it is greater than or equal to 48 meters.)

72. Geometry Problems The length of a rectangle is 3 more than twice the width. If the perimeter is to be at least 51 meters, what are the possible values for the width? (If the perimeter is at least 51 meters, then it is greater than or equal to 51 meters.)

73. Geometry Problems The numerical values of the three sides of a triangle are given by three consecutive even integers. If the perimeter is greater than 24 inches, what are the possibilities for the shortest side?

74. Geometry Problems The numerical values of the three sides of a triangle are given by three consecutive odd integers. If the perimeter is greater than 27 inches, what are the possibilities for the shortest side?

Learning Objectives Assessment

The following problems can be used to help assess if you have successfully met the learning objectives for this section.

75. Solve: $3(9 - 5x) < 72$.

    a. $x < -3$ **b.** $x > -3$ **c.** $x < 3$ **d.** $x > 3$

76. Graph $x > -2$ on the number line.

    a. ![number line, open circle at -2, shaded to the right]   **b.** ![number line, closed circle at -2, shaded to the right]

    c. ![number line, closed circle at -2, shaded to the left]   **d.** ![number line, open circle at -2, shaded to the left]

Maintaining Your Skills

The problems that follow review some of the more important skills you have learned in previous sections and chapters. You can consider the time you spend working these problems as time spent studying for exams.

Answer the following percent problems.

77. What number is 25% of 32?

78. What number is 15% of 75?

79. What number is 20% of 120?

80. What number is 125% of 300?

81. What percent of 36 is 9?

82. What percent of 16 is 9?

83. What percent of 50 is 5?

84. What percent of 140 is 35?

85. 16 is 20% of what number?

86. 6 is 3% of what number?

87. 8 is 2% of what number?

88. 70 is 175% of what number?

Simplify each expression.

89. $-|-5|$

90. $\left(-\dfrac{2}{3}\right)^3$

91. $-3 - 4(-2)$

92. $2^4 + 3^3 \div 9 - 4^2$

93. $5|3 - 8| - 6|2 - 5|$

94. $7 - 3(2 - 6)$

95. $5 - 2[-3(5 - 7) - 8]$

96. $\dfrac{5 + 3(7 - 2)}{2(-3) - 4}$

97. Find the difference of -3 and -9.

98. If you add -4 to the product of -3 and 5, what number results?

99. Apply the distributive property to $\dfrac{1}{2}(4x - 6)$.

100. Use the associative property to simplify $-6\left(\dfrac{1}{3}x\right)$.

For the set $\left\{-3, -\dfrac{4}{5}, 0, \dfrac{5}{8}, 2, \sqrt{5}\right\}$, which numbers are

101. Integers

102. Rational numbers

Chapter 2 Summary

Similar Terms [2.1]

1. The terms $2x$, $5x$, and $-7x$ are all similar because their variable parts are the same.

A term is a number or a number and one or more variables multiplied together. Similar terms are terms with the same variable part.

Simplifying Expressions [2.1]

2. Simplify: $3x + 4x$.
$$3x + 4x = (3 + 4)x$$
$$= 7x$$

In this chapter, we simplified expressions that contained variables by using the distributive property to combine similar terms.

Solution Set [2.2]

3. The solution set for the equation $x + 2 = 5$ is $\{3\}$ because $x = 3$ is the only real number that makes the equation true.

The solution set for an equation (or inequality) is all the numbers that, when used in place of the variable, make the equation (or inequality) a true statement.

Equivalent Equations [2.2]

4. The equations $a - 4 = 3$ and $a - 2 = 5$ are equivalent because both have solution set $\{7\}$.

Two equations are called equivalent if they have the same solution set.

Addition Property of Equality [2.2]

5. Solve: $x - 5 = 12$.
$$x - 5\,(+5) = 12\,(+5)$$
$$x + 0 = 17$$
$$x = 17$$

When the same quantity is added to both sides of an equation, the solution set for the equation is unchanged. Adding the same amount to both sides of an equation produces an equivalent equation.

Multiplication Property of Equality [2.3]

6. Solve: $3x = 18$.
$$\frac{1}{3}(3x) = \frac{1}{3}(18)$$
$$x = 6$$

If both sides of an equation are multiplied by the same nonzero number, the solution set is unchanged. Multiplying both sides of an equation by a nonzero quantity produces an equivalent equation.

Strategy for Solving Linear Equations in One Variable [2.4]

7. Solve: $2(x + 3) = 10$.

$$2x + 6 = 10$$
$$2x + 6 + (-6) = 10 + (-6)$$
$$2x = 4$$
$$\frac{1}{2}(2x) = \frac{1}{2}(4)$$
$$x = 2$$

Step 1a: Use the distributive property to separate terms, if necessary.

1b: If fractions are present, consider multiplying both sides by the LCD to eliminate the fractions. If decimals are present, consider multiplying both sides by a power of 10 to clear the equation of decimals.

1c: Combine similar terms on each side of the equation.

Step 2: Use the addition property of equality to get all variable terms on one side of the equation and all constant terms on the other side. A variable term is a term that contains the variable (for example, $5x$). A constant term is a term that does not contain the variable (the number 3, for example).

Step 3: Use the multiplication property of equality to change the coefficient of the variable term into 1.

Step 4: Check your solution in the original equation to be sure that you have not made a mistake in the solution process.

Formulas [2.5]

8. Solving $P = 2l + 2w$ for l, we have

$$P - 2w = 2l$$
$$\frac{P - 2w}{2} = l$$

A formula is an equation with more than one variable. To solve a formula for one of its variables, we use the addition and multiplication properties of equality to move everything except the variable in question to one side of the equal sign so the variable in question is alone on the other side.

Blueprint for Problem Solving [2.6, 2.7]

Step 1: ***Read*** the problem, and then mentally ***list*** the items that are known and the items that are unknown.

Step 2: ***Assign a variable*** to one of the unknown items. (In most cases this will amount to letting x represent the item that is asked for in the problem.) Then ***translate*** the other ***information*** in the problem to expressions involving the variable.

Step 3: ***Reread*** the problem, and then ***write an equation,*** using the items and variables listed in steps 1 and 2, that describes the situation.

Step 4: ***Solve the equation*** found in step 3.

Step 5: ***Write*** your ***answer*** using a complete sentence.

Step 6: ***Reread*** the problem, and ***check*** your solution with the original words in the problem.

Addition Property for Inequalities [2.8]

9. Solve: $x + 5 < 7$.
$$x + 5 + (-5) < 7 + (-5)$$
$$x < 2$$

Adding the same quantity to both sides of an inequality produces an equivalent inequality, one with the same solution set.

Multiplication Property for Inequalities [2.8]

10. Solve: $-3a \leq 18$.
$$-\frac{1}{3}(-3a) \geq -\frac{1}{3}(18)$$
$$a \geq -6$$

Multiplying both sides of an inequality by a positive number never changes the solution set. If both sides are multiplied by a negative number, the direction of the inequality symbol must be reversed to produce an equivalent inequality.

Strategy for Solving Linear Inequalities in One Variable [2.8]

11. Solve: $3(x - 4) \geq -2$.
$$3x - 12 \geq -2$$
$$3x - 12 + 12 \geq -2 + 12$$
$$3x \geq 10$$
$$\frac{1}{3}(3x) \geq \frac{1}{3}(10)$$
$$x \geq \frac{10}{3}$$

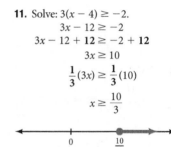

Step 1a: Use the distributive property to separate terms, if necessary.

Step 1b: If fractions are present, consider multiplying both sides by the LCD to eliminate the fractions. If decimals are present, consider multiplying both sides by a power of 10 to clear the inequality of decimals.

Step 1c: Combine similar terms on each side of the inequality.

Step 2: Use the addition property for inequalities to get all variable terms on one side of the inequality and all constant terms on the other side.

Step 3: Use the multiplication property for inequalities to get the variable by itself on one side of the inequality. Remember to reverse the direction of the inequality symbol if both sides are multiplied by a negative number.

Step 4: Graph the solution set.

Chapter 2 Test

Simplify each of the following expressions. [2.1]

1. $5y - 3 - 6y + 4$

2. $3x - 4 + x + 3$

3. $4 - 2(y - 3) - 6$

4. $3(3x - 4) - 2(4x + 5)$

5. Find the value of $3x + 12 + 2x$ when $x = -3$. [2.1]

6. Find the value of $x^2 - 3xy + y^2$ when $x = -2$ and $y = -4$. [2.1]

7. Fill in the tables below to find the sequences formed by substituting the first four counting numbers into the expressions $(n + 2)^2$ and $n^2 + 2$. [2.1]

a.

n	$(n + 2)^2$
1	
2	
3	
4	

b.

n	$n^2 + 2$
1	
2	
3	
4	

Solve the following equations. [2.2, 2.3, 2.4]

8. $3x - 2 = 7$

9. $4y + 15 = y$

10. $\frac{1}{4}x - \frac{1}{12} = \frac{1}{3}x - \frac{1}{6}$

11. $-3(3 - 2x) - 7 = 8$

12. $3x - 9 = -6$

13. $0.05 + 0.07(100 - x) = 3.2$

14. $4(t - 3) + 2(t + 4) = 2t - 16$

15. $4x - 2(3x - 1) = 2x - 8$

For each of the following expressions, write an equivalent equation. [2.5]

16. What number is 40% of 56?

17. 720 is 24% of what number?

18. If $3x - 4y = 16$, find y when $x = 4$.

19. If $3x - 4y = 16$, find x when $y = 2$.

Solve each formula for the appropriate variable. [2.5]

20. Solve $2x + 6y = 12$ for y.

21. Solve $x^2 = v^2 + 2ad$ for a.

Solve each word problem. [2.6, 2.7]

22. **Age Problem** Paul is twice as old as Becca. Five years ago, the sum of their ages was 44. How old are they now?

23. **Geometry** The length of a rectangle is 5 less than 3 times the width. The perimeter is 150 centimeters. What are the length and width?

24. **Coin Problem** A man has a collection of dimes and nickels with a total value of $1.70. If he has 8 more dimes than nickels, how many of each coin does he have?

25. **Investing** A woman has money in two accounts. One account pays 6% annual interest, whereas the other pays 12% annual interest. If she has $500 more invested at 12% than she does at 6% and her total interest for a year is $186, how much does she have in each account?

Solve each inequality, and graph the solution. [2.8]

26. $\frac{1}{2}x - 2 > 3$

27. $-6y \leq 24$

28. $0.3 - 0.2x < 1.1$

29. $3 - 2(n - 1) \geq 9$

Linear Equations and Inequalities in Two Variables

Chapter Outline

iStockphoto.com © AtollPhotography

When light comes into contact with a surface that does not transmit light, then all the light that contacts the surface is either reflected off the surface or absorbed into the surface. If we let R represent the percentage of light reflected and w represent the percentage of light absorbed, then the relationship between these two variables can be written as

$$R + A = 100$$

which is a linear equation in two variables. The following table and graph show the same relationship as that described by the equation. The table is a numerical description; the graph is a visual description.

Reflected and Absorbed Light	
Percent Reflected	Percent Absorbed
0	100
20	80
40	60
60	40
80	20
100	0

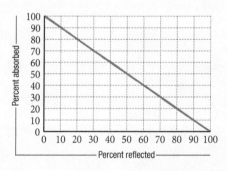

In this chapter, we learn how to build tables and draw graphs from linear equations in two variables.

Try to arrange your daily study habits so that you have very little studying to do the night before your next exam. The next two goals will help you achieve this.

1. **Review with the Exam in Mind** Each day you should review material that will be covered on the next exam. Your review should consist of working problems. Preferably, the problems you work should be problems from your list of difficult problems.

2. **Pay Attention to Instructions** Each of the following is a valid instruction with respect to the equation $y = 3x - 2$, and the result of applying the instructions will be different in each case:

Find x when y is 10.	(Section 2.5)
Solve for x.	(Section 2.5)
Graph the equation.	(Section 3.2)
Find the intercepts.	(Section 3.3)

There are many things to do with the equation $y = 3x - 2$. If you train yourself to pay attention to the instructions that accompany a problem as you work through the assigned problems, you will not find yourself confused about what to do with a problem when you see it on a test.

Learning Objectives

In this section, we will learn how to:

1. Construct and interpret a scatter diagram.

2. Construct and interpret a line graph.

3. Graph an ordered pair on the rectangular coordinate system.

Introduction

This table and figure show the relationship between the table of values for the speed of a race car and the corresponding bar chart. In Figure 1, the horizontal line that shows the elapsed time in seconds is called the *horizontal axis*, and the vertical line that shows the speed in miles per hour is called the *vertical axis*.

The data in the table are called *paired data* because the information is organized so that each number in the first column is paired with a specific number in the second column. Each pair of numbers is associated with one of the solid bars in Figure 1. For example, the third bar in the bar chart is associated with the pair of numbers 3 seconds and 162.8 miles per hour. The first number, 3 seconds, is associated with the horizontal axis, and the second number, 162.8 miles per hour, is associated with the vertical axis.

Speed of a Race Car	
Time in Seconds	Speed in Miles per Hour
0	0
1	72.7
2	129.9
3	162.8
4	192.2
5	212.4
6	228.1

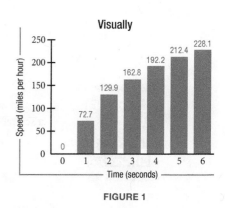

FIGURE 1

Scatter Diagrams and Line Graphs

The information in the table can be visualized with a scatter diagram and line graph as well. Figure 2 is a *scatter diagram* of the information in the table. We use dots instead of the bars shown in Figure 1 to show the speed of the race car at each second during the race. Figure 3 is called a *line graph*. It is constructed by taking the dots in Figure 2 and connecting each one to the next with a straight line.

Notice that we have labeled the axes in these two figures a little differently than we did with the bar chart by making the axes intersect at the number 0.

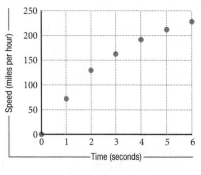

FIGURE 2

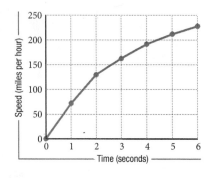

FIGURE 3

The number sequences we have worked with in the past can also be written as paired data by associating each number in the sequence with its position in the sequence. For instance, in the sequence of odd numbers

$$1, 3, 5, 7, 9, \ldots$$

the number 7 is the fourth number in the sequence. Its position is 4, and its value is 7. Here is the sequence of odd numbers written so that the position of each term is noted:

Position	$1, 2, 3, 4, 5, \ldots$
Value	$1, 3, 5, 7, 9, \ldots$

EXAMPLE 1   The tables below give the first five terms of the sequence of odd numbers and the sequence of squares as paired data. In each case construct a scatter diagram.

Odd Numbers	
Position	Value
1	1
2	3
3	5
4	7
5	9

Squares	
Position	Value
1	1
2	4
3	9
4	16
5	25

SOLUTION   The two scatter diagrams are based on the data from these tables shown here. Notice how the dots in Figure 4 seem to line up in a straight line, whereas the dots in Figure 5 give the impression of a curve. We say the points in Figure 4 suggest a linear relationship between the two sets of data, whereas the points in Figure 5 suggest a nonlinear relationship.

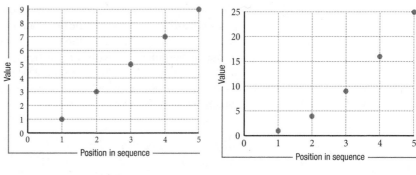

FIGURE 4   **FIGURE 5**

As you know, each dot in Figures 4 and 5 corresponds to a pair of numbers, one of which is associated with the horizontal axis and the other with the vertical axis. Paired data play a very important role in the equations we will solve in the next section. To prepare ourselves for those equations, we need to expand the concept of paired data to include negative numbers. At the same time, we want to standardize the position of the axes in the diagrams that we use to visualize paired data.

The Rectangular Coordinate System

> **DEFINITION** *x-coordinate, y-coordinate*
>
> A pair of numbers enclosed in parentheses and separated by a comma, such as $(-2, 1)$, is called an *ordered pair* of numbers. The first number in the pair is called the *x-coordinate* of the ordered pair; the second number is called the *y-coordinate*. For the ordered pair $(-2, 1)$, the *x*-coordinate is -2 and the *y*-coordinate is 1.

Ordered pairs of numbers are important in the study of mathematics because they give us a way to visualize solutions to equations. To see the visual component of ordered pairs, we need the diagram shown in Figure 6. It is called the *rectangular coordinate system*.

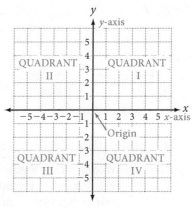

FIGURE 6

The rectangular coordinate system is built from two number lines oriented perpendicular to each other. The horizontal number line is exactly the same as our real number line and is called the *x-axis*. The vertical number line is also the same as our real number line with the positive direction up and the negative direction down. It is called the *y-axis*. The point where the two axes intersect is called the *origin*. As you can see from Figure 6, the axes divide the plane into four *quadrants*, which are numbered I through IV in a counterclockwise direction.

Graphing Ordered Pairs

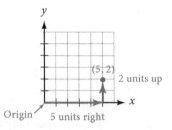

To graph the ordered pair (a, b), we start at the origin and move a units right or left (right if a is positive and left if a is negative). Then we move b units up or down (up if b is positive, down if b is negative). The point where we end up is the graph of the ordered pair (a, b). To graph the ordered pair $(5, 2)$, we start at the origin and move 5 units to the right. Then, from that position, we move 2 units up.

Every ordered pair can be represented graphically as a unique point on the rectangular coordinate system.

> **EXAMPLE 2**   Graph the ordered pairs $(3, 4)$, $(3, -4)$, $(-3, 4)$, and $(-3, -4)$. Also, identify which quadrant each point lies in.

SOLUTION

Note It is very important that you graph ordered pairs quickly and accurately. Remember, the first coordinate goes with the horizontal axis and the second coordinate goes with the vertical axis.

FIGURE 7

We can see in Figure 7 that when we graph ordered pairs, the x-coordinate corresponds to movement parallel to the x-axis (horizontal) and the y-coordinate corresponds to movement parallel to the y-axis (vertical).

The point $(3, 4)$ lies in QI, $(3, -4)$ lies in QIV, $(-3, 4)$ lies in QII, and $(-3, -4)$ lies in QIII. We have labeled each point with its corresponding quadrant in Figure 7.

EXAMPLE 3 Graph the ordered pairs $(-1, 3)$, $(2, 5)$, $(0, 0)$, $(0, -3)$, and $(4, 0)$. State which quadrant each point lies in.

SOLUTION See Figure 8.

Note If we do not label the axes of a coordinate system, we assume that each square is one unit long and one unit wide.

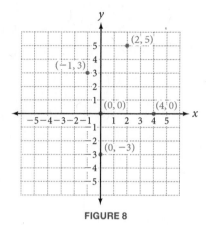

FIGURE 8

The point $(-1, 3)$ lies in QII, and $(2, 5)$ lies in QI. Because $(0, 0)$, $(0, -3)$, and $(4, 0)$ lie on one of the axes, these points are not in a particular quadrant.

Getting Ready for Class

After reading through the preceding section, respond in your own words and in complete sentences.

A. What is an ordered pair of numbers?

B. Explain in words how you would graph the ordered pair $(3, 4)$.

C. How do you construct a rectangular coordinate system?

D. Where is the origin on a rectangular coordinate system?

Problem Set 3.1

Graph each ordered pair on a rectangular coordinate system. Then indicate which quadrant, if any, the corresponding point lies in.

1. $(3, 2)$ **2.** $(3, -2)$ **3.** $(-3, 2)$ **4.** $(-3, -2)$

5. $(5, 1)$ **6.** $(5, -1)$ **7.** $(1, 5)$ **8.** $(1, -5)$

9. $(-1, 5)$ **10.** $(-1, -5)$ **11.** $\left(2, \frac{1}{2}\right)$ **12.** $\left(3, \frac{3}{2}\right)$

13. $\left(-4, -\frac{5}{2}\right)$ **14.** $\left(-5, -\frac{3}{2}\right)$ **15.** $(3, 0)$ **16.** $(-2, 0)$

17. $(0, 5)$ **18.** $(0, 0)$

Give the coordinates of each numbered point in the figure.

19–28.

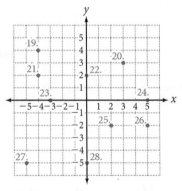

Graph the points $(4, 3)$ and $(-4, -1)$, and draw a straight line that passes through both of them. Then answer the following questions.

29. Does the graph of $(2, 2)$ lie on the line?

30. Does the graph of $(-2, 0)$ lie on the line?

31. Does the graph of $(0, -2)$ lie on the line?

32. Does the graph of $(-6, 2)$ lie on the line?

Graph the points $(-2, 4)$ and $(2, -4)$, and draw a straight line that passes through both of them. Then answer the following questions.

33. Does the graph of $(0, 0)$ lie on the line?

34. Does the graph of $(-1, 2)$ lie on the line?

35. Does the graph of $(2, -1)$ lie on the line?

36. Does the graph of $(1, -2)$ lie on the line?

Draw a straight line that passes through the points $(3, 4)$ and $(3, -4)$. Then answer the following questions.

37. Is the graph of $(3, 0)$ on this line?

38. Is the graph of $(0, 3)$ on this line?

39. Is there any point on this line with an x-coordinate other than 3?

40. If you extended the line, would it pass through a point with a y-coordinate of 10?

Draw a straight line that passes through the points (3, 4) and (−3, 4). Then answer the following questions.

41. Is the graph of (4, 0) on this line?

42. Is the graph of (0, 4) on this line?

43. Is there any point on this line with a y-coordinate other than 4?

44. If you extended the line, would it pass through a point with an x-coordinate of 10?

Applying the Concepts

45. Fibonacci Sequence The table below gives the first six terms of the Fibonacci sequence as paired data. Use the information in the table to construct a scatter diagram.

Fibonacci Sequence	
Position	Value
1	1
2	1
3	2
4	3
5	5
6	8

46. Triangular Numbers The table below gives the first six terms of the sequence of triangular numbers as paired data. Use the information in the table to construct a scatter diagram.

Triangular Numbers	
Position	Value
1	1
2	3
3	6
4	10
5	15
6	21

47. Non-Camera Phone Sales The table and bar chart show the sales of non-camera phones for the years 2006–2010. Use the information from the table and chart to construct a scatter diagram and a line graph.

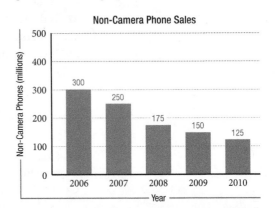

Year	Sales (in Millions)
2006	300
2007	250
2008	175
2009	150
2010	125

48. Camera Phone Sales The table and bar chart show the sales of camera phones from 2006 to 2010. Use the information from the table and chart to construct a scatter diagram and a line graph.

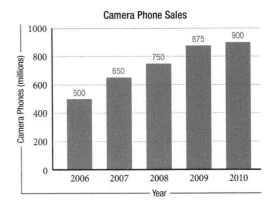

Year	Sales (in Millions)
2006	500
2007	650
2008	750
2009	875
2010	900

49. Hourly Wages Jane takes a job at the local Marcy's department store. Her job pays $8.00 per hour. The graph shows how much Jane earns for working from 0 to 40 hours in a week.

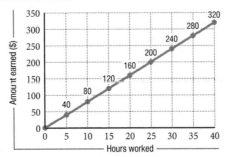

  a. List three ordered pairs that lie on the line graph.

  b. How much will she earn for working 40 hours?

  c. If her check for one week is $240, how many hours did she work?

  d. She works 35 hours one week, but her paycheck before deductions are subtracted out is for $260. Is this correct? Explain.

50. Hourly Wages Judy takes a job at Gigi's boutique. Her job pays $9.00 per hour plus $50 per week in commission. The graph shows how much Judy earns for working from 0 to 40 hours in a week.

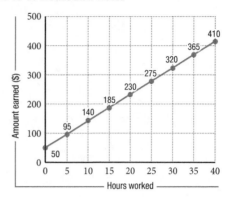

a. List three ordered pairs that lie on the line graph.

b. How much will she earn for working 40 hours?

c. If her check for one week is $230, how many hours did she work?

d. She works 35 hours one week, but her paycheck before deductions are subtracted out is for $365. Is this correct? Explain.

51. Kentucky Derby The line graph gives the monetary bets placed at the Kentucky Derby for specific years. If x represents the year in question and y represents the total wagering for that year, write five ordered pairs that describe the information in the table.

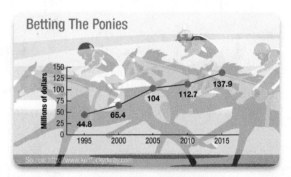

52. Health Care Costs Write 5 ordered pairs that lie on the curve shown below.

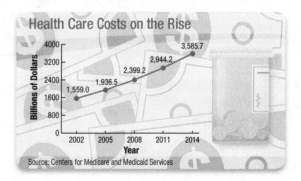

53. Rectangle *ABCD* (Figure 11) has a length of 5 and a width of 3. Point *D* is the ordered pair (7, 2). Find points *A*, *B*, and *C*.

54. Rectangle *ABCD* (Figure 12) has a length of 5 and a width of 3. Point *D* is the ordered pair (−1, 1). Find points *A*, *B*, and *C*.

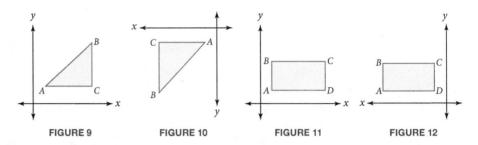

FIGURE 9   FIGURE 10   FIGURE 11   FIGURE 12

Learning Objectives Assessment

The following problems can be used to help assess if you have successfully met the learning objectives for this section.

55. Which of the following ordered pairs appears in the scatter diagram shown below?

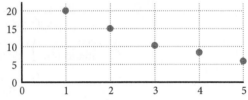

a. (15, 2)   **b.** (10, 4)   **c.** (3, 11)   **d.** (1, 18)

56. The line graph gives the worldwide sales of Apple iPhones for specific years. How many iPhones were sold in 2013?

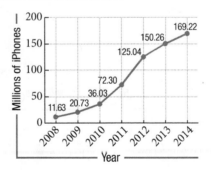

a. 125.04   **b.** 125.04 million

c. 150.26 million   **d.** 150.26

57. Which of the following graphs correctly represents the ordered pair $(-3, 1)$?

a.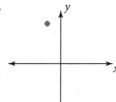

b.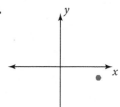

c.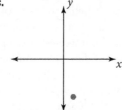

d.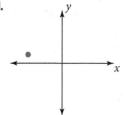

Getting Ready for the Next Section

58. Let $2x + 3y = 6$.

   a. Find x if $y = 4$.   **b.** Find x if $y = -2$.

   c. Find y if $x = 3$.   **d.** Find y if $x = 9$.

59. Let $2x - 5y = 20$.

   a. Find x if $y = 0$.   **b.** Find x if $y = -6$.

   c. Find y if $x = 0$.   **d.** Find y if $x = 5$.

60. Let $y = 2x - 1$.

   a. Find x if $y = 7$.   **b.** Find x if $y = 3$.

   c. Find y if $x = 0$.   **d.** Find y if $x = 5$.

61. Let $y = 3x - 2$.

   a. Find x if $y = 4$.   **b.** Find x if $y = 3$.

   c. Find y if $x = 2$.   **d.** Find y if $x = -3$.

62. Solve $5x + y = 4$ for y.   **63.** Solve $-3x + y = 5$ for y.

64. Solve $3x - 2y = 6$ for y.   **65.** Solve $2x - 3y = 6$ for y.

SPOTLIGHT ON SUCCESS   *Student Instructor CJ*

We are what we repeatedly do.
Excellence, then, is not an act, but a habit.
—Aristotle

Something that has worked for me in college, in addition to completing the assigned homework, is working on some extra problems from each section. Working on these extra problems is a great habit to get into because it helps further your understanding of the material, and you see the many different types of problems that can arise. If you have completed every problem that your book offers, and you still don't feel confident that you have a full grasp of the material, look for more problems. Many problems can be found online or in other books. Your professors may even have some problems that they would suggest doing for extra practice. The biggest benefit to working all the problems in the course's assigned textbook is that often teachers will choose problems either straight from the book or ones similar to problems that were not assigned for tests. Doing this will ensure that you do your best in all your classes.

Graphing Linear Equations in Two Variables

Learning Objectives

In this section, we will learn how to:

1. Determine if an ordered pair is a solution to a linear equation in two variables.

2. Find solutions for a linear equation in two variables.

3. Graph a linear equation in two variables.

4. Graph horizontal and vertical lines.

Introduction

In this section we will begin to investigate equations in two variables. As you will see, equations in two variables have ordered pairs for solutions. We will use the rectangular coordinate system introduced in Section 3.1 to obtain a visual picture of *all* solutions to a linear equation in two variables. The process we use to obtain a visual picture of all solutions to an equation is called *graphing*. The picture itself is called the *graph* of the equation.

Let's begin this section by reviewing the relationship between equations in one variable and their solutions. If we solve the equation $3x - 2 = 10$, the solution is $x = 4$. If we graph this solution, we simply draw the real number line and place a point at the point whose coordinate is 4. The relationship between linear equations in one variable, their solutions, and the graphs of those solutions looks like this:

Equation	Solution	Graph of Solution Set
$3x - 2 = 10$	$x = 4$	(number line with point at 4)

When the equation has one variable, the solution is a single number whose graph is a point on a line.

Solutions to Linear Equations in Two Variables

Consider the equation $2x + y = 3$. The first thing we notice is that there are two variables instead of one. Therefore, a solution to the equation $2x + y = 3$ will be not a single number but a pair of numbers, one for x and one for y, that makes the equation a true statement. One pair of numbers that works is $x = 2$ and $y = -1$, because when we substitute them for x and y in the equation we get a true statement.

$$2(2) + (-1) \stackrel{?}{=} 3$$

$$4 - 1 \stackrel{?}{=} 3$$

$$3 = 3 \qquad \text{A true statement}$$

The pair of numbers $x = 2, y = -1$ is written as $(2, -1)$. As you know from Section 3.1, $(2, -1)$ is called an *ordered pair* because it is a pair of numbers written in a specific order. The first number is always associated with the variable x, and the second number is always associated with the variable y. We call the first number in the ordered pair the *x-coordinate* (or x component) and the second number the *y-coordinate* (or y component) of the ordered pair.

Note If this discussion seems a little long and confusing, you may want to look over some of the examples first and then come back and read this. Remember, it isn't always easy to read material in mathematics. What is important is that you understand what you are doing when you work problems. The reading is intended to assist you in understanding what you are doing. It is important to read everything in the book, but you don't always have to read it in the order it is written.

The ordered pair $(2, -1)$ is not the only solution. Another solution is $(0, 3)$ because when we substitute 0 for x and 3 for y we get

$$2(0) + 3 \overset{?}{=} 3$$

$$0 + 3 \overset{?}{=} 3$$

$$3 = 3 \qquad \text{A true statement}$$

As a matter of fact, for any number we want to use for x, there is another number we can use for y that will make the equation a true statement. There is an infinite number of ordered pairs that satisfy (are solutions to) the equation $2x + y = 3$; we have listed just a couple of them.

VIDEO EXAMPLES

SECTION 3.2

EXAMPLE 1   Which of the ordered pairs $(2, 3)$, $(1, 5)$, and $(-2, -4)$ are solutions to the equation $y = 3x + 2$?

SOLUTION   If an ordered pair is a solution to the equation, then it must satisfy the equation; that is, when the coordinates are used in place of the variables in the equation, the equation becomes a true statement.

Try $(2, 3)$ in $y = 3x + 2$:

$$3 \overset{?}{=} 3(2) + 2$$

$$3 \overset{?}{=} 6 + 2$$

$$3 = 8 \qquad \text{A false statement}$$

Try $(1, 5)$ in $y = 3x + 2$:

$$5 \overset{?}{=} 3(1) + 2$$

$$5 \overset{?}{=} 3 + 2$$

$$5 = 5 \qquad \text{A true statement}$$

Try $(-2, -4)$ in $y = 3x + 2$:

$$-4 \overset{?}{=} 3(-2) + 2$$

$$-4 \overset{?}{=} -6 + 2$$

$$-4 = -4 \qquad \text{A true statement}$$

The ordered pairs $(1, 5)$ and $(-2, -4)$ are solutions to the equation $y = 3x + 2$, and $(2, 3)$ is not.

Now that we know how to determine if a given ordered pair is a solution to a linear equation in two variables, the next question is how can we *find* ordered pairs that will be solutions? The next examples illustrate how this is done.

EXAMPLE 2   Given the equation $2x + 3y = 6$, complete the following ordered pairs so they will be solutions to the equation: $(0, \ )$, $(\ , 1)$, $(3, \ )$.

SOLUTION   To complete the ordered pair $(0, \ )$, we substitute 0 for x in the equation and then solve for y:

$$2(0) + 3y = 6$$

$$3y = 6$$

$$y = 2$$

The ordered pair is $(0, 2)$.

To complete the ordered pair (, 1), we substitute 1 for y in the equation and solve for x:

$$2x + 3(1) = 6$$
$$2x + 3 = 6$$
$$2x = 3$$
$$x = \frac{3}{2}$$

The ordered pair is $\left(\frac{3}{2}, 1\right)$.

To complete the ordered pair (3,), we substitute 3 for x in the equation and solve for y:

$$2(3) + 3y = 6$$
$$6 + 3y = 6$$
$$3y = 0$$
$$y = 0$$

The ordered pair is $(3, 0)$.

Notice in each case that once we have substituted a number in place of one of the variables, the equation becomes a linear equation in one variable. We then use the method explained in Chapter 2 to solve for that variable.

EXAMPLE 3   Complete the following table for the equation $y = 2x - 1$.

x	y
0	
5	
	7
	3

SOLUTION   When $x = 0$, we have   When $x = 5$, we have

$$y = 2(0) - 1 \qquad\qquad y = 2(5) - 1$$
$$y = 0 - 1 \qquad\qquad\quad y = 10 - 1$$
$$y = -1 \qquad\qquad\qquad y = 9$$

When $y = 7$, we have   When $y = 3$, we have

$$7 = 2x - 1 \qquad\qquad 3 = 2x - 1$$
$$8 = 2x \qquad\qquad\quad 4 = 2x$$
$$4 = x \qquad\qquad\qquad 2 = x$$

The completed table is

x	y
0	−1
5	9
4	7
2	3

which means the ordered pairs $(0, -1)$, $(5, 9)$, $(4, 7)$, and $(2, 3)$ are among the solutions to the equation $y = 2x - 1$.

Graphing Linear Equations in Two Variables

We know from Section 3.1 that every ordered pair can be represented graphically as a point on the rectangular coordinate system. To graph a linear equation in two variables, we draw a picture that represents all solutions (ordered pairs) to the equation.

EXAMPLE 4   Graph the solution set for $x + y = 5$.

SOLUTION   We know from our previous work in this section that an infinite number of ordered pairs are solutions to the equation $x + y = 5$. We can't possibly list them all. What we can do is list a few of them and see if there is any pattern to their graphs.

Some ordered pairs that are solutions to $x + y = 5$ are $(0, 5)$, $(2, 3)$, $(3, 2)$, $(5, 0)$. The graph of each is shown in Figure 1.

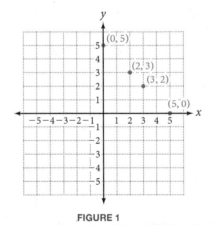

FIGURE 1

As you can see, all four points appear to lie on a line. If we were to continue graphing additional solutions, the gaps between points would start to fill in. Eventually we would have so many points that we would not be able to distinguish one from another, and the resulting image would appear to us as a continuous line.

Note Our ability to graph an equation as we have done in Example 4 is due to the invention of the rectangular coordinate system. The French philosopher René Descartes (1595–1650) is the person usually credited with the invention of the rectangular coordinate system. As a philosopher, Descartes is responsible for the statement "I think, therefore I am." Until Descartes invented his coordinate system in 1637, algebra and geometry were treated as separate subjects. The rectangular coordinate system allows us to connect algebra and geometry by associating geometric shapes with algebraic equations. The study of the relationship between equations in algebra and their associated geometric figures is called *analytic geometry*. The rectangular coordinate system often is referred to as the *Cartesian coordinate system* in honor of Descartes.

So, by drawing a line through these points, we represent the entire solution set for the equation $x + y = 5$. Linear equations in two variables always have graphs that are lines. The graph of the solution set for $x + y = 5$ is shown in Figure 2.

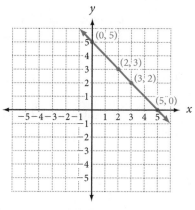

FIGURE 2

Every ordered pair that satisfies $x + y = 5$ has its graph on the line, and any point on the line has coordinates that satisfy the equation. So, there is a one-to-one correspondence between points on the line and solutions to the equation.

Here is the precise definition for a linear equation in two variables.

Note In standard form, we prefer that $a > 0$ and that any fractions have been cleared from the equation by multiplying both sides, if necessary, by the LCD.

(def) DEFINITION   *Linear Equation in Two Variables, Standard Form*

Any equation that can be put in the form $ax + by = c$, where a, b, and c are real numbers and a and b are not both 0, is called a *linear equation in two variables*. The graph of any equation of this form is a straight line (that is why these equations are called "linear"). The form $ax + by = c$ is called *standard form*.

To graph a linear equation in two variables, we simply graph its solution set; that is, we draw a line representing all the points whose coordinates satisfy the equation. Here are the steps to follow.

HOW TO   *Graph a Linear Equation in Two Variables*

Step 1: Find any three ordered pairs that satisfy the equation. This can be done by using a convenient number for one variable and solving for the other variable.

Step 2: Graph the three ordered pairs found in step 1. Actually, we need only two points to graph a straight line. The third point serves as a check. If all three points do not line up, there is a mistake in our work.

Step 3: Draw a line through the three points graphed in step 2.

EXAMPLE 5   Graph the equation $y = 3x - 1$.

SOLUTION   Because $y = 3x - 1$ can be put in the form $ax + by = c$, it is a linear equation in two variables. Hence, the graph of its solution set is a line. We can find some specific solutions by substituting numbers for x and then solving for the corresponding values of y. We are free to choose any numbers for x, so let's use 0, 2, and -1.

<table>
<tr><td>Let $x = 0$:</td><td>$y = 3(0) - 1$</td></tr>
<tr><td></td><td>$y = 0 - 1$</td></tr>
<tr><td></td><td>$y = -1$</td></tr>
</table>

The ordered pair $(0, -1)$ is one solution.

<table>
<tr><td>Let $x = 2$:</td><td>$y = 3(2) - 1$</td></tr>
<tr><td></td><td>$y = 6 - 1$</td></tr>
<tr><td></td><td>$y = 5$</td></tr>
</table>

The ordered pair $(2, 5)$ is a second solution.

<table>
<tr><td>Let $x = -1$:</td><td>$y = 3(-1) - 1$</td></tr>
<tr><td></td><td>$y = -3 - 1$</td></tr>
<tr><td></td><td>$y = -4$</td></tr>
</table>

The ordered pair $(-1, -4)$ is a third solution.

In table form

x	y
0	-1
2	5
-1	-4

Note   It may seem that we have simply picked the numbers 0, 2, and -1 out of the air and used them for x. In fact we have done just that. Could we have used numbers other than these? The answer is yes, we can substitute any number for x; there will always be a value of y to go with it.

Next, we graph the ordered pairs $(0, -1)$, $(2, 5)$, $(-1, -4)$ and draw a line through them.

The line we have drawn in Figure 3 is the graph of $y = 3x - 1$.

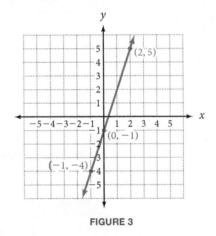

FIGURE 3

EXAMPLE 6   Graph the equation $3x - 2y = 6$.

SOLUTION   It will be easier to find convenient values of x to use in the equation if we first solve the equation for y. To do so, we add $-3x$ to each side, and then we multiply each side by $-\frac{1}{2}$.

$3x - 2y = 6$	Original equation
$-2y = -3x + 6$	Add $-3x$ to each side
$-\frac{1}{2}(-2y) = -\frac{1}{2}(-3x + 6)$	Multiply each side by $-\frac{1}{2}$
$y = \frac{3}{2}x - 3$	Simplify each side

Now, because each value of x will be multiplied by $\frac{3}{2}$, it will be to our advantage to choose values of x that are divisible by 2. That way, we will obtain values of y that do not contain fractions. This time, let's use 0, 2, and 4 for x.

$$\text{When } x = 0: \qquad y = \frac{3}{2}(0) - 3$$

$$y = 0 - 3$$

$$y = -3$$

The ordered pair $(0, -3)$ is one solution.

$$\text{When } x = 2: \qquad y = \frac{3}{2}(2) - 3$$

$$y = 3 - 3$$

$$y = 0$$

The ordered pair $(2, 0)$ is a second solution.

$$\text{When } x = 4: \qquad y = \frac{3}{2}(4) - 3$$

$$y = 6 - 3$$

$$y = 3$$

The ordered pair $(4, 3)$ is a third solution.

Graphing the ordered pairs $(0, -3)$, $(2, 0)$, and $(4, 3)$ and drawing a line through them, we have the graph shown in Figure 4.

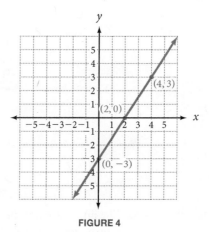

FIGURE 4

Note In Example 6 the values of x we used, 0, 2, and 4 are referred to as convenient values of x because they are easier to work with than some other numbers. For instance, if we let $x = 1$ in the equation $y = \frac{3}{2}x - 3$, we would have to add $\frac{3}{2}$ and -3 to find the corresponding value of y. Not only would the arithmetic be more difficult but also the ordered pair we obtained would have a fraction for its y-coordinate, making it more difficult to graph accurately.

EXAMPLE 7   Graph each of the following lines.

a. $y = \frac{1}{2}x$ **b.** $x = 3$ **c.** $y = -2$

SOLUTION

a. The line $y = \frac{1}{2}x$ passes through the origin because $(0, 0)$ satisfies the equation. To sketch the graph we need at least one more point on the line. When x is 2, we obtain the point $(2, 1)$, and when x is -4, we obtain the point $(-4, -2)$.

The graph of $y = \frac{1}{2}x$ is shown in Figure 5.

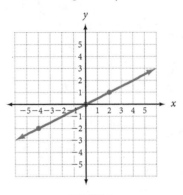

FIGURE 5

b. The line $x = 3$ is the set of all points whose x-coordinate is 3. The variable y does not appear in the equation, so the y-coordinate can be any number. Note that we can write our equation as a linear equation in two variables by writing it as $x + 0y = 3$. Because the product of 0 and y will always be 0, y can be any number.

For instance, if we use -4, 0, and 2 for y, then we obtain the solutions $(3, -4)$, $(3, 0)$, and $(3, 2)$.

The graph of $x = 3$ is shown in Figure 6. As you can see, the graph is a vertical line.

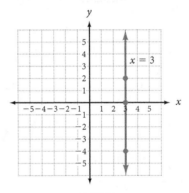

FIGURE 6

c. The line $y = -2$ is the set of all points whose y-coordinate is -2. The variable x does not appear in the equation, so the x-coordinate can be any number. Again, we can write our equation as a linear equation in two variables by writing it as $0x + y = -2$. Because the product of 0 and x will always be 0, x can be any number.

For instance, if we use -3, 0, and 1 for x, then we obtain the solutions $(-3, -2)$, $(0, -2)$, and $(1, -2)$.

The graph of $y = -2$ is shown in Figure 7. As you can see, the graph is a horizontal line.

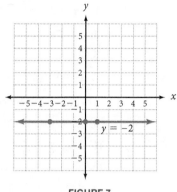

FIGURE 7

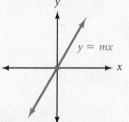 **FACTS FROM GEOMETRY** *Special Equations and Their Graphs*

For the equations below, m, a, and b are real numbers.

Through the Origin

Vertical Line

Horizontal Line

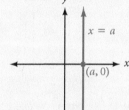

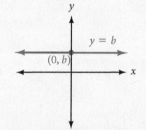

FIGURE 8 Any equation of the form $y = mx$ has a graph that passes through the origin.

FIGURE 9 The graph of an equation of the form $x = a$ is a vertical line passing through the point $(a, 0)$ on the x-axis.

FIGURE 10 The graph of an equation of the form $y = b$ is a horizontal line passing through the point $(0, b)$ on the y-axis.

Getting Ready for Class

After reading through the preceding section, respond in your own words and in complete sentences.

A. How can you tell if an ordered pair is a solution to an equation?

B. How would you find a solution to $y = 3x - 5$?

C. Explain how you would go about graphing the line $x + y = 5$.

D. What kind of equations have horizontal lines for graphs?

Problem Set 3.2

For the following equations, tell which of the given ordered pairs are solutions.

1. $2x - 5y = 10$ $(2, 3), (0, -2), \left(\frac{5}{2}, 1\right)$ **2.** $3x + 7y = 21$ $(0, 3), (7, 0), (1, 2)$

3. $y = 7x - 2$ $(1, 5), (0, -2), (-2, -16)$ **4.** $y = -4x$ $(0, 0), (2, 4), (-3, 12)$

5. $x + y = 0$ $(1, 1), (2, -2), (3, 3)$ **6.** $x - y = 1$ $(0, 1), (0, -1), (1, 2)$

7. $x = 3$ $(3, 0), (3, -3), (5, 3)$ **8.** $y = -4$ $(3, -4), (-4, 4), (0, -4)$

For each equation, complete the given ordered pairs.

9. $2x + y = 6$ $(0,\ ), (\ , 0), (\ , -6)$ **10.** $3x - y = 5$ $(0,\ ), (1,\ ), (\ , 5)$

11. $3x + 4y = 12$ $(0,\ ), (\ , 0), (-4,\ )$ **12.** $5x - 5y = 20$ $(0,\ ), (\ , -2), (1,\ )$

13. $y = 4x - 3$ $(1,\ ), (\ , 0), (5,\ )$ **14.** $y = 3x - 5$ $(\ , 13), (0,\ ), (-2,\ )$

15. $y = 7x - 1$ $(2,\ ), (\ , 6), (0,\ )$ **16.** $y = 8x + 2$ $(3,\ ), (\ , 0), (\ , -6)$

17. $x = -5$ $(\ , 4), (\ , -3), (\ , 0)$ **18.** $y = 2$ $(5,\ ), (-8,\ ), \left(\frac{1}{2},\ \right)$

For each of the following equations, complete the given table.

19. $y = 3x$ **20.** $y = -2x$ **21.** $x + y = 5$ **22.** $x - y = 8$

x	y
1	
-3	
	12
	18

x	y
-4	
0	
	10
	12

x	y
2	
3	
	0
	-4

x	y
0	
4	
	-3
	-2

23. $2x - y = 4$ **24.** $3x - y = 9$ **25.** $y = 6x - 1$ **26.** $y = 5x + 7$

x	y
	0
	2
1	
-3	

x	y
	0
	-9
5	
-4	

x	y
0	
	-7
-3	
	8

x	y
0	
-2	
-4	
	-8

For the following equations, complete the given ordered pairs, and use the results to graph the solution set for the equation.

27. $x + y = 4$ $(0,\ ), (2,\ ), (\ , 0)$ **28.** $x - y = 3$ $(0,\ ), (2,\ ), (\ , 0)$

29. $y = 2x$ $(0,\ ), (-2,\ ), (2,\ )$ **30.** $y = \frac{1}{2}x$ $(0,\ ), (-2,\ ), (2,\ )$

31. $y = \frac{1}{3}x$ $(-3,\ ), (0,\ ), (3,\ )$ **32.** $y = 3x$ $(-2,\ ), (0,\ ), (2,\ )$

33. $y = 2x + 1$ $(0,\ ), (-1,\ ), (1,\ )$ **34.** $y = -2x + 1$ $(0,\ ), (-1,\ ), (1,\ )$

35. $y = 4$ $(0,\ ), (-1,\ ), (2,\ )$ **36.** $x = 3$ $(\ , -2), (\ , 0), (\ , 5)$

37. $y = \frac{1}{2}x + 3$ $(-2,\ ), (0,\ ), (2,\ )$ **38.** $y = \frac{1}{2}x - 3$ $(-2,\ ), (0,\ ), (2,\ )$

39. $y = -\frac{2}{3}x + 1$ $(-3,\ ), (0,\ ), (3,\ )$ **40.** $y = -\frac{2}{3}x - 1$ $(-3,\ ), (0,\ ), (3,\ )$

Solve each equation for y. Then, complete the given ordered pairs, and use them to graph the equation.

41. $2x + y = 3$ $(-1, \ ), (0, \ ), (1, \ )$ **42.** $3x + y = 2$ $(-1, \ ), (0, \ ), (1, \ )$

43. $3x + 2y = 6$ $(0, \ ), (2, \ ), (4, \ )$ **44.** $2x + 3y = 6$ $(0, \ ), (3, \ ), (6, \ )$

45. $-x + 2y = 6$ $(-2, \ ), (0, \ ), (2, \ )$ **46.** $-x + 3y = 6$ $(-3, \ ), (0, \ ), (3, \ )$

47. $4y = 2$ $(-4, \ ), (0, \ ), (4, \ )$ **48.** $2y = -5$ $(-4, \ ), (-2, \ ), (0, \ )$

Find three solutions to each of the following equations, and then graph the solution set.

49. $y = -\dfrac{1}{2}x$ **50.** $y = -2x$ **51.** $y = 3x - 1$ **52.** $y = -3x - 1$

53. $-2x + y = 1$ **54.** $-3x + y = 1$ **55.** $3x + 4y = 8$ **56.** $3x - 4y = 8$

57. $x = -2$ **58.** $y = 3$ **59.** $y = 2$ **60.** $x = -3$

Graph each equation.

61. $y = \dfrac{3}{4}x + 1$ **62.** $y = \dfrac{2}{3}x + 1$ **63.** $y = \dfrac{2}{3}x + \dfrac{2}{3}$ **64.** $y = -\dfrac{3}{4}x + \dfrac{3}{2}$

For each equation in each table below, indicate whether the graph is horizontal (H), or vertical (V), or whether it passes through the origin (O).

65.

Equation	H, V, and/or O
$x = 3$	
$y = 3$	
$y = 3x$	
$y = 0$	

66.

Equation	H, V, and/or O
$x = \dfrac{1}{2}$	
$y = \dfrac{1}{2}$	
$y = \dfrac{1}{2}x$	
$x = 0$	

67.

Equation	H, V, and/or O
$x = -\dfrac{3}{5}$	
$y = -\dfrac{3}{5}$	
$y = -\dfrac{3}{5}x$	
$x = 0$	

68.

Equation	H, V, and/or O
$x = -4$	
$y = -4$	
$y = -4x$	
$y = 0$	

69. Use the graph at the right to complete the table.

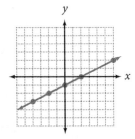

x	y
	-3
-2	
0	
	0
6	

70. Use the graph at the right to complete the table. (*Hint:* Some parts have two answers.)

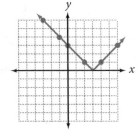

x	y
-3	6
	4
0	3
	1
6	

The next two problems are intended to give you practice reading, and paying attention to, the instructions that accompany the problems you are working. Working these problems is an excellent way to get ready for a test or a quiz.

71. Paying Attention to Instructions Work each problem according to the instructions given.

   a. Solve: $2x + 5 = 10$

   b. Find x when y is 0: $2x + 5y = 10$

   c. Find y when x is 0: $2x + 5y = 10$

   d. Graph: $2x + 5y = 10$

   e. Solve for y: $2x + 5y = 10$

72. Paying Attention to Instructions Work each problem according to the instructions given.

   a. Solve: $x - 2 = 6$

   b. Find x when y is 0: $x - 2y = 6$

   c. Find y when x is 0: $x - 2y = 6$

   d. Graph: $x - 2y = 6$

   e. Solve for y: $x - 2y = 6$

Applying the Concepts

73. Perimeter If the perimeter of a rectangle is 30 inches, then the relationship between the length l and the width w is given by the equation

$$2l + 2w = 30$$

What is the length when the width is 3 inches?

74. Perimeter The relationship between the perimeter P of a square and the length of its side s is given by the formula $P = 4s$. If each side of a square is 5 inches, what is the perimeter? If the perimeter of a square is 28 inches, how long is a side?

75. **Hourly Wages** Janai earns $12 per hour working as a math tutor. We can express the amount she earns each week, y, for working x hours with the equation $y = 12x$. Indicate with a yes or no, which of the following could be one of Janai's paychecks. If you answer no, explain your answer.
    a. $60 for working five hours.
    b. $100 for working nine hours
    c. $80 for working seven hours.
    d. $168 for working 14 hours

76. **Hourly Wages** Erin earns $15 per hour working as a graphic designer. We can express the amount she earns each week, y, for working x hours with the equation $y = 15x$. Indicate with a yes or no which of the following could be one of Erin's paychecks. If you answer no, explain your answer.
    a. $75 for working five hours.
    b. $125 for working nine hours
    c. $90 for working six hours.
    d. $500 for working 35 hours

77. **Depreciation** The equation $V = -45{,}000t + 600{,}000$, can be used to find the value, V, of a small crane at the end of t years, for $0 \leq t \leq 13$.
    a. What is the value of the crane at the end of five years?
    b. When is the crane worth $330,000?
    c. Is it true that the crane will be worth $150,000 after nine years?
    d. How much did the crane cost?

78. **Depreciation** The equation $V = -400t + 2{,}500$, can be used to find the value, V, of a notebook computer at the end of t years, for $0 \leq t \leq 6$.
    a. What is the value of the notebook computer at the end of four years?
    b. When is the notebook computer worth $1,700?
    c. Is it true that the notebook computer will be worth $100 after five years?
    d. How much did the notebook computer cost?

Learning Objectives Assessment

The following problems can be used to help assess if you have successfully met the learning objectives for this section.

79. Which ordered pair is a solution to the equation $3x - 4y = 8$?
    a. $(0, 2)$ b. $(4, -1)$ c. $(-2, 1)$ d. $(-4, -5)$

80. Find an ordered pair with an x-coordinate of 2 that is a solution to $y = -3x + 5$.
    a. $(1, 2)$ b. $(0, 2)$ c. $(2, -1)$ d. $(2, 11)$

81. Which equation has the graph shown in Figure 11?

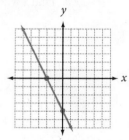

FIGURE 11

    a. $-2x - 4y = 0$ b. $-2x - 4y = 1$
    c. $2x + y = -4$ d. $2x - y = 4$

82. Graph the equation $x = 2$.

a.

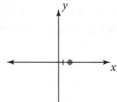

b.

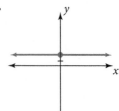

c.

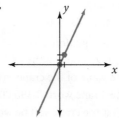

d.

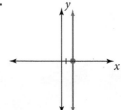

Getting Ready for the Next Section

83. Let $3x + 2y = 6$.

    a. Find x when $y = 0$.   **b.** Find y when $x = 0$.

84. Let $2x - 5y = 10$.

    a. Find x when $y = 0$.   **b.** Find y when $x = 0$.

85. Let $-x + 2y = 4$.

    a. Find x when $y = 0$.   **b.** Find y when $x = 0$.

86. Let $3x - y = 6$.

    a. Find x when $y = 0$.   **b.** Find y when $x = 0$.

87. Let $y = -\dfrac{1}{3}x + 2$.

    a. Find x when $y = 0$.   **b.** Find y when $x = 0$.

88. Let $y = \dfrac{3}{2}x - 3$.

    a. Find x when $y = 0$.   **b.** Find y when $x = 0$.

Learning Objectives

In this section, we will learn how to:

1. Find the x-intercept and y-intercept for a line.

2. Use the intercepts to graph a line.

Introduction

In this section we continue our work with graphing lines by finding the points where a line crosses the axes of our coordinate system. To do so, we use the fact that any point on the x-axis has a y-coordinate of 0 and any point on the y-axis has an x-coordinate of 0. We begin with the following definition.

> **DEFINITION** *x-intercept, y-intercept*
>
> The **x-intercept** of a line is the x-coordinate of the point where the graph crosses the x-axis. The **y-intercept** is defined similarly. It is the y-coordinate of the point where the graph crosses the y-axis.

If the x-intercept is a, then the point $(a, 0)$ lies on the graph. This is true because any point on the x-axis has a y-coordinate of 0.

If the y-intercept is b, then the point $(0, b)$ lies on the graph. This is true because any point on the y-axis has an x-coordinate of 0.

Graphically, the relationship is shown in Figure 1.

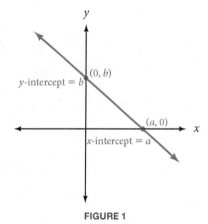

FIGURE 1

EXAMPLE 1   Find the x- and y-intercepts for $3x - 2y = 6$, and then use them to draw the graph.

SOLUTION   To find where the graph crosses the x-axis, we let $y = 0$. (The y-coordinate of any point on the x-axis is 0.)

x-intercept:

When $y = 0$

the equation $3x - 2y = 6$

becomes $3x - 2(0) = 6$

$3x - 0 = 6$

$x = 2$ Multiply each side by $\frac{1}{3}$

The graph crosses the x-axis at $(2, 0)$, which means the x-intercept is 2.

y-intercept:

When $x = 0$

the equation $3x - 2y = 6$

becomes $3(0) - 2y = 6$

$0 - 2y = 6$

$-2y = 6$

$y = -3$ Multiply each side by $-\frac{1}{2}$

The graph crosses the y-axis at $(0, -3)$, which means the y-intercept is -3.

Plotting the x- and y-intercepts and then drawing a line through them, we have the graph of $3x - 2y = 6$, as shown in Figure 2.

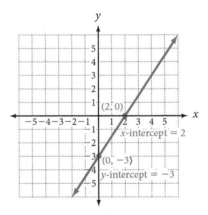

FIGURE 2

EXAMPLE 2 Graph $-x + 2y = 4$ by finding the intercepts and using them to draw the graph.

SOLUTION Again, we find the x-intercept by letting $y = 0$ in the equation and solving for x. Similarly, we find the y-intercept by letting $x = 0$ and solving for y.

x-intercept:

$$\text{When} \qquad\qquad y = 0$$
$$\text{the equation} \qquad -x + 2y = 4$$
$$\text{becomes} \qquad -x + 2(0) = 4$$
$$-x + 0 = 4$$
$$-x = 4$$
$$x = -4 \qquad \text{Multiply each side by } -1$$

The x-intercept is -4, indicating that the point $(-4, 0)$ is on the graph of $-x + 2y = 4$.

y-intercept:

$$\text{When} \qquad\qquad x = 0$$
$$\text{the equation} \qquad -x + 2y = 4$$
$$\text{becomes} \qquad -0 + 2y = 4$$
$$2y = 4$$
$$y = 2 \qquad \text{Multiply each side by } \tfrac{1}{2}$$

The y-intercept is 2, indicating that the point $(0, 2)$ is on the graph of $-x + 2y = 4$.

Plotting the intercepts and drawing a line through them, we have the graph of $-x + 2y = 4$, as shown in Figure 3.

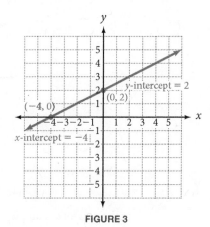

FIGURE 3

Graphing a line by finding the intercepts, as we have done in Examples 1 and 2, is an easy method of graphing if the equation is in standard form $ax + by = c$ and both the numbers a and b divide the number c evenly.

In our next example we use the intercepts to graph a line in which y is given in terms of x.

EXAMPLE 3   Use the intercepts for $y = -\frac{1}{3}x + 2$ to draw its graph.

SOLUTION   Graph the line by finding the intercepts.

***x*-intercept:**

When $\qquad\qquad y = 0$

the equation $\qquad y = -\frac{1}{3}x + 2$

becomes $\qquad\quad 0 = -\frac{1}{3}x + 2$

$$-2 = -\frac{1}{3}x \qquad\qquad\qquad \text{Add } -2 \text{ to each side}$$

$$6 = x \qquad\qquad\qquad\qquad \text{Multiply each side by } -3$$

The *x*-intercept is 6, which means the graph passes through the point $(6, 0)$.

***y*-intercept:**

When $\qquad\qquad x = 0$

the equation $\qquad y = -\frac{1}{3}x + 2$

becomes $\qquad\quad y = -\frac{1}{3}(0) + 2$

$$y = 2$$

The *y*-intercept is 2, which means the graph passes through the point $(0, 2)$.

The graph of $y = -\frac{1}{3}x + 2$ is shown in Figure 4.

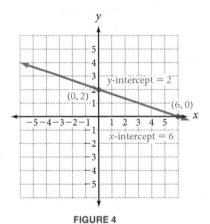

FIGURE 4

In the previous example, notice that the *y*-intercept was given by the constant term in the equation. If the equation is written with the variable *y* isolated, then this will always be true.

Consider the equation $y = ax + b$. To find the y-intercept, we substitute $x = 0$:

When $\qquad x = 0$

the equation $\qquad y = ax + b$

becomes $\qquad y = a(0) + b$

$\qquad\qquad\quad y = b$

We summarize this fact in the following property.

 PROPERTY *y-intercept*

The y-intercept of the line $y = ax + b$ is $y = b$. The graph of the line will cross the y-axis at the point $(0, b)$.

We will investigate this form of a linear equation in more detail in Section 3.5.

EXAMPLES

4. The y-intercept of $y = \dfrac{1}{2}x - 5$ is -5.

5. The y-intercept of $y = 2x + \dfrac{1}{3}$ is $\dfrac{1}{3}$.

6. The y-intercept of $y = 6$ is 6.

7. The y-intercept of $y = 4 - x$ is 4.

Getting Ready for Class

After reading through the preceding section, respond in your own words and in complete sentences.

A. What is the x-intercept for a graph?

B. What is the y-intercept for a graph?

C. How do we find the y-intercept for a line from the equation?

D. How do we graph a line using its intercepts?

Problem Set 3.3

Find the x- and y-intercepts for the following equations. Then use the intercepts to graph each equation.

1. $2x + y = 4$ **2.** $2x + y = 2$ **3.** $-x + y = 3$ **4.** $-x + y = 4$

5. $-x + 2y = 2$ **6.** $-x + 2y = 4$ **7.** $5x + 2y = 10$ **8.** $2x + 5y = 10$

9. $4x - 2y = 8$ **10.** $2x - 4y = 8$ **11.** $-4x + 5y = 20$ **12.** $-5x + 4y = 20$

13. $y = 2x - 6$ **14.** $y = 2x + 6$ **15.** $y = 2x + 2$ **16.** $y = -2x + 2$

17. $y = 2x - 1$ **18.** $y = -2x - 1$ **19.** $y = \frac{1}{2}x + 3$ **20.** $y = \frac{1}{2}x - 3$

21. $y = -\frac{1}{3}x - 2$ **22.** $y = -\frac{1}{3}x + 2$

For each of the following lines the x-intercept and the y-intercept are both 0, which means the graph of each will go through the origin, (0, 0). Graph each line by finding a point on each, other than the origin, and then drawing a line through that point and the origin.

23. $y = -2x$ **24.** $y = \frac{1}{2}x$ **25.** $y = -\frac{1}{3}x$ **26.** $y = -3x$

27. $y = \frac{2}{3}x$ **28.** $y = \frac{3}{2}x$

Complete each table.

29.

Equation	x-intercept	y-intercept
$3x + 4y = 12$		
$3x + 4y = 4$		
$3x + 4y = 3$		
$3x + 4y = 2$		

30.

Equation	x-intercept	y-intercept
$-2x + 3y = 6$		
$-2x + 3y = 3$		
$-2x + 3y = 2$		
$-2x + 3y = 1$		

31.

Equation	x-intercept	y-intercept
$x - 3y = 2$		
$y = \frac{1}{3}x - \frac{2}{3}$		
$x - 3y = 0$		
$y = \frac{1}{3}x$		

32.

Equation	x-intercept	y-intercept
$x - 2y = 1$		
$y = \frac{1}{2}x - \frac{1}{2}$		
$x - 2y = 0$		
$y = \frac{1}{2}x$		

Find the y-intercept for each of the following lines.

33. $y = 2x + 5$

34. $y = 3x - 1$

35. $y = \frac{1}{3}x - \frac{2}{3}$

36. $y = \frac{1}{4}x + \frac{5}{4}$

37. $y = 4 - x$

38. $y = 6 - 5x$

39. $y = \frac{7x + 1}{2}$

40. $y = \frac{2x + 3}{5}$

The next two problems are intended to give you practice reading, and paying attention to, the instructions that accompany the problems you are working. Working these problems is an excellent way to get ready for a test or a quiz.

41. Paying Attention to Instructions Work each problem according to the instructions given.

    a. Solve: $2x - 3 = -3$

    b. Find the x-intercept: $2x - 3y = -3$

    c. Find y when x is 0: $2x - 3y = -3$

    d. Graph: $2x - 3y = -3$

    e. Solve for y: $2x - 3y = -3$

42. Paying Attention to Instructions Work each problem according to the instructions given.

    a. Solve: $3x - 4 = -4$

    b. Find the y-intercept: $3x - 4y = -4$

    c. Find x when y is 0: $3x - 4y = -4$

    d. Graph: $3x - 4y = -4$

    e. Solve for y: $3x - 4y = -4$

From the graphs below, find the x- and y-intercepts for each line.

43.

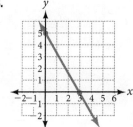

44.

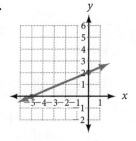

45.

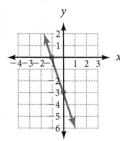

46.

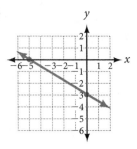

47. Graph the line that passes through the point $(-4, 4)$ and has an x-intercept of -2. What is the y-intercept of this line?

48. Graph the line that passes through the point $(-3, 4)$ and has a y-intercept of 3. What is the x-intercept of this line?

49. A line passes through the point $(1, 4)$ and has a y-intercept of 3. Graph the line and name its x-intercept.

50. A line passes through the point $(3, 4)$ and has an x-intercept of 1. Graph the line and name its y-intercept.

51. Graph the line that passes through the points $(-2, 5)$ and $(5, -2)$. What are the x- and y-intercepts for this line?

52. Graph the line that passes through the points $(5, 3)$ and $(-3, -5)$. What are the x- and y-intercepts for this line?

53. Use the graph at the right to complete the following table.

x	y
-2	
0	
	0
	-2

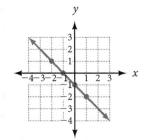

54. Use the graph at the right to complete the following table.

x	y
-2	
	0
	6

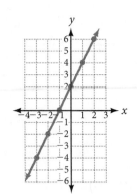

55. The vertical line $x = 3$ has only one intercept. Graph $x = 3$, and name its intercept. [Remember, ordered pairs (x, y) that are solutions to the equation $x = 3$ are ordered pairs with an x-coordinate of 3 and any y-coordinate.]

56. Graph the vertical line $x = -2$. Then name its intercept.

57. The horizontal line $y = 4$ has only one intercept. Graph $y = 4$, and name its intercept. [Ordered pairs (x, y) that are solutions to the equation $y = 4$ are ordered pairs with a y-coordinate of 4 and any x-coordinate.]

58. Graph the horizontal line $y = -3$. Then name its intercept.

Applying the Concepts

59. Complementary Angles The following diagram shows sunlight hitting the ground. Angle α (*alpha*) is called the angle of inclination, and angle θ (*theta*) is called the angle of incidence. As the sun moves across the sky, the values of these angles change. Assume that $\alpha + \theta = 90$, where both α and θ are in degrees. Graph this equation on a coordinate system where the horizontal axis is the α-axis and the vertical axis is the θ-axis. Find the intercepts first, and limit your graph to the first quadrant only.

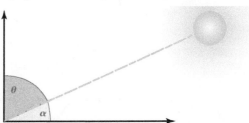

60. Light When light comes into contact with an impenetrable object, such as a thick piece of wood or metal, it is reflected or absorbed, but not transmitted, as shown in the following diagram. If we let R represent the percentage of light reflected and A the percentage of light absorbed by a surface, then the relationship between R and A is $R + A = 100$. Graph this equation on a coordinate system where the horizontal axis is the A-axis and the vertical axis is the R-axis. Find the intercepts first, and limit your graph to the first quadrant.

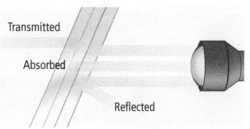

Learning Objectives Assessment

The following problems can be used to help assess if you have successfully met the learning objectives for this section.

61. Find the x-intercept of the line $3x - 4y = 8$.

    a. $\dfrac{3}{8}$ **b.** -2 **c.** 3 **d.** $\dfrac{8}{3}$

62. Find the y-intercept of the line $y = 9x - 4$.

    a. $\dfrac{4}{9}$ **b.** $\dfrac{9}{4}$ **c.** -4 **d.** 9

63. Graph the line having an x-intercept of -3 and a y-intercept of 2.

    a.

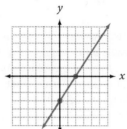

    b.

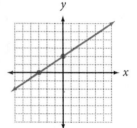

    c.

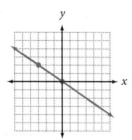

    d.

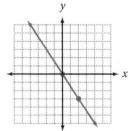

Getting Ready for the Next Section

64. Evaluate.

    a. $\dfrac{5 - 2}{3 - 1}$ **b.** $\dfrac{2 - 5}{1 - 3}$

65. Evaluate.

    a. $\dfrac{-4 - 1}{5 - (-2)}$ **b.** $\dfrac{1 + 4}{-2 - 5}$

66. Evaluate the following expressions when $x = 3$, and $y = 5$.

    a. $\dfrac{y - 2}{x - 1}$ **b.** $\dfrac{2 - y}{1 - x}$

67. Evaluate the following expressions when $x = -2$, and $y = 1$.

    a. $\dfrac{-4 - y}{5 - x}$ **b.** $\dfrac{y + 4}{x - 5}$

Learning Objectives

In this section, we will learn how to:

1. Use two ordered pairs to find the slope of a line.

2. Graph a line given a point and the slope.

3. Interpret slope as a rate of change.

4. Determine if two lines are parallel or perpendicular.

Introduction

In defining the slope of a line, we are looking for a number to associate with the line that does two things. First of all, we want the slope of a line to measure the "steepness" of the line; that is, in comparing two lines, the slope of the steeper line should have the larger absolute value. Second, we want a line that *rises* going from left to right to have a *positive* slope. We want a line that *falls* going from left to right to have a *negative* slope. (A line that neither rises nor falls going from left to right must, therefore, have 0 slope.) These are illustrated in Figure 1.

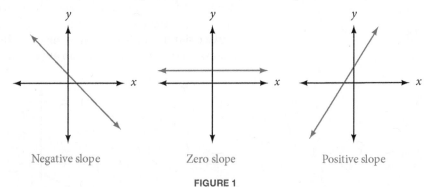

Negative slope   Zero slope   Positive slope

FIGURE 1

Slope

Suppose we know the coordinates of two points on a line. Because we are trying to develop a general formula for the slope of a line, we will use general points—call the two points $P_1(x_1, y_1)$ and $P_2(x_2, y_2)$. They represent the coordinates of any two different points on our line. We define the *slope* of our line to be the ratio of the vertical change to the horizontal change as we move from point (x_1, y_1) to point (x_2, y_2) on the line. (See Figure 2.)

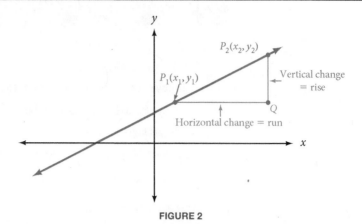

FIGURE 2

We call the vertical change the *rise* in the graph and the horizontal change the *run* in the graph. The slope, then, is

$$\text{Slope} = \frac{\text{vertical change}}{\text{horizontal change}} = \frac{\text{rise}}{\text{run}}$$

We would like to have a numerical value to associate with the rise in the graph and a numerical value to associate with the run in the graph. A quick study of Figure 2 shows that the coordinates of point Q must be (x_2, y_1), because Q is directly below point P_2 and right across from point P_1. We can draw our diagram again in the manner shown in Figure 3. It is apparent from this graph that the rise can be expressed as $(y_2 - y_1)$ and the run as $(x_2 - x_1)$.

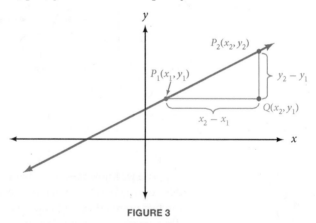

FIGURE 3

We usually denote the slope of a line by the letter m. Here is a formal definition of slope.

DEFINITION   *slope*

If points (x_1, y_1) and (x_2, y_2) are any two different points, then the ***slope*** of the line on which they lie is

$$\text{Slope} = m = \frac{\text{rise}}{\text{run}} = \frac{y_2 - y_1}{x_2 - x_1}$$

This definition of the *slope* of a line does just what we want it to do. If the line rises going from left to right, the slope will be positive. If the line falls from left to right, the slope will be negative. Also, the steeper the line, the larger absolute value the slope will have.

EXAMPLE 1   Find the slope of the line between the points $(1, 2)$ and $(3, 5)$.

SOLUTION   We can let

$$(x_1, y_1) = (1, 2)$$

and

$$(x_2, y_2) = (3, 5)$$

then

$$m = \frac{y_2 - y_1}{x_2 - x_1} = \frac{5 - 2}{3 - 1} = \frac{3}{2}$$

The slope is $\frac{3}{2}$. For every vertical change of 3 units, there will be a corresponding horizontal change of 2 units. (See Figure 4.)

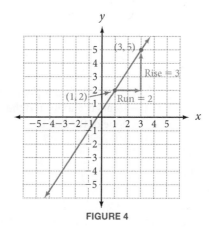

FIGURE 4

EXAMPLE 2   Find the slope of the line through $(-2, 1)$ and $(5, -4)$.

SOLUTION   It makes no difference which ordered pair we call (x_1, y_1) and which we call (x_2, y_2).

$$\text{Slope} = m = \frac{y_2 - y_1}{x_2 - x_1} = \frac{-4 - 1}{5 - (-2)} = -\frac{5}{7}$$

The slope is $-\frac{5}{7}$. Every vertical change of -5 units (down 5 units) is accompanied by a horizontal change of 7 units (to the right 7 units). (See Figure 5.)

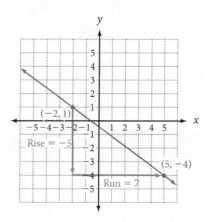

FIGURE 5

EXAMPLE 3   Find the slope of the line shown in Figure 6.

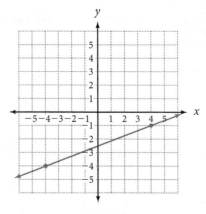

FIGURE 6

SOLUTION From Figure 6, we can see that the vertical change between the two points is 3 units and the horizontal change is 8 units (see Figure 7). Therefore, the slope of the line is

$$m = \frac{\text{rise}}{\text{run}} = \frac{3}{8}$$

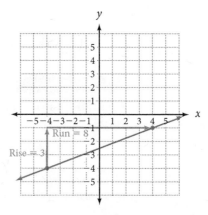

FIGURE 7

Graphing with Slope

| EXAMPLE 4 | Graph the line with slope $-\frac{3}{2}$ passing through the point $(1, 1)$.

SOLUTION   We begin by plotting the point $(1, 1)$, as shown in Figure 8.

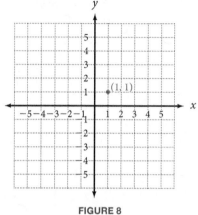

FIGURE 8

There are many lines that pass through the point shown in Figure 8, but only one of those lines has a slope of $-\frac{3}{2}$. The slope, $-\frac{3}{2}$, can be thought of as the rise in the graph divided by the run in the graph. Because the slope is negative, we can associate the negative with either the rise or the run (but not both).

If we think of the slope as $\frac{-3}{2}$, then the rise is -3 and the run is 2. Therefore, if we start at the point $(1, 1)$ and move 3 units down (that's a rise of -3) and then 2 units to the right (a run of 2), we will be at another point on the graph. Figure 9 shows that the point we reach by doing so is the point $(3, -2)$, and shows the resulting line passing through both points.

Or, we can think of the slope as $\frac{3}{-2}$. Then the rise is 3 and the run is -2. If we start at the point $(1, 1)$ and move 3 units up (a rise of 3) and then 2 units left (a run of -2), we will reach another point on the graph at $(-1, 4)$. Figure 10 shows this point and the resulting line.

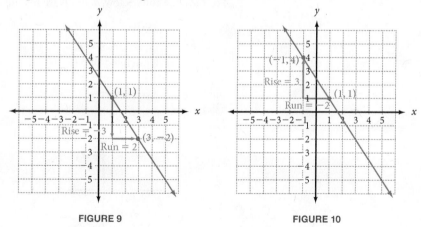

FIGURE 9   **FIGURE 10**

As you can see, the lines in Figures 9 and 10 are identical. It makes no difference whether we choose to associate the negative sign with the rise or the run. We will get the same line in either case.

EXAMPLE 5   Find the slope of the line containing $(3, -1)$ and $(3, 4)$.

SOLUTION   Using the definition for slope, we have

$$m = \frac{y_2 - y_1}{x_2 - x_1} = \frac{4 - (-1)}{3 - 3} = \frac{5}{0}$$

The expression $\frac{5}{0}$ is undefined; that is, there is no real number to associate with it. In this case, we say the line *has an undefined slope*.

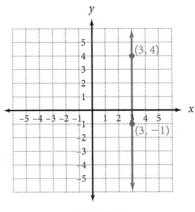

FIGURE 11

The graph of the line is shown in Figure 11. A line with an undefined slope is a vertical line.

The following summary reminds us that all horizontal lines have equations of the form $y = b$ and slopes of 0. Because they cross the y-axis at $(0, b)$, the y-intercept is b; there is no x-intercept. Vertical lines have an undefined slope and equations of the form $x = a$. Each will have an x-intercept at $(a, 0)$ and no y-intercept.

> **FACTS FROM GEOMETRY**   *Special Equations and Their Graphs, Slopes, and Intercepts*
>
> For the equations below, a and b are real numbers.
>
> | **Vertical Line** | **Horizontal Line** |
> |---|---|
> | Equation: $x = a$ | Equation: $y = b$ |
> | Undefined slope | Slope = 0 |
> | x-intercept = a | No x-intercept |
> | No y-intercept | y-intercept = b |
>
>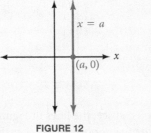
>
> **FIGURE 12**
>
>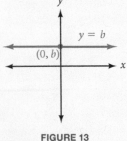
>
> **FIGURE 13**

Slope as Rate of Change

If two quantities have a relationship that can be described by a linear equation, then we can interpret the slope of the line as a *rate of change* between these two quantities. Our next example illustrates how this is done.

EXAMPLE 6   The graph in Figure 14 shows the rise in U.S. retail e-commerce sales over a five-year period, which is approximately linear. Use the graph to find the slope of the line, and then interpret the slope as a rate of change.

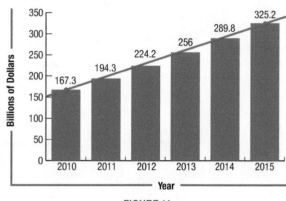

FIGURE 14

SOLUTION Using the points (2010, 167.3) and (2015, 325.2), we have

$$m = \frac{\text{rise}}{\text{run}} = \frac{325.2 - 167.3}{2015 - 2010} = \frac{157.9}{5} = 31.58$$

We see that U.S. retail e-commerce sales increased by $157.9 billion dollars over the five-year period. This means that, on average, the U.S. retail e-commerce sales are increasing at a rate of 31.58 billion dollars per year during the five-year period between 2010 and 2015.

Slopes of Parallel and Perpendicular Lines

In geometry, we call lines in the same plane that never intersect parallel. For two lines to be nonintersecting, they must rise or fall at the same rate. In other words, two lines are *parallel* if and only if they have the *same slope*.

Although it is not as obvious, it is also true that two nonvertical lines are *perpendicular* if and only if the *product of their slopes is* −1. This is the same as saying their slopes are negative reciprocals.

DEFINITION   *parallel and perpendicular lines*

Two distinct, nonvertical lines are *parallel* if they have the same slope, or *perpendicular* if the product of their slopes is −1.

We can state these facts with symbols as follows: If line l_1 has slope m_1 and line l_2 has slope m_2, then

$$l_1 \text{ is parallel to } l_2 \Leftrightarrow m_1 = m_2$$
$$\text{and}$$
$$l_1 \text{ is perpendicular to } l_2 \Leftrightarrow m_1 \cdot m_2 = -1 \text{ or } \left(m_1 = -\frac{1}{m_2} \right)$$

For example, if a line has a slope of $\frac{2}{3}$, then any line parallel to it has a slope of $\frac{2}{3}$. Any line perpendicular to it has a slope of $-\frac{3}{2}$ (the negative reciprocal of $\frac{2}{3}$).

Although we cannot give a formal proof of the relationship between the slopes of perpendicular lines at this level of mathematics, we can offer some justification for the relationship. Figure 15 shows the graphs of two lines. One of the lines has a slope of $\frac{2}{3}$; the other has a slope of $-\frac{3}{2}$. As you can see, the lines are perpendicular.

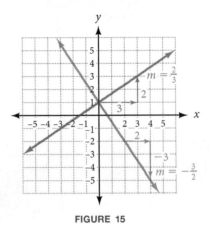

FIGURE 15

Getting Ready for Class

After reading through the preceding section, respond in your own words and in complete sentences.

A. What is the slope of a line?

B. Describe how to obtain the slope of a line if you know the coordinates of two points on the line.

C. Describe how you would graph a line from its slope and a point.

D. How do we know if two lines are parallel or perpendicular?

Find the slope of the line through the following pairs of points. Then plot each pair of points, draw a line through them, and indicate the rise and run in the graph in the same manner shown in Examples 1 and 2.

1. $(2, 1), (4, 4)$ **2.** $(3, 1), (5, 4)$ **3.** $(1, 4), (5, 2)$

4. $(1, 3), (5, 2)$ **5.** $(1, -3), (4, 2)$ **6.** $(2, -3), (5, 2)$

7. $(-3, -2), (1, 3)$ **8.** $(-3, -1), (1, 4)$ **9.** $(-3, 2), (3, -2)$

10. $(-3, 3), (3, -1)$ **11.** $(2, -5), (3, -2)$ **12.** $(2, -4), (3, -1)$

13. $(4, -5), (4, 1)$ **14.** $(-1, 4), (3, 4)$ **15.** $(-4, -2), (-1, -2)$

16. $(-2, 0), (-2, 5)$ **17.** $(0, 0) (-3, -1)$ **18.** $(0, 0), (-3, 2)$

Find the slope for each line.

19.

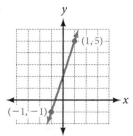

20.

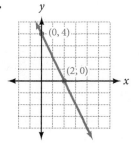

21.

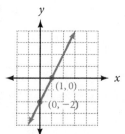

22.

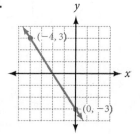

In each of the following problems, graph the line having the given slope and passing through the given point.

23. $m = 2, (0, 1)$ **24.** $m = -2, (0, 4)$ **25.** $m = \frac{2}{3}, (1, 0)$

26. $m = \frac{3}{4}, (-2, 0)$ **27.** $m = \frac{3}{2}, (-1, -3)$ **28.** $m = \frac{4}{3}, (-2, 1)$

29. $m = -\frac{4}{3}, (1, 1)$ **30.** $m = -\frac{3}{5}, (-3, -1)$ **31.** $m = 3, (-1, -4)$

32. $m = -3, (-2, -2)$ **33.** $m = -\frac{1}{5}, (0, 0)$ **34.** $m = \frac{1}{4}, (0, 0)$

35. Graph the line that has an x-intercept of 3 and a y-intercept of -2. What is the slope of this line?

36. Graph the line that has an x-intercept of 2 and a y-intercept of -3. What is the slope of this line?

37. Graph the line with x-intercept 4 and y-intercept 2. What is the slope of this line?

38. Graph the line with x-intercept -4 and y-intercept -2. What is the slope of this line?

39. Graph the line $y = 2x - 3$, then name the slope and y-intercept by looking at the graph.

40. Graph the line $y = -2x + 3$, then name the slope and y-intercept by looking at the graph.

41. Graph the line $y = \frac{1}{2}x + 1$, then name the slope and y-intercept by looking at the graph.

42. Graph the line $y = -\frac{1}{2}x - 2$, then name the slope and y-intercept by looking at the graph.

For each equation in each table, give the slope of the graph.

43.

Equation	Slope
$x = 3$	
$y = 3$	
$y = 3x$	

44.

Equation	Slope
$y = \frac{3}{2}$	
$x = \frac{3}{2}$	
$y = \frac{3}{2}x$	

45.

Equation	Slope
$y = -\frac{2}{3}$	
$x = -\frac{2}{3}$	
$y = -\frac{2}{3}x$	

46.

Equation	Slope
$x = -2$	
$y = -2$	
$y = -2x$	

If a line has the slope that is given, state the slope of a line that is (a) parallel to this line, and (b) perpendicular to this line.

47. $m = \dfrac{2}{3}$ **48.** $m = -\dfrac{3}{2}$ **49.** $m = -\dfrac{1}{4}$ **50.** $m = \dfrac{1}{5}$

51. $m = 2$ **52.** $m = -3$ **53.** $m = 0$ **54.** Undefined slope

Determine if the lines passing through the given pairs of points are parallel, perpendicular or neither.

55. $(-3, 2)$ and $(6, 8)$, $(0, -1)$ and $(3, 1)$

56. $(-4, -4)$ and $(2, 5)$, $(-2, 0)$ and $(0, -3)$

57. $(-2, 6)$ and $(2, 4)$, $(-3, -5)$ and $(1, 3)$

58. $(0, -1)$ and $(4, 7)$, $(-4, -5)$ and $(-1, 1)$

59. $(-4, 0)$ and $(1, 5)$, $(0, -4)$ and $(2, -6)$

60. $(0, -2)$ and $(2, 6)$, $(-4, 1)$ and $(4, -1)$

61. Find y if the line through $(4, 2)$ and $(6, y)$ has a slope of 2.

62. Find y if the line through $(1, y)$ and $(7, 3)$ has a slope of 6.

Applying the Concepts

63. **Garbage Production** The table and completed line graph give the annual production of garbage in the United States for some specific years.
   a. Find the slope of each of the four line segments, A, B, C, and D.
   b. Interpret the slope of line segment A as a rate of change.

Year	Garbage (millions of tons)
1960	88
1970	121
1980	152
1990	205
2000	224

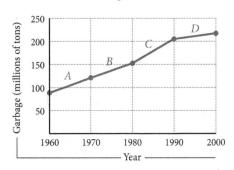

64. **Grass Height** The table and completed line graph give the growth of a certain plant species over time.
   a. Find the slopes of the line segments labeled A, B, and C.
   b. Interpret the slope of segment C as a rate of change.

Day	Plant Height
0	0
2	1
4	3
6	6
8	13
10	23

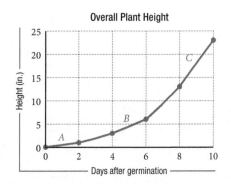

65. **Non-Camera Phone Sales** The table and line graph here each show the projected non-camera phone sales each year from 2006 to 2010.
   a. Find the slope of each of the three line segments, A, B, and C.
   b. Interpret the slope of segment B as a rate of change.

Year	Sales (in millions)
2006	300
2007	250
2008	175
2009	150
2010	125

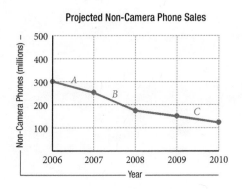

66. Camera Phone Sales The table and line graph here show the projected sales of camera phones from 2006 to 2010.

   a. Find the slopes of line segments A, B, and C.

   b. Interpret the slope of segment C as a rate of change.

Year	Sales (in millions)
2006	500
2007	650
2008	750
2009	875
2010	900

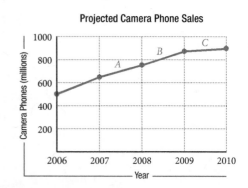

Projected Camera Phone Sales

Learning Objectives Assessment

The following problems can be used to help assess if you have successfully met the learning objectives for this section.

67. Find the slope of the line passing through the points $(-3, 2)$ and $(1, -4)$.

   a. $-\dfrac{3}{2}$ **b.** 1 **c.** $\dfrac{1}{2}$ **d.** $-\dfrac{2}{3}$

68. Sketch the graph of the line with slope 3 and passing through the point $(2, 1)$.

   a.

   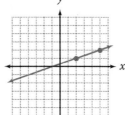

   b.

   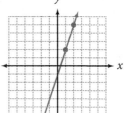

   c.

   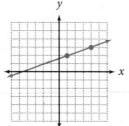

   d.

   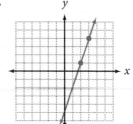

69. The table below shows the federal minimum wage from two past years. Find the slope of the line passing through these two points and then interpret the slope as a rate of change.

Year	Minimum Wage
1979	$2.90
2009	$7.25

    a. The federal minimum wage increased at a rate of $6.90 per year from 1979 to 2009.

    b. The federal Minimum wage increased at a rate of $4.35 per year from 1979 to 2009.

    c. The federal minimum wage increased at a rate of 0.145 years per dollar from 1979 to 2009.

    d. The federal minimum wage increased at a rate of 14.5 cents per year from 1979 to 2009.

70. Find the slope of a line that would be perpendicular to the line passing through $(-1, -3)$ and $(2, 3)$.

    a. $-\dfrac{1}{2}$ **b.** 2 **c.** -2 **d.** $\dfrac{1}{2}$

Getting Ready for the Next Section

Solve each equation for y.

71. $-2x + y = 4$ **72.** $-4x + y = -2$ **73.** $2x + y = 3$

74. $3x + 2y = 6$ **75.** $4x - 5y = 20$ **76.** $-2x - 5y = 10$

SPOTLIGHT ON SUCCESS   *Student Instructor Julieta*

Success is no accident. It is hard work, perseverance, learning, studying, sacrifice, and most of all, love of what you are doing or learning to do.
—*Pelé*

Success really is no accident, nor is it something that happens overnight. Sure you may be sitting there wondering why you don't understand a certain lesson or topic, but you are not alone. There are many others who are sitting in your exact position. Throughout my first year in college (and more specifically in Calculus I) I learned that it is normal for any student to feel stumped every now and then. The students who do well are the ones who keep working, even when they are confused.

Pelé wasn't just born with all that legendary talent. It took dedication and hard work as well. Don't ever feel bad because there's something you don't understand—it's not worth it. Stick with it 100% and just keep working problems; I'm sure you'll be successful with whatever you set your mind to achieve in this course.

Slope-Intercept Form

Learning Objectives

In this section, we will learn how to:

1. Use slope-intercept form to find the slope and *y*-intercept of a line.
2. Use slope-intercept form to graph a line.
3. Use slope-intercept form to find the equation of a line.

Introduction

To this point in the chapter, most of the problems we have worked have used the equation of a line to find different types of information about the line. For instance, given the equation of a line, we can find points on the line, the graph of the line, the intercepts, and the slope of the line. In this section we reverse things somewhat and begin to move in the other direction; we will use information about a line, such as its slope and *y*-intercept, to find the equation of a line.

The Slope-Intercept Form of a Line

EXAMPLE 1   Find the slope and *y*-intercept of the line $y = \frac{3}{2}x + 1$.

SOLUTION   From our work in Section 3.3, we know that the *y*-intercept is given by the constant term when an equation is in this form. Therefore, the *y*-intercept is 1 and the point (0, 1) lies on the line.

To find the slope, we need another point on the line. Using $x = 2$, we have

$$y = \frac{3}{2}(2) + 1 = 3 + 1 = 4$$

So (2, 4) is a second point on the line. Now we can find the slope.

$$m = \frac{y_2 - y_1}{x_2 - x_1} = \frac{4 - 1}{2 - 0} = \frac{3}{2}$$

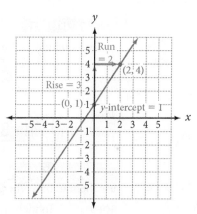

FIGURE 1

The graph of the line is shown in Figure 1.

What is interesting and useful about the equation from the previous example is that the coefficient of x is the slope of the line. It is no coincidence that it turned out this way. Whenever an equation has the form $y = mx + b$, the graph is always a line with slope m and y-intercept b.

To see that this is true in general, suppose we know that the slope of a line is m and the y-intercept is b. Because the y-intercept is b, then the point $(0, b)$ is on the line. If (x, y) is any other point on the line (see Figure 2), then we apply our slope formula to get

$$\frac{y - b}{x - 0} = m \qquad \text{Slope} = \frac{\text{vertical change}}{\text{horizontal change}}$$

$$\frac{y - b}{x} = m \qquad x - 0 = x$$

$$y - b = mx \qquad \text{Multiply each side by } x$$

$$y = mx + b \qquad \text{Add } b \text{ to each side}$$

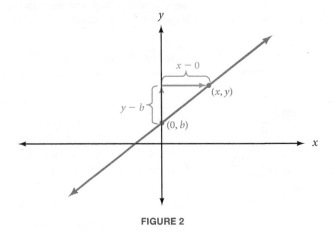

FIGURE 2

Here is a summary of what we have just found.

> **RULE** *Slope-Intercept Form of the Equation of a Line*
>
> The equation of the line with slope m and y-intercept b is always given by
>
> $$y = mx + b$$

Graphing with Slope-Intercept Form

EXAMPLE 2   Find the slope and y-intercept for $-2x + y = -4$. Then, use them to draw the graph.

SOLUTION   To identify the slope and y-intercept from the equation, the equation must be in the form $y = mx + b$ (slope-intercept form). To write our equation in this form, we must solve the equation for y. To do so, we simply add $2x$ to each side of the equation.

$$-2x + y = -4 \qquad \text{Original equation}$$

$$y = 2x - 4 \qquad \text{Add } 2x \text{ to each side}$$

The equation is now in slope-intercept form, so the slope must be 2 and the y-intercept must be -4. The graph, therefore, crosses the y-axis at $(0, -4)$. Because the slope is 2, we can let the rise = 2 and the run = 1 and find a second point on the graph. The graph is shown in Figure 3.

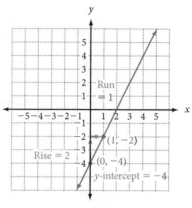

FIGURE 3

EXAMPLE 3   Find the slope and y-intercept for $3x - 2y = 6$. Then use them to draw the graph.

SOLUTION   To find the slope and y-intercept from the equation, we can write the equation in the form $y = mx + b$. This means we must solve the equation $3x - 2y = 6$ for y.

$$3x - 2y = 6 \qquad \text{Original equation}$$

$$-2y = -3x + 6 \qquad \text{Add } -3x \text{ to each side}$$

$$-\frac{1}{2}(-2y) = -\frac{1}{2}(-3x + 6) \qquad \text{Multiply each side by } -\frac{1}{2}$$

$$y = \frac{3}{2}x - 3 \qquad \text{Simplify each side}$$

Now that the equation is written in slope-intercept form, we can identify the slope as $\frac{3}{2}$ and the y-intercept as -3. The graph is shown in Figure 4.

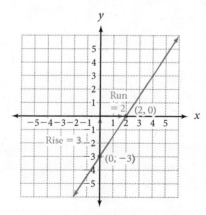

FIGURE 4

Before we move on to finding equations of lines, here is a summary of the methods we have discussed so far for sketching the graph of a line.

Methods of Graphing Lines

1. Substitute convenient values of x into the equation, and find the corresponding values of y. We used this method first for equations like $y = 2x - 3$. To use this method for equations that looked like $2x - 3y = 6$, we first solved them for y.

2. Find the x- and y-intercepts. This method works best for equations of the form $3x + 2y = 6$ where the numbers in front of x and y divide the constant term evenly.

3. Find the slope and y-intercept. This method works best when the equation has the form $y = mx + b$ and b is an integer.

Finding the Equation of a Line

EXAMPLE 4   Find the equation of the line with slope $-\frac{4}{3}$ and y-intercept 5. Then, graph the line.

SOLUTION   Substituting $m = -\frac{4}{3}$ and $b = 5$ into the equation $y = mx + b$, we have

$$y = -\frac{4}{3}x + 5$$

Finding the equation from the slope and y-intercept is just that easy. If the slope is m and the y-intercept is b, then the equation is always $y = mx + b$.

Because the y-intercept is 5, the graph goes through the point $(0, 5)$. To find a second point on the graph, we start at $(0, 5)$ and move 4 units down (that's a rise of -4) and 3 units to the right (a run of 3). The point we reach is $(3, 1)$. Drawing a line that passes through $(0, 5)$ and $(3, 1)$, we have the graph of our equation. (Note that we could also let the rise $= 4$ and the run $= -3$ and obtain the same graph.) The graph is shown in Figure 5.

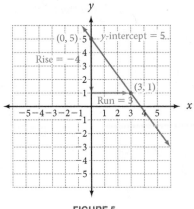

FIGURE 5

EXAMPLE 5   Find the equation of the line with slope -2 that passes through the point $(-4, 3)$. Write the answer in standard form.

SOLUTION We can find the equation using slope-intercept form $y = mx + b$. Because the point $(-4, 3)$ is not on the y-axis, it is not a y-intercept. We are not given the value of b. However we can substitute $x = -4$, $y = 3$, and $m = -2$ into $y = mx + b$ and solve for b.

Using $(x, y) = (-4, 3)$ and $m = -2$

in $y = mx + b$ Slope-intercept form

gives us $3 = -2(-4) + b$ Substitute values

                $3 = 8 + b$ Multiply

                $-5 = b$ Add -8 to both sides

So, the slope-intercept form of the line is $y = -2x - 5$. To write the equation in standard form, we simply add $2x$ to both sides to obtain $2x + y = -5$.

EXAMPLE 6   Find the equation of the line passing through the point $(2, 5)$ and perpendicular to the line $3x + 4y = 12$. Write the answer in slope-intercept form.

SOLUTION First, we must find the slope of the line $3x + 4y = 12$. To do so, we isolate y in order to write the equation in slope-intercept form.

$$3x + 4y = 12$$ Original equation

$$4y = -3x + 12$$ Add $-3x$ to both sides

$$y = -\frac{3}{4}x + 3$$ Multiply each side by $\frac{1}{4}$

The slope of this line is $-\frac{3}{4}$. Therefore, a line perpendicular to this line must have a slope of $\frac{4}{3}$. We can now find the equation of the line that was asked for using the process we followed in the previous example.

Using $(x, y) = (2, 5)$ and $m = \dfrac{4}{3}$

in $y = mx + b$ Slope-intercept form

gives us $5 = \dfrac{4}{3}(2) + b$ Substitute values

                $5 = \dfrac{8}{3} + b$ Multiply

            $5 - \dfrac{8}{3} = b$ Add $-\dfrac{8}{3}$ to both sides

                $\dfrac{7}{3} = b$ Simplify

In slope-intercept form, the desired line has the equation

$$y = \frac{4}{3}x + \frac{7}{3}$$

EXAMPLE 7   Find the equation of the horizontal line passing through the point $(-3, -1)$.

SOLUTION   Any horizontal line has slope $m = 0$. To pass through $(-3, -1)$, the line must also cross the y-axis at $(0, -1)$. Therefore, $b = -1$. This gives us

$$y = mx + b \qquad \text{Slope-intercept form}$$

$$y = 0(x) + (-1) \qquad \text{Substitute values}$$

$$y = -1 \qquad \text{Simplify}$$

Getting Ready for Class

After reading through the preceding section, respond in your own words and in complete sentences.

A. What are m and b in the equation $y = mx + b$?

B. How would you find the slope and y-intercept for the line $3x - 2y = 6$?

C. How would you find the equation of a line given a point on the line and the slope?

D. In Example 6, explain why $b \neq 5$.

Find the slope and y-intercept for each of the following equations.

1. $y = 5x - 3$

2. $y = -4x + 1$

3. $y = -\dfrac{2}{3}x + \dfrac{7}{3}$

4. $y = \dfrac{5}{6}x - \dfrac{11}{6}$

5. $y = x + 9$

6. $y = -x - 8$

7. $y = \dfrac{x}{2} - \dfrac{5}{2}$

8. $y = \dfrac{x}{3} + \dfrac{4}{3}$

9. $y = \dfrac{1}{4} - 2x$

10. $y = \dfrac{2}{5} + 6x$

11. $y = 3x$

12. $y = 4x$

13. $y = -10$

14. $y = 7$

In each of the following problems, graph the line having the given slope m and y-intercept b.

15. $m = \dfrac{2}{3}, b = 1$

16. $m = \dfrac{3}{4}, b = -2$

17. $m = \dfrac{3}{2}, b = -3$

18. $m = \dfrac{4}{3}, b = 2$

19. $m = -\dfrac{4}{3}, b = 5$

20. $m = -\dfrac{3}{5}, b = 4$

21. $m = 3, b = -1$

22. $m = 3, b = -2$

Using the slope and y-intercept to graph each equation.

23. $y = -2x + 3$

24. $y = 2x - 5$

25. $y = \dfrac{3}{4}x + 2$

26. $y = -\dfrac{4}{3}x - 1$

27. $y = \dfrac{3}{2}x$

28. $y = -\dfrac{2}{5}x$

Find the slope and y-intercept for each of the following equations by writing them in the form $y = mx + b$. Then, graph each equation.

29. $-2x + y = 4$

30. $-2x + y = 2$

31. $3x + y = 3$

32. $3x + y = 6$

33. $3x + 2y = 6$

34. $2x + 3y = 6$

35. $4x - 5y = 20$

36. $2x - 5y = 10$

37. $-2x - 5y = 10$

38. $-4x + 5y = 20$

In each of the following problems, give the equation of the line with the given slope and y-intercept.

39. $m = \dfrac{2}{3}, b = 1$

40. $m = \dfrac{3}{4}, b = -2$

41. $m = \dfrac{3}{2}, b = -1$

42. $m = \dfrac{4}{3}, b = 2$

43. $m = -\dfrac{2}{3}, b = 3$

44. $m = -\dfrac{3}{5}, b = 4$

45. $m = 2, b = -4$

46. $m = -2, b = 4$

Find the slope and y-intercept for each line. Then write the equation of each line in slope-intercept form.

47.

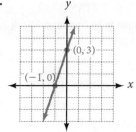

48.

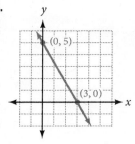

49.

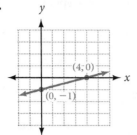

50.

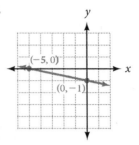

For the following problems, the slope and one point on a line are given. In each case use slope-intercept form to find the equation of the line. Then write your answer in standard form.

51. $(2, 3)$, $m = 2$

52. $(-1, 5)$, $m = 3$

53. $(1, -4)$, $m = -\dfrac{1}{3}$

54. $(-2, -2)$, $m = -\dfrac{1}{4}$

55. $(-2, 6)$, $m = \dfrac{3}{5}$

56. $(0, 0)$, $m = -\dfrac{5}{2}$

57. $(4, 0)$, $m = -\dfrac{4}{3}$

58. $(0, -3)$, $m = \dfrac{3}{4}$

Find the equation of the line passing through the given point and **a.** parallel to the given line, **b.** perpendicular to the given line. Write your answers in slope-intercept form.

59. $(1, 2)$; $y = 3x + 4$ **60.** $(2, -3)$; $y = -2x - 1$ **61.** $(-4, -1)$; $x + 2y = 6$

62. $(-2, 5)$; $x - 4y = 4$ **63.** $(3, 4)$; $2x + 3y = 6$ **64.** $(6, 0)$; $3x - 4y = 12$

65. Find the equation of the horizontal line passing through $(3, 2)$.

66. Find the equation of the horizontal line passing through $(-2, -3)$.

67. Find the equation of the line with zero slope passing through $(-1, 5)$.

68. Find the equation of the line with zero slope passing through the origin.

The next two problems are intended to give you practice reading, and paying attention to, the instructions that accompany the problems you are working. Working these problems is an excellent way to get ready for a test or a quiz.

69. Paying Attention to Instructions Work each problem according to the instructions given.

    a. Solve: $-2x + 1 = 6$

    b. Write in slope-intercept form: $-2x + y = 6$

    c. Find the y-intercept: $-2x + y = 6$

    d. Find the slope: $-2x + y = 6$

    e. Graph: $-2x + y = 6$

70. Paying Attention to Instructions Work each problem according to the instructions given.

    a. Solve: $x + 3 = -6$

    b. Write in slope-intercept form: $x + 3y = -6$

    c. Find the y-intercept: $x + 3y = -6$

    d. Find the slope: $x + 3y = -6$

    e. Graph: $x + 3y = -6$

Applying the Concepts

71. **Value of a Copy Machine** Cassandra buys a new color copier for her small business. It will cost $21,000 and will decrease in value each year. The graph below shows the value of the copier after the first 5 years of ownership.

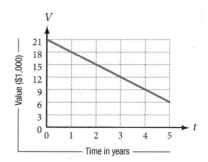

a. How much is the copier worth after 5 years?
b. After how many years is the copier worth $12,000?
c. Find the slope of this line.
d. By how many dollars per year is the copier decreasing in value?
e. Find the equation of this line where V is the value after t years.

72. **Salesperson's Income** Kevin starts a new job in sales next month. He will earn $1,000 per month plus a certain amount for each shirt he sells. The graph below shows the amount Kevin will earn per month based on how many shirts he sells.

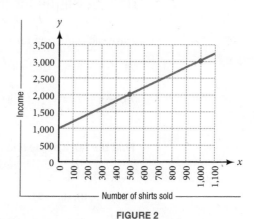

FIGURE 2

a. How much will he earn for selling 1,000 shirts?
b. How many shirts must he sell to earn $2,000 for a month?
c. Find the slope of this line.
d. How much money does Kevin earn for each shirt he sells?
e. Find the equation of this line where y is the amount he earns for selling x number of shirts.

Learning Objectives Assessment

The following problems can be used to help assess if you have successfully met the learning objectives for this section.

73. Find the slope of the line $y = -\dfrac{5}{6}x + \dfrac{13}{6}$.

    a. -5 **b.** $\dfrac{13}{6}$ **c.** $-\dfrac{5}{6}$ **d.** 1

74. To graph $y = \dfrac{1}{2}x - 4$, we would

    a. Plot a point at $(-4, 0)$, then rise 2 units and run 1 unit to locate a second point.

    b. Plot a point at $(-4, 0)$, then rise 1 unit and run 2 units to locate a second point.

    c. Plot a point at $(0, -4)$, then rise 2 units and run 1 unit to locate a second point.

    d. Plot a point at $(0, -4)$, then rise 1 unit and run 2 units to locate a second point.

75. Use slope-intercept form to find the equation of the line with slope 3 and passing through $(-4, 2)$.

    a. $y = 14x + 3$ **b.** $y = -10x + 3$

    c. $y = 3x + 14$ **d.** $y = 3x - 10$

Getting Ready for the Next Section

Solve each equation for y.

76. $-y - 3 = -2(x + 4)$ **77.** $-y + 5 = 2(x + 2)$ **78.** $-y - 3 = -\dfrac{2}{3}(x + 3)$

79. $-y - 1 = -\dfrac{1}{2}(x + 4)$ **80.** $-\dfrac{y - 1}{x} = \dfrac{3}{2}$ **81.** $-\dfrac{y + 1}{x} = \dfrac{3}{2}$

Find the slope of the line through the following pairs of points.

82. $(-3, 3), (3, -1)$ **83.** $(-2, -4), (2, 1)$ **84.** $(0, 0), (4, 1)$

85. $(-3, 0), (0, -3)$ **86.** $(2, 1), (2, 5)$ **87.** $(1, -3), (3, -3)$

Learning Objectives

In this section, we will learn how to:

1. Find the equation of a line using point-slope form.

Introduction

In the previous section, we saw how slope-intercept form could be used to graph a line or to find the equation of a line. Another useful form of the equation of a straight line is the point-slope form.

Let line l contain the point (x_1, y_1) and have slope m. If (x, y) is any other point on l, then by the definition of slope we have

$$\frac{y - y_1}{x - x_1} = m$$

Multiplying both sides by $(x - x_1)$ gives us

$$(x - x_1) \cdot \frac{y - y_1}{x - x_1} = m(x - x_1)$$

$$y - y_1 = m(x - x_1)$$

This last equation is known as the *point-slope form* of the equation of a straight line.

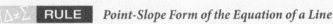

> **RULE**   *Point-Slope Form of the Equation of a Line*
>
> The equation of the line through (x_1, y_1) with slope m is given by
>
> $$y - y_1 = m(x - x_1)$$

This form is used to find the equation of a line, either given one point on the line and the slope, or given two points on the line.

VIDEO EXAMPLES

SECTION 3.6

EXAMPLE 1   Find the equation of the line with slope -2 that contains the point $(-4, 3)$. Write the answer in standard form.

SOLUTION In Section 3.5 we solved this problem using slope-intercept form. Now we will see how it can be done using point-slope form.

Using	$(x_1, y_1) = (-4, 3)$ and $m = -2$	
in	$y - y_1 = m(x - x_1)$	Point-slope form
gives us	$y - 3 = -2(x + 4)$	Note: $x - (-4) = x + 4$
	$y - 3 = -2x - 8$	Multiply out right side
	$2x + y - 3 = -8$	Add $2x$ to each side
	$2x + y = -5$	Add 3 to each side

Figure 1 is the graph of the line that contains $(-4, 3)$ and has a slope of -2. Notice that the y-intercept on the graph matches that of the equation we found.

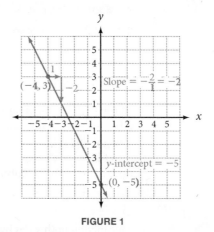

FIGURE 1

EXAMPLE 2   Find the equation of the line that passes through the points $(-3, 3)$ and $(3, -1)$. Write the answer in slope-intercept form.

SOLUTION   We begin by finding the slope of the line:

$$m = \frac{3 - (-1)}{-3 - 3} = \frac{4}{-6} = -\frac{2}{3}$$

Using $(x_1, y_1) = (3, -1)$ and $m = -\frac{2}{3}$ in $y - y_1 = m(x - x_1)$ yields

$$y + 1 = -\frac{2}{3}(x - 3)$$

$$y + 1 = -\frac{2}{3}x + 2 \qquad \text{Multiply out right side}$$

$$y = -\frac{2}{3}x + 1 \qquad \text{Add } -1 \text{ to each side}$$

Figure 2 shows the graph of the line that passes through the points $(-3, 3)$ and $(3, -1)$. As you can see, the slope and y-intercept are $-\frac{2}{3}$ and 1, respectively.

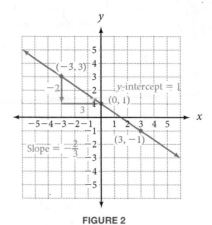

FIGURE 2

Note In Example 2 we could have used the point $(-3, 3)$ instead of $(3, -1)$ and obtained the same equation; that is, using $(x_1, y_1) = (-3, 3)$ and $m = -\frac{2}{3}$ in $y - y_1 = m(x - x_1)$ gives us

$$y - 3 = -\frac{2}{3}(x + 3)$$

$$y - 3 = -\frac{2}{3}x - 2$$

$$y = -\frac{2}{3}x + 1$$

which is the same result we obtained using $(3, -1)$.

EXAMPLE 3   Find the equation of the line passing through $(4, -5)$ with

a. zero slope   **b.** undefined slope

SOLUTION

a. Using $(x_1, y_1) = (4, -5)$ and $m = 0$ in point-slope form gives us

$$y - (-5) = 0(x - 4)$$

$$y + 5 = 0$$

$$y = -5$$

This is the equation of a horizontal line. Recall that the equation of the horizontal line passing through (a, b) is $y = b$. We could have used this fact to get $y = -5$ with less effort, although point-slope form does lead us to the correct equation.

b. Because there is an undefined slope, we cannot use point-slope form. We must recognize that a line having an undefined slope is a vertical line. The equation of the vertical line passing through (a, b) is $x = a$. In this case, we get $x = 4$.

EXAMPLE 4   Find the equation of the line passing through the point $(-3, -2)$ and parallel to the line $3x - 5y = 10$. Write the answer in standard form.

SOLUTION   First, we find the slope of the line $3x - 5y = 10$ by writing the equation in slope-intercept form.

$$3x - 5y = 10$$

$$-5y = -3x + 10 \qquad \text{Add } -3x \text{ to both sides}$$

$$y = \frac{3}{5}x - 2 \qquad \text{Multiply both sides by } -\frac{1}{5}$$

The slope of this line is $m = \frac{3}{5}$. Any line parallel to this line must have the same slope. Using $(x_1, y_1) = (-3, -2)$ and $m = \frac{3}{5}$ in point-slope form gives us

$$y - (-2) = \frac{3}{5}(x - (-3)) \qquad \text{Substitute values}$$

$$y + 2 = \frac{3}{5}(x + 3) \qquad \text{Simplify}$$

$$y + 2 = \frac{3}{5}x + \frac{9}{5} \qquad \text{Distributive property}$$

$$5y + 10 = 3x + 9 \qquad \text{Multiply both sides by 5 to clear fractions}$$

$$-3x + 5y + 10 = 9 \qquad \text{Add } -3x \text{ to each side}$$

$$-3x + 5y = -1 \qquad \text{Add } -10 \text{ to each side}$$

$$3x - 5y = 1 \qquad \text{Multiply both sides by } -1$$

Figure 3 shows the graph of both lines.

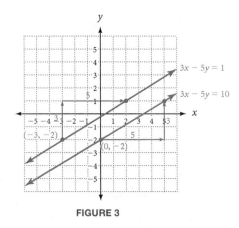

FIGURE 3

Here is a summary of the various equations for a line that we have introduced in this chapter.

Equations of Lines

$ax + by = c$	Standard form
$x = a$	Vertical line through (a, b)
$y = b$	Horizontal line through (a, b)
$y = mx + b$	Slope-intercept form of a line with slope m and y-intercept b.
$y - y_1 = m(x - x_1)$	Point-slope form of line passing through (x_1, y_1) with slope m.

Getting Ready for Class

After reading through the preceding section, respond in your own words and in complete sentences.

A. What is the point-slope form of the equation of a line?

B. What is the point-slope form most useful for?

C. How would you find the equation of a line from two points on the line?

D. Explain why point-slope form cannot be used to find the equation of a vertical line.

For each of the following problems, the slope and one point on a line are given. In each case use the point-slope form to find the equation of that line. Write your answers in standard form.

1. $(-2, -5)$, $m = 2$ **2.** $(-1, -5)$, $m = 2$ **3.** $(-4, 1)$, $m = -\dfrac{1}{2}$

4. $(-2, 1)$, $m = -\dfrac{1}{2}$ **5.** $(2, -3)$, $m = \dfrac{3}{2}$ **6.** $(3, -4)$, $m = \dfrac{4}{3}$

7. $(-1, 4)$, $m = -3$ **8.** $(-2, 5)$, $m = -3$ **9.** $(6, 0)$, $m = -\dfrac{2}{3}$

10. $(-5, 0)$, $m = \dfrac{3}{4}$ **11.** $(0, -1)$, $m = \dfrac{1}{5}$ **12.** $(0, 4)$, $m = -\dfrac{1}{3}$

13. $(5, 3)$, $m = 0$ **14.** $(-3, 5)$, $m = 0$ **15.** $(0, 0)$, $m = \dfrac{3}{2}$

16. $(0, 0)$, $m = -\dfrac{3}{4}$

Find the equation of the line that passes through each pair of points. Write your answers in slope-intercept form when possible.

17. $(-2, -4)$, $(1, -1)$ **18.** $(2, 4)$, $(-3, -1)$ **19.** $(-1, -5)$, $(2, 1)$

20. $(-1, 6)$, $(1, 2)$ **21.** $(-3, -2)$, $(3, 6)$ **22.** $(-3, 6)$, $(3, -2)$

23. $(-3, -1)$, $(3, -5)$ **24.** $(-3, -5)$, $(3, 1)$ **25.** $(2, 0)$, $(0, 3)$

26. $(-4, 0)$, $(0, 1)$ **27.** $(-1, 0)$, $(-1, 5)$ **28.** $(3, -4)$, $(3, 2)$

29. $(1, 1)$, $(5, 1)$ **30.** $(-6, -3)$, $(-2, -3)$

31. Find the equation of the line with x-intercept 3 and y-intercept 2.

32. Find the equation of the line with x-intercept 2 and y-intercept 3.

33. Find the equation of the line with x-intercept -2 and y-intercept -5.

34. Find the equation of the line with x-intercept -3 and y-intercept -5.

35. The equation of the vertical line that passes through the points $(3, -2)$ and $(3, 4)$ is either $x = 3$ or $y = 3$. Which one is it?

36. The equation of the horizontal line that passes through the points $(2, 3)$ and $(-1, 3)$ is either $x = 3$ or $y = 3$. Which one is it?

37. Find the equation of the line passing through the point $(-2, 3)$ with
    a. zero slope   **b.** undefined slope

38. Find the equation of the line passing through the point $(-1, -4)$ with
    a. zero slope   **b.** undefined slope

39. Find the equation of the line through $(6, 2)$ if the line is
    a. horizontal   **b.** vertical

40. Find the equation of the line through $(5, 0)$ if the line is
    a. horizontal   **b.** vertical

For the following problems, find the equation of the line passing through the given point and **a.** parallel to the given line, **b.** perpendicular to the given line. Write your answers in standard form.

41. $(3, -1), y = 2x - 5$

42. $(-1, 2), y = 3x + 4$

43. $(-4, -3), y = -\dfrac{1}{3}x + 1$

44. $(2, -6), y = \dfrac{1}{2}x - 3$

45. $(0, 5), 3x + 4y = 12$

46. $(0, -1), 4x + 3y = 15$

47. $(1, 0), 2x - 3y = 6$

48. $(3, 0), 2x - 5y = -10$

49. $(4, 2), y = -3$

50. $(-5, 1), x = 2$

Applying the Concepts

51. Temperature The following graph shows the relationship between temperature measured in degrees Fahrenheit (°F) and degrees Celsius (°C).

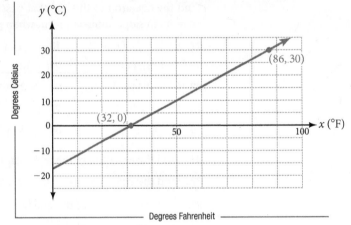

a. Water freezes at a temperature of 32°F. What is the freezing temperature of water in degrees Celsius?

b. Find the slope of this line.

c. Use the two points shown on the graph to find the equation of the line.

d. Water boils at a temperature of 212°F. What is the boiling point of water in degrees Celsius?

52. **Pressure** The following graph shows the relationship between depth below sea level, measured in feet, and the pressure at that depth in pounds per square inch (psi).

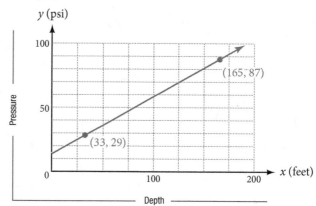

   a. What is the pressure at a depth of 33 feet?
   b. Find the slope of this line.
   c. Use the two points shown on the graph to find the equation of the line.
   d. What pressure would a diver experience at a depth of 100 feet?

Learning Objectives Assessment

The following problems can be used to help assess if you have successfully met the learning objectives for this section.

53. Find the equation of the line passing through $(2, -4)$ with slope $m = -3$.

   a. $y = -3x - 4$ **b.** $y = -3x + 2$
   c. $3x + y = -2$ **d.** $3x + y = -10$

54. Find the equation of the line passing through the points $(-2, 1)$ and $(2, -3)$.

   a. $x - y = -3$ **b.** $x + y = -1$
   c. $y = -x + 1$ **d.** $y = -x - 3$

Getting Ready for the Next Section

Graph each of the following lines.

55. $x + y = 4$ 56. $x - y = -2$ 57. $y = 2x - 3$ 58. $y = 2x + 3$
59. $y = 2x$ 60. $y = -2x$

Linear Inequalities in Two Variables

Learning Objectives

In this section, we will learn how to:

1. Graph the solution set for a linear inequality in two variables.

Introduction

A linear inequality in two variables is any expression that can be put in the form

$$ax + by < c$$

where a, b, and c are real numbers (a and b not both 0). The inequality symbol can be any of the following four: $<, \leq, >, \geq$.

Some examples of linear inequalities are

$$2x + 3y < 6 \qquad y \geq 2x + 1 \qquad x \leq 0 \qquad y > -4$$

Although not all of these inequalities have the form $ax + by < c$, each one can be put in that form.

The solution set for a linear inequality is an entire region of the coordinate plane. The boundary for the region is found by replacing the inequality symbol with an equal sign and graphing the resulting equation. If the inequality symbol used originally is $\leq$ or $\geq$, then the points on the boundary line satisfy the inequality and are part of the solution set. We indicate this by drawing the boundary as a solid line. However, if the original inequality symbol is $<$ or $>$, then the points on the boundary line do not satisfy the inequality and are not part of the solution set. In this case, we draw the boundary as a dashed line. (This is similar to our use of open or closed circles in Section 2.8.)

The boundary equation divides the coordinate plane into two regions. One of these regions is part of the solution set. To determine which region contains solutions, we choose any point not on the boundary and see if it satisfies the inequality.

Let's look at some examples.

VIDEO EXAMPLES

SECTION 3.7

EXAMPLE 1 Graph the solution set for $x + y \leq 4$.

SOLUTION The boundary for the solution set is the line $x + y = 4$. Because the statement $x + y \leq 4$ is true if either $x + y = 4$ or $x + y < 4$, the points on the boundary line are solutions, so we draw the boundary as a solid line.

The graph of the boundary is shown in Figure 1.

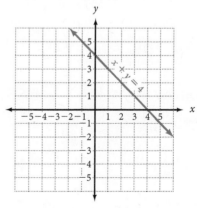

FIGURE 1

The boundary separates the coordinate plane into two regions: the region above the boundary and the region below the boundary. One of the regions contains the remaining solutions, which are the points that satisfy $x + y < 4$. To find the correct region, we simply choose any convenient point that is *not* on the boundary. We then substitute the coordinates of the point into the original inequality $x + y \leq 4$. If the point we choose satisfies the inequality, then it is a member of the solution set, and we can assume that all points on the same side of the boundary as the chosen point are also in the solution set. If the coordinates of our point do not satisfy the original inequality, then the solution set lies on the other side of the boundary.

In this example a convenient point not on the boundary is the origin. Substituting $(0, 0)$ into $x + y \leq 4$ gives us

$$0 + 0 \overset{?}{\leq} 4$$

$$0 \leq 4 \qquad \text{A true statement}$$

Because the origin is a solution to the inequality $x + y \leq 4$, and the origin is below the boundary, all other points below the boundary are also solutions. We indicate this by shading the region of the coordinate plane below the boundary line.

The graph of $x + y \leq 4$ is shown in Figure 2. The solution set consists of all points on or below the line.

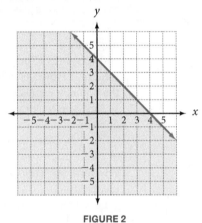

FIGURE 2

Here is a list of steps to follow when graphing the solution set for linear inequalities in two variables.

HOW TO   *Graph the Solution Set for Linear Inequalities in Two Variables*

Step 1: Replace the inequality symbol with an equal sign. The resulting equation represents the boundary for the solution set.

Step 2: Graph the boundary found in step 1 using a *solid line* if the boundary is included in the solution set (that is, if the original inequality symbol was either ≤ or ≥). Use a *dashed line* to graph the boundary if it is *not* included in the solution set. (It is not included if the original inequality was either < or >).

Step 3: Choose any convenient point not on the boundary and substitute the coordinates into the *original* inequality. If the resulting statement is *true*, the solution set lies on the *same* side of the boundary as the chosen point. If the resulting statement is *false*, the solution set lies on the *opposite* side of the boundary.

Step 4: Shade the region on the side of the boundary line that contains solutions.

EXAMPLE 2   Graph the solution set for $y < 2x - 3$.

SOLUTION The boundary is the graph of $y = 2x - 3$. The boundary is not included because the original inequality symbol is <, which does not allow equality. We therefore use a dashed line to represent the boundary, as shown in Figure 3.

A convenient test point is again the origin. Using $(0, 0)$ in $y < 2x - 3$, we have

$$0 \stackrel{?}{<} 2(0) - 3$$

$$0 < -3 \qquad \text{A false statement}$$

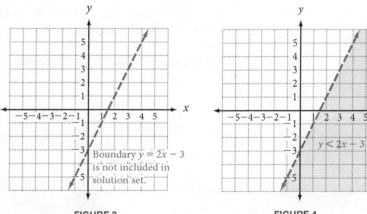

FIGURE 3   **FIGURE 4**

Because our test point gives us a false statement and it lies above the boundary, the solution set must lie on the other side of the boundary. Therefore, we shade the region below the boundary line as shown in Figure 4.

EXAMPLE 3   Graph the inequality $2x + 3y \leq 0$.

SOLUTION   We begin by graphing the boundary $2x + 3y = 0$. The boundary is included in the solution set because the inequality symbol is $\leq$.

Because the origin $(0, 0)$ lies on the boundary line, we cannot use it as a test point. We choose any other point not on the line, such as $(1, 1)$. Using $(1, 1)$ in $2x + 3y \leq 0$, we have

$$2(1) + 3(1) \overset{?}{\leq} 0$$

$$5 \leq 0 \qquad \text{A false statement}$$

Since $(1, 1)$ does not satisfy the inequality and lies above the boundary, the solution set must be the region below the line. We therefore shade below the line, as shown in Figure 5.

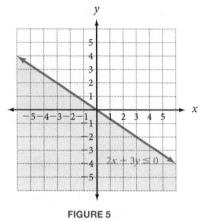

FIGURE 5

EXAMPLE 4   Graph the solution set for $x \leq 5$.

SOLUTION   In this context, the inequality $x \leq 5$ can be interpreted to mean $x + 0y \leq 5$. It is still considered an inequality in two variables. The boundary is $x = 5$, which is a vertical line and is part of the solution set.

If we use $(0, 0)$ as our test point, we see that it yields a true statement when its coordinates are substituted into $x + 0y \leq 5$. The solution set, therefore, lies to the left of the vertical line. Figure 6 shows the graph.

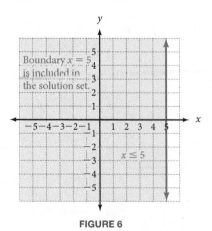

FIGURE 6

Getting Ready for Class

After reading through the preceding section, respond in your own words and in complete sentences.

A. When graphing a linear inequality in two variables, how do you find the equation of the boundary line?

B. What is the significance of a dashed line in the graph of an inequality?

C. When graphing a linear inequality in two variables, how do you know which side of the boundary line to shade?

D. Describe the set of ordered pairs that are solutions to $x + y < 6$.

Problem Set 3.7

Graph the solution set for the following linear inequalities.

1. $2x - 3y < 6$ **2.** $3x + 2y \geq 6$ **3.** $x - 2y \leq 4$ **4.** $2x + y > 4$

5. $x - y \leq 2$ **6.** $x - y \leq 1$ **7.** $3x - 4y \geq 12$ **8.** $4x + 3y < 12$

9. $5x - y \leq 5$ **10.** $4x + y > 4$ **11.** $2x + 6y \leq 12$ **12.** $x - 5y > 5$

13. $x \geq 1$ **14.** $x < 5$ **15.** $y > 2$ **16.** $y \leq -4$

17. $x + 3y \leq 0$ **18.** $3x - y > 0$ **19.** $2x + y > 3$ **20.** $5x + 2y < 2$

21. $y \leq 3x - 1$ **22.** $y \geq 3x + 2$ **23.** $y \leq -\dfrac{1}{2}x + 2$ **24.** $y < \dfrac{1}{3}x + 3$

The next two problems are intended to give you practice reading, and paying attention to, the instructions that accompany the problems you are working.

25. Paying Attention to Instructions Work each problem according to the instructions given.

    a. Solve: $4 + 3y < 12$ **b.** Solve: $4 - 3y < 12$

    c. Solve for y: $4x + 3y = 12$ **d.** Graph: $y < -\dfrac{4}{3}x + 4$

26. Paying Attention to Instructions Work each problem according to the instructions given.

    a. Solve: $3x + 2 \geq 6$ **b.** Solve: $-3x + 2 \geq 6$

    c. Solve for y: $3x + 2y = 6$ **d.** Graph: $y \geq -\dfrac{3}{2}x + 3$

27. Find the equation of the line shown in part a, then use this information to find the inequalities whose solution sets are shown in parts b and c.

   a.   **b.**   **c.**

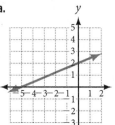 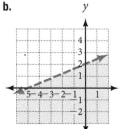 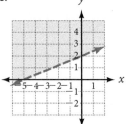

28. Find the equation of the line shown in part a, then use this information to find the inequalities whose solution sets are shown in parts b and c.

   a.   **b.**   **c.**

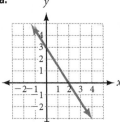 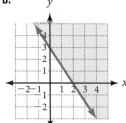 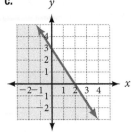

Learning Objectives Assessment

The following problems can be used to help assess if you have successfully met the learning objectives for this section.

29. The boundary for the solution set of $x - 2y > 4$ should be drawn as:
   a. a solid line.
   b. a dashed line.

30. The solution set for $x - 2y > 4$ is:
   a. the line $x - 2y = 4$ and the region above the line.
   b. the line $x - 2y = 4$ and the region below the line.
   c. only the region below the line $x - 2y = 4$.
   d. only the region above the line $x - 2y = 4$.

Maintaining Your Skills

31. Simplify the expression $7 - 3(2x - 4) - 8$.

32. Find the value of $x^2 - 2xy + y^2$ when $x = 3$ and $y = -4$.

Solve each equation.

33. $-\dfrac{3}{2}x = 12$ **34.** $2x - 4 = 5x + 2$ **35.** $8 - 2(x + 7) = 2$

36. $3(2x - 5) - (2x - 4) = 6 - (4x + 5)$

37. Solve the formula $P = 2l + 2w$ for w.

Solve each inequality, and graph the solution set.

38. $-4x < 20$ **39.** $3 - 2x > 5$

40. $3 - 4(x - 2) \geq -5x + 6$

41. Solve the formula $3x - 2y \leq 12$ for y.

42. What number is 12% of 2,000?

43. Geometry The length of a rectangle is 5 inches more than 3 times the width. If the perimeter is 26 inches, find the length and width.

Chapter 3 Summary

Rectangular Coordinate System [3.1]

1. For the point $(-4, -5)$, the x-coordinate is -4 and the y-coordinate is -5. Also, the point lies in the third quadrant, QIII.

A pair of numbers enclosed in parentheses and separated by a comma, such as $(-2, 1)$, is called an *ordered pair* of numbers. The first number in the pair is called the *x-coordinate* of the ordered pair; the second number is called the *y-coordinate*.

Ordered pairs of numbers are important in the study of mathematics because they give us a way to visualize solutions to equations. The visual component of ordered pairs is called the rectangular coordinate system.

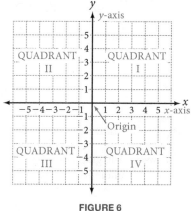

FIGURE 6

Linear Equation in Two Variables [3.2]

2. The equation $3x + 2y = 6$ is an example of a linear equation in two variables.

A linear equation in two variables is any equation that can be put in the form $ax + by = c$. The graph of every linear equation is a straight line.

Strategy for Graphing Linear Equations in Two Variables [3.2]

3. The graph of $y = -\frac{2}{3}x - 1$ is shown below.

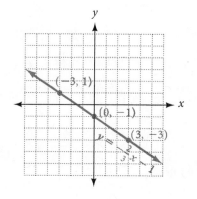

Step 1: Find any three ordered pairs that satisfy the equation. This can be done by using a convenient number for one variable and solving for the other variable.

Step 2: Graph the three ordered pairs found in step 1. Actually, we need only two points to graph a line. The third point serves as a check. If all three points do not line up, there is a mistake in our work.

Step 3: Draw a line through the three points graphed in step 2.

Intercepts [3.3]

4. To find the x-intercept for $3x + 2y = 6$, we let $y = 0$ and get

$$3x = 6$$
$$x = 2$$

In this case the x-intercept is 2, and the graph crosses the x-axis at $(2, 0)$.

The x-intercept of a line is the x-coordinate of the point where the graph crosses the x-axis. The y-intercept is the y-coordinate of the point where the graph crosses the y-axis. We find the y-intercept by substituting $x = 0$ into the equation and solving for y. The x-intercept is found by letting $y = 0$ and solving for x.

Slope of a Line [3.4]

5. The slope of the line through $(3, -5)$ and $(-2, 1)$ is

$$m = \frac{-5 - 1}{3 - (-2)} = \frac{-6}{5} = -\frac{6}{5}$$

The *slope* of the line containing the points (x_1, y_1) and (x_2, y_2) is given by

$$\text{Slope} = m = \frac{y_2 - y_1}{x_2 - x_1} = \frac{\text{rise}}{\text{run}}$$

Vertical and Horizontal Lines [3.2, 3.4]

6. The graph of $x = 3$ is a vertical line, and the graph of $y = 3$ is a horizontal line. The figure below shows both graphs.

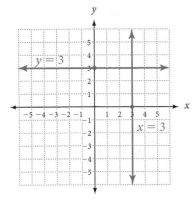

The graph of $x = a$ is a vertical line passing through $(a, 0)$. A vertical line has an undefined slope.

The graph of $y = b$ is a horizontal line passing through $(0, b)$. A horizontal line has slope $m = 0$.

Parallel and Perpendicular Lines [3.4]

7. A line parallel to $y = \frac{2}{3}x + 1$ would have a slope of $m = \frac{2}{3}$. A perpendicular line would have a slope of $m = -\frac{3}{2}$.

Two distinct, nonvertical lines are parallel if they have the same slope. They are perpendicular if the product of their slopes is -1.

Slope-Intercept Form of a Line [3.5]

8. The equation of the line with a slope of 2 and a y-intercept of 5 is

$$y = 2x + 5$$

The equation of the line with a slope of m and a y-intercept of b is

$$y = mx + b$$

Point-Slope Form of a Line [3.6]

9. The equation of the line through $(1, 2)$ with a slope of 3 is
$$y - 2 = 3(x - 1)$$
$$y - 2 = 3x - 3$$
$$y = 3x - 1$$

If a line has a slope of m and contains the point (x_1, y_1), the equation can be written as

$$y - y_1 = m(x - x_1)$$

To Graph a Linear Inequality in Two Variables [3.7]

9. Graph $x - y \geq 3$.

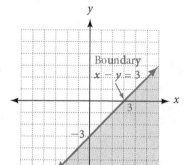

Step 1: Replace the inequality symbol with an equal sign. The resulting equation represents the boundary for the solution set.

Step 2: Graph the boundary found in step 1, using a *solid line* if the original inequality symbol was either $\leq$ or $\geq$. Use a *dashed line* otherwise.

Step 3: Choose any convenient point not on the boundary and substitute the coordinates into the *original* inequality. If the resulting statement is *true*, the graph lies on the *same* side of the boundary as the chosen point. If the resulting statement is *false*, the solution set lies on the *opposite* side of the boundary.

Step 4: Shade the side of the boundary line containing solutions.

Chapter 3 Test

Graph the ordered pairs. [3.1]

1. $(2, -1)$ **2.** $(-4, 3)$ **3.** $(-3, -2)$ **4.** $(0, -4)$

5. Fill in the following ordered pairs for the equation $3x - 2y = 6$. [3.2]

$(0, \ )\ (\ , 0)\ (4, \ )\ (\ , -6)$

6. Which of the following ordered pairs are solutions to $y = -3x + 7$? [3.2]

$(0, 7)\ (2, -1)\ (4, -5)\ (-5, -3)$

Graph each line. [3.2]

7. $y = -\dfrac{1}{2}x + 4$ **8.** $2x - 5y = 10$

9. $x = -3$ **10.** $y = 2$

Find the x- and y-intercepts. [3.3]

11. $8x - 4y = 16$ **12.** $y = \dfrac{3}{2}x + 6$

13. $y = 3$ **14.** $x = -2$

Find the slope of the line through each pair of points. [3.4]

15. $(3, 2), (-5, 6)$ **16.** $(0, 9), (7, 1)$

Find the slope of each line. [3.4]

17. 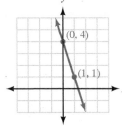   **18.** 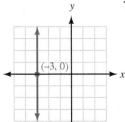   **19.**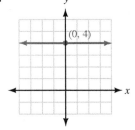

Find the slope and y-intercept for each line. [3.5]

20. $y = -\dfrac{1}{2}x + 6$ **21.** $y = 3x$

22. Find the slope of a line parallel to the line $y = \dfrac{3}{7}x - 5$. [3.4, 3.5]

23. Find the slope of a line perpendicular to $y = -4x + 3$. [3.4, 3.5]

24. Find the equation of the line with a slope of 3 and y-intercept -5. [3.5]

25. Find the equation of the line through $(4, 1)$ with a slope of $-\dfrac{1}{2}$. [3.5, 3.6]

26. Find the equation of the line passing through the points $(3, -4)$ and $(-6, 2)$. [3.6]

27. A line has an x-intercept 3 and contains the point $(-2, 6)$. Find its equation. [3.6]

28. Find the equation of the line passing through $(1, -2)$ and parallel to the line $y = \dfrac{3}{2}x + 3$. Write your answer in standard form. [3.5, 3.6]

29. Find the equation of the line passing through $(-4, 3)$ and perpendicular to the line $3x + 2y = 6$. Write your answer in standard form. [3.5, 3.6]

30. Find the equation of the line with slope $m = 0$ passing through $(5, -5)$. [3.5, 3.6]

31. Find the equation of the vertical line passing through $(-2, -4)$. [3.5, 3.6]

Graph the solution set for each linear inequality in two variables. [3.7]

32. $y > x - 6$ **33.** $6x - 9y \le 18$ **34.** $x \le 2$

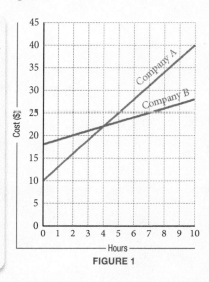

Systems
of Linear Equations

4

Chapter Outline

iStockphoto.com © Yuri Arcurs

Two companies offer Internet access to their customers. Company A charges $10 a month plus $3 for every hour of Internet connection. Company B charges $18 a month plus $1 for every hour of Internet connection. To compare the monthly charges of the two companies we form what is called a system of equations. Here is that system.

$$y = 3x + 10$$
$$y = x + 18$$

The first equation gives us information on company A; the second equation gives information on company B. Tables 1 and 2 and the graphs in Figure 1 give us additional information about this system of equations.

TABLE 1	
Company A	
Hours	Cost
0	$10
1	$13
2	$16
3	$19
4	$22
5	$25
6	$28
7	$31
8	$34
9	$37
10	$40

TABLE 2	
Company B	
Hours	Cost
0	$18
1	$19
2	$20
3	$21
4	$22
5	$23
6	$24
7	$25
8	$26
9	$27
10	$28

FIGURE 1

As you can see from looking at the tables and at the graphs in Figure 1, the monthly charges for the two companies will be equal if Internet use is exactly 4 hours. In this chapter we work with systems of linear equations.

The study skills for this chapter concern the way you approach new situations in mathematics. The first study skill applies to your natural instincts for what does and doesn't work in mathematics. The second study skill gives you a way of testing your instincts.

1. **Don't Let Your Intuition Fool You** As you become more experienced and more successful in mathematics, you will be able to trust your mathematical intuition. For now, though, it can get in the way of success. For example, if you ask a beginning algebra student to "subtract 3 from -5" many will answer -2 or 2. Both answers are incorrect, even though they may seem intuitively true.

2. **Test Properties About Which You Are Unsure** From time to time you will be in a situation in which you would like to apply a property or rule, but you are not sure if it is true. You can always test a property or statement by substituting numbers for variables. For instance, I always have students that rewrite $(x + 3)^2$ as $x^2 + 9$, thinking that the two expressions are equivalent. The fact that the two expressions are not equivalent becomes obvious when we substitute 10 for x in each one.

   When $x = 10$, the expression $(x + 3)^2$ is $(10 + 3)^2 = 13^2 = 169$

   When $x = 10$, the expression $x^2 + 9 = 10^2 + 9 = 100 + 9 = 109$

It is not unusual, nor is it wrong, to try occasionally to apply a property that doesn't exist. If you have any doubt about generalizations you are making, test them by replacing variables with numbers and simplifying.

Learning Objectives

In this section, we will learn how to:

1. Determine if an ordered pair is a solution to a system of linear equations.
2. Solve a linear system by graphing.
3. Identify an inconsistent system.
4. Identify a system with dependent equations.

Introduction

Two linear equations considered at the same time make up what is called a *system of linear equations*. Both equations have graphs that are lines. The following are systems of linear equations:

$$x + y = 3 \qquad y = 2x + 1 \qquad 2x - y = 1$$
$$3x + 4y = 2 \qquad y = 3x + 2 \qquad 3x - 2y = 6$$

Solutions to a Linear System

A solution to a system of linear equations in two variables is an ordered pair that satisfies every equation in the system. For systems with two equations, the ordered pair must make both equations true statements.

VIDEO EXAMPLES

SECTION 4.1

EXAMPLE 1 Determine whether each ordered pair is a solution to the following system:

$$x + y = 3$$
$$3x + 4y = 2$$

a. $(-2, 5)$ **b.** $(10, -7)$

SOLUTION We must determine if the ordered pair satisfies both equations.

a.

When $x = -2$ and $y = 5$ the equation $x + y = 3$ becomes

$-2 + 5 \overset{?}{=} 3$

$3 = 3$

When $x = -2$ and $y = 5$ the equation $3x + 4y = 2$ becomes

$3(-2) + 4(5) \overset{?}{=} 2$

$-6 + 20 \overset{?}{=} 2$

$14 \neq 2$

The ordered pair $(-2, 5)$ satisfies the first equation but not the second, so it is not a solution to the system.

b.

When $x = 10$ and $y = -7$ the equation $x + y = 3$ becomes

$10 + (-7) \overset{?}{=} 3$

$3 = 3$

When $x = 10$ and $y = -7$ the equation $3x + 4y = 2$ becomes

$3(10) + 4(-7) \overset{?}{=} 2$

$30 + (-28) \overset{?}{=} 2$

$2 = 2$

The ordered pair $(10, -7)$ makes both equations true, so it is a solution to the system of equations.

Solving Systems by Graphing

The solution set for a system of linear equations contains all ordered pairs that are solutions to both equations. Each linear equation has a graph that is a line. If the lines intersect at a point, then this point lies on both lines and the corresponding ordered pair must therefore satisfy both equations, making it a solution to the system. So we can solve a linear system graphically by locating intersection points. If we graph both equations on the same coordinate system, we can read the coordinates of the point of intersection and have the solution to our system. Here is an example.

EXAMPLE 2   Solve the following system by graphing.

$$x + y = 4$$
$$x - y = -2$$

SOLUTION   On the same set of coordinate axes we graph each equation separately. Figure 1 shows both graphs, without showing the work necessary to get them. We can see from the graphs that they appear to intersect at the point $(1, 3)$.

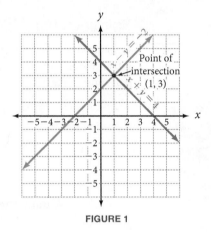

FIGURE 1

We can verify that the ordered pair $(1, 3)$ is a solution to the system by substituting the coordinates $x = 1$, $y = 3$ into both equations to see if they work.

When	$x = 1$	When	$x = 1$
and	$y = 3$	and	$y = 3$
the equation	$x + y = 4$	the equation	$x - y = -2$
becomes	$1 + 3 \overset{?}{=} 4$	becomes	$1 - 3 \overset{?}{=} -2$
	$4 = 4$		$-2 = -2$

The point $(1, 3)$ satisfies both equations, so it is a solution to the system. From Figure 1 we can see that the two lines intersect at a single point, so $(1, 3)$ is the *only* solution to the system. The solution set is $\{(1, 3)\}$.

Here are some steps to follow in solving linear systems by graphing.

> **HOW TO**   *Solve a Linear System by Graphing*
>
> **Step 1:** Graph the first equation by any of the methods described in Chapter 3.
> **Step 2:** Graph the second equation on the same set of axes used for the first equation.
> **Step 3:** Identify the coordinates of the point where the two graphs appear to intersect.
> **Step 4:** Verify the solution in both equations.

EXAMPLE 3   Solve the following system by graphing.

$$x + 2y = 8$$
$$2x - 3y = 2$$

SOLUTION   Graphing each equation on the same coordinate system, we have the lines shown in Figure 2.

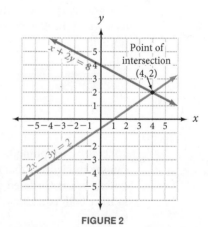

FIGURE 2

From Figure 2, we can see the solution for our system appears to be the point (4, 2). We check this solution as follows.

When	$x = 4$	When	$x = 4$
and	$y = 2$	and	$y = 2$
the equation	$x + 2y = 8$	the equation	$2x - 3y = 2$
becomes	$4 + 2(2) \overset{?}{=} 8$	becomes	$2(4) - 3(2) \overset{?}{=} 2$
	$4 + 4 \overset{?}{=} 8$		$8 - 6 \overset{?}{=} 2$
	$8 = 8$		$2 = 2$

The point (4, 2) satisfies both equations and, therefore, must be the solution to our system. The solution set is $\{(4, 2)\}$.

EXAMPLE 4   Solve the following system by graphing.

$$y = 2x - 3$$
$$x = 3$$

SOLUTION   Graphing both equations on the same set of axes, we have Figure 3.

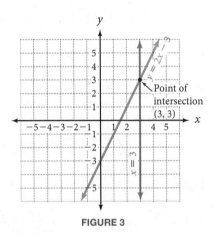

FIGURE 3

The graphs appear to intersect at the point (3, 3). Because (3, 3) satisfies both equations (check for yourself), it is the solution to the system. The solution set is {(3, 3)}.

EXAMPLE 5   Solve the following system by graphing.

$$y = x - 2$$
$$y = x + 1$$

SOLUTION   Graphing both equations produces the lines shown in Figure 4. We can see in Figure 4 that the lines are parallel and therefore do not intersect. Our system has no ordered pair as a solution because there is no ordered pair that satisfies both equations. The solution set is the empty set, which we denote by the symbol $\varnothing$.

Note We know that the lines in Example 5 must be parallel because they both have slope $m = 1$.

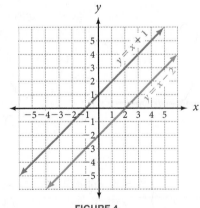

FIGURE 4

EXAMPLE 6   Graph the system.

$$2x + y = 4$$
$$4x + 2y = 8$$

SOLUTION   Both graphs are shown in Figure 5. The two graphs coincide. The reason becomes apparent when we multiply both sides of the first equation by 2:

$$2x + y = 4$$
$$2(2x + y) = 2(4) \qquad \text{Multiply both sides by 2}$$
$$4x + 2y = 8$$

The equations are equivalent and have the same solution set. Any point that lies on one line also lies on the other. Therefore, every point on either line is a solution to the system. Because a line consists of an infinite set of points, the system has an infinite number of solutions.

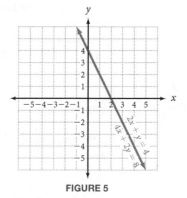

FIGURE 5

Note   When the lines coincide and there are an infinite number of solutions, either of the equations can be used to write the solution set. In Example 6, we could also have written $\{(x, y) \mid 4x + 2y = 8\}$.

We can use set-builder notation to write the solution set as $\{(x, y) \mid 2x + y = 4\}$.

We sometimes use special vocabulary to describe the special cases shown in Examples 5 and 6. When a system of equations has no solution because the lines are parallel (as in Example 5), we say the system is *inconsistent*. When the lines coincide (as in Example 6), we say the equations are *dependent*. The two special cases illustrated in the previous two examples do not happen often. Usually, a system has a single ordered pair as a solution.

Here is a summary of three possible types of solutions to a system of equations in two variables.

One Solution

Lines intersect at a single point

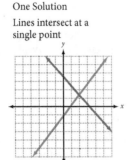

No Solution

Lines are parallel and never cross

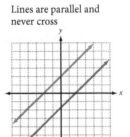

System is inconsistent

Infinite Solutions

Lines coincide

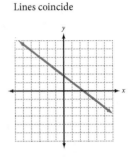

Equations are dependent

Solving a system of linear equations by graphing is useful only when the point of intersection has integers for coordinates. In the next two sections, we will introduce algebraic methods for solving linear systems that will allow us to find the solution even when the ordered pair does not have convenient values for coordinates.

Getting Ready for Class

After reading through the preceding section, respond in your own words and in complete sentences.

A. What is a system of two linear equations in two variables?

B. What is a solution to a system of linear equations?

C. How do we solve a system of linear equations by graphing?

D. Under what conditions will a system of linear equations not have a solution?

For each of the following systems of linear equations, determine if any of the given ordered pairs are solutions to the system.

1. $x - y = 1$
$x + 2y = 4$
a. $(-1, -2)$ **b.** $(2, 1)$ **c.** $(2, 2)$

2. $x + y = 2$
$x - y = 4$
a. $(0, 2)$ **b.** $(-1, -2)$ **c.** $(3, -1)$

3. $2x - 4y = 6$
$-x + 2y = -3$
a. $(5, 1)$ **b.** $(-1, -1)$ **c.** $(3, 0)$

4. $2x - y = -3$
$y = 2x + 3$
a. $(2, -1)$ **b.** $(0, 3)$ **c.** $(-1, 1)$

Solve the following systems of linear equations by graphing, then write the solution set.

5. $x + y = 3$
$x - y = 1$

6. $x + y = 2$
$x - y = 4$

7. $x + y = 1$
$-x + y = 3$

8. $x + y = 1$
$x - y = -5$

9. $x + y = 8$
$-x + y = 2$

10. $x + y = 6$
$-x + y = -2$

11. $3x - 2y = 6$
$x - y = 1$

12. $5x - 2y = 10$
$x - y = -1$

13. $6x - 2y = 12$
$3x + y = -6$

14. $4x - 2y = 8$
$2x + y = -4$

15. $4x + y = 4$
$3x - y = 3$

16. $5x - y = 10$
$2x + y = 4$

17. $x + 2y = 0$
$2x - y = 0$

18. $3x + y = 0$
$5x - y = 0$

19. $3x - 5y = 15$
$-2x + y = 4$

20. $2x - 4y = 8$
$2x - y = -1$

21. $y = 2x + 1$
$y = -2x - 3$

22. $y = 3x - 4$
$y = -2x + 1$

23. $x + 3y = 3$
$y = x + 5$

24. $2x + y = -2$
$y = x + 4$

25. $x + y = 2$
$x = -3$

26. $x + y = 6$
$y = 2$

27. $x = -4$
$y = 6$

28. $x = 5$
$y = -1$

29. $x + y = 4$
$2x + 2y = -6$

30. $x - y = 3$
$2x - 2y = 6$

31. $4x - 2y = 8$
$2x - y = 4$

32. $3x - 6y = 6$
$x - 2y = 4$

33. As you probably have guessed by now, it can be difficult to solve a system of equations by graphing if the solution to the system contains a fraction. The solution to the following system is $\left(\frac{1}{2}, 1\right)$. Solve the system by graphing.

$$y = -2x + 2$$
$$y = 4x - 1$$

34. The solution to the following system is $\left(\frac{1}{3}, -2\right)$. Solve the system by graphing.

$$y = 3x - 3$$
$$y = -3x - 1$$

35. A second difficulty can arise in solving a system of equations by graphing if one or both of the equations is difficult to graph. The solution to the following system is $(2, 1)$. Solve the system by graphing.

$$3x - 8y = -2$$
$$x - y = 1$$

36. The solution to the following system is $(-3, 2)$. Solve the system by graphing.

$$2x + 5y = 4$$
$$x - y = -5$$

37. Find a and b so that $(2, -3)$ is a solution to the system of equations

$$x - y = a$$
$$2x + 3y = b$$

38. Find c and d so that $(-4, 1)$ is a solution to the system of equations

$$3x + y = c$$
$$x - 5y = d$$

39. Consider the following system of equations:

$$y = 3x + 1$$
$$y = ax + b$$

  a. Find the values for a and b so that the system has an infinite number of solutions.

  b. For what values of a and b will the system be inconsistent?

  c. For what values of a will the solution set to the system be a single ordered pair?

40. Figure 6 shows the graphs of both equations in the following linear system.

$$-31x + 61y = 183$$
$$-30x + 59y = -118$$

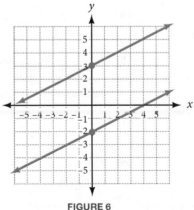

FIGURE 6

The two lines appear to be parallel. Explain how we know this system does have a solution.

Applying the Concepts

41. **Job Comparison** Jane is deciding between two sales positions. She can work for Marcy's and receive $8.00 per hour, or she can work for Gigi's, where she earns $6.00 per hour but also receives a $50 commission per week. The two lines in the following figure represent the money Jane will make for working at each of the jobs.

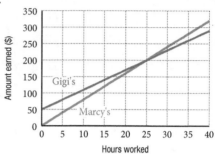

a. From the figure, how many hours would Jane have to work to earn the same amount at each of the positions?

b. If Jane expects to work less than 20 hours a week, which job should she choose?

c. If Jane expects to work more than 30 hours a week, which job should she choose?

42. **Truck Rental** You need to rent a moving truck for two days. Rider Moving Trucks charges $50 per day and $0.50 per mile. UMove Trucks charges $45 per day and $0.75 per mile. The following figure represents the cost of renting each of the trucks for two days.

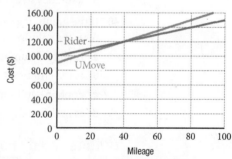

a. From the figure, after how many miles would the trucks cost the same?

b. Which company will give you a better deal if you drive less than 30 miles?

c. Which company will give you a better deal if you drive more than 60 miles?

Learning Objectives Assessment

The following problems can be used to help assess if you have successfully met the learning objectives for this section.

43. Which ordered pair is a solution to the following system?

$$x - y = 5$$
$$x + y = 3$$

a. $(4, -1)$ b. $(6, 1)$ c. $(2, -3)$ d. $(-4, 1)$

44. Which graph represents the solution to the following system of equations?

$$x - 2y = 4$$
$$3x + 2y = 6$$

a.

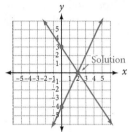

b.

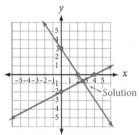

c.

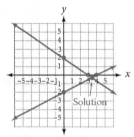

d.

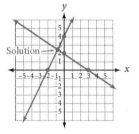

45. The graph of an inconsistent system of linear equations will be:

 a. two lines that coincide

 b. two distinct, parallel lines

 c. two lines that intersect at a single point

 d. two lines with one of the lines vertical

46. If the graph of a system of linear equations consists of two lines that coincide, then the solution set:

 a. is all real numbers

 b. is the empty set

 c. contains an infinite number of ordered pairs

 d. is undefined

Getting Ready For the Next Section

Simplify each of the following.

47. $(x + y) + (x - y)$

48. $(x + 2y) + (-x + y)$

49. $3(2x - y) + (x + 3y)$

50. $3(2x + 4y) - 2(3x + 5y)$

51. $-4(3x + 5y) + 5(5x + 4y)$

52. $(3x + 8y) - (3x - 2y)$

53. $6\left(\dfrac{1}{2}x - \dfrac{1}{3}y\right)$

54. $12\left(\dfrac{1}{4}x + \dfrac{2}{3}y\right)$

55. Let $x + y = 4$. If $x = 3$, find y.

56. Let $x + 2y = 4$. If $y = 3$, find x.

57. Let $x + 3y = 3$. If $x = 3$, find y.

58. Let $2x + 4y = -1$. If $y = \dfrac{1}{2}$, find x.

59. Let $3x + 5y = -7$. If $x = 6$, find y.

60. Let $3x - 2y = 12$. If $y = 6$, find x.

The Elimination Method 4.2

Learning Objectives

In this section, we will learn how to:

1. Solve a system of linear equations using the elimination method.

Introduction

The addition property of equality states that if equal quantities are added to both sides of an equation, the solution set is unchanged. In the past we have used this property to help solve equations in one variable. We will now use it to solve systems of linear equations. Here is another way to state the addition property of equality.

Let A, B, C, and D represent algebraic expressions.

$$\text{If} \qquad A = B$$
$$\text{and} \qquad C = D$$
$$\text{then} \qquad A + C = B + D$$

Because C and D are equal (that is, they represent the same number), what we have done is added the same amount to both sides of the equation $A = B$. Let's see how we can use this form of the addition property of equality to solve a system of linear equations.

EXAMPLE 1 Solve the following system.

$$x + y = 4$$
$$x - y = 2$$

SOLUTION The system is in the form of the addition property of equality as described in this section. It looks like this:

$$A = B$$
$$C = D$$

where A is $x + y$, B is 4, C is $x - y$, and D is 2.

We use the addition property of equality to add the left sides together and the right sides together, performing the addition in a vertical format.

$$\begin{array}{r} x + y = 4 \\ + \; x - y = 2 \\ \hline 2x + 0 = 6 \end{array}$$

> *Note* When adding the left sides together and the right sides together vertically, notice that we are really just combining like terms.

We now solve the resulting equation for x.

$$2x + 0 = 6$$
$$2x = 6$$
$$x = 3$$

The value we get for x is the value of the x-coordinate of the point of intersection of the two lines $x + y = 4$ and $x - y = 2$. To find the y-coordinate, we simply substitute $x = 3$ into either of the two original equations. Using the first equation, we get

$$3 + y = 4$$
$$y = 1$$

The solution to our system is the ordered pair $(3, 1)$. It satisfies both equations.

When	$x = 3$	When	$x = 3$
and	$y = 1$	and	$y = 1$
the equation	$x + y = 4$	the equation	$x - y = 2$
becomes	$3 + 1 \overset{?}{=} 4$	becomes	$3 - 1 \overset{?}{=} 2$
	$4 = 4$		$2 = 2$

If we were to graph both lines, we would see that they intersect at the point (3, 1) as shown in Figure 1.

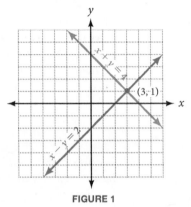

FIGURE 1

The most important part of this method of solving linear systems is eliminating one of the variables when we add the left and right sides together. In our first example, the equations were such that the y variable was eliminated when we added the left and right sides together. This is because the coefficients of the two terms containing y were opposites.

We will not always be able to eliminate a variable by adding the equations as given. We may have to multiply both sides of one (or both) equations by some value to ensure that one of the variables has coefficients that are opposites. The next examples show how this is done.

EXAMPLE 2   Solve the following system.

$$x + 2y = 4$$
$$x - y = -5$$

SOLUTION   Notice that if we were to add the equations together as they are, the resulting equation would have terms in both x and y. Let's eliminate the variable x by multiplying both sides of the second equation by -1 before we add the equations together. (As you will see, we can choose to eliminate either the x or the y variable.) Multiplying both sides of the second equation by -1 will not change its solution, so we do not need to be concerned that we have altered the system.

$$
\begin{array}{lll}
x + 2y = 4 & \xrightarrow{\text{No change}} & x + 2y = 4 \\
x - y = -5 & \xrightarrow[\text{Multiply by }-1]{} & \underline{-x + y = 5} \\
& & 0 + 3y = 9 \qquad \text{Add left and right sides} \\
& & 3y = 9 \\
& & y = 3 \quad \left\{ \begin{array}{l} y\text{-coordinate of the} \\ \text{point of intersection} \end{array} \right.
\end{array}
$$

Substituting $y = 3$ into either of the two original equations, we get $x = -2$. The solution to the system is $(-2, 3)$. It satisfies both equations.

EXAMPLE 3   Solve the following system.

$$2x - y = 6$$
$$x + 3y = 3$$

SOLUTION   Let's eliminate the y variable from the two equations. We can do this by multiplying the first equation by 3 and leaving the second equation unchanged.

$$2x - y = 6 \xrightarrow{\text{3 times both sides}} 6x - 3y = 18$$
$$x + 3y = 3 \xrightarrow[\text{No change}]{} x + 3y = 3$$

The important thing about our system now is that the coefficients (the numbers in front) of the y variables are opposites. When we add the terms on each side of the equal sign, then the terms in y will add to zero and be eliminated.

$$
\begin{array}{r}
6x - 3y = 18 \\
x + 3y = 3 \\
\hline
7x = 21
\end{array}
$$ Add corresponding terms

This gives us $x = 3$. Using this value of x in the second equation of our original system, we have

$$3 + 3y = 3$$
$$3y = 0$$
$$y = 0$$

The solution to our system is the ordered pair $(3, 0)$.

EXAMPLE 4   Solve the system.

$$2x + 4y = -1$$
$$3x + 5y = -2$$

SOLUTION   Let's eliminate x from the two equations. If we multiply the first equation by 3 and the second by -2, the coefficients of x will be 6 and -6, respectively. The x terms in the two equations will then add to zero.

$$2x + 4y = -1 \xrightarrow{\text{Multiply by 3}} 6x + 12y = -3$$
$$3x + 5y = -2 \xrightarrow[\text{Multiply by } -2]{} -6x - 10y = 4$$

We now add the left and right sides of our new system together.

$$
\begin{array}{r}
6x + 12y = -3 \\
-6x - 10y = 4 \\
\hline
2y = 1 \\
y = \dfrac{1}{2}
\end{array}
$$

Substituting $y = \frac{1}{2}$ into the first equation in our original system, we have

$$2x + 4\left(\frac{1}{2}\right) = -1$$
$$2x + 2 = -1$$
$$2x = -3$$
$$x = -\frac{3}{2}$$

The solution to our system is $\left(-\frac{3}{2}, \frac{1}{2}\right)$. It is the only ordered pair that satisfies both equations.

Note   If you are having trouble understanding this method of solution, it is probably because you can't see why we chose to multiply by 3 and -2 in the first step of Example 4. Look at the result of doing so: the $6x$ and $-6x$ will add to 0. We chose to multiply by 3 and -2 because they produce $6x$ and $-6x$, which will add to 0.

EXAMPLE 5   Solve the system.

$$3x + 5y = 2$$
$$5x + 4y = 1$$

SOLUTION   Let's eliminate y by multiplying the first equation by -4 and the second equation by 5.

$$3x + 5y = 2 \xrightarrow{\text{Multiply by } -4} -12x - 20y = -8$$
$$5x + 4y = 1 \xrightarrow[\text{Multiply by } 5]{} 25x + 20y = 5$$
$$13x = -3$$
$$x = -\frac{3}{13}$$

If we substitute $x = -\frac{3}{13}$ into the first equation, we have

$$3\left(-\frac{3}{13}\right) + 5y = 2$$

$$-\frac{9}{13} + 5y = 2$$

$$5y = 2 + \frac{9}{13}$$

$$5y = \frac{35}{13}$$

$$y = \frac{7}{13}$$

As an alternative to working with the fraction in the substitution step above, we can repeat the elimination process, but eliminate x instead of y. To do so, we can multiply the first equation by 5 and the second equation by -3.

$$3x + 5y = 2 \xrightarrow{\text{Multiply by } 5} 15x + 25y = 10$$
$$5x + 4y = 1 \xrightarrow[\text{Multiply by } -3]{} -15x - 12y = -3$$
$$13y = 7$$
$$y = \frac{7}{13}$$

Notice we get the same result for y. Using either approach, we obtain the solution $\left(-\frac{3}{13}, \frac{7}{13}\right)$.

EXAMPLE 6   Solve the system.

$$\frac{1}{2}x - \frac{1}{3}y = 2$$

$$\frac{1}{4}x + \frac{2}{3}y = 6$$

SOLUTION   Although we could solve this system without clearing the equations of fractions, there is probably less chance for error if we have only integer coefficients to work with. So let's begin by multiplying both sides of the first equation by 6 and both sides of the second equation by 12, to clear each equation of fractions.

$$\frac{1}{2}x - \frac{1}{3}y = 2 \xrightarrow{\text{Multiply by 6}} 3x - 2y = 12$$

$$\frac{1}{4}x + \frac{2}{3}y = 6 \xrightarrow[\text{Multiply by 12}]{} 3x + 8y = 72$$

Now we can eliminate x by multiplying the top equation by -1 and leaving the bottom equation unchanged.

$$3x - 2y = 12 \xrightarrow{\text{Multiply by } -1} -3x + 2y = -12$$

$$3x + 8y = 72 \xrightarrow[\text{No change}]{} \underline{3x + 8y = 72}$$

$$10y = 60$$

$$y = 6$$

We can substitute $y = 6$ into any equation that contains both x and y. Let's use $3x - 2y = 12$.

$$3x - 2(6) = 12$$

$$3x - 12 = 12$$

$$3x = 24$$

$$x = 8$$

The solution to the system is $(8, 6)$.

Our next two examples will show what happens when we apply the elimination method to a system of equations consisting of distinct parallel lines and to a system in which the lines coincide.

EXAMPLE 7   Solve the system.

$$2x - y = 2$$
$$4x - 2y = 12$$

SOLUTION   Let us choose to eliminate y from the system. We can do this by multiplying the first equation by -2 and leaving the second equation unchanged.

$$2x - y = 2 \xrightarrow{\text{Multiply by } -2} -4x + 2y = -4$$

$$4x - 2y = 12 \xrightarrow[\text{No change}]{} 4x - 2y = 12$$

If we add both sides of the resulting system, we have

$$-4x + 2y = -4$$

$$\underline{4x - 2y = 12}$$

$$0 + 0 = 8$$

$$0 = 8 \qquad \text{A false statement}$$

Both variables have been eliminated and we end up with the false statement $0 = 8$. We cannot solve for x or y. The system of equations is equivalent to an equation that is always false and therefore has no solution. There are no ordered pairs that satisfy both equations, so the solution set is $\varnothing$.

The reason this happened is that we have tried to solve a system that consists of two parallel lines. Figure 2 is a visual representation of the situation and is conclusive evidence that there is no solution to our system.

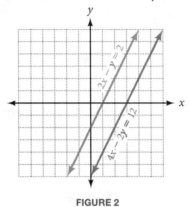

FIGURE 2

EXAMPLE 8   Solve the system.

$$4x - 3y = 2$$
$$8x - 6y = 4$$

SOLUTION   Multiplying the top equation by -2 and adding, we can eliminate the variable x.

$$
\begin{array}{rcl}
4x - 3y = 2 & \xrightarrow{\text{Multiply by } -2} & -8x + 6y = -4 \\
8x - 6y = 4 & \xrightarrow{\text{No change}} & \underline{8x - 6y = 4} \\
& & 0 = 0
\end{array}
$$

Both variables have been eliminated, and the resulting statement $0 = 0$ is true. The system of equations is equivalent to a statement that is always true, meaning that there is a solution corresponding to every real number. It does not imply that *any* ordered pair will satisfy both equations, but that there are an infinite number of ordered pairs that do.

In this case the lines coincide because the equations are equivalent. The solution set consists of all ordered pairs that satisfy either equation, which we can express as $\{(x, y) \mid 4x - 3y = 2\}$.

The preceding two examples illustrate the two special cases in which the graphs of the equations in the system either coincide or are parallel.

Here is a summary of our results from these two examples:

Both variables are eliminated and the resulting statement is false.	$\leftrightarrow$	The lines are parallel and there is no solution to the system.
Both variables are eliminated and the resulting statement is true.	$\leftrightarrow$	The lines coincide and there is an infinite number of solutions to the system.

The main idea in solving a system of linear equations by the elimination method is to use the multiplication property of equality on one or both of the original equations, if necessary, to make the coefficients of either variable opposites. The following box shows some steps to follow when solving a system of linear equations by the elimination method.

 HOW TO *Solve a System of Linear Equations by the Elimination Method*

Step 1: Decide which variable to eliminate. (In some cases one variable will be easier to eliminate than the other. With some practice you will notice which one it is.)

Step 2: If necessary, use the multiplication property of equality on each equation separately to make the coefficients of the variable that is to be eliminated opposites.

Step 3: Add the respective left and right sides of the system together.

Step 4: Solve for the variable remaining.

Step 5: Substitute the value of the variable from step 4 into either of the original equations and solve for the other variable.

Step 6: Check your solution in both equations, if necessary.

Getting Ready for Class

After reading through the preceding section, respond in your own words and in complete sentences.

A. How is the addition property of equality used in the elimination method of solving a system of linear equations?

B. What happens when we use the elimination method to solve a system of linear equations consisting of two parallel lines?

C. What does it mean when we solve a system of linear equations by the elimination method and we end up with the statement $0 = 0$?

D. What is the first step in solving a system of linear equations that contains fractions?

Problem Set 4.2

Solve the following systems of linear equations by elimination.

1. $x + y = 3$
$x - y = 1$

2. $x + y = -2$
$x - y = 6$

3. $x + y = 10$
$-x + y = 4$

4. $x - y = 1$
$-x - y = -7$

5. $x - y = 7$
$-x - y = 3$

6. $x - y = 4$
$2x + y = 8$

7. $x + y = -1$
$3x - y = -3$

8. $2x - y = -2$
$-2x - y = 2$

9. $3x + 2y = 1$
$-3x - 2y = -1$

10. $-2x - 4y = 1$
$2x + 4y = -1$

Solve each of the following systems by eliminating the variable y.

11. $3x - y = 4$
$2x + 2y = 24$

12. $2x + y = 3$
$3x + 2y = 1$

13. $5x - 3y = -2$
$10x - y = 1$

14. $4x - y = -1$
$2x + 4y = 13$

15. $11x - 4y = 11$
$5x + y = 5$

16. $3x - y = 7$
$10x - 5y = 25$

Solve each of the following systems by eliminating the variable x.

17. $3x - 5y = 7$
$-x + y = -1$

18. $4x + 2y = 32$
$x + y = -2$

19. $-x - 8y = -1$
$-2x + 4y = 13$

20. $-x + 10y = 1$
$-5x + 15y = -9$

21. $-3x - y = 7$
$6x + 7y = 11$

22. $-5x + 2y = -6$
$10x + 7y = 34$

Solve each of the following systems of linear equations by the elimination method.

23. $6x - y = -8$
$2x + y = -16$

24. $5x - 3y = -3$
$3x + 3y = -21$

25. $x + 3y = 9$
$2x - y = 4$

26. $x + 2y = 0$
$2x - y = 0$

27. $x - 6y = 3$
$4x + 3y = 21$

28. $8x + y = -1$
$4x - 5y = 16$

29. $2x + 9y = 2$

$5x + 3y = -8$

30. $5x + 2y = 11$

$7x + 8y = 7$

31. $\dfrac{1}{3}x + \dfrac{1}{4}y = \dfrac{7}{6}$

$\dfrac{3}{2}x - \dfrac{1}{3}y = \dfrac{7}{3}$

32. $\dfrac{7}{12}x - \dfrac{1}{2}y = \dfrac{1}{6}$

$\dfrac{2}{5}x - \dfrac{1}{3}y = \dfrac{11}{15}$

33. $3x + 2y = -1$

$6x + 4y = 0$

34. $8x - 2y = 2$

$4x - y = 2$

35. $11x + 6y = 17$

$5x - 4y = 1$

36. $3x - 8y = 7$

$10x - 5y = 45$

37. $\dfrac{1}{2}x + \dfrac{1}{6}y = \dfrac{1}{3}$

$-x - \dfrac{1}{3}y = -\dfrac{1}{6}$

38. $\dfrac{1}{3}x + \dfrac{1}{2}y = \dfrac{2}{3}$

$-\dfrac{2}{3}x - \phantom{\dfrac{1}{2}}y = -\dfrac{4}{3}$

39. Multiply both sides of the second equation in the following system by 100, and then solve as usual.

$$x + y = 22$$
$$0.05x + 0.10y = 1.70$$

40. Multiply both sides of the second equation in the following system by 100, and then solve as usual.

$$x + y = 15,000$$
$$0.06x + 0.07y = 980$$

Learning Objectives Assessment

The following problems can be used to help assess if you have successfully met the learning objectives for this section.

41. Solve the following system using the elimination method.

$$4x - y = -3$$
$$2x + 3y = -5$$

   a. $(1, 7)$ **b.** $(0, 3)$ **c.** $(-1, -1)$ **d.** $\varnothing$

42. Solve the following system using the elimination method.

$$x - 2y = -4$$
$$-3x + 6y = 4$$

   a. $\varnothing$ **b.** $(0, 2)$ **c.** $(2, 3)$ **d.** $\{(x, y) \mid x - 2y = -4\}$

Getting Ready for the Next Section

Solve. Round to the nearest hundredth when necessary.

43. $x + (2x - 1) = 2$ **44.** $2(2y + 7) - 3y = 12$

45. $2(3y - 1) - 3y = 4$ **46.** $-2x + 4(3x + 6) = 14$

47. $4x + 2(-2x + 4) = 8$ **48.** $1.5x + 15 = 0.75x + 24.95$

Solve each equation for the indicated variable.

49. $x - 3y = -1$ for x **50.** $-3x + y = 6$ for y

51. Let $y = 2x - 1$. If $x = 1$, find y.   **52.** Let $y = 2x - 8$. If $x = 5$, find y.

53. Let $x = 3y - 1$. If $y = 2$, find x.   **54.** Let $y = 3x + 6$. If $y = -6$, find x.

Let $y = 1.5x + 15$.

55. If $x = 13$, find y.   **56.** If $x = 14$, find y.

Let $y = 0.75x + 24.95$.

57. If $x = 12$, find y.   **58.** If $x = 16$, find y.

SPOTLIGHT ON SUCCESS   *Student Instructor Penelope*

Never give up on something that you can't go a day
without thinking about.
— Sir Winston Churchill

Since I was young, math has been a part of my life. Both my parents have Mathematics degrees, with one of them earning a doctorate in Math. Least to say, math was ingrained in my mind and a subject I had a knack for. As a child, I was so proud that I knew the square root of 144. Now this math is simple, but back then, I felt smart for knowing the answer. That excitement stayed alive through elementary school. Honestly, there were times when I became frustrated, such as when learning division and factoring for the first time, but I was still enthusiastic.

In middle school and high school, I lost my ability to enjoy math. With classes getting progressively more difficult and having to worry about the future, my focus veered away from wanting to learn more to forcing myself to master the material for the grades. The weight of having parents with math backgrounds became quite heavy. This created high standards and expectations from friends and family that turned into expectations that I placed on myself. I felt like I had to do well, to be more than proficient in math so that I would not let them down. It was not until I went to university that I found my motivation and inspiration again.

While working to attain a degree in Business Administration at Cal Poly, I decided to take the Calculus series. In a college setting, math was even more difficult to understand but I did not let that deter me. I persevered and found myself in the Proofs in Mathematics course, where I learned to truly appreciate math again. The class utilized a different way of thinking than I was used to. It was a challenging class; I struggled throughout most of it, but I was eager to learn the new material despite my grades not being what I desired. It was at that moment that I did not care how my grades ended up. Enjoying and understanding what I was learning was my main priority.

The Substitution Method

Learning Objectives

In this section, we will learn how to:

1. Solve a system of linear equations using the substitution method.

Introduction

There is a third method of solving systems of equations. It is the substitution method, and, like the elimination method, it can be used on any system of linear equations. Some systems, however, lend themselves more to the substitution method than others do.

VIDEO EXAMPLES

SECTION 4.3

EXAMPLE 1   Solve the following system.

$$x + y = 2$$
$$y = 2x - 1$$

SOLUTION   If we were to solve this system by the methods used in the previous section, we would have to rearrange the terms of the second equation so that similar terms would be in the same column. There is no need to do this, however, because the second equation tells us that y is $2x - 1$. We can replace the variable y in the first equation with the expression $2x - 1$ from the second equation; that is, we substitute $2x - 1$ from the second equation for y in the first equation. Here is what it looks like:

$$x + (2x - 1) = 2$$

The equation we end up with contains only the variable x. The variable y has been eliminated by substitution.

Solving the resulting equation, we have

$$x + (2x - 1) = 2$$
$$3x - 1 = 2$$
$$3x = 3$$
$$x = 1$$

This is the x-coordinate of the solution to our system. To find the y-coordinate, we can substitute $x = 1$ into the second equation of our system.

$$y = 2(1) - 1$$
$$y = 2 - 1$$
$$y = 1$$

The solution to our system is the ordered pair $(1, 1)$. It satisfies both of the original equations. Figure 1 provides visual evidence that the substitution method yields the correct solution.

Note   Sometimes this method of solving systems of equations is confusing the first time you see it. If you are confused, you may want to read through this first example more than once.

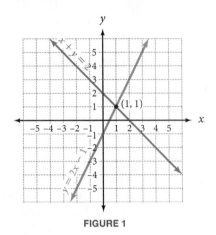

FIGURE 1

EXAMPLE 2 Solve the following system by the substitution method.

$$2x - 3y = 12$$
$$x = 2y + 7$$

SOLUTION This time, the second equation tells us x is $2y + 7$. We can replace the variable x in the first equation with $2y + 7$. Substituting $2y + 7$ from the second equation for x in the first equation, we have

$$2(2y + 7) - 3y = 12$$
$$4y + 14 - 3y = 12$$
$$y + 14 = 12$$
$$y = -2$$

To find the x-coordinate of our solution, we substitute $y = -2$ into the second equation in the original system.

When	$y = -2$
the equation	$x = 2y + 7$
becomes	$x = 2(-2) + 7$
	$x = -4 + 7 = 3$

The solution to our system is $(3, -2)$.

From the first two examples, we see that substitution works using either variable. In general, we usually choose the variable that is easiest to work with. In many cases, one of the variables will be easier to isolate than the other. The next two examples illustrate this situation.

EXAMPLE 3 Solve the following system by solving the first equation for x and then using the substitution method:

$$x - 3y = -1$$
$$2x - 3y = 4$$

SOLUTION Looking at both equations, we observe that the term containing x in the first equation is the only variable term with a coefficient of 1. Therefore, it will be easiest to isolate x in the first equation. We solve the first equation for x by adding $3y$ to both sides to get

$$x = 3y - 1$$

Substituting this expression for x in the second equation, we have

$$2(3y - 1) - 3y = 4$$
$$6y - 2 - 3y = 4$$
$$3y - 2 = 4$$
$$3y = 6$$
$$y = 2$$

Next, we find x.

When $y = 2$

the equation $x = 3y - 1$

becomes $x = 3(2) - 1$

$$x = 6 - 1$$
$$x = 5$$

The solution to our system is $(5, 2)$.

EXAMPLE 4   Solve by substitution.

$$-2x + 4y = 14$$
$$-3x + y = 6$$

SOLUTION   We can solve either equation for either variable. If we look at the system closely, it becomes apparent that solving the second equation for y is the easiest way to go. If we add $3x$ to both sides of the second equation, we have

$$y = 3x + 6$$

Substituting the expression $3x + 6$ back into the first equation in place of y yields the following result.

$$-2x + 4(3x + 6) = 14$$
$$-2x + 12x + 24 = 14$$
$$10x + 24 = 14$$
$$10x = -10$$
$$x = -1$$

Substituting $x = -1$ into the equation $y = 3x + 6$ leaves us with

$$y = 3(-1) + 6$$
$$y = -3 + 6$$
$$y = 3$$

The solution to our system is $(-1, 3)$.

Here are the steps to use in solving a system of equations by the substitution method.

> **HOW TO**   *Solving a System of Linear Equations by the Substitution Method*
>
> **Step 1:** Solve either of the equations for x or y. (This step is not necessary if one of the equations is already in the correct form, as in Examples 1 and 2.)
>
> **Step 2:** Substitute the expression for the variable obtained in step 1 into the other equation and solve it for the remaining variable.
>
> **Step 3:** Substitute the value from step 2 into the equation obtained in step 1 to find the value of the other variable.
>
> **Step 4:** Check your results, if necessary.

EXAMPLE 5   Solve by substitution.

$$4x + 2y = 8$$
$$y = -2x + 4$$

SOLUTION   Substituting the expression $-2x + 4$ for y from the second equation into the first equation, we have

$$4x + 2(-2x + 4) = 8$$
$$4x - 4x + 8 = 8$$
$$8 = 8 \qquad \text{A true statement}$$

Both variables have been eliminated, and we are left with a true statement. Recall from the last section that a true statement in this situation tells us the lines coincide; that is, the equations $4x + 2y = 8$ and $y = -2x + 4$ have exactly the same graph. Any point on that graph has coordinates that satisfy both equations and is a solution to the system. We can write the solution set as $\{(x, y) \mid 4x + 2y = 8\}$.

EXAMPLE 6   The following table shows two monthly contract rates charged by GTE Wireless for cellular phone use. At how many minutes will the two rates cost the same amount?

	Flat Rate	Plus	Per Minute Charge
Plan 1	$15		$1.50
Plan 2	$24.95		$0.75

SOLUTION   If we let $y =$ the monthly charge for x minutes of phone use, then the equations for each plan are

Plan 1: $y = 1.5x + 15$

Plan 2: $y = 0.75x + 24.95$

We can solve this system by substitution by replacing the variable y in Plan 2 with the expression $1.5x + 15$ from Plan 1. If we do so, we have

$$1.5x + 15 = 0.75x + 24.95$$
$$0.75x + 15 = 24.95$$
$$0.75x = 9.95$$
$$x = 13.27 \qquad \text{Round to the nearest hundredth}$$

The monthly bill is based on the number of minutes you use the phone, with any fraction of a minute moving you up to the next minute. If you talk for a total of 13 minutes, you are billed for 13 minutes. If you talk for 13 minutes, 10 seconds, you are billed for 14 minutes. The number of minutes on your bill will always be a whole number. So, to calculate the cost for talking 13.27 minutes, we would replace x with 14 and find y. Let's compare the two plans at $x = 13$ minutes and at $x = 14$ minutes.

Plan 1:	$y = 1.5x + 15$		Plan 2:	$y = 0.75x + 24.95$
When	$x = 13, y = \$34.50$		When	$x = 13, y = \$34.70$
When	$x = 14, y = \$36.00$		When	$x = 14, y = \$35.45$

The two plans will never give the same cost for talking x minutes. If you talk 13 or fewer minutes, Plan 1 will cost less. If you talk for more than 13 minutes, you will be billed for 14 minutes, and Plan 2 will cost less than Plan 1.

Getting Ready for Class

After reading through the preceding section, respond in your own words and in complete sentences.

A. What is the first step in solving a system of linear equations by substitution?

B. When would substitution be more efficient than the elimination method in solving two linear equations?

C. What does it mean when we solve a system of linear equations by the substitution method and we end up with the statement $8 = 8$?

D. How would you begin solving the following system using the substitution method?

$$x + y = 2$$
$$y = 2x - 1$$

Problem Set 4.3

Solve the following systems by substitution. Substitute the expression in the second equation into the first equation and solve.

1. $x + y = 11$
$y = 2x - 1$

2. $x - y = -3$
$y = 3x + 5$

3. $x + y = 20$
$y = 5x + 2$

4. $3x - y = -1$
$x = 2y - 7$

5. $-2x + y = -1$
$y = -4x + 8$

6. $4x - y = 5$
$y = -4x + 1$

7. $3x - 2y = -2$
$x = -y + 6$

8. $2x - 3y = 17$
$x = -y + 6$

9. $5x - 4y = -16$
$y = 4$

10. $6x + 2y = 18$
$x = 3$

11. $5x + 4y = 7$
$y = -3x$

12. $10x + 2y = -6$
$y = -5x$

Solve the following systems by solving one of the equations for x or y and then using the substitution method.

13. $x + 3y = 4$
$x - 2y = -1$

14. $x - y = 5$
$x + 2y = -1$

15. $2x + y = 1$
$x - 5y = 17$

16. $2x - 2y = 2$
$x - 3y = -7$

17. $3x + 5y = -3$
$x - 5y = -5$

18. $2x - 4y = -4$
$x + 2y = 8$

19. $5x + 3y = 0$
$x - 3y = -18$

20. $x - 3y = -5$
$x - 2y = 0$

21. $-3x - 9y = 7$
$x + 3y = 12$

22. $2x + 6y = -18$
$x + 3y = -9$

Solve each system by substitution. You can eliminate the decimals or fractions if you like, but you don't have to. The solution will be the same in either case.

23. $0.05x + 0.10y = 1.70$
$x + y = 22$

24. $0.20x + 0.50y = 3.60$
$x + y = 12$

25. $\dfrac{1}{4}x + \dfrac{1}{3}y = -\dfrac{1}{2}$
$x - y = 2$

26. $\dfrac{1}{2}x + \dfrac{3}{5}y = \dfrac{7}{10}$
$x - y = 3$

Solve the following systems using either the substitution method or the elimination method. Choose the method you feel is best suited for the problem.

27. $5x - 8y = 7$
$2x - y = 5$

28. $7x - 6y = -1$
$x - 2y = -1$

29. $5x - 6y = -4$
$x = y$

30. $2x - 4y = 0$
$y = x$

31. $4x + 2y = 3$
$3x - 12y = -9$

32. $3x + 4y = 10$
$16x - 2y = 30$

33. $-3x + 2y = 6$
$-3x + y = 0$

34. $-2x - y = -3$
$3x + y = 0$

35. $y = -x + 3$
$y = 2x - 12$

36. $y = 2x + 1$
$y = -2x + 1$

37. $7x - 11y = 16$
$y = 10$

38. $9x - 7y = -14$
$x = 7$

39. $-4x + 4y = -8$
$x - y = 2$

40. $-4x + 2y = -10$
$2x - y = 5$

41. $3x + 7y = 2$
$4x + 2y = -1$

42. $2x - 5y = 3$
$3x + 4y = -2$

Applying the Concepts

43. Gas Mileage Daniel is trying to decide whether to buy a car or a truck. The truck he is considering will cost him $250 a month in loan payments, and it gets 20 miles per gallon in gas mileage. The car will cost $340 a month in loan payments, but it gets 35 miles per gallon in gas mileage. Daniel estimates that he will pay $4.20 per gallon for gas. This means that the monthly cost to drive the truck x miles will be $y = \frac{4.20}{20}x + 250$. The total monthly cost to drive the car x miles will be $y = \frac{4.20}{35}x + 340$. The following figure shows the graph of each equation:

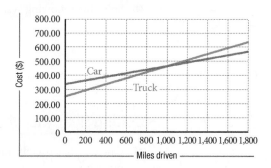

a. At how many miles do the car and the truck cost the same to operate?

b. If Daniel drives more than 1,200 miles, which will be cheaper?

c. If Daniel drives fewer than 800 miles, which will be cheaper?

d. Why do the graphs appear in the first quadrant only?

44. Video Production Pat runs a small company that duplicates videotapes. The daily cost and daily revenue for a company duplicating videos are shown in the following figure. The daily cost for duplicating x videos is $y = \frac{6}{5}x + 20$; the daily revenue (the amount of money he brings in each day) for duplicating x videos is $y = 1.7x$. The graphs of the two lines are shown in the following figure:

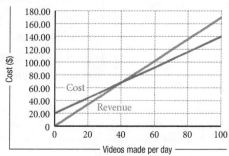

a. Pat will "break even" when his cost and his revenue are equal. How many videos does he need to duplicate to break even?

b. Pat will incur a loss when his revenue is less than his cost. If he duplicates 30 videos in one day, will he incur a loss?

c. Pat will make a profit when his revenue is larger than his costs. For what values of x will Pat make a profit?

d. Why do the graphs appear in the first quadrant only?

Learning Objectives Assessment

The following problems can be used to help assess if you have successfully met the learning objectives for this section.

45. Which substitution could be used to solve the following system?

$$2x + 5y = 4$$
$$x - 4y = -2$$

a. $x = -5y + 2$ **b.** $x = 4y - 2$ **c.** $y = x + 2$ **d.** $y = -x + \dfrac{1}{2}$

46. Solve the following system using the substitution method.

$$2x + y = -1$$
$$x - 2y = 7$$

a. $(-1, 1)$ **b.** $(2, -5)$ **c.** $(1, -3)$ **d.** $\varnothing$

Getting Ready for the Next Section

47. One number is eight more than five times another; their sum is 26. Find the numbers.

48. One number is three less than four times another; their sum is 27. Find the numbers.

49. The difference of two positive numbers is nine. The larger number is six less than twice the smaller number. Find the numbers.

50. The difference of two positive numbers is 17. The larger number is one more than twice the smaller number. Find the numbers.

51. The length of a rectangle is five inches more than three times the width. The perimeter is 58 inches. Find the length and width.

52. The length of a rectangle is three inches less than twice the width. The perimeter is 36 inches. Find the length and width.

53. John has $1.70 in nickels and dimes in his pocket. He has four more nickels than he does dimes. How many of each does he have?

54. Jamie has $2.65 in dimes and quarters in her pocket. She has two more dimes than she does quarters. How many of each does she have?

Applications

Learning Objectives

In this section, we will learn how to:

1. Solve number problems using a system of equations.

2. Solve interest problems using a system of equations.

3. Solve coin problems using a system of equations.

4. Solve mixture problems using a system of equations.

Introduction

I often have heard students remark about the word problems in beginning algebra: "What does this have to do with real life?" Most of the word problems we will encounter don't have much to do with "real life." We are actually just practicing. Ultimately, all problems requiring the use of algebra are word problems; that is, they are stated in words first, then translated to symbols. The problem then is solved by some system of mathematics, like algebra. Most real applications involve calculus or higher levels of mathematics. So, if the problems we solve are upsetting or frustrating to you, then you are probably taking them too seriously.

The word problems in this section have two unknown quantities. We will write two equations in two variables (each of which represents one of the unknown quantities), which of course is a system of equations. We then solve the system by one of the methods developed in the previous sections of this chapter. Here are the steps to follow in solving these word problems.

Note If this Blueprint for Problem Solving looks familiar to you, it should. We introduced it in Section 2.6 when we solved word problems with one variable. In that chapter, all of our problems involved one equation in one variable. Now we are solving problems using a system of equations (two equations in two variables). As you work through the examples in this section, you will see some word problems that are almost identical to ones we solved earlier. The difference is the method we use to solve them.

HOW TO — Use the Blueprint for Problem Solving For a System of Equations

Step 1: *Read* the problem, and then mentally *list* the items that are known and the items that are unknown.

Step 2: *Assign variables* to each of the unknown items; that is, let x be one of the unknown items and y be the other unknown item. Then *translate* the other *information* in the problem to expressions involving the two variables.

Step 3: *Reread* the problem, and then *write a system of equations,* using the items and variables listed in steps 1 and 2, that describes the situation.

Step 4: *Solve the system* found in step 3.

Step 5: *Write* your *answers* using complete sentences.

Step 6: *Reread* the problem, and *check* your solution with the original words in the problem.

Remember, the more problems you work, the more problems you will be able to work. If you have trouble getting started on the problem set, come back to the examples and work through them yourself. The examples are similar to the problems found in the problem set.

Number Problem

EXAMPLE 1   One number is 2 more than 5 times another number. Their sum is 20. Find the two numbers.

SOLUTION   Applying the steps in our blueprint, we have

Step 1:   We know that the two numbers have a sum of 20 and that one of them is 2 more than 5 times the other. We don't know what the numbers themselves are.

Step 2:   Let x represent one of the numbers and y represent the other. "One number is 2 more than 5 times another" translates to

$$y = 5x + 2$$

"Their sum is 20" translates to

$$x + y = 20$$

Step 3:   The system that describes the situation must be

$$x + y = 20$$
$$y = 5x + 2$$

Step 4:   We can solve this system by substituting the expression $5x + 2$ in the second equation for y in the first equation:

$$x + (5x + 2) = 20$$
$$6x + 2 = 20$$
$$6x = 18$$
$$x = 3$$

Using $x = 3$ in either of the first two equations and then solving for y, we get $y = 17$.

Step 5:   So 17 and 3 are the numbers we are looking for.

Step 6:   The number 17 is 2 more than 5 times 3, and the sum of 17 and 3 is 20.

Interest Problem

EXAMPLE 2   Mr. Hicks had $15,000 to invest. He invested some at 6% and the rest at 7%. If he earns $980 in interest, how much did he invest at each rate?

SOLUTION   Remember, step 1 is done mentally.

Step 1:   We do not know the specific amounts invested in the two accounts. We do know that their sum is $15,000 and that the interest rates on the two accounts are 6% and 7%. We also know that the total interest earned is $980.

Step 2:   Let x be the amount invested at 6% and y be the amount invested at 7%. Because Mr. Hicks invested a total of $15,000, we have

$$x + y = 15,000$$

The interest he earns comes from 6% of the amount invested at 6% and 7% of the amount invested at 7%. To find 6% of x, we multiply x by 0.06, which gives us $0.06x$. To find 7% of y, we multiply 0.07 times y and get $0.07y$.

$$\underset{\text{at 6\%}}{\text{Interest}} + \underset{\text{at 7\%}}{\text{Interest}} = \underset{\text{interest}}{\text{Total}}$$

$$0.06x + 0.07y = 980$$

Step 3: The system is

$$x + y = 15,000$$
$$0.06x + 0.07y = 980$$

Step 4: We multiply the first equation by -6 and the second by 100 to eliminate x:

Multiply by -6

$$x + \qquad y = 15,000 \longrightarrow -6x - 6y = -90,000$$
$$0.06x + 0.07y = 980 \qquad \longrightarrow \underline{\quad 6x + 7y = 98,000}$$

Multiply by 100

$$y = 8,000$$

Substituting $y = 8,000$ into the first equation and solving for x, we get $x = 7,000$.

Step 5: He invested $7,000 at 6% and $8,000 at 7%.

Step 6: Checking our solutions in the original problem, we have: The sum of $7,000 and $8,000 is $15,000, the total amount he invested. To complete our check, we find the total interest earned from the two accounts:

The interest on $7,000 at 6% is 0.06(7,000) = $420
The interest on $8,000 at 7% is 0.07(8,000) = $560

The total interest is $980

Coin Problem

EXAMPLE 3   John has $1.70 all in dimes and nickels. He has a total of 22 coins. How many of each kind does he have?

SOLUTION

Step 1: We know that John has 22 coins that are dimes and nickels. We know that a dime is worth 10 cents and a nickel is worth 5 cents. We do not know the specific number of dimes and nickels he has.

Step 2: Let x be the number of nickels and y be the number of dimes. The total number of coins is 22, so

$$x + y = 22$$

The total amount of money he has is $1.70, which comes from nickels and dimes:

$$\begin{array}{ccccc} \text{Amount of money} & + & \text{Amount of money} & = & \text{Total amount} \\ \text{in nickels} & & \text{in dimes} & & \text{of money} \\ 0.05x & + & 0.10y & = & 1.70 \end{array}$$

Step 3: The system that represents the situation is

$$x + y = 22 \qquad \text{The number of coins}$$
$$0.05x + 0.10y = 1.70 \qquad \text{The value of the coins}$$

Step 4: We multiply the first equation by -5 and the second by 100 to eliminate the variable x:

Multiply by -5

$$x + \qquad y = \quad 22 \longrightarrow -5x - 5y = -110$$
$$0.05x + 0.10y = 1.70 \longrightarrow \underline{\quad 5x + 10y = 170}$$

Multiply by 100

$$5y = 60$$
$$y = 12$$

Substituting $y = 12$ into our first equation, we get $x = 10$.

Step 5: John has 12 dimes and 10 nickels.
Step 6: Twelve dimes and 10 nickels total 22 coins.

$$12 \text{ dimes are worth } 12(0.10) = 1.20$$
$$\underline{10 \text{ nickels are worth } 10(0.05) = 0.50}$$
$$\text{The total value is}\quad \$1.70$$

Mixture Problem

EXAMPLE 4   How much of a 20% alcohol solution and 50% alcohol solution must be mixed to get 12 gallons of 30% alcohol solution?

SOLUTION   To solve this problem we must first understand that a 20% alcohol solution is 20% alcohol and 80% water.

Step 1: We know there are two solutions that together must total 12 gallons. 20% of one of the solutions is alcohol and the rest is water, whereas the other solution is 50% alcohol and 50% water. We do not know how many gallons of each individual solution we need.

Step 2: Let x be the number of gallons of 20% alcohol solution needed and y be the number of gallons of 50% alcohol solution needed. Because the total number of gallons we will end up with is 12, and this 12 gallons must come from the two solutions we are mixing, our first equation is

$$x + y = 12$$

To obtain our second equation, we look at the amount of alcohol in our two original solutions and our final solution. The amount of alcohol in the x gallons of 20% solution is $0.20x$, and the amount of alcohol in y gallons of 50% solution is $0.50y$. The amount of alcohol in the 12 gallons of 30% solution is $0.30(12)$. Because the amount of alcohol we start with must equal the amount of alcohol we end up with, our second equation is

$$0.20x + 0.50y = 0.30(12)$$

The information we have so far can also be summarized with a table. Sometimes by looking at a table like the one that follows it is easier to see where the equations come from.

	20% Solution	50% Solution	Final Solution
Number of Gallons	x	y	12
Gallons of Alcohol	$0.20x$	$0.50y$	$0.30(12)$

Step 3: Our system of equations is
$$x + y = 12$$
$$0.20x + 0.50y = 0.30(12)$$

Step 4: We can solve this system by substitution. Solving the first equation for y and substituting the result into the second equation, we have

$$0.20x + 0.50(12 - x) = 0.30(12)$$

Multiplying each side by 10 gives us an equivalent equation that is a little easier to work with.

$$2x + 5(12 - x) = 3(12)$$
$$2x + 60 - 5x = 36$$
$$-3x + 60 = 36$$
$$-3x = -24$$
$$x = 8$$

If x is 8, then y must be 4 because $x + y = 12$.

Step 5: It takes 8 gallons of 20% alcohol solution and 4 gallons of 50% alcohol solution to produce 12 gallons of 30% alcohol solution.

Step 6: Try it and see.

Motion Problem

If an object is moving at a steady speed, we can find the distance the object has traveled during a given time using the rate equation.

$$\text{Distance} = \text{Rate} \cdot \text{Time}$$
$$d = r \cdot t$$

In our last example, we will see how the rate equation can be used when an object is traveling in a current.

Current

EXAMPLE 5 It takes 2 hours for a boat to travel 28 miles downstream (with the current). The same boat can travel 18 miles upstream (against the current) in 3 hours. What is the speed of the boat in still water, and what is the speed of the current of the river?

SOLUTION

Step 1: A boat travels 18 miles upstream and 28 miles downstream. The trip upstream takes 3 hours. The trip downstream takes 2 hours. We don't know the speed of the boat or the speed of the current.

Step 2: Let x be the speed of the boat in still water and let y be the speed of the current. The average speed (rate) of the boat upstream is $x - y$, because it is traveling against the current. The rate of the boat downstream is $x + y$, because the boat is traveling with the current.

Step 3: Putting the information into a table, we have

Note When setting up motion problems involving current or wind, the rate of the object is always first, followed by the rate of the current or wind. That is, the two expressions for r are given by

rate of ± rate of
object current/wind

	d (distance, miles)	r (rate, mph)	t (time, h)
Upstream	18	$x - y$	3
Downstream	28	$x + y$	2

The formula for the relationship between distance d, rate r, and time t is $d = rt$ (the rate equation).

Because $d = r \cdot t$, the system we need to solve the problem is

$$18 = (x - y) \cdot 3$$
$$28 = (x + y) \cdot 2$$

which is equivalent to

$$6 = x - y$$
$$14 = x + y$$

Step 4: Adding the two equations, we have

$$20 = 2x$$

$$x = 10$$

Substituting $x = 10$ into $14 = x + y$, we see that

$$y = 4$$

Step 5: The speed of the boat in still water is 10 miles per hour; the speed of the current is 4 miles per hour.

Step 6: The boat travels at $10 + 4 = 14$ miles per hour downstream, so in 2 hours it will travel $14 \cdot 2 = 28$ miles. The boat travels at $10 - 4 = 6$ miles per hour upstream, so in 3 hours it will travel $6 \cdot 3 = 18$ miles.

Getting Ready for Class

After reading through the preceding section, respond in your own words and in complete sentences.

A. If you were to apply the Blueprint for Problem Solving from Section 2.6 to the examples in this section, what would be the first step?

B. If you were to apply the Blueprint for Problem Solving from Section 2.6 to the examples in this section, what would be the last step?

C. Which method of solving systems of equations do you prefer? Why?

D. Write an application problem for which the solution depends on solving a system of equations.

Solve the following word problems. Be sure to show the equations used.

Number Problems

1. Two numbers have a sum of 25. One number is 5 more than the other. Find the numbers.

2. The difference of two numbers is 6. Their sum is 30. Find the two numbers.

3. The sum of two numbers is 15. One number is 4 times the other. Find the numbers.

4. The difference of two positive numbers is 28. One number is 3 times the other. Find the two numbers.

5. Two positive numbers have a difference of 5. The larger number is one more than twice the smaller. Find the two numbers.

6. One number is 2 more than 3 times another. Their sum is 26. Find the two numbers.

7. One number is 5 more than 4 times another. Their sum is 35. Find the two numbers.

8. The difference of two positive numbers is 8. The larger is twice the smaller decreased by 7. Find the two numbers.

Interest Problems

9. Mr. Wilson invested money in two accounts. His total investment was $20,000. If one account pays 6% in interest and the other pays 8% in interest, how much does he have in each account if he earned a total of $1,380 in interest in 1 year?

10. A total of $11,000 was invested. Part of the $11,000 was invested at 4%, and the rest was invested at 7%. If the investments earn $680 per year, how much was invested at each rate?

11. A woman invested 4 times as much at 5% as she did at 6%. The total amount of interest she earns in 1 year from both accounts is $520. How much did she invest at each rate?

12. Ms. Hagan invested twice as much money in an account that pays 7% interest as she did in an account that pays 6% in interest. Her total investment pays her $1,000 a year in interest. How much did she invest at each rate?

Coin Problems

13. Ron has 14 coins with a total value of $2.30. The coins are nickels and quarters. How many of each coin does he have?

14. Diane has $0.95 in dimes and nickels. She has a total of 11 coins. How many of each kind does she have?

15. Suppose Tom has 21 coins totaling $3.45. If he has only dimes and quarters, how many of each type does he have?

16. A coin collector has 31 dimes and nickels with a total face value of $2.40. How many of each coin does she have?

Mixture Problems

17. How many liters of 50% alcohol solution and 20% alcohol solution must be mixed to obtain 18 liters of 30% alcohol solution?

	50% Solution	20% Solution	Final Solution
Number of Liters	x	y	18
Liters of Alcohol			

18. How many liters of 10% alcohol solution and 5% alcohol solution must be mixed to obtain 40 liters of 8% alcohol solution?

	10% Solution	5% Solution	Final Solution
Number of Liters	x	y	40
Liters of Alcohol			

19. A mixture of 8% disinfectant solution is to be made from 10% and 7% disinfectant solutions. How much of each solution should be used if 30 gallons of 8% solution are needed?

20. How much 50% antifreeze solution and 40% antifreeze solution should be combined to give 50 gallons of 46% antifreeze solution?

Rate Problems

21. It takes a boat 2 hours to travel 24 miles downstream and 3 hours to travel 18 miles upstream. What is the speed of the boat in still water? What is the speed of the current of the river?

22. A boat on a river travels 20 miles downstream in only 2 hours. It takes the same boat 6 hours to travel 12 miles upstream. What are the speed of the boat and the speed of the current?

23. An airplane flying with the wind can cover a certain distance in 2 hours. The return trip against the wind takes $2\frac{1}{2}$ hours. How fast is the plane and what is the speed of the air, if the distance is 600 miles?

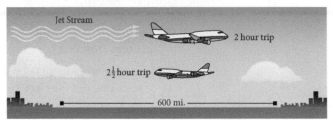

24. An airplane covers a distance of 1,500 miles in 3 hours when it flies with the wind and $3\frac{1}{3}$ hours when it flies against the wind. What is the speed of the plane in still air?

Miscellaneous Problems

25. For a Saturday matinee, adult tickets cost $5.50 and kids under 12 pay only $4.00. If 70 tickets are sold for a total of $310, how many of the tickets were adult tickets and how many were sold to kids under 12?

26. The Bishop's Peak 4-H club is having its annual fundraising dinner. Adults pay $15 apiece and children pay $10 apiece. If the number of adult tickets sold is twice the number of children's tickets sold, and the total income for the dinner is $1,600, how many of each kind of ticket did the 4-H club sell?

27. A farmer has 96 feet of fence with which to make a corral. If he arranges it into a rectangle that is twice as long as it is wide, what are the dimensions?

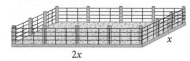

28. If a 22-inch rope is to be cut into two pieces so that one piece is 3 inches longer than twice the other, how long is each piece?

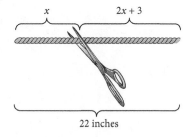

29. A gambler finishes a session of blackjack with $5 chips and $25 chips. If he has 45 chips in all, with a total value of $465, how many of each kind of chip does the gambler have?

30. Tyler has been saving his winning lottery tickets. He has 23 tickets that are worth a total of $175. If each ticket is worth either $5 or $10, how many of each does he have?

31. Mary Jo spends $2,550 to buy stock in two companies. She pays $11 a share to one of the companies and $20 a share to the other. If she ends up with a total of 150 shares, how many shares did she buy at $11 a share and how many did she buy at $20 a share?

32. Kelly sells 62 shares of stock she owns for a total of $433. If the stock was in two different companies, one selling at $6.50 a share and the other at $7.25 a share, how many of each did she sell?

Learning Objectives Assessment

The following problems can be used to help assess if you have successfully met the learning objectives for this section.

For Problems 49-52, determine which system of equations is an appropriate model for solving the given problem.

33. Two numbers have a sum of 49 and a difference of 7. Find the numbers.

a. $x + y = 49$
$x - y = 7$

b. $xy = 49$
$y - x = 7$

c. $x + y = 49$
$y = 7 - x$

d. $x + y = 7$
$x - y = 49$

34. A total of $8,000 was invested in two accounts, one earning 3% interest and the other 5% interest. If the investments earn a total of $352 in interest after one year, find the amount invested at each rate.

a. $x + y = 8{,}000$
$0.03x + 0.05y = 352$

b. $x + y = 352$
$0.03x + 0.05y = 8{,}000$

c. $x + y = 8{,}000$
$3x + 5y = 352$

d. $x + y = 352$
$3x + 5y = 8{,}000$

35. Valerie has $2.50 in nickels and quarters. She has a total of 14 coins. How many of each coin does she have?

a. $x + y = 250$
$25x + 5y = 14$

b. $x + y = 2.50$
$0.25x + 0.05y = 14$

c. $x + y = 14$
$0.25x + 0.05y = 2.50$

d. $x + y = 14$
$25x + 5y = 2.50$

36. How many liters of 40% alcohol solution and 75% alcohol solution must be mixed to obtain 20 liters of 50% alcohol solution?

a. $x + y = 20$
$0.40x + 0.75y = 0.50$

b. $x + y = 20$
$0.40x + 0.75y = 0.50(20)$

c. $x + y = 50$
$40x + 75y = 20$

d. $x + y = 20$
$40x + 75y = 50$

Maintaining Your Skills

Simplify.

37. $6(3 + 4) + 5$

38. $[(1 + 2)(2 + 3)] + (4 \div 2)$

39. $1^2 + 2^2 + 3^2$

40. $(1 + 2 + 3)^2$

41. $5(6 + 3 \cdot 2) + 4 + 3 \cdot 2$

42. $(1 + 2)^3 + [(2 \cdot 3) + (4 \cdot 5)]$

43. $(1^3 + 2^3) + [(2 \cdot 3) + (4 \cdot 5)]$

44. $[2(3 + 4 + 5)] \div 3$

45. $(2 \cdot 3 + 4 + 5) \div 3$

46. $10^4 + 10^3 + 10^2 + 10^1$

47. $6 \cdot 10^3 + 5 \cdot 10^2 + 4 \cdot 10^1$

48. $5 \cdot 10^3 + 2 \cdot 10^2 + 8 \cdot 10^1$

49. $1 \cdot 10^3 + 7 \cdot 10^2 + 6 \cdot 10^1$

50. $4(2 - 1) + 5(3 - 2)$

51. $4 \cdot 2 - 1 + 5 \cdot 3 - 2$

52. $2^3 + 3^2 \cdot 4 - 5$

53. $(2^3 + 3^2) \cdot 4 - 5$

54. $4^2 - 2^4 + (2 \cdot 2)^2$

55. $2(2^2 + 3^2) + 3(3^2)$

56. $2 \cdot 2^2 + 3^2 + 3 \cdot 3^2$

Chapter 4 Summary

EXAMPLES

1. The solution to the system
$$x + 2y = 4$$
$$x - y = 1$$
is the ordered pair (2, 1). It is the only ordered pair that satisfies both equations.

Definitions [4.1]

1. A system of linear equations, as the term is used in this book, is two linear equations that each contain the same two variables.

2. The solution set for a system of equations is the set of all ordered pairs that satisfy *both* equations. The solution set to a system of linear equations will be one of the following:

   - One ordered pair when the graphs of the two equations intersect at only one point (this is the most common situation)
   - No ordered pairs when the graphs of the two equations are distinct, parallel lines
   - An infinite number of ordered pairs when the graphs of the two equations coincide (are the same line)

Solving a System by Graphing [4.1]

2. Solving the system in Example 1 by graphing looks like

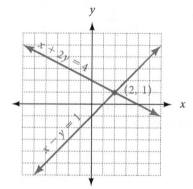

Step 1: Graph the first equation.

Step 2: Graph the second equation on the same set of axes.

Step 3: Identify the coordinates of the point where the graphs appear to cross each other (the coordinates of the point of intersection).

Step 4: Check the solution to verify that it satisfies *both* equations.

Solving a System by the Elimination Method [4.2]

3. We can eliminate the y variable from the system in Example 1 by multiplying both sides of the second equation by 2 and adding the result to the first equation

$$x + 2y = 4 \qquad\qquad x + 2y = 4$$
$$x - y = 1 \xrightarrow[\text{Multiply by 2}]{} 2x - 2y = 2$$
$$\overline{\qquad\qquad\quad 3x \qquad = 6}$$
$$x \qquad = 2$$

Substituting $x = 2$ into either of the original two equations gives $y = 1$. The solution is (2, 1).

Step 1: Look the system over to decide which variable will be easier to eliminate.

Step 2: If necessary, use the multiplication property of equality on each equation separately to ensure that the coefficients of the variable to be eliminated are opposites.

Step 3: Add the respective left and right sides of the system together.

Step 4: Solve for the variable remaining.

Step 5: Substitute the solution from step 4 into either of the original equations, and solve for the other variable.

Step 6: Check your solution in both equations, if necessary.

Solving a System by the Substitution Method [4.3]

4. We can apply the substitution method to the system in Example 1 by first solving the second equation for x to get $x = y + 1$. Substituting this expression for x into the first equation, we have

$$(y + 1) + 2y = 4$$
$$3y + 1 = 4$$
$$3y = 3$$
$$y = 1$$

Using $y = 1$ in either of the original equations gives $x = 2$.

Step 1: Solve either of the equations for one of the variables (this step is not necessary if one of the equations has the correct form already).

Step 2: Substitute the results of step 1 into the other equation, and solve for the remaining variable.

Step 3: Substitute the value from step 2 into the equation obtained in step 1 to find the value of the other variable.

Step 4: Check your solution, if necessary.

Special Cases [4.2, 4.3]

In some cases, using the elimination or substitution method eliminates both variables. The situation is interpreted as follows.

1. If the resulting statement is *false*, then the lines are parallel and there is no solution to the system.

2. If the resulting statement is *true*, then the equations represent the same line (the lines coincide). In this case any ordered pair that satisfies either equation is a solution to the system.

COMMON MISTAKE

The most common mistake encountered in solving linear systems is the failure to complete the problem. Here is an example.

$$x + y = 8$$
$$x - y = 4$$
$$2x = 12$$
$$x = 6$$

This is only half the solution. To find the other half, we must substitute the 6 back into one of the original equations and then solve for y.

Remember, solutions to systems of linear equations always consist of ordered pairs. We need an x-coordinate and a y-coordinate; $x = 6$ can never be a solution to a system of linear equations.

1. Write the solution to the system which is graphed below. [4.1]

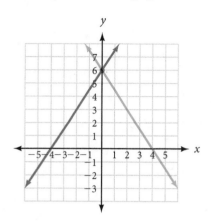

Solve each system by graphing. [4.1]

2. $4x - 2y = 8$

$y = \dfrac{2}{3}x$

3. $3x - 2y = 13$

$y = 4$

4. $2x - 2y = -12$

$-3x - y = 2$

Solve each system by the elimination method. [4.2]

5. $x - y = -9$
$2x + 3y = 7$

6. $3x - y = 1$
$5x - y = 3$

7. $2x + 3y = -3$
$x + 6y = 12$

8. $2x + 3y = 4$
$4x + 6y = 8$

Solve each system by the substitution method. [4.3]

9. $3x - y = 12$
$\quad\ y = 2x - 8$

10. $3x - 6y = 3$
$\quad\ x = 4y - 17$

11. $2x - 3y = -18$
$3x + y = -5$

12. $2x - 3y = 13$
$x - 4y = -1$

Solve the following word problems. In each case, be sure to show the system of equations that describes the situation. [4.4]

13. Number Problem The sum of two numbers is 18. One number is 2 more than 3 times the other. Find the two numbers.

14. Investing Dave has $2,000 to invest. He would like to earn $135.20 per year in interest. How much should he invest at 6% if the rest is to be invested at 7%?

15. Coin Problem Maria has 19 coins that total $1.35. If the coins are all nickels and dimes, how many of each type does she have?

16. Mixture Problem How much 40% antifreeze solution and 70% antifreeze solution should be combined to obtain 30 gallons of 50% antifreeze solution?

17. Fencing Problem A rancher wants to build a rectangular corral using 198 feet of fence. If the length of the corral is to be 15 feet longer than twice the width, find the dimensions of the corral.

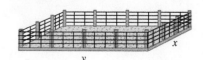

Exponents and Polynomials

5

Chapter Outline

© XYZ Textbooks

I f you were given a penny on the first day of September, and then each day after that you were given twice the amount of money you received the day before, how much money would you receive on September 30th? To begin, Table 1 and Figure 1 show the amount of money you would receive on each of the first 10 days of the month. As you can see, on the tenth day of the month you would receive $5.12.

TABLE 1

Money That Doubles Each Day

Day	Money (in cents)
1	$1 = 2^0$
2	$2 = 2^1$
3	$4 = 2^2$
4	$8 = 2^3$
5	$16 = 2^4$
6	$32 = 2^5$
7	$64 = 2^6$
8	$128 = 2^7$
9	$256 = 2^8$
10	$512 = 2^9$

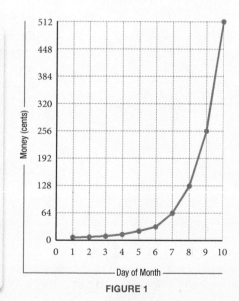

FIGURE 1

To find the amount of money on day 30, we could continue to double the amount on each of the next 20 days. Or, we could notice the pattern of exponents in the second column of the table and reason that the amount of money on day 30 would be 2^{29} cents, which is a very large number. In fact, 2^{29} cents is $5,368,709.12—a little less than $5.4 million. When you are finished with this chapter, you will have a good working knowledge of exponents.

© Steve Debenport / iStockPhoto

Study Skills

The study skills for this chapter are about attitude. They are points of view that point toward success.

1. **Be Focused, Not Distracted** I have students who begin their assignments by asking themselves, "Why am I taking this class?" Or, "When am I ever going to use this stuff?" If you are asking yourself similar questions, you may be distracting yourself away from doing the things that will produce the results you want in this course. Don't dwell on questions and evaluations of the class that can be used as excuses for not doing well. If you want to succeed in this course, focus your energy and efforts toward success, rather than distracting yourself away from your goals.

2. **Be Resilient** Don't let setbacks keep you from your goals. You want to put yourself on the road to becoming a person who can succeed in this class or any class in college. Failing a test or quiz, or having a difficult time on some topics, is normal. No one goes through college without some setbacks. Don't let a temporary disappointment keep you from succeeding in this course. A low grade on a test or quiz is simply a signal that some reevaluation of your study habits needs to take place.

3. **Intend to Succeed** I always have a few students who simply go through the motions of studying without intending to master the material. It is more important to them to look like they are studying than to actually study. You need to study with the intention of being successful in the course. Intend to master the material, no matter what it takes.

Learning Objectives

In this section, we will learn how to:

1. Multiply like bases by adding exponents.
2. Simplify the power of a power.
3. Simplify the power of a product.
4. Write numbers in scientific notation.

Introduction

Recall that an *exponent* is a number written just above and to the right of another number, which is called the *base*. In the expression 5^2, for example, the exponent is 2 and the base is 5. The expression 5^2 is read "5 to the second power" or "5 squared." The meaning of the expression is

$$5^2 = 5 \cdot 5 = 25$$

In the expression 5^3, the exponent is 3 and the base is 5. The expression 5^3 is read "5 to the third power" or "5 cubed." The meaning of the expression is

$$5^3 = 5 \cdot 5 \cdot 5 = 125$$

Here are some further examples.

VIDEO EXAMPLES

SECTION 5.1

EXAMPLE 1 Write each expression as a single number.

a. 4^3 **b.** -3^4 **c.** $(-2)^5$ **d.** $\left(-\dfrac{3}{4}\right)^2$

SOLUTION

a. $4^3 = 4 \cdot 4 \cdot 4 = 16 \cdot 4 = 64$ Exponent 3, base 4

b. $-3^4 = -(3 \cdot 3 \cdot 3 \cdot 3) = -81$ Exponent 4, base 3

c. $(-2)^5 = (-2)(-2)(-2)(-2)(-2) = -32$ Exponent 5, base -2

d. $\left(-\dfrac{3}{4}\right)^2 = \left(-\dfrac{3}{4}\right)\left(-\dfrac{3}{4}\right) = \dfrac{9}{16}$ Exponent 2, base $-\dfrac{3}{4}$

Note Many students have difficulty simplifying expressions like the one in Example 1b, because they tend to treat it like the expression in Example 1c. How are -3^4 and $(-3)^4$ different? In the first case the base is 3. In the second case, the base is -3. It helps if we understand that

$$-3^4 = -1(3^4)$$

Following the order of operations, we must evaluate the exponent first (giving us 81), and then take the opposite of this value to get -81.

Multiplication with Exponents

We can simplify our work with exponents by developing some properties of exponents. We want to list the things we know are true about exponents and then use these properties to simplify expressions that contain exponents.

The first property of exponents applies to products with the same base. We can use the definition of exponents, as indicating repeated multiplication, to simplify expressions like $7^4 \cdot 7^2$.

$$7^4 \cdot 7^2 = (7 \cdot 7 \cdot 7 \cdot 7)(7 \cdot 7)$$

$$= (7 \cdot 7 \cdot 7 \cdot 7 \cdot 7 \cdot 7)$$

$$= 7^6 \qquad \text{Notice: } 4 + 2 = 6$$

As you can see, multiplication with the same base resulted in addition of exponents. We can summarize this result with the following property.

> ⟨Δ≠Σ⟩ **PROPERTY**   *Property 1 for Exponents*
>
> If a is any real number and r and s are integers, then
>
> $$a^r \cdot a^s = a^{r+s}$$
>
> *In words:*   To multiply two expressions with the same base, add exponents and use the common base.

Here is an example using Property 1.

EXAMPLE 2   Use Property 1 to simplify the following expressions. Leave your answers in terms of exponents:

a. $5^3 \cdot 5^6$ **b.** $x^7 \cdot x^8$ **c.** $3^4 \cdot 3^8 \cdot 3^5$

SOLUTION

a. $5^3 \cdot 5^6 = 5^{3+6} = 5^9$

b. $x^7 \cdot x^8 = x^{7+8} = x^{15}$

c. $3^4 \cdot 3^8 \cdot 3^5 = 3^{4+8+5} = 3^{17}$

> *Note* In Example 2, notice that in each case the base in the original problem is the same base that appears in the answer and that it is written only once in the answer. A very common mistake that people make when they first begin to use Property 1 is to write a 2 in front of the base in the answer. For example, people making this mistake would get $2x^{15}$ or $(2x)^{15}$ as the result in Example 2b. To avoid this mistake, you must be sure you understand the meaning of Property 1 exactly as it is written.

Another common type of expression involving exponents is one in which an expression containing an exponent is raised to another power. The expression $(5^3)^2$ is an example:

$$(5^3)^2 = (5^3)(5^3)$$
$$= 5^{3+3}$$
$$= 5^6 \qquad \text{Notice: } 3 \cdot 2 = 6$$

This result offers justification for the second property of exponents.

> ⟨Δ≠Σ⟩ **PROPERTY**   *Property 2 for Exponents*
>
> If a is any real number and r and s are integers, then
>
> $$(a^r)^s = a^{r \cdot s}$$
>
> *In words:*   A power raised to another power is the base raised to the product of the powers.

EXAMPLE 3   Simplify the following expressions:

a. $(4^5)^6$ **b.** $(x^3)^5$ **c.** $(x^4)^3(x^2)^5$

SOLUTION

a. $(4^5)^6 = 4^{5 \cdot 6} = 4^{30}$

b. $(x^3)^5 = x^{3 \cdot 5} = x^{15}$

c. $(x^4)^3(x^2)^5 = x^{12} \cdot x^{10}$ Property 2

$\qquad\qquad\qquad = x^{22}$ Property 1

The third property of exponents applies to expressions in which the product of two or more numbers or variables is raised to a power. Let's look at how the expression $(2x)^3$ can be simplified:

$$(2x)^3 = (2x)(2x)(2x)$$
$$= (2 \cdot 2 \cdot 2)(x \cdot x \cdot x)$$
$$= 2^3 \cdot x^3 \qquad \text{Notice: The exponent 3 distributes}$$
$$\text{over the product } 2x$$
$$= 8x^3$$

We can generalize this result into a third property of exponents.

$\lceil \Delta \neq \Sigma \rceil$ **PROPERTY**   *Property 3 for Exponents*

If a and b are any two real numbers and r is an integer, then

$$(ab)^r = a^r b^r$$

In words: The power of a product is the product of the powers.

Here are some examples using Property 3 to simplify expressions.

EXAMPLE 4   Simplify the following expressions:

a. $(3y)^2$ **b.** $\left(-\dfrac{1}{4}x^2y^3\right)^2$ **c.** $(x^2y^5)^3(x^4y)^2$

SOLUTION

a. $(3y)^2 = 3^2y^2$ Property 3
        $= 9y^2$

b. $\left(-\dfrac{1}{4}x^2y^3\right)^2 = \left(-\dfrac{1}{4}\right)^2(x^2)^2(y^3)^2$ Property 3
               $= \dfrac{1}{16}x^4y^6$ Property 2

c. $(x^2y^5)^3(x^4y)^2 = (x^2)^3(y^5)^3 \cdot (x^4)^2y^2$ Property 3
               $= x^6y^{15} \cdot x^8y^2$ Property 2
               $= (x^6x^8)(y^{15}y^2)$ Commutative and associative properties
               $= x^{14}y^{17}$ Property 1

Note If we include units with the dimensions of the diagrams, then the units for the area will be square units and the units for volume will be cubic units. More specifically,

If a square has a side 5 inches long, then its area will be

$A = (5 \text{ inches})^2 = 25 \text{ inches}^2$

where the unit inches^2 stands for square inches.

If a cube has a side 5 inches long, then its volume will be

$V = (5 \text{ inches})^3 = 125 \text{ inches}^3$

where the unit inches^3 stands for cubic inches.

If a rectangular solid has a length of 5 inches, a width of 4 inches, and a height of 3 inches, then its volume is

$V = (5 \text{ in.})(4 \text{ in.})(3 \text{ in.})$
$= 60 \text{ inches}^3$

FACTS FROM GEOMETRY   *Volume of a Rectangular Solid*

It is easy to see why the phrase "five squared" is associated with the expression 5^2. Simply find the area of the square shown in Figure 1 with a side of 5.

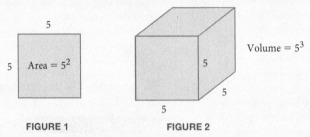

FIGURE 1   FIGURE 2

To see why the phrase "five cubed" is associated with the expression 5^3, we have to find the *volume* of a cube for which all three dimensions are 5 units long. The volume of a cube is a measure of the space occupied by the cube. To calculate the volume of the cube shown in Figure 2, we multiply the three dimensions together to get $5 \cdot 5 \cdot 5 = 5^3$.

The cube shown in Figure 2 is a special case of a general category of three dimensional geometric figures called *rectangular solids*. Rectangular solids have rectangles for sides, and all connecting sides meet at right angles. The three dimensions are length, width, and height. To find the volume of a rectangular solid, we find the product of the three dimensions.

Scientific Notation

Many branches of science require working with very large numbers. In astronomy, for example, distances commonly are given in light-years. A light-year is the distance light travels in a year. It is approximately

5,880,000,000,000 miles

This number is difficult to use in calculations because of the number of zeros it contains. Scientific notation provides a way of writing very large numbers in a more manageable form.

DEFINITION   *scientific notation*

A number is in *scientific notation* when it is written as the product of a number between 1 and 10 and an integer power of 10. A number written in scientific notation has the form

$n \times 10^r$

where $1 \le n < 10$ and r is an integer.

EXAMPLE 5   Write 376,000 in scientific notation.

SOLUTION   We must rewrite 376,000 as the product of a number between 1 and 10 and a power of 10. To do so, we move the decimal point 5 places to the left so that it appears between the 3 and the 7. Then we multiply this number by 10^5. The number that results has the same value as our original number and is written in scientific notation:

$$376,000 = 3.76 \times 100,000 = 3.76 \times 10^5$$

Moved 5 places

Decimal point originally here

Keeps track of the 5 places we moved the decimal point

> **Note**   Moving the decimal point one position to the left in a number is equivalent to *dividing* the number by a factor of 10. To preserve the value of the original number, we must *multiply* this new decimal by a factor of 10.
>
> In Example 5, when moving the decimal point five places to the left we are dividing the number by five factors of 10.
>
> $$3.76 = \frac{376,000}{10^5}$$
>
> Therefore, we must multiply the new decimal 3.76 by five factors of 10 so that the result is the same value of our original number.
>
> $$3.76 \times 10^5 = \frac{376,000}{10^5} \cdot 10^5$$
> $$= 376,000$$

EXAMPLE 6   Write 4.52×10^3 in expanded form.

SOLUTION   Since 10^3 is 1,000, we can think of this as simply a multiplication problem; that is,

$$4.52 \times 10^3 = 4.52 \times 1,000 = 4,520$$

On the other hand, we can think of the exponent 3 as indicating the number of places we need to move the decimal point to write our number in expanded form. Since our exponent is 3, we move the decimal point three places to the right:

$$4.520 \times 10^3 = 4,520$$

The zero we add does not change the value of the decimal.

Getting Ready for Class

After reading through the preceding section, respond in your own words and in complete sentences.

A. Explain the difference between -5^2 and $(-5)^2$.

B. How do you multiply two expressions containing exponents when they each have the same base?

C. Explain the difference between $2x^5$ and $(2x)^5$.

D. When is a number written in scientific notation?

Problem Set 5.1

Name the base and exponent in each of the following expressions. Then use the definition of exponents as repeated multiplication to simplify.

1. 4^2 **2.** 6^2 **3.** $(0.3)^2$ **4.** $(0.03)^2$ **5.** 4^3 **6.** 10^3

7. $(-5)^2$ **8.** -5^2 **9.** -2^3 **10.** $(-2)^3$ **11.** 3^4 **12.** $(-3)^4$

13. $\left(\dfrac{2}{3}\right)^2$ **14.** $\left(\dfrac{2}{3}\right)^3$ **15.** $\left(\dfrac{1}{2}\right)^4$ **16.** $\left(\dfrac{4}{5}\right)^2$

17. a. Complete the following table.

Number x	1	2	3	4	5	6	7
Square x^2							

   b. Using the results of part **a**, fill in the blank in the following statement: For numbers larger than 1, the square of the number is _____ than the number.

18. a. Complete the following table.

Number x	$\dfrac{1}{2}$	$\dfrac{1}{3}$	$\dfrac{1}{4}$	$\dfrac{1}{5}$	$\dfrac{1}{6}$	$\dfrac{1}{7}$	$\dfrac{1}{8}$
Square x^2							

   b. Using the results of part **a**, fill in the blank in the following statement: For numbers between 0 and 1, the square of the number is _____ than the number.

Use Property 1 to simplify the following expressions.

19. $x^4 \cdot x^5$ **20.** $x^7 \cdot x^3$ **21.** $y^{10} \cdot y^{20}$

22. $y^{30} \cdot y^{30}$ **23.** $2^5 \cdot 2^4 \cdot 2^3$ **24.** $4^2 \cdot 4^3 \cdot 4^4$

25. $x^4 \cdot x^6 \cdot x^8 \cdot x^{10}$ **26.** $x^{20} \cdot x^{18} \cdot x^{16} \cdot x^{14}$

Use Property 2 for exponents to write each of the following problems with a single exponent. (Assume all variables are positive numbers.)

27. $(x^2)^5$ **28.** $(x^5)^2$ **29.** $(5^4)^3$ **30.** $(5^3)^4$ **31.** $(y^3)^3$ **32.** $(y^2)^2$

33. $(2^5)^{10}$ **34.** $(10^5)^2$ **35.** $(a^3)^x$ **36.** $(a^5)^x$ **37.** $(b^x)^y$ **38.** $(b^r)^s$

Use Property 3 for exponents to simplify each of the following expressions.

39. $(4x)^2$ **40.** $(2x)^4$ **41.** $(2y)^5$ **42.** $(5y)^2$

43. $(-3x)^4$ **44.** $(-3x)^3$ **45.** $(0.5ab)^2$ **46.** $(0.4ab)^2$

47. $(4xyz)^3$ **48.** $(5xyz)^3$

Simplify the following expressions by using the properties of exponents.

49. $(2x^4)^3$ **50.** $(3x^5)^2$ **51.** $(4a^3)^2$ **52.** $(5a^2)^2$

53. $(x^2)^3(x^4)^2$ **54.** $(x^5)^2(x^3)^5$ **55.** $(a^3)^1(a^2)^4$ **56.** $(a^4)^1(a^1)^3$

57. $(4x^2y^3)^2$ **58.** $(9x^3y^5)^2$ **59.** $\left(\dfrac{2}{3}a^4b^5\right)^3$ **60.** $\left(\dfrac{3}{4}ab^7\right)^3$

61. Complete the following table, and then construct a line graph of the information in the table.

Number x	-3	-2	-1	0	1	2	3
Square x^2							

62. Complete the table, and then construct a line graph of the information in the table.

Number x	-3	-2	-1	0	1	2	3
Cube x^3							

63. Complete the table. When you are finished, notice how the points in this table could be used to refine the line graph you created in Problem 61.

Number x	-2.5	-1.5	-0.5	0	0.5	1.5	2.5
Square x^2							

64. Complete the following table. When you are finished, notice that this table contains exactly the same entries as the table from Problem 63. This table uses fractions, whereas the table from Problem 63 uses decimals.

Number x	$-\frac{5}{2}$	$-\frac{3}{2}$	$-\frac{1}{2}$	0	$\frac{1}{2}$	$\frac{3}{2}$	$\frac{5}{2}$
Square x^2							

Write each number in scientific notation.

65. 43,200

66. 432,000

67. -570

68. -5,700

69. 238,000

70. 2,380,000

Write each number in expanded form.

71. 2.49×10^3

72. 2.49×10^4

73. -3.52×10^2

74. -3.52×10^5

75. 2.8×10^4

76. 2.8×10^3

Applying the Concepts

77. **Volume of a Cube** Find the volume of a cube if each side is 3 inches long.

78. **Volume of a Cube** Find the volume of a cube if each side is 4 feet long.

79. **Volume of a Cube** A bottle of perfume is packaged in a box that is in the shape of a cube. Find the volume of the box if each side is 2.5 inches long. Round to the nearest tenth.

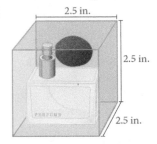

80. **Volume of a Cube** A television set is packaged in a box that is in the shape of a cube. Find the volume of the box if each side is 18 inches long.

81. **Volume of a Box** A rented videotape is in a plastic container that has the shape of a rectangular solid. Find the volume of the container if the length is 8 inches, the width is 4.5 inches, and the height is 1 inch.

82. **Volume of a Box** Your textbook is in the shape of a rectangular solid. Find the volume in cubic inches.

83. **Volume of a Box** If a box has a volume of 42 cubic feet, is it possible for you to fit inside the box? Explain your answer.

84. **Volume of a Box** A box has a volume of 45 cubic inches. Will a can of soup fit inside the box? Explain your answer.

85. **Age in seconds** If you are 21 years old, you have been alive for more than 650,000,000 seconds. Write this last number in scientific notation.

86. **Distance Around the Earth** The distance around the Earth at the equator is more than 130,000,000 feet. Write this number in scientific notation.

87. **Lifetime Earnings** If you earn at least $12 an hour and work full-time for 30 years, you will make at least 7.4×10^5 dollars. Write this last number in expanded form.

88. **Heart Beats per Year** If your pulse is 72, then in one year your heart will beat at least 3.78×10^7 times. Write this last number in expanded form.

89. **Investing** If you put $1,000 into a savings account every year from the time you are 25 years old until you are 55 years old, you will have more than 1.8×10^5 dollars in the account when you reach 55 years of age (assuming 10% annual interest). Write 1.8×10^5 in expanded form.

90. **Investing** If you put $20 into a savings account every month from the time you are 20 years old until you are 30 years old, you will have more than 3.27×10^3 dollars in the account when you reach 30 years of age (assuming 6% annual interest compounded monthly). Write 3.27×10^3 in expanded form.

Displacement The displacement, in cubic inches, of a car engine is given by the formula

$$d = \pi \cdot s \cdot c \cdot \left(\frac{1}{2} \cdot b \right)^2$$

where s is the stroke and b is the bore, as shown in the figure, and c is the number of cylinders.

Calculate the engine displacement for each of the following cars. Use 3.14 to approximate π. Round to the nearest whole number.

91. Ferrari Modena 8 cylinders, 3.35 inches of bore, 3.11 inches of stroke

92. Audi A8 8 cylinders, 3.32 inches of bore, 3.66 inches of stroke

93. Mitsubishi Eclipse 6 cylinders, 3.59 inches of bore, 2.99 inches of stroke

94. Porsche 911 GT3 6 cylinders, 3.94 inches of bore, 3.01 inches of stroke

Learning Objectives Assessment

The following problems can be used to help assess if you have successfully met the learning objectives for this section.

95. Simplify: $x^2 \cdot x^4 \cdot x^6$.

    a. x^{12} **b.** x^{48} **c.** $3x^{12}$ **d.** $3x^{48}$

96. Simplify: $(y^7)^3$.

    a. y^4 **b.** y^{10} **c.** y^{21} **d.** $3y^7$

97. Simplify: $(-2xy)^4$.

    a. $16x^4y^4$ **b.** $-16x^4y^4$ **c.** $-2xy^4$ **d.** $-8xy$

98. Write 340,000 in scientific notation.

    a. 34×10^4 **b.** 3.4×10^5 **c.** 0.34×10^6 **d.** 340×10^3

Getting Ready for the Next Section

Subtract.

99. $4 - 7$ **100.** $-4 - 7$ **101.** $4 - (-7)$

102. $-4 - (-7)$ **103.** $15 - 20$ **104.** $15 - (-20)$

105. $-15 - (-20)$ **106.** $-15 - 20$ **107.** $2(3) - 4$

108. $5(3) - 10$ **109.** $4(3) - 3(2)$ **110.** $-8 - 2(3)$

111. $2(5 - 3)$ **112.** $2(3) - 4 - 3(-4)$ **113.** $5 + 4(-2) - 2(-3)$

114. $2(3) + 4(5) - 5(2)$

Division with Exponents

Learning Objectives

In this section, we will learn how to:

1. Simplify expressions containing negative exponents.
2. Divide like bases by subtracting exponents.
3. Simplify the power of a quotient.
4. Simplify expressions containing exponents of 1 or 0.
5. Use scientific notation with negative exponents.

Introduction

In Section 5.1 we found that multiplication with the same base results in addition of exponents; that is, $a^r \cdot a^s = a^{r+s}$. Since division is the inverse operation of multiplication, we can expect division with the same base to result in subtraction of exponents.

To develop the properties for exponents under division, we again apply the definition of exponents:

$$\frac{x^5}{x^3} = \frac{x \cdot x \cdot x \cdot x \cdot x}{x \cdot x \cdot x} \qquad\qquad \frac{2^4}{2^7} = \frac{2 \cdot 2 \cdot 2 \cdot 2}{2 \cdot 2 \cdot 2 \cdot 2 \cdot 2 \cdot 2 \cdot 2}$$

$$= \frac{x \cdot x \cdot x}{x \cdot x \cdot x} (x \cdot x) \qquad\qquad = \frac{2 \cdot 2 \cdot 2 \cdot 2}{2 \cdot 2 \cdot 2 \cdot 2} \cdot \frac{1}{2 \cdot 2 \cdot 2}$$

$$= 1(x \cdot x) \qquad\qquad\qquad = \frac{1}{2 \cdot 2 \cdot 2}$$

$$= x^2 \quad \text{Notice: } 5 - 3 = 2 \qquad\qquad = \frac{1}{2^3} \quad \text{Notice: } 7 - 4 = 3$$

In both cases division with the same base resulted in subtraction of the smaller exponent from the larger. The problem is deciding whether the answer is a fraction. The following discussion will help us resolve this problem.

Negative Exponents

Consider the product $3^3 \cdot 3^{-1}$. We do not know yet what 3^{-1} represents. But according to Property 1 for exponents, it should be the case that

$$3^3 \cdot 3^{-1} = 3^{3 + (-1)} = 3^2$$

Simplifying the positive exponents, we have

$$27 \cdot 3^{-1} = 9$$

If we solve this equation for 3^{-1}, we find

$$3^{-1} = \frac{9}{27} = \frac{1}{3}$$

It would appear that 3^{-1} represents the reciprocal of 3. This leads us to the following definition.

> **def** **DEFINITION**   *Negative Exponents*
>
> If $a \neq 0$ and r is a positive integer, then
>
> $$a^{-1} = \frac{1}{a}$$
>
> and
>
> $$a^{-r} = \frac{1}{a^r} = \left(\frac{1}{a}\right)^r$$

Notice that a negative exponent indicates a reciprocal of some kind. The following examples illustrate how we use this definition to simplify expressions that contain negative exponents.

VIDEO EXAMPLES

SECTION 5.2

EXAMPLE 1   Write each expression with a positive exponent and then simplify:

a. 2^{-3} **b.** $(-5)^{-2}$ **c.** -5^{-2} **d.** $3x^{-6}$ **e.** $(3x)^{-6}$

SOLUTION

a. $2^{-3} = \dfrac{1}{2^3} = \dfrac{1}{8}$

Notice: Negative exponents do not indicate negative numbers. They indicate reciprocals

b. $(-5)^{-2} = \dfrac{1}{(-5)^2} = \dfrac{1}{25}$

c. $-5^{-2} = -(5^{-2}) = -\left(\dfrac{1}{5^2}\right) = -\dfrac{1}{25}$

d. $3x^{-6} = 3 \cdot \dfrac{1}{x^6} = \dfrac{3}{x^6}$ x is the base

e. $(3x)^{-6} = \dfrac{1}{(3x)^6} = \dfrac{1}{3^6 x^6} = \dfrac{1}{729x^6}$ $3x$ is the base

Division with Exponents

Now let us look back to the problem in the introduction to this section and try to work it again with the help of a negative exponent. We know that $\frac{2^4}{2^7} = \frac{1}{2^3}$. Let us decide now that with division of the same base, we will always subtract the exponent in the denominator from the exponent in the numerator and see if this conflicts with what we know is true.

$$\frac{2^4}{2^7} = 2^{4-7}$$ Subtracting the bottom exponent from the top exponent

$$= 2^{-3}$$ Subtraction

$$= \frac{1}{2^3}$$ Definition of negative exponents

Subtracting the exponent in the denominator from the exponent in the numerator and then using the definition of negative exponents gives us the same result we obtained previously. We can now continue the list of properties of exponents we started in Section 5.1.

> **PROPERTY**   *Property 4 for Exponents*
>
> If a is any real number and r and s are integers, then
>
> $$\frac{a^r}{a^s} = a^{r-s} \qquad (a \neq 0)$$
>
> *In words:*   To divide with the same base, subtract the exponent in the denominator from the exponent in the numerator and raise the base to the exponent that results.

The following examples show how we use Property 4 and the definition for negative exponents to simplify expressions involving division.

EXAMPLE 2   Simplify the following expressions:

a. $\dfrac{x^9}{x^6}$ **b.** $\dfrac{x^4}{x^{10}}$ **c.** $\dfrac{2^{15}}{2^{20}}$

SOLUTION

a. $\dfrac{x^9}{x^6} = x^{9-6} = x^3$

b. $\dfrac{x^4}{x^{10}} = x^{4-10} = x^{-6} = \dfrac{1}{x^6}$

c. $\dfrac{2^{15}}{2^{20}} = 2^{15-20} = 2^{-5} = \dfrac{1}{2^5} = \dfrac{1}{32}$

Our final property of exponents is similar to Property 3 from Section 5.1, but it involves division instead of multiplication. After we have stated the property, we will give a proof of it. The proof shows why this property is true.

> **PROPERTY**   *Property 5 for Exponents*
>
> If a and b are any two real numbers ($b \neq 0$) and r is an integer, then
>
> $$\left(\frac{a}{b}\right)^r = \frac{a^r}{b^r}$$
>
> *In words:*   A quotient raised to a power is the quotient of the powers.

Proof

$$\left(\frac{a}{b}\right)^r = \left(a \cdot \frac{1}{b}\right)^r \qquad \text{By the definition of division}$$

$$= a^r \cdot \left(\frac{1}{b}\right)^r \qquad \text{By Property 3}$$

$$= a^r \cdot b^{-r} \qquad \text{By the definition of negative exponents}$$

$$= a^r \cdot \frac{1}{b^r} \qquad \text{By the definition of negative exponents}$$

$$= \frac{a^r}{b^r} \qquad \text{By the definition of division}$$

EXAMPLE 3   Simplify the following expressions.

a. $\left(\dfrac{x}{2}\right)^3$ **b.** $\left(\dfrac{5}{y}\right)^2$ **c.** $\left(\dfrac{2}{3}\right)^4$

SOLUTION

a. $\left(\dfrac{x}{2}\right)^3 = \dfrac{x^3}{2^3} = \dfrac{x^3}{8}$

b. $\left(\dfrac{5}{y}\right)^2 = \dfrac{5^2}{y^2} = \dfrac{25}{y^2}$

c. $\left(\dfrac{2}{3}\right)^4 = \dfrac{2^4}{3^4} = \dfrac{16}{81}$

Zero and One as Exponents

We have two special exponents left to deal with before our rules for exponents are complete: 0 and 1. To obtain an expression for x^1, we will solve a problem two different ways:

$$\dfrac{x^3}{x^2} = \dfrac{x \cdot x \cdot x}{x \cdot x} = x$$

$$\dfrac{x^3}{x^2} = x^{3-2} = x^1$$

Hence $x^1 = x$

Stated generally, this rule says that $a^1 = a$. This seems reasonable and we will use it since it is consistent with our property of division using the same base.

We use the same procedure to obtain an expression for x^0:

$$\dfrac{5^2}{5^2} = \dfrac{25}{25} = 1$$

$$\dfrac{5^2}{5^2} = 5^{2-2} = 5^0$$

Hence $5^0 = 1$

It seems, therefore, that the best definition of x^0 is 1 for all x except $x = 0$. In the case of $x = 0$, we have 0^0, which we will not define. This definition will probably seem awkward at first. Most people would like to define x^0 as 0 when they first encounter it. Remember, the zero in this expression is an exponent, so x^0 does not mean to multiply by zero. Thus, we can make the general statement that $a^0 = 1$ for all real numbers except $a = 0$.

(def) DEFINITION   *Zero and One as Exponents*

$$a^1 = a$$

$$a^0 = 1 \quad (a \neq 0)$$

Here are some examples involving the exponents 0 and 1.

EXAMPLE 4   Simplify the following expressions:

a. 8^0 **b.** 8^1 **c.** $4^0 + 4^1$ **d.** $(2x^2y)^0$

SOLUTION

a. $8^0 = 1$

b. $8^1 = 8$

c. $4^0 + 4^1 = 1 + 4 = 5$

d. $(2x^2y)^0 = 1$

Here is a summary of the definitions and properties of exponents we have developed so far. For each definition or property in the list, a and b are real numbers, and r and s are integers.

Definitions		Properties	
$a^{-1} = \dfrac{1}{a}$	$a \neq 0$	**1.** $a^r \cdot a^s = a^{r+s}$	
$a^{-r} = \dfrac{1}{a^r} = \left(\dfrac{1}{a}\right)^r$	$a \neq 0$	**2.** $(a^r)^s = a^{r \cdot s}$	
$a^1 = a$		**3.** $(ab)^r = a^r b^r$	
$a^0 = 1$	$a \neq 0$	**4.** $\dfrac{a^r}{a^s} = a^{r-s}$	$a \neq 0$
		5. $\left(\dfrac{a}{b}\right)^r = \dfrac{a^r}{b^r}$	$b \neq 0$

Here are some additional examples. These examples use a combination of the preceding properties and definitions.

EXAMPLES   Simplify each expression. Write all answers with positive exponents only:

Note Because of the order of operations, we must simplify the exponent in the numerator in Example 5 and denominator in Example 6 before using Property 4 to do the division.

5. $\dfrac{(5x^3)^2}{x^4} = \dfrac{25(x^3)^2}{x^4}$ Property 3

$\quad = \dfrac{25x^6}{x^4}$ Property 2

$\quad = 25x^2$ Property 4

6. $\dfrac{x^{-8}}{(x^2)^3} = \dfrac{x^{-8}}{x^6}$ Property 2

$\quad = x^{-8-6}$ Property 4

$\quad = x^{-14}$ Subtraction

$\quad = \dfrac{1}{x^{14}}$ Definition of negative exponents

7. $\left(\dfrac{y^5}{y^3}\right)^2 = \dfrac{(y^5)^2}{(y^3)^2}$ Property 5

$\quad = \dfrac{y^{10}}{y^6}$ Property 2

$\quad = y^4$ Property 4

Notice in Example 7 that we could have simplified inside the parentheses first and then raised the result to the second power:

$$\left(\frac{y^5}{y^3}\right)^2 = (y^2)^2 = y^4$$

8. $(3x^5)^{-2} = \dfrac{1}{(3x^5)^2}$ Definition of negative exponents

$\qquad\qquad = \dfrac{1}{9x^{10}}$ Properties 2 and 3

9. $x^{-8} \cdot x^5 = x^{-8+5}$ Property 1

$\qquad\quad = x^{-3}$ Addition

$\qquad\quad = \dfrac{1}{x^3}$ Definition of negative exponents

10. $\dfrac{(a^3)^2 a^{-4}}{(a^{-4})^3} = \dfrac{a^6 a^{-4}}{a^{-12}}$ Property 2

$\qquad\qquad = \dfrac{a^2}{a^{-12}}$ Property 1

$\qquad\qquad = a^{14}$ Property 4

Applications

In the next two examples we use division to compare the area and volume of geometric figures.

EXAMPLE 11   Suppose you have two squares, one of which is larger than the other. If the length of a side of the larger square is 3 times as long as the length of a side of the smaller square, how many of the smaller squares will it take to cover up the larger square?

SOLUTION   If we let x represent the length of a side of the smaller square, then the length of a side of the larger square is $3x$. The area of each square, along with a diagram of the situation, is given in Figure 1.

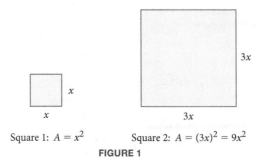

Square 1: $A = x^2$ Square 2: $A = (3x)^2 = 9x^2$

FIGURE 1

To find out how many smaller squares it will take to cover up the larger square, we divide the area of the larger square by the area of the smaller square.

$$\frac{\text{Area of square 2}}{\text{Area of square 1}} = \frac{9x^2}{x^2} = 9$$

It will take 9 of the smaller squares to cover the larger square.

EXAMPLE 12   Suppose you have two boxes, each of which is a cube. If the length of a side in the second box is 3 times as long as the length of a side of the first box, how many of the smaller boxes will fit inside the larger box?

SOLUTION   If we let x represent the length of a side of the smaller box, then the length of a side of the larger box is $3x$. The volume of each box, along with a diagram of the situation, is given in Figure 2.

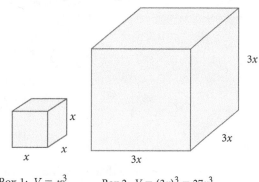

Box 1: $V = x^3$ Box 2: $V = (3x)^3 = 27x^3$

FIGURE 2

To find out how many smaller boxes will fit inside the larger box, we divide the volume of the larger box by the volume of the smaller box.

$$\frac{\text{Volume of box 2}}{\text{Volume of box 1}} = \frac{27x^3}{x^3} = 27$$

We can fit 27 of the smaller boxes inside the larger box.

More on Scientific Notation

Now that we have completed our list of definitions and properties of exponents, we can expand the work we did previously with scientific notation.

Recall that a number is in scientific notation when it is written in the form

$$n \times 10^r$$

where $1 \le n < 10$ and r is an integer.

Since negative exponents give us reciprocals, we can use negative exponents to write very small numbers in scientific notation. For example, the number 0.00057, when written in scientific notation, is equivalent to 5.7×10^{-4}. Here's why:

$$5.7 \times 10^{-4} = 5.7 \times \frac{1}{10^4} = 5.7 \times \frac{1}{10{,}000} = \frac{5.7}{10{,}000} = 0.00057$$

The table below lists some other numbers in both scientific notation and expanded form.

Number Written the Long Way		Number Written Again in Scientific Notation
376,000	=	3.76×10^5
49,500	=	4.95×10^4
3,200	=	3.2×10^3
591	=	5.91×10^2
46	=	4.6×10^1
8	=	8×10^0
0.47	=	4.7×10^{-1}
0.093	=	9.3×10^{-2}
0.00688	=	6.88×10^{-3}
0.0002	=	2×10^{-4}
0.000098	=	9.8×10^{-5}

Notice that in each case, when the number is written in scientific notation, the decimal point in the first number is placed so that the number is between 1 and 10. The exponent on 10 in the second number keeps track of the number of places we moved the decimal point in the original number to get a number between 1 and 10:

$$376,000 = 3.76 \times 10^5$$

Large number = positive exponent

Moved 5 places.

Decimal point was originally here.

Keeps track of the 5 places we moved the decimal point.

$$0.00688 = 6.88 \times 10^{-3}$$

Small number = negative exponent

Moved 3 places.

Keeps track of the 3 places we moved the decimal point.

EXAMPLE 13   Write each number in scientific notation.

a. 36×10^{-4} **b.** 0.36×10^5

SOLUTION

a. 36×10^{-4} is not in scientific notation because 36 is not between 1 and 10. We first write 36 in scientific notation, and then simplify the result using Property 1 for exponents.

$$36 \times 10^{-4} = (3.6 \times 10^1) \times 10^{-4}$$
$$= 3.6 \times 10^{1 + (-4)}$$
$$= 3.6 \times 10^{-3}$$

b. This number is not in scientific notation because 0.36 is less than 1. Following our process above, we have

$$0.36 \times 10^5 = (3.6 \times 10^{-1}) \times 10^5$$
$$= 3.6 \times 10^{-1 + 5}$$
$$= 3.6 \times 10^4$$

Getting Ready for Class

After reading through the preceding section, respond in your own words and in complete sentences.

A. How do you divide two expressions containing exponents when they each have the same base?

B. Explain the difference between 3^2 and 3^{-2}.

C. If a positive base is raised to a negative exponent, can the result be a negative number?

D. Explain what happens when we use zero as an exponent.

Problem Set 5.2

Simplify each expression.

1. 5^{-1} **2.** 4^{-1} **3.** x^{-1} **4.** y^{-1} **5.** 3^{-2} **6.** 3^{-3}

7. 6^{-2} **8.** 2^{-6} **9.** 8^{-2} **10.** 3^{-4} **11.** 5^{-3} **12.** 9^{-2}

13. a^{-4} **14.** b^{-5} **15.** -4^{-2} **16.** -6^{-3} **17.** $-x^{-1}$ **18.** $-y^{-7}$

19. $(-5)^{-3}$ **20.** $(-2)^{-4}$ **21.** $(-4)^{-2}$ **22.** $(-3)^{-3}$ **23.** $2x^{-3}$ **24.** $5x^{-1}$

25. $(2x)^{-3}$ **26.** $(5x)^{-1}$ **27.** $(5y)^{-2}$ **28.** $5y^{-2}$ **29.** 10^{-2} **30.** 10^{-3}

31. Complete the following table.

Number x	Square x^2	Power of 2 2^x
-3		
-2		
-1		
0		
1		
2		
3		

32. Complete the following table.

Number x	Cube x^3	Power of 3 3^x
-3		
-2		
-1		
0		
1		
2		
3		

Use Property 4 to simplify each of the following expressions. Write all answers that contain exponents with positive exponents only.

33. $\dfrac{5^1}{5^3}$ **34.** $\dfrac{7^6}{7^8}$ **35.** $\dfrac{x^{10}}{x^4}$ **36.** $\dfrac{x^4}{x^{10}}$ **37.** $\dfrac{4^3}{4^0}$ **38.** $\dfrac{4^0}{4^3}$

39. $\dfrac{(2x)^7}{(2x)^4}$ **40.** $\dfrac{(2x)^4}{(2x)^7}$ **41.** $\dfrac{6^{11}}{6}$ **42.** $\dfrac{8^7}{8}$ **43.** $\dfrac{6}{6^{11}}$ **44.** $\dfrac{8}{8^7}$

45. $\dfrac{2^{-5}}{2^3}$ **46.** $\dfrac{2^{-5}}{2^{-3}}$ **47.** $\dfrac{2^5}{2^{-3}}$ **48.** $\dfrac{2^{-3}}{2^{-5}}$ **49.** $\dfrac{(3x)^{-5}}{(3x)^{-8}}$ **50.** $\dfrac{(2x)^{-10}}{(2x)^{-15}}$

Simplify the following expressions. Any answers that contain exponents should contain positive exponents only.

51. $(3xy)^4$ **52.** $(4xy)^3$ **53.** 10^0 **54.** 10^1

55. $(2a^2b)^1$ **56.** $(2a^2b)^0$ **57.** $(7y^3)^{-2}$ **58.** $(5y^4)^{-2}$

59. $x^{-3}x^{-5}$ **60.** $x^{-6} \cdot x^8$ **61.** $y^7 \cdot y^{-10}$ **62.** $y^{-4} \cdot y^{-6}$

63. $\dfrac{(x^2)^3}{x^4}$ **64.** $\dfrac{(x^5)^3}{x^{10}}$ **65.** $\dfrac{(a^4)^3}{(a^3)^2}$ **66.** $\dfrac{(a^5)^3}{(a^5)^2}$

67. $\dfrac{y^7}{(y^2)^8}$ **68.** $\dfrac{y^2}{(y^3)^4}$ **69.** $\left(\dfrac{y^7}{y^2}\right)^8$ **70.** $\left(\dfrac{y^2}{y^3}\right)^4$

71. $\dfrac{(x^{-2})^3}{x^{-5}}$ **72.** $\dfrac{(x^2)^{-3}}{x^{-5}}$ **73.** $\left(\dfrac{x^{-2}}{x^{-5}}\right)^3$ **74.** $\left(\dfrac{x^2}{x^{-5}}\right)^{-3}$

75. $\dfrac{(a^3)^2(a^4)^5}{(a^5)^2}$ **76.** $\dfrac{(a^4)^8(a^2)^5}{(a^3)^4}$ **77.** $\dfrac{(a^{-2})^3(a^4)^2}{(a^{-3})^{-2}}$ **78.** $\dfrac{(a^{-5})^{-3}(a^7)^{-1}}{(a^{-3})^5}$

79. Complete the following table, and then construct a line graph of the information in the table.

Number x	-3	-2	-1	0	1	2	3
Power of 2 2^x							

80. Complete the following table, and then construct a line graph of the information in the table.

Number x	-3	-2	-1	0	1	2	3
Power of 3 3^x							

Write each of the following numbers in scientific notation.

81. 0.0048   **82.** 0.000048   **83.** 25   **84.** 35

85. 0.25   **86.** 0.35   **87.** 0.000009   **88.** 0.0009

89. Complete the following table.

Expanded Form	Scientific Notation $n \times 10^r$
0.000357	3.57×10^{-4}
0.00357	
0.0357	
0.357	
3.57	
35.7	
357	
3,570	
35,700	

90. Complete the following table.

Expanded Form	Scientific Notation $n \times 10^r$
0.000123	1.23×10^{-4}
	1.23×10^{-3}
	1.23×10^{-2}
	1.23×10^{-1}
	1.23×10^{0}
	1.23×10^{1}
	1.23×10^{2}
	1.23×10^{3}
	1.23×10^{4}

Write each of the following numbers in expanded form.

91. 4.23×10^{-3} **92.** 4.23×10^{3} **93.** 8×10^{-5} **94.** 8×10^{5}

95. 4.2×10^{0} **96.** 4.2×10^{1} **97.** 2.4×10^{-1} **98.** 2.4×10^{-6}

Applying the Concepts

Scientific Notation Problems

99. Some home computers can do a calculation in 2×10^{-3} seconds. Write this number in expanded form.

100. Some of the cells in the human body have a radius of 3×10^{-5} inches. Write this number in expanded form.

101. Margin of Victory Since 1993, the Nascar races with the smallest margin of victory are shown here. Write each number in scientific notation.

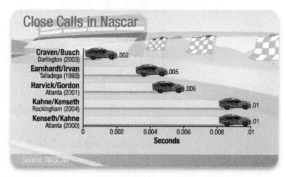

102. Some cameras used in scientific research can take one picture every 0.000000167 second. Write this number in scientific notation.

103. The number 25×10^3 is not in scientific notation because 25 is larger than 10. Write 25×10^3 in scientific notation.

104. The number 0.25×10^3 is not in scientific notation because 0.25 is less than 1. Write 0.25×10^3 in scientific notation.

105. The number 23.5×10^4 is not in scientific notation because 23.5 is not between 1 and 10. Rewrite 23.5×10^4 in scientific notation.

106. The number 375×10^3 is not in scientific notation because 375 is not between 1 and 10. Rewrite 375×10^3 in scientific notation.

107. The number 0.82×10^{-3} is not in scientific notation because 0.82 is not between 1 and 10. Rewrite 0.82×10^{-3} in scientific notation.

108. The number 0.93×10^{-2} is not in scientific notation because 0.93 is not between 1 and 10. Rewrite 0.93×10^{-2} in scientific notation.

Comparing Areas Suppose you have two squares, one of which is larger than the other. Suppose further that the side of the larger square is twice as long as the side of the smaller square.

109. If the length of the side of the smaller square is 10 inches, give the area of each square. Then find the number of smaller squares it will take to cover the larger square.

110. How many smaller squares will it take to cover the larger square if the length of the side of the smaller square is 1 foot?

111. If the length of the side of the smaller square is x, find the area of each square. Then find the number of smaller squares it will take to cover the larger square.

112. Suppose the length of the side of the larger square is 1 foot. How many smaller squares will it take to cover the larger square?

Comparing Volumes Suppose you have two boxes, each of which is a cube. Suppose further that the length of a side of the second box is twice as long as the length of a side of the first box.

113. If the length of a side of the first box is 6 inches, give the volume of each box. Then find the number of smaller boxes that will fit inside the larger box.

114. How many smaller boxes can be placed inside the larger box if the length of a side of the second box is 1 foot?

115. If the length of a side of the first box is x, find the volume of each box. Then find the number of smaller boxes that will fit inside the larger box.

116. Suppose the length of a side of the larger box is 12 inches. How many smaller boxes will fit inside the larger box?

Learning Objectives Assessment

The following problems can be used to help assess if you have successfully met the learning objectives for this section.

117. Simplify: 4^{-3}

    a. -12 **b.** $\dfrac{1}{64}$ **c.** 64 **d.** -64

118. Simplify: $\dfrac{x^2}{x^{-5}}$

    a. x^7 **b.** x^{-3} **c.** x^3 **d.** $\dfrac{1}{x^7}$

119. Simplify $\left(\dfrac{x}{3}\right)^4$

    a. $\dfrac{x^4}{81}$ **b.** $\dfrac{x^4}{3}$ **c.** $\dfrac{x}{81}$ **d.** $\dfrac{4x}{3}$

120. Simplify: $2^0 - 2^1$

    a. 0 **b.** -2 **c.** $\dfrac{1}{2}$ **d.** -1

121. Write 0.00123 in scientific notation.

    a. 123×10^5 **b.** 123×10^{-5} **c.** 1.23×10^3 **d.** 1.23×10^{-3}

Getting Ready for the Next Section

Simplify.

122. $3(4.5)$ **123.** $\dfrac{1}{2} \cdot \dfrac{5}{7}$ **124.** $\dfrac{4}{5}(10)$

125. $\dfrac{9.6}{3}$ **126.** $6.8(3.9)$ **127.** $9 - 20$

128. $-3 + 15$ **129.** $2x \cdot x \cdot \dfrac{1}{2}x$ **130.** $x^5 \cdot x^3$

131. $y^2 \cdot y$ **132.** $\dfrac{x^3}{x^2}$ **133.** $\dfrac{x^2}{x}$

134. $\dfrac{y^3}{y^5}$ **135.** $\dfrac{x^2}{x^5}$

Write in expanded form.

136. 3.4×10^2 **137.** 6.0×10^{-4}

Learning Objectives

In this section, we will learn how to:

1. State the degree of a monomial.
2. Multiply and divide monomials.
3. Multiply and divide numbers written in scientific notation.
4. Add and subtract monomials.

Introduction

We have developed all the tools necessary to perform the four basic operations on the simplest of polynomials: monomials.

> **def** **DEFINITION** *monomial*
>
> A *monomial* is a one-term expression that is either a constant (number) or the product of a constant and one or more variables raised to whole number exponents.

The following are examples of monomials:

$$-3 \qquad 15x \qquad -23x^2y \qquad 49x^4y^2z^4 \qquad \frac{3}{4}a^2b^3$$

The numerical part of each monomial is called the *numerical coefficient*, or just *coefficient*. Monomials are also called *terms*.

> **def** **DEFINITION** *degree of a monomial*
>
> The *degree* of a monomial in one variable is the exponent of the variable. If the monomial contains multiple variables, then the *degree* is the sum of the exponents on the variables. A constant term is defined to have a degree of zero.

VIDEO EXAMPLES

SECTION 5.3

EXAMPLES State the coefficient and degree of each monomial.

1. $8x^5$ Coefficient $= 8$ Degree $= 5$
2. $-\dfrac{1}{2}x$ Coefficient $= -\dfrac{1}{2}$ Degree $= 1$
3. $14x^4y^3$ Coefficient $= 14$ Degree $= 7$
4. -3 Coefficient $= -3$ Degree $= 0$

Multiplication and Division of Monomials

There are two basic steps involved in the multiplication of monomials. First, we rewrite the products using the commutative and associative properties. Then, we simplify by multiplying coefficients and adding exponents of like bases.

EXAMPLE 5   Multiply:

a. $(-3x^2)(4x^3)$ **b.** $\left(\dfrac{4}{5}x^5 \cdot y^2\right)(10x^3 \cdot y)$

SOLUTION

a. $(-3x^2)(4x^3) = (-3 \cdot 4)(x^2 \cdot x^3)$ Commutative and associative properties

$\qquad\qquad\qquad = -12x^5$ Multiply coefficients, add exponents

b. $\left(\dfrac{4}{5}x^5 \cdot y^2\right)(10x^3 \cdot y) = \left(\dfrac{4}{5} \cdot 10\right)(x^5 \cdot x^3)(y^2 \cdot y)$ Commutative and associative properties

$\qquad\qquad\qquad\qquad\quad = 8x^8y^3$ Multiply coefficients, add exponents

You can see that in each case the work was the same—multiply coefficients and add exponents of the same base. We can expect division of monomials to proceed in a similar way. Since our properties are consistent, division of monomials will result in division of coefficients and subtraction of exponents of like bases.

EXAMPLE 6   Divide:

a. $\dfrac{15x^3}{3x^2}$ **b.** $\dfrac{39x^2y^3}{3xy^5}$

SOLUTION

a. $\dfrac{15x^3}{3x^2} = \dfrac{15}{3} \cdot \dfrac{x^3}{x^2}$ Write as separate fractions

$\qquad\quad = 5x$ Divide coefficients, subtract exponents

b. $\dfrac{39x^2y^3}{3xy^5} = \dfrac{39}{3} \cdot \dfrac{x^2}{x} \cdot \dfrac{y^3}{y^5}$ Write as separate fractions

$\qquad\qquad = 13 \cdot x \cdot \dfrac{1}{y^2}$ Divide coefficients, subtract exponents

$\qquad\qquad = \dfrac{13x}{y^2}$ Write answer as a single fraction

> *Note*   Notice that when dividing monomials, the result may not be a monomial. In Example 6b, the expression
>
> $$\dfrac{13x}{y^2} = 13xy^{-2}$$
>
> is not a monomial because it contains a negative exponent.

In Example 6b, the expression $\dfrac{y^3}{y^5}$ simplifies to $\dfrac{1}{y^2}$ because of Property 4 for exponents and the definition of negative exponents. If we were to show all the work in this simplification process, it would look like this:

$$\dfrac{y^3}{y^5} = y^{3-5} \qquad \text{Property 4 for exponents}$$

$$= y^{-2} \qquad \text{Subtraction}$$

$$= \dfrac{1}{y^2} \qquad \text{Definition of negative exponents}$$

The point of this explanation is this: Even though we may not show all the steps when simplifying an expression involving exponents, the result we obtain still can be justified using the properties of exponents. We have not introduced any new properties in Example 6; we have just not shown the details of each simplification.

EXAMPLE 7   Divide $25a^5b^3$ by $50a^2b^7$.

SOLUTION

$$\frac{25a^5b^3}{50a^2b^7} = \frac{25}{50} \cdot \frac{a^5}{a^2} \cdot \frac{b^3}{b^7} \qquad \text{Write as separate fractions}$$

$$= \frac{1}{2} \cdot a^3 \cdot \frac{1}{b^4} \qquad \text{Divide coefficients; subtract exponents}$$

$$= \frac{a^3}{2b^4} \qquad \text{Write answer as a single fraction}$$

Notice in Example 7 that dividing 25 by 50 results in $\frac{1}{2}$. This is the same result we would obtain if we reduced the fraction $\frac{25}{50}$ to lowest terms, and there is no harm in thinking of it that way. Also, notice that the expression $\frac{b^3}{b^7}$ simplifies to $\frac{1}{b^4}$ by Property 4 for exponents and the definition of negative exponents, even though we have not shown the steps involved in doing so.

EXAMPLE 8   Simplify: $\dfrac{(6x^4y)(3x^7y^5)}{9x^5y^2}$.

SOLUTION   We begin by multiplying the two monomials in the numerator:

$$\frac{(6x^4y)(3x^7y^5)}{9x^5y^2} = \frac{18x^{11}y^6}{9x^5y^2} \qquad \text{Simplify numerator}$$

$$= 2x^6y^4 \qquad \text{Divide}$$

EXAMPLE 9   Simplify each expression.

a. $(2y)^3(3y)^2$ **b.** $\dfrac{(6xy^4)^2}{(2x^3y^2)^3}$

SOLUTION   In both cases, we follow the order of operations by applying properties 2 and 3 for exponents first. Then we can perform the multiplication and division.

a. $(2y)^3(3y)^2 = 8y^3 \cdot 9y^2 \qquad \text{Property 3 for exponents}$

$\qquad\qquad\qquad = 72y^5 \qquad \text{Multiply coefficients, add exponents}$

b. $\dfrac{(6xy^4)^2}{(2x^3y^2)^3} = \dfrac{36x^2y^8}{8x^9y^6} \qquad \text{Properties 2 and 3}$

$$= \frac{9}{2} \cdot \frac{1}{x^7} \cdot y^2 \qquad \text{Divide coefficients, subtract exponents}$$

$$= \frac{9y^2}{2x^7} \qquad \text{Write answer as a single fraction}$$

Multiplication and Division of Numbers Written in Scientific Notation

We multiply and divide numbers written in scientific notation using the same steps we used to multiply and divide monomials.

EXAMPLE 10   Multiply: $(4 \times 10^7)(2 \times 10^{-4})$.

SOLUTION   Since multiplication is commutative and associative, we can rearrange the order of these numbers and group them as follows:

$$(4 \times 10^7)(2 \times 10^{-4}) = (4 \times 2)(10^7 \times 10^{-4})$$

$$= 8 \times 10^3$$

Notice that we add exponents, $7 + (-4) = 3$, when we multiply with the same base.

EXAMPLE 11 Divide: $\dfrac{9.6 \times 10^{12}}{3 \times 10^4}$.

SOLUTION We group the numbers between 1 and 10 separately from the powers of 10 and proceed as we did in Example 6:

$$\frac{9.6 \times 10^{12}}{3 \times 10^4} = \frac{9.6}{3} \times \frac{10^{12}}{10^4}$$

$$= 3.2 \times 10^8$$

Notice that the procedure we used in both of these examples is very similar to multiplication and division of monomials, for which we multiplied or divided coefficients and added or subtracted exponents.

EXAMPLE 12 Simplify: $\dfrac{(6.8 \times 10^5)(3.9 \times 10^{-7})}{1.7 \times 10^{-4}}$.

SOLUTION We group the numbers between 1 and 10 separately from the powers of 10:

$$\frac{(6.8)(3.9)}{1.7} \times \frac{(10^5)(10^{-7})}{10^{-4}} = 15.6 \times 10^{5+(-7)-(-4)}$$

$$= 15.6 \times 10^2$$

Our result is not in scientific notation because 15.6 is greater than 10. We convert our answer into scientific notation as follows.

$$15.6 \times 10^2 = (1.56 \times 10^1) \times 10^2$$

$$= 1.56 \times 10^3$$

Addition and Subtraction of Monomials

Addition and subtraction of monomials will be almost identical since subtraction is defined as addition of the opposite. With multiplication and division of monomials, the key was rearranging the numbers and variables using the commutative and associative properties. With addition, the key is application of the distributive property. We sometimes use the phrase *combine monomials* to describe addition and subtraction of monomials.

DEFINITION *similar terms*

Two terms (monomials) with the same variable part (same variables raised to the same powers) are called *similar* (or like) *terms*.

You can add only similar terms. This is because the distributive property (which is the key to addition of monomials) cannot be applied to terms that are not similar.

EXAMPLE 13 Combine the following monomials.
a. $-3x^2 + 15x^2$ **b.** $9x^2y - 20x^2y$ **c.** $5x^2 + 8y^2$

SOLUTION

a. $-3x^2 + 15x^2 = (-3 + 15)x^2$ Distributive property

$$= 12x^2$$ Add coefficients

b. $9x^2y - 20x^2y = (9 - 20)x^2y$ Distributive property

$= -11x^2y$ Add coefficients

c. $5x^2 + 8y^2$ In this case we cannot apply the distributive property, so we cannot add the monomials

EXAMPLE 14 Simplify: $\dfrac{14x^5}{2x^2} + \dfrac{15x^8}{3x^5}$.

SOLUTION Simplifying each expression separately and then combining similar terms gives

$$\frac{14x^5}{2x^2} + \frac{15x^8}{3x^5} = 7x^3 + 5x^3 \qquad \text{Divide}$$

$$= 12x^3 \qquad \text{Add}$$

Application

EXAMPLE 15 A rectangular solid is twice as long as it is wide and one-half as high as it is wide. Write an expression for the volume.

SOLUTION We begin by making a diagram of the object (Figure 1) with the dimensions labeled as given in the problem.

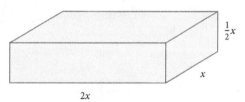

FIGURE 1

The volume is the product of the three dimensions:

$$V = 2x \cdot x \cdot \frac{1}{2}x = x^3$$

The box has the same volume as a cube with side x, as shown in Figure 2.

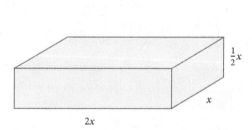 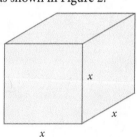

Equal Volumes

FIGURE 2

Getting Ready for Class

After reading through the preceding section, respond in your own words and in complete sentences.

A. What is a monomial?

B. Describe how you would multiply $3x^2$ and $5x^2$.

C. Describe how you would add $3x^2$ and $5x^2$.

D. Describe how you would multiply two numbers written in scientific notation.

State the coefficient and degree for each of the following monomials.

1. $7x^3$ **2.** $-2x^8$ **3.** $-x$ **4.** $\dfrac{x}{3}$ **5.** $\dfrac{1}{2}xy$

6. $\dfrac{3}{4}x^2y$ **7.** $-4a^6b^5$ **8.** $-9a^3b^{11}$ **9.** 8 **10.** -5

Multiply.

11. $(3x^4)(4x^3)$

12. $(6x^5)(-2x^2)$

13. $(-2y^4)(8y^7)$

14. $(5y^{10})(2y^5)$

15. $(8x)(4x)$

16. $(7x)(5x)$

17. $(10a^3)(10a)(2a^2)$

18. $(5a^4)(10a)(10a^4)$

19. $(6ab^2)(-4a^2b)$

20. $(-5a^3b)(4ab^4)$

21. $(4x^2y)(3x^3y^3)(2xy^4)$

22. $(5x^6)(-10xy^4)(-2x^2y^6)$

Divide. Write all answers with positive exponents only.

23. $\dfrac{15x^3}{5x^2}$

24. $\dfrac{25x^5}{5x^4}$

25. $\dfrac{18y^9}{3y^{12}}$

26. $\dfrac{24y^4}{8y^7}$

27. $\dfrac{32a^3}{64a^4}$

28. $\dfrac{25a^5}{75a^6}$

29. $\dfrac{21a^2b^3}{-7ab^5}$

30. $\dfrac{32a^5b^6}{8ab^5}$

31. $\dfrac{3x^3y^2z}{27xy^2z^3}$

32. $\dfrac{5x^5y^4z}{30x^3yz^2}$

33. Fill in the table.

a	b	ab	$\dfrac{a}{b}$	$\dfrac{b}{a}$
10	$5x$			
$20x^3$	$6x^2$			
$25x^5$	$5x^4$			
$3x^{-2}$	$3x^2$			
$-2y^4$	$8y^7$			

34. Fill in the table.

a	b	ab	$\dfrac{a}{b}$	$\dfrac{b}{a}$
$10y$	$2y^2$			
$10y^2$	$2y$			
$5y^3$	15			
5	$15y^3$			
$4y^{-3}$	$4y^3$			

Find each product. Write all answers in scientific notation.

35. $(3 \times 10^3)(2 \times 10^5)$

36. $(4 \times 10^8)(1 \times 10^6)$

37. $(3.5 \times 10^4)(5 \times 10^{-6})$

38. $(7.1 \times 10^5)(2 \times 10^{-8})$

39. $(5.5 \times 10^{-3})(2.2 \times 10^{-4})$

40. $(3.4 \times 10^{-2})(4.5 \times 10^{-6})$

Find each quotient. Write all answers in scientific notation.

41. $\dfrac{8.4 \times 10^5}{2 \times 10^2}$ **42.** $\dfrac{9.6 \times 10^{20}}{3 \times 10^6}$ **43.** $\dfrac{6 \times 10^8}{2 \times 10^{-2}}$

44. $\dfrac{8 \times 10^{12}}{4 \times 10^{-3}}$ **45.** $\dfrac{2.5 \times 10^{-6}}{5 \times 10^{-4}}$ **46.** $\dfrac{4.5 \times 10^{-8}}{9 \times 10^{-4}}$

Combine like terms by adding or subtracting as indicated.

47. $3x^2 + 5x^2$ **48.** $4x^3 + 8x^3$

49. $8x^5 - 19x^5$ **50.** $75x^6 - 50x^6$

51. $2a + a - 3a$ **52.** $5a + a - 6a$

53. $10x^3 - 8x^3 + 2x^3$ **54.** $7x^5 + 8x^5 - 12x^5$

55. $20ab^2 - 19ab^2 + 30ab^2$ **56.** $18a^3b^2 - 20a^3b^2 + 10a^3b^2$

57. Fill in the table.

a	b	ab	$a + b$
$5x$	$3x$		
$4x^2$	$2x^2$		
$3x^3$	$6x^3$		
$2x^4$	$-3x^4$		
x^5	$7x^5$		

58. Fill in the table.

a	b	ab	$a - b$
$2y$	$3y$		
$-2y$	$3y$		
$4y^2$	$5y^2$		
y^3	$-3y^3$		
$5y^4$	$7y^4$		

Simplify. Write all answers with positive exponents only.

59. $(2x)^3(2x)^4$ **60.** $(3x)^2(3x)^3$ **61.** $(3x^2)^3(2x)^4$

62. $(3x)^3(2x^3)^2$ **63.** $(4xy^3)^2(2x^5y)^3$ **64.** $(3x^3y^2)^3(2x^2y^3)^2$

65. $\dfrac{(2x)^5}{(2x)^3}$ **66.** $\dfrac{(3x)^2}{(3x)^4}$ **67.** $\dfrac{(3x^2)^3}{(2x)^4}$

68. $\dfrac{(3x)^3}{(2x^3)^2}$ **69.** $\dfrac{(2x^2y)^4}{(6xy^4)^2}$ **70.** $\dfrac{(4x^2y^3)^3}{(2x^3y^2)^4}$

71. $\dfrac{(3x^2)(8x^5)}{6x^4}$ **72.** $\dfrac{(7x^3)(6x^8)}{14x^5}$ **73.** $\dfrac{(9a^2b)(2a^3b^4)}{18a^5b^7}$

74. $\dfrac{(21a^5b)(2a^8b^4)}{14ab}$ **75.** $\dfrac{(4x^3y^2)(9x^4y^{10})}{(3x^5y)(2x^6y)}$ **76.** $\dfrac{(5x^4y^4)(10x^3y^3)}{(25xy^5)(2xy^7)}$

Simplify each expression, and write all answers in scientific notation.

77. $\dfrac{(6 \times 10^8)(3 \times 10^5)}{9 \times 10^7}$ **78.** $\dfrac{(8 \times 10^4)(5 \times 10^{10})}{2 \times 10^7}$

79. $\dfrac{(5 \times 10^3)(4 \times 10^{-5})}{2 \times 10^{-2}}$ **80.** $\dfrac{(7 \times 10^6)(4 \times 10^{-4})}{1.4 \times 10^{-3}}$

81. $\dfrac{(2.8 \times 10^{-7})(3.6 \times 10^4)}{2.4 \times 10^3}$ **82.** $\dfrac{(5.4 \times 10^2)(3.5 \times 10^{-9})}{4.5 \times 10^6}$

Simplify.

83. $\dfrac{18x^4}{3x} + \dfrac{21x^7}{7x^4}$ **84.** $\dfrac{24x^{10}}{6x^4} + \dfrac{32x^7}{8x}$ **85.** $\dfrac{45a^6}{9a^4} - \dfrac{50a^8}{2a^6}$

86. $\dfrac{16a^9}{4a} - \dfrac{28a^{12}}{4a^4}$ **87.** $\dfrac{6x^7y^4}{3x^2y^2} + \dfrac{8x^5y^8}{2y^6}$ **88.** $\dfrac{40x^{10}y^{10}}{8x^2y^5} + \dfrac{10x^8y^8}{5y^3}$

Learning Objectives Assessment

The following problems can be used to help assess if you have successfully met the learning objectives for this section.

89. State the degree of $5x^7y^2$.

   a. 7 **b.** 9 **c.** 5 **d.** 14

90. Simplify: $\dfrac{(2x^3)(9x^4)}{6x^5}$.

   a. $3x^2$ **b.** $3x^7$ **c.** $\dfrac{27x^2}{4}$ **d.** $\dfrac{27x^7}{4}$

91. Simplify: $(2.6 \times 10^{-5})(3.8 \times 10^3)$.

   a. 6.4×10^{-2} **b.** 6.4×10^{-15} **c.** 9.88×10^{-15} **d.** 9.88×10^{-2}

92. Simplify: $15a^2b^3 - 6a^2b^3$.

   a. $9a^4b^9$ **b.** $-90a^4b^9$ **c.** $9a^2b^3$ **d.** 9

Getting Ready for the Next Section

Simplify.

93. $3 - 8$ **94.** $-5 + 7$ **95.** $-1 + 7$

96. $1 - 8$ **97.** $3(5)^2 + 1$ **98.** $3(-2)^2 - 5(-2) + 4$

99. $2x^2 + 4x^2$ **100.** $3x^2 - x^2$ **101.** $-5x + 7x$

102. $x - 2x$ **103.** $-(2x + 9)$ **104.** $-(4x^2 - 2x - 6)$

105. Find the value of $2x + 3$ when $x = 4$.

106. Find the value of $(3x)^2$ when $x = 3$.

SPOTLIGHT ON SUCCESS   *Student Instructor Gordon*

Math takes time. This fact holds true in the smallest of math problems as much as it does in the most math intensive careers. I see proof in each video I make. My videos get progressively better with each take, though I still make mistakes and find aspects I can improve on with each new video. In order to keep trying to improve in spite of any failures or lack of improvement, something else is needed. For me it is the sense of a specific goal in sight, to help me maintain the desire to put in continued time and effort.

When I decided on the number one university I wanted to attend, I wrote the name of that school in bold block letters on my door, written to remind myself daily of my ultimate goal. Stuck in the back of my head, this end result pushed me little by little to succeed and meet all of the requirements for the university I had in mind. And now I can say I'm at my dream school bringing with me that skill.

I recognize that others may have much more difficult circumstances than my own to endure, with the goal of improving or escaping those circumstances, and I deeply respect that. But that fact demonstrates to me how easy but effective it is, in comparison, to "stay with the problems longer" with a goal in mind of something much more easily realized, like a good grade on a test. I've learned to set goals, small or big, and to stick with them until they are realized.

Addition and Subtraction of Polynomials

Learning Objectives

In this section, we will learn how to:

1. State the degree and leading coefficient for a polynomial in one variable.
2. Evaluate a polynomial.
3. Add polynomials.
4. Subtract polynomials.

In this section we will extend what we learned in Section 5.3 to expressions called polynomials.

Polynomials

We begin this section with the definition of a polynomial.

> **DEFINITION** *polynomial*
>
> A *polynomial* is a finite sum of monomials (terms).

Here are some examples of polynomials:

$$3x^2 + 2x + 1 \qquad 15x^2y + 21xy^2 - 7 \qquad 3a - 2b + 4c - 5d$$

Polynomials can be further classified by the number of terms they contain. A polynomial with two terms is called a *binomial*. If it has three terms, it is a *trinomial*. As stated before, a *monomial* has only one term.

To write a polynomial in *standard form*, we write the terms in order of degree from highest degree to lowest degree. Once we have done so, the first term in the polynomial is called the *leading term*.

> **DEFINITION** *degree of a polynomial*
>
> The *degree* of a polynomial is the degree of the leading term once the polynomial is written in standard form.

For a polynomial in one variable, the degree of the polynomial is the highest power to which the variable is raised.

Various degrees of polynomials:

$3x^5 + 2x^3 + 1$	A trinomial of degree 5
$2x + 1$	A binomial of degree 1
$3x^2 + 2x + 1$	A trinomial of degree 2
$3x^5$	A monomial of degree 5
-9	A monomial of degree 0

EXAMPLE 1   Write $2x - 5 + 3x^4 - x^2$ in standard form. Then state the degree of the polynomial and the leading coefficient.

SOLUTION For standard form, we write the terms in order from highest degree to lowest.

$$3x^4 - x^2 + 2x - 5 \qquad \text{Standard form}$$

The leading term is $3x^4$, so the degree is 4 and the leading coefficient is 3.

Evaluating Polynomials

Evaluating a polynomial means finding the value of a polynomial for a given value of the variable. To find the value of the polynomial $3x^2 + 1$ when x is 5, we replace x with 5 and simplify the result:

$$
\begin{aligned}
\text{When} \qquad & x = 5 \\
\text{the polynomial} \qquad & 3x^2 + 1 \\
\text{becomes} \qquad & 3(5)^2 + 1 = 3(25) + 1 \\
& = 75 + 1 \\
& = 76
\end{aligned}
$$

EXAMPLE 2   Find the value of $3x^2 - 5x + 4$ when $x = -2$.

SOLUTION

$$
\begin{aligned}
\text{When} \qquad & x = -2 \\
\text{the polynomial} \qquad & 3x^2 - 5x + 4 \\
\text{becomes} \qquad & 3(-2)^2 - 5(-2) + 4 = 3(4) + 10 + 4 \\
& = 12 + 10 + 4 \\
& = 26
\end{aligned}
$$

Addition

There are no new rules for adding one or more polynomials. We rely only on our previous knowledge. Here are some examples.

EXAMPLE 3   Add: $(2x^2 - 5x + 3) + (4x^2 + 7x - 8)$.

SOLUTION We use the commutative and associative properties to group similar terms together and then apply the distributive property to add.

$$
\begin{aligned}
& (2x^2 - 5x + 3) + (4x^2 + 7x - 8) \\
&= (2x^2 + 4x^2) + (-5x + 7x) + (3 - 8) && \text{Commutative and} \\
& && \text{associative properties} \\
&= (2 + 4)x^2 + (-5 + 7)x + (3 - 8) && \text{Distributive property} \\
&= 6x^2 + 2x - 5 && \text{Addition}
\end{aligned}
$$

The results here indicate that to add two polynomials, we add coefficients of similar terms.

EXAMPLE 4   Add $x^2 + 3x$ and $2x + 6$.

SOLUTION   The only similar terms here are the two middle terms. We combine them as usual to get

$$x^2 + 3x + 2x + 6 = x^2 + 5x + 6$$

Subtraction

You will recall from Chapter 1 the definition of subtraction: $a - b = a + (-b)$. To subtract one expression from another, we simply add its opposite. The letters a and b in the definition can each represent polynomials.

Before we can subtract, we need to be able to find the *opposite* of a polynomial. The opposite of a polynomial is the opposite of each of its terms. This is equivalent to multiplying the polynomial by a factor of -1 and then distributing.

EXAMPLE 5   Find the opposite of $3x^2 - 5x + 8$.

SOLUTION   To find the opposite, we take the opposite of each term.

$$-(3x^2 - 5x + 8) = -1(3x^2 - 5x + 8)$$

$$= -3x^2 + 5x - 8$$

Now we are ready to subtract polynomials. When you subtract one polynomial from another you add the opposite of each of its terms.

EXAMPLE 6   Subtract: $(3x^2 + x + 4) - (x^2 + 2x + 3)$.

SOLUTION   To subtract $x^2 + 2x + 3$, we change the sign of each of its terms and add.

$$(3x^2 + x + 4) - (x^2 + 2x + 3)$$
$$= 3x^2 + x + 4 - x^2 - 2x - 3 \qquad \text{Take the opposite of each term in the second polynomial}$$

$$= (3x^2 - x^2) + (x - 2x) + (4 - 3)$$
$$= 2x^2 - x + 1$$

EXAMPLE 7   Subtract $-4x^2 + 5x - 7$ from $x^2 - x - 1$.

SOLUTION   The polynomial $x^2 - x - 1$ comes first, then the subtraction sign, and finally the polynomial $-4x^2 + 5x - 7$ in parentheses.

$$(x^2 - x - 1) - (-4x^2 + 5x - 7)$$
$$= x^2 - x - 1 + 4x^2 - 5x + 7 \qquad \text{Take the opposite of each term in the second polynomial}$$

$$= (x^2 + 4x^2) + (-x - 5x) + (-1 + 7)$$
$$= 5x^2 - 6x + 6$$

Getting Ready for Class

After reading through the preceding section, respond in your own words and in complete sentences.

A. What are similar terms?

B. What is the degree of a polynomial?

C. How you would find the value of $3x^2 - 5x + 4$ when x is -2?

D. Describe how you would subtract one polynomial from another.

Identify each of the following polynomials as a trinomial, binomial, or monomial, and give the degree in each case.

1. $2x^3 - 3x^2 + 1$ **2.** $4x^2 - 4x + 1$ **3.** $5 + 8a - 9a^3$

4. $6 + 12x^3 + x^4$ **5.** $2x - 1$ **6.** $4 + 7x$

7. $45x^2 - 1$ **8.** $3a^3 + 8$ **9.** $7a^2$

10. $90x$ **11.** -4 **12.** 56

Write each polynomial in standard form. Then identify the degree and leading coefficient.

13. $2 + 5x^2$ **14.** $5 - 4x^3$ **15.** $3x^2 - x^3 - 6x$

16. $2x^3 - 6 + x^4 - x$ **17.** $6x^2 - 1 + x$ **18.** $4x^2 - 9$

Evaluate each polynomial for the given value of the variable.

19. $4x + 2, x = 3$ **20.** $2x - 4, x = 5$

21. $x^2 - 9, x = -1$ **22.** $16 - y^2, y = -2$

23. $3a^2 - 2a + 4, a = 2$ **24.** $4a^2 + 5a - 9, a = 0$

25. $x^2 - 2x + 1, x = 3$ **26.** $(x - 1)^2, x = 3$

Perform the following additions.

27. $(2x^2 + 3x + 4) + (3x^2 + 2x + 5)$ **28.** $(x^2 + 5x + 6) + (x^2 + 3x + 4)$

29. $(3a^2 - 4a + 1) + (2a^2 - 5a + 6)$ **30.** $(5a^2 - 2a + 7) + (4a^2 - 3a + 2)$

31. $(x^2 + 4x) + (2x + 8)$ **32.** $(y^2 - 18y) + (2y - 12)$

33. $(x^2 - 3x) + (3x - 9)$ **34.** $(x^2 - 5x) + (5x - 25)$

Find the opposite of each polynomial.

35. $10x - 5$ **36.** $2x + 6$ **37.** $5x^2 + x - 2$

38. $3x^2 - 4x + 1$ **39.** $3 + 2x - x^2$ **40.** $12 - x - x^2$

Perform the indicated operation.

41. $(6x^3 - 4x^2 + 2x) - (9x^2 - 6x + 3)$ **42.** $(5x^3 + 2x^2 + 3x) - (2x^2 + 5x + 1)$

43. $(a^2 - a - 1) - (-a^2 + a + 1)$ **44.** $(5a^2 - a - 6) - (-3a^2 - 2a + 4)$

45. $(6x^2 - 3x) - (10x - 5)$ **46.** $(x^2 + 5x) - (3x + 15)$

47. $(3y^2 - 5y) - (6y - 10)$ **48.** $(10x^2 + 30x) - (2x + 6)$

49. $\left(\frac{2}{3}x^2 - \frac{1}{5}x - \frac{3}{4}\right) + \left(\frac{4}{3}x^2 - \frac{4}{5}x + \frac{7}{4}\right)$

50. $\left(\frac{3}{8}x^3 - \frac{5}{7}x^2 - \frac{2}{5}\right) + \left(\frac{5}{8}x^3 - \frac{2}{7}x^2 + \frac{7}{5}\right)$

51. $\left(\frac{5}{9}x^3 + \frac{1}{3}x^2 - 2x + 1\right) - \left(\frac{2}{3}x^3 + x^2 + \frac{1}{2}x - \frac{3}{4}\right)$

52. $\left(4x^3 - \frac{2}{5}x^2 + \frac{3}{8}x - 1\right) - \left(\frac{9}{2}x^3 + \frac{1}{4}x^2 - x + \frac{5}{6}\right)$

53. $(4y^2 - 3y + 2) + (5y^2 + 12y - 4) - (13y^2 - 6y + 20)$

54. $(2y^2 - 7y - 8) - (6y^2 + 6y - 8) + (4y^2 - 2y + 3)$

55. Subtract $10x^2 + 23x - 50$ from $11x^2 - 10x + 13$.

56. Subtract $2x^2 - 3x + 5$ from $4x^2 - 5x + 10$.

57. Subtract $3y^2 + 7y - 15$ from $11y^2 + 11y + 11$.

58. Subtract $15y^2 - 8y - 2$ from $3y^2 - 3y + 2$.

59. Add $50x^2 - 100x - 150$ to $25x^2 - 50x + 75$.

60. Add $7x^2 - 8x + 10$ to $-8x^2 + 2x - 12$.

61. Subtract $2x + 1$ from the sum of $3x - 2$ and $11x + 5$.

62. Subtract $3x - 5$ from the sum of $5x + 2$ and $9x - 1$.

Applying the Concepts

63. Packaging A crystal ball with a diameter of 6 inches is being packaged for shipment. If the crystal ball is placed inside a circular cylinder with radius 3 inches and height 6 inches, how much volume will need to be filled with padding? (The volume of a sphere with radius r is $\frac{4}{3}\pi r^3$, and the volume of a right circular cylinder with radius r and height h is $\pi r^2 h$.) Use 3.14 to approximate π.

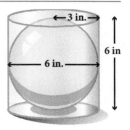

64. Packaging Suppose the circular cylinder of Problem 63 has a radius of 4 inches and a height of 7 inches. How much volume will need to be filled with padding?

Learning Objectives Assessment

The following problems can be used to help assess if you have successfully met the learning objectives for this section.

65. State the degree of the polynomial $2x^3 + x + 3x^4 - 4$.

   a. 3   **b.** 2   **c.** -4 **d.** 4

66. Evaluate $2x^2 - 5x - 3$ if $x = -2$.

   a. 15   **b.** -1 **c.** -5 **d.** 3

67. Add: $(2x^3 - x^2 + 4) + (3x^2 + x - 2)$.

   a. $5x^5 - x^3 + 2$ **b.** $2x^3 + 2x^2 + x + 2$

   c. $3x^3 + 2x + 2$ **d.** $2x^3 - 4x^2 - x + 6$

68. Subtract: $(2x^3 - x^2 + 4) - (3x^2 + x - 2)$.

   a. $2x^3 - 4x^2 - x + 6$ **b.** $2x^3 + 2x^2 + x + 2$

   c. $-x^5 - x^3 + 6$ **d.** $2x^3 - 4x^2 + x + 2$

Getting Ready for the Next Section

Simplify.

69. $(-5)(-1)$

70. $3(-4)$

71. $(-1)(6)$

72. $(-7) \cdot 8$

73. $(5x)(-4x)$

74. $(3x)(2x)$

75. $3x(-7)$

76. $3x(-1)$

77. $5x + (-3x)$

78. $-3x - 10x$

79. $3(2x - 6)$

80. $-4x(x + 5)$

SPOTLIGHT ON SUCCESS   *Student Instructor Ryan*

You do not determine a man's greatness by his talent or wealth, as the world does, but rather by what it takes to discourage him.
— Dr. Jerry Falwell

From very early in school, I seemed to have a knack for math, but I also had a knack for laziness and procrastination. In rare times, I would really focus in class and nail all the material, but more often I would spend my time goofing off with friends and coasting on what came easily to me. My parents tried their hardest to motivate me, to do anything they could to help me succeed, but when it came down to it, it was on me to control the outcome.

At one point, my dad voiced his frustrations with having to pay for such a good education when I wasn't taking advantage of it. He told me that if I didn't get above a 3.8 GPA, that I would be attending a different school the following fall. It was the motivation I needed. Finally, I understood the importance of trying my best in school. That semester I achieved the goal my dad had given to me.

But it wasn't that easy. I encountered numerous things in high school that could have derailed my academic journey. I felt abandoned by people I considered family, I suffered multiple injuries requiring surgery, and I experienced the death of a classmate and teammate. There was so much going on that I could have just shut down and gone back to coasting by, but luckily, I had already learned my lesson. I managed to stay positive and work hard through all the challenges. Everything paid off senior year when I was accepted to California Polytechnic State University and managed to pass every AP test I took. This journey has taught me that one of the most important things we can do is to work hard no matter what the circumstances; if we refuse to be discouraged, then we can achieve greatness.

Multiplication with Polynomials

Learning Objectives

In this section, we will learn how to:

1. Multiply a polynomial by a monomial.
2. Multiply two binomials using the FOIL method.
3. Multiply polynomials.
4. Solve application problems involving multiplication with polynomials.

Introduction

We begin our discussion of multiplication of polynomials by finding the product of a monomial and a trinomial.

EXAMPLE 1 Multiply: $3x^2(2x^2 + 4x + 5)$.

SOLUTION Applying the distributive property gives us

$$3x^2(2x^2 + 4x + 5) = 3x^2(2x^2) + 3x^2(4x) + 3x^2(5) \qquad \text{Distributive property}$$
$$= 6x^4 + 12x^3 + 15x^2 \qquad \text{Multiplication}$$

Multiplying Binomials

The distributive property is the key to multiplication of polynomials. We can use it to find the product of any two polynomials. There are some shortcuts we can use in certain situations, however. Let's look at an example that involves the product of two binomials.

EXAMPLE 2 Multiply: $(3x - 5)(2x - 1)$.

SOLUTION
$$(3x - 5)(2x - 1) = 3x(2x - 1) - 5(2x - 1)$$
$$= 3x(2x) + 3x(-1) + (-5)(2x) + (-5)(-1)$$
$$= 6x^2 - 3x - 10x + 5$$
$$= 6x^2 - 13x + 5$$

If we look closely at the second and third lines of work in this example, we can see that the terms in the answer come from all possible products of terms in the first binomial with terms in the second binomial. This result is generalized as follows.

 RULE

To multiply any two polynomials, multiply each term in the first with each term in the second.

There are several ways we can put this rule to work.

FOIL Method

If we look at the original problem in Example 2 and then to the answer, we see that the first term in the answer came from multiplying the first terms in each binomial:

$$3x \cdot 2x = 6x^2 \qquad \text{First}$$

The middle term in the answer came from adding the products of the two outside terms with the two inside terms in each binomial:

$$3x(-1) = -3x \qquad \text{Outside}$$
$$\underline{-5(2x) = -10x} \qquad \text{Inside}$$
$$= -13x$$

The last term in the answer came from multiplying the two last terms:

$$-5(-1) = 5 \qquad \text{Last}$$

The word FOIL is a mnemonic to help us remember how we obtain the four products that result when we multiply two binomials:

F	O	I	L
First	Outside	Inside	Last

To summarize the FOIL method, we will multiply another two binomials.

EXAMPLE 3   Multiply: $(2x + 3)(5x - 4)$.

SOLUTION $(2x + 3)(5x - 4) = \underset{\text{First}}{\underline{2x(5x)}} + \underset{\text{Outside}}{\underline{2x(-4)}} + \underset{\text{Inside}}{\underline{3(5x)}} + \underset{\text{Last}}{\underline{3(-4)}}$

$$= 10x^2 - 8x + 15x - 12$$

$$= 10x^2 + 7x - 12$$

With practice $-8x + 15x = 7x$ can be done mentally.

EXAMPLE 4   Multiply:

a. $4a^2(2a^2 - 3a + 5) = 4a^2(2a^2) + 4a^2(-3a) + 4a^2(5)$
$$= 8a^4 - 12a^3 + 20a^2$$

b. $(x - 2)(y + 3) = \underset{\text{F}}{x(y)} + \underset{\text{O}}{x(3)} + \underset{\text{I}}{(-2)(y)} + \underset{\text{L}}{(-2)(3)}$
$$= xy + 3x - 2y - 6$$

c. $(x + y)(a - b) = \underset{\text{F}}{x(a)} + \underset{\text{O}}{x(-b)} + \underset{\text{I}}{y(a)} + \underset{\text{L}}{y(-b)}$
$$= xa - xb + ya - yb$$

d. $(5x - 1)(2x + 6) = \underset{\text{F}}{5x(2x)} + \underset{\text{O}}{5x(6)} + \underset{\text{I}}{(-1)(2x)} + \underset{\text{L}}{(-1)(6)}$
$$= 10x^2 + 30x + (-2x) + (-6)$$
$$= 10x^2 + 28x - 6$$

Multiplying Polynomials

The FOIL method can be applied only when multiplying two binomials. To find products of polynomials with more than two terms, we once again apply the distributive property.

EXAMPLE 5   Multiply: $(x^2 - 4x + 2)(3x^2 + x - 5)$.

SOLUTION First, we use the distributive property to multiply each term in the first polynomial by the second polynomial.

$$(x^2 - 4x + 2)(3x^2 + x - 5) =$$

$$= x^2(3x^2 + x - 5) - 4x(3x^2 + x - 5) + 2(3x^2 + x - 5)$$

Now we use the distributive property three more times to perform the multiplication by each monomial.

$$= 3x^4 + x^3 - 5x^2 + (-12x^3 - 4x^2 + 20x) + (6x^2 + 2x - 10)$$

$$= 3x^4 + (x^3 - 12x^3) + (-5x^2 - 4x^2 + 6x^2) + (20x + 2x) - 10$$

$$= 3x^4 - 11x^3 - 3x^2 + 22x - 10$$

The column method of multiplying two polynomials is very similar to long multiplication with whole numbers. It is just another way of finding all possible products of terms in one polynomial with terms in another polynomial.

EXAMPLE 6   Multiply: $(2x + 3)(3x^2 - 2x + 1)$.

SOLUTION

$$
\begin{array}{r}
3x^2 - 2x + 1 \\
\times \quad\quad\quad 2x + 3 \\
\hline
6x^3 - 4x^2 + 2x \qquad \leftarrow 2x(3x^2 - 2x + 1) \\
9x^2 - 6x + 3 \qquad \leftarrow 3(3x^2 - 2x + 1) \\
\hline
6x^3 + 5x^2 - 4x + 3 \qquad \leftarrow \text{Add similar terms}
\end{array}
$$

A third way to multiply polynomials is the rectangle method. We create a rectangle with each term in the first polynomial at the start of a row and each term in the second polynomial at the top of a column. We then fill in each box in the rectangle by multiplying the corresponding monomials. Our next example illustrates this process.

EXAMPLE 7   Multiply: $(3x - 2)(4x^2 + x + 3)$.

SOLUTION   We create a rectangle with two rows and three columns, placing the terms of $3x - 2$ along one side and the terms of $4x^2 + x + 3$ along the other as follows.

	$4x^2$	x	3
$3x$			
-2			

The entry in each box is found by multiplying the monomial at the left with the monomial above.

	$4x^2$	x	3
$3x$	$12x^3$	$3x^2$	$9x$
-2	$-8x^2$	$-2x$	-6

Notice that our rectangle contains six terms

$$\text{binomial} \times \text{trinomial} = 2 \text{ terms} \times 3 \text{ terms} = 6 \text{ terms}$$

Combining like terms gives us the final result.

$$= 12x^3 + (3x^2 - 8x^2) + (9x - 2x) - 6$$

$$= 12x^3 - 5x^2 + 7x - 6$$

It will be to your advantage to become very fast and accurate at multiplying polynomials. Use the method you are most comfortable with and make the fewest mistakes with.

Applications

EXAMPLE 8   The length of a rectangle is 3 more than twice the width. Write an expression for the area of the rectangle.

SOLUTION   We begin by drawing a rectangle and labeling the width with x. Since the length is 3 more than twice the width, we label the length with $2x + 3$.

The area A of a rectangle is the product of the length and width, so we write our formula for the area of this rectangle as

$$A = x(2x + 3)$$

$$A = 2x^2 + 3x \qquad \text{Multiply}$$

Revenue

Suppose that a store sells x items at p dollars per item. The total amount of money obtained by selling the items is called the *revenue*. It can be found by multiplying the number of items sold, x, by the price per item, p. For example, if 100 items are sold for \$6 each, the revenue is $100(6) = \$600$. Similarly, if 500 items are sold for \$8 each, the total revenue is $500(8) = \$4{,}000$. If we denote the revenue with the letter R, then the formula that relates R, x, and p is

$$R = xp$$

In words: Revenue = (number of items sold)(price of each item)

EXAMPLE 9   A store selling cases for cell phones knows from past experience that it can sell x cases each day at a price of p dollars per case, according to the equation $x = 800 - 100p$. Write a formula for the daily revenue that involves only the variables R and p.

SOLUTION   From our previous discussion we know that the revenue R is given by the formula

$$R = xp$$

But, since $x = 800 - 100p$, we can substitute $800 - 100p$ for x in the revenue equation to obtain

$$R = (800 - 100p)p$$
$$R = 800p - 100p^2$$

This last formula gives the revenue, R, in terms of the price, p.

Getting Ready for Class

After reading through the preceding section, respond in your own words and in complete sentences.

A. How do we multiply two polynomials?

B. Describe how the distributive property is used to multiply a monomial and a polynomial.

C. Describe how you would use the foil method to multiply two binomials.

D. Explain how you would multiply two trinomials.

Problem Set 5.5

Multiply the following by applying the distributive property.

1. $2x(3x + 1)$ **2.** $4x(2x - 3)$

3. $2x^2(3x^2 - 2x + 1)$ **4.** $5x(4x^3 - 5x^2 + x)$

5. $2ab(a^2 - ab + 1)$ **6.** $3a^2b(a^3 + a^2b^2 + b^3)$

7. $y^2(3y^2 + 9y + 12)$ **8.** $5y(2y^2 - 3y + 5)$

9. $4x^2y(2x^3y + 3x^2y^2 + 8y^3)$ **10.** $6xy^3(2x^2 + 5xy + 12y^2)$

Multiply the following binomials using the FOIL method.

11. $(x + 3)(x + 4)$ **12.** $(x + 2)(x + 5)$ **13.** $(x + 6)(x + 1)$

14. $(x + 1)(x + 4)$ **15.** $\left(x + \dfrac{1}{2}\right)\left(x + \dfrac{3}{2}\right)$ **16.** $\left(x + \dfrac{3}{5}\right)\left(x + \dfrac{2}{5}\right)$

17. $(a + 5)(a - 3)$ **18.** $(a - 8)(a + 2)$ **19.** $(x - a)(y + b)$

20. $(x + a)(y - b)$ **21.** $(x + 6)(x - 6)$ **22.** $(x + 3)(x - 3)$

23. $\left(y + \dfrac{5}{6}\right)\left(y - \dfrac{5}{6}\right)$ **24.** $\left(y - \dfrac{4}{7}\right)\left(y + \dfrac{4}{7}\right)$ **25.** $(2x - 3)(x - 4)$

26. $(3x - 5)(x - 2)$ **27.** $(a + 2)(2a - 1)$ **28.** $(a - 6)(3a + 2)$

29. $(2x - 5)(3x - 2)$ **30.** $(3x + 6)(2x - 1)$ **31.** $(2x + 3)(a + 4)$

32. $(2x - 3)(a - 4)$ **33.** $(5x - 4)(5x + 4)$ **34.** $(6x + 5)(6x - 5)$

35. $\left(2x - \dfrac{1}{2}\right)\left(x + \dfrac{3}{2}\right)$ **36.** $\left(4x - \dfrac{3}{2}\right)\left(x + \dfrac{1}{2}\right)$ **37.** $(1 - 2a)(3 - 4a)$

38. $(1 - 3a)(3 + 2a)$

Multiply the following polynomials using one of the three methods described in this section.

39. $(a - 3)(a^2 - 3a + 2)$ **40.** $(a + 5)(a^2 + 2a + 3)$

41. $(x + 2)(x^2 - 2x + 4)$ **42.** $(x + 3)(x^2 - 3x + 9)$

43. $(2x + 1)(x^2 + 8x + 9)$ **44.** $(3x - 2)(x^2 - 7x + 8)$

45. $(5x^2 + 2x + 1)(x^2 - 3x + 5)$ **46.** $(2x^2 + x + 1)(x^2 - 4x + 3)$

47. $(3x^2 - 5x - 2)(2x^2 + x - 1)$ **48.** $(4x^2 + 2x - 3)(3x^2 - 2x + 3)$

49. $(a^3 + a + 2)(a^2 - 3a + 4)$ **50.** $(a^3 - 2a^2 - 3)(2a^2 + a + 1)$

51. $(x^2 + 3)(2x^2 - 5)$ **52.** $(4x^3 - 8)(5x^3 + 4)$

53. $(3a^4 + 2)(2a^2 + 5)$ **54.** $(7a^4 - 8)(4a^3 - 6)$

55. $(x + 3)(x + 4)(x + 5)$ **56.** $(x - 3)(x - 4)(x - 5)$

Simplify each expression.

57. $(x - 3)(x - 2) + 2$ **58.** $(2x - 5)(3x + 2) - 4$

59. $(2x - 3)(4x + 3) + 4$ **60.** $(3x + 8)(5x - 7) + 52$

61. $(x + 4)(x - 5) + (-5)(2)$ **62.** $(x + 3)(x - 4) + (-4)(2)$

63. $2(x - 3) + x(x + 2)$ **64.** $5(x + 3) + 1(x + 4)$

65. $3x(x + 1) - 2x(x - 5)$ **66.** $4x(x - 2) - 3x(x - 4)$

67. $x(x + 2) - 3$ **68.** $2x(x - 4) + 6$

69. $a(a - 3) + 6$ **70.** $a(a - 4) + 8$

For each of the following problems, fill in the area of each small rectangle and square, and then add the results together to find the indicated product.

71. $(x + 2)(x + 3)$

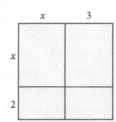

72. $(x + 4)(x + 5)$

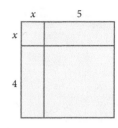

73. $(x + 1)(2x + 2)$

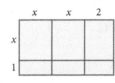

74. $(2x + 1)(2x + 2)$

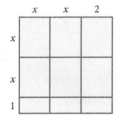

75. Paying Attention to Instructions Work each problem according to the instructions given.

   a. Add $2x + 5$ and $3x - 4$.

   b. Subtract $2x + 5$ from $3x - 4$.

   c. Solve $2x + 5 = 3x - 4$.

   d. Multiply $2x + 5$ by $3x - 4$.

76. Paying Attention to Instructions Work each problem according to the instructions given.

   a. Add $2x - 1$ and $x^2 + 3x + 4$.

   b. Solve $2x - 1 = 0$

   c. Multiply $2x - 1$ by $x^2 + 3x + 4$.

   d. Subtract $2x - 1$ from $x^2 + 3x + 4$.

Applying the Concepts

77. Area The length of a rectangle is 5 units more than twice the width. Write an expression for the area of the rectangle.

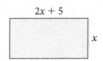

78. Area The length of a rectangle is 2 more than three times the width. Write an expression for the area of the rectangle.

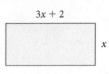

79. Area The width and length of a rectangle are given by two consecutive integers. Write an expression for the area of the rectangle.

80. **Area** The width and length of a rectangle are given by two consecutive even integers. Write an expression for the area of the rectangle.

81. **Revenue** A stationery store can sell x binders each day at a price of p dollars per binder, according to the equation $x = 100 - 10p$. Write a formula for the daily revenue that involves only the variables R and p.

82. **Revenue** A surf shop can sell x packs of board wax each day at a price of p dollars per pack, according to the equation $x = 40 - 5p$. Write a formula for the daily revenue that involves only the variables R and p.

Learning Objectives Assessment

The following problems can be used to help assess if you have successfully met the learning objectives for this section.

83. Multiply: $3x^4(2x^2 - 5x + 4)$.

    a. $5x^6 - 2x^5 + 7x^4$ **b.** $3x^{15}$

    c. $6x^8 - 3x^4$ **d.** $6x^6 - 15x^5 + 12x^4$

84. Multiply $(2x + 7)(x - 4)$ using the FOIL method.

    a. $2x^2 - 28$ **b.** $2x^2 + 5x + 3$

    c. $2x^2 - 15x - 28$ **d.** $2x^2 - x - 28$

85. Multiply: $(x + 4)(2x^2 - x - 3)$.

    a. $2x^3 + 8x^2 - x - 3$ **b.** $2x^3 - 9x^2 + x - 12$

    c. $2x^3 + 7x^2 - 7x - 12$ **d.** $2x^2 + 1$

86. **Area** The length of a rectangle is 4 units less than twice the width. Write an expression for the area of the rectangle if x represents the width.

    a. $2x^2 - 4x$ **b.** $2x^2 - 8x$ **c.** $4x - 2x^2$ **d.** $x^3 - 4x$

Getting Ready for the Next Section

Simplify.

87. $13 \cdot 13$ 88. $3x \cdot 3x$ 89. $2(x)(-5)$

90. $2(2x)(-3)$ 91. $6x + (-6x)$ 92. $3x + (-3x)$

93. $(2x)(-3) + (2x)(3)$ 94. $(2x)(-5y) + (2x)(5y)$

Multiply.

95. $-4(3x - 4)$ 96. $-2x(2x + 7)$ 97. $(x - 1)(x + 2)$

98. $(x + 5)(x - 6)$ 99. $(x + 3)(x + 3)$ 100. $(3x - 2)(3x - 2)$

Learning Objectives

In this section, we will learn how to:

1. Find the square of a binomial.

2. Multiply binomials that differ only in the sign between their terms.

Introduction

In this section we will combine the results of the last section with our definition of exponents to find some special products.

VIDEO EXAMPLES

SECTION 5.6

> **EXAMPLE 1**   Find the square of $(3x - 2)$.

SOLUTION To square $(3x - 2)$, we multiply it by itself:

$$(3x - 2)^2 = (3x - 2)(3x - 2) \qquad \text{Definition of exponents}$$
$$= 9x^2 - 6x - 6x + 4 \qquad \text{FOIL method}$$
$$= 9x^2 - 12x + 4 \qquad \text{Combine similar terms}$$

Notice that the first and last terms in the answer are the square of the first and last terms in the original problem and that the middle term is twice the product of the two terms in the original binomial.

> **EXAMPLE 2**   Expand and multiply each expression.

a. $(a + b)^2$ **b.** $(a - b)^2$

SOLUTION

a. $(a + b)^2 = a^2 + ab + ab + b^2$
$$= a^2 + 2ab + b^2$$

b. $(a - b)^2 = a^2 - ab - ab + b^2$
$$= a^2 - 2ab + b^2$$

Binomial Squares

Binomial squares having the form of Example 2 occur very frequently in algebra. It will be to your advantage to memorize the following rule for squaring a binomial.

Note A very common mistake when squaring binomials is to write

$$(a + b)^2 = a^2 + b^2$$

which just isn't true. The mistake becomes obvious when we substitute 2 for a and 3 for b:

$$(2 + 3)^2 \neq 2^2 + 3^2$$

$$25 \neq 13$$

Exponents do not distribute over addition or subtraction.

> **⟨Δ≠Σ⟩ RULE**
>
> The square of a binomial is a trinomial containing the square of the first term, the square of the last term, and twice the product of the two original terms. In symbols this rule is written as follows:
>
> $$(a + b)^2 = \quad a^2 \quad + \quad 2ab \quad + \quad b^2$$
>
> Square of first term   Twice product of the two terms   Square of last term
>
> $$(a - b)^2 = \quad a^2 \quad - \quad 2ab \quad + \quad b^2$$

EXAMPLES   Multiply using the preceding rule:

		First term squared		Twice their product		Last term squared		Answer
3. $(x - 5)^2$	$=$	x^2	$-$	$2(x)(5)$	$+$	5^2	$=$	$x^2 - 10x + 25$
4. $(x + 2)^2$	$=$	x^2	$+$	$2(x)(2)$	$+$	2^2	$=$	$x^2 + 4x + 4$
5. $(2x - 3y)^2$	$=$	$(2x)^2$	$-$	$2(2x)(3y)$	$+$	$(3y)^2$	$=$	$4x^2 - 12xy + 9y^2$
6. $(5x^2 - 4)^2$	$=$	$(5x^2)^2$	$-$	$2(5x^2)(4)$	$+$	4^2	$=$	$25x^4 - 40x^2 + 16$

Difference of Squares

Another special product that occurs frequently is $(a + b)(a - b)$. The only difference in the two binomials is the sign between the two terms. Here are some examples.

EXAMPLES   Multiply using the FOIL method:

7. $(2x - 3)(2x + 3) = 4x^2 + 6x - 6x - 9$ FOIL method

$\qquad\qquad\qquad = 4x^2 - 9$

8. $(x - 5)(x + 5) = x^2 + 5x - 5x - 25$ FOIL method

$\qquad\qquad\qquad = x^2 - 25$

9. $(3x - 1)(3x + 1) = 9x^2 + 3x - 3x - 1$ FOIL method

$\qquad\qquad\qquad = 9x^2 - 1$

Notice that in each case the middle term is zero and therefore we get a binomial instead of a trinomial. The answers all turn out to be the difference of two squares. Here is a rule to help you memorize the result.

> **RULE**
>
> When multiplying two binomials that differ only in the sign between their terms, subtract the square of the last term from the square of the first term.
>
> $$(a - b)(a + b) = a^2 - b^2$$

Here are some problems that result in the difference of two squares.

EXAMPLES   Multiply using the preceding rule:

		First term squared		Last term squared		Answer
10. $(x + 3)(x - 3)$	$=$	x^2	$-$	3^2	$=$	$x^2 - 9$
11. $(a + 2)(a - 2)$	$=$	a^2	$-$	2^2	$=$	$a^2 - 4$
12. $(1 + 9a)(1 - 9a)$	$=$	1^2	$-$	$(9a)^2$	$=$	$1 - 81a^2$
13. $(2x - 5y)(2x + 5y)$	$=$	$(2x)^2$	$-$	$(5y)^2$	$=$	$4x^2 - 25y^2$
14. $(3a^2 - 7b^2)(3a^2 + 7b^2)$	$=$	$(3a^2)^2$	$-$	$(7b^2)^2$	$=$	$9a^4 - 49b^4$

Although all the problems in this section can be worked correctly using the methods in the previous section, they can be done much faster if the two rules are *memorized*. Here is a summary of the two rules:

$$(a + b)^2 = (a + b)(a + b) = a^2 + 2ab + b^2$$

$$(a - b)^2 = (a - b)(a - b) = a^2 - 2ab + b^2$$

$$(a - b)(a + b) = a^2 - b^2$$

EXAMPLE 15   Write an expression in symbols for the sum of the squares of three consecutive even integers. Then, simplify that expression.

SOLUTION   If we let $x = $ the first of the even integers, then $x + 2$ is the next consecutive even integer, and $x + 4$ is the one after that. An expression for the sum of their squares is

$x^2 + (x + 2)^2 + (x + 4)^2$	Sum of squares
$= x^2 + (x^2 + 4x + 4) + (x^2 + 8x + 16)$	Expand squares
$= 3x^2 + 12x + 20$	Add similar terms

Getting Ready for Class

After reading through the preceding section, respond in your own words and in complete sentences.

A. Explain why $(x + 3)^2 \neq x^2 + 9$.

B. What kind of products result in the difference of two squares?

C. When multiplied out, how will $(x + 3)^2$ and $(x - 3)^2$ differ?

D. Explain how to use the rule for binomial squares to find $(2x - 3)^2$.

Problem Set 5.6

Perform the indicated operations.

1. $(x - 2)^2$ 2. $(x + 2)^2$ 3. $(a + 3)^2$ 4. $(a - 3)^2$

5. $(x - 5)^2$ 6. $(x - 4)^2$ 7. $\left(a - \dfrac{1}{2}\right)^2$ 8. $\left(a + \dfrac{1}{2}\right)^2$

9. $(x + 10)^2$ 10. $(x - 10)^2$ 11. $(a + 0.8)^2$ 12. $(a - 0.4)^2$

13. $(2x - 1)^2$ 14. $(3x + 2)^2$ 15. $(4a + 5)^2$ 16. $(4a - 5)^2$

17. $(3x - 2)^2$ 18. $(2x - 3)^2$ 19. $(3a + 5b)^2$ 20. $(5a - 3b)^2$

21. $(4x - 5y)^2$ 22. $(5x + 4y)^2$ 23. $(x^2 + 5)^2$ 24. $(x^2 + 3)^2$

25. $(a^3 + 1)^2$ 26. $(a^3 - 2)^2$ 27. $(7m^2 + 2n)^2$ 28. $(2m^2 - 7n)^2$

29. $(6x^2 - 10y^2)^2$ 30. $(10x^2 + 6y^2)^2$

Comparing Expressions Fill in each table.

31.

x	$(x + 3)^2$	$x^2 + 9$	$x^2 + 6x + 9$
1			
2			
3			
4			

32.

x	$(x - 5)^2$	$x^2 + 25$	$x^2 - 10x + 25$
1			
2			
3			
4			

33.

a	1	3	3	4
b	1	5	4	5
$(a + b)^2$				
$a^2 + b^2$				
$a^2 + ab + b^2$				
$a^2 + 2ab + b^2$				

34.

a	2	5	2	4
b	1	2	5	3
$(a - b)^2$				
$a^2 - b^2$				
$a^2 - 2ab + b^2$				

Multiply.

35. $(a + 5)(a - 5)$ **36.** $(a - 6)(a + 6)$ **37.** $(y - 1)(y + 1)$

38. $(y - 2)(y + 2)$ **39.** $(9 + x)(9 - x)$ **40.** $(10 - x)(10 + x)$

41. $(2x + 5)(2x - 5)$ **42.** $(3x + 5)(3x - 5)$ **43.** $\left(4x + \dfrac{1}{3}\right)\left(4x - \dfrac{1}{3}\right)$

44. $\left(6x + \dfrac{1}{4}\right)\left(6x - \dfrac{1}{4}\right)$ **45.** $(2a + 7b)(2a - 7b)$ **46.** $(3a + 10b)(3a - 10b)$

47. $(6 - 7x)(6 + 7x)$ **48.** $(7 - 6x)(7 + 6x)$ **49.** $(x^2 + 3)(x^2 - 3)$

50. $(x^2 + 2)(x^2 - 2)$ **51.** $(a^2 + 4b^2)(a^2 - 4b^2)$ **52.** $(a^2 + 9b^2)(a^2 - 9b^2)$

53. $(5y^4 - 8)(5y^4 + 8)$ **54.** $(7y^5 + 6)(7y^5 - 6)$

Multiply and simplify.

55. $(x + 3)(x - 3) + (x - 5)(x + 5)$ **56.** $(x - 7)(x + 7) + (x - 4)(x + 4)$

57. $(2x + 3)^2 - (4x - 1)^2$ **58.** $(3x - 5)^2 - (2x + 3)^2$

59. $(a + 1)^2 - (a + 2)^2 + (a + 3)^2$ **60.** $(a - 1)^2 + (a - 2)^2 - (a - 3)^2$

61. $(2x + 3)^3$ **62.** $(3x - 2)^3$

Applying the Concepts

63. Shortcut The formula for the difference of two squares can be used as a shortcut to multiplying certain whole numbers if they have the correct form. Use the difference of two squares formula to multiply 49(51) by first writing 49 as $(50 - 1)$ and 51 as $(50 + 1)$.

64. Shortcut Use the difference of two squares formula to multiply 101(99) by first writing 101 as $(100 + 1)$ and 99 as $(100 - 1)$.

65. Comparing Expressions Evaluate the expression $(x + 3)^2$ and the expression $x^2 + 6x + 9$ for $x = 2$.

66. Comparing Expressions Evaluate the expression $x^2 - 25$ and the expression $(x - 5)(x + 5)$ for $x = 6$.

67. Number Problem Write an expression for the sum of the squares of two consecutive integers. Then, simplify that expression.

68. Number Problem Write an expression for the sum of the squares of two consecutive odd integers. Then, simplify that expression.

69. Number Problem Write an expression for the sum of the squares of three consecutive integers. Then, simplify that expression.

70. Number Problem Write an expression for the sum of the squares of three consecutive odd integers. Then, simplify that expression.

For each problem, fill in the area of each small rectangle and square, and then add the results together to find the indicated product.

71. Area We can use the concept of area to further justify our rule for squaring a binomial. The length of each side of the square shown in the figure is $a + b$. (The longer line segment has length a and the shorter line segment has length b.) The area of the whole square is $(a + b)^2$. However, the whole area is the sum of the areas of the two smaller squares and the two smaller rectangles that make it up. Write the area of the two smaller squares and the two smaller rectangles and then add them together to verify the formula $(a + b)^2 = a^2 + 2ab + b^2$.

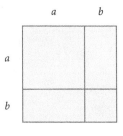

72. Area The length of each side of the large square shown in the figure is $x + 5$. Therefore, its area is $(x + 5)^2$. Find the area of the two smaller squares and the two smaller rectangles that make up the large square, then add them together to verify the formula $(x + 5)^2 = x^2 + 10x + 25$.

Learning Objectives Assessment

The following problems can be used to help assess if you have successfully met the learning objectives for this section.

73. Simplify: $(3x - 4y)^2$.

    a. $9x^2 + 16y^2$ **b.** $9x^2 - 24xy + 16y^2$

    c. $9x^2 - 16y^2$ **d.** $9x^2 - 12xy + 16y^2$

74. Multiply: $(5x + 2)(5x - 2)$.

    a. $25x^2 + 20x - 4$ **b.** $25x^2 - 20x - 4$

    c. $25x^2 + 4$ **d.** $25x^2 - 4$

Getting Ready for the Next Section

Simplify.

75. $\dfrac{10x^3}{5x}$ **76.** $\dfrac{15x^2}{5x}$ **77.** $\dfrac{3x^2}{3}$ **78.** $\dfrac{4x^2}{2}$

79. $\dfrac{9x^2}{3x}$ **80.** $\dfrac{3x^4}{3x^2}$ **81.** $\dfrac{24x^3y^2}{8x^2y}$ **82.** $\dfrac{4xy^3}{8x^2y}$

Divide.

83. $27\overline{)3{,}962}$

84. $13\overline{)18{,}780}$

Multiply.

85. $(x - 3)x$

86. $(x - 3)(-2)$

87. $2x^2(x - 5)$

88. $10x(x - 5)$

Subtract.

89. $(x^2 - 5x) - (x^2 - 3x)$

90. $(2x^3 + 0x^2) - (2x^3 - 10x^2)$

91. $(-2x + 8) - (-2x + 6)$

92. $(4x - 14) - (4x - 10)$

Learning Objectives

In this section, we will learn how to:

1. Divide a polynomial by a monomial.
2. Divide a polynomial by a polynomial.

Dividing by a Monomial

To divide a polynomial by a monomial, we will use the definition of division and apply the distributive property. Follow the steps in this example closely.

VIDEO EXAMPLES

SECTION 5.7

EXAMPLE 1   Divide $10x^3 - 15x^2$ by $5x$.

SOLUTION

$$\frac{10x^3 - 15x^2}{5x} = (10x^3 - 15x^2)\frac{1}{5x}$$ Division by $5x$ is the same as multiplication by $\frac{1}{5x}$

$$= 10x^3\left(\frac{1}{5x}\right) - 15x^2\left(\frac{1}{5x}\right)$$ Distribute $\frac{1}{5x}$ to both terms

$$= \frac{10x^3}{5x} - \frac{15x^2}{5x}$$ Multiplication by $\frac{1}{5x}$ is the same as division by $5x$

$$= 2x^2 - 3x$$ Division of monomials as done in Section 5.3

If we were to leave out the first steps, the problem would look like this:

$$\frac{10x^3 - 15x^2}{5x} = \frac{10x^3}{5x} - \frac{15x^2}{5x}$$

$$= 2x^2 - 3x$$

The problem is much shorter and clearer this way. You may leave out the first two steps from Example 1 when working problems in this section. They are part of Example 1 only to help show you why the following rule is true.

> **⌈Δ≠Σ RULE**
>
> To divide a polynomial by a monomial, simply divide each term in the polynomial by the monomial.

Here are some further examples using our rule for division of a polynomial by a monomial.

EXAMPLE 2   Divide: $\dfrac{3x^2 - 6}{3}$.

SOLUTION   We begin by writing the 3 in the denominator under each term in the numerator. Then we simplify the result:

$$\frac{3x^2 - 6}{3} = \frac{3x^2}{3} - \frac{6}{3}$$ Divide each term in the numerator by 3

$$= x^2 - 2$$ Simplify

EXAMPLE 3   Find the quotient of $27x^3 - 9x^2$ and $3x$.

SOLUTION   We again are asked to divide the first polynomial by the second one:

$$\frac{27x^3 - 9x^2}{3x} = \frac{27x^3}{3x} - \frac{9x^2}{3x} \qquad \text{Divide each term by } 3x$$

$$= 9x^2 - 3x \qquad \text{Simplify}$$

EXAMPLE 4   Divide: $(15x^2y - 21xy^2) \div (-3xy)$.

SOLUTION   This is the same type of problem we have shown in the first three examples; it is just worded a little differently. Note that when we divide each term in the first polynomial by $-3xy$, the negative sign must be taken into account:

$$\frac{15x^2y - 21xy^2}{-3xy} = \frac{15x^2y}{-3xy} - \frac{21xy^2}{-3xy} \qquad \text{Divide each term by } -3xy$$

$$= -5x - (-7y) \qquad \text{Simplify}$$

$$= -5x + 7y \qquad \text{Simplify}$$

EXAMPLE 5   Divide: $\dfrac{24x^3y^2 + 16x^2y^2 - 4xy^3}{8x^2y}$.

SOLUTION   Writing $8x^2y$ under each term in the numerator and then simplifying, we have

$$\frac{24x^3y^2 + 16x^2y^2 - 4xy^3}{8x^2y} = \frac{24x^3y^2}{8x^2y} + \frac{16x^2y^2}{8x^2y} - \frac{4xy^3}{8x^2y}$$

$$= 3xy + 2y - \frac{y^2}{2x}$$

From the first five examples, it is clear that to divide a polynomial by a monomial, we must divide each term in the polynomial by the monomial. Often, students taking algebra for the first time will make the following mistake:

$$\frac{x + 2}{2} = x + 1 \qquad \text{Mistake}$$

The mistake here is in not dividing both terms in the numerator by 2. The correct way to divide $x + 2$ by 2 looks like this:

$$\frac{x + 2}{2} = \frac{x}{2} + \frac{2}{2} = \frac{x}{2} + 1 \qquad \text{Correct}$$

Dividing a Polynomial by a Polynomial

Since long division for polynomials is very similar to long division with whole numbers, we will begin by reviewing a division problem with whole numbers. You may realize when looking at Example 6 that you don't have a very good idea why you proceed as you do with long division. What you do know is that the process always works. We are going to approach the explanations for the following examples in much the same manner; that is, we won't always be sure why the steps we will use are important, only that they always produce the correct result.

EXAMPLE 6   Divide: $27\overline{)3,962}$.

SOLUTION   The divisor is 27 and the dividend is 3,962.

$$
\begin{array}{r}
1 \\
27\overline{)3,962} \\
2\,7 \\
\hline
1\,2
\end{array}
$$

← Estimate 27 into 39
← Multiply $1 \times 27 = 27$
← Subtract $39 - 27 = 12$

$$
\begin{array}{r}
1 \\
27\overline{)3,962} \\
2\,7\downarrow \\
\hline
1\,26
\end{array}
$$

← Bring down the 6

These are the four basic steps in long division. Estimate, multiply, subtract, and bring down the next term. To finish the problem, we simply perform the same four steps again:

$$
\begin{array}{r}
14 \\
27\overline{)3,962} \\
2\,7\downarrow \\
\hline
1\,26 \\
1\,08\downarrow \\
\hline
182
\end{array}
$$

← 4 is the estimate

← Multiply to get 108
← Subtract to get 18, then bring down the 2

One more time.

$$
\begin{array}{r}
146 \\
27\overline{)3,962} \\
2\,7 \\
\hline
1\,26 \\
1\,08 \\
\hline
182 \\
162 \\
\hline
20
\end{array}
$$

← 6 is the estimate

← Multiply to get 162
← Subtract to get 20

Since there is nothing left to bring down, we have our answer. The quotient is 146 and the remainder is 20. We write the result in the form

$$
\frac{\text{Dividend}}{\text{Divisor}} = \text{Quotient} + \frac{\text{Remainder}}{\text{Divisor}}
$$

In this case, we have

$$
\frac{3,962}{27} = 146 + \frac{20}{27} \qquad \text{or} \qquad 146\frac{20}{27}
$$

Here is how it works with polynomials.

EXAMPLE 7   Divide: $\dfrac{x^2 - 5x + 8}{x - 3}$.

SOLUTION The dividend is $x^2 - 5x + 8$ and the divisor is $x - 3$.

$$
\begin{array}{r}
x \quad\quad\quad\quad \leftarrow \text{Estimate } x^2 \div x = x \\
x - 3 \overline{) \; x^2 - 5x + 8} \\
\cancel{+} \; x^2 \cancel{+} 3x \quad\quad \leftarrow \text{Multiply } x(x-3) = x^2 - 3x \\
\hline
-2x \quad\quad\quad \leftarrow \text{Subtract } (x^2 - 5x) - (x^2 - 3x) = -2x
\end{array}
$$

$$
\begin{array}{r}
x \quad\quad\quad\quad \\
x - 3 \overline{) \; x^2 - 5x + 8} \\
\cancel{+} \; x^2 \cancel{+} 3x \quad \downarrow \\
\hline
-2x + 8 \quad \leftarrow \text{Bring down the 8}
\end{array}
$$

Notice that to subtract one polynomial from another, we add its opposite. That is why we change the signs on $x^2 - 3x$ and add what we get to $x^2 - 5x$. (To subtract the second polynomial, simply change the signs and add.)

We perform the same four steps again:

$$
\begin{array}{r}
x - 2 \quad \leftarrow -2 \text{ is the estimate } (-2x \div x = -2) \\
x - 3 \overline{) \; x^2 - 5x + 8} \\
\cancel{+} \; x^2 \cancel{+} 3x \quad\quad \downarrow \\
\hline
-2x + 8 \\
\cancel{+} 2x \cancel{+} 6 \quad \leftarrow \text{Multiply } -2(x - 3) = -2x + 6. \\
\hline
2 \quad \leftarrow \text{Subtract } (-2x + 8) - (-2x + 6) = 2
\end{array}
$$

Since there is nothing left to bring down, we have our answer: The quotient is $x - 2$ and the remainder is 2. We write

$$\frac{x^2 - 5x + 8}{x - 3} = x - 2 + \frac{2}{x - 3}$$

To check our answer, we multiply $(x - 3)(x - 2)$ to get $x^2 - 5x + 6$. Then, adding on the remainder, 2, we have $x^2 - 5x + 8$.

EXAMPLE 8   Divide: $\dfrac{6x^3 - 11x^2 - 14x + 3}{2x^2 - 5x - 1}$.

SOLUTION

$$
\begin{array}{r}
3x + 2 \quad\quad\quad \\
2x^2 - 5x - 1 \overline{) \; 6x^3 - 11x^2 - 14x + 3} \\
\cancel{+} \; 6x^3 \cancel{+} 15x^2 \cancel{+} 3x \quad \downarrow \\
\hline
+ 4x^2 - 11x + 3 \\
\cancel{+} 4x^2 \cancel{+} 10x \cancel{+} 2 \\
\hline
-x + 5
\end{array}
$$

$$\frac{6x^3 - 11x^2 - 14x + 3}{2x^2 - 5x - 1} = 3x + 2 + \frac{-x + 5}{2x^2 - 5x - 1}$$

Polynomial Division with Missing Powers

One last step is sometimes necessary. The two polynomials in a division problem must both be in descending powers of the variable and cannot skip any powers from the highest power down to the constant term. If any powers of the variable or the constant term is missing from either the dividend or the quotient, we can insert zero terms to act as placeholders. This will ensure that like terms are lined up vertically in the long division process.

EXAMPLE 9 Divide: $\dfrac{2x^3 - 3x + 2}{x - 5}$.

SOLUTION Notice that the dividend (the numerator) is missing an x^2 term. We write $2x^3 - 3x + 2$ as $2x^3 + 0x^2 - 3x + 2$. Adding $0x^2$ does not change our original problem, and it will make sure we are always combining like terms.

$$
\begin{array}{r}
2x^2 \\
x - 5 \overline{)\ 2x^3 + \ 0x^2 - 3x + 2} \\
\underline{\ \ \ 2x^3 \ \ 10x^2} \quad \downarrow \\
+ 10x^2 - 3x
\end{array}
$$

← Estimate $2x^3 \div x = 2x^2$

← Multiply $2x^2(x - 5) = 2x^3 - 10x^2$

← Subtract:
$(2x^3 + 0x^2) - (2x^3 - 10x^2) = 10x^2$
Bring down the next term

Adding the term $0x^2$ gives us a column in which to write $10x^2$. (Remember, you can add and subtract only similar terms.)

Here is the completed problem:

$$
\begin{array}{r}
2x^2 + 10x + \ 47 \\
x - 5 \overline{)\ 2x^3 + \ 0x^2 - \ 3x + \ 2} \\
\underline{\ \ \ 2x^3 \ \ 10x^2} \quad \downarrow \\
+ 10x^2 - \ 3x \\
\underline{\ \ 10x^2 \ \ 50x} \quad \downarrow \\
+ 47x + \ 2 \\
\underline{\ \ 47x \ \ 235} \\
237
\end{array}
$$

Our answer is

$$\frac{2x^3 - 3x + 2}{x - 5} = 2x^2 + 10x + 47 + \frac{237}{x - 5}$$

EXAMPLE 10 Divide: $\dfrac{6x^3 + 2x^2 - x}{2x^2 - 3}$.

SOLUTION The dividend is missing the constant term and the divisor is missing an x term. We write the dividend as $6x^3 + 2x^2 - x + 0$ and the divisor as $2x^2 + 0x - 3$.

$$
\begin{array}{r}
3x + 1 \\
2x^2 + 0x - 3 \overline{)\ 6x^3 + 2x^2 - x + 0} \\
\underline{\ \ 6x^3 \ \ 0x^2 \ \ 9x} \quad \downarrow \\
+ 2x^2 + 8x + 0 \\
\underline{\ \ 2x^2 \ \ 0x \ \ 3} \\
8x + 3
\end{array}
$$

The result is

$$\frac{6x^3 + 2x^2 - x}{2x^2 - 3} = 3x + 1 + \frac{8x + 3}{2x^2 - 3}$$

As you can see, long division with polynomials is a mechanical process. Once you have done it correctly a couple of times, it becomes very easy to produce the correct answer.

Getting Ready for Class

After reading through the preceding section, respond in your own words and in complete sentences.

A. What property of real numbers is key to dividing a polynomial by a monomial?

B. Why is our answer to Example 5 not a polynomial?

C. How is division of two polynomials similar to long division with whole numbers?

D. How do we use 0 when dividing the polynomial $2x^3 - 3x + 2$ by $x - 5$?

Divide the following polynomials by $5x$.

1. $5x^2 - 10x$

2. $10x^3 - 15x$

3. $25x^2y - 10xy$

4. $15xy^2 + 20x^2y$

5. $35x^5 - 30x^4 + 25x^3$

6. $75x^6 + 50x^3 - 25x$

Divide the following by $-2a$.

7. $8a^2 - 4a$

8. $a^3 - 6a^2$

9. $12a^3b - 6a^2b^2 + 14ab^3$

10. $4ab^3 - 16a^2b^2 - 22a^3b$

11. $a^2 + 2ab + b^2$

12. $a^2b - 2ab^2 + b^3$

Perform the following monomial divisions (find the following quotients).

13. $\dfrac{6x + 8y}{2}$

14. $\dfrac{9x - 3y}{3}$

15. $\dfrac{7y - 21}{-7}$

16. $\dfrac{14y - 12}{2}$

17. $\dfrac{10xy - 8x}{2x}$

18. $\dfrac{12xy^2 - 18x}{-6x}$

19. $\dfrac{x^2y - x^3y^2}{x}$

20. $\dfrac{x^2y - x^3y^2}{x^2}$

21. $\dfrac{a^2b^2 - ab^2}{-ab^2}$

22. $\dfrac{a^2b^2c - ab^2c^2}{abc}$

23. $\dfrac{x^3 - 3x^2y + xy^2}{x}$

24. $\dfrac{x^2 - 3xy^2 + xy^3}{x}$

25. $\dfrac{10a^2 - 15a^2b + 25a^2b^2}{5a^2}$

26. $\dfrac{6x^2a + 12x^2b - 6x^2c}{36x^2}$

27. $\dfrac{26x^2y^2 - 13xy}{-13xy}$

28. $\dfrac{6x^2y^2 - 3xy}{6xy}$

29. $\dfrac{5a^2x - 10ax^2 + 15a^2x^2}{20a^2x^2}$

30. $\dfrac{12ax - 9bx + 18cx}{6x^2}$

31. $\dfrac{16x^5 + 8x^2 + 12x}{12x^3}$

32. $\dfrac{27x^2 - 9x^3 - 18x^4}{-18x^3}$

Divide. Assume all variables represent positive numbers.

33. $\dfrac{9a^{5m} - 27a^{3m}}{3a^{2m}}$

34. $\dfrac{26a^{3m} - 39a^{5m}}{13a^{3m}}$

35. $\dfrac{10x^{5m} - 25x^{3m} + 35x^m}{5x^m}$

36. $\dfrac{18x^{2m} + 24x^{4m} - 30x^{6m}}{6x^{2m}}$

Simplify each numerator, and then divide.

37. $\dfrac{2x^3(3x + 2) - 3x^2(2x - 4)}{2x^2}$

38. $\dfrac{5x^2(6x - 3) + 6x^3(3x - 1)}{3x}$

39. $\dfrac{(x + 2)^2 - (x - 2)^2}{2x}$

40. $\dfrac{(x - 3)^2 - (x + 3)^2}{3x}$

41. $\dfrac{(x + 5)^2 + (x + 5)(x - 5)}{2x}$

42. $\dfrac{(x - 4)^2 + (x + 4)(x - 4)}{2x}$

Use long division to perform each division.

43. $\dfrac{x^2 - 5x + 6}{x - 3}$

44. $\dfrac{x^2 - 5x + 6}{x - 2}$

45. $\dfrac{a^2 + 9a + 20}{a + 5}$

46. $\dfrac{a^2 + 9a + 20}{a + 4}$

47. $\dfrac{2x^2 + 5x - 3}{2x - 1}$

48. $\dfrac{4x^2 + 4x - 3}{2x - 1}$

49. $\dfrac{x^3 - 9x^2 + 27x - 27}{x^2 - 6x + 9}$

50. $\dfrac{x^3 + 15x^2 + 75x + 125}{x^2 + 10x + 25}$

51. $\dfrac{x^4 - x^3 - x^2 - 2x - 6}{x^2 + 2}$

52. $\dfrac{x^4 + 3x^3 + 2x^2 - 6x - 8}{x^2 - 2}$

53. $\dfrac{x + 3}{x - 2}$

54. $\dfrac{x - 3}{x + 1}$

55. $\dfrac{3x + 4}{x + 2}$

56. $\dfrac{4x - 1}{x - 3}$

57. $\dfrac{x^2 + 5x + 8}{x + 3}$

58. $\dfrac{x^2 + 5x + 4}{x + 3}$

59. $\dfrac{x^2 + 2x + 1}{x - 2}$

60. $\dfrac{x^2 + 6x + 9}{x - 3}$

61. $\dfrac{x^2 + 5x - 6}{x + 1}$

62. $\dfrac{x^2 - x - 6}{x + 1}$

63. $\dfrac{2x^2 - 2x + 5}{2x + 4}$

64. $\dfrac{15x^2 + 19x - 4}{3x + 8}$

65. $\dfrac{6a^2 + 5a + 1}{2a + 3}$

66. $\dfrac{4a^2 + 4a + 3}{2a + 1}$

67. $\dfrac{6a^3 - 13a^2 - 4a + 15}{3a - 5}$

68. $\dfrac{2a^3 - a^2 + 3a + 2}{2a + 1}$

69. $\dfrac{x^2 - 6x + 9}{x^2 - 3x - 2}$

70. $\dfrac{x^2 + 10x + 25}{x^2 + 5x + 4}$

71. $\dfrac{2a^3 - 9a^2 - 5a + 4}{2a^2 + a + 3}$

72. $\dfrac{4a^3 - 8a^2 - 5a + 1}{2a^2 + a - 2}$

Use long division to find the quotients, filling in missing terms with zero place holders.

73. $\dfrac{x^3 + 4x + 5}{x + 1}$

74. $\dfrac{x^3 + 4x^2 - 8}{x + 2}$

75. $\dfrac{x^3 - 1}{x - 1}$

76. $\dfrac{x^3 + 1}{x + 1}$

77. $\dfrac{x^3 - 8}{x - 2}$

78. $\dfrac{x^3 + 27}{x + 3}$

79. $\dfrac{a^2 + 3a + 2}{a^2 + 1}$

80. $\dfrac{a^2 + 4a + 3}{a^2 - 5}$

81. $\dfrac{a^3 + 3a^2 + 1}{a^2 - 2}$

82. $\dfrac{a^3 - a^2 + 3}{a^2 + 1}$

83. $\dfrac{4a^4 + 4a^2 - 2}{2a^2 - 1}$

84. $\dfrac{6a^4 - 2a^2 + 9}{3a^2 + 2}$

85. Comparing Expressions Evaluate the expression $\dfrac{10x + 15}{5}$ and the expression $2x + 3$ when $x = 2$.

86. Comparing Expressions Evaluate the expression $\dfrac{6x^2 + 4x}{2x}$ and the expression $3x + 2$ when $x = 5$.

87. Comparing Expressions Show that the expression $\dfrac{3x + 8}{2}$ is not the same as the expression $3x + 4$ by replacing x with 10 in both expressions and simplifying the results.

88. Comparing Expressions Show that the expression $\dfrac{x + 10}{x}$ is not equal to 10 by replacing x with 5 and simplifying.

Long Division Use the information in the table to find the monthly payment for auto insurance for the cities below. Round to the nearest cent.

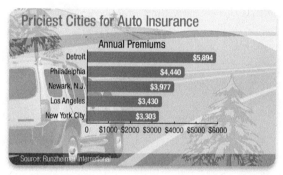

Priciest Cities for Auto Insurance

Annual Premiums

Detroit	$5,894
Philadelphia	$4,440
Newark, N.J.	$3,977
Los Angeles	$3,430
New York City	$3,303

0   $1000 $2000 $3000 $4000 $5000 $6000

Source: Runzheimer International

89. Detroit   **90.** Philadelphia   **91.** Newark, N.J.   **92.** Los Angeles

Learning Objectives Assessment

The following problems can be used to help assess if you have successfully met the learning objectives for this section.

93. Divide: $\dfrac{12x^3y^2 - 3xy^3}{6x^2y^2}$.

  a. $2x - 3xy^3$ **b.** $\dfrac{3}{2}x^2y^3$ **c.** $2x - 2xy$ **d.** $2x - \dfrac{y}{2x}$

94. Divide: $\dfrac{5x^2 - 3x + 2}{x + 4}$.

  a. $5x - 23 + \dfrac{94}{x + 4}$ **b.** $5x + 17 + \dfrac{70}{x + 4}$

  c. $5x - 3 + \dfrac{2}{x + 4}$ **d.** $2x + \dfrac{1}{2}$

Maintaining Your Skills

Simplify each expression. (Write all answers with positive exponents only.)

95. $(5x^3)^2(2x^6)^3$

96. 2^{-3}

97. $\dfrac{x^4}{x^{-3}}$

98. $\dfrac{(20x^2y^3)(5x^4y)}{(2xy^5)(10x^2y^3)}$

99. $(2 \times 10^{-4})(4 \times 10^5)$

100. $\dfrac{9 \times 10^{-3}}{3 \times 10^{-2}}$

101. $20ab^2 - 16ab^2 + 6ab^2$

102. Subtract $6x^2 - 5x - 7$ from $9x^2 + 3x - 2$.

Multiply.

103. $2x^2(3x^2 + 3x - 1)$

104. $(2x + 3)(5x - 2)$

105. $(3y - 5)^2$

106. $(a - 4)(a^2 + 4a + 16)$

107. $(2a^2 + 7)(2a^2 - 7)$

108. Divide: $15x^{10} - 10x^8 + 25x^6$ by $5x^6$.

Chapter 5 Summary

Exponents: Definition and Properties [5.1, 5.2]

EXAMPLES

1. a. $2^3 = 2 \cdot 2 \cdot 2 = 8$

b. $x^5 \cdot x^3 = x^{5+3} = x^8$

c. $\frac{x^5}{x^3} = x^{5-3} = x^2$

d. $(3x)^2 = 3^2 \cdot x^2 = 9x^2$

e. $\left(\frac{2}{3}\right)^3 = \frac{2^3}{3^3} = \frac{8}{27}$

f. $(x^5)^3 = x^{5 \cdot 3} = x^{15}$

g. $3^{-2} = \frac{1}{3^2} = \frac{1}{9}$

Integer exponents indicate repeated multiplications.

$a^r \cdot a^s = a^{r+s}$ To multiply with the same base, you add exponents

$\dfrac{a^r}{a^s} = a^{r-s}$ To divide with the same base, you subtract exponents

$(ab)^r = a^r \cdot b^r$ Exponents distribute over multiplication

$\left(\dfrac{a}{b}\right)^r = \dfrac{a^r}{b^r}$ Exponents distribute over division

$(a^r)^s = a^{r \cdot s}$ A power of a power is the product of the powers

$a^{-r} = \dfrac{1}{a^r}$ Negative exponents imply reciprocals

Scientific Notation [5.1, 5.2]

2. $768{,}000 = 7.68 \times 10^5$
$0.00039 = 3.9 \times 10^{-4}$

A number is in scientific notation when it is written as the product of a number between 1 and 10 and an integer power of 10.

Multiplication of Monomials [5.3]

3. $(5x^2)(3x^4) = 15x^6$

To multiply two monomials, multiply coefficients and add exponents.

Division of Monomials [5.3]

4. $\frac{12x^9}{4x^5} = 3x^4$

To divide two monomials, divide coefficients and subtract exponents.

Addition of Polynomials [5.4]

5. $(3x^2 - 2x + 1) + (2x^2 + 7x - 3)$
$= 5x^2 + 5x - 2$

To add two polynomials, add coefficients of similar terms.

Subtraction of Polynomials [5.4]

6. $(3x + 5) - (4x - 3)$
$= 3x + 5 - 4x + 3$
$= -x + 8$

To subtract one polynomial from another, add the opposite of the second to the first.

Multiplication of Polynomials [5.5]

7. a. $2a^2(5a^2 + 3a - 2)$
$= 10a^4 + 6a^3 - 4a^2$

b. $(x + 2)(3x - 1)$
$= 3x^2 - x + 6x - 2$
$= 3x^2 + 5x - 2$

c. $2x^2 - 3x + 4$
$ 3x - 2$
$\overline{6x^3 - 9x^2 + 12x}$
$ - 4x^2 + 6x - 8$
$\overline{6x^3 - 13x^2 + 18x - 8}$

To multiply a polynomial by a monomial, we apply the distributive property. To multiply two binomials we use the FOIL method. To multiply any two polynomials, we multiply each term in the first polynomial by each term in the second polynomial.

Special Products [5.6]

8. $(x + 3)^2 = x^2 + 6x + 9$
$(x - 3)^2 = x^2 - 6x + 9$
$(x + 3)(x - 3) = x^2 - 9$

$(a + b)^2 = a^2 + 2ab + b^2$

$(a - b)^2 = a^2 - 2ab + b^2$

Binomial squares

$(a + b)(a - b) = a^2 - b^2$

Difference of two squares

Dividing a Polynomial by a Monomial [5.7]

9. $\dfrac{12x^3 - 18x^2}{6x} = \dfrac{12x^3}{6x} - \dfrac{18x^2}{6x}$

$= 2x^2 - 3x$

To divide a polynomial by a monomial, divide each term in the polynomial by the monomial.

Long Division with Polynomials [5.7]

10.
$$\begin{array}{r} x - 2 \\ x - 3 \overline{)\ x^2 - 5x + 8} \\ \end{array}$$
$ \cancel{x^2} \cancel{-} 3x \quad \downarrow$
$ -2x + 8$
$ \cancel{-} 2x \cancel{-} 6$
$ 2$

$\dfrac{x^2 - 5x + 8}{x} - 3$

$= x - 2 + \dfrac{2}{x - 3}$

Division with polynomials is similar to long division with whole numbers. The steps in the process are estimate, multiply, subtract, and bring down the next term.

Simplify each of the following expressions. [5.1]

1. $(-2)^5$ **2.** -4^2 **3.** $x^9 \cdot x^{14}$ **4.** $(4x^2y^3)^2$

Simplify each expression. Write all answers with positive exponents only. [5.2]

5. 4^{-2} **6.** $(4a^5b^3)^0$ **7.** $\dfrac{x^{-4}}{x^{-7}}$

8. $\left(\dfrac{x}{3}\right)^3$ **9.** $\dfrac{(x^{-3})^2(x^{-5})^{-3}}{(x^{-3})^{-4}}$

10. Write 0.04307 in scientific notation. [5.2]

11. Write 7.63×10^6 in expanded form. [5.1]

Simplify. Write all answers with positive exponents only. [5.3]

12. $(6a^2b)(-4ab^3)$ **13.** $\dfrac{17x^2y^5z^3}{51x^4y^2z}$

14. $\dfrac{(3a^3b)(4a^2b^5)}{24a^2b^4}$ **15.** $\dfrac{28x^4}{4x} + \dfrac{30x^7}{6x^4}$

16. $\dfrac{(1.1 \times 10^5)(3 \times 10^{-2})}{4.4 \times 10^{-5}}$

Add or subtract as indicated. [5.4]

17. $(9x^2 - 2x) + (7x + 4)$ **18.** $(4x^2 + 5x - 6) - (2x^2 - x - 4)$

19. Subtract $2x + 7$ from $7x + 3$. [5.4]

20. Find the value of $3a^2 + 4a + 6$ when a is -3. [5.4]

Multiply. [5.5]

21. $3x^2(5x^2 - 2x + 4)$ **22.** $\left(x + \dfrac{1}{4}\right)\left(x - \dfrac{1}{3}\right)$

23. $(2x - 3)(5x + 6)$ **24.** $(x + 4)(x^2 - 4x + 16)$

Multiply. [5.6]

25. $(x - 6)^2$ **26.** $(2a + 4b)^2$

27. $(3x - 6)(3x + 6)$ **28.** $(x^2 - 4)(x^2 + 4)$

29. Divide $18x^3 - 36x^2 + 6x$ by $6x$. [5.7]

Divide. [5.7]

30. $\dfrac{9x^2 - 6x - 4}{3x - 1}$ **31.** $\dfrac{4x^3 + 3x^2 + 1}{x^2 + 2}$

32. Volume Find the volume of a cube if the length of a side is 3.2 inches. Round to the nearest hundredth. [5.1]

33. Volume Find the volume of a rectangular solid if the length is three times the width, and the height is one third the width. [5.3]

Factoring

6

Chapter Outline

istockphoto.com © file

If you watch professional football on television, you will hear the announcers refer to "hang time" when the punter punts the ball. Hang time is the amount of time the ball is in the air, and it depends on only one thing—the initial vertical velocity imparted to the ball by the kicker's foot. We can find the hang time of a football by solving equations. Table 1 shows the equations to solve for hang time, given various initial vertical velocities. Figure 1 is a visual representation of the equations in Table 1. In Figure 1, you can find hang time on the horizontal axis.

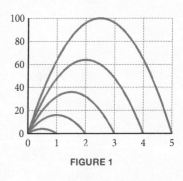

FIGURE 1

TABLE 1		
Hang Time for a Football		
Initial Vertical Velocity	Equation in Factored Form	Hang Time
16	$16t(1 - t) = 0$	1
32	$16t(2 - t) = 0$	2
48	$16t(3 - t) = 0$	3
64	$16t(4 - t) = 0$	4
80	$16t(5 - t) = 0$	5

The equations in the second column of the table are in what is called "factored form." Once the equation is in factored form, hang time can be read from the second factor. In this chapter, we develop techniques that allow us to factor a variety of polynomials. Factoring is the key to solving equations like the ones in Table 1.

This is the last chapter in which we will mention study skills. You know by now what works best for you and what you have to do to achieve your goals for this course. From now on, it is simply a matter of sticking with the things that work for you and avoiding the things that do not. It seems simple, but as with anything that takes effort, it is up to you to see that you maintain the skills that get you where you want to be in the course.

If you intend to take more classes in mathematics and want to ensure your success in those classes, then you can work toward this goal: *Become the type of student who can learn mathematics on his or her own.* Most people who have degrees in mathematics were students who could learn mathematics on their own. This doesn't mean that you must learn it all on your own, or that you study alone, or that you don't ask questions. It means that you know your resources, both internal and external, and you can count on those resources when you need them. Attaining this goal gives you independence and puts you in control of your success in any math class you take.

Learning Objectives

In this section, we will learn how to:

1. Find the greatest common factor for a polynomial.

2. Factor the greatest common factor from a polynomial.

3. Factor a polynomial using grouping.

Introduction

In Chapter 1, we used the following diagram to illustrate the relationship between multiplication and factoring.

$$\text{Factors} \longrightarrow \overset{\text{Multiplication}}{\overset{\frown}{3 \cdot 5 = 15}} \longleftarrow \text{Product}$$
$$\underset{\text{Factoring}}{\underbrace{}}$$

A similar relationship holds for multiplication of polynomials. Reading the following diagram from left to right, we say the product of the binomials $x + 2$ and $x + 3$ is the trinomial $x^2 + 5x + 6$. However, if we read in the other direction, we can say that $x^2 + 5x + 6$ factors into the product of $x + 2$ and $x + 3$.

$$\text{Factors} \longrightarrow \overset{\text{Multiplication}}{\overset{\frown}{(x + 2)(x + 3) = x^2 + 5x + 6}} \longleftarrow \text{Product}$$
$$\underset{\text{Factoring}}{\underbrace{}}$$

In this chapter we develop a systematic method of factoring polynomials. When factoring polynomials, our objective is to change the polynomial (a sum of terms) into a product of two or more factors (quantities connected by multiplication).

The Greatest Common Factor

In this section we will apply the distributive property to polynomials to factor from them what is called the greatest common factor.

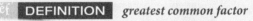

DEFINITION *greatest common factor*

The *greatest common factor* (GCF) for a polynomial is the largest monomial that divides (is a factor of) each term of the polynomial.

We use the term *largest monomial* to mean the monomial with the greatest coefficient and highest power of the variable that will divide evenly into each term.

EXAMPLE 1   Find the greatest common factor for the polynomial:

$$3x^5 + 12x^2$$

SOLUTION   The terms of the polynomial are $3x^5$ and $12x^2$. The largest number that divides the coefficients is 3, and the highest power of x that is a factor of x^5 and x^2 is x^2. Therefore, the greatest common factor for $3x^5 + 12x^2$ is $3x^2$; that is, $3x^2$ is the largest monomial that divides each term of $3x^5 + 12x^2$.

Notice in Example 1 that the variable part of the GCF, x^2, contains the smaller of the two exponents appearing on the variable in the polynomial. In general, this will always be true. To find the variable part of the GCF, choose the smallest exponent of each variable that is common to every term in the polynomial.

EXAMPLE 2   Find the greatest common factor for:

$$8a^3b^2 + 16a^2b^3 + 20a^3b^3$$

SOLUTION   The largest number that divides each of the coefficients is 4. Because both variables a and b appear in every term, the GCF will contain the smallest exponent appearing on these variables, which is a^2 and b^2. The greatest common factor for $8a^3b^2 + 16a^2b^3 + 20a^3b^3$ is $4a^2b^2$. It is the largest monomial that is a factor of each term.

EXAMPLE 3   Find the greatest common factor for $2x + 9$.

SOLUTION   The largest number that divides the coefficients is 1. Because the variable x is not common to both terms, no variable will appear in the GCF. Therefore, the greatest common factor for $2x + 9$ is 1.

Factoring the GCF from a Polynomial

Once we have recognized the greatest common factor of a polynomial, we can apply the distributive property and factor it out of each term. We rewrite the polynomial as the product of its greatest common factor with the polynomial that remains after the greatest common factor has been divided from each term in the original polynomial.

EXAMPLE 4   Factor the greatest common factor from $3x - 15$.

SOLUTION   The greatest common factor for the terms $3x$ and 15 is 3. We can rewrite both $3x$ and 15 so that the greatest common factor 3 is showing in each term. It is important to realize that $3x$ means $3 \cdot x$. The 3 and the x are not "stuck" together:

$$3x - 15 = 3 \cdot x - 3 \cdot 5$$

Now, applying the distributive property, we have:

$$3 \cdot x - 3 \cdot 5 = 3(x - 5)$$

To check a factoring problem like this, we can multiply 3 and $x - 5$ to get $3x - 15$, which is what we started with. Factoring is simply a procedure by which we change sums and differences into products. In this case we changed the difference $3x - 15$ into the product $3(x - 5)$. Note, however, that we have not changed the meaning or value of the expression. The expression we end up with is equivalent to the expression we started with.

EXAMPLE 5   Factor the greatest common factor from:

$$5x^3 - 15x^2$$

SOLUTION   The greatest common factor is $5x^2$. We rewrite the polynomial as:

$$5x^3 - 15x^2 = 5x^2 \cdot x - 5x^2 \cdot 3$$

Then we apply the distributive property to get:

$$5x^2 \cdot x - 5x^2 \cdot 3 = 5x^2(x - 3)$$

To check our work, we simply multiply $5x^2$ and $(x - 3)$ to get $5x^3 - 15x^2$, which is our original polynomial.

Note An alternative approach to Example 5 is to view it from the perspective of division:

$$5x^3 - 15x^2 = 5x^2 \left(\frac{5x^3}{5x^2} - \frac{15x^2}{5x^2} \right)$$
$$= 5x^2(x - 3)$$

EXAMPLE 6   Factor the greatest common factor from:

$$16x^5 - 20x^4 + 8x^3$$

SOLUTION   The greatest common factor is $4x^3$. We rewrite the polynomial so we can see the greatest common factor $4x^3$ in each term; then we apply the distributive property to factor it out.

$$16x^5 - 20x^4 + 8x^3 = 4x^3 \cdot 4x^2 - 4x^3 \cdot 5x + 4x^3 \cdot 2$$
$$= 4x^3(4x^2 - 5x + 2)$$

Notice that the terms in the grouping symbol are what remains when the GCF of $4x^3$ is divided out of each term in the trinomial.

EXAMPLE 7   Factor the greatest common factor from:

$$-6x^3y - 18x^2y^2 + 12xy^3$$

SOLUTION   Notice that the leading term is negative. When this is the case, we will include a negative sign with our GCF. As a result, the greatest common factor is $-6xy$. We rewrite the polynomial in terms of $-6xy$ and then apply the distributive property as follows.

$$-6x^3y - 18x^2y^2 + 12xy^3 = -6xy(x^2) - 6xy(3xy) - 6xy(-2y^2)$$

$$= -6xy(x^2 + 3xy - 2y^2)$$

Again, notice the terms in the grouping symbols are the quotients that result when $-6xy$ is divided out of each term in the original trinomial:

$$-6xy(x^2 + 3xy - 2y^2)$$

$$\frac{-6x^3y}{-6xy} \qquad \frac{-18x^2y^2}{-6xy} \qquad \frac{12xy^3}{-6xy}$$

To check our answer, we can multiply $x^2 + 3xy - 2y^2$ by $-6xy$ and verify the resulting product is equal to the original polynomial.

EXAMPLE 8   Factor the greatest common factor from:

$$3a^2b - 6a^3b^2 + 9a^3b^3$$

SOLUTION   The greatest common factor is $3a^2b$:

$$3a^2b - 6a^3b^2 + 9a^3b^3 = 3a^2b(1) - 3a^2b(2ab) + 3a^2b(3ab^2)$$
$$= 3a^2b(1 - 2ab + 3ab^2)$$

Factoring by Grouping

To develop our next method of factoring, called *factoring by grouping*, we start by examining the polynomial $xc + yc$. The greatest common factor for the two terms is c. Factoring c from each term we have:

$$xc + yc = c(x + y)$$

But suppose that c itself was a more complicated expression, such as $a + b$, so that the expression we were trying to factor was $x(a + b) + y(a + b)$, instead of $xc + yc$. The greatest common factor for $x(a + b) + y(a + b)$ is the binomial $(a + b)$. Factoring this common factor from each term looks like this:

$$x(a + b) + y(a + b) = (a + b)(x + y)$$

To see how all of this applies to factoring polynomials, consider the polynomial

$$xy + 3x + 2y + 6$$

There is no greatest common factor other than the number 1. However, if we group the terms together two at a time, we can factor an x from the first two terms and a 2 from the last two terms:

$$xy + 3x + 2y + 6 = x(y + 3) + 2(y + 3)$$

The expression on the right can be thought of as having two terms: $x(y + 3)$ and $2(y + 3)$. Each of these expressions contains the common factor $y + 3$, which can be factored out using the distributive property:

$$x(y + 3) + 2(y + 3) = (y + 3)(x + 2)$$

This last expression is in factored form. The process we used to obtain it is called factoring by grouping. Here are some additional examples.

EXAMPLE 9   Factor: $ax + bx + ay + by$.

SOLUTION   We begin by factoring x from the first two terms and y from the last two terms:

$$ax + bx + ay + by = x(a + b) + y(a + b)$$

We can see that the binomial $a + b$ is now a common factor, which we factor out to obtain

$$x(a + b) + y(a + b) = (a + b)(x + y)$$

To convince yourself that this is factored correctly, multiply the two factors $(a + b)$ and $(x + y)$.

Note In Example 10, if we factored out a y instead of a $-y$, we would have

$2x^2 + 5ax - 2xy - 5ay =$
$x(2x + 5a) + y(-2x - 5a)$

Grouping would not work because the resulting binomials, $2x + 5a$ and $-2x - 5a$, are not the same. These binomials must be identical so that we have a common factor for the second step.

EXAMPLE 10   Factor: $2x^2 + 5ax - 2xy - 5ay$.

SOLUTION   From the first two terms we factor x. From the second two terms we factor $-y$ because the leading term in that pair is negative. Remember, we are actually dividing each term in the second pair by $-y$. This means that the resulting terms in the grouping symbol will both be positive.

$$2x^2 + 5ax - 2xy - 5ay = x(2x + 5a) - y(2x + 5a)$$
$$= (2x + 5a)(x - y)$$

Another way to accomplish the same result is to use the commutative property to interchange the middle two terms, and then factor by grouping:

$$2x^2 + 5ax - 2xy - 5ay = 2x^2 - 2xy + 5ax - 5ay \qquad \text{Commutative property}$$
$$= 2x(x - y) + 5a(x - y)$$
$$= (x - y)(2x + 5a)$$

This is the same result we obtained previously.

In some cases, grouping may not work with the terms in the original order. If so, we can try rearranging the terms and try again. The last example illustrates this situation.

EXAMPLE 11   Factor: $3ax - 10 + 15x - 2a$.

SOLUTION   The first pair of terms, $3ax - 10$, has a GCF of 1. The same is true of the last pair of terms. This is not helpful if we are to factor the expression. However, if we rearrange terms we can make common factors (other than 1) appear.

$$3ax - 10 + 15x - 2a = 3ax + 15x - 10 - 2a \qquad \text{Commutative property}$$
$$= 3x(a + 5) - 2(5 + a) \qquad \text{Grouping}$$
$$= 3x(a + 5) - 2(a + 5) \qquad 5 + a = a + 5$$
$$= (3x - 2)(a + 5)$$

Getting Ready for Class

After reading through the preceding section, respond in your own words and in complete sentences.

A. What is the greatest common factor for a polynomial?

B. After factoring a polynomial, how can you check your result?

C. When would you try to factor by grouping?

D. What is the relationship between multiplication and factoring?

Problem Set 6.1

Find the greatest common factor for each expression.

1. $3x - 12$

2. $6x + 14$

3. $2x^3 - 18x$

4. $12y^3 - 3y$

5. $8a^3b^4 - 12a^4b + 20a^2b^3$

6. $6a^3b^3 + 12a^2b^4 - 8ab^5$

7. $3x(2x + 1) - 4(2x + 1)$

8. $4x^2(x - 3) - 9(x - 3)$

Factor the following by taking out the greatest common factor.

9. $15x + 25$

10. $14x + 21$

11. $6a + 9$

12. $8a + 10$

13. $4x - 8y$

14. $9x - 12y$

15. $3x^2 - 6x - 9$

16. $2x^2 + 6x + 4$

17. $3a^2 - 3a - 60$

18. $2a^2 - 18a + 28$

19. $24y^2 - 52y + 24$

20. $18y^2 + 48y + 32$

21. $9x^2 - 8x^3$

22. $7x^3 - 4x^2$

23. $13a^2 - 26a^3$

24. $5a^2 - 10a^3$

25. $21x^2y - 28xy^2$

26. $30xy^2 - 25x^2y$

27. $22a^2b^2 - 11ab^2$

28. $15x^3 - 25x^2 + 30x$

29. $7x^3 + 21x^2 - 28x$

30. $16x^4 - 20x^2 - 16x$

31. $121y^4 - 11x^4$

32. $25a^4 - 5b^4$

33. $100x^4 - 50x^3 + 25x^2$

34. $36x^5 + 72x^3 - 81x^2$

35. $8a^2 + 16b^2 + 32c^2$

36. $9a^2 - 18b^2 - 27c^2$

37. $4a^2b - 16ab^2 + 32a^2b^2$

38. $5ab^2 + 10a^2b^2 + 15a^2b$

39. $121a^3b^2 - 22a^2b^3 + 33a^3b^3$

40. $20a^4b^3 - 18a^3b^4 + 22a^4b^4$

41. $12x^2y^3 - 72x^5y^3 - 36x^4y^4$

42. $49xy - 21x^2y^2 + 35x^3y^3$

Factor by grouping.

43. $xy + 5x + 3y + 15$

44. $xy + 2x + 4y + 8$

45. $xy + 6x + 2y + 12$

46. $xy + 2y + 6x + 12$

47. $ab + 7a - 3b - 21$

48. $ab + 3b - 7a - 21$

49. $ax - bx + ay - by$

50. $ax - ay + bx - by$

51. $2ax + 5a - 2x - 5$

52. $3ax + 21x - a - 7$

53. $27by - 6y + 9b - 2$

54. $4by - 24y + b - 6$

55. $3xb - 4b - 6x + 8$

56. $3xb - 4b - 15x + 20$

57. $x^2 + 2a + 2x + ax$

58. $x^2 + 3a + ax + 3x$

59. $x^2 + ab - ax - bx$

60. $x^2 - ab + ax - bx$

Factor by grouping. You can group the terms together two at a time or three at a time. Either way will produce the same result.

61. $ax + ay + bx + by + cx + cy$

62. $ax + bx + cx + ay + by + cy$

Factor the following polynomials by grouping the terms together two at a time.

63. $6x^2 + 9x + 4x + 6$

64. $6x^2 - 9x - 4x + 6$

65. $20x^2 - 2x + 50x - 5$

66. $20x^2 + 25x + 4x + 5$

67. $20x^2 + 4x + 25x + 5$

68. $20x^2 + 4x - 25x - 5$

69. $x^3 + 2x^2 + 3x + 6$

70. $x^3 - 5x^2 - 4x + 20$

71. $6x^3 - 4x^2 + 15x - 10$

72. $8x^3 - 12x^2 + 14x - 21$

73. The greatest common factor of the binomial $3x + 6$ is 3. The greatest common factor of the binomial $2x + 4$ is 2. What is the greatest common factor of their product $(3x + 6)(2x + 4)$ when it has been multiplied out?

74. The greatest common factors of the binomials $4x + 2$ and $5x + 10$ are 2 and 5, respectively. What is the greatest common factor of their product $(4x + 2)(5x + 10)$ when it has been multiplied out?

75. The following factorization is incorrect. Find the mistake, and correct the right-hand side:

$$12x^2 + 6x + 3 = 3(4x^2 + 2x)$$

76. Find the mistake in the following factorization, and then rewrite the right-hand side correctly:

$$10x^2 + 2x + 6 = 2(5x^2 + 3)$$

Applying the Concepts

77. Investing If you invest \$1,000 in an account with an annual interest rate of r compounded annually, the amount of money you have in the account after one year is:

$$A = 1,000 + 1,000r$$

Write this formula again with the right side in factored form. Then, find the amount of money in this account at the end of one year if the interest rate is 12%.

78. Investing If you invest P dollars in an account with an annual interest rate of 8% compounded annually, then the amount of money in that account after one year is given by the formula:

$$A = P + 0.08P$$

Rewrite this formula with the right side in factored form, and then find the amount of money in the account at the end of one year if \$500 was the initial investment.

79. Biological Growth If 1,000,000 bacteria are placed in a petri dish and the bacteria have a growth rate of r (a percent expressed as a decimal) per hour, then 1 hour later the amount of bacteria will be $A = 1,000,000 + 1,000,000r$ bacteria.

a. Factor the right side of the equation.

b. If $r = 30\%$, find the number of bacteria present after one hour.

80. Biological Growth If there are B E. coli bacteria present initially in a petri dish and their growth rate is r (a percent expressed as a decimal) per hour, then after one hour there will be $A = B + Br$ bacteria present.

a. Factor the right side of this equation.

b. The following bar graph shows the number of E. coli bacteria present initially and the number of bacteria present hours later. Use the bar chart to find B and A in the preceding equation.

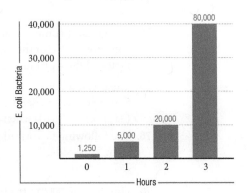

Learning Objectives Assessment

The following problems can be used to help assess if you have successfully met the learning objectives for this section.

81. Find the greatest common factor for $9a^2b^4 - 15a^3b$.

    a. $3a^2b$ **b.** $3a^3b^4$ **c.** ab **d.** $45a^5b^5$

82. Factor: $10x^2y - 25xy^3$

    a. $5xy(2x - 5y^2)$ **b.** $5x^2y^3(2y^2 - 5x)$

    c. $2xy(5x - 12y^2)$ **d.** $-15xy^2$

83. Factor by grouping: $2ax + 6x - 5a - 15$

    a. $(2x - 5)(a + 3)(a - 3)$ **b.** $(2x - 5)(a + 3)^2$

    c. $(2x - 5)(a + 3)$ **d.** $(2x + 5)(a + 3)$

Getting Ready for the Next Section

Multiply.

84. $(x - 7)(x + 2)$

85. $(x - 7)(x - 2)$

86. $(x - 3)(x + 2)$

87. $(x + 3)(x - 2)$

88. $(x + 3)(x^2 - 3x + 9)$

89. $(x - 2)(x^2 + 2x + 4)$

90. $(2x + 1)(x^2 + 4x - 3)$

91. $(3x + 2)(x^2 - 2x - 4)$

92. $3x^4(6x^3 - 4x^2 + 2x)$

93. $2x^4(5x^3 + 4x^2 - 3x)$

94. $\left(x + \dfrac{1}{3}\right)\left(x + \dfrac{2}{3}\right)$

95. $\left(x + \dfrac{1}{4}\right)\left(x + \dfrac{3}{4}\right)$

96. $(6x + 4y)(2x - 3y)$

97. $(8a - 3b)(4a - 5b)$

98. $(9a + 1)(9a - 1)$

99. $(7b + 1)(7b + 1)$

100. $(x - 9)(x - 9)$

101. $(x - 8)(x - 8)$

102. $(x + 2)(x^2 - 2x + 4)$

103. $(x - 3)(x^2 + 3x + 9)$

SPOTLIGHT ON SUCCESS   *Student Instructor Stefanie*

Never confuse a single defeat with a final defeat.
—F. Scott Fitzgerald

The idea that has worked best for my success in college, and more specifically in my math courses, is to stay positive and be resilient. I have learned that a 'bad' grade doesn't make me a failure; if anything it makes me strive to do better. That is why I never let a bad grade on a test or even in a class get in the way of my overall success.

By sticking with this positive attitude, I have been able to achieve my goals. My grades have never represented how well I know the material. This is because I have struggled with test anxiety and it has consistently lowered my test scores in a number of courses. However, I have not let it defeat me. When I applied to graduate school, I did not meet the grade requirements for my top two schools, but that did not stop me from applying.

One school asked that I convince them that my knowledge of mathematics was more than my grades indicated. If I had let my grades stand in the way of my goals, I wouldn't have been accepted to both of my top two schools, and wouldn't be attending one of them in the Fall, on my way to becoming a mathematics teacher.

Learning Objectives

In this section, we will learn how to:

1. Factor trinomials whose leading coefficient is 1.

Introduction

In this section, we will factor trinomials in which the coefficient of the squared term is 1. The more familiar we are with multiplication of binomials the easier factoring trinomials will be.

Recall multiplication of binomials using the FOIL method from Chapter 4:

$$(x + 3)(x + 4) = x^2 + \underbrace{4x + 3x}_{} + 12$$
$$= x^2 + \quad 7x \quad + 12$$

$$(x - 5)(x + 2) = x^2 + \underbrace{2x - 5x}_{} - 10$$
$$= x^2 - \quad 3x - \quad 10$$

The first term in the answer is the product of the first terms in each binomial. The last term in the answer is the product of the last terms in each binomial. The middle term in the answer comes from adding the product of the outside terms to the product of the inside terms.

Let's have a and b represent real numbers and look at the product of $(x + a)$ and $(x + b)$:

$$(x + a)(x + b) = x^2 + ax + bx + ab$$
$$= x^2 + (a + b)x + ab$$

The coefficient of the middle term is the sum of a and b. The last term is the product of a and b. Writing this as a factoring problem, we have:

$$x^2 + \underset{\text{Sum}}{(a + b)}x + \underset{\text{Product}}{ab} = (x + a)(x + b)$$

To factor a trinomial in which the coefficient of x^2 is 1, we need only find the numbers a and b whose sum is the coefficient of the middle term and whose product is the constant term (last term).

EXAMPLE 1 Factor: $x^2 + 8x + 12$.

SOLUTION The coefficient of x^2 is 1. We need two numbers whose sum is 8 and whose product is 12. Because the product is positive and the sum is also positive, both numbers must be positive. The numbers are 6 and 2:

$$x^2 + 8x + 12 = (x + 6)(x + 2)$$

We can easily check our work by multiplying $(x + 6)$ and $(x + 2)$.

$$\text{Check:} \quad (x + 6)(x + 2) = x^2 + 2x + 6x + 12$$
$$= x^2 + 8x + 12$$

VIDEO EXAMPLES

SECTION 6.2

Note As you will see as we progress through the book, factoring is a tool that is used in solving a number of problems. Before seeing how it is used, however, we first must learn how to do it. So, in this section and the two sections that follow, we will be developing our factoring skills.

Note Because multiplication is commutative, it does not matter which order we write the factors. In Example 1, we could have said
$x^2 + 8x + 12 = (x + 2)(x + 6)$
and still be correct.

Note Again, we can check our results by multiplying our factors to see if their product is the original polynomial.

EXAMPLE 2   Factor: $x^2 - 7x + 12$.

SOLUTION   Observe the leading coefficient is 1. We need two numbers whose sum is -7 and whose product is 12. This time, because the product is positive but the sum is negative, both numbers must be negative. The numbers that work are -3 and -4:

$$x^2 - 7x + 12 = (x - 3)(x - 4)$$

EXAMPLE 3   Factor: $x^2 - 2x - 15$.

SOLUTION   The coefficient of x^2 is again 1. We need to find a pair of numbers whose sum is -2 and whose product is -15. Because the product is negative, the two numbers must have opposite signs. Here are all the possibilities for products that are -15.

Products	Sums
$-1(15) = -15$	$-1 + 15 = 14$
$1(-15) = -15$	$1 + (-15) = -14$
$-5(3) = -15$	$-5 + 3 = -2$
$5(-3) = -15$	$5 + (-3) = 2$

The third line gives us what we want. Notice that, for the sum to be negative, the number with the larger absolute value is negative. The factors of $x^2 - 2x - 15$ are $(x - 5)$ and $(x + 3)$:

$$x^2 - 2x - 15 = (x - 5)(x + 3)$$

EXAMPLE 4   Factor $x^2 + 3x - 18$.

SOLUTION   We must find a pair of numbers whose sum is 3 and whose product is -18. Here are the possibilities.

Products	Sums
$-1(18) = -18$	$-1 + 18 = 17$
$1(-18) = -18$	$1 + (-18) = -17$
$-2(9) = -18$	$-2 + 9 = 7$
$2(-9) = -18$	$2 + (-9) = -7$
$-3(6) = -18$	$-3 + 6 = 3$
$3(-6) = -18$	$3 + (-6) = -3$

From the fifth line we see that the numbers are -3 and 6. Notice that the number with the larger absolute value is positive. The factors of $x^2 + 3x - 18$ are $(x - 3)$ and $(x + 6)$.

$$x^2 + 3x - 18 = (x - 3)(x + 6)$$

Based upon our work from the first four examples, we can make the following observations about factoring trinomials whose leading coefficient is 1.

> $[\Delta \neq \Sigma$ **RULE**   *Factoring trinomials with leading coefficient of 1*
>
> To factor $x^2 + bx + c$:
> **1.** If c is positive, then the numbers in the factors will have the same sign as b.
>
> **2.** If c is negative, then the numbers in the factors will have opposite signs, and the number with the larger absolute value will have the same sign as b.

EXAMPLE 5   Factor: $x^2 + 8xy + 12y^2$.

SOLUTION   We need two numbers whose product is 12 and whose sum is 8 (see Example 1 in this section). However, because the third term contains y^2, the last terms in the two binomials must each include a factor of y:

$$x^2 + 8xy + 12y^2 = (x + 6y)(x + 2y)$$

Note Trinomials in which the coefficient of the second-degree term is 1 are the easiest to factor. Success in factoring any type of polynomial is directly related to the amount of time spent working the problems. The more we practice, the more accomplished we become at factoring.

You should convince yourself that these factors are correct by finding their product. When you do, notice that the product of the outer terms and the product of the inner terms both contain the expression xy.

To conclude this section, we look at some trinomials that include a greatest common factor. We factor out the GCF first, and then (if possible) factor the remaining trinomial.

EXAMPLE 6   Factor: $2x^2 + 10x - 28$.

SOLUTION   We begin by factoring out the greatest common factor, which is 2:

$$2x^2 + 10x - 28 = 2(x^2 + 5x - 14)$$

Note In Example 6 we began by factoring out the greatest common factor. The first step in factoring any trinomial is to look for the greatest common factor. If the trinomial in question has a greatest common factor other than 1, we factor it out first and then try to factor the trinomial that remains.

Now, we factor the remaining trinomial by finding a pair of numbers whose sum is 5 and whose product is -14. The numbers must have opposite signs, with the larger of the two positive. The only choices are -1 and 14, or -2 and 7. Since $-2 + 7 = 5$, we see that the factors of $x^2 + 5x - 14$ are $(x + 7)$ and $(x - 2)$. Here is the complete problem:

$$2x^2 + 10x - 28 = 2(x^2 + 5x - 14)$$
$$= 2(x + 7)(x - 2)$$

EXAMPLE 7   Factor: $3x^3 - 3x^2 - 18x$.

SOLUTION   We begin by factoring out the greatest common factor, which is $3x$. Then we factor the remaining trinomial. Without showing the table of products and sums as we did in Examples 3 and 4, here is the complete problem:

$$3x^3 - 3x^2 - 18x = 3x(x^2 - x - 6)$$
$$= 3x(x - 3)(x + 2)$$

EXAMPLE 8   Factor: $-y^2 + 11y - 24$.

SOLUTION   The leading coefficient is -1, not 1, so we begin by factoring out a GCF of -1 so that the remaining trinomial has a positive leading term.

$$-y^2 + 11y - 24 = -1(y^2 - 11y + 24)$$

To factor the remaining trinomial, we need two negative numbers whose product is 24 and whose sum is -11. The numbers are -3 and -8. Here is the complete problem:

$$-y^2 + 11y - 24 = -1(y^2 - 11y + 24)$$

$$= -1(y - 3)(y - 8)$$

Getting Ready for Class

After reading through the preceding section, respond in your own words and in complete sentences.

A. When the leading coefficient of a trinomial is 1, what is the relationship between the other two coefficients and the factors of the trinomial?

B. How can you check to see that you have factored a trinomial correctly?

C. Describe how you would find the factors of $x^2 + 8x + 12$.

D. If the third term of the trinomial is negative, how do we decide which of the two factors has a plus sign and which has a minus sign?

Factor the following trinomials.

1. $x^2 + 7x + 12$ **2.** $x^2 + 7x + 10$

3. $x^2 + 3x + 2$ **4.** $x^2 + 7x + 6$

5. $a^2 + 10a + 21$ **6.** $a^2 - 7a + 12$

7. $x^2 - 7x + 10$ **8.** $x^2 - 3x + 2$

9. $y^2 - 10y + 21$ **10.** $y^2 - 7y + 6$

11. $x^2 - x - 12$ **12.** $x^2 - 4x - 5$

13. $y^2 + y - 12$ **14.** $y^2 + 3y - 18$

15. $x^2 + 5x - 14$ **16.** $x^2 - 5x - 24$

17. $r^2 - 8r - 9$ **18.** $r^2 - r - 2$

19. $x^2 - x - 30$ **20.** $x^2 + 8x + 12$

21. $a^2 + 15a + 56$ **22.** $a^2 - 9a + 20$

23. $y^2 - y - 42$ **24.** $y^2 + y - 42$

25. $x^2 + 13x + 42$ **26.** $x^2 - 13x + 42$

27. $x^2 + 5xy + 6y^2$ **28.** $x^2 - 5xy + 6y^2$

29. $x^2 - 9xy + 20y^2$ **30.** $x^2 + 9xy + 20y^2$

31. $a^2 + 2ab - 8b^2$ **32.** $a^2 - 2ab - 8b^2$

33. $a^2 - 10ab + 25b^2$ **34.** $a^2 + 6ab + 9b^2$

35. $a^2 + 10ab + 25b^2$ **36.** $a^2 - 6ab + 9b^2$

37. $x^2 + 2xa - 48a^2$ **38.** $x^2 - 3xa - 10a^2$

39. $x^2 - 5xb - 36b^2$ **40.** $x^2 - 13xb + 36b^2$

Factor the following problems completely. First, factor out the greatest common factor, and then factor the remaining trinomial.

41. $2x^2 + 6x + 4$ **42.** $3x^2 - 6x - 9$

43. $3a^2 - 3a - 60$ **44.** $2a^2 - 18a + 28$

45. $100x^2 - 500x + 600$ **46.** $100x^2 - 900x + 2,000$

47. $100p^2 - 1,300p + 4,000$ **48.** $100p^2 - 1,200p + 3,200$

49. $x^4 - x^3 - 12x^2$ **50.** $x^4 - 11x^3 + 24x^2$

51. $2r^3 + 4r^2 - 30r$ **52.** $5r^3 + 45r^2 + 100r$

53. $2y^4 - 6y^3 - 8y^2$ **54.** $3r^3 - 3r^2 - 6r$

55. $x^5 + 4x^4 + 4x^3$ **56.** $x^5 + 13x^4 + 42x^3$

57. $3y^4 - 12y^3 - 15y^2$ **58.** $5y^4 - 10y^3 + 5y^2$

59. $4x^4 - 52x^3 + 144x^2$ **60.** $3x^3 - 3x^2 - 18x$

61. $-a^2 - 11a - 30$ **62.** $-a^2 + 11a - 18$

63. $56 - x - x^2$ **64.** $44 + 7x - x^2$

Factor completely.

65. $x^4 - 5x^2 + 6$ **66.** $x^6 - 2x^3 - 15$

67. $x^2 - 80x - 2,000$ **68.** $x^2 - 190x - 2,000$

69. $x^2 - x + \dfrac{1}{4}$ **70.** $x^2 - \dfrac{2}{3}x + \dfrac{1}{9}$

71. $x^2 + 0.6x + 0.08$ **72.** $x^2 + 0.8x + 0.15$

73. If one of the factors of $x^2 + 24x + 128$ is $x + 8$, what is the other factor?

74. If one factor of $x^2 + 260x + 2,500$ is $x + 10$, what is the other factor?

75. What polynomial, when factored, gives $(4x + 3)(x - 1)$?

76. What polynomial factors to $(4x - 3)(x + 1)$?

Learning Objectives Assessment

The following problems can be used to help assess if you have successfully met the learning objectives for this section.

77. Factor: $x^2 + 8x + 12$.

    a. $(x + 4)(x + 3)$ **b.** $(x + 2)(x + 6)$

    c. $(x - 2)(x - 6)$ **d.** $(x + 10)(x - 2)$

78. Factor: $x^2 - 9x + 8$.

    a. $(x + 1)(x + 8)$ **b.** $(x - 2)(x - 4)$

    c. $(x + 2)(x + 4)$ **d.** $(x - 1)(x - 8)$

79. Factor: $a^2 - 5a - 6$.

    a. $(a + 6)(a - 1)$ **b.** $(a - 2)(a - 3)$

    c. $(a - 6)(a + 1)$ **d.** $(a + 2)(a - 3)$

80. Factor: $a^2 + 10a - 24$.

    a. $(a + 4)(a + 6)$ **b.** $(a - 4)(a - 6)$

    c. $(a - 12)(a + 2)$ **d.** $(a + 12)(a - 2)$

Getting Ready for the Next Section

Multiply using the FOIL method.

81. $(6a + 1)(a + 2)$ **82.** $(6a - 1)(a - 2)$

83. $(3a + 2)(2a + 1)$ **84.** $(3a - 2)(2a - 1)$

85. $(6a + 2)(a + 1)$ **86.** $(3a + 1)(2a + 2)$

More on Factoring Trinomials

Learning Objectives

In this section, we will learn how to:

1. Factor trinomials by trial and error.

2. Factor trinomials by grouping.

3. Solve applications that involve factoring trinomials.

Introduction

We will now consider trinomials whose greatest common factor is 1 and whose leading coefficient (the coefficient of the squared term) is a number other than 1.

Trial and Error

Suppose we want to factor the trinomial $2x^2 - 5x - 3$. We know the factors (if they exist) will be a pair of binomials. The product of their first terms is $2x^2$, so the first terms must be $2x$ and x. The product of their last terms is -3, so the last terms must be 3 and 1, with the binomials having opposite signs. Let us list all the possible factors along with the trinomial that would result if we were to multiply them together. Remember, the middle term comes from the product of the inside terms plus the product of the outside terms.

Binomial Factors	First Term	Middle Term	Last Term
$(2x - 3)(x + 1)$	$2x^2$	$-x$	-3
$(2x + 3)(x - 1)$	$2x^2$	$+x$	-3
$(2x - 1)(x + 3)$	$2x^2$	$+5x$	-3
$(2x + 1)(x - 3)$	$2x^2$	$-5x$	-3

We can see from the last line that the factors of $2x^2 - 5x - 3$ are $(2x + 1)$ and $(x - 3)$. There is no straightforward way, as there was in the previous section, to find the factors, other than by trial and error or by simply listing all the possibilities. We look for possible factors that, when multiplied, will give the correct first and last terms, and then we see if we can adjust them to give the correct middle term.

EXAMPLE 1   Factor: $6a^2 + 7a + 2$.

SOLUTION   We list all the possible pairs of factors that, when multiplied together, give a trinomial whose first term is $6a^2$ and whose last term is $+2$. The first terms can either be $6a$ and $1a$, or $2a$ and $3a$. The last terms must be 1 and 2, with both binomials positive.

Binomial Factors	First Term	Middle Term	Last Term
$(6a + 1)(a + 2)$	$6a^2$	$+13a$	$+2$
$(6a + 2)(a + 1)$	$6a^2$	$+8a$	$+2$
$(3a + 1)(2a + 2)$	$6a^2$	$+8a$	$+2$
$(3a + 2)(2a + 1)$	$6a^2$	$+7a$	$+2$

We can rule out the second line because the first factor has a 2 common to each term and so could be factored again, giving $2(3a + 1)(a + 1)$. Since our original trinomial, $6a^2 + 7a + 2$, did *not* have a greatest common factor of 2, neither of its factors will. Likewise, we can rule out the third line because $2a + 2$ has a greatest common factor of 2 also. The fourth line gives the correct middle term, so the factors of $6a^2 + 7a + 2$ are $(3a + 2)$ and $(2a + 1)$.

Check: $(3a + 2)(2a + 1) = 6a^2 + 7a + 2$

> **Note**   Remember, we can always check our results by multiplying the factors we have and comparing that product with our original polynomial.

EXAMPLE 2   Factor: $4x^2 - x - 3$.

SOLUTION   The choices for the first terms are $4x$ and x, or $2x$ and $2x$. The last terms must be 1 and 3 with the binomials having opposite signs. We list all the possible factors that, when multiplied, give a trinomial whose first term is $4x^2$ and whose last term is -3.

Binomial Factors	First Term	Middle Term	Last Term
$(4x + 1)(x - 3)$	$4x^2$	$-11x$	-3
$(4x - 1)(x + 3)$	$4x^2$	$+11x$	-3
$(4x + 3)(x - 1)$	$4x^2$	$-x$	-3
$(4x - 3)(x + 1)$	$4x^2$	$+x$	-3
$(2x + 1)(2x - 3)$	$4x^2$	$-4x$	-3
$(2x - 1)(2x + 3)$	$4x^2$	$+4x$	-3

The third line shows that the factors are $(4x + 3)$ and $(x - 1)$.

Check: $(4x + 3)(x - 1) = 4x^2 - x - 3$

You will find that the more practice you have at factoring this type of trinomial, the faster you will get the correct factors. You will pick up some shortcuts along the way, or you may come across a system of eliminating some factors as possibilities. Whatever works best for you is the method you should use. Factoring is a very important tool, and you must be good at it.

EXAMPLE 3   Factor: $12y^3 + 10y^2 - 12y$.

SOLUTION   We begin by factoring out the greatest common factor, $2y$:

$$12y^3 + 10y^2 - 12y = 2y(6y^2 + 5y - 6)$$

> **Note**   Once again, the first step in any factoring problem is to factor out the greatest common factor if it is other than 1.

The choices for the first terms are $3y$ and $2y$, or $6y$ and y. The choices for the last terms are 2 and 3, or 1 and 6. The binomials must have opposite signs. We now list all possible factors of a trinomial with the first term $6y^2$ and last term -6, along with the associated middle terms.

Possible Factors	Middle Term When Multiplied
$(3y + 2)(2y - 3)$	$-5y$
$(3y - 2)(2y + 3)$	$+5y$
$(6y + 1)(y - 6)$	$-35y$
$(6y - 1)(y + 6)$	$+35y$

Notice that we did not list any possibilities where either factor would have a greatest common factor, such as $(6y + 2)(y - 3)$. The second line gives the correct factors. The complete problem is:

$$12y^3 + 10y^2 - 12y = 2y(6y^2 + 5y - 6)$$
$$= 2y(3y - 2)(2y + 3)$$

Factoring Trinomials by Grouping

Factoring trinomials by trial and error works well as long as there are not too many possibilities to test for the factors. When the coefficients of the first and third terms have many possible factors, it may take a considerable time to find the correct combination, and it can be easy to overlook some possibilities. In this case, we can use a second method to factor the trinomial that involves grouping (sometimes this process is referred to as the AC method or splitting the middle term).

The main idea behind this second method is to write the middle term as a sum of two new terms. This changes the trinomial into a polynomial with 4 terms, allowing grouping to be used.

Let's revisit the trinomial from the beginning of this section. To factor $2x^2 - 5x - 3$, we begin by multiplying the coefficients of the first and third terms:

$$(\text{first coefficient})(\text{third coefficient}) = 2(-3) = -6$$

Then we list all possible factors of -6 and their corresponding sums.

Factors	Sum
$1(-6)$	$1 + (-6) = -5$
$-1(6)$	$-1 + (6) = 5$
$2(-3)$	$2 + (-3) = -1$
$-2(3)$	$-2 + 3 = 1$

We want the factors whose sum gives us the coefficient of the middle term. The first line shows that the correct factors are 1 and -6. Writing $-5x$ as $x + (-6x)$, we have

$$2x^2 - 5x - 3 = 2x^2 + x - 6x - 3$$

It does not matter in which order we write the new terms. It would work just as well if we wrote $2x^2 - 6x + x - 3$.

We can now factor the resulting expression using grouping. Here is the complete process:

$$2x^2 - 5x - 3 = 2x^2 + x - 6x - 3$$
$$= x(2x + 1) - 3(2x + 1)$$
$$= (2x + 1)(x - 3)$$

Notice we obtain the same result as we did using trial and error.

EXAMPLE 4   Factor: $6x^2 - 17x + 12$.

SOLUTION   The product of the first and third coefficients is $6(12) = 72$. We need factors of 72 whose sum is -17. Because the product is positive and the middle term is negative, both factors must be negative. Here are the possible factors:

Factors	Sum
$-1(-72)$	$-1 + (-72) = -73$
$-2(-36)$	$-2 + (-36) = -38$
$-3(-24)$	$-3 + (-24) = -27$
$-4(-18)$	$-4 + (-18) = -22$
$-6(-12)$	$-6 + (-12) = -18$
$-8(-9)$	$-8 + (-9) = -17$

The last line shows that the correct factors are -8 and -9. Writing $-17x$ as $-8x + (-9x)$, we have:

$$6x^2 - 17x + 12 = 6x^2 - 8x - 9x + 12$$
$$= 2x(3x - 4) - 3(3x - 4)$$
$$= (2x - 3)(3x - 4)$$

EXAMPLE 5   Factor: $8x^2 + 26x - 15$.

SOLUTION   We need two numbers whose product is $8(-15) = -120$ and whose sum is 26. The numbers must have opposite signs, and the number with the larger absolute value must be positive for the sum to be positive. We begin listing possible factors and their sums.

Factors	Sum
$-1(120)$	$-1 + (120) = 119$
$-2(60)$	$-2 + (60) = 58$
$-3(40)$	$-3 + (40) = 37$
$-4(30)$	$-4 + (30) = 26$

The fourth line shows the correct numbers. Writing $26x$ as $-4x + 30x$, we have:

$$8x^2 + 26x - 15 = 8x^2 - 4x + 30x - 15$$
$$= 4x(2x - 1) + 15(2x - 1)$$
$$= (2x - 1)(4x + 15)$$

EXAMPLE 6   Factor: $30x^2y - 5xy^2 - 10y^3$.

SOLUTION   The greatest common factor is $5y$:

$$30x^2y - 5xy^2 - 10y^3 = 5y(6x^2 - xy - 2y^2)$$

Writing $-xy$ as $3xy - 4xy$, we have

$$= 5y(6x^2 + 3xy - 4xy - 2y^2)$$
$$= 5y[3x(2x + y) - 2y(2x + y)]$$
$$= 5y[(2x + y)(3x - 2y)]$$
$$= 5y(2x + y)(3x - 2y)$$

Note   In Example 6, we came up with $3xy - 4xy$ by mentally reviewing the possible factors and their sums.

Application

EXAMPLE 7 A ball is tossed into the air with an upward velocity of 16 feet per second from the top of a building 32 feet high. The equation that gives the height h of the ball above the ground at any time t is

$$h = 32 + 16t - 16t^2$$

Factor the right side of this equation and then find h when t is 2.

SOLUTION We begin by factoring out the greatest common factor, -16. Then, we factor the trinomial that remains:

$$h = -16t^2 + 16t + 32$$
$$h = -16(t^2 - t - 2)$$
$$h = -16(t - 2)(t + 1) \qquad \text{Letting } t = 2 \text{ in the equation, we have}$$
$$h = -16(0)(3) = 0$$

When t is 2, h is 0.

Getting Ready for Class

After reading through the preceding section, respond in your own words and in complete sentences.

A. Describe the criteria you would use to set up a table of possible factors of a trinomial using trial and error.

B. Describe the criteria you would use to set up a table of possible factors for a trinomial using the grouping method.

C. In factoring $2a^2 + a - 6$ by grouping, explain why the correct pair of numbers is 4 and -3, not 2 and 3.

D. What does it mean if you factor a trinomial and one of your factors has a greatest common factor of 3?

Problem Set 6.3

Factor the following trinomials using either method.

1. $2x^2 + 7x + 3$

2. $2x^2 + 5x + 3$

3. $2a^2 - a - 3$

4. $2a^2 + a - 3$

5. $3x^2 + 2x - 5$

6. $3x^2 - 2x - 5$

7. $3y^2 + 2y - 5$

8. $3y^2 + 14y - 5$

9. $6x^2 + 13x + 6$

10. $6x^2 - 13x + 6$

11. $4x^2 - 12xy + 9y^2$

12. $4x^2 + 12xy + 9y^2$

13. $4y^2 - 11y - 3$

14. $4y^2 + y - 3$

15. $20x^2 - 41x + 20$

16. $20x^2 + 9x - 20$

17. $20a^2 + 48ab - 5b^2$

18. $20a^2 + 29ab + 5b^2$

19. $20x^2 - 21x - 5$

20. $20x^2 - 48x - 5$

21. $12m^2 + 16m - 3$

22. $12m^2 + 20m + 3$

23. $20x^2 + 37x + 15$

24. $20x^2 + 13x - 15$

25. $12a^2 - 25ab + 12b^2$

26. $12a^2 + 7ab - 12b^2$

27. $3x^2 - xy - 14y^2$

28. $3x^2 + 19xy - 14y^2$

29. $14x^2 + 29x - 15$

30. $14x^2 + 11x - 15$

31. $6x^2 - 43x + 55$

32. $6x^2 - 7x - 55$

33. $15t^2 - 67t + 38$

34. $15t^2 - 79t - 34$

Factor each of the following completely. Look first for the greatest common factor.

35. $4x^2 + 2x - 6$

36. $6x^2 - 51x + 63$

37. $24a^2 - 50a + 24$

38. $18a^2 + 48a + 32$

39. $10 + 13x - 3x^2$

40. $10 - x - 3x^2$

41. $-12x^2 + 10x + 8$

42. $-18x^2 + 51x - 15$

43. $10x^3 - 23x^2 + 12x$

44. $10x^4 + 7x^3 - 12x^2$

45. $6x^4 - 11x^3 - 10x^2$

46. $6x^3 + 19x^2 + 10x$

47. $10a^3 - 6a^2 - 4a$

48. $6a^3 + 15a^2 + 9a$

49. $15x^3 - 102x^2 - 21x$

50. $2x^4 - 24x^3 + 64x^2$

51. $35y^3 - 60y^2 - 20y$

52. $14y^4 - 32y^3 + 8y^2$

53. $15a^4 - 2a^3 - a^2$

54. $10a^5 - 17a^4 + 3a^3$

55. $24x^2y - 6xy - 45y$

56. $8x^2y^2 + 26xy^2 + 15y^2$

57. $12x^3y - 34xy^2 + 14y^3$

58. $12x^2y - 46xy^2 + 14y^3$

59. Evaluate the expression $2x^2 + 7x + 3$ and the expression $(2x + 1)(x + 3)$ for $x = 2$.

60. Evaluate the expression $2a^2 - a - 3$ and the expression $(2a - 3)(a + 1)$ for $a = 5$.

61. What polynomial factors to $(2x + 3)(2x - 3)$?

62. What polynomial factors to $(5x + 4)(5x - 4)$?

63. What polynomial factors to $(x + 3)(x - 3)(x^2 + 9)$?

64. What polynomial factors to $(x + 2)(x - 2)(x^2 + 4)$?

Applying the Concepts

65. Archery Margaret shoots an arrow into the air. The equation for the height (in feet) of the tip of the arrow is:

$$h = 8 + 62t - 16t^2$$

Factor the right side of this equation. Then fill in the table for various heights of the arrow, using the factored form of the equation.

Time t (seconds)	0	1	2	3	4
Height h (feet)					

66. Coin Toss At the beginning of every football game, the referee flips a coin to see who will kick off. The equation that gives the height (in feet) of the coin tossed in the air is:

$$h = 6 + 29t - 16t^2$$

a. Factor this equation.

b. Use the factored form of the equation to find the height of the coin after 0 seconds, 1 second, and 2 seconds.

67. Constructing a Box Yesterday I was experimenting with how to cut and fold a certain piece of cardboard to make a box with different volumes. Unfortunately, today I have lost both the cardboard and most of my notes. I remember that I made the box by cutting equal squares from the corners then folding up the side flaps.

I don't remember how big the cardboard was, and I can only find the last page of notes, which says that if x is the length of a side of a small square (in inches), then the volume is $V = 99x - 40x^2 + 4x^3$.

a. Factor the right side of this expression completely.

b. What were the dimensions of the original piece of cardboard?

68. Constructing a Box Repeat Problem 67 if the remaining formula is $V = 15x - 16x^2 + 4x^3$.

Learning Objectives Assessment

The following problems can be used to help assess if you have successfully met the learning objectives for this section.

69. Factor $4x^2 - 5x - 6$ by trial and error. Which factor appears in the answer?

    a. $2x + 3$ **b.** $2x - 1$ **c.** $x - 3$ **d.** $x - 2$

70. In factoring $6x^2 + 11x - 7$ by grouping, what is the correct way to rewrite the middle term $11x$?

    a. $-3x + 14x$ **b.** $9x + 2x$ **c.** $12x - x$ **d.** $18x - 7x$

71. A water balloon is tossed in the air. The equation $h = 8 + 28t - 16t^2$ gives the height of the water balloon after t seconds. If the equation is factored completely, which factor appears in the answer?

    a. $t + 2$ **b.** $t - 2$ **c.** $16t + 1$ **d.** $8t - 1$

Getting Ready for the Next Section

Multiply each of the following.

72. $(x + 3)(x - 3)$ **73.** $(x - 4)(x + 4)$

74. $(2x - 3y)(2x + 3y)$ **75.** $(5x - 6y)(5x + 6y)$

76. $(x^2 + 4)(x + 2)(x - 2)$ **77.** $(x^2 + 9)(x + 3)(x - 3)$

78. $(x + 3)^2$ **79.** $(x - 4)^2$

80. $(2x + 3)^2$ **81.** $(3x - y)^2$

82. $(4x - 2y)^2$ **83.** $(5x - 6y)^2$

84.   **a.** 1^3 **b.** 2^3 **c.** 3^3 **d.** 4^3 **e.** 5^3

85.   **a.** $(-1)^3$ **b.** $(-2)^3$ **c.** $(-3)^3$ **d.** $(-4)^3$ **e.** $(-5)^3$

86.   **a.** $x(x^2 - 2x + 4)$ **b.** $2(x^2 - 2x + 4)$ **c.** $(x + 2)(x^2 - 2x + 4)$

87.   **a.** $x(x^2 + 2x + 4)$ **b.** $-2(x^2 + 2x + 4)$ **c.** $(x - 2)(x^2 + 2x + 4)$

88.   **a.** $x(x^2 - 3x + 9)$ **b.** $3(x^2 - 3x + 9)$ **c.** $(x + 3)(x^2 - 3x + 9)$

89.   **a.** $x(x^2 + 3x + 9)$ **b.** $-3(x^2 + 3x + 9)$ **c.** $(x - 3)(x^2 + 3x + 9)$

Learning Objectives

In this section, we will learn how to:

1. Factor a perfect square trinomial.

2. Factor a difference of two squares.

3. Factor a sum or difference of two cubes.

Introduction

In Chapter 5, we listed the following three special products:

$$(a + b)^2 = (a + b)(a + b) = a^2 + 2ab + b^2$$
$$(a - b)^2 = (a - b)(a - b) = a^2 - 2ab + b^2$$
$$(a + b)(a - b) = a^2 - b^2$$

Since factoring is the reverse of multiplication, we can also consider the three special products as three special factoring patterns:

$$a^2 + 2ab + b^2 = (a + b)^2$$
$$a^2 - 2ab + b^2 = (a - b)^2$$
$$a^2 - b^2 = (a + b)(a - b)$$

We begin by considering the first two of these formulas.

Perfect Square Trinomials

Any trinomial of the form $a^2 + 2ab + b^2$ or $a^2 - 2ab + b^2$ is called a *perfect square trinomial* because it can be factored as the square of a binomial. For convenience, we repeat both formulas as follows.

 RULE   *Perfect Square Trinomials*

$$a^2 + 2ab + b^2 = (a + b)^2$$
$$a^2 - 2ab + b^2 = (a - b)^2$$

Perfect square trinomials can be factored using the methods of the two previous sections, but if we recognize that a trinomial is a perfect square trinomial, it can often be factored more quickly using the special pattern.

EXAMPLE 1   Factor: $25x^2 - 60x + 36$.

SOLUTION   We notice that the first and last terms are the perfect squares $(5x)^2$ and $(6)^2$, and that the middle term involves the product $2(5x)(6) = 60x$. This means we have a perfect square trinomial with $a = 5x$ and $b = 6$. Thus, we have

$$25x^2 - 60x + 36 = (5x)^2 - 2(5x)(6) + (6)^2$$

$$= (5x - 6)^2$$

The trinomial $25x^2 - 60x + 36$ factors to $(5x - 6)(5x - 6) = (5x - 6)^2$.

 EXAMPLE 2   Factor: $5x^2 + 30x + 45$.

SOLUTION   We begin by factoring out the greatest common factor, which is 5. Then we notice that the trinomial that remains is a perfect square trinomial with $a = x$ and $b = 3$:

$$5x^2 + 30x + 45 = 5(x^2 + 6x + 9)$$

$$= 5(x^2 + 2(x)(3) + 3^2)$$

$$= 5(x + 3)^2$$

> *Note*   As we have indicated before, perfect square trinomials like the ones in Examples 1 and 2 can be factored by the methods developed in previous sections. Recognizing that they factor to binomial squares simply saves time in factoring.

Factoring Binomials

Our third special product gives us one way to factor certain binomials whose terms are both perfect squares.

> **⟍Δ≠Σ RULE**   *Difference of Squares*
>
> $$a^2 - b^2 = (a + b)(a - b)$$

Notice that this pattern requires the binomial to have a subtraction. Other than a possible greatest common factor, the expression $a^2 + b^2$ is prime, meaning there is no special pattern by which it can be factored.

EXAMPLE 3   Factor: $16x^2 - 25$.

SOLUTION   We can see that both terms are perfect squares. This fact becomes even more obvious if we rewrite the problem as:

$$16x^2 - 25 = (4x)^2 - (5)^2$$

The first term is the square of the quantity $4x$, and the last term is the square of 5. The completed problem looks like this:

$$16x^2 - 25 = (4x)^2 - (5)^2$$

$$= (4x + 5)(4x - 5)$$

To check our results, we multiply:

$$(4x + 5)(4x - 5) = 16x^2 - 20x + 20x - 25$$

$$= 16x^2 - 25$$

EXAMPLE 4   Factor: $1 - 36a^2$.

SOLUTION   We rewrite the two terms to show they are perfect squares and then factor. Remember, 1 is its own square, $1^2 = 1$.

$$1 - 36a^2 = (1)^2 - (6a)^2$$

$$= (1 + 6a)(1 - 6a)$$

To check our results, we multiply:

$$(1 + 6a)(1 - 6a) = 1 - 6a + 6a - 36a^2$$

$$= 1 - 36a^2$$

EXAMPLE 5   Factor: $4x^2 + 16y^2$.

SOLUTION   We begin by factoring out the greatest common factor of 4:

$$4x^2 + 16y^2 = 4(x^2 + 4y^2)$$

Both terms of the resulting binomial, $x^2 + 4y^2$, are perfect squares. However, because the binomial is a *sum* of squares, it cannot be factored any further.

EXAMPLE 6   Factor: $x^4 - y^4$.

SOLUTION x^4 is the perfect square $(x^2)^2$, and y^4 is $(y^2)^2$:

$$x^4 - y^4 = (x^2)^2 - (y^2)^2$$
$$= (x^2 + y^2)(x^2 - y^2)$$

The factor $(x^2 - y^2)$ is itself the difference of two squares and therefore can be factored again. The factor $(x^2 + y^2)$ is the *sum* of two squares and cannot be factored again. The complete problem is this:

$$x^4 - y^4 = (x^2)^2 - (y^2)^2$$
$$= (x^2 + y^2)(x^2 - y^2)$$
$$= (x^2 + y^2)(x + y)(x - y)$$

> *Note*   If you think the sum of two squares $x^2 + y^2$ factors, you should try it. Write down the factors you think it has, and then multiply them using the FOIL method. You won't get $x^2 + y^2$.

EXAMPLE 7   Factor: $(x - 3)^2 - 25$.

SOLUTION   This example has the form $a^2 - b^2$, where a is $x - 3$ and b is 5. We factor it according to the formula for the difference of two squares:

$$(x - 3)^2 - 25 = (x - 3)^2 - 5^2 \qquad \text{Write 25 as } 5^2$$
$$= [(x - 3) + 5][(x - 3) - 5] \qquad \text{Factor}$$
$$= (x + 2)(x - 8) \qquad \text{Simplify}$$

Notice in this example we could have expanded $(x - 3)^2$, subtracted 25, and then factored to obtain the same result:

$$(x - 3)^2 - 25 = x^2 - 6x + 9 - 25 \qquad \text{Expand } (x - 3)^2$$
$$= x^2 - 6x - 16 \qquad \text{Simplify}$$
$$= (x - 8)(x + 2) \qquad \text{Factor}$$

Just as we can factor certain binomials whose terms are both perfect squares, we can also factor binomials whose terms are both perfect cubes. The formulas that allow us to factor the sum of two cubes and the difference of two cubes are not as simple as the formula for factoring the difference of two squares.

> **RULE**   *Sum or Difference of Cubes*
>
> $$a^3 + b^3 = (a + b)(a^2 - ab + b^2)$$
> $$a^3 - b^3 = (a - b)(a^2 + ab + b^2)$$

Let's begin our work with these two formulas by showing that they are true. To do so, we multiply out the right side of each formula.

EXAMPLE 8   Verify the two formulas.

SOLUTION   We verify the formulas by multiplying the right sides and comparing the results with the left sides:

$$\begin{array}{r} a^2 - ab\ + b^2 \\ \times \underline{\qquad a\ + b} \\ a^3 - a^2b + ab^2 \\ + \underline{\qquad a^2b - ab^2 + b^3} \\ a^3 \qquad\qquad\ + b^3 \end{array} \qquad \begin{array}{r} a^2 + ab\ + b^2 \\ \times \underline{\qquad a\ - b} \\ a^3 + a^2b + ab^2 \\ + \underline{\qquad - a^2b - ab^2 - b^3} \\ a^3 \qquad\qquad\ - b^3 \end{array}$$

The first formula is correct.   The second formula is correct.

Here are some examples that use the formulas for factoring the sum and difference of two cubes.

EXAMPLE 9   Factor: $x^3 - 8$.

SOLUTION   Since both terms are perfect cubes, we write them as such and apply the formula:

$$x^3 - 8 = x^3 - 2^3$$
$$= (x - 2)(x^2 + 2x + 2^2) \qquad \text{Formula using } a = x, b = 2$$
$$= (x - 2)(x^2 + 2x + 4)$$

EXAMPLE 10   Factor: $y^3 + 27$.

SOLUTION   Proceeding as we did in Example 9, we first write 27 as 3^3. Then, we apply the formula for factoring the sum of two cubes, which is $a^3 + b^3 = (a + b)(a^2 - ab + b^2)$:

$$y^3 + 27 = y^3 + 3^3$$
$$= (y + 3)(y^2 - 3y + 3^2) \qquad \text{Formula using } a = y, b = 3$$
$$= (y + 3)(y^2 - 3y + 9)$$

Here are some additional examples using the formulas for factoring the sum and difference of two cubes.

EXAMPLE 11   Factor: $64 + t^3$.

SOLUTION   The first term is the cube of 4 and the second term is the cube of t. Therefore,

$$64 + t^3 = 4^3 + t^3$$
$$= (4 + t)(4^2 - 4t + t^2)$$
$$= (4 + t)(16 - 4t + t^2)$$

EXAMPLE 12 Factor: $27x^3 + 125y^3$.

SOLUTION Writing both terms as perfect cubes, we have

$$27x^3 + 125y^3 = (3x)^3 + (5y)^3$$
$$= (3x + 5y)((3x)^2 - 3x(5y) + (5y)^2)$$
$$= (3x + 5y)(9x^2 - 15xy + 25y^2)$$

EXAMPLE 13 Factor: $a^3 - \dfrac{1}{8}$.

SOLUTION The first term is the cube of a, whereas the second term is the cube of $\frac{1}{2}$:

$$a^3 - \frac{1}{8} = a^3 - \left(\frac{1}{2}\right)^3$$
$$= \left(a - \frac{1}{2}\right)\left(a^2 + \frac{1}{2}a + \left(\frac{1}{2}\right)^2\right)$$
$$= \left(a - \frac{1}{2}\right)\left(a^2 + \frac{1}{2}a + \frac{1}{4}\right)$$

EXAMPLE 14 Factor: $x^6 - y^6$.

SOLUTION We have a choice of how we want to write the two terms to begin. We can write the expression as the difference of two squares, $(x^3)^2 - (y^3)^2$, or as the difference of two cubes, $(x^2)^3 - (y^2)^3$. It is better to use the difference of two squares if we have a choice. Then we factor again, using the formulas for the difference and sum of two cubes.

$$x^6 - y^6 = (x^3)^2 - (y^3)^2$$
$$= (x^3 - y^3)(x^3 + y^3)$$
$$= (x - y)(x^2 + xy + y^2)(x + y)(x^2 - xy + y^2)$$

Getting Ready for Class

After reading through the preceding section, respond in your own words and in complete sentences.

A. What is a perfect square trinomial?

B. What are the different ways that a binomial can be factored?

C. Describe how you factor the difference of two squares.

D. How are you going to remember that the sum of two cubes factors, while the sum of two squares is prime?

Problem Set 6.4

Factor each trinomial.

1. $x^2 - 2x + 1$

2. $x^2 - 6x + 9$

3. $x^2 + 2x + 1$

4. $x^2 + 6x + 9$

5. $a^2 - 10a + 25$

6. $a^2 + 10a + 25$

7. $y^2 + 4y + 4$

8. $y^2 - 8y + 16$

9. $x^2 - 4x + 4$

10. $x^2 + 8x + 16$

11. $m^2 - 12m + 36$

12. $m^2 + 12m + 36$

13. $4a^2 + 12a + 9$

14. $9a^2 - 12a + 4$

15. $49x^2 - 14x + 1$

16. $64x^2 - 16x + 1$

17. $9y^2 - 30y + 25$

18. $25y^2 + 30y + 9$

19. $x^2 + 10xy + 25y^2$

20. $25x^2 + 10xy + y^2$

21. $9a^2 + 6ab + b^2$

22. $9a^2 - 6ab + b^2$

Factor the following by first factoring out the greatest common factor.

23. $3a^2 + 18a + 27$

24. $4a^2 - 16a + 16$

25. $2x^2 + 20xy + 50y^2$

26. $3x^2 + 30xy + 75y^2$

27. $5x^3 + 30x^2y + 45xy^2$

28. $12x^2y - 36xy^2 + 27y^3$

Factor each binomial.

29. $x^2 - 9$

30. $x^2 - 25$

31. $a^2 - 36$

32. $a^2 - 64$

33. $x^2 - 49$

34. $x^2 - 121$

35. $4a^2 - 16$

36. $4a^2 + 16$

37. $9x^2 + 25$

38. $16x^2 - 36$

39. $25x^2 - 169$

40. $x^2 - y^2$

41. $9a^2 - 16b^2$

42. $49a^2 - 25b^2$

43. $9 - m^2$

44. $16 - m^2$

45. $25 - 4x^2$

46. $36 - 49y^2$

47. $2x^2 - 18$

48. $3x^2 - 27$

49. $x^3 - y^3$

50. $x^3 + y^3$

51. $a^3 + 8$

52. $a^3 - 8$

53. $27 + x^3$

54. $27 - x^3$

55. $y^3 - 1$

56. $y^3 + 1$

57. $64 - y^3$

58. $64 + y^3$

59. $125h^3 - t^3$

60. $t^3 + 125h^3$

61. $x^3 - 216$

62. $216 + x^3$

63. $2y^3 - 54$

64. $81 + 3y^3$

65. $64 + 27a^3$

66. $27 - 64a^3$

67. $8x^3 - 27y^3$

68. $27x^3 - 8y^3$

69. $32a^2 - 128$

70. $3a^3 - 48a$

71. $8x^2y - 18y$

72. $50a^2b - 72b$

73. $2a^3 - 128b^3$

74. $120a^3 + 2b^3$

75. $2x^3 + 432y^3$

76. $432x^3 - 2y^3$

77. $10a^3 - 640b^3$

78. $640a^3 + 10b^3$

79. $10r^3 - 1{,}250$

80. $10r^3 + 1{,}250$

81. $t^3 + \dfrac{1}{27}$

82. $t^3 - \dfrac{1}{27}$

83. $27x^3 - \dfrac{1}{27}$

84. $8x^3 + \dfrac{1}{8}$

85. $64a^3 + 125b^3$

86. $125a^3 - 27b^3$

87. $\dfrac{1}{8}x^3 - \dfrac{1}{27}y^3$

88. $\dfrac{1}{27}x^3 + \dfrac{1}{8}y^3$

89. $a^4 - b^4$

90. $a^4 - 16$

91. $16m^4 - 81$

92. $81 - m^4$

93. $3x^3y - 75xy^3$

94. $2xy^3 - 8x^3y$

95. $a^6 - b^6$

96. $x^6 - 64y^6$

97. $64x^6 - y^6$

98. $x^6 - (3y)^6$

99. $x^6 - (5y)^6$

100. $(4x)^6 - (7y)^6$

Factor by grouping the first three terms together.

101. $x^2 + 6x + 9 - y^2$ **102.** $x^2 + 10x + 25 - y^2$

103. $x^2 + 2xy + y^2 - 9$ **104.** $a^2 + 2ab + b^2 - 25$

105. Find a value for b so that the polynomial $x^2 + bx + 49$ factors to $(x + 7)^2$.

106. Find a value of b so that the polynomial $x^2 + bx + 81$ factors to $(x + 9)^2$.

107. Find the value of c for which the polynomial $x^2 + 10x + c$ factors to $(x + 5)^2$.

108. Find the value of a for which the polynomial $ax^2 + 12x + 9$ factors to $(2x + 3)^2$.

Applying the Concepts

109. Area

    a. What is the area of the following figure?

    b. Factor the answer from part **a**.

    c. Find a way to cut the figure into two pieces and put them back together to show that the factorization in part **b**. is correct.

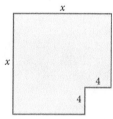

110. Area

    a. What is the area of the following figure?

    b. Factor the expression from part **a**.

    c. Cut and rearrange the figure to show that the factorization is correct.

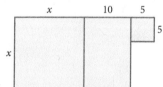

Find the area for the shaded regions; then write your result in factored form.

111.

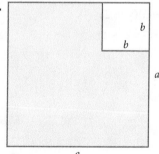

112.

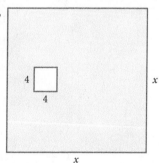

Learning Objectives Assessment

The following problems can be used to help assess if you have successfully met the learning objectives for this section.

113. Factor: $9x^2 - 48x + 64$.

    a. $(3x + 8)(3x - 8)$ **b.** $(3x + 8)^2$

    c. $(3x - 8)^2$ **d.** $(9x - 64)(x + 1)$

114. Factor: $4 - 9a^2$.

    a. Prime   **b.** $(2 + 3a)^2$

    c. $(2 - 3a)^2$ **d.** $(2 + 3a)(2 - 3a)$

115. Factor: $4y^2 + 25$.

    a. $(2y + 5)(2y - 5)$ **b.** Prime

    c. $(2y + 5)^2$ **d.** $(2y - 5)$

116. Factor: $8x^3 + 1$.

    a. Prime   **b.** $(2x + 1)(2x^2 - 4x + 1)$

    c. $(2x + 1)(4x^2 + 2x + 1)$ **d.** $(2x + 1)(4x^2 - 2x + 1)$

Getting Ready for the Next Section

Multiply each of the following.

117. $2x^3(x + 2)(x - 2)$ **118.** $3x^2(x + 3)(x - 3)$

119. $3x^2(x - 3)^2$ **120.** $2x^2(x + 5)^2$

121. $y(y^2 + 25)$ **122.** $y^3(y^2 + 36)$

123. $(5a - 2)(3a + 1)$ **124.** $(3a - 4)(2a - 1)$

125. $4x^2(x - 5)(x + 2)$ **126.** $6x(x - 4)(x + 2)$

127. $2ab^3(b^2 - 4b + 1)$ **128.** $2a^3b(a^2 + 3a + 1)$

Factoring: A General Review

Learning Objectives

In this section, we will learn how to:

1. Use a factoring strategy to factor a variety of polynomials.

Introduction

In this section we will review the different methods of factoring that we presented in the previous sections of the chapter. This section is important because it will give you an opportunity to factor a variety of polynomials. Prior to this section, the polynomials you worked with were grouped together according to the method used to factor them. What usually happens in a situation like this is that you become proficient at factoring the kind of polynomial you are working with at the time but have trouble when given a variety of polynomials to factor.

We begin this section with a strategy that can be used in factoring polynomials of any type. When you have finished this section and the problem set that follows, you want to be proficient enough at factoring that the checklist is second nature to you.

HOW TO *Factor a polynomial*

Step 1: If the polynomial has a greatest common factor other than 1, then factor out the greatest common factor.

Step 2: If the polynomial has two terms (it is a binomial), then see if it is the difference of squares or a sum or difference of cubes.

Step 3: If the polynomial has three terms (a trinomial), then either it is a perfect square trinomial, which will factor into the square of a binomial, or it is not a perfect square trinomial, in which case you use the methods developed in Sections 6.2 and 6.3.

Step 4: If the polynomial has more than three terms, try to factor it by grouping.

Step 5: As a final check, see if any of the factors you have written can be factored further. If you have overlooked a common factor, you can catch it here.

Here are some examples illustrating how we use the checklist.

VIDEO EXAMPLES

SECTION 6.5

EXAMPLE 1 Factor: $2x^5 - 8x^3$.

SOLUTION First, we check to see if the greatest common factor is other than 1. Since the greatest common factor is $2x^3$, we begin by factoring it out. Once we have done so, we notice that the binomial that remains is the difference of two squares:

$$2x^5 - 8x^3 = 2x^3(x^2 - 4) \qquad \text{Factor out the greatest common factor, } 2x^3$$

$$= 2x^3(x + 2)(x - 2) \qquad \text{Factor the difference of two squares}$$

Note that the greatest common factor $2x^3$ that we factored from each term in the first step of Example 1 remains as part of the answer to the problem. This is because it is one of the factors of the original binomial. Remember, the expression we end up with when factoring must be equal to the expression we start with. We can't just drop a factor and expect the resulting expression to equal the original expression.

EXAMPLE 2   Factor: $3x^4 - 18x^3 + 27x^2$.

SOLUTION   Step 1 is to factor out the greatest common factor, $3x^2$. After we have done so, we notice that the trinomial that remains is a perfect square trinomial, which will factor as the square of a binomial:

$$3x^4 - 18x^3 + 27x^2 = 3x^2(x^2 - 6x + 9) \qquad \text{Factor out } 3x^2$$
$$= 3x^2(x - 3)^2 \qquad \begin{array}{l} x^2 - 6x + 9 \text{ is the} \\ \text{square of } x - 3 \end{array}$$

EXAMPLE 3   Factor: $y^4 + 27y$.

SOLUTION   We begin by factoring out the y that is common to both terms. The binomial that remains after we have done so is the sum of two cubes:

$$y^4 + 27y = y(y^3 + 27) \qquad \text{Factor out the greatest common factor of } y$$
$$= y(y + 3)(y^2 - 3y + 9) \quad \text{Sum of cubes pattern}$$

EXAMPLE 4   Factor: $6a^2 - 11a + 4$.

SOLUTION   Here we have a trinomial that does not have a greatest common factor other than 1. Since it is not a perfect square trinomial, we factor it by trial and error or by grouping. Without showing all the different possibilities, here is the answer by grouping:

$$6a^2 - 11a + 4 = 6a^2 - 3a - 8a + 4$$
$$= 3a(2a - 1) - 4(2a - 1)$$
$$= (3a - 4)(2a - 1)$$

EXAMPLE 5   Factor: $6x^3 - 12x^2 - 48x$.

SOLUTION   This trinomial has a greatest common factor of $6x$. The trinomial that remains after the $6x$ has been factored from each term must be factored using the rules from Section 6.2.

$$6x^3 - 12x^2 - 48x = 6x(x^2 - 2x - 8)$$
$$= 6x(x - 4)(x + 2)$$

EXAMPLE 6 Factor: $2ab^5 + 8ab^4 + 2ab^3$.

SOLUTION The greatest common factor is $2ab^3$. We begin by factoring it from each term. After that we find the trinomial that remains cannot be factored further:

$$2ab^5 + 8ab^4 + 2ab^3 = 2ab^3(b^2 + 4b + 1)$$

EXAMPLE 7 Factor: $xy + 8x + 3y + 24$.

SOLUTION Since our polynomial has four terms, we try factoring by grouping:

$$xy + 8x + 3y + 24 = x(y + 8) + 3(y + 8)$$
$$= (y + 8)(x + 3)$$

Getting Ready for Class

After reading through the preceding section, respond in your own words and in complete sentences.

A. What is the first step in factoring any polynomial?

B. If a polynomial has four terms, what method of factoring should you try?

C. If a polynomial has two terms, what method of factoring should you try?

D. What is the last step in factoring any polynomial?

Problem Set 6.5

Factor each of the following polynomials completely; that is, once you are finished factoring, none of the factors you obtain should be factorable any further. Also, note that the even-numbered problems are not necessarily similar to the odd-numbered problems that precede them in this problem set.

1. $x^2 - 81$　　　　**2.** $x^2 - 18x + 81$　　　　**3.** $x^2 + 2x - 15$

4. $15x^2 + 11x - 6$　　**5.** $x^2 + 6x + 9$　　　　**6.** $12x^2 - 11x + 2$

7. $y^2 - 10y + 25$　　**8.** $21y^2 - 25y - 4$　　**9.** $2a^3b + 6a^2b + 2ab$

10. $6a^2 - ab - 15b^2$　**11.** $x^2 + x + 1$　　　　**12.** $2x^2 - 4x + 2$

13. $12a^2 - 75$　　　　**14.** $16a^3 - 250$　　　　**15.** $9x^2 - 12xy + 4y^2$

16. $x^3 - x^2$　　　　　**17.** $4x^3 + 16xy^2$　　　　**18.** $16x^2 + 49y^2$

19. $2y^3 + 20y^2 + 50y$　　　　　　　**20.** $3y^2 - 9y - 30$

21. $a^6 + 4a^4b^2$　　　　　　　　　　**22.** $5a^2 - 45b^2$

23. $xy + 3x + 4y + 12$　　　　　　　**24.** $xy + 7x + 6y + 42$

25. $x^4 - 16$　　　　　　　　　　　　**26.** $x^4 - 81$

27. $xy - 5x + 2y - 10$　　　　　　　**28.** $xy - 7x + 3y - 21$

29. $5a^2 + 10ab + 5b^2$　　　　　　　**30.** $3a^3b^2 + 15a^2b^2 + 3ab^2$

31. $64 + x^3$　　　　　　　　　　　　**32.** $49 + x^2$

33. $3x^2 + 15xy + 18y^2$　　　　　　　**34.** $3x^2 + 27xy + 54y^2$

35. $2x^2 + 15x - 38$　　　　　　　　　**36.** $2x^2 + 7x - 85$

37. $100x^2 - 300x + 200$　　　　　　　**38.** $100x^2 - 400x + 300$

39. $x^2 - 64$　　　　　　　　　　　　**40.** $x^3 - 64$

41. $x^2 + 3x + ax + 3a$　　　　　　　**42.** $x^2 + 4x + bx + 4b$

43. $49a^7 - 9a^5$　　　　　　　　　　**44.** $a^4 - 1$

45. $49x^2 + 9y^2$　　　　　　　　　　**46.** $12x^4 - 62x^3 + 70x^2$

47. $25a^3 + 20a^2 + 3a$　　　　　　　**48.** $36a^4 - 100a^2$

49. $xa - xb + ay - by$　　　　　　　**50.** $xy - bx + ay - ab$

51. $48a^4b - 3a^2b$　　　　　　　　　**52.** $18a^4b^2 - 12a^3b^3 + 8a^2b^4$

53. $5x^5 - 40x^2$　　　　　　　　　　**54.** $16x^3 + 16x^2 + 3x$

55. $3x^2 + 35xy - 82y^2$　　　　　　　**56.** $3x^2 + 37xy - 86y^2$

57. $16x^5 - 44x^4 + 30x^3$　　　　　　**58.** $16x^2 + 16x - 1$

59. $2x^2 + 2ax + 3x + 3a$　　　　　　**60.** $2x^2 + 2ax + 5x + 5a$

61. $y^4 - 1$　　　　　　　　　　　　**62.** $25y^7 - 16y^5$

63. $12x^4y^2 + 36x^3y^3 + 27x^2y^4$　　　**64.** $16x^3y^2 - 4xy^2$

Learning Objectives Assessment

The following problems can be used to help assess if you have successfully met the learning objectives for this section.

For problems 65-68, match each polynomial with the factoring method by which it could be factored.

65. $6x^2 + 7x - 10$

66. $x^2 - 16y^2$

67. $4x^2 + 64y^2$

68. $x^2 - 6x + xy - by$

a. Greatest common factor

b. Grouping

c. Trial and error

d. Difference of squares

Getting Ready for the Next Section

Solve each equation.

69. $3x - 6 = 9$

70. $5x - 1 = 14$

71. $2x + 3 = 0$

72. $4x - 5 = 0$

73. $4x + 3 = 0$

74. $3x - 1 = 0$

Learning Objectives

In this section, we will learn how to:

1. Use the Zero-Factor Property to solve a quadratic equation.

2. Solve a quadratic equation by factoring.

Introduction

In this section we will use the methods of factoring developed in previous sections, along with a special property of 0, to solve quadratic equations.

> **def** **DEFINITION** *quadratic equation*
>
> Any equation that can be put in the form $ax^2 + bx + c = 0$, where a, b, and c are real numbers ($a \neq 0$), is called a *quadratic equation.* The equation $ax^2 + bx + c = 0$ is called *standard form* for a quadratic equation.

Notice that a quadratic equation in standard form is simply a polynomial of degree 2 that has been set equal to zero.

The number 0 has a special property. If we multiply two numbers and the product is 0, then one or both of the original two numbers must be 0. In symbols, this property looks like this.

> **$\{A \neq \Sigma$** **PROPERTY** *Zero-Factor Property*
>
> Let a and b represent real numbers. If $a \cdot b = 0$, then $a = 0$ or $b = 0$.

Note The zero-factor property allows us to solve a quadratic equation by replacing it with two linear equations in one variable.

Suppose we want to solve the quadratic equation $x^2 + 5x + 6 = 0$. We can factor the left side into $(x + 2)(x + 3)$. Then we have:

$$x^2 + 5x + 6 = 0$$
$$(x + 2)(x + 3) = 0$$

Now, $(x + 2)$ and $(x + 3)$ both represent real numbers. Their product is 0; therefore, either $(x + 3)$ is 0 or $(x + 2)$ is 0. Either way we have a solution to our equation. We use the property of 0 stated above to finish the problem:

$$x^2 + 5x + 6 = 0$$
$$(x + 2)(x + 3) = 0$$
$$x + 2 = 0 \quad \text{or} \quad x + 3 = 0$$
$$x = -2 \quad \text{or} \quad x = -3$$

Our solution set is $\{-2, -3\}$. Our equation has two solutions. To check our solutions we have to check each one separately to see that they both produce a true statement when used in place of the variable:

When	$x = -3$
the equation	$x^2 + 5x + 6 = 0$
becomes	$(-3)^2 + 5(-3) + 6 \stackrel{?}{=} 0$
	$9 + (-15) + 6 \stackrel{?}{=} 0$
	$0 = 0$

When	$x = -2$
the equation	$x^2 + 5x + 6 = 0$
becomes	$(-2)^2 + 5(-2) + 6 \stackrel{?}{=} 0$
	$4 + (-10) + 6 \stackrel{?}{=} 0$
	$0 = 0$

Since substituting $x = 3$ and $x = -2$ into the original equation produces true statements, both solutions check. We have solved a quadratic equation by replacing it with two linear equations in one variable.

HOW TO   *Strategy for solving a quadratic equation by factoring*

Step 1: Put the equation in standard form; that is, 0 on one side and decreasing powers of the variable on the other.

Step 2: Factor completely.

Step 3: Use the zero-factor property to set each variable factor from step 2 equal to 0.

Step 4: Solve each equation produced in step 3.

Step 5: Check each solution, if necessary.

VIDEO EXAMPLES

SECTION 6.6

EXAMPLE 1   Solve: $(2x - 5)(x + 4) = 0$.

SOLUTION   The first two steps have already been done. That is, the equation has 0 on one side and the other side is factored. We can proceed directly with the zero-factor property in Step 3.

Step 3: Set each factor equal to 0:

$$2x - 5 = 0 \quad \text{or} \quad x + 4 = 0$$

Step 4: Solve each of the equations from Step 3:

$$2x - 5 = 0 \quad \text{or} \quad x + 4 = 0$$

$$2x = 5 \quad \text{or} \quad x = -4$$

$$x = \frac{5}{2}$$

Step 5:   Check solutions:

$$\text{Check: } x = \frac{5}{2} \qquad\qquad \text{Check: } x = -4$$

$$\left(2 \cdot \frac{5}{2} - 5\right)\left(\frac{5}{2} + 4\right) \overset{?}{=} 0 \qquad (2(-4) - 5)(-4 + 4) \overset{?}{=} 0$$

$$(5 - 5)\left(\frac{5}{2} + \frac{8}{2}\right) \overset{?}{=} 0 \qquad\qquad (-8 - 5)(0) \overset{?}{=} 0$$

$$0\left(\frac{13}{2}\right) \overset{?}{=} 0 \qquad\qquad -13(0) \overset{?}{=} 0$$

$$0 = 0 \qquad\qquad 0 = 0$$

EXAMPLE 2   Solve the equation $2x^2 - 5x = 12$.

SOLUTION

Step 1:   Begin by adding -12 to both sides, so the equation is in standard form:

$$2x^2 - 5x = 12$$

$$2x^2 - 5x - 12 = 0$$

Step 2:   Factor the left side completely:

$$(2x + 3)(x - 4) = 0$$

Step 3:   Set each factor to 0:

$$2x + 3 = 0 \qquad \text{or} \qquad x - 4 = 0$$

Step 4:   Solve each of the equations from Step 3:

$$2x + 3 = 0 \qquad\qquad x - 4 = 0$$

$$2x = -3 \qquad\qquad x = 4$$

$$x = -\frac{3}{2}$$

Step 5:   Substitute each solution into $2x^2 - 5x = 12$ to check:

$$\text{Check: } x = -\frac{3}{2} \qquad\qquad \text{Check: } x = 4$$

$$2\left(-\frac{3}{2}\right)^2 - 5\left(-\frac{3}{2}\right) \overset{?}{=} 12 \qquad 2(4)^2 - 5(4) \overset{?}{=} 12$$

$$2\left(\frac{9}{4}\right) + 5\left(\frac{3}{2}\right) \overset{?}{=} 12 \qquad 2(16) - 20 \overset{?}{=} 12$$

$$\frac{9}{2} + \frac{15}{2} \overset{?}{=} 12 \qquad\qquad 32 - 20 \overset{?}{=} 12$$

$$\frac{24}{2} \overset{?}{=} 12 \qquad\qquad 12 = 12$$

$$12 = 12$$

EXAMPLE 3   Solve for a: $16a^2 - 25 = 0$.

SOLUTION   The equation is already in standard form:

$$16a^2 - 25 = 0$$

$$(4a - 5)(4a + 5) = 0 \qquad \text{Factor the left side}$$

$$4a - 5 = 0 \quad \text{or} \quad 4a + 5 = 0 \qquad \text{Set each factor equal to 0}$$

$$4a = 5 \qquad\qquad 4a = -5 \qquad \text{Solve the resulting equations}$$

$$a = \frac{5}{4} \qquad\qquad a = -\frac{5}{4}$$

The solutions are $\frac{5}{4}$ and $-\frac{5}{4}$.

EXAMPLE 4   Solve: $4x^2 = 8x$.

SOLUTION   We begin by adding $-8x$ to each side of the equation to put it in standard form. Then we factor the left side of the equation by factoring out the greatest common factor.

$$4x^2 = 8x$$

$$4x^2 - 8x = 0 \qquad \text{Add } -8x \text{ to each side}$$

$$4x(x - 2) = 0 \qquad \text{Factor the left side}$$

$$4x = 0 \quad \text{or} \quad x - 2 = 0 \qquad \text{Set each factor equal to 0}$$

$$x = 0 \quad \text{or} \qquad x = 2 \qquad \text{Solve the resulting equations}$$

The solutions are 0 and 2.

EXAMPLE 5   Solve: $x(2x + 3) = 44$.

SOLUTION   We must multiply out the left side first and then put the equation in standard form:

$$x(2x + 3) = 44$$

$$2x^2 + 3x = 44 \qquad \text{Multiply out the left side}$$

$$2x^2 + 3x - 44 = 0 \qquad \text{Add } -44 \text{ to each side}$$

$$(2x + 11)(x - 4) = 0 \qquad \text{Factor the left side}$$

$$2x + 11 = 0 \quad \text{or} \quad x - 4 = 0 \qquad \text{Set each factor equal to 0}$$

$$2x = -11 \quad \text{or} \qquad x = 4 \qquad \text{Solve the resulting equations}$$

$$x = -\frac{11}{2}$$

The two solutions are $-\frac{11}{2}$ and 4.

Note   In Example 5, even though the left side of the equation was factored originally, we cannot say:

$x = 44$ or $2x + 3 = 44$

It simply is not true. The fact that the two numbers have a product of 44 does not mean one of the numbers must equal 44. For example $2 \cdot 22 = 44$. The zero-factor property is only valid when the product is equal to 0.

EXAMPLE 6 Solve for x: $5^2 = x^2 + (x + 1)^2$.

SOLUTION Before we can put this equation in standard form we must square the binomial. Remember, to square a binomial, we use the formula $(a + b)^2 = a^2 + 2ab + b^2$:

$$5^2 = x^2 + (x + 1)^2$$

$$25 = x^2 + x^2 + 2x + 1 \qquad \text{Expand } 5^2 \text{ and } (x+1)^2$$

$$25 = 2x^2 + 2x + 1 \qquad \text{Simplify the right side}$$

$$0 = 2x^2 + 2x - 24 \qquad \text{Add } -25 \text{ to each side}$$

$$0 = x^2 + x - 12 \qquad \text{Divide both sides by 2}$$

$$0 = (x + 4)(x - 3) \qquad \text{Factor completely}$$

$$x + 4 = 0 \quad \text{or} \quad x - 3 = 0 \qquad \text{Set each factor equal to 0}$$

$$x = -4 \quad \text{or} \qquad x = 3$$

Notice that it makes no difference which side of the equation is 0 when we write the equation in standard form.

Although the equation in the next example is not a quadratic equation, it can be solved by the method shown in the first six examples.

EXAMPLE 7 Solve $24x^3 = -10x^2 + 6x$ for x.

SOLUTION First, we write the equation in standard form:

$$24x^3 + 10x^2 - 6x = 0 \qquad \text{Standard form}$$

$$2x(12x^2 + 5x - 3) = 0 \qquad \text{Factor out } 2x$$

$$2x(3x - 1)(4x + 3) = 0 \qquad \text{Factor remaining trinomial}$$

$$2x = 0 \quad \text{or} \quad 3x - 1 = 0 \quad \text{or} \quad 4x + 3 = 0 \qquad \text{Set factors equal to 0}$$

$$x = 0 \quad \text{or} \qquad x = \frac{1}{3} \quad \text{or} \qquad x = -\frac{3}{4} \qquad \text{Solutions}$$

Getting Ready for Class

After reading through the preceding section, respond in your own words and in complete sentences.

A. When is an equation in standard form?

B. What is the first step in solving an equation by factoring?

C. Describe the zero-factor property in your own words.

D. Describe how you would solve the equation $2x^2 - 5x = 12$.

Problem Set 6.6

The following equations are already in factored form. Use the zero-factor property to solve.

1. $(x + 2)(x - 1) = 0$ **2.** $(x + 3)(x + 2) = 0$

3. $(a - 4)(a - 5) = 0$ **4.** $(a + 6)(a - 1) = 0$

5. $x(x + 1)(x - 3) = 0$ **6.** $x(2x + 1)(x - 5) = 0$

7. $(3x + 2)(2x + 3) = 0$ **8.** $(4x - 5)(x - 6) = 0$

9. $m(3m + 4)(3m - 4) = 0$ **10.** $m(2m - 5)(3m - 1) = 0$

11. $2y(3y + 1)(5y + 3) = 0$ **12.** $3y(2y - 3)(3y - 4) = 0$

Solve the following equations.

13. $x^2 + 3x + 2 = 0$ **14.** $x^2 - x - 6 = 0$

15. $x^2 - 9x + 20 = 0$ **16.** $x^2 + 2x - 3 = 0$

17. $a^2 - 2a - 24 = 0$ **18.** $a^2 - 11a + 30 = 0$

19. $100x^2 - 500x + 600 = 0$ **20.** $100x^2 - 300x + 200 = 0$

21. $x^2 = -6x - 9$ **22.** $x^2 = 10x - 25$

23. $a^2 - 16 = 0$ **24.** $a^2 - 36 = 0$

25. $2x^2 + 5x - 12 = 0$ **26.** $3x^2 + 14x - 5 = 0$

27. $9x^2 + 12x + 4 = 0$ **28.** $12x^2 - 24x + 9 = 0$

29. $a^2 + 25 = 10a$ **30.** $a^2 + 16 = 8a$

31. $0 = 20 + 3x - 2x^2$ **32.** $0 = 2 + x - 6x^2$

33. $3m^2 = 20 - 7m$ **34.** $2m^2 = -18 + 15m$

35. $4x^2 - 49 = 0$ **36.** $16x^2 - 25 = 0$

37. $x^2 + 6x = 0$ **38.** $x^2 + 5x = 0$

39. $3x - x^2 = 0$ **40.** $8x - x^2 = 0$

41. $2x^2 = 8x$ **42.** $2x^2 = 10x$

43. $3x^2 = 15x$ **44.** $5x^2 = 15x$

45. $1,400 = 400 + 700x - 100x^2$ **46.** $2,700 = 700 + 900x - 100x^2$

47. $6x^2 = -5x + 4$ **48.** $9x^2 = 12x - 4$

49. $x(2x - 3) = 20$ **50.** $x(3x - 5) = 12$

51. $t(t + 2) = 80$ **52.** $t(t + 2) = 99$

53. $4,000 = (1,300 - 100p)p$ **54.** $3,200 = (1,200 - 100p)p$

55. $x(14 - x) = 48$ **56.** $x(12 - x) = 32$

57. $(x + 5)^2 = 2x + 9$ **58.** $(x + 7)^2 = 2x + 13$

59. $(y - 6)^2 = y - 4$ **60.** $(y + 4)^2 = y + 6$

61. $10^2 = (x + 2)^2 + x^2$ **62.** $15^2 = (x + 3)^2 + x^2$

63. $2x^3 + 11x^2 + 12x = 0$ **64.** $3x^3 + 17x^2 + 10x = 0$

65. $4y^3 - 2y^2 - 30y = 0$ **66.** $9y^3 + 6y^2 - 24y = 0$

67. $8x^3 + 16x^2 = 10x$ **68.** $24x^3 - 22x^2 = -4x$

69. $20a^3 = -18a^2 + 18a$ **70.** $12a^3 = -2a^2 + 10a$

71. $16t^2 - 32t + 12 = 0$ **72.** $16t^2 - 64t + 48 = 0$

Simplify each side as much as possible, then solve the equation.

73. $(a - 5)(a + 4) = -2a$

74. $(a + 2)(a - 3) = -2a$

75. $3x(x + 1) - 2x(x - 5) = -42$

76. $4x(x - 2) - 3x(x - 4) = -3$

77. $2x(x + 3) = x(x + 2) - 3$

78. $3x(x - 3) = 2x(x - 4) + 6$

79. $a(a - 3) + 6 = 2a$

80. $a(a - 4) + 8 = 2a$

81. $15(x + 20) + 15x = 2x(x + 20)$

82. $15(x + 8) + 15x = 2x(x + 8)$

83. $15 = a(a + 2)$

84. $6 = a(a - 5)$

Use factoring by grouping to solve the following equations.

85. $x^3 + 3x^2 - 4x - 12 = 0$

86. $x^3 + 5x^2 - 9x - 45 = 0$

87. $x^3 + x^2 - 16x - 16 = 0$

88. $4x^3 + 12x^2 - 9x - 27 = 0$

89. Paying Attention to Instructions Work each problem according to the instructions given.

    a. Solve: $2x^2 + 7x - 4 = 0$.

    b. Factor: $2x^2 + 7x - 4$.

    c. Solve: $2x^2 + 7x - 4 = -7$.

    d. Solve: $2x + 7x - 4 = 0$.

90. Paying Attention to Instructions Work each problem according to the instructions given.

    a. Multiply: $(3x + 2)(x - 4)$.

    b. Solve: $(3x + 2)(x - 4) = 0$.

    c. Solve: $(3x + 2)(x - 4) = 17$.

    d. Evaluate $(3x + 2)(x - 4)$ if $x = 2$.

Learning Objectives Assessment

The following problems can be used to help assess if you have successfully met the learning objectives for this section.

91. Solve: $(5x + 2)(x - 3) = 0$

    a. $-3, \dfrac{2}{5}$ **b.** $-\dfrac{2}{5}, 3$ **c.** $\dfrac{3}{5}, 2$ **d.** $5x^2 - 13x - 6$

92. Solve: $(x - 4)(x - 2) = 3$

    a. $2, 4$ **b.** $5, 7$ **c.** $1, 5$ **d.** $-5, -1$

Getting Ready for the Next Section

Write each sentence as an algebraic equation.

93. The product of two consecutive integers is 72.

94. The product of two consecutive even integers is 80.

95. The product of two consecutive odd integers is 99.

96. The product of two consecutive odd integers is 63.

97. The product of two consecutive even integers is 10 less than 5 times their sum.

98. The product of two consecutive odd integers is 1 less than 4 times their sum.

The following word problems are taken from the book *Academic Algebra*, written by William J. Milne and published by the American Book Company in 1901. Solve each problem.

99. Cost of a Bicycle and a Suit A bicycle and a suit cost $90. How much did each cost, if the bicycle cost 5 times as much as the suit?

100. Cost of a Cow and a Calf A man bought a cow and a calf for $36, paying 8 times as much for the cow as for the calf. What was the cost of each?

101. Cost of a House and a Lot A house and a lot cost $3,000. If the house cost 4 times as much as the lot, what was the cost of each?

102. Daily Wages A plumber and two helpers together earned $7.50 per day. How much did each earn per day, if the plumber earned 4 times as much as each helper?

Applications

Learning Objectives

In this section, we will learn how to:

1. Solve number problems.
2. Solve area problems.
3. Solve problems involving the Pythagorean theorem.
4. Solve cost and revenue problems.

In this section we will look at some application problems, the solutions to which require solving a quadratic equation. We will also introduce the Pythagorean theorem, one of the oldest theorems in the history of mathematics. The person whose name we associate with the theorem, Pythagoras (of Samos), was a Greek philosopher and mathematician who lived from about 560 B.C. to 480 B.C. According to the British philosopher Bertrand Russell, Pythagoras was "intellectually one of the most important men that ever lived."

Also in this section, the solutions to the examples show only the essential steps from our Blueprint for Problem Solving that we introduced in Section 2.6. Recall that Step 1 is done mentally; we read the problem and mentally list the items that are known and the items that are unknown. This is an essential part of problem solving. However, now that you have had experience with application problems, you are doing Step 1 automatically.

Number Problems

EXAMPLE 1   The product of two consecutive odd integers is 63. Find the integers.

SOLUTION   Let x be the first odd integer; then $x + 2$ is the second odd integer. An equation that describes the situation is:

$$x(x + 2) = 63 \qquad \text{Their product is 63}$$

We solve the equation:

$$x(x + 2) = 63$$
$$x^2 + 2x = 63$$
$$x^2 + 2x - 63 = 0$$
$$(x - 7)(x + 9) = 0$$
$$x - 7 = 0 \qquad \text{or} \qquad x + 9 = 0$$
$$x = 7 \qquad \text{or} \qquad x = -9$$

If the first odd integer is 7, the next odd integer is $7 + 2 = 9$. If the first odd integer is -9, the next consecutive odd integer is $-9 + 2 = -7$. We have two pairs of consecutive odd integers that are solutions. They are 7, 9 and -9, -7.

We check to see that their products are 63:

$$7(9) = 63$$
$$-7(-9) = 63$$

Suppose we know that the sum of two numbers is 50. We want to find a way to represent each number using only one variable. If we let x represent one of the two numbers, how can we represent the other? Let's suppose for a moment that x turns out to be 30. Then the other number will be 20, because their sum is 50; that is, if two numbers add up to 50 and one of them is 30, then the other must be $50 - 30 = 20$. Generalizing this to any number x, we see that if two numbers have a sum of 50 and one of the numbers is x, then the other must be $50 - x$. The table that follows shows some additional examples.

If two numbers have a sum of	and one of them is	then the other must be
50	x	$50 - x$
100	x	$100 - x$
10	y	$10 - y$
12	n	$12 - n$

Now, let's look at an example that uses this idea.

EXAMPLE 2   The sum of two numbers is 13. Their product is 40. Find the numbers.

SOLUTION   If we let x represent one of the numbers, then $13 - x$ must be the other number because their sum is 13. Since their product is 40, we can write:

$$x(13 - x) = 40 \qquad \text{The product of the two numbers is 40}$$

$$13x - x^2 = 40 \qquad \text{Multiply the left side}$$

$$x^2 - 13x = -40 \qquad \text{Multiply both sides by } -1 \text{ and reverse the order of the terms on the left side}$$

$$x^2 - 13x + 40 = 0 \qquad \text{Add 40 to each side}$$

$$(x - 8)(x - 5) = 0 \qquad \text{Factor the left side}$$

$$x - 8 = 0 \quad \text{or} \quad x - 5 = 0$$

$$x = 8 \quad \text{or} \quad x = 5$$

The two solutions are 8 and 5. If x is 8, then the other number is

$$13 - x = 13 - 8 = 5$$

Likewise, if x is 5, the other number is $13 - x = 13 - 5 = 8$. Therefore, the two numbers we are looking for are 8 and 5. Their sum is 13 and their product is 40.

Area Problems

Many word problems dealing with area can best be described algebraically by quadratic equations.

EXAMPLE 3   The length of a rectangle is 3 more than twice the width. The area is 44 square inches. Find the dimensions (find the length and width).

SOLUTION   As shown in Figure 1, let x be the width of the rectangle. Then $2x + 3$ is the length of the rectangle because the length is three more than twice the width.

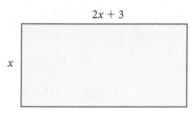

$2x + 3$

x

FIGURE 1

Since the area is 44 square inches, an equation that describes the situation is

$$x(2x + 3) = 44 \qquad \text{Width} \cdot \text{length} = \text{area}$$

We now solve the equation:

$$x(2x + 3) = 44$$
$$2x^2 + 3x = 44$$
$$2x^2 + 3x - 44 = 0$$
$$(2x + 11)(x - 4) = 0$$
$$2x + 11 = 0 \qquad \text{or} \quad x - 4 = 0$$
$$x = -\frac{11}{2} \quad \text{or} \qquad x = 4$$

The solution $x = -\frac{11}{2}$ cannot be used since length and width are always given in positive units. The width is 4. The length is 3 more than twice the width or $2(4) + 3 = 11$.

$$\text{Width} = 4 \text{ inches}$$
$$\text{Length} = 11 \text{ inches}$$

The solutions check in the original problem since $4(11) = 44$.

EXAMPLE 4   The numerical value of the area of a square is twice its perimeter. What is the length of its side?

SOLUTION   As shown in Figure 2, let x be the length of its side. Then x^2 is the area of the square and $4x$ is the perimeter of the square:

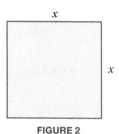

FIGURE 2

An equation that describes the situation is

$$x^2 = 2(4x) \qquad \text{The area is 2 times the perimeter}$$

$$x^2 = 8x$$

$$x^2 - 8x = 0$$

$$x(x - 8) = 0$$

$$x = 0 \quad \text{or} \quad x = 8$$

Since $x = 0$ does not make sense in our original problem, we use $x = 8$. If the side has length 8, then the perimeter is $4(8) = 32$ and the area is $8^2 = 64$. Since 64 is twice 32, our solution is correct.

The Pythagorean Theorem

FACTS FROM GEOMETRY   *The Pythagorean Theorem*

Next, we will work some problems involving the Pythagorean theorem, which we mentioned in the introduction to this section. It may interest you to know that Pythagoras formed a secret society around the year 540 B.C. Known as the Pythagoreans, members kept no written record of their work; everything was handed down by spoken word. They influenced not only mathematics, but religion, science, medicine, and music as well. Among other things, they discovered the correlation between musical notes and the reciprocals of counting numbers, $\frac{1}{2}, \frac{1}{3}, \frac{1}{4}$, and so on. In their daily lives, they followed strict dietary and moral rules to achieve a higher rank in future lives.

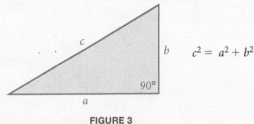

> THEOREM   *Pythagorean Theorem*
>
> In any right triangle (Figure 3), the square of the longest side (called the hypotenuse) is equal to the sum of the squares of the other two sides (called legs).
>
> **FIGURE 3**

EXAMPLE 5   The three sides of a right triangle are three consecutive integers. Find the lengths of the three sides.

SOLUTION   Let x be the first integer (shortest side)

then $x + 1$ = the next consecutive integer

and $x + 2$ = the last consecutive integer (longest side)

A diagram of the triangle is shown in Figure 4.

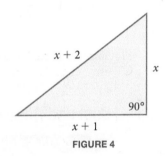

FIGURE 4

The Pythagorean theorem tells us that the square of the longest side $(x + 2)^2$ is equal to the sum of the squares of the two shorter sides, $(x + 1)^2 + x^2$. Here is the equation:

$$(x + 2)^2 = (x + 1)^2 + x^2$$
$$x^2 + 4x + 4 = x^2 + 2x + 1 + x^2 \qquad \text{Expand squares}$$
$$x^2 - 2x - 3 = 0 \qquad \text{Standard form}$$
$$(x - 3)(x + 1) = 0 \qquad \text{Factor}$$
$$x - 3 = 0 \quad \text{or} \quad x + 1 = 0 \qquad \text{Set factors to 0}$$
$$x = 3 \quad \text{or} \qquad x = -1$$

Note   Many students make the mistake of assuming if
   $(x + 2)^2 = (x + 1)^2 + x^2$
then
   $x + 2 = (x + 1) + x$
Unfortunately, this is simply not true. We do not get an equivalent equation by "dropping" the squares. For instance,
   $5^2 = 4^2 + 3^2$
is a true statement, but
   $5 \neq 4 + 3$.

Since a triangle cannot have a side with a negative number for its length, we must not use -1 for a solution to our original problem; therefore, the shortest side is 3. The other two sides are the next two consecutive integers, 4 and 5.

EXAMPLE 6   The hypotenuse of a right triangle is 13 inches, and one leg is 7 inches longer than the other leg. Find the lengths of the two legs.

SOLUTION   If we let x be the length of the shortest leg, then the longer leg must be $x + 7$. A diagram of the triangle is shown in Figure 5.

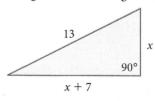

FIGURE 5

The Pythagorean theorem tells us that the square of the longest side, 13^2, is equal to the sum of the squares of the two shorter sides, $x^2 + (x + 7)^2$. Here is the equation:

$$13^2 = x^2 + (x + 7)^2 \qquad \text{Pythagorean theorem}$$
$$169 = x^2 + x^2 + 14x + 49 \qquad \text{Expand } 13^2 \text{ and } (x+7)^2$$
$$169 = 2x^2 + 14x + 49 \qquad \text{Simplify the right side}$$
$$0 = 2x^2 + 14x - 120 \qquad \text{Add } -169 \text{ to each side}$$
$$0 = x^2 + 7x - 60 \qquad \text{Divide both sides by 2}$$
$$0 = (x + 12)(x - 5) \qquad \text{Factor completely}$$
$$x + 12 = 0 \quad \text{or} \quad x - 5 = 0 \qquad \text{Set factors equal to 0}$$
$$x = -12 \quad \text{or} \qquad x = 5$$

Since a triangle cannot have a side with a negative number for its length, we cannot use -12; therefore, the shortest leg must be 5 inches. The other leg is $x + 7 = 5 + 7 = 12$ inches.

Cost and Revenue

EXAMPLE 7   A company can manufacture x hundred items for a total cost of $C = 300 + 500x - 100x^2$. How many items were manufactured if the total cost is $900?

SOLUTION   We are looking for x when C is 900. We begin by substituting 900 for C in the cost equation. Then we solve for x:

When $C = 900$

the equation $C = 300 + 500x - 100x^2$

becomes $900 = 300 + 500x - 100x^2$

We can write this equation in standard form by adding -300, $-500x$, and $100x^2$ to each side. The result looks like this:

$$100x^2 - 500x + 600 = 0$$
$$x^2 - 5x + 6 = 0 \qquad \text{Divide both sides by 100}$$
$$(x - 2)(x - 3) = 0 \qquad \text{Factor completely}$$
$$x - 2 = 0 \quad \text{or} \quad x - 3 = 0 \qquad \text{Set variable factors to 0}$$
$$x = 2 \quad \text{or} \qquad x = 3$$

Our solutions are 2 and 3, which means that the company can manufacture 2 hundred items or 3 hundred items for a total cost of $900.

EXAMPLE 8 A manufacturer of small portable radios knows that the number of radios she can sell each week is related to the price of the radios by the equation $x = 1{,}300 - 100p$ (x is the number of radios and p is the price per radio). What price should she charge for the radios to have a weekly revenue of $4,000?

SOLUTION First, we must find the revenue equation. The equation for total revenue is $R = xp$, where x is the number of units sold and p is the price per unit. Since we want R in terms of p, we substitute $1{,}300 - 100p$ for x in the equation $R = xp$:

$$\text{If} \quad R = xp$$
$$\text{and} \quad x = 1{,}300 - 100p$$
$$\text{then} \quad R = (1{,}300 - 100p)p$$

We want to find p when R is 4,000. Substituting 4,000 for R in the equation gives us:

$$4{,}000 = (1{,}300 - 100p)p$$

If we multiply out the right side, we have:

$$4{,}000 = 1{,}300p - 100p^2$$

To write this equation in standard form, we add $100p^2$ and $-1{,}300p$ to each side:

$$100p^2 - 1{,}300p + 4{,}000 = 0 \qquad \text{Add } 100p^2 \text{ and } -1{,}300p$$
$$p^2 - 13p + 40 = 0 \qquad \text{Divide both sides by 100}$$
$$(p - 5)(p - 8) = 0 \qquad \text{Factor completely}$$
$$p - 5 = 0 \quad \text{or} \quad p - 8 = 0 \qquad \text{Set factors equal to 0}$$
$$p = 5 \quad \text{or} \quad p = 8$$

If she sells the radios for $5 each or for $8 each, she will have a weekly revenue of $4,000.

Getting Ready for Class

After reading through the preceding section, respond in your own words and in complete sentences.

A. What are consecutive integers?

B. Explain the Pythagorean theorem in words.

C. If the sum of two numbers is 20 and x is one of the numbers, what is the other number?

D. If $x^2 + (x + 2)^2 = (x + 4)^2$, we cannot conclude that $x + (x + 2) = (x + 4)$. Show that the expressions are not equivalent by substituting 6 for x in each one.

Problem Set 6.7

Solve the following word problems. Be sure to show the equation used.

Number Problems

1. The product of two consecutive even integers is 80. Find the two integers.
2. The product of two consecutive integers is 72. Find the two integers.
3. The product of two consecutive odd integers is 99. Find the two integers.
4. The product of two consecutive integers is 132. Find the two integers.
5. The product of two consecutive even integers is 10 less than 5 times their sum. Find the two integers.
6. The product of two consecutive odd integers is 1 less than 4 times their sum. Find the two integers.
7. The sum of two numbers is 14. Their product is 48. Find the numbers.
8. The sum of two numbers is 12. Their product is 32. Find the numbers.
9. One number is 2 more than 5 times another. Their product is 24. Find the numbers.
10. One number is 1 more than twice another. Their product is 55. Find the numbers.
11. One number is 4 times another. Their product is 4 times their sum. Find the numbers.
12. One number is 2 more than twice another. Their product is 2 more than twice their sum. Find the numbers.

Geometry Problems

13. The length of a rectangle is 1 more than the width. The area is 12 square inches. Find the dimensions.
14. The length of a rectangle is 3 more than twice the width. The area is 44 square inches. Find the dimensions.
15. The height of a triangle is twice the base. The area is 9 square inches. Find the base.
16. The height of a triangle is 2 more than twice the base. The area is 20 square feet. Find the base.
17. The hypotenuse of a right triangle is 10 inches. The lengths of the two legs are given by two consecutive even integers. Find the lengths of the two legs.
18. The hypotenuse of a right triangle is 15 inches. One of the legs is 3 inches more than the other. Find the lengths of the two legs.
19. The shorter leg of a right triangle is 5 meters. The hypotenuse is 1 meter longer than the longer leg. Find the length of the longer leg.
20. The shorter leg of a right triangle is 12 yards. If the hypotenuse is 20 yards, how long is the other leg?

Business Problems

21. A company can manufacture x hundred items for a total cost of $C = 400 + 700x - 100x^2$. Find x if the total cost is $1,400.

22. If the total cost C of manufacturing x hundred items is given by the equation $C = 700 + 900x - 100x^2$, find x when C is $2,700.

23. The relationship between the number of calculators a company sells per week, x, and the price p of each calculator is given by the equation $x = 1,700 - 100p$. At what price should the calculators be sold if the weekly revenue is to be $7,000?

24. The relationship between the number of pencil sharpeners a company can sell each week, x, and the price p of each sharpener is given by the equation $x = 1,800 - 100p$. At what price should the sharpeners be sold if the weekly revenue is to be $7,200?

Other Applications

25. **Pythagorean Theorem** A 13-foot ladder is placed so that it reaches to a point on the wall that is 2 feet higher than twice the distance from the base of the wall to the base of the ladder.

    a. How far from the wall is the base of the ladder?

    b. How high does the ladder reach?

26. **Constructing a Box** I have a piece of cardboard that is twice as long as it is wide. If I cut a 2-inch by 2-inch square from each corner and fold up the resulting flaps, I get a box with a volume of 32 cubic inches. What are the dimensions of the cardboard?

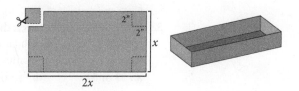

27. **Projectile Motion** A gun fires a bullet almost straight up from the edge of a 100-foot cliff. If the bullet leaves the gun with a speed of 396 feet per second, its height at time t is given by $h(t) = -16t^2 + 396t + 100$, measured from the ground below the cliff.

    a. When will the bullet land on the ground below the cliff? (*Hint:* What is its height when it lands? Remember that we are measuring from the ground below, not from the cliff.)

    b. Make a table showing the bullet's height every five seconds, from the time it is fired ($t = 0$) to the time it lands. (*Note:* It is faster to substitute into the factored form.)

28. **Height of a Projectile** If a rocket is fired vertically into the air with a speed of 240 feet per second, its height at time t seconds is given by $h(t) = -16t^2 + 240t$. At what time(s) will the rocket be the following number of feet above the ground?

    a. 704 feet

    b. 896 feet

    c. Why do parts **a.** and **b.** each have two answers?

    d. How long will the rocket be in the air? (*Hint:* How high is it when it hits the ground?)

    e. When the equation for part **d.** is solved, one of the answers is $t = 0$ seconds. What does this represent?

Learning Objectives Assessment

The following problems can be used to help assess if you have successfully met the learning objectives for this section.

29. One number is 1 less than twice another. Their product is 120. Find the numbers. One of the numbers is:

    a. 8   **b.** 12   **c.** 6   **d.** 5

30. The length of a rectangle is 5 feet more than the width. The area of the rectangle is 36 square feet. Find the width.

    a. 2   **b.** 3   **c.** 4   **d.** 6

31. The hypotenuse of a right triangle is 17 meters. One leg is 7 meters longer than the other. Which of the following equations can be used as a model to solve this problem?

    a. $x(x + 7) = 17$ **b.** $x + (x + 7) = 17$

    c. $x^2 + (x - 7)^2 = 17$ **d.** $x^2 + (x + 7)^2 = 289$

32. The relationship between the number of lattes a café can sell each week, x, and the price, p, of each latte is given by the equation $x = 700 - 100p$. At what price should the lattes be sold if the weekly revenue is to be \$1,200?

    a. \$3 or \$4   **b.** \$3 or \$5   **c.** \$4 or \$5   **d.** \$2 or \$5

Maintaining Your Skills

33. Fill in each ordered pair so that it is a solution to $y = \frac{1}{2}x + 3$.

    $$(-2,), (0,), (2,)$$

34. Graph the line $y = \frac{1}{2}x + 3$.

35. Graph the line $x = -2$.

36. Graph $3x - 2y = 6$.

37. Find the slope of the line through (2, 5) and (0, 1).

38. Find the slope and y-intercept for the line $2x - 5y = 10$.

39. Find the equation of the line through $(-2, 1)$ with slope $\frac{1}{2}$.

40. Write the equation of the line with slope -2 and y-intercept $\frac{3}{2}$.

41. Find the equation of the line through (2, 5) and (0, 1).

42. Graph the solution set for $2x - y < 4$.

Chapter 6 Summary

Greatest Common Factor [6.1]

The largest monomial that divides each term of a polynomial is called the greatest common factor for that polynomial. We begin all factoring by factoring out the greatest common factor.

Factoring by Grouping [6.1]

2. $2x + ax + 2y + ay$
$= x(2 + a) + y(2 + a)$
$= (2 + a)(x + y)$

Try factoring the greatest common factor from pairs of terms to create a common binomial factor that can be factored out.

Factoring Trinomials [6.2, 6.3]

3. $x^2 + 5x + 6 = (x + 2)(x + 3)$
$\quad x^2 - 5x + 6 = (x - 2)(x - 3)$
$\quad 6x^2 - x - 2 = (2x + 1)(3x - 2)$
$\quad 6x^2 + 7x + 2 = (2x + 1)(3x + 2)$

One method of factoring a trinomial is to list all pairs of binomials whose product of the first terms gives the first term of the trinomial and whose product of the last terms gives the last term of the trinomial. We then choose the pair that gives the correct middle term for the original trinomial.

Perfect Square Trinomials [6.4]

4. $x^2 + 10x + 25 = (x + 5)^2$
$\quad x^2 - 10x + 25 = (x - 5)^2$

$$a^2 + 2ab + b^2 = (a + b)^2$$

$$a^2 - 2ab + b^2 = (a - b)^2$$

Factoring Binomials [6.4]

5. $x^2 - 25 = (x + 5)(x - 5)$
$\quad x^3 - 27 = (x - 3)(x^2 + 3x + 9)$
$\quad x^3 + 27 = (x + 3)(x^2 - 3x + 9)$

$$a^2 - b^2 = (a + b)(a - b) \qquad \text{Difference of two squares}$$

$$a^3 - b^3 = (a - b)(a^2 + ab + b^2) \qquad \text{Difference of two cubes}$$

$$a^3 + b^3 = (a + b)(a^2 - ab + b^2) \qquad \text{Sum of two cubes}$$

Strategy for Factoring a Polynomial [6.5]

6. a. $2x^5 - 8x^3 = 2x^3(x^2 - 4)$
$\qquad\qquad\;\; = 2x^3(x + 2)(x - 2)$

b. $3x^4 - 18x^3 + 27x^2$
$\quad = 3x^2(x^2 - 6x + 9)$
$\quad = 3x^2(x - 3)^2$

c. $6x^3 - 12x^2 - 48x$
$\quad = 6x(x^2 - 2x - 8)$
$\quad = 6x(x - 4)(x + 2)$

d. $x^2 + ax + bx + ab$
$\quad = x(x + a) + b(x + a)$
$\quad = (x + a)(x + b)$

Step 1: If the polynomial has a greatest common factor other than 1, then factor out the greatest common factor.

Step 2: If the polynomial has two terms (it is a binomial), then see if it is the difference of squares or the sum or difference of cubes, and then factor accordingly. Remember, if it is the sum of squares, it will not factor.

Step 3: If the polynomial has three terms (a trinomial), then it is either a perfect square trinomial that will factor into the square of a binomial, or it is not a perfect square trinomial, in which case you use the methods developed in Sections 6.2 and 6.3.

Step 4: If the polynomial has more than three terms, then try to factor it by grouping.

Step 5: As a final check, see if any of the factors you have written can be factored further. If you have overlooked a common factor, you can catch it here.

Strategy for Solving a Quadratic Equation [6.6]

7. Solve $x^2 - 6x = -8$.
$$x^2 - 6x + 8 = 0$$
$$(x - 4)(x - 2) = 0$$
$$x - 4 = 0 \quad \text{or} \quad x - 2 = 0$$
$$x = 4 \quad \text{or} \qquad x = 2$$
Both solutions check.

Step 1: Write the equation in standard form $ax^2 + bx + c = 0$.

Step 2: Factor completely.

Step 3: Use the zero-factor property and set each variable factor equal to 0.

Step 4: Solve the equations found in step 3.

Step 5: Check solutions, if necessary.

The Pythagorean Theorem [6.7]

8. The hypotenuse of a right triangle is 5 inches, and the lengths of the two legs (the other two sides) are given by two consecutive integers. Find the lengths of the two legs.

     If we let $x = $ the length of the shortest side, then the other side must be $x + 1$. The Pythagorean theorem tells us that
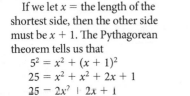
$$5^2 = x^2 + (x + 1)^2$$
$$25 = x^2 + x^2 + 2x + 1$$
$$25 = 2x^2 + 2x + 1$$
$$0 = 2x^2 + 2x - 24$$
$$0 = 2(x^2 + x - 12)$$
$$0 = 2(x + 4)(x - 3)$$
$$x + 4 = 0 \qquad \text{or} \qquad x - 3 = 0$$
$$x = -4 \qquad \text{or} \qquad\;\; x = 3$$
Since a triangle cannot have a side with a negative number for its length, we cannot use -4. One leg is $x = 3$ and the other leg is $x + 1 = 3 + 1 = 4$.

In any right triangle, the square of the longest side (called the hypotenuse) is equal to the sum of the squares of the other two sides (called legs).

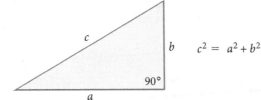

$$c^2 = a^2 + b^2$$

⚠️ **COMMON MISTAKE**

It is a mistake to apply the zero-factor property to numbers other than zero. For example, consider the equation $(x - 3)(x + 4) = 18$. A fairly common mistake is to attempt to solve it with the following steps:

$$(x - 3)(x + 4) = 18$$

$$x - 3 = 18 \quad \text{or} \quad x + 4 = 18 \leftarrow \text{Mistake}$$

$$x = 21 \quad \text{or} \quad x = 14$$

These are obviously not solutions, as a quick check will verify:

$$\text{Check: } x = 21 \qquad \text{Check: } x = 14$$

$$(21 - 3)(21 + 4) \stackrel{?}{=} 18 \qquad (14 - 3)(14 + 4) \stackrel{?}{=} 18$$

$$18 \cdot 25 \stackrel{?}{=} 18 \qquad\qquad 11 \cdot 18 \stackrel{?}{=} 18$$

$$450 = 18 \xleftarrow{\text{False statements}} 198 = 18$$

The mistake is in setting each factor equal to 18. It is not necessarily true that when the product of two numbers is 18, either one of them is itself 18. The correct solution looks like this:

$$(x - 3)(x + 4) = 18$$

$$x^2 + x - 12 = 18$$

$$x^2 + x - 30 = 0$$

$$(x + 6)(x - 5) = 0$$

$$x + 6 = 0 \qquad \text{or} \qquad x - 5 = 0$$

$$x = -6 \qquad \text{or} \qquad x = 5$$

To avoid this mistake, remember that before you factor a quadratic equation, you must write it in standard form. It is in standard form only when 0 is on one side and decreasing powers of the variable are on the other.

Chapter 6 Test

Factor out the greatest common factor. [6.1]

1. $6x + 18$

2. $12a^2b - 24ab + 8ab^2$

Factor by grouping. [6.1]

3. $x^2 + 3ax - 2bx - 6ab$

4. $15y - 5xy - 12 + 4x$

Factor the following completely. [6.2–6.5]

5. $x^2 + x - 12$

6. $x^2 - 4x - 21$

7. $x^2 - 25$

8. $x^4 - 16$

9. $x^2 + 36$

10. $18x^2 - 32y^2$

11. $x^3 + 4x^2 - 3x - 12$

12. $x^2 + bx - 3x - 3b$

13. $4x^2 - 6x - 10$

14. $4n^2 + 13n - 12$

15. $12c^2 + c - 6$

16. $12x^3 + 12x^2 - 9x$

17. $x^3 + 125y^3$

18. $54b^3 - 128$

Solve the following equations. [6.6]

19. $x^2 - 2x - 15 = 0$

20. $x^2 - 7x + 12 = 0$

21. $x^2 - 25 = 0$

22. $x^2 = 5x + 14$

23. $x^2 + x = 30$

24. $y^3 = 9y$

25. $2x^2 = -5x + 12$

26. $15x^3 - 65x^2 - 150x = 0$

Solve the following word problems. Be sure to show the system of equations used. [6.7]

27. Number Problem Two numbers have a sum of 18. Their product is 72. Find the numbers.

28. Consecutive Integers The product of two consecutive even integers is 14 more than their sum. Find the integers.

29. Geometry The length of a rectangle is 1 foot more than 3 times the width. The area is 52 square feet. Find the dimensions.

30. Geometry One leg of a right triangle is 2 feet more than the other. The hypotenuse is 10 feet. Find the lengths of the two legs.

31. Production Cost A company can manufacture x hundred items for a total cost C, given the equation $C = 100 + 500x - 100x^2$. How many items can be manufactured if the total cost is to be $700?

32. Price and Revenue A manufacturer knows that the number of items he can sell each week, x, is related to the price p of each item by the equation $x = 800 - 100p$. What price should he charge for each item to have a weekly revenue of $1,500? (*Remember: $R = xp$.*)

Rational Expressions

iStockphoto.com © YinYang

First Bank of San Luis Obispo charges $2.00 per month and $0.15 per check for a regular checking account. If we write x checks in one month, the total monthly cost of the checking account will be $C = 2.00 + 0.15x$. From this formula we see that the more checks we write in a month, the more we pay for the account. But, it is also true that the more checks we write in a month, the lower the cost per check. To find the average cost per check, we divide the total cost by the number of checks written:

$$\text{Average cost} = A = \frac{C}{x} = \frac{2.00 + 0.15x}{x}$$

We can use this formula to create Table 1 and Figure 1, giving us a visual interpretation of the relationship between the number of checks written and the average cost per check.

TABLE 1

Number of Checks	Average Cost Per Check
1	2.15
2	1.15
5	0.55
10	0.35
15	0.28
20	0.25

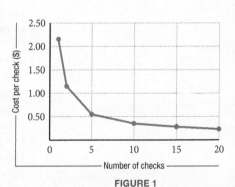

FIGURE 1

As you can see, if we write one check per month, the cost per check is relatively high, $2.15. However, if we write 20 checks per month, each check costs us only $0.25. Using average cost per check is a good way to compare different checking accounts. The expression $\frac{2.00 + 0.15x}{x}$ in the average cost formula is a rational expression. When you have finished this chapter you will have a good working knowledge of rational expressions.

iStockphoto.com © IPGGutenbergUKLtd

If you have made it this far, then you have the study skills necessary to be successful in this course. Success skills are more general in nature and will help you with all your classes and ensure your success in college as well.

Let's start with a question:

Question: What quality is most important for success in any college course?

Answer: Independence. You want to become an independent learner.

We all know people like this. They are generally happy. They don't worry about getting the right instructor, or whether or not things work out every time. They have a confidence that comes from knowing that they are responsible for their success or failure in the goals they set for themselves.

Here are some of the qualities of an independent learner:

- Intends to succeed.
- Doesn't let setbacks deter them.
- Knows their resources.
  - Instructor's office hours
  - Math lab
  - Student Solutions Manual
  - Group study
  - Internet
- Doesn't mistake activity for achievement.
- Has a positive attitude.

There are other traits as well. The first step in becoming an independent learner is doing a little self-evaluation and then making of list of traits that you would like to acquire. What skills do you have that align with those of an independent learner? What attributes do you have that keep you from being an independent learner? What qualities would you like to obtain that you don't have now?

Reducing Rational Expressions to Lowest Terms

Learning Objectives

In this section, we will learn how to:

1. Evaluate a rational expression.
2. Determine the values for which a rational expression is undefined.
3. Reduce rational expressions.
4. Solve problems involving ratios.

Introduction

In Chapter 1 we defined the set of rational numbers to be the set of all numbers that could be put in the form $\frac{a}{b}$, where a and b are integers ($b \neq 0$):

$$\text{Rational numbers} = \left\{ \frac{a}{b} \,\middle|\, a \text{ and } b \text{ are integers}, b \neq 0 \right\}$$

We will now extend this idea to fractions involving polynomials.

Rational Expressions

> **def** **DEFINITION** *Rational Expression*
>
> A ***rational expression*** is any expression that can be put in the form $\frac{P}{Q}$, where P and Q are polynomials and $Q \neq 0$:
>
> $$\text{Rational expressions} = \left\{ \frac{P}{Q} \,\middle|\, P \text{ and } Q \text{ are polynomials}, Q \neq 0 \right\}$$

Each of the following is an example of a rational expression:

$$\frac{2x + 3}{x} \qquad \frac{x^2 - 6x + 9}{x^2 - 4} \qquad \frac{5}{x^2 + 6} \qquad \frac{2x^2 + 3x + 4}{2}$$

For the rational expression

$$\frac{x^2 - 6x + 9}{x^2 - 4}$$

the polynomial on top, $x^2 - 6x + 9$, is called the numerator, and the polynomial on the bottom, $x^2 - 4$, is called the denominator. The same is true of the other rational expressions.

Evaluating Rational Expressions

We can find the value of a rational expression for a given value of the variable by substituting the given value in place of the variable and simplifying the result.

EXAMPLE 1   Evaluate $\dfrac{x^2 - 6x + 9}{x^2 - 4}$ for $x = 3$ and $x = -2$.

SOLUTION   We replace x with each given value and simplify.

When $x = 3$ When $x = -2$

the expression $\dfrac{x^2 - 6x + 9}{x^2 - 4}$ the expression $\dfrac{x^2 - 6x + 9}{x^2 - 4}$

becomes $\dfrac{(3)^2 - 6(3) + 9}{(3)^2 - 4}$ becomes $\dfrac{(-2)^2 - 6(-2) + 9}{(-2)^2 - 4}$

$= \dfrac{9 - 18 + 9}{9 - 4}$ $= \dfrac{4 + 12 + 9}{4 - 4}$

$= \dfrac{0}{5}$ $= \dfrac{25}{0}$

$= 0$ which is undefined

The value of the rational expression is 0 when $x = 3$, and when $x = -2$ the rational expression is undefined.

EXAMPLE 2   In the introduction to this chapter, we saw that the average cost per check of writing x checks in one month at a certain bank is given by the rational expression

$$A = \frac{2.00 + 0.15x}{x}$$

Find the average cost per check if 8 checks are written in a month.

SOLUTION   We substitute $x = 8$ into the expression and simplify.

$$A = \frac{2.00 + 0.15(8)}{8}$$

$$= \frac{2.00 + 1.20}{8}$$

$$= \frac{3.20}{8}$$

$$= 0.40$$

The average cost is $0.40, or 40¢, per check.

Restricting the Variable

As we saw in Example 1, some values of the variable may cause a rational expression to be undefined. We must be careful that we do not use a value of the variable that will give us a denominator of zero. Remember, division by zero is not defined.

EXAMPLE 3   State the restrictions on the variable:

$$\frac{x + 2}{x - 3}$$

SOLUTION   The variable x can be any real number except $x = 3$ since, when $x = 3$, the denominator is $3 - 3 = 0$. We state this restriction by writing $x \neq 3$.

EXAMPLE 4   Determine any values of the variable for which the rational expression $\dfrac{5}{x^2 - x - 6}$ will be undefined.

SOLUTION   We must find any values of x that will make the denominator, $x^2 - x - 6$, equal to zero. That is, we need to solve the equation

$$x^2 - x - 6 = 0$$

This is a quadratic equation, which we can solve by factoring using the zero-factor property from the previous chapter.

$$x^2 - x - 6 = 0$$

$$(x - 3)(x + 2) = 0 \qquad \text{Factor}$$

$$x - 3 = 0 \quad \text{or} \quad x + 2 = 0 \qquad \text{Zero-factor property}$$

$$x = 3 \quad \text{or} \quad x = -2$$

Our restrictions are $x \neq 3$ and $x \neq -2$ since either one makes $x^2 - x - 6 = 0$.

We will not always list each restriction on a rational expression, but we should be aware of them and keep in mind that no rational expression can have a denominator of zero.

Reducing Rational Expressions

The two fundamental properties of rational expressions are listed next. We will use these two properties many times in this chapter.

⟨Δ≠Σ⟩   PROPERTY   *Properties of Rational Expressions*

Property 1
Multiplying the numerator and denominator of a rational expression by the same nonzero quantity will not change the value of the rational expression.

Property 2
Dividing the numerator and denominator of a rational expression by the same nonzero quantity will not change the value of the rational expression.

We can use Property 2 to reduce rational expressions to lowest terms. Since this process is almost identical to the process of reducing fractions to lowest terms, let's recall how the fraction $\frac{6}{15}$ is reduced to lowest terms:

$$\frac{6}{15} = \frac{2 \cdot 3}{5 \cdot 3} \qquad \text{Factor numerator and denominator}$$

$$= \frac{2 \cdot \cancel{3}}{5 \cdot \cancel{3}} \qquad \text{Divide out the common factor, 3}$$

$$= \frac{2}{5} \qquad \text{Reduce to lowest terms}$$

The same procedure applies to reducing rational expressions to lowest terms. The process is summarized in the following rule.

RULE

To reduce a rational expression to lowest terms, first factor the numerator and denominator completely and then divide both the numerator and denominator by any factors they have in common.

EXAMPLE 5   Reduce $\dfrac{x^2 - 9}{x^2 + 5x + 6}$ to lowest terms.

SOLUTION   We begin by factoring:

$$\frac{x^2 - 9}{x^2 + 5x + 6} = \frac{(x - 3)(x + 3)}{(x + 2)(x + 3)}$$

Notice that both polynomials contain the factor $(x + 3)$. If we divide the numerator by $(x + 3)$, we are left with $(x - 3)$. If we divide the denominator by $(x + 3)$, we are left with $(x + 2)$. The complete problem looks like this:

$$\frac{x^2 - 9}{x^2 + 5x + 6} = \frac{(x - 3)(x + 3)}{(x + 2)(x + 3)}$$ Factor the numerator and denominator completely

$$= \frac{(x - 3)\cancel{(x + 3)}}{(x + 2)\cancel{(x + 3)}}$$ Divide out the common factor, $x + 3$

$$= \frac{x - 3}{x + 2}$$

Note   It is convenient to draw a line through the factors as we divide them out. It is especially helpful when the problems become longer.

Note   Students sometimes make the mistake of dividing out common terms:

$$\frac{\cancel{x^2} - 9}{\cancel{x^2} + 5x + 6} \neq \frac{-9}{5x + 6}$$

This does not give us an equivalent expression. We can only divide out common factors, which usually requires that we factor the rational expression first.

EXAMPLE 6   Reduce to lowest terms: $\dfrac{10a + 20}{20 - 5a^2}$.

SOLUTION   We begin by factoring out the greatest common factor from the numerator and denominator:

$$\frac{10a + 20}{20 - 5a^2} = \frac{10(a + 2)}{-5(a^2 - 4)}$$ Factor the greatest common factor from the numerator and denominator

$$= \frac{10(a + 2)}{-5(a + 2)(a - 2)}$$ Factor the denominator as the difference of two squares

$$= -\frac{2}{a - 2}$$ Divide out the common factors 5 and $a + 2$

EXAMPLE 7   Reduce $\dfrac{2x^3 + 2x^2 - 24x}{x^3 + 2x^2 - 8x}$ to lowest terms.

SOLUTION   We begin by factoring the numerator and denominator completely. Then we divide out all factors common to the numerator and denominator. Here is what it looks like:

$$\frac{2x^3 + 2x^2 - 24x}{x^3 + 2x^2 - 8x} = \frac{2x(x^2 + x - 12)}{x(x^2 + 2x - 8)}$$ Factor out the greatest common factor first

$$= \frac{2x(x - 3)(x + 4)}{x(x - 2)(x + 4)}$$ Factor the remaining trinomials

$$= \frac{2(x - 3)}{x - 2}$$ Divide out the factors common to the numerator and denominator

EXAMPLE 8 Reduce $\dfrac{x-5}{x^2-25}$ to lowest terms. Also, state any restrictions on the variable.

SOLUTION First, we reduce the expression by dividing out common factors.

$$\frac{x-5}{x^2-25} = \frac{x-5}{(x-5)(x+5)} \qquad \text{Factor numerator and denominator completely}$$

$$= \frac{1}{x+5} \qquad \text{Divide out the common factor, } x-5$$

To find any restrictions on the variable, we must find any values of x that make the *original* expression undefined. This will be the case if $x^2 - 25 = 0$.

$$x^2 - 25 = 0$$

$$(x+5)(x-5) = 0 \qquad \text{Factor}$$

$$x + 5 = 0 \qquad \text{or} \qquad x - 5 = 0 \qquad \text{Zero-factor property}$$

$$x = -5 \qquad \text{or} \qquad x = 5$$

Our restrictions are $x \neq -5$ and $x \neq 5$.

> *Note* Even though the rational expression in Example 8 can be reduced, the original expression is undefined for both $x = -5$ and $x = 5$. When determining any restrictions on the variable, we must work with the original denominator prior to reducing the expression.

Ratios

For the rest of this section we will concern ourselves with *ratios*, a topic closely related to reducing fractions and rational expressions to lowest terms. Let's start with a definition.

> **(dĕf) DEFINITION** *Ratio*
>
> If a and b are any two numbers, $b \neq 0$, then the **ratio** of a and b is
>
> $$\frac{a}{b}$$

As you can see, ratios are another name for fractions or rational numbers. They are a way of comparing quantities. Since we also can think of $\frac{a}{b}$ as the quotient of a and b, ratios are also quotients. The following table gives some ratios in words and as fractions.

Ratio	As a Fraction	In Lowest Terms	
25 to 75	$\frac{25}{75}$	$\frac{1}{3}$	
8 to 2	$\frac{8}{2}$	$\frac{4}{1}$	With ratios it is common to leave the 1 in the denominator.
20 to 16	$\frac{20}{16}$	$\frac{5}{4}$	

EXAMPLE 9   A solution of hydrochloric acid (HCl) and water contains 49 milliliters of water and 21 milliliters of HCl. Find the ratio of HCl to water and of HCl to the total volume of the solution.

SOLUTION   The ratio of HCl to water is 21 to 49, or

$$\frac{21}{49} = \frac{3}{7}$$

The amount of total solution volume is $49 + 21 = 70$ milliliters. Therefore, the ratio of HCl to total solution is 21 to 70, or

$$\frac{21}{70} = \frac{3}{10}$$

Rate Equation

Many of the problems in this chapter will use what is called the *rate equation*. You use this equation on an intuitive level when you are estimating how long it will take you to drive long distances. For example, if you drive at a steady speed of 50 miles per hour for 2 hours, you will travel 100 miles. Here is the rate equation:

$$\text{Distance} = \text{rate} \cdot \text{time}$$
$$d = r \cdot t$$

The rate equation has two equivalent forms, the most common of which is obtained by solving for r. Here it is:

$$r = \frac{d}{t}$$

The rate r in the rate equation is the ratio of distance to time and also is referred to as *average speed*. The units for rate are miles per hour, feet per second, kilometers per hour, and so on.

L = 5,649 feet

EXAMPLE 10   The Comstock Express chair lift at the Northstar California ski resort in Lake Tahoe is 5,649 feet long. If a ride on this chair lift takes 6 minutes, what is the average speed of the lift in feet per minute?

SOLUTION   To find the speed of the lift, we find the ratio of distance covered to time. (Our answer is rounded to the nearest whole number.)

$$\text{Rate} = \frac{\text{distance}}{\text{time}} = \frac{5{,}649 \text{ feet}}{6 \text{ minutes}} = \frac{5{,}649}{6} \text{ feet/minute} \approx 942 \text{ feet/minute}$$

Note how we separate the numerical part of the problem from the units. In the next section, we will convert this rate to miles per hour.

Getting Ready for Class

After reading through the preceding section, respond in your own words and in complete sentences.

A. For what values of the variable is a rational expression undefined?

B. What are the properties we use to manipulate rational expressions?

C. How do you reduce a rational expression to lowest terms?

D. What is a ratio?

Evaluate each rational expression for the given values of the variable.

1. $\dfrac{x-3}{x+4}$ for $x = 2$, $x = 3$, and $x = -4$

2. $\dfrac{x+2}{x-5}$ for $x = -2$, $x = 4$, and $x = 5$

3. $\dfrac{2x+1}{x^2+x-2}$ for $x = -3$, $x = 0$, and $x = 1$

4. $\dfrac{x^2-4}{x^2+4}$ for $x = 0$, $x = 2$, and $x = -1$

Determine any values of the variable for which the rational expression is undefined.

5. $\dfrac{x-2}{x}$

6. $\dfrac{3x}{x-6}$

7. $\dfrac{x+1}{(x+2)(x-3)}$

8. $\dfrac{x-1}{x(x-4)}$

9. $\dfrac{2x+5}{3x^2-2x-1}$

10. $\dfrac{x^2-9}{x^2+9}$

11. $\dfrac{x+4}{x^2+4}$

12. $\dfrac{6x+10}{4x^2-25}$

Reduce the following rational expressions to lowest terms, if possible. Also, specify any restrictions on the variable.

13. $\dfrac{5}{5x-10}$

14. $\dfrac{-4}{2x-8}$

15. $\dfrac{a-3}{a^2-9}$

16. $\dfrac{a+4}{a^2-16}$

17. $\dfrac{x+5}{x^2-25}$

18. $\dfrac{x-2}{x^2-4}$

19. $\dfrac{2x^2-8}{4}$

20. $\dfrac{5x-10}{x-2}$

21. $\dfrac{2x-10}{3x-6}$

22. $\dfrac{4x-8}{x-2}$

23. $\dfrac{10a+20}{5a+10}$

24. $\dfrac{11a+33}{6a+18}$

Reduce each rational expression to lowest terms.

25. $\dfrac{5x^2-5}{4x+4}$

26. $\dfrac{7x^2-28}{2x+4}$

27. $\dfrac{x-3}{x^2-6x+9}$

28. $\dfrac{x^2-10x+25}{x-5}$

29. $\dfrac{3x+15}{3x^2+24x+45}$

30. $\dfrac{5x+15}{5x^2+40x+75}$

31. $\dfrac{a^2-3a}{a^3-8a^2+15a}$

32. $\dfrac{a^2-3a}{a^3+2a^2-15a}$

33. $\dfrac{3x-2}{9x^2-4}$

34. $\dfrac{2x-3}{4x^2-9}$

35. $\dfrac{x^2+8x+15}{x^2+5x+6}$

36. $\dfrac{x^2-8x+15}{x^2-x-6}$

37. $\dfrac{2m^3-2m^2-12m}{m^2-5m+6}$

38. $\dfrac{2m^3+4m^2-6m}{m^2-m-12}$

39. $\dfrac{x^3+3x^2-4x}{x^3-16x}$

40. $\dfrac{3a^2-8a+4}{9a^3-4a}$

41. $\dfrac{4x^3-10x^2+6x}{2x^3+x^2-3x}$

42. $\dfrac{3a^3-8a^2+5a}{4a^3-5a^2+1a}$

43. $\dfrac{4x^2 - 12x + 9}{4x^2 - 9}$

44. $\dfrac{5x^2 + 18x - 8}{5x^2 + 13x - 6}$

45. $\dfrac{x + 3}{x^4 - 81}$

46. $\dfrac{x^2 + 9}{x^4 - 81}$

47. $\dfrac{3x^2 + x - 10}{x^4 - 16}$

48. $\dfrac{5x^2 - 16x + 12}{x^4 - 16}$

49. $\dfrac{42x^3 - 20x^2 - 48x}{6x^2 - 5x - 4}$

50. $\dfrac{36x^3 + 132x^2 - 135x}{6x^2 + 25x - 9}$

51. $\dfrac{x^3 - y^3}{x^2 - y^2}$

52. $\dfrac{x^3 + y^3}{x^2 - y^2}$

53. $\dfrac{x^3 + 8}{x^2 - 4}$

54. $\dfrac{x^3 - 125}{x^2 - 25}$

55. $\dfrac{x^3 + 8}{x^2 + x - 2}$

56. $\dfrac{x^2 - 2x - 3}{x^3 - 27}$

To reduce each of the following rational expressions to lowest terms, you will have to use factoring by grouping. Be sure to factor each numerator and denominator completely before dividing out any common factors. (Remember, factoring by grouping takes two steps.)

57. $\dfrac{xy + 3x + 2y + 6}{xy + 3x + 5y + 15}$

58. $\dfrac{xy + 7x + 4y + 28}{xy + 3x + 4y + 12}$

59. $\dfrac{x^2 - 3x + ax - 3a}{x^2 - 3x + bx - 3b}$

60. $\dfrac{x^2 - 6x + ax - 6a}{x^2 - 7x + ax - 7a}$

The next two problems are intended to give you practice reading, and paying attention to, the instructions that accompany the problems you're working. Working these problems is an excellent way to get ready for a test or quiz.

61. Paying Attention to Instructions Work each problem according to the instructions given:

    a. Add: $(x^2 - 4x) + (4x - 16)$

    b. Subtract: $(x^2 - 4x) - (4x - 16)$

    c. Multiply: $(x^2 - 4x)(4x - 16)$

    d. Reduce: $\dfrac{x^2 - 4x}{4x - 16}$

62. Paying Attention to Instructions Work each problem according to the instructions given:

    a. Add: $(9x^2 - 3x) + (6x - 2)$

    b. Subtract: $(9x^2 - 3x) - (6x - 2)$

    c. Multiply: $(9x^2 - 3x)(6x - 2)$

    d. Reduce: $\dfrac{9x^2 - 3x}{6x - 2}$

Write each ratio as a fraction in lowest terms.

63. 8 to 6   **64.** 6 to 8   **65.** 200 to 250   **66.** 250 to 200

67. 32 to 4   **68.** 4 to 32

Applying the Concepts

69. **Cost and Average Cost** As we mentioned in the introduction to this chapter, if a bank charges $2.00 per month and $0.15 per check for one of its checking accounts, then the total monthly cost to write x checks is $C = 2.00 + 0.15x$, and the average cost of each of the x checks written is $A = \frac{2.00 + 0.15x}{x}$. Compare these two formulas by filling in the following table. Round to the nearest cent.

Checks Written x	Total Cost $2.00 + 0.15x$	Cost per Check $\frac{2.00 + 0.15x}{x}$
0		
5		
10		
15		
20		

70. **Cost and Average Cost** A rewritable Blu-ray drive for a computer costs $60. An individual BD-RE disc for the drive costs $4.00 and can store 50 gigabytes of information. The total cost of filling x discs with information is $C = 60 + 4x$ dollars. The average cost per gigabyte of information is given by $A = \frac{4x + 60}{50x}$. Compare the total cost and average cost per gigabyte of storage by completing the following table. Round all answers to the nearest cent.

Discs Purchased x	Total Cost $60 + 4x$	Cost per Gigabyte $\frac{4x + 60}{50x}$
0		
5		
10		
15		
20		

71. **Speed of a Car** A car travels 122 miles in 3 hours. Find the average speed of the car in miles per hour. Round to the nearest tenth.

72. **Speed of a Bullet** A bullet fired from a gun travels a distance of 4,500 feet in 3 seconds. Find the average speed of the bullet in feet per second.

73. Baseball For the four pitchers mentioned in the chart, calculate the number of strikeouts per inning. Round to the nearest hundredth.

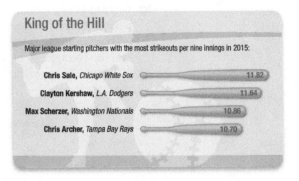

King of the Hill

Major league starting pitchers with the most strikeouts per nine innings in 2015:

Chris Sale, *Chicago White Sox*	11.82
Clayton Kershaw, *L.A. Dodgers*	11.64
Max Scherzer, *Washington Nationals*	10.86
Chris Archer, *Tampa Bay Rays*	10.70

74. Ferris Wheel A person riding a Ferris Wheel travels once around the wheel, a distance of 188 feet, in 30 seconds. What is the average speed of the rider in feet per second? Round to the nearest tenth.

75. Jogging A jogger covers a distance of 3 miles in 24 minutes. Find the average speed of the jogger in miles per minute.

76. Fuel Consumption An economy car travels 168 miles on 3.5 gallons of gas. Give the average fuel consumption of the car in miles per gallon.

Learning Objectives Assessment

The following problems can be used to help assess if you have successfully met the learning objectives for this section.

77. Evaluate $\frac{2x-3}{x^2-4}$ for $x = -1$.

    a. 1   **b.** Undefined   **c.** $-\frac{3}{5}$ **d.** $\frac{5}{3}$

78. For what values of x is $\frac{x-5}{x+6}$ undefined?

    a. 5   **b.** -6 **c.** -6 and 5   **d.** none

79. Reduce to lowest terms: $\frac{x^2-4x}{x^2-16}$.

    a. $\frac{x}{4}$ **b.** $\frac{x}{x+4}$

    c. $\frac{x}{x-4}$ **d.** $\frac{1}{4}$

80. In 2002, the Hubbard Glacier surged forward 170 meters in six weeks (42 days). Find the approximate average speed by which the glacier advanced during this period.

    a. 4 meters per day   **b.** 0.25 meters per day

    c. 17 meters per day   **d.** 7,140 meters per day

Getting Ready for the Next Section

Perform the indicated operation.

81. $\dfrac{3}{4} \cdot \dfrac{10}{21}$ **82.** $\dfrac{2}{9} \cdot \dfrac{15}{22}$ **83.** $\dfrac{4}{5} \div \dfrac{8}{9}$ **84.** $\dfrac{3}{5} \div \dfrac{15}{7}$

Factor completely.

85. $x^2 - 9$ **86.** $x^2 - 25$ **87.** $3x - 9$ **88.** $2x - 4$

89. $x^2 - x - 20$ **90.** $x^2 + 7x + 12$ **91.** $a^2 + 5a$ **92.** $a^2 - 4a$

Reduce to lowest terms.

93. $\dfrac{a(a + 5)(a - 5)(a + 4)}{a^2 + 5a}$ **94.** $\dfrac{a(a + 2)(a - 4)(a + 5)}{a^2 - 4a}$

Multiply. Give the answers as decimals rounded to the nearest tenth.

95. $\dfrac{5603}{11} \cdot \dfrac{1}{2580} \cdot \dfrac{60}{1}$ **96.** $\dfrac{772}{2.2} \cdot \dfrac{1}{2580} \cdot \dfrac{60}{1}$

SPOTLIGHT ON SUCCESS   *Student Instructor Aaron*

*Sometimes you have to take a step back
in order to get a running start forward.*
—Anonymous

As a high school senior I was encouraged to go to college immediately after graduating. I earned good grades in high school and I knew that I would have a pretty good group of schools to pick from. Even though I felt like "more school" was not quite what I wanted, the counselors had so much faith and had done this process so many times that it was almost too easy to get the applications out. I sent out applications to schools I knew I could get into and a "dream school."

One night in my email inbox there was a letter of acceptance from my dream school. There was just one problem with getting into this school. It was going to be difficult and I still had senioritis. Going into my first quarter of college was as exciting and difficult as I knew it would be. But after my first quarter I could see that this was not the time for me to be here. I was interested in the subject matter but I could not find my motivating purpose like I had in high school. Instead of dropping out completely, I decided a community college would be a good way for me to stay on track. Without necessarily knowing my direction, I could take the general education classes and get those out of the way while figuring out exactly what and where I felt a good place for me to be.

Now I know what I want to go to school for and the next time I walk onto a four year campus it will be on my terms with my reasons for being there driving me to succeed. I encourage everyone to continue school after high school, even if you have no clue as to what you want to study. There are always stepping stones, like community colleges, that can help you get a clearer picture of what you want to strive for.

Multiplication and Division of Rational Expressions

Learning Objectives

In this section, we will learn how to:

1. Multiply rational expressions.
2. Divide rational expressions.
3. Use a conversion factor to convert units.

Introduction

Recall that to multiply two fractions we simply multiply numerators and multiply denominators and then reduce to lowest terms, if possible:

$$\frac{3}{4} \cdot \frac{10}{21} = \frac{30}{84} \quad \leftarrow \text{Multiply numerators}$$
$$\phantom{\frac{3}{4} \cdot \frac{10}{21}} \quad \leftarrow \text{Multiply denominators}$$
$$= \frac{5}{14} \quad \leftarrow \text{Reduce to lowest terms}$$

Recall also that the same result can be achieved by factoring numerators and denominators first and then dividing out the factors they have in common:

$$\frac{3}{4} \cdot \frac{10}{21} = \frac{3}{2 \cdot 2} \cdot \frac{2 \cdot 5}{3 \cdot 7} \quad \text{Factor}$$
$$= \frac{3 \cdot 2 \cdot 5}{2 \cdot 2 \cdot 3 \cdot 7} \quad \begin{array}{l}\text{Multiply numerators}\\\text{Multiply denominators}\end{array}$$
$$= \frac{5}{14} \quad \text{Divide out common factors}$$

We can apply the second process to the product of two rational expressions, as the following example illustrates.

VIDEO EXAMPLES

SECTION 7.2

EXAMPLE 1 Multiply: $\dfrac{x - 2}{x + 3} \cdot \dfrac{x^2 - 9}{2x - 4}$.

SOLUTION We begin by factoring numerators and denominators as much as possible. Then we multiply the numerators and denominators. The last step consists of dividing out all factors common to the numerator and denominator:

$$\frac{x - 2}{x + 3} \cdot \frac{x^2 - 9}{2x - 4} = \frac{x - 2}{x + 3} \cdot \frac{(x - 3)(x + 3)}{2(x - 2)} \quad \text{Factor completely}$$
$$= \frac{(x - 2)(x - 3)(x + 3)}{(x + 3)(2)(x - 2)} \quad \begin{array}{l}\text{Multiply numerators and}\\\text{denominators}\end{array}$$
$$= \frac{x - 3}{2} \quad \text{Divide out common factors}$$

EXAMPLE 2   Multiply $\dfrac{3a + 6}{a^2} \cdot \dfrac{a}{2a + 4}$.

SOLUTION

$$\dfrac{3a + 6}{a^2} \cdot \dfrac{a}{2a + 4}$$

$$= \dfrac{3(a + 2)}{a^2} \cdot \dfrac{a}{2(a + 2)} \qquad \text{Factor completely}$$

$$= \dfrac{3(a + 2)a}{a^2(2)(a + 2)} \qquad \text{Multiply}$$

$$= \dfrac{3}{2a} \qquad\qquad\qquad \text{Divide numerator and denominator}$$
$$\phantom{= \dfrac{3}{2a} \qquad\qquad\qquad} \text{by common factors } a(a + 2)$$

In Chapter 1 we defined division as the equivalent of multiplication by the reciprocal. This is how it looks with fractions:

$$\dfrac{4}{5} \div \dfrac{8}{9} = \dfrac{4}{5} \cdot \dfrac{9}{8} \qquad \text{Multiply by the reciprocal of the divisor}$$

$$= \dfrac{2 \cdot 2 \cdot 3 \cdot 3}{5 \cdot 2 \cdot 2 \cdot 2}$$
$$= \dfrac{9}{10} \qquad\qquad \text{Factor and divide out common factors}$$

The same idea holds for division with rational expressions. The rational expression that follows the division symbol is called the *divisor;* to divide, we multiply by the reciprocal of the divisor.

EXAMPLE 3   Divide: $\dfrac{x^2 + 7x + 12}{x^2 - 16} \div \dfrac{x^2 + 6x + 9}{2x - 8}$.

SOLUTION We begin by taking the reciprocal of the divisor and writing the problem again in terms of multiplication. We then factor, multiply, and, finally, divide out all factors common to the numerator and denominator of the resulting expression. The complete problem looks like this:

$$\dfrac{x^2 + 7x + 12}{x^2 - 16} \div \dfrac{x^2 + 6x + 9}{2x - 8}$$

$$= \dfrac{x^2 + 7x + 12}{x^2 - 16} \cdot \dfrac{2x - 8}{x^2 + 6x + 9} \qquad \text{Multiply by the reciprocal of the}$$
$$\phantom{= \dfrac{x^2 + 7x + 12}{x^2 - 16} \cdot \dfrac{2x - 8}{x^2 + 6x + 9} \qquad} \text{divisor}$$

$$= \dfrac{(x + 3)(x + 4)}{(x - 4)(x + 4)} \cdot \dfrac{2(x - 4)}{(x + 3)(x + 3)} \qquad \text{Factor}$$

$$= \dfrac{(x + 3)(x + 4)(2)(x - 4)}{(x - 4)(x + 4)(x + 3)(x + 3)} \qquad \text{Multiply}$$

$$= \dfrac{2}{x + 3} \qquad\qquad\qquad\qquad \text{Divide out common factors}$$

As you can see, factoring is the single most important tool we use in working with rational expressions. Most of the work we have done or will do with rational expressions is accomplished most easily if the rational expressions are in factored form. Here are some more examples of multiplication and division with rational expressions.

EXAMPLE 4   Divide: $\dfrac{3x-9}{x^2-x-20} \div \dfrac{15-2x-x^2}{x^2-25}$.

SOLUTION

$$\dfrac{3x-9}{x^2-x-20} \div \dfrac{15-2x-x^2}{x^2-25}$$

$$= \dfrac{3x-9}{x^2-x-20} \cdot \dfrac{x^2-25}{15-2x-x^2} \qquad \text{Multiply by the reciprocal of the divisor}$$

$$= \dfrac{3x-9}{x^2-x-20} \cdot \dfrac{x^2-25}{-1(x^2+2x-15)} \qquad \text{Factor a } -1 \text{ from the second denominator}$$

$$= \dfrac{3(x-3)(x-5)(x+5)}{(x+4)(x-5)(-1)(x+5)(x-3)} \qquad \text{Factor and multiply}$$

$$= -\dfrac{3}{x+4} \qquad \text{Divide out common factors}$$

In Example 4 we factored and multiplied the two expressions in a single step. This saves writing the problem one extra time.

EXAMPLE 5   Multiply: $(49 - x^2)\left(\dfrac{x+4}{x-7}\right)$.

SOLUTION We can think of the polynomial $49 - x^2$ as having a denominator of 1. Thinking of $49 - x^2$ in this way allows us to proceed as we did in previous examples:

$$(49 - x^2)\left(\dfrac{x+4}{x-7}\right)$$

$$= \dfrac{49-x^2}{1} \cdot \dfrac{x+4}{x-7} \qquad \text{Write } x^2 - 49 \text{ with denominator 1}$$

$$= \dfrac{-1(x^2-49)}{1} \cdot \dfrac{x+4}{x-7} \qquad \text{Factor and multiply}$$

$$= \dfrac{-1(x+7)(x-7)(x+4)}{x-7}$$

$$= -1(x+7)(x+4) \qquad \text{Divide out common factors}$$

In this section let's agree to leave our answers in factored form.

EXAMPLE 6   Multiply: $a(a+5)(a-5)\left(\dfrac{a+4}{a^2+5a}\right)$.

SOLUTION We can think of the expression $a(a+5)(a-5)$ as having a denominator of 1:

$$a(a+5)(a-5)\left(\dfrac{a+4}{a^2+5a}\right)$$

$$= \dfrac{a(a+5)(a-5)}{1} \cdot \dfrac{a+4}{a^2+5a}$$

$$= \dfrac{a(a+5)(a-5)(a+4)}{a(a+5)} \qquad \text{Factor and multiply}$$

$$= (a-5)(a+4) \qquad \text{Divide out common factors}$$

Unit Analysis

Unit analysis is a method of converting between units of measure by multiplying by the number 1. Here is our first illustration: Suppose you are flying in a commercial airliner and the pilot tells you the plane has reached its cruising altitude of 35,000 feet. How many miles is the plane above the ground?

If you know that 1 mile is 5,280 feet, then it is simply a matter of deciding what to do with the two numbers, 5,280 and 35,000. By using unit analysis, this decision is unnecessary:

$$35,000 \text{ feet} = \frac{35,000 \text{ feet}}{1} \cdot \frac{1 \text{ mile}}{5,280 \text{ feet}}$$

We treat the units common to the numerator and denominator in the same way we treat factors common to the numerator and denominator; common units can be divided out, just as common factors are. In the previous expression, we have feet common to the numerator and denominator. Dividing them out leaves us with miles only. Here is the complete problem:

$$35,000 \text{ feet} = \frac{35,000 \text{ feet}}{1} \cdot \frac{1 \text{ mile}}{5,280 \text{ feet}}$$

$$= \frac{35,000}{5,280} \text{ miles}$$

$$= 6.6 \text{ miles to the nearest tenth of a mile}$$

The expression $\frac{1 \text{ mile}}{5,280 \text{ feet}}$ is called a *conversion factor*. It is simply the number 1 written in a convenient form. Because it is the number 1, we can multiply any other number by it and always be sure we have not changed that number. The key to unit analysis is choosing the right conversion factors.

Note Realizing that conversion factors, such as $\frac{1 \text{ mile}}{5,280}$ feet, are equivalent to the number 1 may take some getting used to. For example, you know that $\frac{2}{2} = 1$ since the numerator and denominator are equal. The same goes for conversion factors; since 1 mile = 5,280 feet, the numerator and denominator are equal, and the fraction is equivalent to 1.

EXAMPLE 7   The Mall of America in the Twin Cities covers 78 acres of land. If 1 square mile = 640 acres, how many square miles does the Mall of America cover? Round your answer to the nearest hundredth of a square mile.

SOLUTION   We are starting with acres and want to end up with square miles. We need to multiply by a conversion factor that will allow acres to divide out and leave us with square miles:

$$78 \text{ acres} = \frac{78 \text{ acres}}{1} \cdot \frac{1 \text{ square mile}}{640 \text{ acres}}$$

$$= \frac{78}{640} \text{ square miles}$$

$$= 0.12 \text{ square miles to the nearest hundredth}$$

The next example is a continuation of Example 10 from Section 7.1.

L = 5,649 feet

EXAMPLE 8   The Comstock Express chair lift at the Northstar California ski resort in Lake Tahoe is 5,649 feet long. If a ride on this chair lift takes 6 minutes, what is the average speed of the lift in miles per hour?

SOLUTION   First, we find the speed of the lift in feet per second, as we did in Example 10 of Section 7.1, by taking the ratio of distance to time.

$$\text{Rate} = \frac{\text{distance}}{\text{time}} = \frac{5{,}649 \text{ feet}}{6 \text{ minutes}} = \frac{5{,}649}{6} \text{ feet per minute}$$

$$\approx 942 \text{ feet per minute}$$

Next, we convert feet per minute to miles per hour. To do this, we need to know that

$$1 \text{ mile} = 5{,}280 \text{ feet}$$

$$1 \text{ hour} = 60 \text{ minutes}$$

$$\text{Average speed} = 942 \text{ feet per minute} = \frac{942 \text{ feet}}{1 \text{ minute}} \cdot \frac{1 \text{ mile}}{5{,}280 \text{ feet}} \cdot \frac{60 \text{ minutes}}{1 \text{ hour}}$$

$$= \frac{942 \cdot 60}{5{,}280} \text{ miles per hour}$$

$$= 10.7 \text{ mph to the nearest tenth}$$

Getting Ready for Class

After reading through the preceding section, respond in your own words and in complete sentences.

A. How do we multiply rational expressions?

B. Explain the steps used to divide rational expressions.

C. What part does factoring play in multiplying and dividing rational expressions?

D. Why are all conversion factors the same as the number 1?

Problem Set 7.2

Multiply or divide as indicated. Be sure to reduce all answers to lowest terms. (The numerator and denominator of the answer should not have any factors in common.)

1. $\dfrac{x+y}{3} \cdot \dfrac{6}{x+y}$

2. $\dfrac{x-1}{x+1} \cdot \dfrac{5}{x-1}$

3. $\dfrac{2x+10}{x^2} \cdot \dfrac{x^3}{4x+20}$

4. $\dfrac{3x^4}{3x-6} \cdot \dfrac{x-2}{x^2}$

5. $\dfrac{9}{2a-8} \div \dfrac{3}{a-4}$

6. $\dfrac{8}{a^2-25} \div \dfrac{16}{a+5}$

7. $\dfrac{x+1}{x^2-9} \div \dfrac{2x+2}{x+3}$

8. $\dfrac{-11}{x-2} \div \dfrac{22}{2x^2-8}$

9. $\dfrac{a^2+5a}{7a} \cdot \dfrac{4a^2}{a^2+4a}$

10. $\dfrac{4a^2+4a}{a^2-25} \cdot \dfrac{a^2-5a}{8a}$

11. $\dfrac{y^2-5y+6}{2y+4} \div \dfrac{2y-6}{y+2}$

12. $\dfrac{y^2-7y}{3y^2-48} \div \dfrac{y^2-9}{y^2-7y+12}$

13. $\dfrac{2x-8}{x^2-4} \cdot \dfrac{x^2+6x+8}{x-4}$

14. $\dfrac{x^2+5x+1}{7x-7} \cdot \dfrac{x-1}{x^2+5x+1}$

15. $\dfrac{x-1}{6+x-x^2} \cdot \dfrac{x^2+5x+6}{x^2-1}$

16. $\dfrac{x^2-3x-10}{x^2-4x+3} \cdot \dfrac{x^2-5x+6}{10+3x-x^2}$

17. $\dfrac{a^2+10a+25}{a+5} \div \dfrac{a^2-25}{a-5}$

18. $\dfrac{a^2+a-2}{a^2+5a+6} \div \dfrac{a-1}{a}$

19. $\dfrac{y^3-5y^2}{y^4+3y^3+2y^2} \div \dfrac{y^2-5y+6}{y^2-2y-3}$

20. $\dfrac{y^2-5y}{y^2+7y+12} \div \dfrac{y^3-7y^2+10y}{y^2+9y+18}$

21. $\dfrac{2x^2+17x+21}{x^2+2x-35} \cdot \dfrac{25-x^2}{2x^2-7x-15}$

22. $\dfrac{x^2-13x+42}{4x^2-31x+21} \cdot \dfrac{4x^2+5x-6}{4-x^2}$

23. $\dfrac{2x^2+10x+12}{4x^2+24x+32} \cdot \dfrac{2x^2+18x+40}{x^2+8x+15}$

24. $\dfrac{3x^2-3}{6x^2+18x+12} \cdot \dfrac{2x^2-8}{x^2-3x+2}$

25. $\dfrac{2a^2+7a+3}{a^2-16} \div \dfrac{4a^2+8a+3}{2a^2-5a-12}$

26. $\dfrac{3a^2+7a-20}{a^2+3a-4} \div \dfrac{3a^2-2a-5}{a^2-2a+1}$

27. $\dfrac{4y^2-12y+9}{36-y^2} \div \dfrac{2y^2-5y+3}{y^2+5y-6}$

28. $\dfrac{5y^2-6y+1}{1-y^2} \div \dfrac{16y^2-9}{4y^2+7y+3}$

29. $\dfrac{x^2-1}{6x^2+18x+12} \cdot \dfrac{7x^2+17x+6}{x+1} \cdot \dfrac{6x+30}{7x^2-11x-6}$

30. $\dfrac{4x^2-1}{3x-15} \cdot \dfrac{4x^2-17x-15}{4x^2-9x-9} \cdot \dfrac{3x-3}{x^2-9}$

31. $\dfrac{18x^3+21x^2-60x}{21x^2-25x-4} \cdot \dfrac{28x^2-17x-3}{16x^3+28x^2-30x}$

32. $\dfrac{56x^3+54x^2-20x}{8x^2-2x-15} \cdot \dfrac{6x^2+5x-21}{63x^3+129x^2-42x}$

The next two problems are intended to give you practice reading, and paying attention to, the instructions that accompany the problems you are working. Working these problems is an excellent way to get ready for a test or quiz.

33. Paying Attention to Instructions Work each problem according to the instructions given:

a. Simplify: $\dfrac{9-1}{27-1}$

b. Reduce: $\dfrac{x^2-1}{x^3-1}$

c. Multiply: $\dfrac{x^2-1}{x^3-1} \cdot \dfrac{x-2}{x+1}$

d. Divide: $\dfrac{x^2-1}{x^3-1} \div \dfrac{x-1}{x^2+x+1}$

34. Paying Attention to Instructions Work each problem according to the instructions given:

a. Simplify: $\dfrac{16 - 9}{16 + 24 + 9}$

b. Reduce: $\dfrac{4x^2 - 9}{4x^2 + 12x + 9}$

c. Multiply: $\dfrac{4x^2 - 9}{4x^2 + 12x + 9} \cdot \dfrac{2x + 3}{2x - 3}$

d. Divide: $\dfrac{4x^2 - 9}{4x^2 + 12x + 9} \div \dfrac{2x + 3}{2x - 3}$

Multiply the following expressions using the method shown in Examples 5 and 6 in this section.

35. $(x^2 - 9)\left(\dfrac{2}{x + 3}\right)$

36. $(x^2 - 9)\left(\dfrac{-3}{x - 3}\right)$

37. $(x^2 - x - 6)\left(\dfrac{x + 1}{x - 3}\right)$

38. $(x^2 - 2x - 8)\left(\dfrac{x + 3}{x - 4}\right)$

39. $(x^2 - 4x - 5)\left(\dfrac{-2x}{x + 1}\right)$

40. $(x^2 - 6x + 8)\left(\dfrac{4x}{x - 2}\right)$

Each of the following problems involves some factoring by grouping. Remember, before you can divide out factors common to the numerators and denominators of a product, you must factor completely.

41. $\dfrac{x^2 - 9}{x^2 - 3x} \cdot \dfrac{2x + 10}{xy + 5x + 3y + 15}$

42. $\dfrac{x^2 - 16}{x^2 - 4x} \cdot \dfrac{3x + 18}{xy + 6x + 4y + 24}$

43. $\dfrac{2x^2 + 4x}{x^2 - y^2} \cdot \dfrac{x^2 + 3x + xy + 3y}{x^2 + 5x + 6}$

44. $\dfrac{x^2 - 25}{3x^2 + 3xy} \cdot \dfrac{x^2 + 4x + xy + 4y}{x^2 + 9x + 20}$

45. $\dfrac{x^3 - 3x^2 + 4x - 12}{x^4 - 16} \cdot \dfrac{3x^2 + 5x - 2}{3x^2 - 10x + 3}$

46. $\dfrac{x^3 - 5x^2 + 9x - 45}{x^4 - 81} \cdot \dfrac{5x^2 + 18x + 9}{5x^2 - 22x - 15}$

Simplify each expression. Work inside parentheses first, and then divide out common factors.

47. $\left(1 - \dfrac{1}{2}\right)\left(1 - \dfrac{1}{3}\right)\left(1 - \dfrac{1}{4}\right)\left(1 - \dfrac{1}{5}\right)$

48. $\left(1 + \dfrac{1}{2}\right)\left(1 + \dfrac{1}{3}\right)\left(1 + \dfrac{1}{4}\right)\left(1 + \dfrac{1}{5}\right)$

The dots in the following problems represent factors not written that are in the same pattern as the surrounding factors. Simplify.

49. $\left(1 - \dfrac{1}{2}\right)\left(1 - \dfrac{1}{3}\right)\left(1 - \dfrac{1}{4}\right)\ldots\left(1 - \dfrac{1}{99}\right)\left(1 - \dfrac{1}{100}\right)$

50. $\left(1 - \dfrac{1}{3}\right)\left(1 - \dfrac{1}{4}\right)\left(1 - \dfrac{1}{5}\right)\ldots\left(1 - \dfrac{1}{98}\right)\left(1 - \dfrac{1}{99}\right)$

Applying the Concepts

51. Mount Whitney The top of Mount Whitney, the highest point in California, is 14,494 feet above sea level. Give this height in miles to the nearest tenth of a mile.

52. Motor Displacement The relationship between liters and cubic inches, both of which are measures of volume, is 0.0164 liters = 1 cubic inch. If a Ford Mustang has a motor with a displacement of 4.9 liters, what is the displacement in cubic inches? Round your answer to the nearest cubic inch.

53. Speed of Sound The speed of sound is 1,088 feet per second. Convert the speed of sound to miles per hour. Round your answer to the nearest whole number.

54. Average Speed A car travels 122 miles in 3 hours. Find the average speed of the car in feet per second. Round to the nearest whole number.

55. Ferris Wheel The first Ferris wheel was built in 1893. It was a large wheel with a circumference of 785 feet. If one trip around the circumference of the wheel took 20 minutes, find the average speed of a rider in miles per hour. Round to the nearest hundredth.

56. Unit Analysis If we assume light travels 186,000 miles in 1 second, we can find the number of miles in 1 light-year by converting 186,000 miles/second to miles/year. Find the number of miles in 1 light-year. Write your answer in expanded form and in scientific notation.

57. Ferris Wheel A Ferris wheel called Colossus has a circumference of 518 feet. If a trip around the circumference of Colossus takes 40 seconds, find the average speed of a rider in miles per hour. Round to the nearest tenth.

58. Fitness Walking The guidelines for fitness now indicate that a person who walks 10,000 steps daily is physically fit. According to *The Walking Site* on the Internet, "The average person's stride length is approximately 2.5 feet long. That means it takes just over 2,000 steps to walk one mile, and 10,000 steps is close to 5 miles." Use your knowledge of unit analysis to determine if these facts are correct.

Learning Objectives Assessment

The following problems can be used to help assess if you have successfully met the learning objectives for this section.

59. Multiply: $\dfrac{x^2 - x - 6}{2x - 10} \cdot \dfrac{6x - 30}{x^2 + 3x + 2}$.

a. $\dfrac{6x^3 - 36x^2 + 6x + 180}{2x^3 - 4x^2 + 26x - 20}$

b. $\dfrac{3(x - 3)}{x + 1}$

c. $\dfrac{3(x - 6)}{x + 2}$

d. -13

60. Divide: $\dfrac{x^2 - 3x - 4}{6} \div \dfrac{2x - 8}{x + 1}$.

a. $\dfrac{(x - 4)^2}{3}$

b. $\dfrac{x(x - 1)}{3}$

c. $\dfrac{(x + 1)^2}{12}$

d. $\dfrac{1}{3}$

61. Convert 10 miles per hour to feet per minute.

a. 0.00003 ft/min

b. 880 ft/min

c. 3,168,000 ft/min

d. 0.11 ft/min

Getting Ready for the Next Section

Perform the indicated operation.

62. $\dfrac{1}{5} + \dfrac{3}{5}$ **63.** $\dfrac{1}{7} + \dfrac{5}{7}$ **64.** $\dfrac{1}{10} + \dfrac{3}{14}$ **65.** $\dfrac{1}{21} + \dfrac{4}{15}$

66. $\dfrac{1}{10} - \dfrac{3}{14}$ **67.** $\dfrac{1}{21} - \dfrac{4}{15}$

Multiply.

68. $2(x - 3)$ **69.** $x(x + 2)$ **70.** $(x + 4)(x - 5)$ **71.** $(x + 3)(x - 4)$

Reduce to lowest terms.

72. $\dfrac{x + 3}{x^2 - 9}$ **73.** $\dfrac{x + 7}{x^2 - 49}$

74. $\dfrac{x^2 - x - 30}{50 - 2x^2}$ **75.** $\dfrac{x^2 - x - 20}{32 - 2x^2}$

Simplify.

76. $(x + 4)(x - 5) - 10$ **77.** $(x + 3)(x - 4) - 8$

Learning Objectives

In this section, we will learn how to:

1. Add and subtract rational expressions with a common denominator.
2. Identify the least common denominator for a set of rational expressions.
3. Add and subtract rational expressions that do not have a common denominator.

Introduction

In Chapter 1, we combined fractions having the same denominator by combining their numerators and putting the result over the common denominator. We use the same process to add two rational expressions with the same denominator.

Addition and Subtraction with Common Denominators

EXAMPLE 1   Add: $\dfrac{5}{x} + \dfrac{3}{x}$.

SOLUTION The two rational expressions have a common denominator of x. Adding numerators, we have:

$$\frac{5}{x} + \frac{3}{x} = \frac{8}{x}$$

EXAMPLE 2   Add: $\dfrac{x}{x^2 - 9} + \dfrac{3}{x^2 - 9}$.

SOLUTION   Since both expressions have the same denominator, we add numerators and reduce to lowest terms:

$$\frac{x}{x^2 - 9} + \frac{3}{x^2 - 9} = \frac{x + 3}{x^2 - 9}$$

$$= \frac{x + 3}{(x + 3)(x - 3)} \quad \left.\begin{array}{l} \text{Reduce to lowest terms by} \\ \text{factoring the denominator and} \\ \text{then dividing out the common} \\ \text{factor } x + 3 \end{array}\right.$$

$$= \frac{1}{x - 3}$$

EXAMPLE 3   Subtract: $\dfrac{6x - 13}{x^2 - 2x - 3} - \dfrac{2x - 1}{x^2 - 2x - 3}$.

SOLUTION The rational expressions have a common denominator, so we can subtract numerators and then reduce:

$$\frac{6x - 13}{x^2 - 2x - 3} - \frac{2x - 1}{x^2 - 2x - 3} = \frac{6x - 13 - (2x - 1)}{x^2 - 2x - 3} \quad \text{Subtract numerators}$$

$$= \frac{6x - 13 - 2x + 1}{x^2 - 2x - 3} \quad \begin{array}{l}\text{Distribute the} \\ \text{negative sign}\end{array}$$

$$= \frac{4x - 12}{x^2 - 2x - 3} \quad \text{Combine like terms}$$

$$= \frac{4(x - 3)}{(x + 1)(x - 3)} \quad \text{Factor}$$

$$= \frac{4}{x + 1} \quad \begin{array}{l}\text{Divide out common} \\ \text{factor of } x - 3\end{array}$$

Least Common Denominator

Remember, it is the distributive property that allows us to add rational expressions by simply adding numerators. Because of this, we must begin all addition problems involving rational expressions by first making sure all the expressions have the same denominator.

> **def   DEFINITION**   *least common denominator*
>
> The *least common denominator* (LCD) for a set of denominators is the simplest quantity that is evenly divisible by all the denominators.

If all of the denominators have been factored, then the LCD will be the product of each factor raised to the highest exponent it appears within any of the denominators.

Before we attempt to add or subtract rational expressions with different denominators, we will practice finding the least common denominator.

EXAMPLE 4   Find the least common denominator for the rational expressions

$$\frac{2}{x} \quad \text{and} \quad \frac{4}{x - 3}$$

SOLUTION   There are only two factors, x and $x - 3$. Since they both appear to the first power, the LCD is $x(x - 3)$. This is the simplest quantity divisible by both x and $x - 3$.

Note Because of the subtraction sign, the x appearing in the denominator $x - 3$ is a term, not a factor. That is why the LCD in Example 4 requires an additional x.

EXAMPLE 5   Find the least common denominator for the rational expressions

$$\frac{x - 5}{2x^2 + 4x + 2} \quad \text{and} \quad \frac{3x}{2x^2 - 2}$$

SOLUTION   Factoring both denominators, we have

$$2x^2 + 4x + 2 = 2(x^2 + 2x + 1) \quad \text{and} \quad 2x^2 - 2 = 2(x^2 - 1)$$
$$= 2(x + 1)^2 \qquad\qquad\qquad = 2(x + 1)(x - 1)$$

The factors appearing in the two denominators are 2, $x + 1$, and $x - 1$. The factors 2 and $x - 1$ only appear to the first power. The highest exponent of the factor $x + 1$ is 2. So we have:

$$\text{LCD} = 2(x - 1)(x + 1)^2$$

Notice that, even though the factor 2 appears in both denominators, it does not show up twice in the LCD. Likewise, the LCD only contains $(x + 1)^2$, not $(x + 1)^3$.

Addition and Subtraction with Different Denominators

Now that we are able to identify the least common denominator for a set of rational expressions, we are ready to add and subtract when the denominators are not identical. We will begin with an example that does not involve any variables.

EXAMPLE 6 Add: $\dfrac{1}{10} + \dfrac{3}{14}$.

SOLUTION

Step 1: Find the LCD for 10 and 14. To do so, we factor each denominator and build the LCD from the factors:

$$\left.\begin{array}{l} 10 = 2 \cdot 5 \\ 14 = 2 \cdot 7 \end{array}\right\} \quad \text{LCD} = 2 \cdot 5 \cdot 7 = 70$$

We know the LCD is divisible by 10 because it contains the factors 2 and 5. It is also divisible by 14 because it contains the factors 2 and 7.

Step 2: Change to equivalent fractions that each have a denominator of 70. To accomplish this task, we multiply the numerator and denominator of each fraction by any factors of the LCD that are not also factors of its denominator:

Original Fractions		Denominators in Factored Form		Multiply by Factor Needed to Obtain LCD		These Have the Same Value as the Original Fractions
$\dfrac{1}{10}$	$=$	$\dfrac{1}{2 \cdot 5}$	$=$	$\dfrac{1}{2 \cdot 5} \cdot \dfrac{7}{7}$	$=$	$\dfrac{7}{70}$
$\dfrac{3}{14}$	$=$	$\dfrac{3}{2 \cdot 7}$	$=$	$\dfrac{3}{2 \cdot 7} \cdot \dfrac{5}{5}$	$=$	$\dfrac{15}{70}$

The fraction $\frac{7}{70}$ has the same value as the fraction $\frac{1}{10}$. Likewise, the fractions $\frac{15}{70}$ and $\frac{3}{14}$ are equivalent; they have the same value.

Step 3: Add numerators and put the result over the LCD:

$$\frac{7}{70} + \frac{15}{70} = \frac{7 + 15}{70} = \frac{22}{70}$$

Step 4: Reduce to lowest terms:

$$\frac{22}{70} = \frac{11}{35} \qquad \text{Divide numerator and denominator by 2}$$

The main idea in adding fractions is to write each fraction again with the LCD for a denominator. Once we have done that, we simply add numerators. The same process can be used to add rational expressions, as the next example illustrates.

EXAMPLE 7 Subtract: $\dfrac{3}{x} - \dfrac{1}{2}$.

SOLUTION

Step 1: The LCD for x and 2 is $2x$. It is the smallest expression divisible by x and by 2.

Step 2: To change to equivalent expressions with the denominator $2x$, we multiply the first fraction by $\frac{2}{2}$ and the second by $\frac{x}{x}$:

$$\frac{3}{x} \cdot \frac{2}{2} = \frac{6}{2x}$$

$$\frac{1}{2} \cdot \frac{x}{x} = \frac{x}{2x}$$

Note If you have had difficulty in the past with addition and subtraction of fractions with different denominators, this is the time to get it straightened out. Go over Example 6 as many times as is necessary for you to understand the process.

Step 3:   Subtracting numerators of the rational expressions in step 2, we have

$$\frac{6}{2x} - \frac{x}{2x} = \frac{6 - x}{2x}$$

Step 4:   Since $6 - x$ and $2x$ do not have any factors in common, we cannot reduce any further. Here is the complete problem:

$$\frac{3}{x} - \frac{1}{2} = \frac{3}{x} \cdot \frac{2}{2} - \frac{1}{2} \cdot \frac{x}{x}$$

$$= \frac{6}{2x} - \frac{x}{2x}$$

$$= \frac{6 - x}{2x}$$

EXAMPLE 8   Add: $\dfrac{5}{2x - 6} + \dfrac{x}{x - 3}$.

SOLUTION   If we factor $2x - 6$, we have $2x - 6 = 2(x - 3)$. The LCD is $2(x - 3)$. We need only multiply the second rational expression in our problem by $\frac{2}{2}$ to have two expressions with the same denominator:

$$\frac{5}{2x - 6} + \frac{x}{x - 3} = \frac{5}{2(x - 3)} + \frac{x}{x - 3}$$

$$= \frac{5}{2(x - 3)} + \frac{2}{2}\left(\frac{x}{x - 3}\right)$$

$$= \frac{5}{2(x - 3)} + \frac{2x}{2(x - 3)}$$

$$= \frac{2x + 5}{2(x - 3)}$$

EXAMPLE 9   Add: $\dfrac{1}{x + 4} + \dfrac{8}{x^2 - 16}$.

SOLUTION   After writing each denominator in factored form, we find that the least common denominator is $(x + 4)(x - 4)$. To change the first rational expression to an equivalent rational expression with the common denominator, we multiply its numerator and denominator by $x - 4$:

$$\frac{1}{x + 4} + \frac{8}{x^2 - 16}$$

$$= \frac{1}{x + 4} + \frac{8}{(x + 4)(x - 4)} \qquad \text{Factor each denominator}$$

$$= \frac{1}{x + 4} \cdot \frac{x - 4}{x - 4} + \frac{8}{(x + 4)(x - 4)} \qquad \text{Change to equivalent rational expressions}$$

$$= \frac{x - 4}{(x + 4)(x - 4)} + \frac{8}{(x + 4)(x - 4)} \qquad \text{Simplify}$$

$$= \frac{x + 4}{(x + 4)(x - 4)} \qquad \text{Add numerators}$$

$$= \frac{1}{x - 4} \qquad \text{Divide out common factor } x + 4$$

EXAMPLE 10   Subtract: $\dfrac{2x-1}{x^2+5x+6} - \dfrac{x+1}{x^2-9}$.

SOLUTION

Step 1:   We factor each denominator and build the LCD from the factors:

$$\left.\begin{array}{r} x^2+5x+6=(x+2)(x+3) \\ x^2-9=(x+3)(x-3) \end{array}\right\} \quad \text{LCD} = (x+2)(x+3)(x-3)$$

Step 2:   Change to equivalent rational expressions:

Note In Step 2 of Example 10, we are using the FOIL method to find the product in each numerator.

$$\frac{2x-1}{x^2+5x+6} = \frac{2x-1}{(x+2)(x+3)} \cdot \frac{(x-3)}{(x-3)} = \frac{2x^2-7x+3}{(x+2)(x+3)(x-3)}$$

$$\frac{x+1}{x^2-9} = \frac{x+1}{(x+3)(x-3)} \cdot \frac{(x+2)}{(x+2)} = \frac{x^2+3x+2}{(x+2)(x+3)(x-3)}$$

Step 3:   Subtract numerators of the rational expressions produced in step 2:

$$\frac{2x^2-7x+3}{(x+2)(x+3)(x-3)} - \frac{x^2+3x+2}{(x+2)(x+3)(x-3)}$$

$$= \frac{2x^2-7x+3-(x^2+3x+2)}{(x+2)(x+3)(x-3)}$$

$$= \frac{2x^2-7x+3-x^2-3x-2}{(x+2)(x+3)(x-3)} \qquad \text{Distribute the}$$
$$\text{negative sign}$$

$$= \frac{x^2-10x+1}{(x+2)(x+3)(x-3)} \qquad \text{Combine like terms}$$

The numerator and denominator do not have any factors in common, so the expression cannot be simplified any further.

EXAMPLE 11   Subtract: $\dfrac{x+4}{2x+10} - \dfrac{5}{x^2-25}$.

SOLUTION   We begin by factoring each denominator:

$$\frac{x+4}{2x+10} - \frac{5}{x^2-25} = \frac{x+4}{2(x+5)} - \frac{5}{(x+5)(x-5)}$$

The LCD is $2(x+5)(x-5)$. Completing the problem, we have:

$$= \frac{x+4}{2(x+5)} \cdot \frac{(x-5)}{(x-5)} + \frac{-5}{(x+5)(x-5)} \cdot \frac{2}{2}$$

$$= \frac{x^2-x-20}{2(x+5)(x-5)} + \frac{-10}{2(x+5)(x-5)}$$

$$= \frac{x^2-x-30}{2(x+5)(x-5)}$$

To see if this expression will reduce, we factor the numerator into $(x-6)(x+5)$:

Note In the last step we reduced the rational expression to lowest terms by dividing out the common factor of $x+5$.

$$= \frac{(x-6)(x+5)}{2(x+5)(x-5)}$$

$$= \frac{x-6}{2(x-5)} \quad .$$

EXAMPLE 12   Write an expression for the sum of a number and its reciprocal, and then simplify that expression.

SOLUTION   If we let x be the number, then its reciprocal is $\frac{1}{x}$. To find the sum of the number and its reciprocal, we add them:

$$x + \frac{1}{x}$$

The first term x can be thought of as having a denominator of 1. Since the denominators are 1 and x, the least common denominator is x.

$$x + \frac{1}{x} = \frac{x}{1} + \frac{1}{x} \qquad \text{Write } x \text{ as } \frac{x}{1}$$

$$= \frac{x}{1} \cdot \frac{x}{x} + \frac{1}{x} \qquad \text{The LCD is } x$$

$$= \frac{x^2}{x} + \frac{1}{x}$$

$$= \frac{x^2 + 1}{x} \qquad \text{Add numerators}$$

Getting Ready for Class

After reading through the preceding section, respond in your own words and in complete sentences.

A. How do we add two rational expressions that have the same denominator?

B. What is the least common denominator for two fractions?

C. What role does factoring play in finding a least common denominator?

D. Explain how to find a common denominator for two rational expressions.

Find the following sums and differences.

1. $\dfrac{3}{x} + \dfrac{4}{x}$

2. $\dfrac{5}{x} + \dfrac{3}{x}$

3. $\dfrac{9}{a} - \dfrac{5}{a}$

4. $\dfrac{8}{a} - \dfrac{7}{a}$

5. $\dfrac{1}{x+1} + \dfrac{x}{x+1}$

6. $\dfrac{x}{x-3} - \dfrac{3}{x-3}$

7. $\dfrac{y^2}{y-1} - \dfrac{1}{y-1}$

8. $\dfrac{y^2}{y+3} - \dfrac{9}{y+3}$

9. $\dfrac{x^2}{x+2} + \dfrac{4x+4}{x+2}$

10. $\dfrac{x^2-6x}{x-3} + \dfrac{9}{x-3}$

11. $\dfrac{x^2}{x-2} - \dfrac{4x-4}{x-2}$

12. $\dfrac{x^2}{x-5} - \dfrac{10x-25}{x-5}$

13. $\dfrac{x+2}{x+6} - \dfrac{x-4}{x+6}$

14. $\dfrac{x+5}{x+2} - \dfrac{x+3}{x+2}$

Find the least common denominator for each pair of rational expresssions.

15. $\dfrac{2}{x}, \dfrac{x}{5}$

16. $\dfrac{x}{2}, \dfrac{3}{x+1}$

17. $\dfrac{4}{x}, \dfrac{x+5}{x-3}$

18. $\dfrac{4x}{x+2}, \dfrac{1}{x-2}$

19. $\dfrac{3}{2y^2}, \dfrac{y-1}{y(y+4)}$

20. $\dfrac{9}{(y+3)^2}, \dfrac{y-6}{4(y+3)}$

21. $\dfrac{a+5}{a^2-6a+8}, \dfrac{2a+1}{a^2+a-6}$

22. $\dfrac{a-2}{a^2-1}, \dfrac{4a}{a^2-6a+5}$

23. $\dfrac{4x-3}{x^2+6x+9}, \dfrac{x-1}{x^2+5x+6}$

24. $\dfrac{x+4}{3x^3-12x^2}, \dfrac{5x+2}{x^2-8x+16}$

Find the following sums and differences.

25. $\dfrac{y}{2} - \dfrac{2}{y}$

26. $\dfrac{3}{y} + \dfrac{y}{3}$

27. $\dfrac{a}{3} + \dfrac{1}{2}$

28. $\dfrac{2a}{5} + \dfrac{2}{3}$

29. $\dfrac{x}{x+1} + \dfrac{3}{4}$

30. $\dfrac{x}{x-3} + \dfrac{1}{3}$

31. $\dfrac{x+1}{x-2} - \dfrac{4x+7}{5x-10}$

32. $\dfrac{3x+1}{2x-6} - \dfrac{x+2}{x-3}$

33. $\dfrac{4x-2}{3x+12} - \dfrac{x-2}{x+4}$

34. $\dfrac{6x+5}{5x-25} - \dfrac{x+2}{x-5}$

35. $\dfrac{6}{x(x-2)} + \dfrac{3}{x}$

36. $\dfrac{10}{x(x+5)} - \dfrac{2}{x}$

37. $\dfrac{4}{a} - \dfrac{12}{a^2+3a}$

38. $\dfrac{5}{a} + \dfrac{20}{a^2-4a}$

39. $\dfrac{2}{x+5} - \dfrac{10}{x^2-25}$

40. $\dfrac{6}{x^2-1} + \dfrac{3}{x+1}$

41. $\dfrac{x-4}{x-3} + \dfrac{6}{x^2-9}$

42. $\dfrac{x+1}{x-1} - \dfrac{4}{x^2-1}$

43. $\dfrac{a-4}{a-3} + \dfrac{5}{a^2-a-6}$

44. $\dfrac{a+2}{a+1} + \dfrac{7}{a^2-5a-6}$

45. $\dfrac{8}{x^2-16} - \dfrac{7}{x^2-x-12}$

46. $\dfrac{6}{x^2-9} - \dfrac{5}{x^2-x-6}$

47. $\dfrac{4y}{y^2+6y+5} - \dfrac{3y}{y^2+5y+4}$

48. $\dfrac{3y}{y^2+7y+10} - \dfrac{2y}{y^2+6y+8}$

49. $\dfrac{4x+1}{x^2+5x+4} - \dfrac{x+3}{x^2+4x+3}$

50. $\dfrac{2x-1}{x^2+x-6} - \dfrac{x+2}{x^2+5x+6}$

51. $\dfrac{x-3}{x^2+4x+4} - \dfrac{x+1}{x^2-4}$

52. $\dfrac{2x-1}{x^2-6x+9} - \dfrac{x+3}{x^2+x-12}$

53. $\dfrac{1}{x} + \dfrac{x}{3x+9} - \dfrac{3}{x^2+3x}$

54. $\dfrac{1}{x} + \dfrac{x}{2x+4} - \dfrac{2}{x^2+2x}$

55. Paying Attention to Instructions Work each problem according to the instructions given.

a. Multiply: $\dfrac{4}{9} \cdot \dfrac{1}{6}$

b. Divide: $\dfrac{4}{9} \div \dfrac{1}{6}$

c. Add: $\dfrac{4}{9} + \dfrac{1}{6}$

d. Multiply: $\dfrac{x+2}{x-2} \cdot \dfrac{3x+10}{x^2-4}$

e. Divide: $\dfrac{x+2}{x-2} \div \dfrac{3x+10}{x^2-4}$

f. Subtract: $\dfrac{x+2}{x-2} - \dfrac{3x+10}{x^2-4}$

56. Paying Attention to Instructions Work each problem according to the instructions given.

a. Multiply: $\dfrac{9}{25} \cdot \dfrac{1}{15}$

b. Divide: $\dfrac{9}{25} \div \dfrac{1}{15}$

c. Subtract: $\dfrac{9}{25} - \dfrac{1}{15}$

d. Multiply: $\dfrac{3x-2}{3x+2} \cdot \dfrac{15x+6}{9x^2-4}$

e. Divide: $\dfrac{3x-2}{3x+2} \div \dfrac{15x+6}{9x^2-4}$

f. Subtract: $\dfrac{3x+2}{3x-2} - \dfrac{15x+6}{9x^2-4}$

Complete the following tables.

57.

Number	Reciprocal	Sum	Quotient
x	$\dfrac{1}{x}$	$1 + \dfrac{1}{x}$	$\dfrac{x+1}{x}$
1			
2			
3			
4			

58.

Number	Reciprocal	Difference	Quotient
x	$\dfrac{1}{x}$	$1 - \dfrac{1}{x}$	$\dfrac{x-1}{x}$
1			
2			
3			
4			

Add and subtract as indicated.

59. $1 + \dfrac{1}{x + 2}$ **60.** $1 - \dfrac{1}{x + 2}$ **61.** $1 - \dfrac{1}{x + 3}$ **62.** $1 + \dfrac{1}{x + 3}$

The following problems involve more than one operation. Simplify inside the parentheses first, then multiply.

63. $\left(1 - \dfrac{1}{x}\right)\left(1 - \dfrac{1}{x + 1}\right)\left(1 - \dfrac{1}{x + 2}\right)$ **64.** $\left(1 + \dfrac{1}{x}\right)\left(1 + \dfrac{1}{x + 1}\right)\left(1 + \dfrac{1}{x + 2}\right)$

65. $\left(1 + \dfrac{1}{x + 3}\right)\left(1 + \dfrac{1}{x + 2}\right)\left(1 + \dfrac{1}{x + 1}\right)$

66. $\left(1 - \dfrac{1}{x + 3}\right)\left(1 - \dfrac{1}{x + 2}\right)\left(1 - \dfrac{1}{x + 1}\right)$

Applying the Concepts

67. Number Problem Write an expression for the sum of a number and twice its reciprocal. Then, simplify that expression. (If the reciprocal of a number is $\frac{1}{x}$, then twice that is $\frac{2}{x}$, not $\frac{1}{2x}$.)

68. Number Problem Write an expression for the sum of a number and 3 times its reciprocal. Then, simplify that expression.

69. Number Problem One number is twice another. Write an expression for the sum of their reciprocals. Then, simplify that expression. Hint: The numbers are x and $2x$. Their reciprocals are, respectively, $\frac{1}{x}$ and $\frac{1}{2x}$.

70. Number Problem One number is three times another. Write an expression for the sum of their reciprocals. Then, simplify that expression.

Learning Objectives Assessment

The following problems can be used to help assess if you have successfully met the learning objectives for this section.

71. Add: $\dfrac{x^2 - 4x}{x - 5} + \dfrac{x - 10}{x - 5}$.

   a. $\dfrac{x^2 - 3x - 10}{(x - 5)^2}$ **b.** $\dfrac{x^2 - 5x + 10}{x - 5}$ **c.** $x + 2$ **d.** $\dfrac{x + 2}{2}$

72. Subtract: $\dfrac{3x + 2}{x + 4} - \dfrac{2x - 3}{x + 4}$.

   a. $\dfrac{x + 5}{x + 4}$ **b.** $\dfrac{x - 1}{x + 4}$ **c.** $x + 5$ **d.** $x - 1$

73. Find the least common denominator for $\dfrac{x + 2}{x^3 + 4x^2}$ and $\dfrac{x - 3}{x^2 - x}$.

   a. $(x^3 + 4x^2)(x^2 - x)$ **b.** $x^3(x + 4)(x - 1)$

   c. $x^2(x + 4)(x - 1)$ **d.** $x(x + 4)(x - 1)$

74. Add: $\dfrac{5x}{x^2 + 7x + 6} + \dfrac{3}{x^2 + 4x - 12}$.

   a. $\dfrac{5x + 3}{2x + 11x - 6}$ **b.** $5x^2 - 7x + 3$

   c. $\dfrac{5x^3 + 23x - 39x + 18}{(x + 1)(x - 2)(x + 6)}$ **d.** $\dfrac{5x^2 - 7x + 3}{(x + 1)(x + 6)(x - 2)}$

Getting Ready for the Next Section

Simplify.

75. $\dfrac{1}{2} \div \dfrac{2}{3}$ **76.** $\dfrac{1}{3} \div \dfrac{3}{4}$ **77.** $1 + \dfrac{1}{2}$ **78.** $1 + \dfrac{2}{3}$

79. $y^5 \cdot \dfrac{2x^3}{y^2}$ **80.** $y^7 \cdot \dfrac{3x^5}{y^4}$ **81.** $\dfrac{2x^3}{y^2} \cdot \dfrac{y^5}{4x}$ **82.** $\dfrac{3x^5}{y^4} \cdot \dfrac{y^7}{6x^2}$

Factor.

83. $x^2y + x$ **84.** $xy^2 + y$

Reduce.

85. $\dfrac{2x^3y^2}{4x}$ **86.** $\dfrac{3x^5y^3}{6x^2}$ **87.** $\dfrac{x^2 - 4}{x^2 - x - 6}$ **88.** $\dfrac{x^2 - 9}{x^2 - 5x + 6}$

Complex Fractions

Learning Objectives

In this section, we will learn how to:

1. Simplify complex fractions using the LCD method.

2. Simplify complex fractions using the division method.

Introduction

A complex fraction is a fraction or rational expression that contains other fractions in its numerator or denominator. Each of the following is a *complex fraction*:

$$\frac{\dfrac{1}{2}}{\dfrac{2}{3}} \qquad \frac{x + \dfrac{1}{y}}{y + \dfrac{1}{x}} \qquad \frac{\dfrac{a+1}{a^2-9}}{\dfrac{2}{a+3}}$$

We will begin this section by simplifying the first of these complex fractions.

VIDEO EXAMPLES

SECTION 7.4

EXAMPLE 1   Simplify $\dfrac{\dfrac{1}{2}}{\dfrac{2}{3}}$.

SOLUTION   There are two methods we can use to solve this problem.

LCD Method

We can multiply the numerator and denominator of this complex fraction by the LCD for both fractions. In this case the LCD is 6:

$$\frac{\dfrac{1}{2}}{\dfrac{2}{3}} = \frac{6 \cdot \dfrac{1}{2}}{6 \cdot \dfrac{2}{3}} = \frac{3}{4}$$

Division Method

We can treat this as a division problem. Instead of dividing by $\frac{2}{3}$, we can multiply by its reciprocal $\frac{3}{2}$:

$$\frac{\dfrac{1}{2}}{\dfrac{2}{3}} = \frac{1}{2} \div \frac{2}{3} = \frac{1}{2} \cdot \frac{3}{2} = \frac{3}{4}$$

Using either method, we obtain the same result.

EXAMPLE 2   Simplify: $\dfrac{\dfrac{2x^3}{y^2}}{\dfrac{4x}{y^5}}$.

SOLUTION

LCD Method
The LCD for each rational expression is y^5. Multiplying the numerator and denominator of the complex fraction by y^5, we have:

$$\frac{\dfrac{2x^3}{y^2}}{\dfrac{4x}{y^5}} = \frac{y^5 \cdot \dfrac{2x^3}{y^2}}{y^5 \cdot \dfrac{4x}{y^5}} = \frac{2x^3 y^3}{4x} = \frac{x^2 y^3}{2}$$

Division Method
Instead of dividing by $\dfrac{4x}{y^5}$ we can multiply by its reciprocal, $\dfrac{y^5}{4x}$:

$$\frac{\dfrac{2x^3}{y^2}}{\dfrac{4x}{y^5}} = \frac{2x^3}{y^2} \div \frac{4x}{y^5} = \frac{2x^3}{y^2} \cdot \frac{y^5}{4x} = \frac{x^2 y^3}{2}$$

Again the result is the same using either method.

EXAMPLE 3   Simplify: $\dfrac{x + \dfrac{1}{y}}{y + \dfrac{1}{x}}$

SOLUTION

Division Method
To apply the division method as we did in the first two examples, we first have to simplify the numerator and denominator separately to obtain a single rational expression for both before we can multiply by the reciprocal. Here are the steps:

$$\frac{x + \dfrac{1}{y}}{y + \dfrac{1}{x}} = \left(x + \frac{1}{y}\right) \div \left(y + \frac{1}{x}\right)$$

$$= \left(\frac{xy}{y} + \frac{1}{y}\right) \div \left(\frac{xy}{x} + \frac{1}{x}\right)$$

$$= \frac{xy + 1}{y} \div \frac{xy + 1}{x}$$

$$= \frac{xy + 1}{y} \cdot \frac{x}{xy + 1}$$

$$= \frac{x}{y}$$

LCD Method
It is much easier, in this case, to multiply the numerator and denominator by the LCD, which is xy:

$$\frac{x + \dfrac{1}{y}}{y + \dfrac{1}{x}} = \frac{xy\left(x + \dfrac{1}{y}\right)}{xy\left(y + \dfrac{1}{x}\right)}$$

Multiply numerator and denominator by xy

$$= \frac{xy \cdot x + xy \cdot \dfrac{1}{y}}{xy \cdot y + xy \cdot \dfrac{1}{x}}$$

Distributive property

$$= \frac{x^2y + x}{xy^2 + y}$$

Simplify

We can factor x from $x^2y + x$ and y from $xy^2 + y$ and then reduce to lowest terms:

$$= \frac{x(xy + 1)}{y(xy + 1)}$$

$$= \frac{x}{y}$$

Both the division method and the LCD method can be used to simplify any complex fraction. In choosing which method to use, you may find these guidelines helpful:

> If the numerator and denominator of the complex fraction are single fractions, the division method is usually faster.

> If the numerator or denominator contains more than one fraction (two or more terms), the LCD method is typically faster.

EXAMPLE 4 Simplify: $\dfrac{1 - \dfrac{4}{x^2}}{1 - \dfrac{1}{x} - \dfrac{6}{x^2}}$

SOLUTION The easiest way to simplify this complex fraction is to multiply the numerator and denominator by the LCD, x^2:

$$\frac{1 - \dfrac{4}{x^2}}{1 - \dfrac{1}{x} - \dfrac{6}{x^2}} = \frac{x^2\left(1 - \dfrac{4}{x^2}\right)}{x^2\left(1 - \dfrac{1}{x} - \dfrac{6}{x^2}\right)}$$

Multiply numerator and denominator by x^2

$$= \frac{x^2 \cdot 1 - x^2 \cdot \dfrac{4}{x^2}}{x^2 \cdot 1 - x^2 \cdot \dfrac{1}{x} - x^2 \cdot \dfrac{6}{x^2}}$$

Distributive property

$$= \frac{x^2 - 4}{x^2 - x - 6}$$

Simplify

$$= \frac{(x - 2)(x + 2)}{(x - 3)(x + 2)}$$

Factor

$$= \frac{x - 2}{x - 3}$$

Reduce

In the introduction to Chapter 1, we mentioned a sequence of numbers that was related closely to the numbers in the Fibonacci sequence. In our next example, we find the relationship between that sequence and the numbers in the Fibonacci sequence.

EXAMPLE 5   Simplify each term in the following sequence, and then explain how this sequence is related to the Fibonacci sequence:

$$1 + \frac{1}{1+1}, \quad 1 + \frac{1}{1+\dfrac{1}{1+1}}, \quad 1 + \frac{1}{1+\dfrac{1}{1+\dfrac{1}{1+1}}}, \ldots$$

SOLUTION   We can simplify our work somewhat if we notice that the first term $1 + \frac{1}{1+1}$ is the denominator of the complex fraction in the second term and that the second term is the denominator of the complex fraction in the third term:

First term: $1 + \dfrac{1}{1+1} = 1 + \dfrac{1}{2} = \dfrac{2}{2} + \dfrac{1}{2} = \dfrac{3}{2}$

Second term: $1 + \dfrac{1}{1+\dfrac{1}{1+1}} = 1 + \dfrac{1}{\dfrac{3}{2}} = 1 + \dfrac{2}{3} = \dfrac{3}{3} + \dfrac{2}{3} = \dfrac{5}{3}$

Third term: $1 + \dfrac{1}{1+\dfrac{1}{1+\dfrac{1}{1+1}}} = 1 + \dfrac{1}{\dfrac{5}{3}} = 1 + \dfrac{3}{5} = \dfrac{5}{5} + \dfrac{3}{5} = \dfrac{8}{5}$

Here are the simplified numbers for the first three terms in our sequence:

$$\frac{3}{2}, \frac{5}{3}, \frac{8}{5}, \ldots$$

Recall the Fibonacci sequence:

$$1, 1, 2, 3, 5, 8, 13, 21, \ldots$$

As you can see, each term in the sequence we have simplified is the ratio of two consecutive numbers in the Fibonacci sequence. If the pattern continues in this manner, the next number in our sequence will be $\frac{13}{8}$.

Getting Ready for Class

After reading through the preceding section, respond in your own words and in complete sentences.

A. What is a complex fraction?

B. Explain the division method of simplifying complex fractions.

C. How is a least common denominator used to simplify a complex fraction?

D. What types of complex fractions can be rewritten as division problems?

Simplify each complex fraction using either method.

1. $\dfrac{\frac{3}{4}}{\frac{1}{8}}$

2. $\dfrac{\frac{1}{3}}{\frac{5}{6}}$

3. $\dfrac{\frac{2}{3}}{\frac{4}{}}$

4. $\dfrac{5}{\frac{1}{2}}$

5. $\dfrac{\frac{x^2}{y}}{\frac{x}{y^3}}$

6. $\dfrac{\frac{x^5}{y^3}}{\frac{x^2}{y^8}}$

7. $\dfrac{\frac{4x^3}{y^6}}{\frac{8x^2}{y^7}}$

8. $\dfrac{\frac{6x^4}{y}}{\frac{2x}{y^5}}$

9. $\dfrac{y + \frac{1}{x}}{x + \frac{1}{y}}$

10. $\dfrac{y - \frac{1}{x}}{x - \frac{1}{y}}$

11. $\dfrac{1 + \frac{1}{a}}{1 - \frac{1}{a}}$

12. $\dfrac{\frac{1}{a} - 1}{\frac{1}{a} + 1}$

13. $\dfrac{\frac{x+1}{x^2-9}}{\frac{2}{x+3}}$

14. $\dfrac{\frac{3}{x-5}}{\frac{x+1}{x^2-25}}$

15. $\dfrac{\frac{1}{a+2}}{\frac{1}{a^2-a-6}}$

16. $\dfrac{\frac{1}{a^2+5a+6}}{\frac{1}{a+3}}$

17. $\dfrac{1 - \frac{9}{y^2}}{1 - \frac{1}{y} - \frac{6}{y^2}}$

18. $\dfrac{1 - \frac{4}{y^2}}{1 - \frac{2}{y} - \frac{8}{y^2}}$

19. $\dfrac{\frac{1}{y} + \frac{1}{x}}{\frac{1}{xy}}$

20. $\dfrac{\frac{1}{xy}}{\frac{1}{y} - \frac{1}{x}}$

21. $\dfrac{1 - \frac{1}{a^2}}{1 - \frac{1}{a}}$

22. $\dfrac{1 + \frac{1}{a}}{1 - \frac{1}{a^2}}$

23. $\dfrac{\frac{1}{10x} - \frac{y}{10x^2}}{\frac{1}{10} - \frac{y}{10x}}$

24. $\dfrac{\frac{1}{2x} + \frac{y}{2x^2}}{\frac{1}{4} + \frac{y}{4x}}$

25. $\dfrac{\frac{1}{a+1} + 2}{\frac{1}{a+1} + 3}$

26. $\dfrac{\frac{2}{a+1} + 3}{\frac{3}{a+1} + 4}$

27. Simplify each term in the following sequence.

$$2 + \frac{1}{2+1}, \, 2 + \cfrac{1}{2 + \cfrac{1}{2+1}}, \, 2 + \cfrac{1}{2 + \cfrac{1}{2 + \cfrac{1}{2+1}}}, \ldots$$

28. Simplify each term in the following sequence.

$$2 + \frac{3}{2+3}, \, 2 + \cfrac{3}{2 + \cfrac{3}{2+3}}, \, 2 + \cfrac{3}{2 + \cfrac{3}{2 + \cfrac{3}{2+3}}}, \ldots$$

Complete the following tables.

29.

Number	Reciprocal	Quotient	Square
x	$\dfrac{1}{x}$	$\dfrac{x}{\frac{1}{x}}$	x^2
1			
2			
3			
4			

30.

Number	Reciprocal	Quotient	Square
x	$\dfrac{1}{x}$	$\dfrac{\frac{1}{x}}{x}$	x^2
1			
2			
3			
4			

31.

Number	Reciprocal	Sum	Quotient
x	$\dfrac{1}{x}$	$1 + \dfrac{1}{x}$	$\dfrac{1 + \frac{1}{x}}{\frac{1}{x}}$
1			
2			
3			
4			

32.

Number	Reciprocal	Difference	Quotient
x	$\dfrac{1}{x}$	$1 - \dfrac{1}{x}$	$\dfrac{1 - \frac{1}{x}}{\frac{1}{x}}$
1			
2			
3			
4			

Learning Objectives Assessment

The following problems can be used to help assess if you have successfully met the learning objectives for this section.

33. Simplify using the division method: $\dfrac{\dfrac{5x^2}{x^2-16}}{\dfrac{2x}{x+4}}$.

a. $\dfrac{10x^3}{(x+4)^2(x-4)}$

b. $\dfrac{2(x-4)}{5x}$

c. $\dfrac{5x}{2}$

d. $\dfrac{5x}{2(x-4)}$

34. Simplify using the LCD method: $\dfrac{\dfrac{2}{3}+\dfrac{4}{x}}{\dfrac{3}{x}+\dfrac{1}{2}}$.

a. 2

b. 1

c. $\dfrac{4}{3}$

d. $\dfrac{3(x+2)}{2(x+3)}$

Getting Ready for the Next Section

Simplify.

35. $6\left(\dfrac{1}{2}\right)$

36. $10\left(\dfrac{1}{5}\right)$

37. $\dfrac{0}{5}$

38. $\dfrac{0}{2}$

39. $\dfrac{5}{0}$

40. $\dfrac{2}{0}$

41. $1-\dfrac{5}{2}$

42. $1-\dfrac{5}{3}$

Use the distributive property to simplify.

43. $6\left(\dfrac{x}{3}+\dfrac{5}{2}\right)$

44. $10\left(\dfrac{x}{2}+\dfrac{3}{5}\right)$

45. $x^2\left(1-\dfrac{5}{x}\right)$

46. $x^2\left(1-\dfrac{3}{x}\right)$

Solve.

47. $2x+15=3$

48. $15=3x-3$

49. $-2x-9=x-3$

50. $a^2-a-22=-2$

SPOTLIGHT ON SUCCESS   *Instructor Edwin*

You never fail until you stop trying.
                                    —*Albert Einstein*

Coming to the United States at the age of 10 and not knowing how to speak English was a very difficult hurdle to overcome. However, with hard work and dedication I was able to rise above those obstacles. When I came to the U.S. our school did not have a strong English development program as it was known at that time, English as a Second Language (ESL). The approach back then was "sink or swim." When my self-esteem was low, my mom and my three older sisters were always there for me and they would always encourage me to do well. My mom was a single parent, and her number one priority was that we would receive a good education. My mother's perseverance is what has made me the person I am today. At a young age I was able to see that she had overcome more than what my situation was, and I would always tell myself, "if Mom can do it, I could also do it." Not only did she not have an education, but she also saved us from a civil war that was happening in my home country of El Salvador.

When things in school got hard, I would always reflect on all the hard work, sacrifice and effort of my mother. I would just tell myself that I should not have any excuses and that I needed to keep going. If my mother, who worked as a housekeeper, could send all four of her kids to college doesn't motivate you, I don't know what does. It definitely motivated me. The day everything began to change for me was when I was in eighth grade. I was sitting in my biology class not paying attention to the teacher because I was really focusing on a piece of paper on the wall. It said, "You never fail until you stop trying." I read it over and over, trying to digest what the quote meant. With my limited English I was doing my best to translate what it meant in my native language. It finally clicked! I was able to figure out what those seven words meant. I memorized the quote and began to apply it to my academics and to real-life situations. I began to really focus in my studies. I wanted to do well in school, and most important I wanted to improve my English. To this day I always reflect to that quote when I feel I can't do something.

I was able to finish junior high successfully. Going to high school was a lot easier and I ended up with very good grades and eventually I was accepted to an excellent college. I was never the smartest student on campus, but I always did well because I never quit. I earned my college degree and now I teach at a dual immersion elementary school. I have that same quote in my classroom and I constantly remind my students to never stop trying.

Learning Objectives

In this section, we will learn how to:

1. Solve an equation containing rational expressions using the LCD.

2. Identify extraneous solutions to rational equations.

Introduction

The first step in solving an equation that contains one or more rational expressions is to find the LCD for all denominators in the equation. Once the LCD has been found, we multiply both sides of the equation by the LCD in order to clear fractions. The resulting equation should be equivalent to the original one (unless we inadvertently multiplied by zero) and free from any denominators except the number 1.

VIDEO EXAMPLES

SECTION 7.5

EXAMPLE 1 Solve $\dfrac{x}{3} + \dfrac{5}{2} = \dfrac{1}{2}$ for x.

SOLUTION The LCD for 3 and 2 is 6. If we multiply both sides by 6, we have:

$$6\left(\frac{x}{3} + \frac{5}{2}\right) = 6\left(\frac{1}{2}\right) \qquad \text{Multiply both sides by 6}$$

$$6\left(\frac{x}{3}\right) + 6\left(\frac{5}{2}\right) = 6\left(\frac{1}{2}\right) \qquad \text{Distributive property}$$

$$2x + 15 = 3$$

$$2x = -12$$

$$x = -6$$

We can check our solution by replacing x with -6 in the original equation:

$$-\frac{6}{3} + \frac{5}{2} \overset{?}{=} \frac{1}{2}$$

$$\frac{1}{2} = \frac{1}{2}$$

Multiplying both sides of an equation containing fractions by the LCD clears the equation of all denominators, because the LCD has the property that all denominators will divide it evenly.

EXAMPLE 2 Solve for x: $\dfrac{3}{x-1} = \dfrac{3}{5}$.

SOLUTION The LCD for $(x-1)$ and 5 is $5(x-1)$. Multiplying both sides by $5(x-1)$, we have:

$$5(x-1) \cdot \frac{3}{x-1} = 5(x-1) \cdot \frac{3}{5}$$

$$5 \cdot 3 = (x-1) \cdot 3$$

$$15 = 3x - 3$$

$$18 = 3x$$

$$6 = x$$

If we substitute $x = 6$ into the original equation, we have:

$$\frac{3}{6-1} \stackrel{?}{=} \frac{3}{5}$$

$$\frac{3}{5} = \frac{3}{5}$$

The solution set is {6}.

EXAMPLE 3   Solve: $1 + \dfrac{6}{x^2} = \dfrac{5}{x}$.

SOLUTION   The LCD is x^2. Multiplying both sides by x^2, we have

$$x^2\left(1 + \frac{6}{x^2}\right) = x^2\left(\frac{5}{x}\right) \qquad \text{Multiply both sides by } x^2$$

$$x^2(1) + x^2\left(\frac{6}{x^2}\right) = x^2\left(\frac{5}{x}\right) \qquad \text{Apply distributive property to the left side}$$

$$x^2 + 6 = 5x \qquad \text{Simplify each side}$$

We have a quadratic equation, which we write in standard form, factor, and solve as we did in Chapter 6.

$$x^2 - 5x + 6 = 0 \qquad\qquad \text{Standard form}$$

$$(x - 2)(x - 3) = 0 \qquad\qquad \text{Factor}$$

$$x - 2 = 0 \quad \text{or} \quad x - 3 = 0 \qquad \text{Set factors equal to } 0$$

$$x = 2 \quad \text{or} \qquad x = 3$$

The two possible solutions are 2 and 3. Checking each in the original equation, we find they both give true statements. They are both solutions to the original equation:

Check $x = 2$ Check $x = 3$

$$1 + \frac{6}{4} \stackrel{?}{=} \frac{5}{2} \qquad\qquad 1 + \frac{6}{9} \stackrel{?}{=} \frac{5}{3}$$

$$1 + \frac{3}{2} \stackrel{?}{=} \frac{5}{2} \qquad\qquad 1 + \frac{2}{3} \stackrel{?}{=} \frac{5}{3}$$

$$\frac{2}{2} + \frac{3}{2} \stackrel{?}{=} \frac{5}{2} \qquad\qquad \frac{3}{3} + \frac{2}{3} \stackrel{?}{=} \frac{5}{3}$$

$$\frac{5}{2} = \frac{5}{2} \qquad\qquad\qquad \frac{5}{3} = \frac{5}{3}$$

EXAMPLE 4 Solve: $\dfrac{x}{x^2 - 9} - \dfrac{3}{x - 3} = \dfrac{1}{x + 3}$.

SOLUTION The factors of $x^2 - 9$ are $(x + 3)(x - 3)$, so the LCD is $(x + 3)(x - 3)$:

$$(x + 3)(x - 3) \cdot \frac{x}{(x + 3)(x - 3)} - (x + 3)(x - 3) \cdot \frac{3}{x - 3}$$

$$= (x + 3)(x - 3) \cdot \frac{1}{x + 3}$$

$$x - (x + 3)(3) = (x - 3)1$$

$$x - 3x - 9 = x - 3$$

$$-2x - 9 = x - 3$$

$$-3x = 6$$

$$x = -2$$

The solution is $x = -2$. It checks when replaced for x in the original equation.

EXAMPLE 5 Solve: $\dfrac{x}{x - 3} + \dfrac{3}{2} = \dfrac{3}{x - 3}$.

SOLUTION We begin by multiplying each term on both sides of the equation by $2(x - 3)$:

$$2(x - 3) \cdot \frac{x}{x - 3} + 2(x - 3) \cdot \frac{3}{2} = 2(x - 3) \cdot \frac{3}{x - 3}$$

$$2x + (x - 3) \cdot 3 = 2 \cdot 3$$

$$2x + 3x - 9 = 6$$

$$5x - 9 = 6$$

$$5x = 15$$

$$x = 3$$

Our only possible solution is $x = 3$. If we substitute $x = 3$ into the original equation, we get:

$$\frac{3}{3 - 3} + \frac{3}{2} \overset{?}{=} \frac{3}{3 - 3}$$

$$\frac{3}{0} + \frac{3}{2} = \frac{3}{0}$$

Two of the terms are undefined, so the equation is meaningless. Because $x = 3$ does not satisfy the equation, it is not a solution. Therefore, the equation has no solution, and the solution set is $\varnothing$.

The value of $x = 3$ in Example 5 is called an *extraneous solution*. When we multiply both sides of an equation by an LCD that contains a variable, we could be multiplying both sides by zero. The equation produced by doing this is not equivalent to the original equation, and it may result in extraneous solutions.

We always must check our solution when we multiply both sides of an equation by an expression containing the variable to make sure we have not multiplied both sides by zero.

EXAMPLE 6   Solve $\dfrac{a + 4}{a^2 + 5a} = \dfrac{-2}{a^2 - 25}$ for a.

SOLUTION   Factoring each denominator, we have:

$$a^2 + 5a = a(a + 5)$$

$$a^2 - 25 = (a + 5)(a - 5)$$

The LCD is $a(a + 5)(a - 5)$. Multiplying both sides of the equation by the LCD gives us:

$$a(a + 5)(a - 5) \cdot \frac{a + 4}{a(a + 5)} = a(a + 5)(a - 5) \cdot \frac{-2}{(a + 5)(a - 5)}$$

$$(a - 5)(a + 4) = -2a$$

$$a^2 - a - 20 = -2a$$

The result is a quadratic equation, which we write in standard form, factor, and solve:

$$a^2 + a - 20 = 0 \qquad\qquad\qquad \text{Add } 2a \text{ to both sides}$$

$$(a + 5)(a - 4) = 0 \qquad\qquad\qquad \text{Factor}$$

$$a + 5 = 0 \quad \text{ or } \quad a - 4 = 0 \qquad \text{Set factors equal to 0}$$

$$a = -5 \quad \text{ or } \qquad a = 4$$

The two possible solutions are -5 and 4. There is no problem with $a = 4$. It checks when substituted for a in the original equation. However, -5 is not a solution. Substituting -5 into the original equation gives:

$$\frac{-5 + 4}{(-5)^2 + 5(-5)} \overset{?}{=} \frac{-2}{(-5)^2 - 25}$$

$$\frac{-1}{0} = \frac{-2}{0}$$

Because $a = -5$ does not satisfy the original equation, it is an extraneous solution. The only valid solution to the equation is $a = 4$.

Getting Ready for Class

After reading through the preceding section, respond in your own words and in complete sentences.

A. What is the first step in solving an equation that contains rational expressions?

B. Explain how the LCD is used to clear an equation of fractions.

C. Why do we sometimes get extraneous solutions when solving rational equations?

D. How do we check for extraneous solutions to an equation containing rational expressions?

Solve the following equations. Be sure to check for extraneous solutions if you multiply both sides by an expression that contains the variable.

1. $\dfrac{x}{3} + \dfrac{1}{2} = -\dfrac{1}{2}$

2. $\dfrac{x}{2} + \dfrac{4}{3} = -\dfrac{2}{3}$

3. $\dfrac{4}{a} = \dfrac{1}{5}$

4. $\dfrac{2}{3} = \dfrac{6}{a}$

5. $\dfrac{3}{x} + 1 = \dfrac{2}{x}$

6. $\dfrac{4}{x} + 3 = \dfrac{1}{x}$

7. $\dfrac{3}{a} - \dfrac{2}{a} = \dfrac{1}{5}$

8. $\dfrac{7}{a} + \dfrac{1}{a} = 2$

9. $\dfrac{3}{x} + 2 = \dfrac{1}{2}$

10. $\dfrac{5}{x} + 3 = \dfrac{4}{3}$

11. $\dfrac{1}{y} - \dfrac{1}{2} = -\dfrac{1}{4}$

12. $\dfrac{3}{y} - \dfrac{4}{5} = -\dfrac{1}{5}$

13. $1 - \dfrac{8}{x} = \dfrac{-15}{x^2}$

14. $1 - \dfrac{3}{x} = \dfrac{-2}{x^2}$

15. $\dfrac{x}{2} - \dfrac{4}{x} = -\dfrac{7}{2}$

16. $\dfrac{x}{2} - \dfrac{5}{x} = -\dfrac{3}{2}$

17. $\dfrac{x-3}{2} + \dfrac{2x}{3} = \dfrac{5}{6}$

18. $\dfrac{x-2}{3} + \dfrac{5x}{2} = 5$

19. $\dfrac{x+1}{3} + \dfrac{x-3}{4} = \dfrac{1}{6}$

20. $\dfrac{x+2}{3} + \dfrac{x-1}{5} = -\dfrac{3}{5}$

21. $\dfrac{6}{x+2} = \dfrac{3}{5}$

22. $\dfrac{4}{x+3} = \dfrac{1}{2}$

23. $\dfrac{3}{y-2} = \dfrac{2}{y-3}$

24. $\dfrac{5}{y+1} = \dfrac{4}{y+2}$

25. $\dfrac{x}{x-2} + \dfrac{2}{3} = \dfrac{2}{x-2}$

26. $\dfrac{x}{x-5} + \dfrac{1}{5} = \dfrac{5}{x-5}$

27. $\dfrac{x}{x-2} + \dfrac{3}{2} = \dfrac{9}{2(x-2)}$

28. $\dfrac{x}{x+1} + \dfrac{4}{5} = \dfrac{-14}{5(x+1)}$

29. $\dfrac{5}{x+2} + \dfrac{1}{x+3} = \dfrac{-1}{x^2+5x+6}$

30. $\dfrac{3}{x-1} + \dfrac{2}{x+3} = \dfrac{-3}{x^2+2x-3}$

31. $\dfrac{8}{x^2-4} + \dfrac{3}{x+2} = \dfrac{1}{x-2}$

32. $\dfrac{10}{x^2-25} - \dfrac{1}{x-5} = \dfrac{3}{x+5}$

33. $\dfrac{a}{2} + \dfrac{3}{a-3} = \dfrac{a}{a-3}$

34. $\dfrac{a}{2} + \dfrac{4}{a-4} = \dfrac{a}{a-4}$

35. $\dfrac{6}{y^2-4} = \dfrac{4}{y^2+2y}$

36. $\dfrac{2}{y^2-9} = \dfrac{5}{y^2+3y}$

37. $\dfrac{2}{a^2-9} = \dfrac{3}{a^2+a-12}$

38. $\dfrac{2}{a^2-1} = \dfrac{6}{a^2-2a-3}$

39. $\dfrac{3x}{x-5} - \dfrac{2x}{x+1} = \dfrac{-42}{x^2-4x-5}$

40. $\dfrac{4x}{x-4} - \dfrac{3x}{x-2} = \dfrac{-3}{x^2-6x+8}$

41. $\dfrac{2x}{x+2} = \dfrac{x}{x+3} - \dfrac{3}{x^2+5x+6}$

42. $\dfrac{3x}{x-4} = \dfrac{2x}{x-3} + \dfrac{6}{x^2-7x+12}$

43. Solve each equation.

a. $5x - 1 = 0$

b. $\dfrac{5}{x} - 1 = 0$

c. $\dfrac{x}{5} - 1 = \dfrac{2}{3}$

d. $\dfrac{5}{x} - 1 = \dfrac{2}{3}$

e. $\dfrac{5}{x^2} + 5 = \dfrac{26}{x}$

44. Solve each equation.

a. $2x - 3 = 0$

b. $2 - \dfrac{3}{x} = 0$

c. $\dfrac{x}{3} - 2 = \dfrac{1}{2}$

d. $\dfrac{3}{x} - 2 = \dfrac{1}{2}$

e. $\dfrac{1}{x} + \dfrac{3}{x^2} = 2$

45. Paying Attention to Instructions Work each problem according to the instructions given.

  a. Divide: $\dfrac{7}{a^2 - 5a - 6} \div \dfrac{a + 2}{a + 1}$

  b. Add: $\dfrac{7}{a^2 - 5a - 6} + \dfrac{a + 2}{a + 1}$

  c. Solve: $\dfrac{7}{a^2 - 5a - 6} + \dfrac{a + 2}{a + 1} = 2$

46. Paying Attention to Instructions Work each problem according to the instructions given.

  a. Divide: $\dfrac{6}{x^2 - 9} \div \dfrac{x - 4}{x - 3}$

  b. Add: $\dfrac{6}{x^2 - 9} + \dfrac{x - 4}{x - 3}$

  c. Solve: $\dfrac{6}{x^2 - 9} + \dfrac{x - 4}{x - 3} = \dfrac{3}{4}$

Learning Objectives Assessment

The following problems can be used to help assess if you have successfully met the learning objectives for this section.

47. Solve: $\dfrac{2x}{x + 3} - \dfrac{1}{2} = \dfrac{6}{x + 3}$.

  a. 5   **b.** $\dfrac{3(x - 5)}{2(x + 3)}$ **c.** 3   **d.** $\varnothing$

48. Which value is an extraneous solution to the following equation?

$$\frac{x}{x + 4} + \frac{1}{x - 4} = \frac{8}{(x + 4)(x - 4)}$$

  a. -1 **b.** -4 **c.** 4   **d.** 0

Getting Ready for the Next Section

Solve.

49. $21 = 6x$ **50.** $72 = 2x$ **51.** $x^2 + x = 6$ **52.** $x^2 + 2x = 8$

Proportions

Learning Objectives

In this section, we will learn how to:

1. Solve a proportion.
2. Solve applied problems involving proportions.

Introduction

A proportion is two equal ratios; that is, if $\frac{a}{b}$ and $\frac{c}{d}$ are ratios, then:

$$\frac{a}{b} = \frac{c}{d}$$

is a proportion.

Each of the four numbers in a proportion is called a *term* of the proportion. We number the terms as follows:

$$\begin{array}{l} \text{First term} \rightarrow a \\ \text{Second term} \rightarrow b \end{array} \frac{}{} \begin{array}{l} c \leftarrow \text{Third term} \\ d \leftarrow \text{Fourth term} \end{array}$$

The first and fourth terms are called the *extremes*, and the second and third terms are called the *means*:

$$\text{Means} \quad \frac{a}{b} = \frac{c}{d} \quad \text{Extremes}$$

For example, in the proportion:

$$\frac{3}{8} = \frac{12}{32}$$

the extremes are 3 and 32, and the means are 8 and 12.

∆≠∑ PROPERTY *Means-Extremes Property*

Let a, b, c, and d be real numbers with $b \neq 0$ and $d \neq 0$.

If $\quad \frac{a}{b} = \frac{c}{d}$

then $\quad ad = bc$

In words: In any proportion, the product of the extremes is equal to the product of the means.

This property of proportions comes from the multiplication property of equality. We can use it to solve for a missing term in a proportion.

EXAMPLE 1   Solve the proportion $\dfrac{3}{x} = \dfrac{6}{7}$ for x.

SOLUTION   We could solve for x by using the method developed in Section 7.5; that is, multiplying both sides by the LCD of $7x$. Instead, let's use our new means-extremes property:

$$\dfrac{3}{x} = \dfrac{6}{7} \qquad \text{Extremes are 3 and 7; means are } x \text{ and 6}$$

$$21 = 6x \qquad \text{Product of extremes} = \text{product of means}$$

$$\dfrac{21}{6} = x \qquad \text{Divide both sides by 6}$$

$$x = \dfrac{7}{2} \qquad \text{Reduce to lowest terms}$$

If x is replaced with $\frac{7}{2}$ in the proportion, the result is a true statement. Therefore, the solution set is $\left\{ \frac{7}{2} \right\}$.

EXAMPLE 2   Solve for x: $\dfrac{x+1}{2} = \dfrac{3}{x}$.

SOLUTION   Again, we want to point out that we could solve for x by using the method we used in Section 7.5. Using the means-extremes property is simply an alternative to the method developed in Section 7.5:

$$\dfrac{x+1}{2} = \dfrac{3}{x} \qquad \text{Extremes are } x + 1 \text{ and } x\,; \text{ means are 2 and 3}$$

$$x^2 + x = 6 \qquad \text{Product of extremes} = \text{product of means}$$

$$x^2 + x - 6 = 0 \qquad \text{Standard form for a quadratic equation}$$

$$(x + 3)(x - 2) = 0 \qquad \text{Factor}$$

$$x + 3 = 0 \quad \text{or} \quad x - 2 = 0 \qquad \text{Set factors equal to 0}$$

$$x = -3 \quad \text{or} \quad x = 2$$

Because both values satisfy the proportion, we have two solutions: -3 and 2.

Applications

EXAMPLE 3   A manufacturer knows that during a production run, 8 out of every 100 parts produced by a certain machine will be defective. If the machine produces 1,450 parts, how many can be expected to be defective?

SOLUTION   The ratio of defective parts to total parts produced is $\frac{8}{100}$. If we let x represent the number of defective parts out of the total of 1,450 parts, then we can write this ratio again as $\frac{x}{1,450}$. This gives us a proportion to solve:

$$\underset{\substack{\text{Defective parts in numerator} \\ \text{Total parts in denominator}}}{\dfrac{x}{1,450}} = \dfrac{8}{100} \qquad \substack{\text{Extremes are } x \text{ and 100;} \\ \text{means are 1,450 and 8}}$$

$$100x = 11,600 \qquad \substack{\text{Product of extremes} \\ = \text{ product of means}}$$

$$x = 116$$

The manufacturer can expect 116 defective parts out of the total of 1,450 parts if the machine usually produces 8 defective parts for every 100 parts it produces.

EXAMPLE 4   A woman drives her car 270 miles in 6 hours. If she continues at the same rate, how far will she travel in 10 hours?

SOLUTION   We let x represent the distance traveled in 10 hours. Using x, we translate the problem into the following proportion:

$$\text{Miles} \longrightarrow \frac{x}{10} = \frac{270}{6} \longleftarrow \text{Miles}$$
$$\text{Hours} \longrightarrow \qquad\qquad \longleftarrow \text{Hours}$$

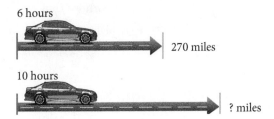

6 hours

270 miles

10 hours

? miles

Notice that the two ratios in the proportion compare the same quantities. That is, both ratios compare miles to hours. In words this proportion says:

x miles is to 10 hours as 270 miles is to 6 hours

$$\frac{x}{10} = \frac{270}{6}$$

Next, we solve the proportion.

$$6x = 2700$$
$$x = 450 \text{ miles}$$

If the woman continues at the same rate, she will travel 450 miles in 10 hours.

EXAMPLE 5   A baseball player gets 8 hits in the first 18 games of the season. If he continues at the same rate, how many hits will he get in 45 games?

SOLUTION   We let x represent the number of hits he will get in 45 games. Then

x is to 45 as 8 is to 18

$$\text{Hits} \rightarrow \frac{x}{45} = \frac{8}{18} \leftarrow \text{Hits}$$
$$\text{Games} \rightarrow \qquad\qquad \leftarrow \text{Games}$$

Notice again that the two ratios are comparing the same quantities, hits to games. We solve the proportion as follows:

$$18x = 360$$
$$x = 20$$

If he continues to hit at the rate of 8 hits in 18 games, he will get 20 hits in 45 games.

Getting Ready for Class

After reading through the preceding section, respond in your own words and in complete sentences.

A. What is a proportion?

B. What are the means and extremes of a proportion?

C. What is the relationship between the means and the extremes in a proportion? (It is called the means-extremes property of proportions.)

D. Explain in your own words how to solve a proportion.

Solve each of the following proportions.

1. $\dfrac{x}{2} = \dfrac{6}{12}$

2. $\dfrac{x}{4} = \dfrac{6}{8}$

3. $\dfrac{2}{5} = \dfrac{4}{x}$

4. $\dfrac{3}{8} = \dfrac{9}{x}$

5. $\dfrac{10}{20} = \dfrac{20}{x}$

6. $\dfrac{15}{60} = \dfrac{60}{x}$

7. $\dfrac{a}{3} = \dfrac{5}{12}$

8. $\dfrac{a}{2} = \dfrac{7}{20}$

9. $\dfrac{2}{x} = \dfrac{6}{7}$

10. $\dfrac{4}{x} = \dfrac{6}{7}$

11. $\dfrac{x+1}{3} = \dfrac{4}{x}$

12. $\dfrac{x+1}{6} = \dfrac{7}{x}$

13. $\dfrac{x}{2} = \dfrac{8}{x}$

14. $\dfrac{x}{9} = \dfrac{4}{x}$

15. $\dfrac{4}{a+2} = \dfrac{a}{2}$

16. $\dfrac{3}{a+2} = \dfrac{a}{5}$

17. $\dfrac{1}{x} = \dfrac{x-5}{6}$

18. $\dfrac{1}{x} = \dfrac{x-6}{7}$

19. $\dfrac{26}{x-3} = \dfrac{38}{x+3}$

20. $\dfrac{9}{x-2} = \dfrac{11}{x+2}$

Applying the Concepts

21. **Baseball** A baseball player gets 6 hits in the first 18 games of the season. If he continues hitting at the same rate, how many hits will he get in the first 45 games?

22. **Basketball** A basketball player makes 8 of 12 free throws in the first game of the season. If she shoots with the same accuracy in the second game, how many of the 15 free throws she attempts will she make?

23. **Mixture Problem** A solution contains 12 milliliters of alcohol and 16 milliliters of water. If another solution is to have the same concentration of alcohol in water but is to contain 28 milliliters of water, how much alcohol must it contain?

24. **Mixture Problem** A solution contains 15 milliliters of HCl and 42 milliliters of water. If another solution is to have the same concentration of HCl in water but is to contain 140 milliliters of water, how much HCl must it contain?

25. **Nutrition** If 100 grams of ice cream contains 13 grams of fat, how much fat is in 350 grams of ice cream?

26. **Nutrition** A 6-ounce serving of grapefruit juice contains 159 grams of water. How many grams of water are in 20 ounces of grapefruit juice?

27. **Map Reading** A map is drawn so that every 3.5 inches on the map corresponds to an actual distance of 100 miles. If the actual distance between the two cities is 420 miles, how far apart are they on the map?

28. **Map Reading** The scale on a map indicates that 1 inch on the map corresponds to an actual distance of 105 miles. Two cities are 4.5 inches apart on the map. What is the actual distance between the two cities?

29. **Distance** A man drives his car 245 miles in 5 hours. At this rate, how far will he travel in 7 hours?

30. **Distance** An airplane flies 1,380 miles in 3 hours. How far will it fly in 5 hours?

Learning Objectives Assessment

The following problems can be used to help assess if you have successfully met the learning objectives for this section.

31. Solve: $\dfrac{4}{x+3} = \dfrac{x}{10}$.

    a. $8, -5$ **b.** 5 **c.** 8 **d.** $-8, 5$

32. **Nutrition** If 12 ounces of a popular soda contain 45 milligrams of sodium, how many milligrams of sodium will 34 ounces of the soda contain?

    a. 96 **b.** 67 **c.** 127.5 **d.** 9.1

Getting Ready for the Next Section

Solve.

33. $\dfrac{1}{x} + \dfrac{1}{2x} = \dfrac{9}{2}$

34. $\dfrac{50}{x+5} = \dfrac{30}{x-5}$

35. $\dfrac{1}{10} - \dfrac{1}{15} = \dfrac{1}{x}$

36. $\dfrac{15}{x} + \dfrac{15}{x+20} = 2$

Find the value of $y = \dfrac{-6}{x}$ for the given value of x.

37. $x = -6$ 38. $x = -3$ 39. $x = 2$ 40. $x = 1$

Learning Objectives

In this section, we will learn how to:

1. Solve number problems involving rational expressions.
2. Solve motion problems involving rational expressions.
3. Solve work problems involving rational expressions.

In this section we will solve some word problems whose equations involve rational expressions. Like the other word problems we have encountered, the more you work with them, the easier they become.

Number Problems

VIDEO EXAMPLES

SECTION 7.7

EXAMPLE 1   One number is twice another. The sum of their reciprocals is $\frac{9}{2}$. Find the two numbers.

SOLUTION   Let x represent the smaller number. The larger then must be $2x$. Their reciprocals are $\frac{1}{x}$ and $\frac{1}{2x}$, respectively. An equation that describes the situation is:

$$\frac{1}{x} + \frac{1}{2x} = \frac{9}{2}$$

We can multiply both sides by the LCD of $2x$ and then solve the resulting equation:

$$2x\left(\frac{1}{x}\right) + 2x\left(\frac{1}{2x}\right) = 2x\left(\frac{9}{2}\right)$$

$$2 + 1 = 9x$$

$$3 = 9x$$

$$x = \frac{3}{9} = \frac{1}{3}$$

The smaller number is $\frac{1}{3}$. The other number is twice as large, or $\frac{2}{3}$. If we add their reciprocals, we have:

$$\frac{3}{1} + \frac{3}{2} = \frac{6}{2} + \frac{3}{2} = \frac{9}{2}$$

The solutions check with the original problem.

Motion Problems

Recall from Section 7.1 that if an object travels at a constant rate r for a specified time t, then the distance traveled is given by the rate equation

$$\text{Distance} = \text{Rate} \cdot \text{Time}$$

$$d = rt$$

If we know the distance traveled and the rate, then we can find the time by dividing the distance by the rate:

$$\text{Time} = \frac{\text{Distance}}{\text{Rate}}$$

$$t = \frac{d}{r}$$

The next two examples use this version of the rate equation to solve problems involving motion.

EXAMPLE 2   A boat travels 30 miles up a river in the same amount of time it takes to travel 50 miles down the same river. If the current is 5 miles per hour, what is the speed of the boat in still water?

SOLUTION   The easiest way to work a problem like this is with a table. The top row of the table is labeled with d for distance, r for rate, and t for time. The left column of the table is labeled with the two trips: upstream and downstream. Here is what the table looks like:

	d	r	t
Upstream			
Downstream			

The next step is to read the problem over again and fill in as much of the table as we can with the information in the problem. The distance the boat travels upstream is 30 miles and the distance downstream is 50 miles. Since we are asked for the speed of the boat in still water, we will let that be x. If the speed of the boat in still water is x, then its speed upstream (against the current) must be $x - 5$, and its speed downstream (with the current) must be $x + 5$. Putting these four quantities into the appropriate positions in the table, we have

	d	r	t
Upstream	30	$x - 5$	
Downstream	50	$x + 5$	

The last positions in the table are filled in by using the equation $t = \dfrac{d}{r}$.

	d	r	t
Upstream	30	$x - 5$	$\dfrac{30}{x - 5}$
Downstream	50	$x + 5$	$\dfrac{50}{x + 5}$

Reading the problem again, we find that the time for the trip upstream is equal to the time for the trip downstream. Setting these two quantities equal to each other, we have our equation:

$$\text{time (downstream)} = \text{time (upstream)}$$
$$\frac{50}{x + 5} = \frac{30}{x - 5}$$

Notice the resulting equation is a proportion. We can solve for x using the means-extremes property.

$$50(x - 5) = 30(x + 5)$$

$$50x - 250 = 30x + 150$$

$$20x = 400$$

$$x = 20$$

The speed of the boat in still water is 20 miles per hour.

EXAMPLE 3   Tina is training for a biathlon. To train for the bicycle portion, she rides her bike 15 miles up a hill and then 15 miles back down the same hill. The complete trip takes her 2 hours. If her downhill speed is 20 miles per hour faster than her uphill speed, how fast does she ride uphill?

SOLUTION   Again, we make a table. As in the previous example, we label the top row with distance, rate, and time. We label the left column with the two trips, uphill and downhill.

Total distance = 30 miles
Total time = 2 hours

	d	r	t
Uphill			
Downhill			

Next, we fill in the table with as much information as we can from the problem. We know the distance traveled is 15 miles uphill and 15 miles downhill, which allows us to fill in the distance column. To fill in the rate column, we first note that she rides 20 miles per hour faster downhill than uphill. Therefore, if we let x be her rate uphill, then her rate downhill is $x + 20$. Filling in the table with this information gives us

	d	r	t
Uphill	15	x	
Downhill	15	$x + 20$	

Since time is distance divided by rate, $t = \frac{d}{r}$, we can fill in the last column in the table.

	d	r	t
Uphill	15	x	$\frac{15}{x}$
Downhill	15	$x + 20$	$\frac{15}{x + 20}$

Rereading the problem, we find that the total time (the time riding uphill plus the time riding downhill) is two hours. We write our equation as follows:

$$\text{time (uphill)} + \text{time (downhill)} = 2$$

$$\frac{15}{x} + \frac{15}{x + 20} = 2$$

We solve this equation for x by first finding the LCD and then multiplying each term in the equation by it to clear the equation of all denominators. The LCD is $x(x + 20)$. Here is our solution:

$$x(x + 20)\frac{15}{x} + x(x + 20)\frac{15}{x + 20} = 2 \cdot [x(x + 20)]$$

$$x(x + 20)\frac{15}{\cancel{x}} + x(x + 20)\frac{15}{\cancel{x + 20}} = 2 \cdot [x(x + 20)]$$

$$15(x + 20) + 15x = 2x(x + 20)$$

$$15x + 300 + 15x = 2x^2 + 40x$$

$$0 = 2x^2 + 10x - 300$$

$$0 = x^2 + 5x - 150 \qquad \text{Divide both sides by 2}$$

$$0 = (x + 15)(x - 10)$$

$$x + 15 = 0 \qquad \text{or} \qquad x - 10 = 0$$

$$x = -15 \qquad\qquad x = 10$$

Since we cannot have a negative speed, the only valid solution is $x = 10$. Tina rides her bike at a rate of 10 miles per hour when going uphill. (Her downhill speed is $x + 20 = 30$ miles per hour.)

Work Problems

Work problems involve two or more people or objects attempting to complete some task. If a person or object works at a constant rate, and the time it takes them to complete the task is given by t, then the fraction of the task completed in one unit of time will be $\frac{1}{t}$. That is, the rate at which they work is found by taking the reciprocal of the time it takes to do the job.

EXAMPLE 4   Allison can clean the house in 5 hours. Working together, she and Kaitlin can clean the house in 3 hours. How long would it take Kaitlin, working alone, to clean the house?

SOLUTION   Let x be the amount of time it takes Kaitlin to clean the house. We now consider the fraction of the task completed in 1 hour for each girl working alone, and for the girls working together.

1. If Allison can clean the house in 5 hours, then in 1 hour she cleans $\frac{1}{5}$ of the house.

2. If Kaitlin can clean the house in x hours, then in 1 hour she cleans $\frac{1}{x}$ of the house.

3. If it takes 3 hours for both girls to clean the house working together, then in 1 hour they clean $\frac{1}{3}$ of the house.

Therefore, in 1 hour we have

$$\frac{1}{5} + \frac{1}{x} = \frac{1}{3}$$

Amount of the house cleaned by Allison

Amount of the house cleaned by Kaitlin

Amount of the house cleaned by both girls

Multiplying both sides of the equation by the LCD of $15x$, we have:

$$15x\left(\frac{1}{5}\right) + 15x\left(\frac{1}{x}\right) = 15x\left(\frac{1}{3}\right)$$

$$3x + 15 = 5x$$

$$15 = 2x$$

$$7.5 = x$$

It would take Kaitlin 7.5 hours to clean the house by herself.

Inlet Pipe
10 hours
to fill

Outlet Pipe
15 hours
to empty

EXAMPLE 5   An inlet pipe can fill a water tank in 10 hours, while an outlet pipe can empty the same tank in 15 hours. By mistake, both pipes are left open. How long will it take to fill the water tank with both pipes open?

SOLUTION   Let x be the amount of time to fill the tank with both pipes open.

One method of solving this type of problem is to think in terms of how much of the job is done by a pipe in 1 hour.

1. If the inlet pipe fills the tank in 10 hours, then in 1 hour the inlet pipe fills $\frac{1}{10}$ of the tank.

2. If the outlet pipe empties the tank in 15 hours, then in 1 hour the outlet pipe empties $\frac{1}{15}$ of the tank.

3. If it takes x hours to fill the tank with both pipes open, then in 1 hour the tank is $\frac{1}{x}$ full.

Here is how we set up the equation. In 1 hour,

$$\frac{1}{10} \quad - \quad \frac{1}{15} \quad = \quad \frac{1}{x}$$

Amount of water let in by inlet pipe

Amount of water let out by outlet pipe

Total amount of water in tank

Note   In solving a problem of this type, we have to assume that the thing doing the work (whether it is a pipe, a person, or a machine) is working at a constant rate; that is, as much work gets done in the first hour as is done in the last hour and any other hour in between.

The LCD for our equation is $30x$. We multiply both sides by the LCD and solve:

$$30x\left(\frac{1}{10}\right) - 30x\left(\frac{1}{15}\right) = 30x\left(\frac{1}{x}\right)$$

$$3x - 2x = 30$$

$$x = 30$$

It takes 30 hours with both pipes open to fill the tank.

Getting Ready for Class

After reading through the preceding section, respond in your own words and in complete sentences.

A. If we know the distance an object travels at a constant rate, how can we find the time it traveled?

B. How does the current of a river affect the speed of a motor boat traveling against the current?

C. How does the current of a river affect the speed of a motor boat traveling in the same direction as the current?

D. What is the relationship between the total number of minutes it takes for a drain to empty a sink and the amount of water that drains out of the sink in 1 minute?

Number Problems

1. One number is 3 times as large as another. The sum of their reciprocals is $\frac{16}{3}$. Find the two numbers.

2. If $\frac{3}{5}$ is added to twice the reciprocal of a number, the result is 1. Find the number.

3. The sum of a number and its reciprocal is $\frac{13}{6}$. Find the number.

4. The sum of a number and 10 times its reciprocal is 7. Find the number.

5. If a certain number is added to both the numerator and denominator of the fraction $\frac{7}{9}$, the result is $\frac{5}{7}$. Find the number.

6. The numerator of a certain fraction is 2 more than the denominator. If $\frac{1}{3}$ is added to the fraction, the result is 2. Find the fraction.

7. The sum of the reciprocals of two consecutive even integers is $\frac{5}{12}$. Find the integers.

8. The sum of the reciprocals of two consecutive integers is $\frac{7}{12}$. Find the two integers.

Motion Problems

9. A boat travels 26 miles up the river in the same amount of time it takes to travel 38 miles down the same river. If the current is 3 miles per hour, what is the speed of the boat in still water?

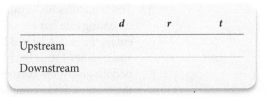

	d	r	t
Upstream			
Downstream			

10. A boat can travel 9 miles up a river in the same amount of time it takes to travel 11 miles down the same river. If the current is 2 miles per hour, what is the speed of the boat in still water?

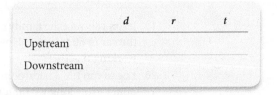

	d	r	t
Upstream			
Downstream			

11. An airplane flying against the wind travels 140 miles in the same amount of time it would take the same plane to travel 160 miles with the wind. If the wind speed is a constant 20 miles per hour, how fast would the plane travel in still air?

12. An airplane flying against the wind travels 500 miles in the same amount of time that it would take to travel 600 miles with the wind. If the speed of the wind is 50 miles per hour, what is the speed of the plane in still air?

13. One plane can travel 20 miles per hour faster than another. One of them goes 285 miles in the same time it takes the other to go 255 miles. What are their speeds?

14. One car travels 300 miles in the same amount of time it takes a second car, traveling 5 miles per hour slower than the first, to go 275 miles. What are the speeds of the cars?

15. Tina, whom we mentioned in Example 3 of this section, is training for a biathlon. To train for the running portion of the race, she runs 8 miles each day, over the same course. The first 2 miles of the course are on level ground, while the last 6 miles are downhill. She runs 3 miles per hour slower on level ground than she runs downhill. If the complete course takes 1 hour, how fast does she run on the downhill part of the course?

16. Jerri is training for the same biathlon as Tina (Example 3 and Problem 15). To train for the bicycle portion of the race, she rides 24 miles out a straight road, then turns around and rides 24 miles back. The trip out is against the wind, whereas the trip back is with the wind. If she rides 10 miles per hour faster with the wind than she does against the wind, and the complete trip out and back takes 2 hours, how fast does she ride when she rides against the wind?

17. To train for the running of a triathlon, Jerri jogs 1 hour each day over the same 9-mile course. Five miles of the course is downhill, whereas the other 4 miles is on level ground. Jerri figures that she runs 2 miles per hour faster downhill than she runs on level ground. Find the rate at which Jerri runs on level ground.

18. Travis paddles his kayak in the harbor at Morro Bay, California, where the incoming tide has caused a current in the water. From the point where he enters the water, he paddles 1 mile against the current, then turns around and paddles 1 mile back to where he started. His average speed when paddling with the current is 4 miles per hour faster than his speed against the current. If the complete trip (out and back) takes him 1.2 hours, find his average speed when he paddles against the current.

Work Problems

19. Jason can wax the family car in 90 minutes, while his brother Kevin can wax the car in 60 minutes. How long would it take Jason and Kevin to wax the car working together?

20. Logan can tile a bathroom in 4 hours. His partner Lance can do the job in 6 hours. How long would it take Logan and Lance to tile a bathroom working together?

21. Valerie can install a car stereo in 45 minutes. Working together with her trainee, Peggy, the installation only takes 30 minutes. How long does it take Peggy to do the installation on her own?

22. It takes Marie 15 hours to install wood flooring in a small house. If she works together with Curtis, they can do the installation in 9 hours. How long would it take Curtis to do the job by himself?

23. An inlet pipe can fill a pool in 12 hours, while an outlet pipe can empty it in 15 hours. If both pipes are left open, how long will it take to fill the pool?

24. A water tank can be filled in 20 hours by an inlet pipe and emptied in 25 hours by an outlet pipe. How long will it take to fill the tank if both pipes are left open?

25. A bathtub can be filled by the cold water faucet in 10 minutes and by the hot water faucet in 12 minutes. How long does it take to fill the tub if both faucets are open?

26. A water faucet can fill a sink in 12 minutes, whereas the drain can empty it in 6 minutes. If the sink is full, how long will it take to empty if both the faucet and the drain are open?

27. A sink can be filled by the cold water faucet in 3 minutes. The drain can empty a full sink in 4 minutes. If the sink is empty and both the cold water faucet and the drain are open, how long will it take the sink to fill?

28. A bathtub can be filled by the cold water faucet in 9 minutes and by the hot water faucet in 10 minutes. The drain can empty the tub in 5 minutes. Can the tub be filled if both faucets and the drain are open?

Learning Objectives Assessment

The following problems can be used to help assess if you have successfully met the learning objectives for this section.

29. The sum of a number and twice its reciprocal is $\frac{41}{12}$. Which equation can be used as a model to find the number?

    a. $2\left(x + \dfrac{1}{x}\right) = \dfrac{41}{12}$ b. $x + \dfrac{1}{2x} = \dfrac{41}{12}$

    c. $x + \dfrac{2}{x} = \dfrac{41}{12}$ d. $x + \dfrac{1}{x + 2} = \dfrac{41}{12}$

30. A kayaker can paddle 6 miles against a current in the same time it takes to paddle 10 miles with the current. If the current is 1 mile per hour, which equation can be used as a model to find the rate of the kayaker in still water?

    a. $\dfrac{6}{x - 1} = \dfrac{10}{x + 1}$ b. $\dfrac{6}{x + 1} = \dfrac{10}{x - 1}$

    c. $\dfrac{6}{1 - x} = \dfrac{10}{1 + x}$ d. $\dfrac{6}{1 + x} = \dfrac{10}{1 - x}$

31. A hot tub can be filled in 10 hours by the inlet pipe. If a hose is used, the hot tub can be filled in 8 hours. Which equation could be used to find the time required to fill the hot tub using both the inlet pipe and hose?

    a. $\dfrac{1}{10} + \dfrac{1}{x} = \dfrac{1}{8}$ b. $10 + 8 = \dfrac{1}{x}$

    c. $\dfrac{1}{10} - \dfrac{1}{8} = \dfrac{1}{x}$ d. $\dfrac{1}{10} + \dfrac{1}{8} = \dfrac{1}{x}$

Getting Ready for the Next Section

Use the formula $y = 5x$ to find y when

32. $x = 4$ **33.** $x = 3$

Use the formula $y = \dfrac{20}{x}$ to find y when

34. $x = 10$ **35.** $x = 5$

Use the formula $y = 2x^2$ to find x when

36. $y = 50$ **37.** $y = 72$

Use the formula $y = Kx$ to find K when

38. $y = 15$ and $x = 3$ **39.** $y = 72$ and $x = 4$

Use the formula $y = Kx^2$ to find K when

40. $y = 32$ and $x = 4$ **41.** $y = 45$ and $x = 3$

Variation

Learning Objectives

In this section, we will learn how to:

1. Express a direct variation in symbols.
2. Express an inverse variation in symbols.
3. Solve variation problems.
4. Solve application problems involving direct or inverse variation.

Direct Variation

Two variables are said to *vary directly* if one is a constant multiple of the other. For instance, y varies directly as x if $y = Kx$, where K is a constant. The constant K is called the *constant of variation*. The following examples give the relationship between direct variation statements and their equivalent algebraic equations.

VIDEO EXAMPLES

SECTION 7.8

EXAMPLES

Statement	Equation
1. y varies directly as x	$y = Kx$
2. y varies directly as the square of x	$y = Kx^2$
3. s varies directly as the square root of t	$s = K\sqrt{t}$
4. r varies directly as the cube of s	$r = Ks^3$

Any time we run across a statement similar to those in the previous examples, we immediately can write an equivalent expression involving variables and a constant of variation K.

EXAMPLE 5 Suppose y varies directly as x. When y is 15, x is 3. Find y when x is 4.

SOLUTION From the first sentence we can write the relationship between x and y as

$$y = Kx$$

We now use the second sentence to find the value of K. Since y is 15 when x is 3, we have

$$15 = K(3) \quad \text{or} \quad K = 5$$

Now we can rewrite the relationship between x and y more specifically as

$$y = 5x$$

To find the value of y when x is 4 we simply substitute $x = 4$ into our last equation.

$$
\begin{array}{ll}
\text{Substituting} & x = 4 \\
\text{into} & y = 5x \\
\text{we have} & y = 5(4) \\
& y = 20
\end{array}
$$

EXAMPLE 6   Suppose y varies directly as the square of x. When x is 4, y is 32. Find x when y is 50.

SOLUTION   The first sentence gives us

$$y = Kx^2$$

Since y is 32 when x is 4, we have

$$32 = K(4)^2$$

$$32 = 16K$$

$$K = 2$$

The equation now becomes

$$y = 2x^2$$

When y is 50, we have

$$50 = 2x^2$$

$$25 = x^2$$

$$x = \pm 5$$

There are two possible solutions, $x = 5$ or $x = -5$.

Inverse Variation

Two variables are said to *vary inversely* if one is a constant multiple of the reciprocal of the other. For example, y varies inversely as x if $y = \frac{K}{x}$, where K is a real number constant. Again, K is called the constant of variation. The examples that follow give some inverse variation statements and their associated algebraic equations.

EXAMPLES

Statement	**Equation**
7. y varies inversely as x	$y = \frac{K}{x}$
8. y varies inversely as the square of x	$y = \frac{K}{x^2}$
9. F varies inversely as the square root of t	$F = \frac{K}{\sqrt{t}}$
10. r varies inversely as the cube of s	$r = \frac{K}{s^3}$

EXAMPLE 11   Suppose y varies inversely as x. When y is 4, x is 5. Find y when x is 10.

SOLUTION   The first sentence gives us the relationship between x and y:

$$y = \frac{K}{x}$$

We use the second sentence to find the value of the constant K:

$$4 = \frac{K}{5} \quad \text{or} \quad K = 20$$

We can now write the relationship between x and y more specifically as:

$$y = \frac{20}{x}$$

We use this equation to find the value of y when x is 10.

Substituting $x = 10$

into $y = \dfrac{20}{x}$

we have $y = \dfrac{20}{10}$

$$y = 2$$

Applications

EXAMPLE 12   The cost of a certain kind of candy varies directly with the weight of the candy. If 12 ounces of the candy cost $1.68, how much will 16 ounces cost?

SOLUTION   Let $x = $ the number of ounces of candy and $y = $ the cost of the candy. Then $y = Kx$. Since y is 1.68 when x is 12, we have

$$1.68 = K \cdot 12$$

$$K = \frac{1.68}{12}$$

$$= 0.14$$

The equation must be

$$y = 0.14x$$

When x is 16, we have

$$y = 0.14(16)$$

$$= 2.24$$

The cost of 16 ounces of candy is $2.24.

EXAMPLE 13   The intensity (I) of light from a source varies inversely as the square of the distance (d) from the source. Ten feet away from the source the intensity is 200 footcandles. What is the intensity 5 feet from the source?

SOLUTION

$$I = \frac{K}{d^2}$$

Since $I = 200$ when $d = 10$, we have

$$200 = \frac{K}{10^2}$$

$$200 = \frac{K}{100}$$

$$K = 20{,}000$$

The equation becomes

$$I = \frac{20{,}000}{d^2}$$

When $d = 5$, we have

$$I = \frac{20{,}000}{5^2}$$

$$= \frac{20{,}000}{25}$$

$$= 800 \text{ footcandles}$$

Getting Ready for Class

After reading through the preceding section, respond in your own words and in complete sentences.

A. What does it mean when we say "y varies directly with x"?

B. Give an example of a sentence that is a direct variation statement.

C. Translate the equation $y = \frac{K}{x}$ into words.

D. Give an example of an everyday situation where one quantity varies inversely with another.

Determine whether each of the following equations represents a direct variation or inverse variation. Also, specify the constant of variation.

1. $y = 10x$ **2.** $E = 14c^2$ **3.** $t = \dfrac{40}{r}$ **4.** $R = \dfrac{1}{T}$

5. $V = \dfrac{4}{3}\pi r^3$ **6.** $b = \dfrac{1}{2\sqrt{n}}$ **7.** $I = \dfrac{1}{9d^2}$ **8.** $S = \dfrac{P}{4}$

Express each sentence algebraically as an equation. Use K for the constant of variation.

9. C varies directly as the square of r.
10. F varies inversely as the square of d.
11. P varies inversely as V.
12. y varies directly as the cube root of x.
13. R varies directly as the square root of n.
14. f varies inversely as the sum of a and b.

For each of the following problems, y varies directly as x.

15. If $y = 10$ when $x = 5$, find y when x is 4.
16. If $y = -18$ when $x = 6$, find y when x is 3.
17. If $y = 30$ when $x = -15$, find x when y is 8.
18. If $y = 30$ when $x = 4$, find y when x is 7.

For each of the following problems, y varies inversely as x.

19. If $y = 5$ when $x = 2$, find y when x is 5.
20. If $y = 2$ when $x = 1$, find y when x is 4.
21. If $y = 5$ when $x = 3$, find x when y is 15.
22. If $y = 15$ when $x = 2$, find x when y is 6.

Solve each of the following variation problems by first expressing the relationship algebraically as an equation.

23. If y varies directly as the square of x, and $y = 75$ when $x = 5$, find y when x is 1.

24. If m varies directly as the square of n, and $m = -72$ when $n = 6$, find m when n is 3.

25. If z varies inversely as the square of w, and $z = 5$ when $w = 2$, find z when w is 6.

26. If y varies inversely as the square of t, and $y = 4$ when $t = 3$, find y when t is 2.

27. If F varies directly as the square root of h, and $F = 24$ when $h = 4$, find F when h is 25.

28. If H varies inversely as the square root of d, and $H = 2$ when $d = 9$, find H when d is 4.

Applying the Concepts

29. **Tension in a Spring** The tension t in a spring varies directly with the distance d the spring is stretched. If the tension is 42 pounds when the spring is stretched 2 inches, find the tension when the spring is stretched twice as far.

30. **Fill Time** The time t it takes to fill a bucket varies directly with the volume g of the bucket. If it takes 1 minute to fill a 4-gallon bucket, how long will it take to fill a 6-gallon bucket?

31. **Electricity** The power P in an electric circuit varies directly with the square of the current I. If $P = 30$ when $I = 2$, find P when $I = 7$.

32. **Electricity** The resistance R in an electric circuit varies directly with the voltage V. If $R = 20$ when $V = 120$, find R when $V = 240$.

33. **Wages** The amount of money M a woman makes per week varies directly with the number of hours h she works per week. If she works 20 hours and earns $185, how much does she make if she works 30 hours?

34. **Volume** The volume V of a gas varies directly as the temperature T. If $V = 3$ when $T = 150$, find V when T is 200.

35. **Weight** The weight F of a body varies inversely with the square of the distance d between the body and the center of the Earth. If a man weighs 150 pounds 4,000 miles from the center of the Earth, how much will he weigh at a distance of 5,000 miles from the center of the Earth?

36. **Light Intensity** The intensity I of a light source varies inversely with the square of the distance d from the source. Four feet from the source, the intensity is 9 footcandles. What is the intensity 3 feet from the source?

37. **Electricity** The current I in an electric circuit varies inversely with the resistance R. If a current of 30 amperes is produced by a resistance of 2 ohms, what current will be produced by a resistance of 5 ohms?

38. **Pressure** The pressure exerted by a gas on the container in which it is held varies inversely with the volume of the container. A pressure of 40 pounds per square inch is exerted on a container of volume 2 cubic feet. What is the pressure on a container whose volume is 8 cubic feet?

Learning Objectives Assessment

The following problems can be used to help assess if you have successfully met the learning objectives for this section.

39. Express as an equation: "T varies directly as r."

    a. $T = \dfrac{1}{r}$ **b.** $T = r$ **c.** $T = Kr$ **d.** $T = \dfrac{K}{r}$

40. Express as an equation: "f varies inversely as the square of h."

    a. $f = Kh^2$ **b.** $f = \dfrac{K}{h^2}$ **c.** $f = \dfrac{1}{\sqrt{h}}$ **d.** $f = \sqrt{h}$

41. If y varies directly as the square of x, and $y = 27$ when $x = 3$, find y when x is 5.

    a. 75   **b.** 45   **c.** $\dfrac{81}{5}$ **d.** $\dfrac{243}{25}$

42. The current I in an electric circuit varies inversely with the resistance R. If a current of 36 amperes is produced by a resistance of 2 ohms, what current will be produced by a resistance of 9 ohms?

a. 8 amperes   **b.** 2 amperes   **c.** 16 amperes   **d.** 162 amperes

Maintaining Your Skills

43. Reduce to lowest terms: $\dfrac{x^2 - x - 6}{x^2 - 9}$.

44. Divide using long division: $\dfrac{x^2 - 2x + 6}{x - 4}$.

Perform the indicated operations.

45. $\dfrac{x^2 - 25}{x + 4} \cdot \dfrac{2x + 8}{x^2 - 9x + 20}$

46. $\dfrac{3x + 6}{x^2 - 4x + 3} \div \dfrac{x^2 + x - 2}{x^2 + 2x - 3}$

47. $\dfrac{x}{x^2 - 16} + \dfrac{4}{x^2 - 16}$

48. $\dfrac{2}{x^2 - 1} - \dfrac{5}{x^2 + 3x - 4}$

49. $\dfrac{1 - \dfrac{25}{x^2}}{1 - \dfrac{8}{x} + \dfrac{15}{x^2}}$

Solve each equation.

50. $\dfrac{x}{2} - \dfrac{5}{x} = -\dfrac{3}{2}$

51. $\dfrac{x}{x^2 - 9} - \dfrac{3}{x - 3} = \dfrac{1}{x + 3}$

52. **Speed of a Boat** A boat travels 30 miles up a river in the same amount of time it takes to travel 50 miles down the same river. If the current is 5 miles per hour, what is the speed of the boat in still water?

53. **Filling a Pool** A pool can be filled by an inlet pipe in 8 hours. The drain will empty the pool in 12 hours. How long will it take to fill the pool if both the inlet pipe and the drain are open?

54. **Mixture Problem** If 30 liters of a certain solution contains 2 liters of alcohol, how much alcohol is in 45 liters of the same solution?

55. y varies directly with x. If $y = 8$ when x is 12, find y when x is 36.

Chapter 7 Summary

EXAMPLES

Rational Expressions [7.1]

1. We reduce rational expressions to lowest terms by factoring the numerator and denominator and then dividing out any factors they have in common:

$$\frac{x-3}{x^2-9} = \frac{x-3}{(x-3)(x+3)} = \frac{1}{x+3}$$

Any expression of the form $\frac{P}{Q}$, where P and Q are polynomials ($Q \neq 0$), is a rational expression.

Multiplying or dividing the numerator and denominator of a rational expression by the same nonzero quantity always produces a rational expression equivalent to the original one.

Restricting the Variable [7.1]

2. The rational expression

$$\frac{x-3}{x^2-9}$$

is undefined if

$$x^2 - 9 = 0$$

Solving for x, we have

$$(x+3)(x-3) = 0$$
$$x+3 = 0 \quad \text{or} \quad x-3 = 0$$
$$x = -3 \qquad\qquad x = 3$$

The restrictions are $x \neq -3$, $x \neq 3$.

A rational expression is undefined only for values of the variable that make the denominator equal to zero. To find the restriction on the variable, we set the denominator equal to 0 and solve the resulting equation.

Multiplication [7.2]

3. $\dfrac{x-1}{x^2+2x-3} \cdot \dfrac{x^2-9}{x-2}$

$$= \frac{x-1}{(x+3)(x-1)} \cdot \frac{(x-3)(x+3)}{x-2}$$

$$= \frac{x-3}{x-2}$$

To multiply two rational expressions, multiply numerators, multiply denominators, and divide out any factors common to the numerator and denominator:

For rational expressions $\dfrac{P}{Q}$ and $\dfrac{R}{S}$, $\dfrac{P}{Q} \cdot \dfrac{R}{S} = \dfrac{PR}{QS}$

Division [7.2]

4. $\dfrac{2x}{x^2-25} \div \dfrac{4}{x-5}$

$$= \frac{2x}{(x-5)(x+5)} \cdot \frac{(x-5)}{(2 \cdot 2)}$$

$$= \frac{x}{2(x+5)}$$

To divide by a rational expression, simply multiply by its reciprocal:

For rational expressions $\dfrac{P}{Q}$ and $\dfrac{R}{S}$, $\dfrac{P}{Q} \div \dfrac{R}{S} = \dfrac{P}{Q} \cdot \dfrac{S}{R} = \dfrac{PS}{QR}$

Least Common Denominator [7.3]

5. The least common denominator for

$$\frac{3}{(x+1)(x-1)} \quad \text{and} \quad \frac{4}{(x+1)^2}$$

is $(x+1)^2(x-1)$.

The least common denominator (LCD) for a set of denominators is the simplest expression that is evenly divisible by all the denominators. If the denominators are factored, then the LCD will be the product of each factor raised to the highest exponent it appears within any of the denominators.

Addition and Subtraction [7.3]

6. $\dfrac{4}{x-1} - \dfrac{x}{2}$

$= \dfrac{4}{x-1} \cdot \dfrac{2}{2} - \dfrac{x}{2} \cdot \dfrac{x-1}{x-1}$

$= \dfrac{8}{2(x-1)} - \dfrac{x^2-x}{2(x-1)}$

$= \dfrac{8 - x^2 + x}{2(x-1)}$

$= -\dfrac{x^2-x-8}{2(x-1)}$

To add or subtract two rational expressions, find a common denominator, change each expression to an equivalent expression having the common denominator, and then add/subtract numerators and reduce if possible:

For rational expressions $\dfrac{P}{S}$ and $\dfrac{Q}{S}$,

$$\dfrac{P}{S} + \dfrac{Q}{S} = \dfrac{P+Q}{S} \quad \text{and} \quad \dfrac{P}{S} - \dfrac{Q}{S} = \dfrac{P-Q}{S}$$

When subtracting, be sure to distribute the negative sign on the second numerator.

Complex Fractions [7.4]

7. $\dfrac{1 - \dfrac{4}{x}}{x - \dfrac{16}{x}} = \dfrac{x\left(1 - \dfrac{4}{x}\right)}{x\left(x - \dfrac{16}{x}\right)}$

$= \dfrac{x-4}{x^2 - 16}$

$= \dfrac{x-4}{(x-4)(x+4)}$

$= \dfrac{1}{x+4}$

A rational expression that contains a fraction in its numerator or denominator is called a complex fraction. The most common method of simplifying a complex fraction is to multiply the top and bottom by the LCD for all denominators.

Equations [7.5]

8. Solve $\dfrac{1}{2} + \dfrac{3}{x} = 5$.

$2x\left(\dfrac{1}{2}\right) + 2x\left(\dfrac{3}{x}\right) = 2x(5)$

$x + 6 = 10x$

$6 = 9x$

$x = \dfrac{2}{3}$

To solve equations involving rational expressions, first find the least common denominator (LCD) for all denominators. Then multiply both sides by the LCD and solve as usual. Check all solutions in the original equation to be sure there are no extraneous solutions.

Ratio and Proportion [7.1, 7.6]

9. Solve for x: $\dfrac{3}{x} = \dfrac{5}{20}$.

$3 \cdot 20 = 5 \cdot x$

$60 = 5x$

$x = 12$

The ratio of a to b is:

$$\dfrac{a}{b}$$

Two equal ratios form a proportion. In the proportion

$$\dfrac{a}{b} = \dfrac{c}{d}$$

a and d are the *extremes*, and b and c are the *means*. In any proportion the product of the extremes is equal to the product of the means.

$$\text{If } \dfrac{a}{b} = \dfrac{c}{d}, \text{ then } ad = bc.$$

Direct Variation [7.8]

10. If y varies directly as the square of x, then

$$y = Kx^2$$

The variable y is said to vary directly as the variable x if $y = Kx$, where K is a real number. The constant K is called the constant of variation.

Inverse Variation [7.8]

11. If y varies inversely as the cube of x, then

$$y = \frac{K}{x^3}$$

The variable y is said to vary inversely as the variable x if $y = \dfrac{K}{x}$, where K is a real number.

Chapter 7 Test

Evaluate each rational expression when $x = -2$. [7.1]

1. $\dfrac{2x + 5}{3x^2 - 2x - 1}$

2. $\dfrac{x^2 - 4}{x^2 + 4}$

Determine any values of the variable for which the given rational expression is undefined. [7.1]

3. $\dfrac{2x}{x - 5}$

4. $\dfrac{x + 1}{x^2 + x - 12}$

Reduce to lowest terms. [7.1]

5. $\dfrac{x^2 - 9}{x^2 - 6x + 9}$

6. $\dfrac{15a + 30}{5a^2 - 10a - 40}$

Multiply or divide as indicated. [7.2]

7. $\dfrac{2x - 6}{3} \cdot \dfrac{9}{4x - 12}$

8. $\dfrac{x^2 - 9}{x - 4} \div \dfrac{x + 3}{x^2 - 16}$

9. $\dfrac{x^2 + x - 6}{x^2 + 4x + 3} \div \dfrac{x^2 + 2x - 8}{2x^2 - x - 3}$

10. $(x^2 - 16)\left(\dfrac{x - 1}{x - 4}\right)$

Add or subtract as indicated. [7.3]

11. $\dfrac{7}{x - 8} - \dfrac{9}{x - 8}$

12. $\dfrac{x}{x^2 - 16} + \dfrac{3}{3x - 12}$

13. $\dfrac{3}{(x - 3)(x + 3)} - \dfrac{1}{(x - 3)(x - 1)}$

Simplify each complex fraction. [7.4]

14. $\dfrac{1 + \dfrac{2}{x}}{1 - \dfrac{2}{x}}$

15. $\dfrac{1 - \dfrac{9}{x^2}}{1 - \dfrac{1}{x} - \dfrac{6}{x^2}}$

Solve the following equations. [7.5]

16. $\dfrac{3}{5} = \dfrac{x + 3}{7}$

17. $\dfrac{25}{x - 3} = \dfrac{7}{x}$

18. $\dfrac{6}{x - 3} - \dfrac{5}{x + 1} = \dfrac{7}{x^2 - 2x - 3}$

19. Mixture A solution of alcohol and water contains 29 milliliters of alcohol and 87 milliliters of water. What is the ratio of alcohol to water and the ratio of alcohol to total volume? [7.6]

20. Ratio A manufacturer knows that during a production run 6 out of every 150 parts produced by a certain machine will be defective. If the machine produces 2,550 parts, how many can be expected to be defective? [7.6]

21. Speed of a Boat It takes a boat 3 hours to travel upstream. It takes the same boat 2 hours to travel the same distance downstream. If the current is 3 miles per hour, what is the speed of the boat in still water? [7.7]

22. Emptying a Pool An inlet pipe can fill a pool in 12 hours, whereas an outlet pipe can empty it in 8 hours. If the pool is full and both pipes are open, how long will it take to empty?[7.7]

23. Direct Variation Suppose y varies directly as the cube of x. If y is 16 when x is 2, find y when x is 3. [7.8]

24. Inverse Variation If y varies inversely as the square of x, and y is 8 when x is 3, find y when x is 6. [7.8]

Transitions

8

Chapter Outline

iStockphoto.com © Andresr

Martina is an international student who is planning on taking some of her college courses here in the U.S. Because her country uses the Celsius scale, she is not familiar with temperatures measured in degrees Fahrenheit. The formula

$$F = \frac{9}{5}C + 32$$

gives the relationship between the Celsius and Fahrenheit temperature scales. Using this formula, we can construct a table that shows the Fahrenheit values for a variety of temperatures measured in degrees Celsius.

Degrees Celsius	Degrees Fahrenheit
20°	68°
25°	77°
30°	86°
35°	95°
40°	104°

In this chapter we will see how Martina could use a linear equation or compound inequality to find the Celsius values for temperatures given in degrees Fahrenheit.

Never mistake activity for achievement.

— John Wooden, legendary UCLA basketball coach

You may think that the John Wooden quote above has to do with being productive and efficient, or using your time wisely, but it is really about being honest with yourself. I have had students come to me after failing a test saying, "I can't understand why I got such a low grade after I put so much time in studying." One student even had help from a tutor and felt she understood everything that we covered. After asking her a few questions, it became clear that she spent all her time studying with a tutor and the tutor was doing most of the work. The tutor can work all the homework problems, but the student cannot. She has mistaken activity for achievement.

Can you think of situations in your life when you are mistaking activity for achievement?

How would you describe someone who is mistaking activity for achievement in the way they study for their math class?

Which of the following best describes the idea behind the John Wooden quote?

- Always be efficient.
- Don't kid yourself.
- Take responsibility for your own success.
- Study with purpose.

Learning Objectives

In this section, we will learn how to:

1. Solve linear equations.
2. Solve quadratic equations by factoring.
3. Identify a contradiction.
4. Identify an identity.

Introduction

This chapter marks the transition from introductory algebra to intermediate algebra. Some of the material here is a review of material we covered earlier, and some of the material here is new. If you cover all the sections in this chapter, you will review all the important points contained in the first six chapters of the book. So, it is a good idea to put some extra time and effort into this chapter to ensure that you get a good start with the rest of the course. Let's begin by reviewing the methods we use to solve equations.

iStockPhoto.com/©zorani

Linear Equations in One Variable

A *linear equation in one variable* is any equation that can be put in the form

$$ax + b = c$$

where a, b, and c are constants and $a \neq 0$. For example, each of the equations

$$5x + 3 = 2 \qquad 2x = 7 \qquad 2x + 5 = 0$$

is linear because it can be put in the form $ax + b = c$. In the first equation, $5x$, 3, and 2 are called *terms* of the equation: $5x$ is a variable term; 3 and 2 are constant terms.

> **DEFINITION** *solution set*
>
> The *solution set* for an equation is the set of all numbers that, when used in place of the variable, make the equation a true statement.

> **DEFINITION** *equivalent equations*
>
> Two or more equations with the same solution set are called *equivalent equations.*

The equations $2x - 5 = 9$, $x - 1 = 6$, and $x = 7$ are all equivalent equations because the solution set for each is {7}.

Properties of Equality

The first property of equality states that adding the same quantity to both sides of an equation preserves equality. Or, more importantly, adding the same amount to both sides of an equation *never changes* the solution set. This property is called the *addition property of equality* and is stated in symbols as follows:

Note Because subtraction is defined in terms of addition and division is defined in terms of multiplication, we do not need to introduce separate properties for subtraction and division. The solution set for an equation will never be changed by subtracting the same amount from both sides or by dividing both sides by the same nonzero quantity.

PROPERTY   *Addition Property of Equality*

For any three algebraic expressions A, B, and C,

$$\text{if} \qquad A = B$$
$$\text{then} \qquad A + C = B + C$$

In words: Adding the same quantity to both sides of an equation will not change the solution set.

Our second property is called the *multiplication property of equality* and is stated as follows:

PROPERTY   *Multiplication Property of Equality*

For any three algebraic expressions A, B, and C, where $C \neq 0$,

$$\text{if} \qquad A = B$$
$$\text{then} \qquad AC = BC$$

In words: Multiplying both sides of an equation by the same nonzero quantity will not change the solution set.

VIDEO EXAMPLES

SECTION 8.1

Note We know that multiplication by a number and division by its reciprocal always produce the same result. Because of this fact, instead of multiplying each side of our equation by $\frac{1}{9}$, we could just as easily divide each side by 9. If we did so, the last two lines in our solution would look like this:

$$\frac{9a}{9} = \frac{6}{9}$$
$$a = \frac{2}{3}$$

EXAMPLE 1   Find the solution set for $3a - 5 = -6a + 1$.

SOLUTION   To solve for a, we must isolate it on one side of the equation. Let's decide to isolate a on the left side. We start by adding $6a$ to both sides of the equation.

$$3a - 5 = -6a + 1$$

$$3a + 6a - 5 = -6a + 6a + 1 \qquad \text{Add } 6a \text{ to both sides}$$

$$9a - 5 = 1$$

$$9a - 5 + 5 = 1 + 5 \qquad \text{Add 5 to both sides}$$

$$9a = 6$$

$$\frac{1}{9}(9a) = \frac{1}{9}(6) \qquad \text{Multiply both sides by } \frac{1}{9}$$

$$a = \frac{2}{3} \qquad \frac{1}{9}(6) = \frac{6}{9} = \frac{2}{3}$$

The solution set is $\left\{ \dfrac{2}{3} \right\}$.

The next example involves fractions. The least common denominator, which is the smallest expression that is divisible by each of the denominators, can be used with the multiplication property of equality to simplify equations containing fractions.

EXAMPLE 2 Solve $\frac{2}{3}x + \frac{1}{2} = -\frac{3}{8}$.

SOLUTION We can solve this equation by applying our properties and working with fractions, or we can begin by eliminating the fractions. Let's work the problem using both methods.

Method 1: *Working with the fractions*

$$\frac{2}{3}x + \frac{1}{2} + \left(-\frac{1}{2}\right) = -\frac{3}{8} + \left(-\frac{1}{2}\right) \quad \text{Add } -\frac{1}{2} \text{ to each side.}$$

$$\frac{2}{3}x = -\frac{7}{8} \qquad\qquad -\frac{3}{8} + \left(-\frac{1}{2}\right) = -\frac{3}{8} + \left(-\frac{4}{8}\right)$$

$$\frac{3}{2}\left(\frac{2}{3}x\right) = \frac{3}{2}\left(-\frac{7}{8}\right) \qquad\qquad \text{Multiply each side by } \frac{3}{2}$$

$$x = -\frac{21}{16}$$

Method 2: *Eliminating the fractions in the beginning*

Our original equation has denominators of 3, 2, and 8. The least common denominator, abbreviated LCD, for these three denominators is 24, and it has the property that all three denominators will divide it evenly. Therefore, if we multiply both sides of our equation by 24, each denominator will divide into 24, and we will be left with an equation that does not contain any denominators other than 1.

$$24\left(\frac{2}{3}x + \frac{1}{2}\right) = 24\left(-\frac{3}{8}\right) \quad \text{Multiply each side by the LCD 24}$$

$$24\left(\frac{2}{3}x\right) + 24\left(\frac{1}{2}\right) = 24\left(-\frac{3}{8}\right) \quad \text{Distributive property on the left side}$$

$$16x + 12 = -9 \qquad\qquad \text{Multiply}$$

$$16x = -21 \qquad\qquad \text{Add } -12 \text{ to each side}$$

$$x = -\frac{21}{16} \qquad\qquad \text{Multiply each side by } \frac{1}{16}$$

As the third line above indicates, multiplying each side of the equation by the LCD eliminates all the fractions from the equation. Both methods yield the same solution.

EXAMPLE 3 Solve the equation $0.06x + 0.05(10{,}000 - x) = 560$.

SOLUTION We can solve the equation in its original form by working with the decimals, or we can eliminate the decimals first by using the multiplication property of equality and solve the resulting equation. Here are both methods.

Method 1: *Working with the decimals*

$$0.06x + 0.05(10{,}000 - x) = 560 \qquad\qquad \text{Original equation}$$

$$0.06x + 0.05(10{,}000) - 0.05x = 560 \qquad\qquad \text{Distributive property}$$

$$0.01x + 500 = 560 \qquad\qquad \text{Simplify the left side}$$

$$0.01x + 500 + (-500) = 560 + (-500) \quad \text{Add } -500 \text{ to each side}$$

$$0.01x = 60$$

$$\frac{0.01x}{0.01} = \frac{60}{0.01} \qquad\qquad \text{Divide each side by 0.01}$$

$$x = 6{,}000$$

Method 2: *Eliminating the decimals in the beginning*
To move the decimal point two places to the right in $0.06x$ and 0.05, we multiply each side of the equation by 100.

$$0.06x + 0.05(10{,}000 - x) = 560 \qquad \text{Original equation}$$

$$0.06x + 500 - 0.05x = 560 \qquad \text{Distributive property}$$

$$100(0.06x) + 100(500) - 100(0.05x) = 100(560) \qquad \text{Multiply each side by 100}$$

$$6x + 50{,}000 - 5x = 56{,}000 \qquad \text{Multiply}$$

$$x + 50{,}000 = 56{,}000 \qquad \text{Simplify the left side}$$

$$x = 6{,}000 \qquad \text{Add } -50{,}000 \text{ to each side}$$

Using either method, the solution to our equation is 6,000. We check our work (to be sure we have not made a mistake in applying the properties or an arithmetic mistake) by substituting 6,000 into our original equation and simplifying each side of the result separately.

Check: Substituting 6,000 for x in the original equation, we have

$$0.06(6{,}000) + 0.05(10{,}000 - 6{,}000) \overset{?}{=} 560$$

$$0.06(6{,}000) + 0.05(4{,}000) \overset{?}{=} 560$$

$$360 + 200 \overset{?}{=} 560$$

$$560 = 560 \qquad \text{A true statement}$$

Note   We are placing question marks over the equal signs because we don't know yet if the expressions on the left will be equal to the expressions on the right.

Here is a list of steps to use as a guideline for solving linear equations in one variable.

HOW TO   *Solve Linear Equations in One Variable*

Step 1a: Use the distributive property to separate terms, if necessary.

     1b: If fractions are present, consider multiplying both sides by the LCD to eliminate the fractions. If decimals are present, consider multiplying both sides by a power of 10 to clear the equation of decimals.

     1c: Combine similar terms on each side of the equation.

Step 2:   Use the addition property of equality to get all variable terms on one side of the equation and all constant terms on the other side. A variable term is a term that contains the variable. A constant term is a term that does not contain the variable (the number 3, for example).

Step 3:   Use the multiplication property of equality to get the variable by itself on one side of the equation.

Step 4:   Check your solution in the original equation to be sure that you have not made a mistake in the solution process.

As you work through the problems in the problem set, you will see that it is not always necessary to use all four steps when solving equations. The number of steps used depends on the equation. In Example 4, there are no fractions or decimals in the original equation, so step 1b will not be used.

EXAMPLE 4 Solve the equation $8 - 3(4x - 2) + 5x = 35$.

SOLUTION We must begin by distributing the -3 across the quantity $4x - 2$. (It would be a mistake to subtract 3 from 8 first, because the rule for order of operations indicates we are to do multiplication before subtraction.) After we have simplified the left side of our equation, we apply the addition property and the multiplication property. In this example, we will show only the results:

$$8 - 3(4x - 2) + 5x = 35 \qquad \text{Original equation}$$

Step 1a:
$$8 - 12x + 6 + 5x = 35 \qquad \text{Distributive property}$$

Step 1c:
$$-7x + 14 = 35 \qquad \text{Simplify}$$

Step 2:
$$-7x = 21 \qquad \text{Add } -14 \text{ to each side}$$

Step 3:
$$x = -3 \qquad \text{Multiply by } -\tfrac{1}{7}$$

Step 4: When x is replaced by -3 in the original equation, a true statement results. Therefore, -3 is the solution to our equation.

Solving Equations by Factoring

Next we will use our knowledge of factoring to solve equations. Most of the equations we will see are *quadratic equations*.

---

def **DEFINITION** *quadratic equations*

Any equation that can be written in the form

$$ax^2 + bx + c = 0$$

where a, b, and c are constants and a is not 0 ($a \neq 0$), is called a *quadratic equation*. The form $ax^2 + bx + c = 0$ is called *standard form* for quadratic equations.

Note For a quadratic equation written in standard form, the first term ax^2 is called the *quadratic term*, the second term bx is the *linear term*, and the last term c is called the *constant term*.

Each of the following is a quadratic equation:

$$2x^2 = 5x + 3 \qquad 5x^2 = 75 \qquad 4x^2 - 3x + 2 = 0$$

The number 0 is a special number, and is the key to solving quadratic equations. If we multiply two expressions and get 0, then one, or both, of the expressions must have been 0. In other words, the only way to multiply and get 0 for an answer is to multiply by 0. This fact allows us to solve certain quadratic equations. We state this fact as follows:

$\triangle \neq \Sigma$ **PROPERTY** *Zero-Factor Property*

For all real numbers r and s,

$$r \cdot s = 0 \qquad \text{if and only if} \qquad r = 0 \qquad \text{or} \qquad s = 0 \qquad \text{(or both)}$$

EXAMPLE 5   Solve $x^2 - 2x - 24 = 0$.

SOLUTION   We begin by factoring the left side as $(x - 6)(x + 4)$ and get

$$(x - 6)(x + 4) = 0$$

Now both $(x - 6)$ and $(x + 4)$ represent real numbers. We notice that their product is 0. By the zero-factor property, one or both of them must be 0:

$$x - 6 = 0 \quad \text{or} \quad x + 4 = 0$$

We have used factoring and the zero-factor property to rewrite our original second-degree equation as two first-degree equations connected by the word *or*. Completing the solution, we solve the two first-degree equations:

$$x - 6 = 0 \quad \text{or} \quad x + 4 = 0$$
$$x = 6 \quad \text{or} \quad x = -4$$

We check our solutions in the original equation as follows:

Check $x = 6$	Check $x = -4$
$6^2 - 2(6) - 24 \overset{?}{=} 0$	$(-4)^2 - 2(-4) - 24 \overset{?}{=} 0$
$36 - 12 - 24 \overset{?}{=} 0$	$16 + 8 - 24 \overset{?}{=} 0$
$0 = 0$	$0 = 0$

In both cases the result is a true statement, which means that both 6 and -4 are solutions to the original equation.

To generalize, here are the steps used in solving a quadratic equation by factoring.

HOW TO   *Solve an Equation by Factoring*

Step 1: Write the equation in standard form.
Step 2: Factor the left side.
Step 3: Use the zero-factor property to set each factor equal to 0.
Step 4: Solve the resulting linear equations.
Step 5: Check the solutions in the original equation.

EXAMPLE 6   Solve $100x^2 = 300x$.

SOLUTION   We begin by writing the equation in standard form and factoring:

$$100x^2 = 300x$$
$$100x^2 - 300x = 0 \qquad \text{Standard form}$$
$$100x(x - 3) = 0 \qquad \text{Factor}$$

Using the zero-factor property to set each factor to 0, we have:

$$100x = 0 \quad \text{or} \quad x - 3 = 0$$
$$x = 0 \quad \text{or} \quad x = 3$$

The two solutions are 0 and 3.

EXAMPLE 7 Solve $(x - 2)(x + 1) = 4$.

SOLUTION We begin by multiplying the two factors on the left side. (Notice that it would be incorrect to set each of the factors on the left side equal to 4. The fact that the product is 4 does not imply that either of the factors must be 4.)

$$(x - 2)(x + 1) = 4$$
$$x^2 - x - 2 = 4 \qquad \text{Multiply the left side}$$
$$x^2 - x - 6 = 0 \qquad \text{Standard form}$$
$$(x - 3)(x + 2) = 0 \qquad \text{Factor}$$
$$x - 3 = 0 \quad \text{or} \quad x + 2 = 0 \qquad \text{Zero-factor property}$$
$$x = 3 \quad \text{or} \quad x = -2$$

We can use factoring to solve other types of equations that contain polynomial expressions, as illustrated in the next two examples.

EXAMPLE 8 Solve $2x^3 = 5x^2 + 3x$.

SOLUTION First we add $-5x^2$ and $-3x$ to each side so the right side will become 0.

$$2x^3 - 5x^2 - 3x = 0 \qquad \text{Standard Form}$$

We factor the left side and then use the zero-factor property to set each factor to 0.

$$x(2x^2 - 5x - 3) = 0 \qquad \text{Factor out the greatest common factor}$$
$$x(2x + 1)(x - 3) = 0 \qquad \text{Continue factoring}$$
$$x = 0 \quad \text{or} \quad 2x + 1 = 0 \quad \text{or} \quad x - 3 = 0 \qquad \text{Zero-factor property}$$

Solving each of the resulting equations, we have

$$x = 0 \quad \text{or} \quad x = -\frac{1}{2} \quad \text{or} \quad x = 3$$

EXAMPLE 9 Solve for x: $x^3 + 2x^2 - 9x - 18 = 0$

SOLUTION We start with factoring by grouping.

$$x^3 + 2x^2 - 9x - 18 = 0$$
$$x^2(x + 2) - 9(x + 2) = 0$$
$$(x + 2)(x^2 - 9) = 0$$
$$(x + 2)(x - 3)(x + 3) = 0 \qquad \text{The difference of two squares}$$
$$x + 2 = 0 \quad \text{or} \quad x - 3 = 0 \quad \text{or} \quad x + 3 = 0$$
$$x = -2 \quad \text{or} \quad x = 3 \quad \text{or} \quad x = -3$$

We have three solutions: -2, 3, and -3.

Identities and Equations with No Solution

There are two special cases associated with solving linear equations in one variable, which are illustrated in the following examples.

EXAMPLE 10 Solve for x: $2(3x - 4) = 3 + 6x$

SOLUTION Applying the distributive property to the left side gives us

$$6x - 8 = 3 + 6x \qquad \text{Distributive property}$$

Now, if we add $-6x$ to each side, we are left with

$$-8 = 3$$

which is a false statement. This means that there is no solution to our equation. Any number we substitute for x in the original equation will lead to a similar false statement. We call this type of equation a *contradiction*.

EXAMPLE 11 Solve for x: $-15 + 3x = 3(x - 5)$

SOLUTION We start by applying the distributive property to the right side.

$$-15 + 3x = 3x - 15 \qquad \text{Distributive property}$$

If we add $-3x$ to each side, we are left with the true statement

$$-15 = -15$$

In this case, our result tells us that any number we use in place of x in the original equation will lead to a true statement. Therefore, all real numbers are solutions to our equation. We say the original equation is an *identity* because the left side is always identically equal to the right side.

Applications

EXAMPLE 12 In the chapter opener we mentioned that the relationship between temperature in degrees Fahrenheit, F, and degrees Celsius, C, is given by the formula

$$F = \frac{9}{5}C + 32$$

Solve the following equation to find the temperature in degrees Celsius if it is 77 degrees Fahrenheit.

$$77 = \frac{9}{5}C + 32$$

SOLUTION First, we multiply both sides of the equation by the LCD, which is 5, to eliminate fractions. Then we isolate C.

$$5(77) = 5\left(\frac{9}{5}C + 32\right) \qquad \text{Multiply each side by the LCD 5}$$

$$5(77) = 5\left(\frac{9}{5}C\right) + 5(32) \qquad \text{Distributive property on the right side}$$

$$385 = 9C + 160 \qquad \text{Multiply}$$

$$225 = 9C \qquad \text{Add } -160 \text{ to each side}$$

$$25 = C \qquad \text{Multiply each side by } \frac{1}{9}$$

A temperature of 77°F corresponds to 25°C.

Getting Ready for Class

After reading through the preceding section, respond in your own words and in complete sentences.

A. Name the constant terms in the equation $5x + 3 = 2$.

B. What is the first step in solving the equation $100x^2 = 300x$?

C. How do you use the zero-factor property to help solve a quadratic equation by factoring?

D. Explain how to recognize a contradiction or an identity.

Problem Set 8.1

Each odd/even pair of problems below is matched to an example in the text. If you have any trouble with any of these problems, go to the example that is matched with that problem.

Solve each of the following equations.

1. $7y - 4 = 2y + 11$

2. $5 - 2x = 3x + 1$

3. $-\dfrac{2}{5}x + \dfrac{2}{15} = \dfrac{2}{3}$

4. $\dfrac{1}{2}x + \dfrac{1}{4} = \dfrac{1}{3}x + \dfrac{5}{4}$

5. $0.14x + 0.08(10,000 - x) = 1220$

6. $-0.3y + 0.1 = 0.5$

7. $5(y + 2) - 4(y + 1) = 3$

8. $6(y - 3) - 5(y + 2) = 8$

9. $x^2 - 5x - 6 = 0$

10. $x^2 - x - 12 = 0$

11. $9a^3 = 16a$

12. $-100x = 10x^2$

13. $(x + 6)(x - 2) = -7$

14. $(x - 7)(x + 5) = -20$

15. $2y^3 - 9y = -3y^2$

16. $3y^2 + 10y = 17y^2$

17. $4x^3 + 12x^2 - 9x - 27 = 0$

18. $2x^3 + x^2 - 18x - 9 = 0$

19. Paying Attention to Instructions Work each problem according to the instructions given.

   a. Solve: $8x - 5 = 0$

   b. Add: $(8x - 5) + (2x - 3)$

   c. Multiply: $(8x - 5)(2x - 3)$

   d. Solve: $16x^2 - 34x + 15 = 0$

20. Paying Attention to Instructions Work each problem according to the instructions given.

   a. Subtract: $(3x + 5) - (7x - 4)$

   b. Solve: $3x + 5 = 7x - 4$

   c. Multiply: $(3x + 5)(7x - 4)$

   d. Solve: $21x^2 + 23x - 20 = 0$

21. Solve each equation.

   a. $9x - 25 = 0$

   b. $9x^2 - 25 = 0$

   c. $9x^2 - 25 = 56$

   d. $9x^2 - 25 = 30x - 50$

22. Solve each equation.

   a. $5x - 6 = 0$

   b. $(5x - 6)^2 = 0$

   c. $25x^2 - 36 = 0$

   d. $25x^2 - 36 = 28$

Now that you have practiced solving a variety of equations, we can turn our attention to the types of equations you will see as you progress through the book. Each equation appears later in the book exactly as you see it below.

Solve each equation.

23. $-3 - 4x = 15$

24. $-\dfrac{3}{5}a + 2 = 8$

25. $x^3 - 5x^2 + 6x = 0$

26. $x^3 + 3x^2 - 4x - 12 = 0$

27. $0 = 6400a + 70$

28. $.07x = 1.4$

29. $5(2x + 1) = 12$

30. $50 = \dfrac{K}{48}$

31. $100P = 2,400$

32. $2x - 3(3x - 5) = -6$

33. $5\left(-\dfrac{19}{15}\right) + 5y = 9$

34. $2\left(-\dfrac{29}{22}\right) - 3y = 4$

35. $3x^2 + x = 10$

36. $12(x + 3) + 12(x - 3) = 3(x^2 - 9)$

37. $(y + 3)^2 + y^2 = 9$

38. $3x + (x - 2) \cdot 2 = 6$

39. $15 - 3(x - 1) = x - 2$

40. $2(2x - 3) + 2x = 45$

41. $2(20 + x) = 3(20 - x)$

42. $2x + 1.5(75 - x) = 127.5$

43. $0.08x + 0.09(9{,}000 - x) = 750$

44. $0.12x + 0.10(15{,}000 - x) = 1{,}600$

45. $(x + 3)^2 + 1^2 = 2$

46. $(x + 2)(x) = 2^3$

Solve each equation, if possible.

47. $3x - 6 = 3(x + 4)$

48. $4y + 2 - 3y + 5 = 3 + y + 4$

49. $2(4t - 1) + 3 = 5t + 4 + 3t$

50. $7x - 3(x - 2) = -4(5 - x)$

51. $7(x + 2) - 4(2x - 1) = 18 - x$

52. $2x^2 + x - 1 = (2x + 3)(x - 1)$

Applying the Concepts

53. Temperature and Altitude As an airplane gains altitude, the temperature outside the plane decreases. The relationship between temperature T (in degrees) and altitude A (in feet) can be described with the formula

$$T = -0.0035A + 70$$

when the temperature on the ground is 70°F. Solve the equation below to find the altitude at which the temperature outside the plane is -35°F.

$$-35 = -0.0035A + 70$$

iStockPhoto.com/©Mikael Damkier

54. Revenue A company manufactures and sells DVDs. The revenue obtained by selling x DVDs is given by the formula

$$R = 11.5x - 0.05x^2$$

Solve the equation below to find the number of DVDs they must sell to receive $650 in revenue.

$$650 = 11.5x - 0.05x^2$$

Learning Objectives Assessment

The following problems can be used to help assess if you have successfully met the learning objectives for this section.

55. Solve: $11 + 4x = 2x - 3$

    a. 4   **b.** -4 **c.** 7   **d.** -7

56. Which of the following is an identity?

    a. $2x + 3 = 2(x + 1) + 1$ **b.** $2x + 3 = 2(x + 1) - 1$

    c. $2x + 3 = 2(x + 1) + x$ **d.** $2x + 3 = 2(x + 1) - x$

57. Solve: $x^2 - x - 12 = 0$.

    a. $-3, 4$ **b.** $3, -4$ **c.** $2, -6$ **d.** $-2, 6$

58. Solve: $2x^3 + x^2 - 18x - 9 = 0$.

    a. $-\dfrac{1}{2}$ **b.** $-3, \dfrac{1}{2}$ **c.** $-3, -\dfrac{1}{2}, 3$ **d.** $3, \dfrac{1}{2}$

Getting Ready for the Next Section

To understand all of the explanations and examples in the next section you must be able to work the problems below.

Solve each equation.

59. $2a - 1 = -7$ **60.** $3x - 6 = 9$ **61.** $\frac{2}{3}x - 3 = 7$

62. $\frac{2}{3}x - 3 = -7$ **63.** $x - 5 = x - 7$ **64.** $x + 3 = x + 8$

65. $x - 5 = -x + 7$ **66.** $x + 3 = -x - 8$

Reviewing Elementary Algebra

As you progress through this chapter, you will find a set of review problems at the end of each problem set. These problems review material from the first seven chapters of the book. If you are starting the course in this chapter, these problems will help you get ready for the rest of the course.

Simplify each expression.

67. $|-3|$ **68.** $-|-3|$ **69.** $-|3|$ **70.** $-(-3)$

71. Give a definition for the absolute value of x that involves the number line. (This is the geometric definition.)

72. Give a definition of the absolute value of x that does not involve the number line. (This is the algebraic definition.)

73. $-|-5|$ **74.** $\left(-\frac{2}{3}\right)^3$ **75.** $-3 - 4(-2)$

76. $2^4 + 3^3 \div 9 - 4^2$ **77.** $5|3 - 8| - 6|2 - 5|$ **78.** $7 - 3(2 - 6)$

79. $5 - 2[-3(5 - 7) - 8]$ **80.** $\dfrac{5 + 3(7 - 2)}{2(-3) - 4}$

81. Find the difference of -3 and -9.

82. If you add -4 to the product of -3 and 5, what number results?

83. Apply the distributive property to $\frac{1}{2}(4x - 6)$.

84. Use the associative property to simplify $-6\left(\frac{1}{3}x\right)$.

For the set $\left\{-3, -\frac{4}{5}, 0, \frac{5}{8}, 2, \sqrt{5}\right\}$, which numbers are

85. Integers   **86.** Rational numbers

Learning Objectives

In this section we will learn how to:

1. Use the property of absolute value equations to solve an equation containing a single absolute value.

2. Solve an absolute value equation having a single solution or no solution.

3. Solve an equation containing two absolute value expressions.

Introduction

At one time, Amtrak's annual passenger revenue could be modeled approximately by the formula

$$R = -60|x - 11| + 962$$

where R is the annual revenue in millions of dollars and x is the number of years after 1980 (Association of American Railroads, Washington, DC, *Railroad Facts, Statistics of Railroads of Class 1*, annual). Notice the absolute symbols in the equation.

iStockPhoto.com/©Rob Vomund

Equations Containing Absolute Value

You may recall that the *absolute value* of x, $|x|$, is the distance between x and 0 on the number line. The absolute value of a number measures its distance from 0.

VIDEO EXAMPLES

SECTION 8.2

EXAMPLE 1   Solve for x: $|x| = 5$.

SOLUTION   Using the definition of absolute value, we can read the equation as, "The distance between x and 0 on the number line is 5." If x is 5 units from 0, then x can be 5 or -5:

$$\text{If } |x| = 5 \quad \text{then} \quad x = 5 \quad \text{or} \quad x = -5$$

In general, then, we can see that any equation of the form $|x| = b$ is equivalent to the equations $x = b$ or $x = -b$, as long as $b > 0$. We generalize this result with the following property.

> $\lceil \Delta \neq \Sigma \rceil$ **PROPERTY**   *Absolute Value Equations*
>
> For any algebraic expression A and positive constant b,
>
> $$\text{If} \quad |A| = b$$
>
> $$\text{then} \quad A = b \quad \text{or} \quad A = -b$$

EXAMPLE 2   Solve $|2a - 1| = 7$.

SOLUTION   We can read this question as "$2a - 1$ is 7 units from 0 on the number line." The quantity $2a - 1$ must be equal to 7 or -7:

$$|2a - 1| = 7$$

$$2a - 1 = 7 \quad \text{or} \quad 2a - 1 = -7$$

We have transformed our absolute value equation into two equations that do not involve absolute value. We can solve each equation using the method in Section 8.1:

$$2a - 1 = 7 \quad \text{or} \quad 2a - 1 = -7$$

$$2a = 8 \quad \text{or} \quad 2a = -6 \qquad \text{Add 1 to both sides}$$

$$a = 4 \quad \text{or} \quad a = -3 \qquad \text{Multiply by } \tfrac{1}{2}$$

Our solution set is $\{-3, 4\}$.

To check our solutions, we put them into the original absolute value equation:

When	$a = 4$	When	$a = -3$
the equation	$\lvert 2a - 1 \rvert \stackrel{?}{=} 7$	the equation	$\lvert 2a - 1 \rvert \stackrel{?}{=} 7$
becomes	$\lvert 2(4) - 1 \rvert \stackrel{?}{=} 7$	becomes	$\lvert 2(-3) - 1 \rvert \stackrel{?}{=} 7$
	$\lvert 7 \rvert \stackrel{?}{=} 7$		$\lvert -7 \rvert \stackrel{?}{=} 7$
	$7 = 7$		$7 = 7$

HOW TO   *Solve an Absolute Value Equation*

Step 1: Isolate the absolute value on one side of the equation.

Step 2: If the constant term on the other side of the equation is positive, proceed to Step 3. If it is zero or negative, treat the problem as a special case.

Step 3: Use the property of absolute value equations to write two equations that do not involve an absolute value.

Step 4: Solve for the variable in the resulting two equations.

Step 5: Check the solutions in the original equation.

EXAMPLE 3   Solve: $\left\lvert \dfrac{2}{3}x - 3 \right\rvert + 5 = 12$.

SOLUTION   To use the property of absolute value equations to solve this problem, we must isolate the absolute value on the left side of the equal sign. To do so, we add -5 to both sides of the equation to obtain

$$\left\lvert \frac{2}{3}x - 3 \right\rvert = 7$$

Now that the equation is in the correct form, we can write

$$\frac{2}{3}x - 3 = 7 \quad \text{or} \quad \frac{2}{3}x - 3 = -7$$

$$\frac{2}{3}x = 10 \quad \text{or} \quad \frac{2}{3}x = -4 \qquad \text{Add 3 to both sides}$$

$$x = 15 \quad \text{or} \quad x = -6 \qquad \text{Multiply by } \tfrac{3}{2}$$

The solution set is $\{-6, 15\}$.

The next two examples illustrate the special cases where the constant term is zero or negative after the absolute value is isolated.

EXAMPLE 4   Solve: $|3a - 6| + 4 = 0$.

SOLUTION   First, we isolate the absolute value by adding -4 to both sides of the equation to obtain

$$|3a - 6| = -4$$

The solution set is $\varnothing$ because the right side is negative but the left side cannot be negative. No matter what we try to substitute for the variable a, the quantity $|3a - 6|$ will always be positive or zero. It can never be -4.

> *Note*   Recall that $\varnothing$ is the symbol we use to denote the empty set. When we use it to indicate the solutions to an equation, then we are saying the equation has no solution.

EXAMPLE 5   Solve: $|2 - 5x| = 0$.

SOLUTION   The absolute value is already isolated, but we have 0 on the right side, which makes this a special case. Because there is no difference between 0 and -0, the property of absolute value equations results in the following single equation:

$$2 - 5x = 0$$
$$-5x = -2$$
$$x = \frac{2}{5}$$

The solution set is $\left\{ \frac{2}{5} \right\}$. Notice that we get a single solution in this case.

Consider the statement $|a| = |b|$. What can we say about a and b? We know they are equal in absolute value. By the definition of absolute value, they are the same distance from 0 on the number line. They must be equal to each other or opposites of each other. In symbols, we write:

$$|a| = |b| \quad \Leftrightarrow \quad a = b \quad \text{or} \quad a = -b$$

$$\underset{\substack{\uparrow \\ \text{Equal in} \\ \text{absolute value}}}{} \qquad \underset{\substack{\uparrow \\ \text{Equals}}}{} \quad \text{or} \quad \underset{\substack{\uparrow \\ \text{Opposites}}}{}$$

> *Note* $\Leftrightarrow$ means "if and only if" and "is equivalent to"

EXAMPLE 6   Solve $|3a + 2| = |2a + 3|$.

SOLUTION   The quantities $3a + 2$ and $2a + 3$ have equal absolute values. They are, therefore, the same distance from 0 on the number line. They must be equals or opposites:

$$|3a + 2| = |2a + 3|$$

Equals	Opposites
$3a + 2 = 2a + 3$ $\quad$ or	$3a + 2 = -(2a + 3)$
$a + 2 = 3$	$3a + 2 = -2a - 3$
$a = 1$	$5a + 2 = -3$
	$5a = -5$
	$a = -1$

The solution set is $\{1, -1\}$.

It makes no difference in the outcome of the problem if we take the opposite of the first or second expression. It is very important, once we have decided which one to take the opposite of, that we take the opposite of both its terms and not just the first term. That is, the opposite of $2a + 3$ is $-(2a + 3)$, which we can think of as $-1(2a + 3)$. Distributing the -1 across *both* terms, we have

$$-1(2a + 3) = -2a - 3$$

EXAMPLE 7   Solve $|x - 5| = |x - 7|$.

SOLUTION   As was the case in Example 6, the quantities $x - 5$ and $x - 7$ must be equal or they must be opposites, because their absolute values are equal:

Equals		Opposites
$x - 5 = x - 7$	or	$x - 5 = -(x - 7)$
$-5 = -7$		$x - 5 = -x + 7$
$\uparrow$		$2x - 5 = 7$
No solution here		$2x = 12$
		$x = 6$

Because the first equation leads to a false statement, it will not give us a solution. (If either of the two equations were to reduce to a true statement, it would mean all real numbers would satisfy the original equation.) In this case, our only solution is $x = 6$.

Getting Ready for Class

After reading through the preceding section, respond in your own words and in complete sentences.

A. Why do some of the equations in this section have two solutions instead of one?

B. Translate $|x| = 6$ into words using the definition of absolute value.

C. Explain in words what the equation $|x - 3| = 4$ means with respect to distance on the number line.

D. In your own words, describe the process for solving an equation that contains two absolute value expressions.

Use the property of absolute value equations to solve each of the following problems.

1. $|x| = 4$ **2.** $|x| = 7$ **3.** $2 = |a|$

4. $5 = |a|$ **5.** $|x| = -3$ **6.** $|x| = -4$

7. $|a| + 2 = 3$ **8.** $|a| - 5 = 2$ **9.** $|y| + 4 = 3$

10. $|y| + 3 = 1$ **11.** $|a - 4| = \dfrac{5}{3}$ **12.** $|a + 2| = \dfrac{7}{5}$

13. $\left|\dfrac{3}{5}a + \dfrac{1}{2}\right| = 1$ **14.** $\left|\dfrac{2}{7}a + \dfrac{3}{4}\right| = 1$ **15.** $60 = |20x - 40|$

16. $800 = |400x - 200|$ **17.** $|2x + 1| = -3$ **18.** $|2x - 5| = -7$

19. $\left|\dfrac{3}{4}x - 6\right| = 9$ **20.** $\left|\dfrac{4}{5}x - 5\right| = 15$ **21.** $\left|1 - \dfrac{1}{2}a\right| = 3$

22. $\left|2 - \dfrac{1}{3}a\right| = 10$ **23.** $|2x - 5| = 3$ **24.** $|3x + 1| = 4$

25. $|4 - 7x| = 5$ **26.** $|9 - 4x| = 1$ **27.** $\left|3 - \dfrac{2}{3}y\right| = 5$

28. $\left|-2 - \dfrac{3}{4}y\right| = 6$ **29.** $|3x + 12| = 0$ **30.** $|8 - 6x| = 0$

Solve each equation.

31. $|3x + 4| + 1 = 7$ **32.** $|5x - 3| - 4 = 3$

33. $|3 - 2y| + 4 = 3$ **34.** $|8 - 7y| + 9 = 1$

35. $3 + |4t - 1| = 8$ **36.** $2 + |2t - 6| = 10$

37. $5 + |3a + 2| = 5$ **38.** $|6a - 5| - 11 = -11$

39. $\left|9 - \dfrac{3}{5}x\right| + 6 = 12$ **40.** $\left|4 - \dfrac{2}{7}x\right| + 2 = 14$

41. $5 = \left|\dfrac{2}{7}x + \dfrac{4}{7}\right| - 3$ **42.** $7 = \left|\dfrac{3}{5}x + \dfrac{1}{5}\right| + 2$

43. $2 = -8 + \left|4 - \dfrac{1}{2}y\right|$ **44.** $1 = -3 + \left|2 - \dfrac{1}{4}y\right|$

45. $|3(x + 1)| - 4 = -1$ **46.** $|2(2x + 3)| - 5 = -1$

47. $|1 + 3(2x - 1)| = 5$ **48.** $|3 + 4(3x + 1)| = 7$

49. $3 = -2 + \left|5 - \dfrac{2}{3}a\right|$ **50.** $4 = -1 + \left|6 - \dfrac{4}{5}a\right|$

51. $6 = |7(k + 3) - 4|$ **52.** $5 = |6(k - 2) + 1|$

53. $|3a + 1| = |2a - 4|$ **54.** $|5a + 2| = |4a + 7|$

55. $\left| x - \dfrac{1}{3} \right| = \left| \dfrac{1}{2}x + \dfrac{1}{6} \right|$ **56.** $\left| \dfrac{1}{10}x - \dfrac{1}{2} \right| = \left| \dfrac{1}{5}x + \dfrac{1}{10} \right|$

57. $|y - 2| = |y + 3|$ **58.** $|y - 5| = |y - 4|$

59. $|3x - 1| = |3x + 1|$ **60.** $|5x - 8| = |5x + 8|$

61. $|0.03 - 0.01x| = |0.04 + 0.05x|$ **62.** $|0.07 - 0.01x| = |0.08 - 0.02x|$

63. $|x - 2| = |2 - x|$ **64.** $|x - 4| = |4 - x|$

65. $\left| \dfrac{x}{5} - 1 \right| = \left| 1 - \dfrac{x}{5} \right|$ **66.** $\left| \dfrac{x}{3} - 1 \right| = \left| 1 - \dfrac{x}{3} \right|$

67. $\left| \dfrac{2}{3}b - \dfrac{1}{4} \right| = \left| \dfrac{1}{6}b + \dfrac{1}{2} \right|$ **68.** $\left| -\dfrac{1}{4}x + 1 \right| = \left| \dfrac{1}{2}x - \dfrac{1}{3} \right|$

69. $|0.1a - 0.04| = |0.3a + 0.08|$ **70.** $|-0.4a + 0.6| = |1.3 - 0.2a|$

71. Paying Attention to Instructions Work each problem according to the instructions given.

    a. Solve: $4x - 5 = 0$ **b.** Solve: $|4x - 5| = 0$

    c. Solve: $4x - 5 = 3$ **d.** Solve: $|4x - 5| = 3$

    e. Solve: $|4x - 5| = |2x + 3|$

72. Paying Attention to Instructions Work each problem according to the instructions given.

    a. Solve: $3x + 6 = 0$ **b.** Solve: $|3x + 6| = 0$

    c. Solve: $3x + 6 = 4$ **d.** Solve: $|3x + 6| = 4$

    e. Solve: $|3x + 6| = |7x + 4|$

Applying the Concepts

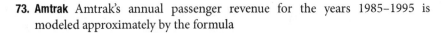

73. Amtrak Amtrak's annual passenger revenue for the years 1985–1995 is modeled approximately by the formula

$$R = -60|x - 11| + 962$$

where R is the annual revenue in millions of dollars and x is the number of years after 1980 (Association of American Railroads, Washington, DC, *Railroad Facts, Statistics of Railroads of Class 1*, annual). In what years was the passenger revenue $722 million?

74. Corporate Profits The corporate profits for various U.S. industries vary from year to year. An approximate model for profits of U.S. "communications companies" during a given year between 1990 and 1997 is given by

$$P = -3{,}400|x - 5.5| + 36{,}000$$

where P is the annual profits (in millions of dollars) and x is the number of years after 1990 (U.S. Bureau of Economic Analysis, Income and Product Accounts of the U.S. (1929–1994), *Survey of Current Business*, September 1998). Use the model to determine the years in which profits of "communications companies" were $31.5 billion ($31,500 million).

Learning Objectives Assessment

The following problems can be used to help assess if you have successfully met the learning objectives for this section.

75. Solve: $|x + 9| - 3 = 5$.

  a. $\{-1, -11\}$ **b.** $\{-1, -17\}$ **c.** $\{-1\}$ **d.** $\varnothing$

76. Solve: $8 + |3x + 7| = 5$.

  a. $\left\{-\dfrac{4}{3}, -\dfrac{10}{3}\right\}$ **b.** $\left\{-\dfrac{20}{3}, -\dfrac{10}{3}\right\}$ **c.** $\varnothing$ **d.** $\left\{-\dfrac{10}{3}\right\}$

77. Solve: $|2a + 3| = |a - 4|$.

  a. $\{-7\}$ **b.** $\left\{-7, -\dfrac{7}{3}\right\}$ **c.** $\left\{-7, \dfrac{1}{3}\right\}$ **d.** $\varnothing$

Getting Ready for the Next Section

To understand all of the explanations and examples in the next section you must be able to work the problems below.

Graph each interval on a number line.

78. $(-\infty, 4)$ **79.** $[-1, \infty)$ **80.** $[-2, \infty)$ **81.** $(-\infty, -1)$

Graph the solution set for each inequality on a number line.

82. $x \geq -2$ **83.** $x > 3$ **84.** $x < 2$ **85.** $x \leq -\dfrac{11}{3}$

Solve each inequality.

86. $3(1 - 4x) \leq 27$ **87.** $5x - 9 > 2x + 3$

88. $3x + 7 \geq 4$ **89.** $3x + 7 \leq -4$

90. $-3 \leq 2x - 5$ **91.** $2x - 5 \leq 3$

Reviewing Elementary Algebra

Simplify each expression. Assume all variables represent nonzero real numbers, and write your answer with positive exponents only.

92. 3^{-2} **93.** $\dfrac{x^6}{x^{-4}}$ **94.** $\dfrac{15x^3y^8}{5xy^{10}}$

95. $(2a^{-3}b^4)^2$ **96.** $\dfrac{(3x^{-3}y^5)^{-2}}{(9xy^{-2})^{-1}}$ **97.** $(3x^4y)^2(5x^3y^4)^3$

Write each number in scientific notation.

98. 54,000   **99.** 0.0359

Write each number in expanded form.

100. 6.44×10^3 **101.** 2.5×10^{-2}

Simplify each expression as much as possible. Write all answers in scientific notation.

102. $(3 \times 10^8)(4 \times 10^{-5})$ **103.** $\dfrac{8 \times 10^5}{2 \times 10^{-8}}$

Learning Objectives

In this section we will learn how to:

1. Use interval notation and graph inequalities.

1. Find the union of two intervals.

2. Find the intersection of two intervals.

3. Solve compound inequalities involving union.

4. Solve compound inequalities involving intersection.

Introduction

A company is about to introduce a new product. Their revenue is given by the formula $R = 15x$ and their cost by the formula $C = 400 + 3x$, where x is the number of units produced and sold each month. To be successful, the company needs a monthly revenue of at least \$12,000, but they must keep their monthly costs to no more than \$5,500. As a result, the company must determine how many units of their product, x, to produce so that

$$15x \geq 12,000 \quad \text{and} \quad 400 + 3x \leq 5,500$$

Solving both inequalities gives us $x \geq 800$ and $x \leq 1,700$. The company can produce between 800 and 1,700 units per month, inclusive, to remain successful. This scenario leads us to the concept of a *compound inequality*. But before we can address compound inequalities, we must first introduce some new notation and then extend our work with sets.

Interval Notation and Graphing

As we saw in Section 2.8, the solution set to a linear inequality in one variable is typically a subset of the real numbers, which can be represented graphically by an entire portion of the number line. A continuous segment of the number line is called an *interval*, and we can describe an interval using *interval notation*. In doing so, we always work from left to right on the number line, indicating where the interval begins on the left, followed by where it ends on the right. In general, if an interval begins at a and ends at b, then the notation will look like this:

$$(a, b) \quad [a, b) \quad (a, b] \quad [a, b]$$

An endpoint is included in the interval if a bracket is used.
An endpoint is not included in the interval if a parenthesis is used.

If the interval extends indefinitely to the left, the symbol $-\infty$ is used for the left endpoint a. If the interval extends indefinitely to the right, the symbol ∞ is used for the right endpoint b. If the values a and b are included in the solution set, then brackets are used. Otherwise parentheses are used. A parenthesis is always used with $-\infty$ or ∞.

Using interval notation, the solution set $x \geq 800$ would be expressed as $[800, \infty)$, indicating that the solution set is all real numbers beginning with 800 and continuing indefinitely.

The following table shows the connection between set-builder notation, interval notation, and number line graphs. We have included the graphs with open and closed circles for those of you who have used this type of graph previously. In this book, we will continue to show our graphs using the parentheses/brackets method.

Note The English mathematician John Wallis (1616–1703) was the first person to use the ∞ symbol to represent infinity. When we encounter the interval $[800, \infty)$, we read it as "the interval from 800 to infinity," and we mean the set of real numbers that are greater than or equal to 800. Likewise, the interval $(-\infty, 1,700)$ is read "the interval from negative infinity to 1,700," which is all real numbers less than or equal to 1,700.

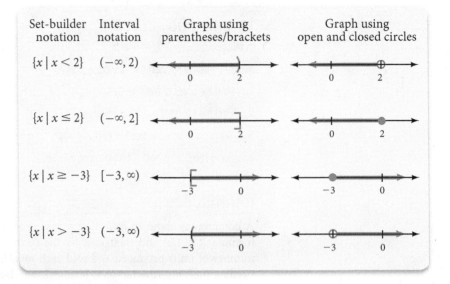

Note Because we always describe an interval from left to right on the number line, the notation $[7, -\infty)$ would be incorrect for the solution set to $x \leq 7$.

EXAMPLE 1   For each inequality, describe the solution set in words. Then write the solution set using set-builder and interval notation, and graph the solution set on the number line.

a. $x \leq 7$ **b.** $x > 0$

SOLUTION

a. The solution set is all real numbers up to and including 7.

Set-builder notation	Interval notation	Graph using parentheses/brackets	Graph using open and closed circles
$\{x \mid x \leq 7\}$	$(-\infty, 7]$		

b. The solution set is all real numbers to the right of, but not including, 0.

Set-builder notation	Interval notation	Graph using parentheses/brackets	Graph using open and closed circles
$\{x \mid x > 0\}$	$(0, \infty)$		

Union and Intersection

DEFINITION   *union*

The union of two sets A and B is the set of all elements that are in either A or B, and is denoted by $A \cup B$.

The idea behind the union is to merge the two sets into a single set. Everything in A should appear in the union and everything in B should also appear in the union. The word *or* is the key word in the definition.

> **(def)   DEFINITION**   *intersection*
>
> The intersection of two sets A and B is the set of all elements contained in both A and B, and is denoted by $A \cap B$.

With the intersection, we are looking for the things that are common to both sets, or where the two sets overlap. Everything in the intersection must appear in A and also in B. The key word in the definition is *and*.

EXAMPLE 2   If $A = \{2, 4, 6, 8\}$ and $B = \{6, 7, 8, 9\}$, find $A \cup B$ and $A \cap B$.

SOLUTION   For the union, we combine the two sets into a single set.

$$A \cup B = \{2, 4, 6, 7, 8, 9\}$$

Notice that we only list the elements 6 and 8 once.

The intersection contains the common elements, which are 6 and 8.

$$A \cap B = \{6, 8\}$$

Because intervals are sets of real numbers, we can also find the union and intersection of two intervals. We illustrate this in the next couple of examples.

EXAMPLE 3   If $A = (-\infty, 4)$ and $B = [-1, \infty)$, find $A \cup B$ and $A \cap B$.

SOLUTION   With intervals, it is helpful to graph both intervals on a single number line. We have done this below using different colors for A and B.

For the union, we identify the portion of the number line that is covered by either color. In this case, the whole number line is covered by either blue or green, so

$$A \cup B = (-\infty, \infty)$$

To find the intersection, we look for the overlap of the two colors; that is, the portion of the number line that is covered by both blue and green. We see that

$$A \cap B = [-1, 4)$$

The endpoint -1 is included in the intersection because of the bracket. It is a value contained in both intervals. However, because of the parenthesis, 4 is not an element of set A, and therefore not included in the intersection.

EXAMPLE 4   If $A = [-2, \infty)$ and $B = [3, \infty)$, find $A \cup B$ and $A \cap B$.

SOLUTION   We begin by graphing both intervals on a common number line.

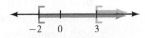

The portion of the number line covered by either color begins at -2, so

$$A \cup B = [-2, \infty)$$

The portion of the number line covered by both colors (the overlap) begins at 3. Therefore,

$$A \cap B = [3, \infty)$$

EXAMPLE 5   If $A = (-\infty, -1)$ and $B = (1, \infty)$, find $A \cup B$ and $A \cap B$.

SOLUTION   The graph of the two intervals is shown below.

We see that

$$A \cup B = (-\infty, -1) \cup (1, \infty)$$

and

$$A \cap B = \varnothing$$

Because the union consists of two separate segments of the number line, it cannot be expressed as a single interval. Also, since the two intervals never overlap, the intersection is the empty set.

Compound Inequalities

We can use the concepts of union and intersection, together with our methods of graphing inequalities, to graph some *compound inequalities*. Compound inequalities are expressions containing two inequalities together with the word *and* or *or*.

EXAMPLE 6   Solve: $x \geq -2$ or $x > 3$. Graph the solution set.

SOLUTION   We begin by graphing each inequality on a single number line:

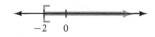

The two inequalities are connected by the word *or*, which indicates a union. The compound inequality will be true for any value of x that satisfies either inequality. So the solution set for the compound inequality is the union of the two intervals we have graphed. In interval notation, the union is

$$[-2, \infty)$$

and the graph of the union is

EXAMPLE 7   Solve: $x > -1$ and $x < 2$. Graph the solution set.

SOLUTION   We first graph each inequality on a single number line:

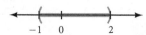

Because the two inequalities are connected by the word *and*, an intersection is indicated. The compound inequality will be true for any value of x that satisfies both inequalities. Thus, the solution set is the intersection of the two intervals we have graphed. Using interval notation, we have

$$(-1, 2)$$

The graph of the solution set is shown below:

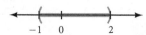

Here is a summary of the general process for solving a compound inequality.

> **🔍 HOW TO** *Solve a Compound Inequality*
>
> **Step 1:** Solve the individual inequalities appearing in the compound inequality.
> **Step 2:** Graph the solution sets of the individual inequalities on a common number line.
> **Step 3:** If the word *or* is used in the compound inequality, find the union of the two solution sets. If the word *and* is used, find the intersection of the two solution sets.
> **Step 4:** Write your answer using interval notation and graph it on a number line.

The next examples illustrate this process.

EXAMPLE 8 Solve: $3t + 7 \le -4$ or $3t + 7 \ge 4$. Graph the solution set.

SOLUTION First, we solve each individual inequality separately by isolating the variable.

$$3t + 7 \le -4 \quad \text{or} \quad 3t + 7 \ge 4$$
$$3t \le -11 \quad \text{or} \quad 3t \ge -3 \qquad \text{Add } -7$$
$$t \le -\frac{11}{3} \quad \text{or} \quad t \ge -1 \qquad \text{Multiply by } \frac{1}{3}$$

Now we graph the two solution sets as intervals on a number line.

The word *or* indicates a union. We write the union using interval notation and graph it on a number line.

Interval Notation   Number Line Graph

$\left(-\infty, -\frac{11}{3}\right] \cup [-1, \infty)$

EXAMPLE 9 Solve: $3(1 - 4x) \le 27$ and $5x - 9 > 2x + 3$. Graph the solution set.

SOLUTION We begin by solving the two individual inequalities.

$$3(1 - 4x) \le 27 \quad \text{and} \quad 5x - 9 > 2x + 3$$
$$3 - 12x \le 27 \quad \text{and} \quad 3x - 9 > 3$$
$$-12x \le 24 \quad \text{and} \quad 3x > 12$$
$$x \ge -2 \quad \text{and} \quad x > 4$$

The graphs of the individual solution sets are shown below.

The word *and* indicates an intersection. From the graph, we see that the intersection of these intervals is all real numbers greater than 4. The interval notation and number line graph of the solution set for the compound inequality is

Interval Notation   Number Line Graph

$(4, \infty)$

Continued Inequalities

Sometimes compound inequalities that use the word *and* as the connecting word can be written in a shorter form. For example, the compound inequality $-3 \leq x$ and $x \leq 4$ can be written $-3 \leq x \leq 4$. The word *and* does not appear when an inequality is written in this form. It is implied. Inequalities of the form $-3 \leq x \leq 4$ are called *continued inequalities*. This new notation is useful because writing it takes fewer symbols. The graph of $-3 \leq x \leq 4$ is

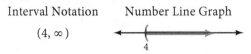

   The table below shows the connection between set-builder notation, interval notation, and number line graphs for a variety of continued inequalities. Again, we have included the graphs with open and closed circles for those of you who have used this type of graph previously. Remember, however, that in this book we will be using the parentheses/brackets method of graphing.

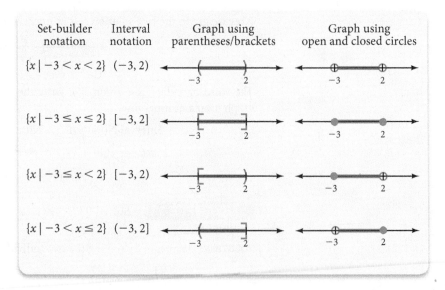

EXAMPLE 10   Solve $-3 \le 2x - 5 \le 3$ and graph the solution set.

SOLUTION   The continued inequality is equivalent to the compound inequality

$$-3 \le 2x - 5 \quad \text{and} \quad 2x - 5 \le 3$$

We could solve this compound inequality using the process we have illustrated in the previous examples. However, with continued inequalities it is much simpler to solve using the original format and not rewriting the problem as a compound inequality.

We can extend our properties for addition and multiplication to cover this situation. If we add a number to the middle expression, we must add the same number to the outside expressions. If we multiply the center expression by a number, we must do the same to the outside expressions, remembering to reverse the direction of the inequality symbols if we multiply by a negative number. We begin by adding 5 to all three parts of the inequality:

$$-3 \le 2x - 5 \le 3$$
$$2 \le \quad 2x \quad \le 8 \qquad \text{Add 5 to all three members}$$
$$1 \le \quad x \quad \le 4 \qquad \text{Multiply through by } \tfrac{1}{2}$$

The solution set is all real numbers between 1 and 4, inclusive. The interval notation and graph are shown below.

Interval Notation   Number Line Graph

[1, 4]

Notice that we did not need to graph individual solution sets or find an intersection. By isolating x in the continued inequality we are led directly to the solution set of the equivalent compound inequality.

EXAMPLE 11   In the chapter opener, we introduced the formula $F = \tfrac{9}{5}C + 32$, which gives the relationship between the Celsius and Fahrenheit temperature scales. If the temperature range on a certain day is 86° to 104° Fahrenheit, what is the temperature range in degrees Celsius?

SOLUTION   From the given information, we can write $86 \le F \le 104$. However, because F is equal to $\tfrac{9}{5}C + 32$, we can also write:

$$86 \le \frac{9}{5}C + 32 \le 104$$
$$54 \le \quad \frac{9}{5}C \quad \le 72 \qquad \text{Add } -32 \text{ to each number}$$
$$\frac{5}{9}(54) \le \frac{5}{9}\left(\frac{9}{5}C\right) \le \frac{5}{9}(72) \qquad \text{Multiply each number by } \tfrac{5}{9}$$
$$30 \le \quad C \quad \le 40$$

A temperature range of 86° to 104° Fahrenheit corresponds to a temperature range of 30° to 40° Celsius.

Getting Ready for Class

After reading through the preceding section, respond in your own words and in complete sentences.

A. What is the difference between the union and the intersection of two sets?

B. How do we solve a compound inequality containing the word *or*?

C. If a compound inequality contained the word *and*, how would your answer to B be different?

D. In your own words, explain how to solve a continued inequality.

For each of the following inequalities, write the solution set in set-builder and interval notation, and graph the solution set on a number line.

1. $x < 6$ **2.** $x \le -2$ **3.** $x \ge -1$ **4.** $x > 0$

5. $x > \dfrac{3}{2}$ **6.** $x \ge \dfrac{13}{3}$ **7.** $x \le -\dfrac{5}{4}$ **8.** $x < -\dfrac{7}{6}$

For each of the following graphs, express the interval shown using interval notation.

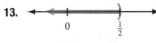

9.

10.

11.

12.

13.

14.

15.

16.

Find the union, $A \cup B$, for each of the following pairs of sets.

17. $A = \{1, 2, 3\}$, $B = \{4, 5, 6\}$

18. $A = \{5, 10, 15, 20\}$, $B = \{10, 20\}$

19. $A = \{5, 6, 7, 8\}$, $B = \{2, 4, 6, 8\}$

20. $A = \{3, 13, 23\}$, $B = \varnothing$

21. $A = (1, \infty)$, $B = (6, \infty)$

22. $A = [-5, \infty)$, $B = [2, \infty)$

23. $A = (-\infty, -3]$, $B = (-\infty, -4)$

24. $A = (-\infty, 0)$, $B = \left(-\infty, \dfrac{3}{2}\right]$

25. $A = (-\infty, -7)$, $B = (7, \infty)$

26. $A = \left(-\infty, -\dfrac{1}{4}\right]$, $B = \left[\dfrac{1}{4}, \infty\right)$

27. $A = \left(-\infty, \dfrac{3}{5}\right]$, $B = (-2, \infty)$

28. $A = (-\infty, 9)$, $B = \left(\dfrac{7}{3}, \infty\right)$

Find the intersection, $A \cap B$, for each of the following pairs of sets.

29. $A = \{1, 2, 3\}$, $B = \{4, 5, 6\}$

30. $A = \{5, 10, 15, 20\}$, $B = \{10, 20\}$

31. $A = \{5, 6, 7, 8\}$, $B = \{2, 4, 6, 8\}$

32. $A = \{3, 13, 23\}$, $B = \varnothing$

33. $A = (1, \infty)$, $B = (6, \infty)$

34. $A = [-5, \infty)$, $B = [2, \infty)$

35. $A = (-\infty, -3]$, $B = (-\infty, -4)$

36. $A = (-\infty, 0)$, $B = \left(-\infty, \dfrac{3}{2}\right]$

37. $A = (-\infty, -7)$, $B = (7, \infty)$

38. $A = \left(-\infty, -\dfrac{1}{4}\right]$, $B = \left[\dfrac{1}{4}, \infty\right)$

39. $A = \left(-\infty, \dfrac{3}{5}\right]$, $B = (-2, \infty)$

40. $A = (-\infty, 9)$, $B = \left(\dfrac{7}{3}, \infty\right)$

Solve the following compound inequalities. Write the solution set using interval notation and graph it on a number line (when possible).

41. $x < 4$ or $x > 1$

42. $x < -1$ or $x > -5$

43. $x \ge -9$ or $x \ge -2$

44. $x \le -3$ or $x \le 6$

45. $2x - 9 < 5$ or $5x + 1 \le 6$

46. $3x + 4 > 13$ or $6x - 2 \ge -8$

47. $10 - x \leq 15$ or $7 + x \geq 4$ **48.** $3 + x < 12$ or $3 - x > 4$

49. $x + 5 \leq -2$ or $x + 5 \geq 2$ **50.** $3x + 2 < -3$ or $3x + 2 > 3$

51. $5y + 1 \leq -4$ or $5y + 1 \geq 4$ **52.** $7y - 5 \leq -2$ or $7y - 5 \geq 2$

53. $5 - 3x > 3x$ or $8x + 1 \geq 2x$ **54.** $3 - 5x \leq x$ or $4x < x + 2$

55. $2x + 5 < 3x - 1$ or $x - 4 < 2x + 6$

56. $3x - 1 > 2x + 4$ or $5x - 2 > 3x + 4$

57. $2(3y + 1) \geq 3(y - 4)$ or $7(2y + 3) \geq 4(3y - 1)$

58. $5(2y - 1) \leq 4(y + 3)$ or $6(y - 2) \geq 2(4y + 3)$

59. $\dfrac{1}{2} \geq -\dfrac{1}{6} - \dfrac{2}{9}x$ or $4 - \dfrac{1}{2}x < \dfrac{2}{3}x - 5$

60. $\dfrac{9}{5} < -\dfrac{1}{5} - \dfrac{1}{2}x$ or $5 - \dfrac{1}{3}x > \dfrac{1}{4}x + 2$

Solve the following compound inequalities. Write the solution set using interval notation and graph it on a number line (when possible).

61. $x < 3$ and $x > 1$ **62.** $x \leq -2$ and $x \geq -6$

63. $x \geq -8$ and $x \geq -3$ **64.** $x < -4$ and $x < 5$

65. $3x - 4 > 2$ and $6x + 2 > -10$ **66.** $2x + 9 < 1$ and $5x - 1 < 14$

67. $3x + 1 < -8$ and $-2x + 1 \leq -3$ **68.** $2x - 5 \leq -1$ and $-3x - 6 < -15$

69. $x + 3 \geq -1$ and $x + 3 \leq 1$ **70.** $2x - 5 > -3$ and $2x - 5 < 3$

71. $4y - 1 > -2$ and $4y - 1 < 2$ **72.** $5y + 7 \geq -4$ and $5y + 7 \leq 4$

73. $4 - 2x \leq x$ and $7x > x - 5$ **74.** $3x + 5 > 4x$ and $1 - 8x \geq 5x$

75. $3(y - 5) < 4(2y + 3)$ and $2(5y + 1) < 9(y + 2)$

76. $6(y + 1) > 5(3y - 2)$ and $3(4y - 5) > 4(y - 8)$

77. $\dfrac{1}{2} - \dfrac{x}{12} \leq \dfrac{7}{12}$ and $3 - \dfrac{x}{5} < 5 - \dfrac{x}{4}$

78. $\dfrac{1}{2} - \dfrac{x}{10} < -\dfrac{1}{5}$ and $-2 + \dfrac{x}{3} \geq \dfrac{x}{2} - 5$

Solve the following continued inequalities. Use interval notation to write each solution set.

79. $-2 \leq m - 5 \leq 2$ **80.** $-3 \leq m + 1 \leq 3$

81. $-60 < 20a + 20 < 60$ **82.** $-60 < 50a - 40 < 60$

83. $0.5 \leq 0.3a - 0.7 \leq 1.1$ **84.** $0.1 \leq 0.4a + 0.1 \leq 0.3$

85. $3 < \dfrac{1}{2}x + 5 < 6$ **86.** $5 < \dfrac{1}{4}x + 1 < 9$

87. $4 < 6 + \dfrac{2}{3}x < 8$ **88.** $3 < 7 + \dfrac{4}{5}x < 15$

Translate each of the following phrases into an equivalent inequality statement.

89. x is greater than -2 and at most 4   **90.** x is less than 9 and at least -3

91. x is less than -4 or at least 1   **92.** x is at most 1 or more than 6

Applying the Concepts

93. Temperature Range Each of the following temperature ranges is in degrees Fahrenheit. Use the formula $F = \frac{9}{5}C + 32$ to find the corresponding temperature range in degrees Celsius.

    a. $95°$ to $113°$ **b.** $68°$ to $86°$ **c.** $-13°$ to $14°$ **d.** $-4°$ to $23°$

94. Survival Rates for 'Apapane Here is what the United States Geological Survey has to say about the survival rates of the 'Apapane, one of the endemic birds of Hawaii.

> Annual survival rates based on 1,584 recaptures of 429 banded individuals 0.72 ± 0.11 for adults and 0.13 ± 0.07 for juveniles.

Write the survival rates using inequalities. Then give the survival rates in terms of percent.

95. Survival Rates for Sea Gulls Here is part of a report concerning the survival rates of Western Gulls that appeared on the web site of Cornell University.

> Survival of eggs to hatching is 70%–80%; of hatched chicks to fledglings 50%–70%; of fledglings to age of first breeding <50%.

Write the survival rates using inequalities without percent.

Learning Objectives Assessment

The following problems can be used to help assess if you have successfully met the learning objectives for this section.

96. Find the union of $[-2, \infty)$ and $(3, \infty)$.

    a. $[-2, 3)$ **b.** $(-\infty, \infty)$ **c.** $(3, \infty)$ **d.** $[-2, \infty)$

97. Find the intersection of $[-2, \infty)$ and $(3, \infty)$.

    a. $[-2, 3)$ **b.** $\varnothing$ **c.** $(3, \infty)$ **d.** $[-2, \infty)$

98. Solve the compound inequality $2x + 5 \leq 3$ or $4 - x \leq 9$.

    a. $[-5, -1]$ **b.** $(-\infty, -5] \cup [-1, \infty)$

    c. $(-\infty, \infty)$ **d.** $\varnothing$

99. Solve the compound inequality $5x - 3 > 2$ and $x + 9 < 4$.

    a. $(-5, 1)$ **b.** $(-\infty, -5) \cup (1, \infty)$

    c. $(-\infty, \infty)$ **d.** $\varnothing$

Getting Ready for the Next Section

To understand all of the explanations and examples in the next section you must be able to work the problems below.

Solve each inequality. Do not graph the solution set.

100. $2x - 5 < 3$ **101.** $-3 < 2x - 5$ **102.** $-4 \leq 3a + 7$

103. $3a + 2 \leq 4$ **104.** $4t - 3 \leq -9$ **105.** $4t - 3 \geq 9$

Reviewing Elementary Algebra

For each of the following straight lines, identify the x-intercept, y-intercept, and slope, and sketch the graph.

106. $2x + y = 6$ **107.** $y = \dfrac{3}{2}x + 4$ **108.** $x = -2$

Find the equation for each line.

109. Give the equation of the line through $(-1, 3)$ that has slope $m = 2$.

110. Give the equation of the line through $(-3, 2)$ and $(4, -1)$.

111. Line l contains the point $(5, -3)$ and has a graph parallel to the graph of $2x - 5y = 10$. Find the equation for l.

112. Give the equation of the vertical line through $(4, -7)$.

Learning Objectives

In this section we will learn how to:

1. Use the property of absolute value inequalities to solve an inequality involving an absolute value.

2. Solve special cases of absolute value inequalities.

iStockPhoto.com/©bluestocking

Introduction

In a student survey conducted by the University of Minnesota, it was found that 30% of students were solely responsible for their finances. The survey was reported to have a margin of error plus or minus 3.74%. This means that the difference between the sample estimate of 30% and the actual percent of students who are responsible for their own finances is most likely less than 3.74%. We can write this as an inequality:

$$|x - 0.30| \leq 0.0374$$

where x represents the true percent of students who are responsible for their own finances.

In this section, we will apply the definition of absolute value to solve inequalities involving absolute value. Again, the absolute value of x, which is denoted $|x|$, represents the distance that x is from 0 on the number line. We will begin by considering three absolute value expressions and their verbal translations:

Expression	In Words
$|x| = 5$	x is exactly 5 units from 0 on the number line.
$|a| < 5$	a is less than 5 units from 0 on the number line.
$|y| > 5$	y is greater than 5 units from 0 on the number line.

Once we have translated the expression into words, we can use the translation to graph the original equation or inequality. The graph is then used to write a final equation or inequality that does not involve absolute value.

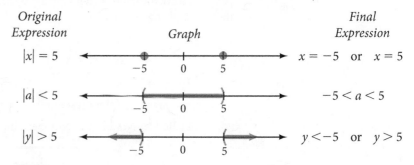

Although we will not always write out the verbal translation of an absolute value inequality, it is important that we understand the translation. Our second expression, $|a| < 5$, means a is within 5 units of 0 on the number line. That is, a must lie *between* the values -5 and 5, as expressed by the continued inequality $-5 < a < 5$. With the third expression, $|y| > 5$, notice that y must lie *outside* the values -5 and 5. That is, y must lie further to the left of -5 or further to the right of 5. The compound inequality $y < -5$ or $y > 5$ expresses this fact.

Absolute Value Inequalities

We can follow this same kind of reasoning to solve more complicated absolute value inequalities by generalizing these results as follows:

> **⟨Δ≠Σ⟩   PROPERTY**   *Absolute Value Inequalities*
>
> For any algebraic expression A and positive constant b,
>
> $$\text{if } |A| < b \text{ then } -b < A < b \quad (A \text{ is between } -b \text{ and } b.)$$
>
> and
>
> $$\text{if } |A| > b \text{ then } A < -b \text{ or } A > b \quad (A \text{ is outside } -b \text{ and } b.)$$
>
> These properties also hold if the strict inequalities are replaced with appropriate inclusive inequality symbols $\leq$ and $\geq$.

EXAMPLE 1   Graph the solution set: $|2x - 5| < 3$

SOLUTION   The absolute value of $2x - 5$ is the distance that $2x - 5$ is from 0 on the number line. We can translate the inequality as, "$2x - 5$ is less than 3 units from 0 on the number line." That is, $2x - 5$ must appear between -3 and 3 on the number line.

A picture of this relationship is

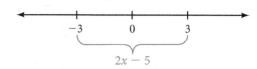

Using the picture, we can write an inequality without absolute value that describes the situation. The value of $2x - 5$ must lie between -3 and 3:

$$-3 < 2x - 5 < 3$$

Next, we solve the continued inequality by first adding 5 to all three members and then multiplying all three by $\frac{1}{2}$.

$$-3 < 2x - 5 < 3$$

$$2 < \quad 2x \quad < 8 \qquad \text{Add 5 to all three expressions}$$

$$1 < \quad x \quad < 4 \qquad \text{Multiply each expression by } \tfrac{1}{2}$$

We can express the solution set in three ways:

Set-Builder Notation	Number Line Graph	Interval Notation
$\{x \mid 1 < x < 4\}$	⟵(——)⟶ 1 4	$(1, 4)$

We can see from the solution that for the quantity $2x - 5$ to be within 3 units of 0 on the number line, x must be between 1 and 4.

EXAMPLE 2 Solve $|x - 3| > 5$, and graph the solution set.

SOLUTION We interpret the absolute value inequality to mean that $x - 3$ is more than 5 units from 0 on the number line. The values of $x - 3$ must lie outside -5 and 5; that is, to the left of -5 or to the right of 5. Here is a picture of the relationship:

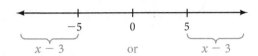

An inequality without absolute value that also describes this situation is

$$x - 3 < -5 \quad \text{or} \quad x - 3 > 5$$

Adding 3 to both sides of each inequality we have

$$x < -2 \quad \text{or} \quad x > 8$$

Here are three ways to write our result:

Set-Builder Notation   Number Line Graph   Interval Notation

$\{x \mid x < -2 \text{ or } x > 8\}$ $(-\infty, -2) \cup (8, \infty)$

We can see from Examples 1 and 2 that to solve an inequality involving absolute value, we must be able to write an equivalent expression that does not involve absolute value.

HOW TO *Solve an Absolute Value Inequality*

Step 1: Isolate the absolute value on one side of the inequality.

Step 2: If the constant term on the other side of the inequality is positive, proceed to Step 3. If it is zero or negative, treat the problem as a special case.

Step 3: Use the property of absolute value inequalities to write an equivalent expression that does not involve an absolute value.

Step 4: Solve for the variable in the resulting expression.

Step 5: Write the solution set using set-builder or interval notation, and graph it on a number line.

EXAMPLE 3 Solve and graph the solution set for $|3a + 7| + 6 \le 10$.

SOLUTION First, we isolate the absolute value by adding -6 to both sides.

$$|3a + 7| \le 4$$

We can read the resulting inequality as, "The distance between $3a + 7$ and 0 is less than or equal to 4." Or, "$3a + 7$ is within 4 units of 0 on the number line." The value of $3a + 7$ must lie between -4 and 4, inclusive. This relationship can be written without absolute value as:

$$-4 \le 3a + 7 \le 4$$

Solving as usual, we have

$$-4 \le 3a + 7 \le 4$$
$$-11 \le \quad 3a \quad \le -3 \qquad \text{Add } -7 \text{ to all three members}$$
$$-\frac{11}{3} \le \quad a \quad \le -1 \qquad \text{Multiply each expression by } \frac{1}{3}$$

We can now express the solution set in three ways:

Set-Builder Notation	Number Line Graph	Interval Notation
$\left\{ a \mid -\frac{11}{3} \le a \le -1 \right\}$		$\left[-\frac{11}{3}, -1 \right]$

EXAMPLE 4   Graph the solution set: $2|4t - 3| \ge 18$.

SOLUTION   We must first isolate the absolute value by multiplying both sides of the inequality by $\frac{1}{2}$.

$$|4t - 3| \ge 9$$

The quantity $4t - 3$ is greater than or equal to 9 units from 0. The value of $4t - 3$ must equal -9 or 9, or lie outside of these numbers; that is, to the left of -9 or to the right of 9.

$$4t - 3 \le -9 \qquad \text{or} \qquad 4t - 3 \ge 9$$
$$4t \le -6 \qquad \text{or} \qquad 4t \ge 12 \qquad \text{Add 3}$$
$$t \le -\frac{6}{4} \qquad \text{or} \qquad t \ge \frac{12}{4} \qquad \text{Multiply by } \frac{1}{4}$$
$$t \le -\frac{3}{2} \qquad \text{or} \qquad t \ge 3$$

Here are three ways to write the solution:

Set-Builder Notation	Number Line Graph	Interval Notation
$\left\{ t \mid t \le -\frac{3}{2} \text{ or } t \ge 3 \right\}$		$\left(-\infty, -\frac{3}{2} \right] \cup [3, \infty)$

EXAMPLE 5   Solve and graph the solution set for $|4 - 2t| > 2$.

SOLUTION   Because the absolute value is already isolated, we can use the property of absolute value inequalities to write an equivalent expression without absolute value symbols as

$$4 - 2t < -2 \qquad \text{or} \qquad 4 - 2t > 2$$

To solve these inequalities we begin by adding -4 to each side.

$$4 + (-4) - 2t < -2 + (-4) \qquad \text{or} \qquad 4 + (-4) - 2t > 2 + (-4)$$
$$-2t < -6 \qquad \text{or} \qquad -2t > -2$$

Next we must multiply both sides of each inequality by $-\frac{1}{2}$. When we do so, we must also reverse the direction of each inequality symbol.

$$-2t < -6 \qquad \text{or} \qquad -2t > -2$$

$$-\frac{1}{2}(-2t) > -\frac{1}{2}(-6) \qquad \text{or} \qquad -\frac{1}{2}(-2t) < -\frac{1}{2}(-2)$$
$$t > 3 \qquad \text{or} \qquad t < 1$$

Although in situations like this we are used to seeing the "less than" symbol written first, the meaning of the solution is clear. We want all real numbers that are either greater than 3 or less than 1. Here are three ways to express this:

Set-Builder Notation   Number Line Graph   Interval Notation

$\{t \mid t < 1 \text{ or } t > 3\}$ $(-\infty, 1) \cup (3, \infty)$

We can use the results of our first few examples and the material in the previous section to summarize the information we have related to absolute value equations and inequalities.

⌈∆≠Σ⌉   *Rewriting Absolute Value Equations and Inequalities*

If c is a positive real number, then each of the following statements on the left is equivalent to the corresponding statement on the right.

With Absolute Value	Without Absolute Value
$\mid x \mid = c$	$x = -c \quad \text{or} \quad x = c$
$\mid x \mid < c$	$-c < x < c$
$\mid x \mid > c$	$x < -c \quad \text{or} \quad x > c$
$\mid ax + b \mid = c$	$ax + b = -c \quad \text{or} \quad ax + b = c$
$\mid ax + b \mid < c$	$-c < ax + b < c$
$\mid ax + b \mid > c$	$ax + b < -c \quad \text{or} \quad ax + b > c$

Special Cases

Because absolute value always results in a nonnegative quantity, we sometimes come across special cases when a negative number or zero appears on the right side of an absolute value inequality after the absolute value has been isolated.

EXAMPLE 6   Solve: $|7y - 1| < -2$.

SOLUTION   The *left* side is never negative because it is an absolute value. The *right* side is negative. We have a positive quantity (or zero) less than a negative quantity, which is impossible. The solution set is the empty set, $\varnothing$. There is no real number to substitute for y to make this inequality a true statement.

EXAMPLE 7   Solve: $|6x + 2| \geq -5$.

SOLUTION   This is the opposite case from that in Example 6. No matter what real number we use for x on the *left* side, the result will always be positive, or zero. The *right* side is negative. We have a positive quantity (or zero) greater than or equal to a negative quantity. Every real number we choose for x gives us a true statement. The absolute value will never *equal* -5, but it will always be *greater than* -5. Therefore, the solution set is the set of all real numbers.

EXAMPLE 8   Solve: $|3 - 4a| \leq 0$.

SOLUTION   For any value of a, it is not possible for the absolute value on the left side to be *less than* zero, but it is possible for the absolute value to *equal* zero. Therefore, we must solve the equation

$$|3 - 4a| = 0$$

$$3 - 4a = 0 \qquad \text{Special case}$$

$$-4a = -3 \qquad \text{Add } -3 \text{ to both sides}$$

$$a = \frac{3}{4} \qquad \text{Divide both sides by } -4$$

The solution set is a single value, $\left\{ \frac{3}{4} \right\}$.

Getting Ready for Class

After reading through the preceding section, respond in your own words and in complete sentences.

A. Write an inequality containing absolute value, the solution to which is all the numbers between -5 and 5 on the number line.

B. Translate $|x| \geq 3$ into words using the definition of absolute value.

C. Explain in words what the inequality $|x - 5| < 2$ means with respect to distance on the number line.

D. Why is there no solution to the inequality $|2x - 3| < 0$?

Solve each of the following inequalities using the definition of absolute value. Write your answer using interval notation (when possible), and graph the solution set in each case.

1. $|x| < 3$ **2.** $|x| \leq 7$ **3.** $|x| \geq 2$ **4.** $|x| > 4$

5. $|x| + 2 < 5$ **6.** $|x| - 3 < -1$ **7.** $|t| - 3 > 4$ **8.** $|t| + 5 > 8$

9. $|y| < -5$ **10.** $|y| > -3$ **11.** $|x| \geq -2$ **12.** $|x| \leq -4$

13. $|x - 3| < 7$ **14.** $|x + 4| < 2$ **15.** $|a + 5| \geq 4$ **16.** $|a - 6| \geq 3$

17. $|b + 1| < 0$ **18.** $|b - 9| \leq 0$ **19.** $|b - 2| \geq 0$ **20.** $|b + 8| > 0$

Solve each inequality and graph the solution set.

21. $|a - 1| < -3$ **22.** $|a + 2| \geq -5$ **23.** $|2x - 4| < 6$

24. $|2x + 6| < 2$ **25.** $|3y + 9| \geq 6$ **26.** $|5y - 1| \geq 4$

27. $|2k + 3| \geq 7$ **28.** $|2k - 5| \geq 3$ **29.** $|x - 3| + 2 < 6$

30. $|x + 4| - 3 < -1$ **31.** $|2a + 1| + 4 \geq 7$ **32.** $|2a - 6| - 1 \geq 2$

33. $|3x + 5| - 8 < 5$ **34.** $|6x - 1| - 4 \leq 2$

35. $9 + |5y - 6| < 4$ **36.** $15 + |3y + 7| \geq 1$

Solve each inequality and write your answer using interval notation. Keep in mind that if you multiply or divide both sides of an inequality by a negative number you must reverse the sense of the inequality.

37. $|x - 3| \leq 5$ **38.** $|a + 4| < 6$ **39.** $|3y + 1| < 5$

40. $|2x - 5| \leq 3$ **41.** $|a + 4| \geq 1$ **42.** $|y - 3| > 6$

43. $|2x + 5| > 2$ **44.** $|-3x + 1| \geq 7$ **45.** $|-5x + 3| \leq 8$

46. $|-3x + 4| \leq 7$ **47.** $|-3x + 7| < 2$ **48.** $|-4x + 2| < 6$

Solve each inequality and graph the solution set.

49. $|5 - x| > 3$ **50.** $|7 - x| > 2$ **51.** $\left|3 - \frac{2}{3}x\right| \geq 5$

52. $\left|3 - \frac{3}{4}x\right| \geq 9$ **53.** $\left|2 - \frac{1}{2}x\right| > 1$ **54.** $\left|3 - \frac{1}{3}x\right| > 1$

Solve each inequality.

55. $|x - 1| < 0.01$ **56.** $|x + 1| < 0.01$ **57.** $|2x + 1| \geq \frac{1}{5}$

58. $|2x - 1| \geq \frac{1}{8}$ **59.** $|3x - 2| \leq \frac{1}{3}$ **60.** $|2x + 5| < \frac{1}{2}$

61. $\left|\frac{3x + 1}{2}\right| > \frac{1}{2}$ **62.** $\left|\frac{2x - 5}{3}\right| \geq \frac{1}{6}$ **63.** $\left|\frac{4 - 3x}{2}\right| \geq 1$

64. $\left|\frac{2x - 3}{4}\right| < 0.35$ **65.** $\left|\frac{3x - 2}{5}\right| \leq \frac{1}{2}$ **66.** $\left|\frac{4x - 3}{2}\right| \leq \frac{1}{3}$

67. $\left|2x - \frac{1}{5}\right| < 0.3$ **68.** $\left|3x - \frac{3}{5}\right| < 0.2$

69. Write the continued inequality $-4 \le x \le 4$ as a single inequality involving absolute value.

70. Write the continued inequality $-8 \le x \le 8$ as a single inequality involving absolute value.

71. Write $-1 \le x - 5 \le 1$ as a single inequality involving absolute value.

72. Write $-3 \le x + 2 \le 3$ as a single inequality involving absolute value.

73. Paying Attention to Instructions Work each problem according to the instructions given.

    a. Evaluate when $x = 0$: $|5x + 3|$ **b.** Solve: $|5x + 3| = 7$

    c. Is 0 a solution to $|5x + 3| > 7$ **d.** Solve: $|5x + 3| > 7$

74. Paying Attention to Instructions Work each problem according to the instructions given.

    a. Evaluate when $x = 0$: $|-2x - 5|$ **b.** Solve: $|-2x - 5| = 1$

    c. Is 0 a solution to $|-2x - 5| > 1$ **d.** Solve: $|-2x - 5| > 1$

Applying the Concepts

75. Speed Limits The interstate speed limit for cars is 75 miles per hour in Nebraska, Nevada, New Mexico, Oklahoma, South Dakota, Utah, and Wyoming and is the highest in the United States. To discourage passing, minimum speeds are also posted, so that the difference between the fastest and slowest moving traffic is no more than 20 miles per hour. Write an absolute value inequality that describes the relationship between the minimum allowable speed and a maximum speed of 75 miles per hour.

76. Wavelengths of Light When white light from the sun passes through a prism, it is broken down into bands of light that form colors. The wavelength, v, (in nanometers) of some common colors are:

Blue: $424 < v < 491$
Green: $491 < v < 575$
Yellow: $575 < v < 585$
Orange: $585 < v < 647$
Red: $647 < v < 700$

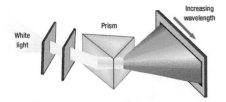

When a fireworks display made of copper is burned, it lets out light with wavelengths, v, that satisfy the relationship $|v - 455| < 23$. Write this inequality without absolute values, find the range of possible values for v, and then using the preceding list of wavelengths, determine the color of that copper fireworks display.

Learning Objectives Assessment

The following problems can be used to help assess if you have successfully met the learning objectives for this section.

77. Solve: $|x - 9| + 5 \le 10$.

    a. $(-\infty, 14]$ **b.** $[-6, 14]$ **c.** $(-\infty, 4] \cup [14, \infty)$ **d.** $[4, 14]$

78. Solve: $|x + 4| > 2$.

    a. $(-2, \infty)$ **b.** $(-6, \infty)$ **c.** $(-\infty, -6) \cup (-2, \infty)$ **d.** $(-6, 2)$

79. Solve: $|5 - y| < -7$.

    a. $\varnothing$ **b.** $(12, \infty)$
    c. $(-\infty, -2) \cup (12, \infty)$ **d.** All real numbers

80. Solve: $|2y + 8| + 11 \ge 9$.

    a. $[-5, \infty)$ **b.** $(-\infty, -5] \cup [-3, \infty)$
    c. $\varnothing$ **d.** All real numbers

Getting Ready for the Next Section

Simplify each expression.

81. $(4x + 3y) - (6x + 3y)$ **82.** $2x - 3(3x - 5)$

83. Solve $x - 2y = 6$ for x.   **84.** Solve $2x - y = 9$ for y.

85. Solve $2x + y = 4$ for y if $x = 1$.   **86.** Solve $2x - 3y = 1$ for x if $y = 7$.

Determine which ordered pair satisfies the equation.

87. $4x + 3y = 10$, $(-1, 5)$ or $(1, 2)$ **88.** $2x - 3y = -6$, $(3, 4)$ or $(2, 3)$

Reviewing Elementary Algebra

Multiply.

89. $(x + 7)(-5x + 4)$ **90.** $(3x - 2)(2x^2 + 6x - 5)$

91. $(3a^4 - 7)^2$ **92.** $(2x + 3)(2x - 3)$

93. $x(x - 7)(3x + 4)$ **94.** $\left(2x - \dfrac{1}{7}\right)\left(7x + \dfrac{1}{2}\right)$

Divide.

95. $\dfrac{24x^3y + 12x^2y^2 - 16xy^3}{4xy}$ **96.** $\dfrac{2x^3 - 9x^2 + 10}{2x - 1}$

Factor the following expressions.

97. $x^2 - 6x + 5$ **98.** $15x^4 + 33x^2 - 36$

99. $81x^4 - 16y^4$ **100.** $6ax - ay + 18b^2x - 3b^2y$

101. $y^3 - \dfrac{1}{27}$ **102.** $3x^4y^4 + 15x^3y^5 - 72x^2y^6$

Learning Objectives

In this section we will learn how to:

1. Solve a system of linear equations in two variables graphically.

2. Solve a system of linear equations in two variables using the addition method.

3. Solve a system of linear equations in two variables using substitution.

4. Recognize an inconsistent system or a system with dependent equations.

Introduction

Previously, we found the graph of an equation of the form $ax + by = c$ to be a straight line. Because the graph is a straight line, the equation is said to be a *linear equation*. Two linear equations considered together form a *linear system* of equations. For example,

$$3x - 2y = 6$$
$$2x + 4y = 20$$

is a linear system. The solution set to the system is the set of all ordered pairs that satisfy both equations. If we graph each equation on the same set of axes, we can see the solution set (see Figure 1).

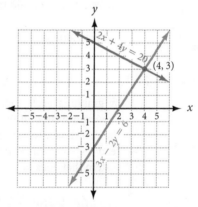

FIGURE 1

The point $(4, 3)$ lies on both lines and therefore must satisfy both equations. It is obvious from the graph that it is the only point that does so. The solution set for the system is $\{(4, 3)\}$.

More generally, if $a_1x + b_1y = c_1$ and $a_2x + b_2y = c_2$ are linear equations, then the solution set for the system

$$a_1x + b_1y = c_1$$
$$a_2x + b_2y = c_2$$

can be illustrated through one of the graphs in Figure 2.

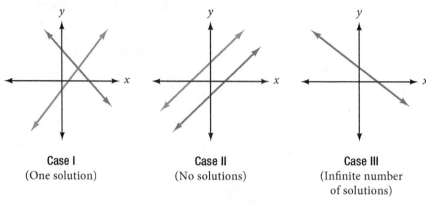

FIGURE 2

Case I   The two lines intersect at one and only one point. The coordinates of the point give the solution to the system. This is what usually happens.

Case II   The lines are parallel and therefore have no points in common. The solution set to the system is the empty set, $\varnothing$. In this case, we say the equations are *inconsistent*.

Case III   The lines coincide. That is, their graphs represent the same line. The solution set consists of all ordered pairs that satisfy either equation. In this case, the equations are said to be *dependent*.

In the beginning of this section, we found the solution set for the system

$$3x - 2y = 6$$
$$2x + 4y = 20$$

by graphing each equation and then reading the solution set from the graph. Solving a system of linear equations by graphing is the least accurate method. If the coordinates of the point of intersection are not integers, it can be difficult to read the solution set from the graph. There is another method of solving a linear system that does not depend on the graph. It is called the *addition method*.

> *Note*   A system of equations is *consistent* if it has at least one solution. It is *inconsistent* if it has no solution. Two equations are *dependent* if one is a multiple of the other. Otherwise, they are *independent*.

The Addition Method

VIDEO EXAMPLES

SECTION 8.5

EXAMPLE 1   Solve the system.

$$4x + 3y = 10$$
$$2x + y = 4$$

SOLUTION   If we multiply the bottom equation by -3, the coefficients of y in the resulting equation and the top equation will be opposites:

$$4x + 3y = 10 \xrightarrow{\text{No Change}} 4x + 3y = 10$$
$$2x + y = 4 \xrightarrow[\text{Multiply by } -3]{} -6x - 3y = -12$$

Adding the left and right sides of the resulting equations, we have

$$4x + 3y = 10$$
$$\underline{-6x - 3y = -12}$$
$$-2x = -2$$

The result is a linear equation in one variable. We have eliminated the variable y from the equations by addition. (It is for this reason we call this method of solving a linear system the *addition method*.) Solving $-2x = -2$ for x, we have

$$x = 1$$

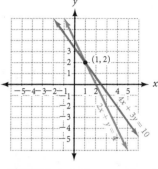

FIGURE 3 *A visual representation of the solution to the system in Example 1*

This is the x-coordinate of the solution to our system. To find the y-coordinate, we substitute $x = 1$ into any of the equations containing both the variables x and y. Let's try the second equation in our original system:

$$2(1) + y = 4$$
$$\underline{2 + y = 4}$$
$$y = 2$$

This is the y-coordinate of the solution to our system. The ordered pair $(1, 2)$ is the solution to the system.

Checking Solutions

We can check our solution by substituting it into both of our equations.

Substituting $x = 1$ and $y = 2$ into $4x + 3y = 10$, we have

$$4(1) + 3(2) \overset{?}{=} 10$$
$$4 + 6 \overset{?}{=} 10$$
$$10 = 10 \quad \text{A true statement}$$

Substituting $x = 1$ and $y = 2$ into $2x + y = 4$, we have

$$2(1) + 2 \overset{?}{=} 4$$
$$2 + 2 \overset{?}{=} 4$$
$$4 = 4 \quad \text{A true statement}$$

Our solution satisfies both equations; therefore, it is a solution to our system of equations.

> **Note** If we had put $x = 1$ into the first equation in our system, we would have obtained $y = 2$ also:
>
> $$4(1) + 3y = 10$$
> $$3y = 6$$
> $$y = 2$$

EXAMPLE 2 Solve the system.

$$2x - 3y = 4$$
$$4x + 5y = 3$$

SOLUTION We can eliminate x by multiplying the top equation by -2 and adding it to the bottom equation:

$$2x - 3y = 4 \xrightarrow{\text{Multiply by } -2} -4x + 6y = -8$$
$$4x + 5y = 3 \xrightarrow[\text{No Change}]{} 4x + 5y = 3$$
$$\underline{}$$
$$11y = -5$$
$$y = -\frac{5}{11}$$

The *y*-coordinate of our solution is $-\frac{5}{11}$. If we were to substitute this value of *y* back into either of our original equations, we would find the arithmetic necessary to solve for *x* cumbersome. For this reason, it is probably best to go back to the original system and solve it a second time—for *x* instead of *y*. Here is how we do that:

$$2x - 3y = 4 \xrightarrow{\text{Multiply by 5}} 10x - 15y = 20$$

$$4x + 5y = 3 \xrightarrow[\text{Multiply by 3}]{} \underline{12x + 15y = 9}$$

$$22x \qquad = 29$$

$$x = \frac{29}{22}$$

The solution to our system is $\left(\dfrac{29}{22}, -\dfrac{5}{11} \right)$.

The main idea in solving a system of linear equations by the addition method is to use the multiplication property of equality on one or both of the original equations, if necessary, to make the coefficients of either variable opposites. The following box shows some steps to follow when solving a system of linear equations by the addition method.

HOW TO   *Solve a System of Linear Equations by the Addition Method*

Step 1: Decide which variable to eliminate. (In some cases, one variable will be easier to eliminate than the other. With some practice, you will notice which one it is.)

Step 2: Use the multiplication property of equality on each equation separately to make the coefficients of the variable that is to be eliminated opposites.

Step 3: Add the respective left and right sides of the system together.

Step 4: Solve for the remaining variable.

Step 5: Substitute the value of the variable from step 4 into an equation containing both variables and solve for the other variable. (Or repeat steps 2–4 to eliminate the other variable.)

Step 6: Check your solution in both equations, if necessary.

EXAMPLE 3   Solve the system.

$$5x - 2y = 5$$
$$-10x + 4y = 15$$

SOLUTION   We can eliminate *y* by multiplying the first equation by 2 and adding the result to the second equation:

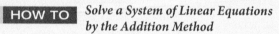

$$5x - 2y = 5 \xrightarrow{\text{Multiply by 2}} 10x - 4y = 10$$

$$-10x + 4y = 15 \xrightarrow[\text{No Change}]{} \underline{-10x + 4y = 15}$$

$$0 = 25$$

The result is the false statement $0 = 25$, which indicates there is no solution to the system. If we were to graph the two lines, we would find that they are parallel. In a case like this, we say the system is *inconsistent*. Whenever both variables have been eliminated and the resulting statement is false, the solution set for the system will be the empty set, $\varnothing$.

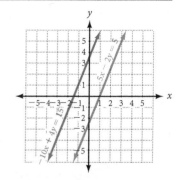

FIGURE 4 *A visual representation of the situation in Example 4—the two lines are parallel*

EXAMPLE 4   Solve the system.

$$4x + 3y = 2$$
$$8x + 6y = 4$$

SOLUTION   Multiplying the top equation by -2 and adding, we can eliminate the variable x:

$$4x + 3y = 2 \xrightarrow{\text{Multiply by } -2} -8x - 6y = -4$$
$$8x + 6y = 4 \xrightarrow[\text{No Change}]{} \underline{ 8x + 6y = 4}$$
$$0 = 0$$

Both variables have been eliminated and the resulting statement $0 = 0$ is true. In this case, the lines coincide and the system is said to be *dependent*. The solution set consists of all ordered pairs that satisfy either equation. We can write the solution set as $\{(x, y) | 4x + 3y = 2\}$ or $\{(x, y) | 8x + 6y = 4\}$.

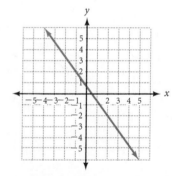

FIGURE 5 *A visual representation of the situation in Example 5—both equations produce the same graph*

Special Cases

The previous two examples illustrate the two special cases in which the graphs of the equations in the system either coincide or are parallel. In both cases the left-hand sides of the equations were multiples of each other. In the case of the dependent equations the right-hand sides were also multiples. We can generalize these observations for the system

$$a_1 x + b_1 y = c_1$$
$$a_2 x + b_2 y = c_2$$

Inconsistent System

What happens	*Geometric Intrepretation*	*Algebraic Intrepretation*
Both variables are eliminated, and the resulting statement is false.	The lines are parallel, and there is no solution to the system.	$\dfrac{a_1}{a_2} = \dfrac{b_1}{b_2} \neq \dfrac{c_1}{c_2}$

Dependent Equations

What happens	*Geometric Interpretation*	*Algebraic Interpretation*
Both variables are eliminated, and the resulting statement is true.	The lines coincide, and there are an infinite number of solutions to the system.	$\dfrac{a_1}{a_2} = \dfrac{b_1}{b_2} = \dfrac{c_1}{c_2}$

The Substitution Method

We end this section by considering another method of solving a linear system. The method is called the *substitution method* and is shown in the following examples.

EXAMPLE 5   Solve the system.

$$2x - 3y = -6$$
$$y = 3x - 5$$

SOLUTION   The second equation tells us y is $3x - 5$. Substituting the expression $3x - 5$ for y in the first equation, we have

$$2x - 3(3x - 5) = -6$$

The result of the substitution is the elimination of the variable y. Solving the resulting linear equation in x as usual, we have

$$2x - 9x + 15 = -6$$
$$-7x + 15 = -6$$
$$-7x = -21$$
$$x = 3$$

Putting $x = 3$ into the second equation in the original system, we have

$$y = 3(3) - 5$$
$$= 9 - 5$$
$$= 4$$

The solution to the system is $(3, 4)$.

Checking Solution

Checking $(3, 4)$ in each equation looks like this

Substituting $x = 3$ and $y = 4$ into $2x - 3y = -6$, we have

$$2(3) - 3(4) \stackrel{?}{=} -6$$
$$6 - 12 \stackrel{?}{=} -6$$
$$-6 = -6 \qquad \text{A true statement}$$

Substituting $x = 3$ and $y = 4$ into $y = 3x - 5$, we have

$$4 \stackrel{?}{=} 3(3) - 5$$
$$4 \stackrel{?}{=} 9 - 5$$
$$4 = 4 \qquad \text{A true statement}$$

Our solution satisfies both equations, so $(3, 4)$ is a solution to our system.

Here are the steps to use in solving a system of equations by the substitution method.

> ### HOW TO   *Solve a System of Equations by the Substitution Method*
>
> **Step 1:** Solve either one of the equations for x or y. (This step is not necessary if one of the equations is already in the correct form, as in Example 7.)
>
> **Step 2:** Substitute the expression for the variable obtained in step 1 into the other equation and solve it.
>
> **Step 3:** Substitute the solution from step 2 into any equation in the system that contains both variables and solve it.
>
> **Step 4:** Check your results, if necessary.

Note Both the substitution method and the addition method can be used to solve any system of linear equations in two variables. Systems like the one in Example 5, however, are easier to solve using the substitution method, because one of the variables is already written in terms of the other. A system like the one in Example 2 is easier to solve using the addition method, because solving for one of the variables would lead to an expression involving fractions. The system in Example 6 could be solved easily by either method, because solving the second equation for x is a one-step process.

EXAMPLE 6   Solve by substitution

$$2x + 3y = 5$$
$$x - 2y = 6$$

SOLUTION   To use the substitution method, we must solve one of the two equations for x or y. We can solve for x in the second equation by adding $2y$ to both sides:

$$x - 2y = 6$$
$$x = 2y + 6 \qquad \text{Add } 2y \text{ to both sides}$$

Substituting the expression $2y + 6$ for x in the first equation of our system, we have

$$2(2y + 6) + 3y = 5$$
$$4y + 12 + 3y = 5$$
$$7y + 12 = 5$$
$$7y = -7$$
$$y = -1$$

Using $y = -1$ in either equation in the original system, we find $x = 4$. The solution is $(4, -1)$.

Getting Ready for Class

After reading through the preceding section, respond in your own words and in complete sentences.

A. Two linear equations, each with the same two variables, form a system of equations. How do we define a solution to this system? That is, what form will a solution have, and what properties does a solution possess?

B. When would substitution be more efficient than the addition method in solving two linear equations?

C. Explain what an inconsistent system of linear equations looks like graphically and what would result algebraically when attempting to solve the system.

D. When might the graphing method of solving a system of equations be more desirable than the other techniques, and when might it be less desirable?

Problem Set 8.5

Solve each system by graphing both equations on the same set of axes and then reading the solution from the graph.

1. $3x - 2y = 6$

  $x - y = 1$

2. $5x - 2y = 10$

  $x - y = -1$

3. $\quad y = \dfrac{3}{5}x - 3$

  $2x - y = -4$

4. $\quad y = \dfrac{1}{2}x - 2$

  $2x - y = -1$

5. $y = \dfrac{1}{2}x$

  $y = -\dfrac{3}{4}x + 5$

6. $y = \dfrac{2}{3}x$

  $y = -\dfrac{1}{3}x + 6$

7. $3x + 3y = -2$

  $y = -x + 4$

8. $2x - y = 5$

  $y = 2x - 5$

Solve each of the following systems by the addition method.

9. $3x + y = 5$

  $3x - y = 3$

10. $-x - y = 4$

  $-x + 2y = -3$

11. $x + 2y = 0$

  $2x - 6y = 5$

12. $x + 3y = 3$

  $2x - 9y = 1$

13. $2x - 5y = 16$

  $4x - 3y = 11$

14. $5x - 3y = -11$

  $7x + 6y = -12$

15. $6x + 3y = -1$

  $9x + 5y = 1$

16. $5x + 4y = -1$

  $7x + 6y = -2$

17. $4x + 3y = 14$

  $9x - 2y = 14$

18. $7x - 6y = 13$

  $6x - 5y = 11$

19. $2x - 5y = 3$

  $-4x + 10y = 3$

20. $-3x - 2y = -1$

  $-6x + 4y = -2$

21. $\dfrac{1}{2}x + \dfrac{1}{3}y = 13$

  $\dfrac{2}{5}x + \dfrac{1}{4}y = 10$

22. $\dfrac{1}{2}x + \dfrac{1}{3}y = \dfrac{2}{3}$

  $\dfrac{2}{3}x + \dfrac{2}{5}y = \dfrac{14}{15}$

23. $\dfrac{2}{3}x + \dfrac{2}{5}y = -4$

  $\dfrac{1}{3}x - \dfrac{1}{2}y = -\dfrac{1}{3}$

24. $\dfrac{1}{2}x - \dfrac{1}{3}y = \dfrac{5}{6}$

  $-\dfrac{2}{5}x + \dfrac{1}{2}y = -\dfrac{9}{10}$

Solve each of the following systems by the substitution method.

25. $7x - y = 24$

  $x = 2y + 9$

26. $3x - y = -8$

  $y = 6x + 3$

27. $6x - y = 10$

  $y = -\dfrac{3}{4}x - 1$

28. $2x - y = 6$

  $y = -\dfrac{4}{3}x + 1$

29. $y = 3x - 2$

  $y = 4x - 4$

30. $y = 5x - 2$

  $y = -2x + 5$

31. $2x - y = 5$

  $4x - 2y = 10$

32. $-10x + 8y = -6$

  $y = \dfrac{5}{4}x$

33. $\dfrac{1}{3}x - \dfrac{1}{2}y = 0$

  $x = \dfrac{3}{2}y$

34. $\dfrac{2}{5}x - \dfrac{2}{3}y = 0$

  $\phantom{\dfrac{2}{5}x}y = \dfrac{3}{5}x$

You may want to read Example 2 again before solving the systems that follow.

35. $4x - 7y = 3$
$\quad\ \ 5x + 2y = -3$

36. $3x - 4y = 7$
$\quad\ \ 6x - 3y = 5$

37. $9x - 8y = 4$
$\quad\ \ 2x + 3y = 6$

38. $\quad 4x - 7y = 10$
$\quad -3x + 2y = -9$

39. $3x - 5y = 2$
$\quad\ \ 7x + 2y = 1$

40. $4x - 3y = -1$
$\quad\ \ 5x + 8y = 2$

Solve each of the following systems by using either the addition or substitution method. Choose the method that is most appropriate for the problem.

41. $x - 3y = 7$

$\quad\ \ 2x + y = -6$

42. $2x - y = 9$

$\quad\ \ x + 2y = -11$

43. $y = \frac{1}{2}x + \frac{1}{3}$

$\quad\ \ y = -\frac{1}{3}x + 2$

44. $y = \frac{3}{4}x - \frac{4}{5}$

$\quad\ \ y = \frac{1}{2}x - \frac{1}{2}$

45. $3x - 4y = 12$

$\quad\ \ x = \frac{2}{3}y - 4$

46. $-5x + 3y = -15$

$\quad\ \ x = \frac{4}{5}y - 2$

47. $\quad 4x - 3y = -7$

$\quad -8x + 6y = -11$

48. $3x - 4y = 8$

$\quad\ \ y = \frac{3}{4}x - 2$

49. $\quad 3y + z = 17$

$\quad\ \ 5y + 20z = 65$

50. $\quad x + y = 850$

$\quad\ \ 1.5x + y = 1,100$

51. $\frac{3}{4}x - \frac{1}{3}y = 1$

$\quad\ \ y = \frac{1}{4}x$

52. $-\frac{2}{3}x + \frac{1}{2}y = -1$

$\quad\ \ y = -\frac{1}{3}x$

53. $\frac{1}{4}x - \frac{1}{2}y = \frac{1}{3}$

$\quad\ \ \frac{1}{3}x - \frac{1}{4}y = -\frac{2}{3}$

54. $\frac{1}{5}x - \frac{1}{10}y = -\frac{1}{5}$

$\quad\ \ \frac{2}{3}x - \frac{1}{2}y = -\frac{1}{6}$

55. Paying Attention to Instructions Work each problem according to the instructions given.

   a. Simplify: $(3x - 4y) - 3(x - y)$

   b. Find y when x is 0 in $3x - 4y = 8$.

   c. Find the y-intercept: $3x - 4y = 8$

   d. Graph: $3x - 4y = 8$

   e. Find the point where the graphs of $3x - 4y = 8$ and $x - y = 2$ cross

56. Paying Attention to Instructions Work each problem according to the instructions given.

   a. Solve: $4x - 5 = 20$

   b. Solve for y: $4x - 5y = 20$

   c. Solve for x: $x - y = 5$

   d. Solve the system:

$$4x - 5 = 20$$
$$x - y = 5$$

57. Multiply both sides of the second equation in the following system by 100, and then solve as usual.

$$x + y = 10,000$$
$$0.06x + 0.05y = 560$$

58. What value of c will make the following system a dependent system (one in which the lines coincide)?

$$6x - 9y = 3$$
$$4x - 6y = c$$

59. Where do the graphs of the lines $x + y = 4$ and $x - 2y = 4$ intersect?

60. Where do the graphs of the line $x = -1$ and $x - 2y = 4$ intersect?

Learning Objectives Assessment

The following problems can be used to help assess if you have successfully met the learning objectives for this section.

61. Figure 7 shows the graphs of two linear equations in two variables. Which of the following could be a solution to the system consisting of the two equations?

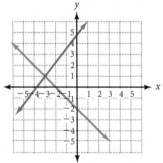

FIGURE 7

    a. $(0, 4)$ **b.** $(-4, 0)$ **c.** $(-3, 1)$ **d.** $(3, -1)$

62. Solve the following system using the addition method. Which value is part of the solution?

$$3x - 2y = 9$$
$$x + 5y - 1$$

    a. $y = \dfrac{1}{5}$ **b.** $y = -\dfrac{6}{17}$ **c.** $x = \dfrac{5}{2}$ **d.** $x = \dfrac{7}{4}$

63. Solve the following system using substitution. Which value is part of the solution?

$$5x + y = 2$$
$$2x - 3y = 4$$

a. $y = 2$ **b.** $y = -\dfrac{14}{17}$ **c.** $x = \dfrac{2}{5}$ **d.** $x = \dfrac{10}{17}$

64. For which value of c will the following system have an infinite number of solutions?

$$x - 2y = 1$$
$$-2x + 4y = c$$

a. 1   **b.** -1 **c.** 2   **d.** -2

Getting Ready for the Next Section

Simplify.

65. $2 - 2(6)$

66. $2(1) - 2 + 3$

67. $(x + 3y) - 1(x - 2z)$

68. $(x + y + z) + (2x - y + z)$

Solve.

69. $-9y = -9$

70. $30x = 38$

71. $3(1) + 2z = 9$

72. $4\left(\dfrac{19}{15}\right) - 2y = 4$

Apply the distributive property, then simplify if possible.

73. $2(5x - z)$

74. $-1(x - 2z)$

75. $3(3x + y - 2z)$

76. $2(2x - y + z)$

Reviewing Elementary Algebra

Perform the indicated operations.

77. $\dfrac{2a + 10}{a^3} \cdot \dfrac{a^2}{3a + 15}$

78. $\dfrac{4a + 8}{a^2 - a - 6} \div \dfrac{a^2 + 7a + 12}{a^2 - 9}$

79. $(x^2 - 9)\left(\dfrac{x + 2}{x + 3}\right)$

80. $\dfrac{1}{x + 4} + \dfrac{8}{x^2 - 16}$

81. $\dfrac{2x - 7}{x - 2} - \dfrac{x - 5}{x - 2}$

82. $2 + \dfrac{25}{5x - 1}$

Simplify each expression.

83. $\dfrac{\dfrac{1}{x} - \dfrac{1}{3}}{\dfrac{1}{x} + \dfrac{1}{3}}$

84. $\dfrac{1 - \dfrac{9}{x^2}}{1 - \dfrac{1}{x} - \dfrac{6}{x^2}}$

Systems of Linear Equations in Three Variables

Learning Objectives

In this section we will learn how to:

1. Determine if an ordered triple is a solution to a system of linear equations in three variables.
2. Solve a system of three linear equations in three variables.
3. Recognize a system of linear equations in three variables having dependent equations.
4. Recognize an inconsistent system of linear equations in three variables.

Introduction

A solution to an equation in three variables such as

$$2x + y - 3z = 6$$

is an ordered triple of numbers (x, y, z). For example, the ordered triples $(0, 0, -2)$, $(2, 2, 0)$, and $(0, 9, 1)$ are solutions to the equation $2x + y - 3z = 6$, because they produce a true statement when their coordinates are substituted for x, y, and z in the equation.

> **DEFINITION** *solution set*
>
> The *solution set* for a system of three linear equations in three variables is the set of ordered triples that satisfies all three equations.

VIDEO EXAMPLES

SECTION 8.6

EXAMPLE 1 Determine if the given ordered triple is a solution to the system.

$$\begin{aligned} x + y + 2z &= 4 \\ 2x - y + z &= -1 \\ -x - 2y + 3z &= 5 \end{aligned}$$

a. $(2, 4, -1)$ **b.** $(-1, 1, 2)$

SOLUTION All we need to do is see if the ordered triple satisfies all three equations.

a. Substituting $x = 2$, $y = 4$, and $z = -1$ we get

$$2 + 4 + 2(-1) \overset{?}{=} 4$$
$$4 = 4 \qquad \text{True}$$

$$2(2) - 4 + (-1) \overset{?}{=} -1$$
$$-1 = -1 \qquad \text{True}$$

$$-2 - 2(4) + 3(-1) \overset{?}{=} 5$$
$$-13 \neq 5 \qquad \text{False}$$

The ordered triple $(2, 4, -1)$ is not a solution because it does not satisfy the third equation.

b. Substituting $x = -1$, $y = 1$, and $z = 2$ gives us

$$-1 + 1 + 2(2) \stackrel{?}{=} 4$$

$$4 = 4 \qquad \text{True}$$

$$2(-1) - 1 + 2 \stackrel{?}{=} -1$$

$$-1 = -1 \qquad \text{True}$$

$$-(-1) - 2(1) + 3(2) \stackrel{?}{=} 5$$

$$5 = 5 \qquad \text{True}$$

The ordered triple $(-1, 1, 2)$ satisfies all three equations, so it is a solution to the system.

EXAMPLE 2   Solve the system.

$$x + y + z = 6 \qquad (1)$$
$$2x - y + z = 3 \qquad (2)$$
$$x + 2y - 3z = -4 \qquad (3)$$

SOLUTION   We want to find the ordered triple (x, y, z) that satisfies all three equations. We have numbered the equations so it will be easier to keep track of where they are and what we are doing.

There are many ways to proceed. The main idea is to take two different pairs of equations and eliminate the same variable from each pair. We begin by adding equations (1) and (2) to eliminate the y-variable. The resulting equation is numbered (4):

$$
\begin{array}{ll}
x + y + z = 6 & (1) \\
\underline{2x - y + z = 3} & (2) \\
3x \quad + 2z = 9 & (4)
\end{array}
$$

Adding twice equation (2) to equation (3) will also eliminate the variable y. The resulting equation is numbered (5):

$$
\begin{array}{ll}
4x - 2y + 2z = 6 & \text{Twice (2)} \\
\underline{x + 2y - 3z = -4} & (3) \\
5x \quad - z = 2 & (5)
\end{array}
$$

Equations (4) and (5) form a linear system in two variables. By multiplying equation (5) by 2 and adding the result to equation (4), we succeed in eliminating the variable z from the new pair of equations:

$$
\begin{array}{ll}
3x + 2z = 9 & (4) \\
\underline{10x - 2z = 4} & \text{Twice (5)} \\
13x \quad = 13 & \\
x \quad = 1 &
\end{array}
$$

Substituting $x = 1$ into equation (4), we have

$$3(1) + 2z = 9$$
$$2z = 6$$
$$z = 3$$

Using $x = 1$ and $z = 3$ in equation (1) gives us

$$1 + y + 3 = 6$$
$$y + 4 = 6$$
$$y = 2$$

The solution is the ordered triple $(1, 2, 3)$.

EXAMPLE 3   Solve the system.

$$2x + y - z = 3 \qquad (1)$$
$$3x + 4y + z = 6 \qquad (2)$$
$$2x - 3y + z = 1 \qquad (3)$$

SOLUTION   It is easiest to eliminate z from the equations. The equation produced by adding (1) and (2) is

$$5x + 5y = 9 \qquad (4)$$

The equation that results from adding (1) and (3) is

$$4x - 2y = 4 \qquad (5)$$

Equations (4) and (5) form a linear system in two variables. We can eliminate the variable y from this system as follows:

$$5x + 5y = 9 \xrightarrow{\text{Multiply by 2}} 10x + 10y = 18$$
$$4x - 2y = 4 \xrightarrow{\text{Multiply by 5}} \underline{20x - 10y = 20}$$
$$30x \qquad\quad = 38$$
$$x = \frac{38}{30}$$
$$= \frac{19}{15}$$

Now we substitute $x = \frac{19}{15}$ into equation (5) or equation (4) and solve for y. Using equation (4), we obtain

$$5\left(\frac{19}{15}\right) + 5y = 9$$
$$\frac{19}{3} + 5y = 9 \qquad\qquad \text{Reduce}$$
$$19 + 15y = 27 \qquad\qquad \text{Multiply both sides by 3}$$
$$15y = 8$$
$$y = \frac{8}{15}$$

Finally, we substitute $x = \frac{19}{15}$ and $y = \frac{8}{15}$ into equation (1), (2), or (3) and solve for z. Using equation (3) gives us

$$2\left(\frac{19}{15}\right) - 3\left(\frac{8}{15}\right) + z = 1$$

$$\frac{38}{15} - \frac{24}{15} + z = 1$$

$$\frac{14}{15} + z = 1$$

$$z = 1 - \frac{14}{15}$$

$$z = \frac{1}{15}$$

The ordered triple that satisfies all three equations is $\left(\frac{19}{15}, \frac{8}{15}, \frac{1}{15}\right)$.

EXAMPLE 4   Solve the system.

$$2x + 3y - z = 5 \qquad (1)$$
$$4x + 6y - 2z = 10 \qquad (2)$$
$$x - 4y + 3z = 5 \qquad (3)$$

SOLUTION   Multiplying equation (1) by -2 and adding the result to equation (2) looks like this:

$$
\begin{aligned}
-4x - 6y + 2z &= -10 \qquad -2 \text{ times (1)} \\
4x + 6y - 2z &= 10 \qquad (2) \\
\hline
0 &= 0
\end{aligned}
$$

All three variables have been eliminated, and we are left with a true statement. This implies that the two equations are dependent. With a system of three equations in three variables, however, a dependent system can have no solution or an infinite number of solutions. After we have concluded the examples in this section, we will discuss the geometry behind these systems. Doing so will give you some additional insight into dependent systems.

EXAMPLE 5   Solve the system.

$$x - 5y + 4z = 8 \qquad (1)$$
$$3x + y - 2z = 7 \qquad (2)$$
$$-9x - 3y + 6z = 5 \qquad (3)$$

SOLUTION   Multiplying equation (2) by 3 and adding the result to equation (3) produces

$$
\begin{aligned}
9x + 3y - 6z &= 21 \qquad 3 \text{ times (2)} \\
-9x - 3y + 6z &= 5 \qquad (3) \\
\hline
0 &= 26
\end{aligned}
$$

In this case, all three variables have been eliminated, and we are left with a false statement. The two equations are inconsistent; there are no ordered triples that satisfy both equations. The solution set for the system is the empty set, $\varnothing$. If equations (2) and (3) have no ordered triples in common, then certainly (1), (2), and (3) do not either.

EXAMPLE 6   Solve the system.

$$x + 3y = 5 \quad (1)$$
$$6y + z = 12 \quad (2)$$
$$x - 2z = -10 \quad (3)$$

SOLUTION   It may be helpful to rewrite the system as

$$x + 3y \quad\quad = \quad 5 \quad (1)$$
$$6y + z = 12 \quad (2)$$
$$x \quad\quad - 2z = -10 \quad (3)$$

Equation (2) does not contain the variable x. If we multiply equation (3) by -1 and add the result to equation (1), we will be left with another equation that does not contain the variable x:

$$x + 3y \quad\quad = 5 \quad (1)$$
$$-x \quad\quad + 2z = 10 \quad\quad -1 \text{ times (3)}$$
$$\overline{\quad\quad\quad 3y + 2z = 15 \quad (4)\quad\quad}$$

Equations (2) and (4) form a linear system in two variables. Multiplying equation (2) by -2 and adding the result to equation (4) eliminates the variable z:

$$6y + z = 12 \quad\xrightarrow{\text{Multiply by } -2}\quad -12y - 2z = -24$$
$$3y + 2z = 15 \quad\xrightarrow[\text{No Change}]{}\quad \underline{\quad 3y + 2z = \quad 15\quad}$$
$$-9y \quad\quad = -9$$
$$y = 1$$

Using $y = 1$ in equation (4) and solving for z, we have

$$z = 6$$

Substituting $y = 1$ into equation (1) gives

$$x = 2$$

The ordered triple that satisfies all three equations is $(2, 1, 6)$.

The Geometry Behind Equations in Three Variables

We can graph an ordered triple on a coordinate system with three axes. The graph will be a point in space. The coordinate system is drawn in perspective; you have to imagine that the x-axis comes out of the paper and is perpendicular to both the y-axis and the z-axis. To graph the point $(3, 4, 5)$, we move 3 units in the x-direction, 4 units in the y-direction, and then 5 units in the z-direction, as shown in Figure 1.

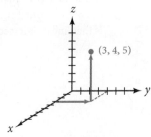

FIGURE 1

Although in actual practice it is sometimes difficult to graph equations in three variables, if we were to graph a linear equation in three variables, we would find that the graph was a plane in space. A system of three equations in three variables is represented by three planes in space.

There are a number of possible ways in which these three planes can intersect, some of which are shown below. And there are still other possibilities that are not among those shown.

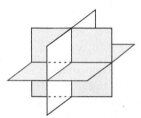

CASE 1   *The three planes have exactly one point in common. In this case we get one solution to our system, as in Examples 2, 3, and 6.*

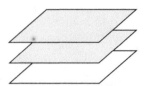

CASE 2   *The three planes have no points in common because they are all parallel to one another. The system they represent is an inconsistent system.*

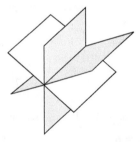

CASE 3   *The three planes intersect in a line. Any point on the line is a solution to the system of equations represented by the planes, so there is an infinite number of solutions to the system. This is an example of a dependent system.*

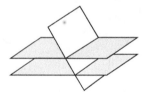

CASE 4   *Two of the planes are parallel; the third plane intersects each of the parallel planes. In this case, the three planes have no points in common. There is no solution to the system; it is an inconsistent system.*

In Example 4, we found that equations (1) and (2) were dependent equations. They represent the same plane. That is, they have all their points in common. But the system of equations that they came from has either no solution or an infinite number of solutions. It all depends on the third plane. If the third plane coincides with the first two, then the solution to the system is a plane. If the third plane is parallel to the first two, then there is no solution to the system. Finally, if the third plane intersects the first two but does not coincide with them, then the solution to the system is that line of intersection.

In Example 5 we found that trying to eliminate a variable from the second and third equations resulted in a false statement. This means that the two planes represented by these equations are parallel. It makes no difference where the third plane is; there is no solution to the system in Example 5. (If we were to graph the three planes from Example 5, we would obtain a diagram similar to Case 2 or Case 4.)

If, in the process of solving a system of linear equations in three variables, we eliminate all the variables from a pair of equations and are left with a false statement, we will say the system is inconsistent. If we eliminate all the variables and are left with a true statement, then we will say the system is a dependent one.

Getting Ready for Class

After reading through the preceding section, respond in your own words and in complete sentences.

A. What is an ordered triple of numbers?

B. Explain what it means for (1, 2, 3) to be a solution to a system of linear equations in three variables.

C. Explain in a general way the procedure you would use to solve a system of three linear equations in three variables.

D. How do you know when a system of linear equations in three variables has no solution?

Determine if each ordered triple is a solution to the given system.

1. $2x + y - z = 2$
$x + y + z = -1$
$3x - 2y + 2z = 3$

a. $(2, 1, 3)$ **b.** $(1, -1, -1)$

2. $3x - 2y + z = -4$
$x - y - 2z = 0$
$-2x + y - z = 6$

a. $(-9, -11, 1)$ **b.** $(-4, -4, 0)$

Solve the following systems.

3. $x + y + z = 4$
$x - y + 2z = 1$
$x - y - 3z = -4$

4. $x - y - 2z = -1$
$x + y + z = 6$
$x + y - z = 4$

5. $x + y + z = 6$
$x - y + 2z = 7$
$2x - y - 4z = -9$

6. $x + y + z = 0$
$x + y - z = 6$
$x - y + 2z = -7$

7. $x + 2y + z = 3$
$2x - y + 2z = 6$
$3x + y - z = 5$

8. $2x + y - 3z = -14$
$x - 3y + 4z = 22$
$3x + 2y + z = 0$

9. $2x + 3y - 2z = 4$
$x + 3y - 3z = 4$
$3x - 6y + z = -3$

10. $4x + y - 2z = 0$
$2x - 3y + 3z = 9$
$-6x - 2y + z = 0$

11. $-x + 4y - 3z = 2$
$2x - 8y + 6z = 1$
$3x - y + z = 0$

12. $4x + 6y - 8z = 1$
$-6x - 9y + 12z = 0$
$x - 2y - 2z = 3$

13. $\frac{1}{2}x - y + z = 0$

$2x + \frac{1}{3}y + z = 2$

$x + y + z = -4$

14. $\frac{1}{3}x + \frac{1}{2}y + z = -1$

$x - y + \frac{1}{5}z = -1$

$x + y + z = -5$

15. $2x - y - 3z = 1$
$x + 2y + 4z = 3$
$4x - 2y - 6z = 2$

16. $3x + 2y + z = 3$
$x - 3y + z = 4$
$-6x - 4y - 2z = 1$

17. $2x - y + 3z = 4$
$x + 2y - z = -3$
$4x + 3y + 2z = -5$

18. $6x - 2y + z = 5$
$3x + y + 3z = 7$
$x + 4y - z = 4$

19. $x + y = 9$
$y + z = 7$
$x - z = 2$

20. $x - y = 1$
$x + z = 2$
$y - z = 7$

21. $2x + y = 2$
$y + z = 3$
$4x - z = 0$

22. $2x + y = 6$
$3y - 2z = -8$
$x + z = 5$

23. $2x - 3y = 0$
$6y - 4z = 1$
$x + 2z = 1$

24. $3x + 2y = 3$
$y + 2z = 2$
$6x - 4z = 1$

25.
$$x + y - z = 2$$
$$2x + y + 3z = 4$$
$$x - 2y + 2z = 6$$

26.
$$x + 2y - 2z = 4$$
$$3x + 4y - z = -2$$
$$2x + 3y - 3z = -5$$

27.
$$2x + 3y = -\frac{1}{2}$$
$$4x + 8z = 2$$
$$3y + 2z = -\frac{3}{4}$$

28.
$$3x - 5y = 2$$
$$4x + 6z = \frac{1}{3}$$
$$5y - 7z = \frac{1}{6}$$

29.
$$\frac{1}{3}x + \frac{1}{2}y - \frac{1}{6}z = 4$$
$$\frac{1}{4}x - \frac{3}{4}y + \frac{1}{2}z = \frac{3}{2}$$
$$\frac{1}{2}x - \frac{2}{3}y - \frac{1}{4}z = -\frac{16}{3}$$

30.
$$-\frac{1}{4}x + \frac{3}{8}y + \frac{1}{2}z = -1$$
$$\frac{2}{3}x - \frac{1}{6}y - \frac{1}{2}z = 2$$
$$\frac{3}{4}x - \frac{1}{2}y - \frac{1}{8}z = 1$$

31.
$$x - \frac{1}{2}y - \frac{1}{3}z = -\frac{4}{3}$$
$$\frac{1}{3}x - \frac{1}{2}z = 5$$
$$-\frac{1}{4}x + \frac{2}{3}y - z = -\frac{3}{4}$$

32.
$$x + \frac{1}{3}y - \frac{1}{2}z = -\frac{3}{2}$$
$$\frac{1}{2}x - y + \frac{1}{3}z = 8$$
$$\frac{1}{3}x - \frac{1}{4}y - z = -\frac{5}{6}$$

Applying the Concepts

33. Electric Current In the following diagram of an electrical circuit, x, y, and z represent the amount of current (in amperes) flowing across the 5-ohm, 20-ohm, and 10-ohm resistors, respectively. (In circuit diagrams, resistors are represented by ⌇⌇ and potential differences by ⊣⊢.)

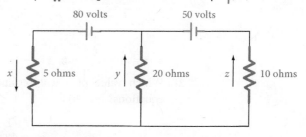

The system of equations used to find the three currents x, y, and z is

$$x - y - z = 0$$
$$5x + 20y = 80$$
$$20y - 10z = 50$$

Solve the system for all variables.

34. Cost of a Rental Car If a car rental company charges $10 a day and 8¢ a mile to rent one of its cars, then the cost z, in dollars, to rent a car for x, days and drive y miles can be found from the equation

$$z = 10x + 0.08y$$

a. How much does it cost to rent a car for 2 days and drive it 200 miles under these conditions?

b. A second company charges $12 a day and 6¢ a mile for the same car. Write an equation that gives the cost z, in dollars, to rent a car from this company for x days and drive it y miles.

c. A car is rented from each of the companies mentioned in parts a and b for 2 days. To find the mileage at which the cost of renting the cars from each of the two companies will be equal, solve the following system for y:

$$z = 10x + 0.08y$$
$$z = 12x + 0.06y$$
$$x = 2$$

Learning Objectives Assessment

The following problems can be used to help assess if you have successfully met the learning objectives for this section.

35. Which ordered triple is a solution to the following system?

$$2x - 3y = 1$$
$$x + 4z = 3$$
$$y - 2z = 4$$

a. $(2, 1, -1)$ **b.** $(-1, -1, 1)$ **c.** $\left(5, 3, -\dfrac{1}{2}\right)$ **d.** $\left(8, 5, \dfrac{1}{2}\right)$

36. Solve the system. Which value of z appears in the solution?

$$x - y + z = 2$$
$$-x - y + 2z = -4$$
$$2x - 2y - z = -2$$

a. $z = 0$ **b.** $z = -1$ **c.** $z = 2$ **d.** $z = 4$

37. Which value of c will result in the following system having dependent equations?

$$x + 2y - z = 3$$
$$2x + 4y - 2z = c$$
$$x - y + z = 1$$

a. 3   **b.** 6   **c.** 0   **d.** -3

38. Which value of c will result in the following system being inconsistent?

$$x + y - z = 2$$
$$-x - y + z = c$$
$$2x + y - 3z = 0$$

a. -2 **b.** 2

Getting Ready for the Next Section

Translate into symbols.

39. Two more than 3 times a number

40. One less than twice a number

Simplify.

41. $25 - \dfrac{385}{9}$

42. $0.30(12)$

43. $0.08(4,000)$

44. $500(1.5)$

45. $10(0.2x + 0.5y)$

46. $100(0.09x + 0.08y)$

Solve.

47. $x + (3x + 2) = 26$

48. $5x = 2,500$

Solve each system.

49. $\begin{aligned} -2y - 4z &= -18 \\ -7y + 4z &= 27 \end{aligned}$

50. $\begin{aligned} -x + 2y &= 200 \\ 4x - 2y &= 1,300 \end{aligned}$

Reviewing Elementary Algebra

Solve each equation.

51. $\dfrac{t}{3} - \dfrac{1}{2} = -1$

52. $\dfrac{x}{x-2} + \dfrac{2}{3} = \dfrac{2}{x-2}$

53. $2 + \dfrac{5}{y} = \dfrac{3}{y^2}$

54. $1 - \dfrac{1}{y} = \dfrac{12}{y^2}$

Solve each application problem.

55. The sum of a number and its reciprocal is $\dfrac{41}{20}$. Find the number.

56. It takes an inlet pipe 8 hours to fill a tank. The drain can empty the tank in 6 hours. If the tank is full and both the inlet pipe and drain are open, how long will it take to drain the tank?

SPOTLIGHT ON SUCCESS   *Student Instructor Lauren*

There are a lot of word problems in algebra and many of them involve topics that I don't know much about. I am better off solving these problems if I know something about the subject. So, I try to find something I can relate to. For instance, an example may involve the amount of fuel used by a pilot in a jet airplane engine. In my mind, I'd change the subject to something more familiar, like the mileage I'd be getting in my car and the amount spent on fuel, driving from my hometown to my college. Changing these problems to more familiar topics makes math much more interesting and gives me a better chance of getting the problem right. It also helps me to understand how greatly math affects and influences me in my everyday life. We really do use math more than we would like to admit—budgeting our income, purchasing gasoline, planning a day of shopping with friends—almost everything we do is related to math. So the best advice I can give with word problems is to learn how to associate the problem with something familiar to you.

You should know that I have always enjoyed math. I like working out problems and love the challenges of solving equations like individual puzzles. Although there are more interesting subjects to me, and I don't plan on pursuing a career in math or teaching, I do think it's an important subject that will help you in any profession.

Learning Objectives

In this section, we will learn how to:

1. Solve applications with two unknowns using a system of two linear equations in two variables.

2. Solve applications with three unknowns using a system of three linear equations in three variables.

Introduction

Many times word problems involve more than one unknown quantity. If a problem is stated in terms of two unknowns and we represent each unknown quantity with a different variable, then we must write the relationships between the variables with two equations. The two equations written in terms of the two variables form a system of linear equations that we solve using the methods developed in this chapter. If we find a problem that relates three unknown quantities, then we need three equations to form a linear system we can solve.

For your convenience, we repeat our Blueprint for Problem Solving from Section 4.4.

HOW TO   *Use the Blueprint for Problem Solving for a System of Equations*

Step 1: *Read* the problem, and then mentally *list* the items that are known and the items that are unknown.

Step 2: *Assign variables* to each of the unknown items. That is, let $x =$ one of the unknown items and $y =$ the other unknown item (and $z =$ the third unknown item, if there is a third one). Then *translate* the other *information* in the problem to expressions involving the two (or three) variables.

Step 3: *Reread* the problem, and then *write a system of equations*, using the items and variables listed in steps 1 and 2, that describes the situation.

Step 4: *Solve the system* found in step 3.

Step 5: *Write your answers* using complete sentences.

Step 6: *Reread* the problem, and *check* your solution with the original words in the problem.

Systems of Two Linear Equations

EXAMPLE 1   One number is 2 more than 3 times another. Their sum is 26. Find the two numbers.

SOLUTION   Applying the steps from our Blueprint, we have:

Step 1: *Read and list.*

We know that we have two numbers, whose sum is 26. One of them is 2 more than 3 times the other. The unknown quantities are the two numbers.

Step 2: *Assign variables and translate information.*

Let x be one of the numbers and y be the other number.

Step 3: *Write a system of equations.*

The first sentence in the problem translates into $y = 3x + 2$. The second sentence gives us a second equation: $x + y = 26$. Together, these two equations give us the following system of equations:

$$x + y = 26$$
$$y = 3x + 2$$

Step 4: *Solve the system.*

Substituting the expression for y from the second equation into the first and solving for x yields

$$x + (3x + 2) = 26$$
$$4x + 2 = 26$$
$$4x = 24$$
$$x = 6$$

Using $x = 6$ in $y = 3x + 2$ gives the second number:

$$y = 3(6) + 2$$
$$y = 20$$

Step 5: *Write answers.*

The two numbers are 6 and 20.

Step 6: *Reread and check.*

The sum of 6 and 20 is 26, and 20 is 2 more than 3 times 6.

EXAMPLE 2   Suppose 850 tickets were sold for a game for a total of $1,100. If adult tickets cost $1.50 and children's tickets cost $1.00, how many of each kind of ticket were sold?

SOLUTION

Step 1: *Read and list.*

The total number of tickets sold is 850. The total income from tickets is $1,100. Adult tickets are $1.50 each. Children's tickets are $1.00 each. We don't know how many of each type of ticket have been sold.

Step 2: *Assign variables and translate information.*

We let x be the number of adult tickets and y be the number of children's tickets.

Step 3: *Write a system of equations.*

The total number of tickets sold is 850, giving us our first equation.

$$x + y = 850$$

Because each adult ticket costs $1.50, and each children's ticket costs $1.00, and the total amount of money paid for tickets was $1,100, a second equation is

$$1.50x + 1.00y = 1,100$$

The same information can also be obtained by summarizing the problem with a table. One such table follows. Notice that the two equations we obtained previously are given by the two rows of the table.

	Adult Tickets	Children's Tickets	Total
Number	x	y	850
Value	$1.50x$	$1.00y$	1,100

Whether we use a table to summarize the information in the problem or just talk our way through the problem, the system of equations that describes the situation is

$$x + y = 850$$
$$1.50x + 1.00y = 1,100$$

Step 4: *Solve the system.*

If we multiply the second equation by 10 to clear it of decimals, we have the system

$$x + y = 850$$
$$15x + 10y = 11,000$$

Multiplying the first equation by -10 and adding the result to the second equation eliminates the variable y from the system:

$$-10x - 10y = -8,500$$
$$\underline{15x + 10y = 11,000}$$
$$5x = 2,500$$
$$x = 500$$

The number of adult tickets sold was 500. To find the number of children's tickets, we substitute $x = 500$ into $x + y = 850$ to get

$$500 + y = 850$$
$$y = 350$$

Step 5: *Write answers.*

The number of children's tickets is 350, and the number of adult tickets is 500.

Step 6: *Reread and check.*

The total number of tickets is $350 + 500 = 850$. The amount of money from selling the two types of tickets is

350 children's tickets at $1.00 each is $350(1.00) = \$350$
$\underline{500 \text{ adult tickets at } \$1.50 \text{ each is} 500(1.50) = \$750}$

The total income from ticket sales is $1,100

Note Example 2 involves the concept of *value*. In writing the second equation we use the formula

$$P \cdot Q = V$$

where *P* is the price of each item, *Q* is the quantity (number) of items, and *V* is the total value of these items.

Systems of Three Linear Equations

EXAMPLE 3   Suppose a person invests a total of $9,000 in three accounts that earn 3%, 4%, and 6% in annual interest. The amount invested at 6% is twice as much as the combined amount invested at the other two rates. If the total interest earned from all three accounts in a year is $468, how much was invested in each account?

SOLUTION

Step 1: *Read and list.*

The total investment is $9,000 split between three accounts. One account earns 3% annually, another earns 4% annually, and the third earns 6% annually. The amount invested at 6% is double the total investment at 3% and 4%. The interest from all three accounts is $468 in 1 year. We don't know how much is in each account.

Step 2: *Assign variables and translate information.*

We let x be the amount invested at 3%, y be the amount invested at 4%, and z be the amount invested at 6%.

Step 3: *Write a system of equations.*

The total investment is $9,000, so one relationship between x, y, and z can be written as

$$x + y + z = 9{,}000$$

Because twice as much is invested at 6% as the combined total at 3% and 4%, a second equation is

$$z = 2(x + y)$$

which we can write as

$$2x + 2y - z = 0$$

The total interest earned from all three accounts is $468. The amount of interest earned on x dollars at 3% is $0.03x$, the amount of interest earned on y dollars at 4% is $0.04y$, and the amount of interest earned on z dollars at 6% is $0.06z$. This relationship is represented by the equation

$$0.03x + 0.04y + 0.06z = 468$$

Two of the equations we have just written can also be found by first summarizing the information from the problem in a table. Again, the two rows of the table yield two of the equations we found previously. Here is the table.

Note   The interest earned in each account is found using the simple interest formula

$$R \cdot P = I$$

where R is the interest rate (the percent in decimal form), P is the principal (the amount of money invested), and I is the interest earned after one year.

	Dollars at 3%	Dollars at 4%	Dollars at 6%	Total
Number	x	y	z	9,000
Interest	$0.03x$	$0.04y$	$0.06z$	468

Here is our system, with the three equations numbered for reference.

$$x + y + z = 9{,}000 \qquad (1)$$
$$2x + 2y - z = 0 \qquad (2)$$
$$0.03x + 0.04y + 0.06z = 468 \qquad (3)$$

Step 4: *Solve the system.*

Multiplying the third equation by 100 will clear it of decimals. The system that results after doing so is

$$x + y + z = 9{,}000$$
$$2x + 2y - z = 0$$
$$3x + 4y + 6z = 46{,}800$$

Let's begin by eliminating z from the first and second equations. Adding the two equations gives us a new equation containing only x and y. We call this equation (4).

$$3x + 3y = 9{,}000 \qquad (4)$$

If we multiply equation (2) by 6 and add the result to equation (3), we have

$$15x + 16y = 46{,}800 \qquad (5)$$

We can eliminate x from equations (4) and (5) by adding -5 times (4) and (5). Here is the result:

$$y = 1{,}800$$

Substituting $y = 1{,}800$ into (4) gives us $x = 1{,}200$. Substituting $x = 1{,}200$ and $y = 1{,}800$ into (1) gives us $z = 6{,}000$.

Step 5: *Write answers.*

The amount invested at 3% is $1,200, the amount invested at 4% is $1,800, and the amount invested at 6% is $6,000.

Step 6: *Reread and check.*

The total investment is $1,200 + $1,800 + $6,000 = $9,000. The total amount invested at 3% and 4% is $1,200 + $1,800 = $3,000, and the amount invested at 6% is twice as much. The amount of interest earned from the three accounts is

In 1 year, $1,200 invested at 3% earns 0.03(1,200) = $36

In 1 year, $1,800 invested at 4% earns 0.04(1,800) = $72

In 1 year, $6,000 invested at 6% earns 0.06(6,000) = $360

The total interest from the three accounts is $468

EXAMPLE 4 How much 20% alcohol solution, 30% alcohol solution, and 50% alcohol solution must be mixed to get 12 gallons of 40% alcohol solution, if twice as much of the 20% solution as 30% solution is used?

SOLUTION To solve this problem, we must first understand that a 20% alcohol solution is 20% alcohol and 80% water.

Step 1: *Read and list.*

We will mix three solutions to obtain 12 gallons of solution that is 40% alcohol. One of the solutions is 20% alcohol, one is 30% alcohol, and the other 50% alcohol. The amount of 20% solution used needs to be twice the amount of 30% solution. We don't know how much of each solution we need.

Step 2: *Assign variables and translate information.*

Let x be the number of gallons of 20% alcohol solution needed, y be the number of gallons of 30% alcohol solution needed, and z be the number of gallons of 50% alcohol solution needed.

Step 3: *Write a system of equations.*

Because we must end up with a total of 12 gallons of solution, one equation for the system is

$$x + y + z = 12$$

The amount of alcohol in the x gallons of 20% solution is $0.20x$, while the amount of alcohol in the y gallons of 30% solution is $0.30y$, and the amount of alcohol in the z gallons of 50% solution is $0.50z$. Because the total amount of alcohol in the 20%, 30%, and 50% solutions must add up to the amount of alcohol in the 12 gallons of 40% solution, the second equation in our system can be written as

$$0.20x + 0.30y + 0.50z = 0.40(12) = 4.8$$

Again, let's make a table that summarizes the information we have to this point in the problem.

> **Note** For mixture problems we use the formula
>
> $$P \cdot Q = A$$
>
> where P is the percent of some item (expressed as a decimal), Q is the quantity of the solution, and A is the amount of this item contained in the solution.

	20% Solution	30% Solution	50% Solution	Final Solution
Total number of gallons	x	y	z	12
Gallons of alcohol	$0.20x$	$0.30y$	$0.50z$	$0.40(12)$

Because we must use twice as much of the 20% solution as the 30% solution, we also have $x = 2y$, which is equivalent to $x - 2y = 0$. Our system of equations is

$$
\begin{aligned}
x + \quad y + \quad z &= 12 \\
0.20x + 0.30y + 0.50z &= 4.8 \\
x - \quad 2y \quad\;\;\; &= 0
\end{aligned}
$$

> **Note** In mixture problems, it is a common mistake to forget that the right side of our second equation must also be the *product* of a percent times a quantity, and is not just the percent itself.

Step 4: *Solve the system.*

Multiplying the second equation by 10 gives us an equivalent system:

$$
\begin{aligned}
x + \; y + \; z &= 12 & (1) \\
2x + 3y + 5z &= 48 & (2) \\
x - 2y \quad\;\; &= 0 & (3)
\end{aligned}
$$

Adding -5 times equation (1) to equation (2) gives us

$$-3x - 2y = -12 \qquad (4)$$

Multiplying equation (4) by -1 and adding the result to equation (3), we have

$$
\begin{aligned}
4x &= 12 \\
x &= 3
\end{aligned}
$$

Substituting $x = 3$ into equation (3) gives us $y = 1.5$. Substituting $x = 3$ and $y = 1.5$ into equation (1) gives us $z = 7.5$.

Step 5: *Write answers.*

It takes 3 gallons of 20% alcohol solution, 1.5 gallons of 30% alcohol solution, and 7.5 gallons of 50% alcohol solution to produce 12 gallons of 40% alcohol solution.

Step 6: *Reread and check.*

If we mix 3 gallons of 20% solution with 1.5 gallons of 30% solution and 7.5 gallons of 50% solution, we end up with a total of 12 gallons of solution. To check the percentages we look for the total amount of alcohol in the three initial solutions and in the final solution.

In the initial solutions

The amount of alcohol in 3 gallons of 20% solution is $0.20(3) = 0.60$ gallons
The amount of alcohol in 1.5 gallons of 30% solution is $0.30(1.5) = 0.45$ gallons
The amount of alcohol in 7.5 gallons of 50% solution is $0.50(7.5) = 3.75$ gallons

The total amount of alcohol in the initial solutions is 4.8 gallons

In the final solution

The amount of alcohol in 12 gallons of 40% solution is $0.40(12) = 4.8$ gallons. Also, twice the amount of 30% solution is $2(1.5) = 3$ gallons, which is equal to the amount of 20% solution used.

EXAMPLE 5 A coin collection consists of 14 coins with a total value of $1.35. If the coins are nickels, dimes, and quarters, and the number of nickels is 3 less than twice the number of dimes, how many of each coin is there in the collection?

SOLUTION

Step 1: *Read and list.*

We have 14 coins with a total value of $1.35. The coins are nickels, dimes, and quarters. The number of nickels is 3 less than twice the number of dimes. We do not know how many of each coin we have.

Step 2: *Assign variables and translate information.*

Because we have three types of coins, we will have to use three variables. Let's let x be the number of nickels, y be the number of dimes, and z be the number of quarters.

Step 3: *Write a system of equations.*

Because the total number of coins is 14, our first equation is

$$x + y + z = 14$$

Because the number of nickels is 3 less than twice the number of dimes, a second equation is

$$x = 2y - 3 \qquad \text{which is equivalent to} \qquad x - 2y = -3$$

Our last equation is obtained by considering the value of each coin and the total value of the collection. Let's write the equation in terms of cents, so we won't have to clear it of decimals later.

$$5x + 10y + 25z = 135$$

Here is our system:

$$
\begin{aligned}
x + y + z &= 14 &\quad (1) \\
x - 2y &= -3 &\quad (2) \\
5x + 10y + 25z &= 135 &\quad (3)
\end{aligned}
$$

Step 4: *Solve the system.*

Let's begin by eliminating x from the first and second equations, and the first and third equations. Adding -1 times the second equation to the first equation gives us an equation in only y and z. We call this equation (4).

$$3y + z = 17 \qquad (4)$$

Adding -5 times equation (1) to equation (3) gives us

$$5y + 20z = 65 \qquad (5)$$

We can eliminate z from equations (4) and (5) by adding -20 times (4) to (5). Here is the result:

$$-55y = -275$$

$$y = 5$$

Substituting $y = 5$ into equation (4) gives us $z = 2$. Substituting $y = 5$ and $z = 2$ into equation (1) gives us $x = 7$.

Step 5: *Write answers.*

The collection consists of 7 nickels, 5 dimes, and 2 quarters.

Step 6: *Reread and check.*

The total number of coins is $7 + 5 + 2 = 14$. The number of nickels, 7, is 3 less than twice the number of dimes, 5. To find the total value of the collection, we have

The value of the 7 nickels is	$7(0.05) = \$0.35$
The value of the 5 dimes is	$5(0.10) = \$0.50$
The value of the 2 quarters is	$2(0.25) = \$0.50$

The total value of the collection is $\$1.35$

EXAMPLE 6   A ball is tossed into the air and its height above the ground after 1, 2, and 4 seconds is recorded as shown in the following table.

t (sec)	h (ft)
1	60
2	72
4	0

If the relationship between the height of the ball h and the time t is quadratic, then the relationship can be written as

$$h = at^2 + bt + c$$

Use the information in the table to find the values of a, b, and c in the quadratic model.

SOLUTION

Step 1: *Read and list.*

We have three ordered pairs of t and h values: $(1, 60)$, $(2, 72)$, and $(4, 0)$. These pairs must all satisfy the equation $h = at^2 + bt + c$. We do not know the values of a, b, and c.

Step 2: *Assign variables and translate information.*

Our variables are the unknown coefficients a, b, and c.

Step 3: *Write a system of equations.*

If we substitute each of the pairs of values of t and h into the model $h = at^2 + bt + c$, we will get three equations containing the unknowns a, b, and c.

Using $t = 1$ and $h = 60$, we get

$$60 = a(1)^2 + b(1) + c$$

which we can write as

$$a + b + c = 60$$

Using $t = 2$ and $h = 72$, we obtain

$$72 = a(2)^2 + b(2) + c$$

which simplifies to

$$4a + 2b + c = 72$$

Using $t = 4$ and $h = 0$, we get

$$0 = a(4)^2 + b(4) + c$$

which we write as

$$16a + 4b + c = 0$$

This gives us the system of equations

$$
\begin{aligned}
a + b + c &= 60 &\quad (1) \\
4a + 2b + c &= 72 &\quad (2) \\
16a + 4b + c &= 0 &\quad (3)
\end{aligned}
$$

Step 4: *Solve the system.*

Multiplying equation (1) by -1 and adding the result to equation (2) gives us

$$3a + b = 12 \qquad (4)$$

Adding -1 times equation (1) to equation (3) gives us

$$15a + 3b = -60 \qquad (5)$$

Adding -3 times equation (4) to equation (5) gives us

$$
\begin{aligned}
6a &= -96 \\
a &= -16
\end{aligned}
$$

Substituting $a = -16$ into equation (4) gives us $b = 60$. Substituting $a = -16$ and $b = 60$ into equation (1) gives us $c = 16$.

Step 5: *Write answers.*

The relationship between t and h is given by the model

$$h = -16t^2 + 60t + 16$$

Step 6: *Reread and check.*

If $t = 1$, then $h = -16(1)^2 + 60(1) + 16 = 60$.
If $t = 2$, then $h = -16(2)^2 + 60(2) + 16 = 72$.
If $t = 4$, then $h = -16(4)^2 + 60(4) + 16 = 0$.

The quadratic model $h = -16t^2 + 60t + 16$ gives the correct values that match the data from the table.

Getting Ready for Class

After reading through the preceding section, respond in your own words and in complete sentences.

A. Two of the equations in the system for Example 3 represent totals. What is being totaled in each of these equations?

B. In Example 4, why is the third equation $x = 2y$ and not $y = 2x$?

C. How can we clear decimals in an equation?

D. How do we get the three equation that can be used to find a quadratic model given three ordered pairs?

Problem Set 8.7

Number Problems

1. One number is 3 more than twice another. The sum of the numbers is 18. Find the two numbers.

2. The sum of two numbers is 32. One of the numbers is 4 less than 5 times the other. Find the two numbers.

3. The sum of three numbers is 8. Twice the smallest is 2 less than the largest, while the sum of the largest and smallest is 5. Use a linear system in three variables to find the three numbers.

4. The sum of three numbers is 14. The largest is 4 times the smallest, while the sum of the smallest and twice the largest is 18. Use a linear system in three variables to find the three numbers.

Ticket and Interest Problems

5. A total of 925 tickets were sold for a game for a total of $1,150. If adult tickets sold for $2.00 and children's tickets sold for $1.00, how many of each kind of ticket were sold?

6. If tickets for a show cost $2.00 for adults and $1.50 for children, how many of each kind of ticket were sold if a total of 300 tickets were sold for $525?

7. Mr. Jones has $20,000 to invest. He invests part at 6% and the rest at 7%. If he earns $1,280 in interest after 1 year, how much did he invest at each rate?

8. A woman earns $1,350 in interest from two accounts in 1 year. If she has three times as much invested at 7% as she does at 6%, how much does she have in each account?

9. A man invests $2,200 in three accounts that pay 6%, 8%, and 9% in annual interest, respectively. He has three times as much invested at 9% as he does at 6%. If his total interest for the year is $178, how much is invested at each rate?

10. A student has money in three accounts that pay 5%, 7%, and 8% in annual interest. She has three times as much invested at 8% as she does at 5%. If the total amount she has invested is $1,600 and her interest for the year comes to $115, how much money does she have in each account?

Mixture Problems

11. How many ounces of 30% hydrochloric acid solution and 80% hydrochloric acid solution must be mixed to get 10 ounces of 50% hydrochloric acid solution?

12. Paul mixes nuts worth $1.55 per pound with oats worth $1.35 per pound to get 25 pounds of trail mix worth $1.45 per pound. How many pounds of nuts and how many pounds of oats did he use?

13. A chemist has three different acid solutions. The first acid solution contains 20% acid, the second contains 40%, and the third contains 60%. He wants to use all three solutions to obtain a mixture of 60 liters containing 50% acid, using twice as much of the 60% solution as the 40% solution. How many liters of each solution should be used?

14. How many gallons of 10% alcohol solution, 30% alcohol solution, and 60% alcohol solution must be mixed to get 40 gallons of 41% alcohol solution if the amount of 60% solution used must be the same as the total amount of the other two solutions?

15. Juan mixes coffee beans worth $8 per pound, coffee beans worth $9 per pound, and coffee beans worth $12 per pound to get 50 pounds of beans worth $10 per pound. If the amount of $9 beans is twice the amount of $8 beans, how many pounds of each type of coffee bean does he use?

16. Cynthia mixes nuts worth $4 per pound, $6 per pound, and $11 per pound to make 40 pounds of a mix that is worth $7 per pound. If she uses twice as much of the $11 nuts as $4 nuts, how many pounds of each type of nut does she use?

Coin Problems

17. Bob has 20 coins totaling $1.40. If he has only dimes and nickels, how many of each coin does he have?

18. If Amy has 15 coins totaling $2.70, and the coins are quarters and dimes, how many of each coin does she have?

19. A collection of nickels, dimes, and quarters consists of 9 coins with a total value of $1.20. If the number of dimes is equal to the number of nickels, find the number of each type of coin.

20. A coin collection consists of 12 coins with a total value of $1.20. If the collection consists only of nickels, dimes, and quarters, and the number of dimes is two more than twice the number of nickels, how many of each type of coin are in the collection?

21. A collection of nickels, dimes, and quarters amount to $10.00. If there are 140 coins in all and there are twice as many dimes as there are quarters, find the number of nickels.

22. A cash register contains a total of 95 coins consisting of pennies, nickels, dimes, and quarters. There are only 5 pennies and the total value of the coins is $12.05. Also, there are 5 more quarters than dimes. How many of each coin is in the cash register?

Modeling

23. Height of a Ball A ball is tossed into the air so that the height after 1, 3, and 5 seconds is as given in the following table.

t (sec)	h (ft)
1	128
3	128
5	0

If the relationship between the height of the ball h and the time t is quadratic, then the relationship can be written as

$$h = at^2 + bt + c$$

Use the information in the table to write a system of three equations in three variables a, b, and c. Solve the system to find the exact relationship between h and t.

24. Height of a Ball A ball is tossed into the air and its height above the ground after 1, 3, and 4 seconds is recorded as shown in the following table.

t (sec)	h (ft)
1	96
3	64
4	0

The relationship between the height of the ball h and the time t is quadratic and can be written as

$$h = at^2 + bt + c$$

Use the information in the table to write a system of three equations in three variables a, b, and c. Solve the system to find the exact relationship between the variables h and t.

Learning Objectives Assessment

The following problems can be used to help assess if you have successfully met the learning objectives for this section.

25. A 25% salt solution and a 60% salt solution are to be mixed to obtain 10 gallons of a 50% salt solution. Which system of equations correctly models this problem?

a. $x + y = 50$
   $0.25x + 0.60y = 10$

b. $x + y = 10$
   $0.25x + 0.60y = 0.50$

c. $x + y = 10$
   $0.25x + 0.60y = 5$

d. $x + y = 0.50$
   $25x + 60y = 10$

26. A collection of nickels, dimes, and quarters amount to $2.00. If there are 16 coins in all and there are three more nickels than dimes, how many nickels are in the collection?

a. 7   b. 4   c. 5   d. 9

Getting Ready for the Next Section

27. Does the graph of $x + y < 4$ include the boundary line?

28. Does the graph of $-x + y \leq 3$ include the boundary line?

29. Where do the graphs of the lines $x + y = 4$ and $x - 2y = 4$ intersect?

30. Where do the graphs of the line $x = -1$ and $x - 2y = 4$ intersect?

Solve.

31. $20x + 9{,}300 > 18{,}000$

32. $20x + 4{,}800 > 18{,}000$

Reviewing Elementary Algebra

Apply the distributive property to each of the following expressions. Simplify when possible.

33. $-\dfrac{1}{4}(2x - 4)$

34. $6\left(\dfrac{x}{3} - \dfrac{1}{2}\right)$

35. $x\left(\dfrac{4}{x} + 3\right)$

36. $-36\left(\dfrac{x}{4} - \dfrac{y}{9}\right)$

37. $a\left(\dfrac{7}{a} + \dfrac{1}{a}\right)$

38. $-4(3x - 1) - 8$

39. $-3(4x + 5) - 20$

40. $\left[\dfrac{1}{2}(-10)\right]^2$

41. $\left(\dfrac{1}{2} \cdot 5\right)^2$

42. $0.04(x + 7{,}000)$

43. $0.06(x + 800)$

44. $a\left(1 - \dfrac{1}{a}\right)$

Learning Objectives

In this section, we will learn how to:

1. Determine if an ordered pair is a solution to a system of linear inequalities in two variables.

2. Graph the solution set to a system of linear inequalities in two variables.

3. Use a system of linear inequalities in two variables to solve applied problems.

Introduction

In Section 3.6, we graphed linear inequalities in two variables. To review, the solution set for a linear inequality is a *section of the coordinate plane*. The *boundary* for the section is found by replacing the inequality symbol with an equal sign and graphing the resulting equation. The boundary is included in the solution set (and is represented with a *solid line*) if the inequality symbol used originally is $\leq$ or $\geq$. The boundary is not included (and is represented with a *broken line*) if the original symbol is $<$ or $>$.

In the following example, we review the process for solving a single linear inequality in two variables.

VIDEO EXAMPLES

SECTION 8.8

EXAMPLE 1   Graph the solution set for $x + y \leq 4$.

SOLUTION   The boundary for the graph is the graph of $x + y = 4$. The boundary is included in the solution set because the inequality symbol is $\leq$.
Figure 1 is the graph of the boundary:

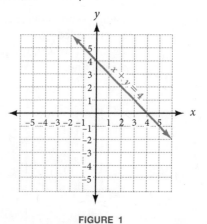

FIGURE 1

The boundary separates the coordinate plane into two regions: the region above the boundary and the region below it. The solution set for $x + y \leq 4$ is one of these two regions along with the boundary. To find the correct region, we simply choose any convenient point that is *not* on the boundary. We then substitute the coordinates of the point into the original inequality $x + y \leq 4$. If the point we choose satisfies the inequality, then it is a member of the solution set, and we can assume that all points on the same side of the boundary as the chosen point are also in the solution set. If the coordinates of our point do not satisfy the original inequality, then the solution set lies on the other side of the boundary.

In this example, a convenient point that is not on the boundary is the origin.

Substituting $(0, 0)$

into $x + y \le 4$

gives us $0 + 0 \le 4$

                      $0 \le 4$ A true statement

Because the origin is a solution to the inequality $x + y \le 4$ and the origin is below the boundary, all other points below the boundary are also solutions. We indicate this by shading the region below the boundary.

Figure 2 is the graph of $x + y \le 4$.

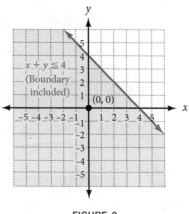

FIGURE 2

Systems of Linear Inequalities

Figure 3 shows the graph of the inequality $x + y < 4$. Note that the boundary is not included in the solution set, and is therefore drawn with a broken line. Figure 4 shows the graph of $-x + y \le 3$. Note that the boundary is drawn with a solid line, because it is part of the solution set.

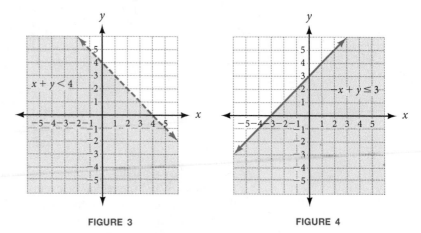

FIGURE 3   **FIGURE 4**

If we form a system of inequalities with the two inequalities, the solution set will be all the points common to both solution sets shown in the two figures above. It is the intersection of the two solution sets. Therefore, the solution set for the system of inequalities

$$x + y < 4$$
$$-x + y \leq 3$$

is all the ordered pairs that satisfy both inequalities. It is the set of points that are below the line $x + y = 4$, and also below (and including) the line $-x + y = 3$. The graph of the solution set to this system is shown in Figure 5. We have written the system in Figure 5 with the word *and* just to remind you that the solution set to a system of equations or inequalities is all the points that satisfy both equations or inequalities.

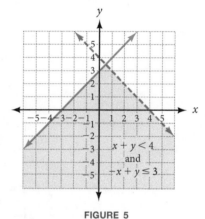

$x + y < 4$
and
$-x + y \leq 3$

FIGURE 5

EXAMPLE 2   Determine if each ordered pair is a solution to the system of linear inequalities.

$$x + y < 4$$
$$x - 2y \leq -2$$

a. $(3, 2)$ b. $(1, -1)$ **c.** $(-1, 3)$

SOLUTION   We check each ordered pair to see if it satisfies both inequalities in the system.

a. Because $3 + 2 < 4$ is a false statement, $(3, 2)$ does not satisfy the first inequality. It cannot be a solution.

b. Substituting $x = 1$ and $y = -1$ we find

$$1 + (-1) < 4$$

$$0 < 4 \qquad \text{A true statement}$$

$$\text{and} \quad 1 - 2(-1) \leq -2$$

$$3 \leq -2 \qquad \text{A false statement}$$

Because $(1, -1)$ does not satisfy the second inequality, it is not a solution to the system.

c. Using $x = -1$ and $y = 3$ we obtain

$$-1 + 3 < 4$$
$$2 < 4 \qquad \text{A true statement}$$
$$\text{and} \quad -1 - 2(3) \le -2$$
$$-7 \le -2 \qquad \text{A true statement}$$

The pair $(-1, 3)$ is a solution because it satisfies both inequalities.

> **EXAMPLE 3**   Graph the solution set for the system of inequalities.

$$y < \frac{1}{2}x + 3$$

$$y \ge \frac{1}{2}x - 2$$

SOLUTION   Figures 6 and 7 show the solution set for each of the inequalities separately.

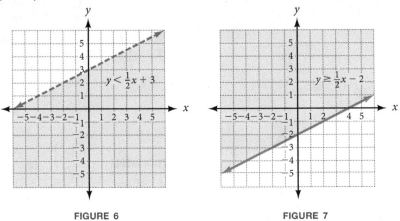

FIGURE 6   FIGURE 7

Figure 8 is the solution set to the system of inequalities. It is the region consisting of points whose coordinates satisfy both inequalities.

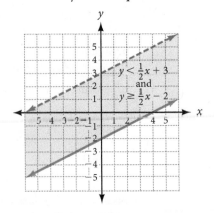

FIGURE 8

EXAMPLE 4 Graph the solution set for the system of inequalities.

$$x + y < 4$$
$$x \geq 0$$
$$y \geq 0$$

SOLUTION We graphed the first inequality, $x + y < 4$, in Figure 3 at the beginning of this section. The solution set to the inequality $x \geq 0$, shown in Figure 9, is all the points to the right of the y-axis; that is, all the points with x-coordinates that are greater than or equal to 0. Figure 10 shows the graph of $y \geq 0$. It consists of all points with y-coordinates greater than or equal to 0; that is, all points from the x-axis up.

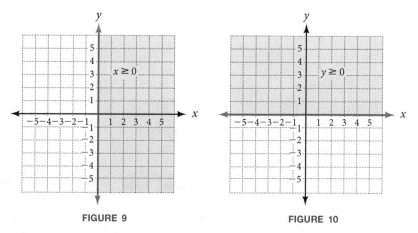

FIGURE 9   FIGURE 10

The regions shown in Figures 9 and 10 overlap in the first quadrant. Therefore, putting all three regions together we have the points in the first quadrant that are below the line $x + y = 4$. This region is shown in Figure 11, and it is the solution to our system of inequalities.

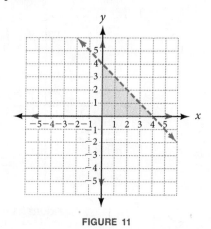

FIGURE 11

EXAMPLE 5   Graph the solution set for the system of inequalities.

$$x \leq 4$$
$$y \geq -3$$

SOLUTION   The solution to this system will consist of all points to the left of and including the vertical line $x = 4$ that intersect with all points above and including the horizontal line $y = -3$. The solution set is shown in Figure 12.

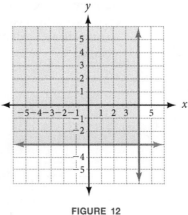

FIGURE 12

EXAMPLE 6   Graph the solution set for the system of inequalities.

$$y \geq 2x + 3$$
$$2x - y > 2$$

SOLUTION   The solution set for the first inequality includes all points above and including the line $y = 2x + 3$ as shown in Figure 13. Figure 14 shows the solution set for the second inequality, which consists of all points below the line $2x - y = 2$.

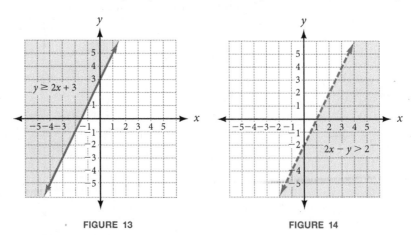

FIGURE 13   **FIGURE 14**

If we isolate y in the second inequality, we obtain $y < 2x - 2$. The lines in Figure 13 and Figure 14 have the same slope, and are therefore parallel. Looking at both graphs, it is evident the two shaded regions will never overlap. There are no ordered pairs that will satisfy both inequalities, so the system has no solution.

EXAMPLE 7   Graph the solution set for the following system.

$$x - 2y \leq 4$$
$$x + y \leq 4$$
$$x \geq -1$$

SOLUTION   We have three linear inequalities, representing three sections of the coordinate plane. The graph of the solution set for this system will be the intersection of these three sections. The graph of $x - 2y \leq 4$ is the section above and including the boundary $x - 2y = 4$. The graph of $x + y \leq 4$ is the section below and including the boundary line $x + y = 4$. The graph of $x \geq -1$ is all the points to the right of, and including, the vertical line $x = -1$. The intersection of these three graphs is shown in Figure 15.

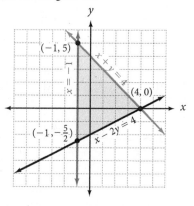

FIGURE 15

EXAMPLE 8   A college basketball arena plans on charging $20 for certain seats and $15 for others. They want to bring in more than $18,000 from all ticket sales and have reserved at least 500 tickets at the $15 rate. Find a system of inequalities describing all possibilities and sketch the graph. If 620 tickets are sold for $15, at least how many tickets are sold for $20?

SOLUTION   Let x = the number of $20 tickets and y = the number of $15 tickets. We need to write a list of inequalities that describe this situation. That list will form our system of inequalities. First of all, we note that we cannot use negative numbers for either x or y. So, we have our first inequalities:

$$x \geq 0$$
$$y \geq 0$$

Next, we note that they are selling at least 500 tickets for $15, so we can replace our second inequality with $y \geq 500$. Now our system is

$$x \geq 0$$
$$y \geq 500$$

Now the amount of money brought in by selling $20 tickets is $20x$, and the amount of money brought in by selling $15 tickets is $15y$. If the total income from ticket sales is to be more than $18,000, then $20x + 15y$ must be greater than 18,000.

This gives us our last inequality and completes our system.

$$20x + 15y > 18{,}000$$
$$x \geq 0$$
$$y \geq 500$$

We have used all the information in the problem to arrive at this system of inequalities. The solution set contains all the values of x and y that satisfy all the conditions given in the problem. Here is the graph of the solution set.

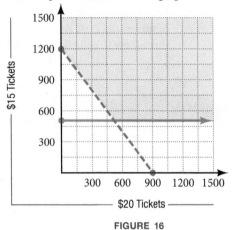

FIGURE 16

If 620 tickets are sold for $15, then we substitute 620 for y in our first inequality to obtain

$$20x + 15(620) > 18000 \qquad \text{Substitute 620 for } y$$
$$20x + 9300 > 18000 \qquad \text{Multiply}$$
$$20x > 8700 \qquad \text{Add } -9300 \text{ to each side}$$
$$x > 435 \qquad \text{Divide each side by 20}$$

If they sell 620 tickets for $15 each, then they need to sell more than 435 tickets at $20 each to bring in more than $18,000.

Getting Ready for Class

After reading through the preceding section, respond in your own words and in complete sentences.

A. What does it mean for an ordered pair to be a solution to a system of linear inequalities in two variables?

B. Explain the process of solving a system of linear inequalities in two variables.

C. What are the circumstances for which a system of linear inequalities in two variables will have no solution?

D. Is it possible for a system of linear inequalities in two variables to have a solution set consisting of the entire xy-plane? Explain why or why not.

Graph the solution set for each linear inequality.

1. $x + y < 5$

2. $x - y \geq -3$

3. $2x + 3y < 6$

4. $-x + 2y > -4$

5. $2x + y < 5$

6. $y < 2x - 1$

7. $3x - 4y < 12$

8. $-2x + 3y < 6$

9. $-5x + 2y \leq 10$

10. $4x - 2y \leq 8$

Determine if each ordered pair is a solution to the system of linear inequalities.

11. $x + y \leq -2$
$x - y < \ 0$

   a. $(0, 0)$ **b.** $(-3, -1)$ **c.** $(1, -4)$ **d.** $(-2, 0)$

12. $3x - y > 3$
$\ \ \ \ \ y \leq 2$

   a. $(3, 2)$ **b.** $(0, -1)$ **c.** $(4, 3)$ **d.** $(1, -2)$

Graph the solution set for each system of linear inequalities.

13. $x + y < 5$
$\ \ \ \ 2x - y > 4$

14. $x + y < 5$
$\ \ \ \ 2x - y < 4$

15. $y < \frac{1}{3}x + 4$
$y \geq \frac{1}{3}x - 3$

16. $y < 2x + 4$
$y \geq 2x - 3$

17. $x \geq -3$
$y < -2$

18. $x \leq 4$
$y \geq -2$

19. $1 \leq x \leq 3$
$2 \leq y \leq 4$

20. $-4 \leq x \leq -2$
$\ \ \ 1 \leq y \leq \ \ 3$

21. $x + 2y < \ \ 4$
$x + 2y \leq -4$

22. $x \geq 3$
$x > -2$

23. $y > 1$
$y < -3$

24. $x - y \leq -3$
$x - y \geq \ \ 1$

25. $x + y \leq 4$
$\ \ \ \ \ x \geq 0$
$\ \ \ \ \ y \geq 0$

26. $x - y \leq 2$
$\ \ \ \ \ x \geq 0$
$\ \ \ \ \ y \leq 0$

27. $x + \ \ y \leq \ \ 3$
$x - 3y \leq \ \ 3$
$\ \ \ \ \ \ \ x \geq -2$

28. $x - \ \ y \leq \ \ 4$
$x + 2y \leq \ \ 4$
$\ \ \ \ \ \ \ x \geq -1$

29. $\ \ x + y \leq \ \ 2$
$-x + y \leq \ \ 2$
$\ \ \ \ \ \ \ y \geq -2$

30. $\ \ x - y \leq \ \ 3$
$-x - y \leq \ \ 3$
$\ \ \ \ \ \ \ y \leq -1$

31. $x + y < 5$
$\ \ \ \ \ y > x$
$\ \ \ \ \ y \geq 0$

32. $x + y < 5$
$\ \ \ \ \ y > x$
$\ \ \ \ \ x \geq 0$

33. $2x + 3y \leq 6$
$\ \ \ \ \ \ \ x \geq 0$
$\ \ \ \ \ \ \ y \geq 0$

34. $\ \ x + 2y \leq 10$
$3x + 2y \leq 12$
$\ \ \ \ \ \ \ x \geq 0$
$\ \ \ \ \ \ \ y \geq 0$

For each figure below, find a system of inequalities that describes the shaded region.

35.

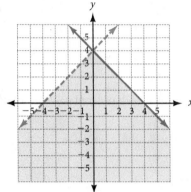

36.

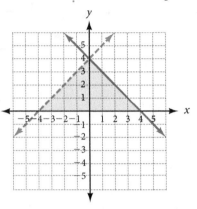

37.

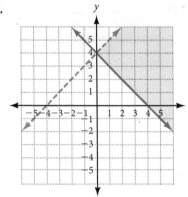

38.

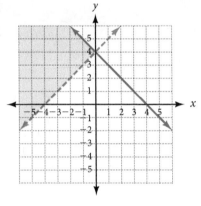

39.

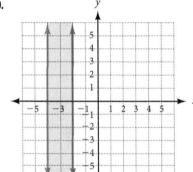

40.

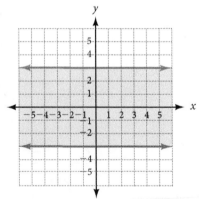

Applying the Concepts

41. Office Supplies An office worker wants to purchase some $0.55 postage stamps and also some $0.65 postage stamps totaling no more than $40. It is also desired to have at least twice as many $0.55 stamps and more than 15 $0.55 stamps.

   a. Find a system of inequalities describing all the possibilities and sketch the graph.

   b. If he purchases 20 $0.55 stamps, what is the maximum number of $0.65 stamps he can purchase?

42. **Inventory** A store sells two brands of DVD players. Customer demand indicates that it is necessary to stock at least twice as many DVD players of brand A as of brand B. At least 30 of brand A and 15 of brand B must be on hand. In the store, there is room for not more than 100 DVD players in the store.

   a. Find a system of inequalities describing all possibilities, then sketch the graph.

   b. If there are 35 DVD players of brand A, what is the most number of brand B DVD players on hand?

Learning Objectives Assessment

The following problems can be used to help assess if you have successfully met the learning objectives for this section.

43. Which of the following ordered pairs is a solution to the given system of linear inequalities?

$$x + 3y < 6$$
$$2x - y \geq 4$$

   a. $(0, 0)$ b. $(4, 1)$ c. $(1, 3)$ d. $(3, -1)$

44. Graph the solution set for the system of linear inequalities.

$$x > y$$
$$x \leq 2$$

a.

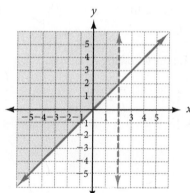

b.

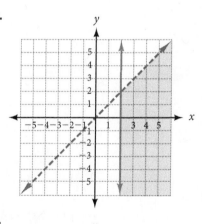

c.

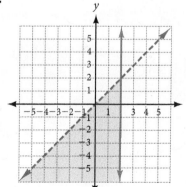

d.

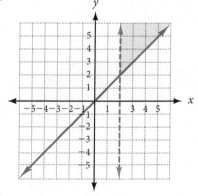

45. You need to purchase some cookies and cupcakes for an office party. Cookies cost \$1.25 each and cupcakes cost \$1.75 each. You can spend at most \$100 and need at least twice as many cookies as cupcakes. Which system of linear inequalities describes all the possibilities?

a. $x + y \leq 100$

    $1.25x \geq 1.75y + 2$

       $x \geq 0$

       $y \geq 0$

b. $2x + y \leq 100$

    $1.25x \geq 1.75y$

       $x \geq 0$

       $y \geq 0$

c. $1.25x + 1.75y \leq 100$

       $x \geq 2y$

       $x \geq 0$

       $y \geq 0$

d. $1.25x + 1.75y \leq 100$

       $y \geq 2x$

       $x \geq 0$

       $y \geq 0$

Maintaining Your Skills

Solve each equation.

46. $5 - \dfrac{4}{7}a = -11$

47. $\dfrac{1}{5}x - \dfrac{1}{2} - \dfrac{1}{10}x + \dfrac{2}{5} = \dfrac{3}{10}x + \dfrac{1}{2}$

48. $5(x - 1) - 2(2x + 3) = 5x - 4$

49. $0.07 - 0.02(3x + 1) = -0.04x + 0.01$

Solve the following inequalities. Write the solution set using interval notation.

50. $-5t \leq 30$

51. $5 - \dfrac{3}{2}x > -1$

52. $1.6x - 2 < 0.8x + 2.8$

53. $3(2y + 4) \geq 5(y - 8)$

Solve the following equations.

54. $\left| \dfrac{1}{4}x - 1 \right| = \dfrac{1}{2}$

55. $\left| \dfrac{2}{3}a + 4 \right| = 6$

56. $|3 - 2x| + 5 = 2$

57. $5 = |3y + 6| - 4$

Chapter 8 Summary

Strategy for Solving Linear Equations in One Variable [8.1]

EXAMPLES

1. Solve: $3(2x - 1) = 9$.

$$3(2x - 1) = 9$$
$$6x - 3 = 9$$
$$6x - 3 + 3 = 9 + 3$$
$$6x = 12$$
$$\frac{1}{6}(6x) = \frac{1}{6}(12)$$
$$x = 2$$

Step 1:
   a. Use the distributive property to separate terms, if necessary.

   b. If fractions are present, consider multiplying both sides by the LCD to eliminate the fractions. If decimals are present, consider multiplying both sides by a power of 10 to clear the equation of decimals.

   c. Combine similar terms on each side of the equation.

Step 2: Use the addition property of equality to get all variable terms on one side of the equation and all constant terms on the other side. A variable term is a term that contains the variable (for example, $5x$). A constant term is a term that does not contain the variable (the number 3, for example).

Step 3: Use the multiplication property of equality to get the variable by itself on one side of the equation.

Step 4: Check your solution in the original equation to be sure that you have not made a mistake in the solution process.

Absolute Value Equations [8.2]

2. To solve

$$|2x - 1| + 2 = 7$$

we first isolate the absolute value on the left side by adding -2 to each side to obtain

$$|2x - 1| = 5$$

$$\begin{array}{lll} 2x - 1 = 5 & \text{or} & 2x - 1 = -5 \\ 2x = 6 & \text{or} & 2x = -4 \\ x = 3 & \text{or} & x = -2 \end{array}$$

To solve an equation that involves absolute value, we isolate the absolute value on one side of the equation and then rewrite the absolute value equation as two separate equations that do not involve absolute value. In general, if b is a positive real number, then

$$|A| = b \quad \text{is equivalent to} \quad A = b \quad \text{or} \quad A = -b$$

Compound Inequalities [8.3]

3. Solve: $3x - 1 \leq 5$ and $x + 4 > 1$.

$$\begin{array}{lll} 3x - 1 \leq 5 & \text{and} & x + 4 > 1 \\ 3x \leq 6 & \text{and} & x > -3 \\ x \leq 2 \end{array}$$

The intersection of $x \leq 2$ and $x > -3$ is $-3 < x \leq 2$, or $(-3, 2]$ using interval notation.

To solve a compound inequality that contains the word "and," solve the two inequalities separately and then find the intersection of the two solution sets.

To solve a compound inequality that contains the word "or," solve the two inequalities separately and then find the union of the two solution sets.

Absolute Value Inequalities [8.4]

4. To solve

$$|x - 3| + 2 < 6$$

we first add -2 to both sides to obtain

$$|x - 3| < 4$$

which is equivalent to

$$-4 < x - 3 < 4$$
$$-1 < \ x \ < 7$$

To solve an inequality that involves absolute value, we first isolate the absolute value on the left side of the inequality symbol. Then we rewrite the absolute value inequality as an equivalent continued or compound inequality that does not contain absolute value symbols. In general, if b is a positive real number, then

$$|A| < b \qquad \text{is equivalent to} \qquad -b < A < b$$

and

$$|A| > b \qquad \text{is equivalent to} \qquad A < -b \qquad \text{or} \qquad A > b$$

To Solve a System by the Addition Method [8.5]

5. We can eliminate the y-variable from the system in Example 1 by multiplying both sides of the second equation by 2 and adding the result to the first equation:

$$x + 2y = 4 \xrightarrow{\text{No Change}} x + 2y = 4$$
$$x - \ y = 1 \xrightarrow{\text{Multiply by 2}} 2x - 2y = 2$$
$$\underline{\hspace{3cm}}$$
$$3x \qquad = 6$$
$$x \qquad = 2$$

Substituting $x = 2$ into either of the original two equations gives $y = 1$. The solution is $(2, 1)$.

Step 1: Look the system over to decide which variable will be easier to eliminate.

Step 2: Use the multiplication property of equality on each equation separately, if necessary, to ensure that the coefficients of the variable to be eliminated are opposites.

Step 3: Add the left and right sides of the system produced in step 2, and solve the resulting equation.

Step 4: Substitute the solution from step 3 back into any equation with both x- and y-variables, and solve.

Step 5: Check your solution in both equations if necessary.

To Solve a System by the Substitution Method [8.5]

6. We can apply the substitution method to the system in Example 1 by first solving the second equation for x to get

$$x = y + 1$$

Substituting this expression for x into the first equation we have

$$(y + 1) + 2y = 4$$
$$3y + 1 = 4$$
$$3y = 3$$
$$y = 1$$

Using $y = 1$ in either of the original equations gives $x = 2$.

Step 1: Solve either of the equations for one of the variables (this step is not necessary if one of the equations has the correct form already).

Step 2: Substitute the results of step 1 into the other equation, and solve.

Step 3: Substitute the results of step 2 into an equation with both x-and y-variables, and solve. (The equation produced in step 1 is usually a good one to use.)

Step 4: Check your solution if necessary.

Inconsistent and Dependent Equations [8.5]

7. If the two lines are parallel, then the system will be inconsistent and the solution is $\varnothing$. If the two lines coincide, then the equations are dependent.

A system of two linear equations that have no solutions in common is said to be an *inconsistent* system, whereas two linear equations that have all their solutions in common are said to be *dependent* equations.

8. The solution to the system

$$x + y + z = 6$$
$$2x - y + z = 3$$
$$x + 2y - 3z = -4$$

is the ordered triple $(1, 2, 3)$.

Systems of Linear Equations in Three Variables [8.6]

The solution set to a linear system in three variables consists of the ordered triples that satisfy each equation in the system. We solve this type of system by repeated use of the addition method.

Linear Inequalities in Two Variables [8.8]

9. The graph of

$$x - y \le 3$$

is

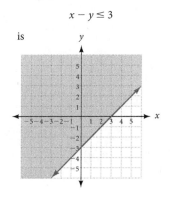

An inequality of the form $ax + by < c$ is a *linear inequality in two variables*. The equation for the boundary of the solution set is given by $ax + by = c$. (This equation is found by simply replacing the inequality symbol with an equal sign.)

To graph a linear inequality, first graph the boundary, using a solid line if the boundary is included in the solution set and a broken line if the boundary is not included in the solution set. Next, choose any point not on the boundary and substitute its coordinates into the original inequality. If the resulting statement is true, the graph lies on the same side of the boundary as the test point. A false statement indicates that the solution set lies on the other side of the boundary.

Systems of Linear Inequalities [8.8]

A system of linear inequalities is two or more linear inequalities considered at the same time. To find the solution set to the system, we graph each of the inequalities on the same coordinate system. The solution set is the region that is common to all the regions graphed.

> ### ⚠ COMMON MISTAKE
>
> A very common mistake in solving inequalities is to forget to reverse the direction of the inequality symbol when multiplying both sides by a negative number. When this mistake occurs, the graph of the solution set is always drawn on the wrong side of the endpoint.

Chapter 8 Test

Solve the following equations. [8.1]

1. $5 - \dfrac{4}{7}a = -11$

2. $\dfrac{1}{5}x - \dfrac{1}{2} - \dfrac{1}{10}x + \dfrac{2}{5} = \dfrac{3}{10}x + \dfrac{1}{2}$

3. $5(x - 1) - 2(2x + 3) = 5x - 4$

4. $0.07 - 0.02(3x + 1) = -0.04x + 0.01$

Solve each equation. [8.1]

5. $\dfrac{1}{4}x^2 = -\dfrac{21}{8}x - \dfrac{5}{4}$

6. $243x^3 = 81x^4$

7. $(x + 5)(x - 2) = 8$

8. $x^3 + 5x^2 - 9x - 45 = 0$

Solve the following equations. [8.2]

9. $|x + 6| - 3 = 1$

10. $\left|\dfrac{1}{4}x - 1\right| = \dfrac{1}{2}$

11. $|3 - 2x| + 5 = 2$

12. $|x - 1| = |5x + 2|$

Find the union. [8.3]

13. $\{1, 2, 3\} \cup \{2, 4, 6\}$

14. $(-\infty, -1) \cup (-\infty, 4]$

Find the intersection. [8.3]

15. $\{1, 2, 3\} \cap \{2, 4, 6\}$

16. $(-\infty, -1) \cap (-\infty, 4]$

Solve the compound inequality. [8.3]

17. $x + 5 \leq 9$ or $x - 2 > -8$

18. $5x - 3 < 7$ and $4 - x > 7$

Solve the following inequalities and graph the solution sets. [8.4]

19. $|6x - 1| > 7$

20. $|3x - 5| - 4 \leq 3$

21. $|5 - 4x| \geq -7$

22. $|4t - 1| < -3$

Solve the following systems by the addition method. [8.5]

23. $2x + 4y = 3$
$-4x - 8y = -6$

24. $4x - 7y = -2$
$-5x + 6y = -3$

Solve the following systems by the substitution method. [8.5]

25. $2x - 5y = -8$
$3x + \ \ y = \ \ 5$

26. $2x - 4y = 0$
$-x + 2y = 5$

Solve each system. [8.6]

27. $2x - y + z = \ \ 9$
$x + y - 3z = -2$
$3x + y - z = \ \ 6$

28. $2x - y + 3z = 2$
$x - 4y - z = 6$
$3x - 2y + z = 4$

29. $x + 2y - \ \ z = \ \ 7$
$3x - 4y - 3z = -4$
$2x + \ \ y - 2z = \ \ 1$

Solve each word problem. [8.7]

30. Investing John invests twice as much money at 6% as he does at 5%. If his investments earn a total of $680 in 1 year, how much does he have invested at each rate?

31. Mixture Problem How much 30% alcohol solution and 70% alcohol solution must be mixed to get 16 gallons of 60% solution?

32. Coin Problem A collection of nickels, dimes, and quarters consists of 15 coins with a total value of $1.10. If the number of nickels is 1 less than 4 times the number of dimes, how many of each coin are contained in the collection?

Graph the following linear inequalities. [8.8]

33. $3x - 4y < 12$ **34.** $y \le -x + 2$

Graph the solution set for each system of linear inequalities. [8.8]

35. $x + 4y \le 4$
$-3x + 2y > -12$

36. $x + y \le -3$
$y \ge 2 - x$

37. $y < -\dfrac{1}{2}x + 4$
$x \ge 0$
$y \ge 0$

Functions

iStockphoto.com © ishmeriev

A student is working with a spring in a physics lab. As she adds various weights to the spring, the spring stretches by various amounts. She records the weights applied and the corresponding length by which the spring stretches. The table below shows some of the data she collects. The scatter diagram gives a visual representation of the data in the table.

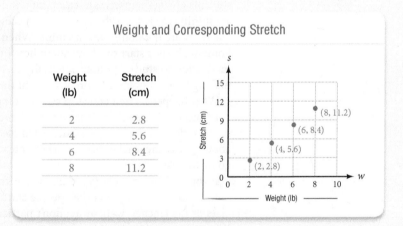

Weight and Corresponding Stretch

Weight (lb)	Stretch (cm)
2	2.8
4	5.6
6	8.4
8	11.2

The exact relationship between the weight and amount of stretch in the spring is given by the following formula, which is an example of a direct variation.

$$s = 1.4w$$

We have three ways to describe the relationship between the weight and amount of stretch in the spring: a table, a graph, and an equation. But, most important to us, we don't need to accept this formula on faith. Later, you will derive the formula from the data in the table above. We will also see that this relationship can be expressed as a function, $f(w) = 1.4w$, because the amount of stretch depends upon the weight applied to the spring.

621

Success Skills

"Once you replace negative thoughts with positive ones, you'll start having positive results."
— Willie Nelson

Do you complain to your classmates about your teacher? If you do, it could be getting in the way of your success in the class.

I have students that tell me that they like the way I teach and that they are enjoying my class. I have other students, in the same class, that complain to each other about me. They say I don't explain things well enough. Are the complaining students giving themselves a reason for not doing well in the class? I think so. They are shifting the responsibility for their success from themselves to me. It's not their fault they are not doing well, it's mine. When these students are alone, trying to do homework, they start thinking about how unfair everything is and they lose their motivation to study. Without intending to, they have set themselves up to fail by making their complaints more important than their progress in the class.

What happens when you stop complaining? You put yourself back in charge of your success. When there is no one to blame if things don't go well, you are more likely to do well. I have had students tell me that, once they stopped complaining about a class, the teacher became a better teacher and they started to actually enjoy going to class.

If you find yourself complaining to your friends about a class or a teacher, make a decision to stop. When other people start complaining to each other about the class or the teacher, walk away; don't participate in the complaining session. Try it for a day, or a week, or for the rest of the term. It may be difficult to do at first, but I'm sure you will like the results, and if you don't, you can always go back to complaining.

Learning Objectives

In this section we will learn how to:

1. Differentiate between a relation and a function.
2. Find the domain and range for a relation or function.
3. Use the vertical line test to identify if a graph represents a function.
4. Sketch the graph of a relation or function.

Introduction

Kaitlin was given an assignment in her math class. For a particular number, which we will call x, she was to ask her friends two questions:

1. What is the square of x?
2. Can you tell me a number whose square is x?

When Kaitlin performed this experiment on her friends, she found that their answer to the first question was always predictable. For example, if $x = 4$, her friends all gave an answer of 16. However, when she asked for a number whose square is 4, even though most of her friends gave an answer of 2, sometimes they would say -2. She found she could not reliably predict which answer her friends would give to the second question.

If we let y represent the answer given to each question, then we can rephrase the two questions as follows:

1. What is y if $y = x^2$?
2. What is y if $y^2 = x$?

The tables below show the results of Kaitlin's experiment.

TABLE 1	$y = x^2$
x	y
1	1
4	16
9	81

TABLE 2	$y^2 = x$
x	y
1	1
1	-1
4	2
4	-2
9	3
9	3

Both of these tables express a relationship between values of x and y, and therefore both are an example of a *relation*. The first table is also an example of a *function*. It is the predictable nature of functions that makes them so useful as models in describing relationships in the real world.

Relations

Any relationship between two sets that can be described in terms of ordered pairs is called a relation.

> **DEFINITION**   *relation*
>
> A *relation* is a rule of correspondence that pairs each element in one set, called the domain, with *one or more elements* from a second set, called the *range*.

> **ALTERNATE DEFINITION**   *relation*
>
> A *relation* is a set of ordered pairs. The set of all first coordinates is the *domain* of the relation. The set of all second coordinates is the *range* of the relation.

EXAMPLE 1   State the domain and range for the relation

$$\{(1, -1), (1, 1), (4, -2), (4, 2), (9, -3), (9, 3)\}$$

SOLUTION   This relation consists of six ordered pairs. The domain is the set of all first coordinates and the range is the set of all second coordinates. Thus, we have

$$\text{Domain} = \{1, 4, 9\}$$

$$\text{Range} = \{-3, -2, -1, 1, 2, 3\}$$

EXAMPLE 2   Table 3 shows the prices of used Ford Mustangs that were listed in the local newspaper. Graph this relation, and give the domain and range.

TABLE 3 Used Mustang Prices	
Year x	Price ($) y
1997	13,925
1997	11,850
1997	9,995
1996	10,200
1996	9,600
1995	9,525
1994	8,675
1994	7,900
1993	6,975

SOLUTION   The graph is shown in Figure 1. This type of graph is called a *scatter diagram*.

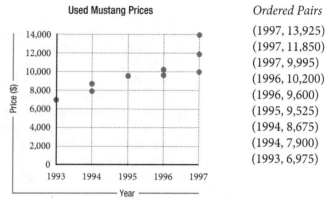

Used Mustang Prices

Ordered Pairs

(1997, 13,925)
(1997, 11,850)
(1997, 9,995)
(1996, 10,200)
(1996, 9,600)
(1995, 9,525)
(1994, 8,675)
(1994, 7,900)
(1993, 6,975)

FIGURE 1   *Scatter diagram of data in Table 3*

The domain is the set of all years listed in Table 3 and the range is the set of the listed prices.

$$\text{Domain} = \{1993, 1994, 1995, 1996, 1997\}$$
$$\text{Range} = \{6,975, 7,900, 8,675, 9,525, 9,995, 10,200, 11,850, 13,925\}$$

Sometimes a relation can be defined by an equation. The equation acts as the "rule of correspondence," and the relation consists of all ordered pairs that satisfy the equation.

EXAMPLE 3   Sketch the graph of the relation $x = y^2$, and state the domain and range.

SOLUTION   We graph the relation $x = y^2$ by finding a number of ordered pairs that satisfy the equation, plotting these points, then drawing a smooth curve that connects them. Table 4 shows some values for x and y that satisfy the equation. The graph of $x = y^2$ is shown in Figure 2.

TABLE 4	
x	*y*
0	0
1	1
1	−1
4	2
4	−2
9	3
9	−3

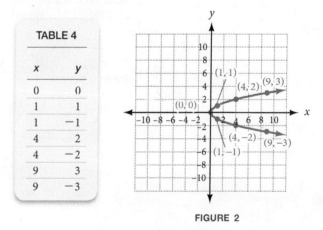

FIGURE 2

To find the domain and range, we must identify *all* values of x and y that satisfy the equation $x = y^2$. We cannot get the domain and range simply by looking at Table 4. For example, the ordered pairs $\left(\frac{1}{4}, \frac{1}{2}\right)$ and $\left(5, \sqrt{5}\right)$ satisfy the equation but are not listed in the table.

From the graph we can see that every point on the graph has a first coordinate that is either positive or zero. In addition, for every real number x greater than or equal to zero, there is a corresponding point on the graph. Therefore, the domain for this relation is $\{x \mid x \geq 0\}$, or $[0, \infty)$ in interval notation.

In contrast, the second coordinates can be positive or negative. Because the graph will continue to widen as we travel further to the right, every real number y will ultimately appear as a second coordinate. (For example, $y = -100$ will appear as a second coordinate in the point $(10{,}000, -100)$, which we could observe if we extended the graph far enough to the right.) Therefore, the range is $\{y \mid y$ is any real number$\}$, which we can write in interval notation as $(-\infty, \infty)$.

Functions

Suppose you have a job that pays $7.50 per hour and that you work anywhere from 0 to 40 hours per week. The amount of money you make in one week *depends* on the number of hours you work that week. In mathematics, we say that your weekly earnings are a *function* of the number of hours you work.

If we let the variable x represent hours and the variable y represent the money you make, then the relationship between x and y can be written as

$$y = 7.5x \qquad \text{for} \qquad 0 \leq x \leq 40$$

This equation defines a relation in which each value of x in the interval $[0, 40]$ will correspond to a single value of y. This leads us to the following definition.

> **DEFINITION**   *function*
>
> A *function* is a relation that pairs each element in the *domain* with exactly one element from the *range*.

If we think of each domain value as an input and the corresponding range value as an output, then a function is a rule for which each input is paired with exactly one output.

| Domain: The set of all inputs | The Function Rule → | Range: The set of all outputs |

EXAMPLE 4   Construct a table and graph for the function $y = 7.5x$ for $0 \leq x \leq 40$, and state the domain and range.

SOLUTION   Table 5 gives some of the paired data that satisfy the equation $y = 7.5x$. Figure 3 is the graph of the equation with the restriction $0 \leq x \leq 40$.

TABLE 5	Weekly Wages	
Hours Worked	Rule	Pay
x	$y = 7.5x$	y
0	$y = 7.5(0)$	0
10	$y = 7.5(10)$	75
20	$y = 7.5(20)$	150
30	$y = 7.5(30)$	225
40	$y = 7.5(40)$	300

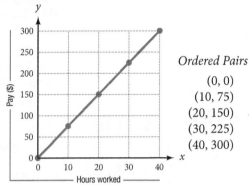

Ordered Pairs

$(0, 0)$
$(10, 75)$
$(20, 150)$
$(30, 225)$
$(40, 300)$

FIGURE 3 *Weekly wages at $7.50 per hour*

The equation $y = 7.5x$ with the restriction $0 \leq x \leq 40$, Table 5, and Figure 3 are three ways to describe the same relationship between the number of hours you work in one week and your gross pay for that week. In all three, we *input* values of x, and then use the function rule to *output* values of y.

The domain is the set of all inputs, or the values that x can assume. Because of the restriction on the number of hours worked, the domain is $\{x \mid 0 \leq x \leq 40\}$, or $[0, 40]$ in interval notation. From the line graph in Figure 3, we see that the corresponding values of y range from 0 to 300. Therefore, the range is $\{y \mid 0 \leq y \leq 300\}$, or $[0, 300]$ in interval notation.

Function Maps

Another way to visualize the relationship between x and y in Example 4 is with the diagram in Figure 4, which we call a *function map*.

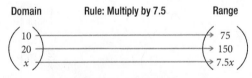

FIGURE 4 *A function map*

Although the diagram in Figure 4 does not show all the values that x and y can assume, it does give us a visual description of how x and y are related. It shows that values of y in the range come from values of x in the domain according to a specific rule (multiply by 7.5 each time).

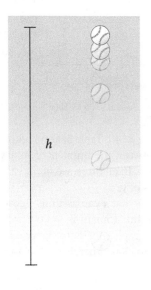

EXAMPLE 5   Kendra tosses a softball into the air with an underhand motion. The distance of the ball above her hand is given by the function

$$h = 32t - 16t^2 \quad \text{for} \quad 0 \le t \le 2$$

where h is the height of the ball in feet and t is the time in seconds. Construct a table that gives the height of the ball at quarter-second intervals, starting with $t = 0$ and ending with $t = 2$, then graph the function.

SOLUTION   We construct Table 6 using the following values of t: $0, \frac{1}{4}, \frac{1}{2}, \frac{3}{4}, 1, \frac{5}{4}, \frac{3}{2}, \frac{7}{4}, 2$. Then we construct the graph in Figure 5 from the table. The graph appears only in the first quadrant because neither t nor h can be negative.

TABLE 6 Tossing a Softball into the Air		
Input		**Output**
Time (sec) t	Function Rule $h = 32t - 16t^2$	Distance (ft) h
0	$h = 32(0) - 16(0)^2 = 0 - 0 = 0$	0
$\frac{1}{4}$	$h = 32\left(\frac{1}{4}\right) - 16\left(\frac{1}{4}\right)^2 = 8 - 1 = 7$	7
$\frac{1}{2}$	$h = 32\left(\frac{1}{2}\right) - 16\left(\frac{1}{2}\right)^2 = 16 - 4 = 12$	12
$\frac{3}{4}$	$h = 32\left(\frac{3}{4}\right) - 16\left(\frac{3}{4}\right)^2 = 24 - 9 = 15$	15
1	$h = 32(1) - 16(1)^2 = 32 - 16 = 16$	16
$\frac{5}{4}$	$h = 32\left(\frac{5}{4}\right) - 16\left(\frac{5}{4}\right)^2 = 40 - 25 = 15$	15
$\frac{3}{2}$	$h = 32\left(\frac{3}{2}\right) - 16\left(\frac{3}{2}\right)^2 = 48 - 36 = 12$	12
$\frac{7}{4}$	$h = 32\left(\frac{7}{4}\right) - 16\left(\frac{7}{4}\right)^2 = 56 - 49 = 7$	7
2	$h = 32(2) - 16(2)^2 = 64 - 64 = 0$	0

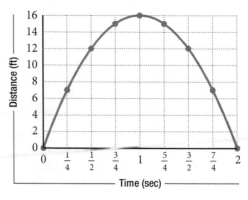

FIGURE 5

Here is a summary of what we know about functions as it applies to this example: We input values of t and output values of h according to the function rule

$$h = 32t - 16t^2 \quad \text{for} \quad 0 \le t \le 2$$

The domain is given by the inequality that follows the equation; it is

$$\text{Domain} = \{\, t \mid 0 \le t \le 2 \,\} = [0, 2]$$

The range is the set of all outputs that are possible by substituting the values of t from the domain into the equation. From our table and graph, it seems that the range is

$$\text{Range} = \{\, h \mid 0 \le h \le 16 \,\} = [0, 16]$$

USING TECHNOLOGY *More About Example 5*

Most graphing calculators can easily produce the information in Table 6. Simply set Y_1 equal to $32X - 16X^2$. Then set up the table so it starts at 0 and increases by an increment of 0.25 each time. (On a TI-82/83, use the $\boxed{\text{TBLSET}}$ key to set up the table.)

Plot1 Plot2 Plot3
\Y₁ ▆ $32X - 16X^2$
\Y₂ =
\Y₃ =
\Y₄ =
\Y₅ =
\Y₆ =
\Y₇ =

TABLE SETUP
TblStart = 0
ΔTbl = .25
Indpnt: **Auto** Ask
Depend: **Auto** Ask

The table will look like this:

X	Y_1	
0	0	
.25	7	
.5	12	
.75	15	
1	16	
1.25	15	
1.5	12	

Graph each equation and build a table as indicated.

1. $y = 64t - 16t^2$ TblStart = 0   ΔTbl = 1

2. $y = \dfrac{1}{2}x - 4$ TblStart = -5 ΔTbl = 1

3. $y = \dfrac{12}{x}$ TblStart = 0.5   ΔTbl = 0.5

Identifying Functions

Because every function is a relation, the function rule also produces ordered pairs of numbers. We use this result to write an alternative definition for a function.

ALTERNATE DEFINITION *function*

A *function* is a set of ordered pairs in which no two different ordered pairs have the same first coordinate. The set of all first coordinates is the *domain* of the function. The set of all second coordinates is the *range* of the function.

The restriction on first coordinates in the alternative definition keeps us from assigning a number in the domain to more than one number in the range.

Here are some facts that will help clarify the distinction between relations and functions:

1. Any rule that assigns numbers from one set to numbers in another set is a relation. If that rule makes the assignment so no input has more than one output, then it is also a function.
2. Any set of ordered pairs is a relation. If none of the first coordinates of those ordered pairs is repeated, the set of ordered pairs is also a function.
3. Every function is a relation.
4. Not every relation is a function.

Note   A function *may* use a *range* value in any number of ordered pairs. This is why the first relation in Example 6 is a function, even though there are different ordered pairs having the same second coordinate.

EXAMPLE 6   Determine if each of the following relations is also a function.

a. $\{(-2, 2), (-1, 1), (0, 0), (1, 1), (2, 2)\}$

b. $\{(1, -1), (1, 1), (4, -2), (4, 2)\}$

SOLUTION   In order to be a function, no two different ordered pairs can have the same first coordinate.

a. This relation is a function. No domain value is repeated as a first coordinate.

b. This relation is not a function. There are two ordered pairs having the same first coordinate of $x = 1$ (and two ordered pairs having the first coordinate $x = 4$). To be a function, each domain value can appear in only one ordered pair.

EXAMPLE 7   In the introduction to this section we described an experiment where students were asked two questions, which can be represented by the equations $y = x^2$ and $y^2 = x$. Determine if these equations represent functions.

SOLUTION   Looking at Table 1, we can see that each value of x gets paired with a single value of y. Once we choose an input, the square of that input is uniquely determined. The relation $y = x^2$ is a function because no two ordered pairs will have the same first coordinate.

On the other hand, a quick glance at Table 2 shows us that the equation $y^2 = x$ does not represent a function. For any positive real number x, we can always find two different values of y whose square is x (one positive and one negative). Different ordered pairs can have the same first coordinate, such as $(1, -1)$ and $(1, 1)$.

Vertical Line Test

Look back at the scatter diagram for used Mustang prices shown in Figure 1. Notice that some of the points on the diagram lie above and below each other along vertical lines. This is an indication that the data do not constitute a function. Two data points that lie on the same vertical line must have come from two ordered pairs with the same first coordinates.

Now, look at the graph shown in Figure 2. The reason this graph is the graph of a relation, but not of a function, is that some points on the graph have the same first coordinates, for example, the points $(4, 2)$ and $(4, -2)$. Furthermore, any time two points on a graph have the same first coordinates, those points must lie on a vertical line. [To convince yourself, connect the points $(4, 2)$ and $(4, -2)$ with a straight line. You will see that it must be a vertical line.] This allows us to write the following test that uses the graph to determine whether a relation is also a function.

⟨Δ≠Σ⟩ **RULE**   *Vertical Line Test*

If a vertical line crosses the graph of a relation in more than one place, the relation cannot be a function. If no vertical line can be found that crosses a graph in more than one place, then the graph represents a function.

If we look back to the graph of $h = 32t - 16t^2$ as shown in Figure 5, we see that no vertical line can be found that crosses this graph in more than one place. The graph shown in Figure 5 is therefore the graph of a function.

EXAMPLE 8   Match each relation with its graph, then indicate which relations are functions

a. $y = |x| - 4$ **b.** $y = x^2 - 4$ **c.** $y = 2x + 2$

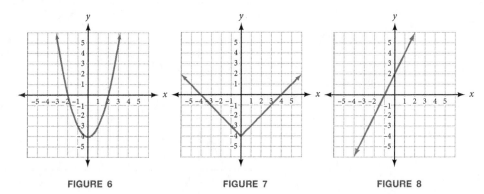

FIGURE 6   FIGURE 7   FIGURE 8

SOLUTION   Using the basic graphs for a guide along with our knowledge of translations, we have the following:

a. Figure 7   **b.** Figure 6   **c.** Figure 8

And, since all graphs pass the vertical line test, all are functions.

Getting Ready for Class

After reading through the preceding section, respond in your own words and in complete sentences.

A. What is a function?

B. How is a relation different from a function?

C. What is the vertical line test?

D. Is every line the graph of a function? Explain.

Problem Set 9.1

For each of the following relations, give the domain and range, and indicate which are also functions.

1. $\{(1, 2), (3, 4), (5, 6), (7, 8)\}$

2. $\{(2, 1), (4, 3), (6, 5), (8, 7)\}$

3. $\{(2, 5), (3, 4), (1, 4), (0, 6)\}$

4. $\{(0, 4), (1, 6), (2, 4), (1, 5)\}$

5. $\{(a, 3), (b, 4), (c, 3), (d, 5)\}$

6. $\{(a, 5), (b, 5), (c, 4), (d, 5)\}$

7. $\{(a, 1), (a, 2), (a, 3), (a, 4)\}$

8. $\{(a, 1), (b, 1), (c, 1), (d, 1)\}$

State whether each of the following graphs represents a function.

9.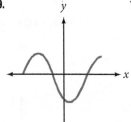

10.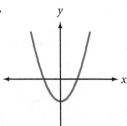

11.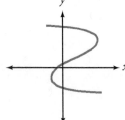

12.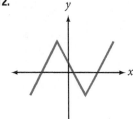

13.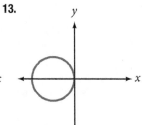

14.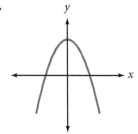

15.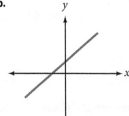

16.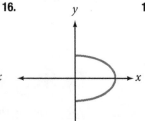

17.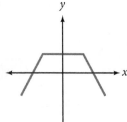

18.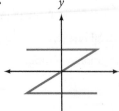

19.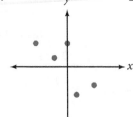

20.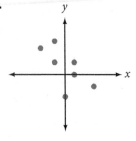

Determine the domain and range of the following functions. Assume the *entire* function is shown.

21.

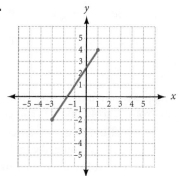

22.

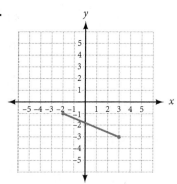

23.

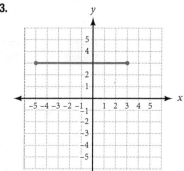

24.

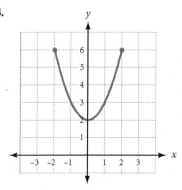

25.

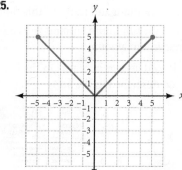

26.

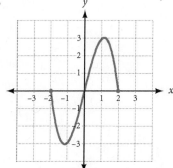

27.

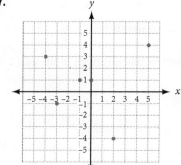

28.

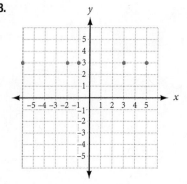

Graph each of the following relations. In each case, use the graph to find the domain and range, and indicate whether the graph is the graph of a function.

29. $y = 2x - 3$ **30.** $y = -\dfrac{1}{3}x + 2$ **31.** $x = 4$ **32.** $y = -5$

33. $y = -|x|$ **34.** $x = |y|$ **35.** $y = x^2 - 1$ **36.** $y = x^2 + 4$

37. $x = 3 - y^2$ **38.** $x = y^2 - 1$

39. Wages Suppose you have a job that pays $8.50 per hour and you work anywhere from 10 to 40 hours per week.

    a. Write an equation, with a restriction on the variable x, that gives the amount of money, y, you will earn for working x hours in one week.

    b. Use the function rule you have written in part a to complete Table 7.

TABLE 7	Weekly Wages	
Hours Worked	Function Rule	Gross Pay ($)
x		y
10		
20		
30		
40		

    c. Construct a line graph from the information in Table 7.

    d. State the domain and range of this function.

    e. What is the minimum amount you can earn in a week with this job? What is the maximum amount?

40. Wages The ad shown here was in the local newspaper. Suppose you are hired for the job described in the ad.

    a. If x is the number of hours you work per week and y is your weekly gross pay, write the equation for y. (Be sure to include any restrictions on the variable x that are given in the ad.)

b. Use the function rule you have written in part *a* to complete Table 8.

TABLE 8   Weekly Wages

Hours Worked	Function Rule	Gross Pay ($)
x		y
15		
20		
25		
30		

c. Construct a line graph from the information in Table 8.

d. State the domain and range of this function.

e. What is the minimum amount you can earn in a week with this job? What is the maximum amount?

41. Camera Phones The chart shows the estimated number of camera phones and non-camera phones sold from 2004 to 2010. Using the chart, list all the values in the domain and range for the total phones sales.

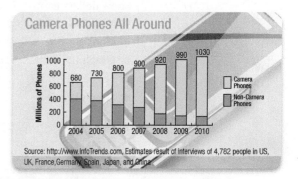

42. Light Bulbs The chart shows a comparison of power usage between incandescent and energy efficient light bulbs. Use the chart to state the domain and range of the function for an energy efficient bulb.

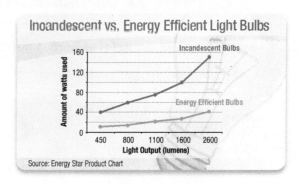

43. Profits Match each of the following statements to the appropriate graph indicated by labels I–IV in Figure 9.

a. Sarah works 25 hours to earn $250.

b. Justin works 35 hours to earn $560.

c. Rosemary works 30 hours to earn $360.

d. Marcus works 40 hours to earn $320.

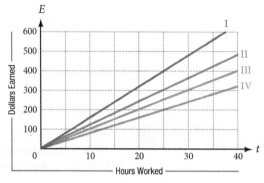

FIGURE 9

44. Find an equation for each of the functions shown in the graph in Figure 9. Show dollars earned, E, as a function of hours worked, t. Then, indicate the domain and range of each function.

a. Graph I: $E =$ Domain $= \{\, t \,|$ $\}$ Range $= \{\, E \,|$ $\}$

b. Graph II: $E =$ Domain $= \{\, t \,|$ $\}$ Range $= \{\, E \,|$ $\}$

c. Graph III: $E =$ Domain $= \{\, t \,|$ $\}$ Range $= \{\, E \,|$ $\}$

d. Graph IV: $E =$ Domain $= \{\, t \,|$ $\}$ Range $= \{\, E \,|$ $\}$

Learning Objectives Assessment

The following problems can be used to help assess if you have successfully met the learning objectives for this section.

45. Which of the following statements are true? (You may choose more than one.)

a. Every relation is a function.

b. Every function is a relation.

c. To be a function, no two ordered pairs can have the same first coordinate.

d. To be a function, no two ordered pairs can have the same second coordinate.

46. Find the domain of the relation whose graph is shown in Figure 10.

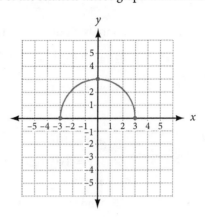

FIGURE 10

    a. $\{-3, 0, 3\}$ **b.** $\{0, 3\}$ **c.** $\{x \mid -3 \le x \le 3\}$ **d.** $\{y \mid 0 \le y \le 3\}$

47. Which of the following graphs represents a function?

    a.

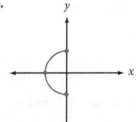

    b.

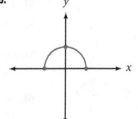

    c.

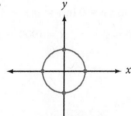

    d.

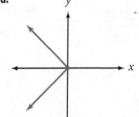

48. Which of the following ordered pairs corresponds to a point on the graph of the function $y = x^2 - 9$?

    a. $(-8, 1)$ **b.** $(2, 5)$ **c.** $(9, 0)$ **d.** $(-2, -5)$

Getting Ready for the Next Section

Simplify. Round to the nearest whole number if necessary.

49. $4(3.14)(9)$

50. $\frac{4}{3}(3.14) \cdot 3^3$

51. $4(-2) - 1$

52. $3(3)^2 + 2(3) - 1$

53. If $s = \dfrac{60}{t}$, find s when
    a. $t = 10$ **b.** $t = 8$

54. If $y = 3x^2 + 2x - 1$, find y when
    a. $x = 0$ **b.** $x = -2$

55. Find the value of $x^2 + 2$ for
    a. $x = 5$ **b.** $x = -2$

56. Find the value of $125 \cdot 2^t$ for
    a. $t = 0$ **b.** $t = 1$

For the equation $y = x^2 - 3$:

57. Find y if x is 2.

58. Find y if x is -2.

59. Find y if x is 0.

60. Find y if x is -4.

The problems that follow review some of the more important skills you have learned in previous sections and chapters.

61. If $x - 2y = 4$, and $x = \frac{8}{5}$ find y.

62. If $\frac{x^2}{25} + \frac{y^2}{9} = 1$, find y when x is -4.

63. Let $x = 0$ and $y = 0$ in $y = a(x - 8)^2 + 70$ and solve for a.

64. Find R if $p = 2.5$ and $R = (900 - 300p)p$.

Learning Objectives

In this section we will learn how to:

1. Use function notation to represent an ordered pair for a function.
2. Evaluate a function using an equation.
3. Evaluate a function using a table.
4. Evaluate a function using a graph.

Introduction

Let's return to an example we considered in the previous section. If a job pays $7.50 per hour for working from 0 to 40 hours a week, then the amount of money y earned in one week is a function of the number of hours worked x. The exact relationship between x and y is written

$$y = 7.5x \quad \text{for} \quad 0 \le x \le 40$$

Because the amount of money earned y depends on the number of hours worked x, we call y the *dependent variable* and x the *independent variable*. Furthermore, if we let f represent all the ordered pairs produced by the equation, then we can write

$$f = \{(x, y) \,|\, y = 7.5x \quad \text{and} \quad 0 \le x \le 40\}$$

Once we have named a function with a letter, we can use an alternative notation to represent the dependent variable y. The alternative notation for y is $f(x)$. It is read "f of x" and can be used instead of the variable y when working with functions. The notation y and the notation $f(x)$ are equivalent. That is,

$$y = 7.5x \Leftrightarrow f(x) = 7.5x$$

When we use the notation $f(x)$ we are using *function notation*.

Function Notation

The benefit of using function notation is that we can write more information with fewer symbols than we can by using just the variable y. For example, in the preceding discussion, asking how much money a person will make for working 20 hours is simply a matter of asking for $f(20)$. Without function notation, we would have to say, "Find the value of y that corresponds to a value of $x = 20$." To illustrate further, using the variable y, we can say "y is 150 when x is 20." Using the notation $f(x)$, we simply say "$f(20) = 150$." Each expression indicates that you will earn $150 for working 20 hours.

> (def) **DEFINITION** *function notation*
>
> If we let f represent the rule of correspondence defining y as a function of x, then the notation $y = f(x)$ is used to indicate that y is the range value assigned by the function to the domain value x.

EXAMPLE 1   If the function f is given by

$$f = \{(-2, 0), (3, -1), (2, 4), (7, 5)\}$$

express each ordered pair using function notation.

SOLUTION   We have the following:

$(-2, 0)$	becomes	$f(-2) = 0$
$(3, -1)$	becomes	$f(3) = -1$
$(2, 4)$	becomes	$f(2) = 4$
$(7, 5)$	becomes	$f(7) = 5$

Evaluating Functions

When we use a function to find the value of y for a given value of x, we call this *evaluating the function*. Because a function is often defined by an equation which performs some operations on x, we sometimes refer to a domain value as an *input* and the corresponding range value as an *output*.

Domain Value	Function	Range Value
$x \longrightarrow$	$\boxed{f}$	$\longrightarrow y = f(x)$
Input	*Rule of Correspondence*	*Output*

Our next example illustrates this process of finding outputs for given inputs.

EXAMPLE 2   If $f(x) = 7.5x$, find $f(0)$, $f(10)$, and $f(20)$.

SOLUTION   To find $f(0)$, we substitute 0 for x in the expression $7.5x$ and simplify. We find $f(10)$ and $f(20)$ in a similar manner — by substitution.

If $f(x) = 7.5x$

then $f(0) = 7.5(0) = 0$

$f(10) = 7.5(10) = 75$

$f(20) = 7.5(20) = 150$

We can also express the relationships between inputs and outputs from Example 2 using a function map as shown in Figure 1.

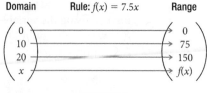

FIGURE 1

EXAMPLE 3   If $f(x) = 3x^2 + 2x - 1$, find $f(0)$, $f(3)$, and $f(-2)$.

SOLUTION   Since $f(x) = 3x^2 + 2x - 1$, we have

$$f(0) = 3(0)^2 + 2(0) - 1 = 0 - 1 = -1$$

$$f(3) = 3(3)^2 + 2(3) - 1 = 27 + 6 - 1 = 32$$

$$f(-2) = 3(-2)^2 + 2(-2) - 1 = 12 - 4 - 1 = 7$$

Keep in mind that a function is a relation, which is a set of ordered pairs. In Example 3, because $f(0) = -1$, $(0, -1)$ is an ordered pair in f. Likewise, $(3, 32)$ and $(-2, 7)$ are also ordered pairs in f.

EXAMPLE 4   If $f(x) = 4x - 1$ and $g(x) = x^2 + 2$, then

$$f(5) = 4(5) - 1 = 19 \qquad \text{and} \qquad g(5) = 5^2 + 2 = 27$$

$$f(-2) = 4(-2) - 1 = -9 \qquad \text{and} \qquad g(-2) = (-2)^2 + 2 = 6$$

$$f(a) = 4a - 1 \qquad \text{and} \qquad g(a) = a^2 + 2$$

$$f(x + 3) = 4(x + 3) - 1 \qquad \text{and} \quad g(x + 3) = (x + 3)^2 + 2$$
$$= 4x + 12 - 1 \qquad\qquad\qquad = (x^2 + 6x + 9) + 2$$
$$= 4x + 11 \qquad\qquad\qquad\quad = x^2 + 6x + 11$$

$$f(x) + 3 = (4x - 1) + 3 \qquad \text{and} \quad g(x) + 3 = (x^2 + 2) + 3$$
$$= 4x + 2 \qquad\qquad\qquad\qquad = x^2 + 5$$

$$3\,f(x) = 3(4x - 1) \qquad \text{and} \qquad 3\,g(x) = 3(x^2 + 2)$$
$$= 12x - 3 \qquad\qquad\qquad\qquad = 3x^2 + 6$$

USING TECHNOLOGY   *More About Example 4*

Most graphing calculators can use tables to evaluate functions. To work Example 4 using a graphing calculator table, set Y_1 equal to $4X - 1$ and Y_2 equal to $X^2 + 2$. Then set the independent variable in the table to Ask instead of Auto. Go to your table and input 5, -2, and 0. Under Y_1 in the table, you will find $f(5)$, $f(-2)$, and $f(0)$. Under Y_2, you will find $g(5)$, $g(-2)$, and $g(0)$.

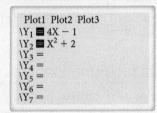

Plot1 Plot2 Plot3
$\backslash Y_1 \blacksquare 4X - 1$
$\backslash Y_2 \blacksquare X^2 + 2$
$\backslash Y_3 =$
$\backslash Y_4 =$
$\backslash Y_5 =$
$\backslash Y_6 =$
$\backslash Y_7 =$

TABLE SETUP
TblStart $= 0$
ΔTbl $= 1$
Indpnt: Auto Ask
Depend: Auto Ask

The table will look like this:

X	Y_1	Y_2
5	19	27
-2	-9	6
0	-1	2

Although the calculator asks us for a table increment, the increment doesn't matter because we are inputting the X values ourselves.

EXAMPLE 5   If $f(x) = 2x^2$ and $g(x) = 3x - 1$, find
a. $f[g(2)]$ **b.** $g[f(2)]$

SOLUTION   The expression $f[g(2)]$ is read "f of g of 2."

a. Because $g(2) = 3(2) - 1 = 5$,
$$f[g(2)] = f(5) = 2(5)^2 = 50$$

b. Because $f(2) = 2(2)^2 = 8$,
$$g[f(2)] = g(8) = 3(8) - 1 = 23$$

Evaluating Functions Using a Table

In the previous examples we have seen how to evaluate a function that is defined by an equation. Another way to define a function is using a table. Because a function is simply a set of ordered pairs, we can specify the ordered pairs in table format.

If (x, y) is an ordered pair in f, then the first coordinate is an input (domain value) and the second coordinate is the corresponding output (range value). To evaluate a function from a table, we identify the ordered pair having the given value of x. The y-coordinate of that pair is the function value $f(x)$.

EXAMPLE 6   Given $y = f(x)$, use the table below to find
a. $f(2)$ **b.** $f(-1)$

x	-2	-1	0	1	2
y	0	-5	2	-1	3

SOLUTION

a. The ordered pair from the table having an x-coordinate of 2 is $(2, 3)$, so $f(2) = 3$.

b. The ordered pair from the table having an x-coordinate of -1 is $(-1, -5)$, so $f(-1) = -5$.

Evaluating Functions Using a Graph

If we plot every ordered pair (x, y) for a function on a rectangular coordinate system, the result is the graph of the function.

DEFINITION   *graph of a function*

The **graph** of a function $y = f(x)$ is the set of all points in the plane $(x, f(x))$, where x is an element of the domain and $f(x)$ is the corresponding element from the range.

Notice that the second coordinate of any point on the graph of a function is the *value* of the function for some input x. This means we can evaluate a function from a graph. We locate the point having the given x-value. The y-value of this point will be $f(x)$.

EXAMPLE 7   Figure 2 shows the graph of the function $y = f(x)$ introduced in the beginning of this section. Use the graph to evaluate $f(30)$ and $f(40)$.

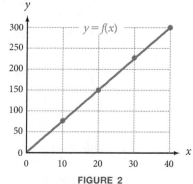

FIGURE 2

SOLUTION   From Figure 2, we can see that the point on the graph having an x-coordinate of 30 is $(30, 225)$, so $f(30) = 225$. Likewise, the point on the graph having an x-coordinate of 40 is $(40, 300)$, so $f(40) = 300$. We illustrate this in Figure 3.

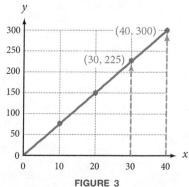

FIGURE 3

Using Function Notation in Applications

The next examples show a variety of ways to use and interpret function notation.

EXAMPLE 8   If it takes Lorena t minutes to run a mile, then her average speed s, in miles per hour, is given by the formula

$$s(t) = \frac{60}{t} \qquad \text{for} \qquad t > 0$$

Find $s(10)$ and $s(8)$, and then explain what they mean.

SOLUTION   To find $s(10)$, we substitute 10 for t in the equation and simplify:

$$s(10) = \frac{60}{10} = 6$$

In words: When Lorena runs a mile in 10 minutes, her average speed is 6 miles per hour.

We calculate $s(8)$ by substituting 8 for t in the equation. Doing so gives us

$$s(8) = \frac{60}{8} = 7.5$$

In words: Running a mile in 8 minutes is running at a rate of 7.5 miles per hour.

EXAMPLE 9   A painting is purchased as an investment for $125. If its value increases continuously so that it doubles every 5 years, then its value is given by the function

$$V(t) = 125 \cdot 2^{t/5} \quad \text{for} \quad t \geq 0$$

where t is the number of years since the painting was purchased, and V is its value (in dollars) at time t. Find $V(5)$ and $V(10)$, and explain what they mean.

SOLUTION   The expression $V(5)$ is the value of the painting when $t = 5$ (5 years after it is purchased). We calculate $V(5)$ by substituting 5 for t in the equation $V(t) = 125 \cdot 2^{t/5}$. Here is our work:

$$V(5) = 125 \cdot 2^{5/5} = 125 \cdot 2^1 = 125 \cdot 2 = 250$$

In words: After 5 years, the painting is worth $250.

The expression $V(10)$ is the value of the painting after 10 years. To find this number, we substitute 10 for t in the equation:

$$V(10) = 125 \cdot 2^{10/5} = 125 \cdot 2^2 = 125 \cdot 4 = 500$$

In words: The value of the painting 10 years after it is purchased is $500.

EXAMPLE 10   A balloon has the shape of a sphere with a radius of 3 inches. Use the following formulas to find the volume and surface area of the balloon.

$$V(r) = \frac{4}{3}\pi r^3 \qquad S(r) = 4\pi r^2$$

SOLUTION   As you can see, we have used function notation to write the formulas for volume and surface area, because each quantity is a function of the radius. To find these quantities when the radius is 3 inches, we evaluate $V(3)$ and $S(3)$:

$$V(3) = \frac{4}{3}\pi \cdot 3^3 = \frac{4}{3}\pi \cdot 27$$

$$= 36\pi \text{ cubic inches, or } 113 \text{ cubic inches}$$
(to the nearest whole number)

$$S(3) = 4\pi \cdot 3^2$$

$$= 36\pi \text{ square inches, or } 113 \text{ square inches}$$
(to the nearest whole number)

The fact that $V(3) = 36\pi$ means that the ordered pair $(3, 36\pi)$ belongs to the function V. Likewise, the fact that $S(3) = 36\pi$ tells us that the ordered pair $(3, 36\pi)$ is a member of function S.

USING TECHNOLOGY *More About Example 10*

If we look at Example 10, we see that when the radius of a sphere is 3, the numerical values of the volume and surface area are equal. How unusual is this? Are there other values of r for which $V(r)$ and $S(r)$ are equal? We can answer this question by looking at the graphs of both V and S.

To graph the function $V(r) = \frac{4}{3}\pi r^3$, set $Y_1 = 4\pi X^3/3$. To graph $S(r) = 4\pi r^2$, set $Y_2 = 4\pi X^2$. Graph the two functions in each of the following windows:

$$\text{Window 1:} \quad \text{X from } -4 \text{ to } 4, \text{ Y from } -2 \text{ to } 10$$

$$\text{Window 2:} \quad \text{X from } 0 \text{ to } 4, \text{ Y from } 0 \text{ to } 50$$

$$\text{Window 3:} \quad \text{X from } 0 \text{ to } 4, \text{ Y from } 0 \text{ to } 150$$

Then use the Trace and Zoom features of your calculator to locate the point in the first quadrant where the two graphs intersect. How do the coordinates of this point compare with the results in Example 10?

Getting Ready for Class

After reading through the preceding section, respond in your own words and in complete sentences.

A. Explain what you are calculating when you find $f(2)$ for a given function f.

B. If $f(x) = 7.5x$, how do you find $f(10)$?

C. If $f(2) = 3$ for a function f, what is the relationship between the numbers 2 and 3 and the graph of f?

D. Explain how you would evaluate $f(6)$ using a table.

Problem Set 9.2

1. If $f(3) = 8$, then what ordered pair is in f?
2. If $f(8) = 3$, then what ordered pair is in f?
3. If $g(-1) = 5$, then what ordered pair is in g?
4. If $g(5) = -1$, then what ordered pair is in g?

If each of the following ordered pairs belongs to the function $y = f(x)$, express each pair using function notation.

5. $(4, 0)$ 6. $(0, 3)$ 7. $(-1, 9)$ 8. $(2, -2)$

9. $(10, 0.1)$ 10. $(0.25, 0.5)$ 11. $\left(-\dfrac{1}{5}, -\dfrac{1}{10}\right)$ 12. $\left(-\dfrac{1}{3}, \dfrac{1}{9}\right)$

Let $f(x) = 2x - 5$ and $g(x) = x^2 + 3x + 4$. Evaluate the following.

13. $f(2)$ 14. $f(3)$ 15. $f(-3)$ 16. $g(-2)$

17. $g(-1)$ 18. $f(-4)$ 19. $g(-3)$ 20. $g(2)$

21. $g(a)$ 22. $f(a)$ 23. $f(a + 6)$ 24. $g(a + 6)$

Let $f(x) = 3x^2 - 4x + 1$ and $g(x) = 2x - 1$. Evaluate the following.

25. $f(0)$ 26. $g(0)$ 27. $g(-4)$ 28. $f(1)$

29. $f(-1)$ 30. $g(-1)$ 31. $g\left(\dfrac{1}{2}\right)$ 32. $g\left(\dfrac{1}{4}\right)$

33. $f(a)$ 34. $g(a)$ 35. $f(a + 2)$ 36. $g(a + 2)$

Let $f(x) = \dfrac{1}{x + 3}$ and $g(x) = \dfrac{1}{x} + 1$. Evaluate the following.

37. $f\left(\dfrac{1}{3}\right)$ 38. $g\left(\dfrac{1}{3}\right)$ 39. $f\left(-\dfrac{1}{2}\right)$ 40. $g\left(-\dfrac{1}{2}\right)$

41. $f(-3)$ 42. $g(0)$

Let $f(x) = x^2 - 2x$ and $g(x) = 5x - 4$. Evaluate the following.

43. $f(-2) + g(-1)$ 44. $f(-1) + g(-2)$ 45. $f(2) - g(3)$

46. $f(3) - g(2)$ 47. $f[g(3)]$ 48. $g[f(3)]$

If $f = \{(1, 4), (-2, 0), \left(3, \frac{1}{2}\right), (\pi, 0)\}$ and $g = \{(1, 1), (-2, 2), \left(\frac{1}{2}, 0\right)\}$, find each of the following values of f and g.

49. $f(1)$ 50. $g(1)$ 51. $g\left(\dfrac{1}{2}\right)$ 52. $f(3)$

53. $g(-2)$ 54. $f(\pi)$

If $y = f(x)$, use the table given below to find each value.

x	-3	-2	-1	0	1	2	3
y	4	5	1	-2	-1	0	2

55. $f(0)$ 56. $f(-3)$ 57. $f(3)$ 58. $f(1)$

59. $f(-1)$ 60. $f(2)$ 61. $3f(-2)$ 62. $-2f(3)$

Use the graphs of $y = f(x)$ and $y = g(x)$ shown to find the following values of f and g.

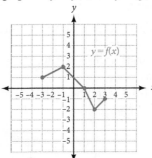
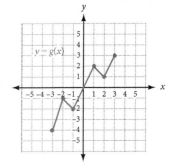

63. $f(3)$ **64.** $g(3)$ **65.** $f(-1)$ **66.** $f(0)$

67. $g(0)$ **68.** $g(-1)$ **69.** $g(-2)$ **70.** $f(-3)$

71. For the function $f(x) = x^2 - 4$, evaluate each of the following expressions.

    a. $f(a) - 3$ **b.** $f(a - 3)$ **c.** $f(x) + 2$ **d.** $f(x + 2)$

    e. $f(a + b)$ **f.** $f(x + h)$ **g.** $f(3x)$ **h.** $3f(x)$

72. For the function $f(x) = 3x^2$, evaluate each of the following expressions.

    a. $f(a) - 2$ **b.** $f(a - 2)$ **c.** $f(x) + 5$ **d.** $f(x + 5)$

    e. $f(a + b)$ **f.** $f(x + h)$ **g.** $f(2x)$ **h.** $2f(x)$

73. Graph the function $f(x) = x^2$. Then use the graph to evaluate $f(1)$, $f(2)$, and $f(3)$.

74. Graph the function $f(x) = x^2 - 2$. Then use the graph to evaluate $f(2)$ and $f(3)$.

Applying the Concepts

75. Investing in Art A painting is purchased as an investment for \$150. If its value increases continuously so that it doubles every 3 years, then its value is given by the function

$$V(t) = 150 \cdot 2^{t/3} \qquad \text{for} \qquad t \geq 0$$

where t is the number of years since the painting was purchased, and $V(t)$ is its value (in dollars) at time t. Find $V(3)$ and $V(6)$, and then explain what they mean.

76. Average Speed If it takes Minke t minutes to run a mile, then her average speed $s(t)$, in miles per hour, is given by the formula

$$s(t) = \frac{60}{t} \qquad \text{for} \qquad t > 0$$

Find $s(4)$ and $s(5)$, and then explain what they mean.

77. Antidepressant Sales Suppose x represents one of the years in the chart. Suppose further that we have three functions f, g, and h that do the following:

- f pairs each year with the total sales of Zoloft in billions of dollars for that year.
- g pairs each year with the total sales of Effexor in billions of dollars for that year.
- h pairs each year with the total sales of Wellbutrin in billions of dollars for that year.

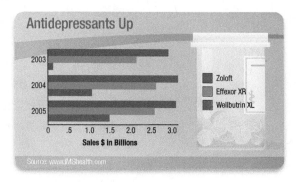

For each statement below, indicate whether the statement is true or false.

a. The domain of g is { 2003, 2004, 2005 }

b. The domain of g is $\{\, x \mid 2003 \le x \le 2005 \,\}$

c. $f(2004) > g(2004)$

d. $h(2005) > 1.5$

e. $h(2005) > h(2004) > h(2003)$

78. Mobile Phone Sales Suppose x represents one of the years in the chart. Suppose further that we have three functions f, g, and h that do the following:

- f pairs each year with the number of camera phones sold that year.
- g pairs each year with the number of non-camera phones sold that year.
- h is such that $h(x) = f(x) + g(x)$.

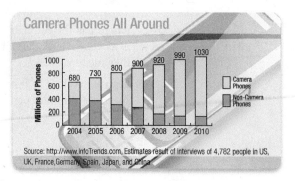

For each statement below, indicate whether the statement is true or false.

a. The domain of f is {2004, 2005, 2006, 2007, 2008, 2009, 2010}

b. $h(2005) = 741,000,000$

c. $f(2009) > g(2009)$

d. $f(2004) < f(2005)$

e. $h(2010) > h(2007) > h(2004)$

79. Length of a Spring The linear function $S(x) = 1.4x$ gives the amount of stretch in a spring, $S(x)$, in centimeters, when a weight of x pounds is added to the spring.

  a. How much will the spring stretch if a weight of 2.5 pounds is added?

  b. What amount of weight will cause the spring to stretch 5.6 cm?

  c. Graph the function for $0 \le x \le 10$.

80. Step Function Figure 4 shows the graph of the step function C that was used to calculate the first-class postage on a letter weighing x ounces in 2006. Use this graph to answer questions a through d.

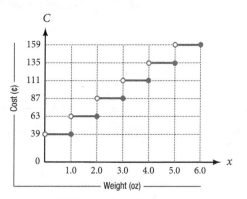

FIGURE 4 *The graph of $C(x)$*

  a. Fill in the following table:

Weight (ounces)	0.6	1.0	1.1	2.5	3.0	4.8	5.0	5.3
Cost (cents)								

  b. If a letter cost 87 cents to mail, how much does it weigh? State your answer in words. State your answer as an inequality.

  c. If the entire function is shown in Figure 5, state the domain.

  d. State the range of the function shown in Figure 5.

Learning Objectives Assessment

The following problems can be used to help assess if you have successfully met the learning objectives for this section.

81. If $(-2, 6)$ is an ordered pair in a function f, express this using function notation.

    a. $-2f = 6$ **b.** $6f = -2$ **c.** $f(-2) = 6$ **d.** $f(6) = -2$

82. If $f(x) = 3x^2 - 4x$, find $f(-2)$.

    a. 4 **b.** 20 **c.** -4 **d.** $-6x^2 + 8x$

83. If $y = f(x)$, use the table below to evaluate $f(1)$.

x	-1	1	2	4
y	-2	-3	1	0

    a. -3 **b.** 2 **c.** -2 **d.** 0

84. Use the graph of $y = g(x)$ shown in Figure 5 to evaluate $g(-1)$.

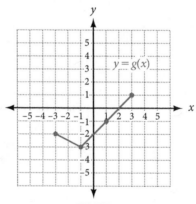

FIGURE 5

    a. 1 **b.** -1 **c.** 3 **d.** -3

Getting Ready for the Next Section

Multiply.

85. $x(35 - 0.1x)$ **86.** $0.6(M - 70)$

87. $(4x - 3)(x - 1)$ **88.** $(4x - 3)(4x^2 - 7x + 3)$

Simplify.

89. $(35x - 0.1x^2) - (8x + 500)$ **90.** $(4x - 3) + (4x^2 - 7x + 3)$

91. $(4x^2 + 3x + 2) - (2x^2 - 5x - 6)$ **92.** $(4x^2 + 3x + 2) + (2x^2 - 5x - 6)$

93. $4(2)^2 - 3(2)$ **94.** $4(-1)^2 - 7(-1)$

Algebra and Composition with Functions

Learning Objectives

In this section we will learn how to:

1. Evaluate the sum, difference, product, or quotient of two functions.

2. Find the formulas for the sum, difference, product, and quotient of two functions.

3. Evaluate a composition of functions.

4. Find the formula for a composition of two functions.

iStockPhoto.com/©Slobo Mitic

Introduction

A company produces and sells copies of an accounting program for home computers. The price they charge for the program is related to the number of copies sold by the demand function

$$p(x) = 35 - 0.1x$$

We find the revenue for this business by multiplying the number of items sold by the price per item. When we do so, we are forming a new function by combining two existing functions. That is, if $n(x) = x$ is the number of items sold and $p(x) = 35 - 0.1x$ is the price per item, then revenue is

$$R(x) = n(x) \cdot p(x) = x(35 - 0.1x) = 35x - 0.1x^2$$

In this case, the revenue function is the product of two functions. When we combine functions in this manner, we are applying our rules for algebra to functions.

To carry this situation further, we know the profit function is the difference between two functions. If the cost function for producing x copies of the accounting program is $C(x) = 8x + 500$, then the profit function is

$$P(x) = R(x) - C(x) = (35x - 0.1x^2) - (8x + 500) = -500 + 27x - 0.1x^2$$

The relationship between these last three functions is represented visually in Figure 1.

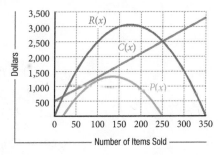

FIGURE 1

Algebra with Functions

Again, when we combine functions in the manner shown, we are applying our rules for algebra to functions. To begin this section, we take a formal look at addition, subtraction, multiplication, and division with functions.

If we are given two functions f and g with a common domain, we can define four other functions as follows.

> ### Operations with Functions
>
> If f and g are functions and x is in the domain of both f and g, then
>
> $(f + g)(x) = f(x) + g(x)$ The function $f + g$ is the sum of the functions f and g.
>
> $(f - g)(x) = f(x) - g(x)$ The function $f - g$ is the difference of the functions f and g.
>
> $(fg)(x) = f(x)g(x)$ The function fg is the product of the functions f and g.
>
> $\left(\dfrac{f}{g}\right)(x) = \dfrac{f(x)}{g(x)}$ The function $\dfrac{f}{g}$ is the quotient of the functions f and g, where $g(x) \neq 0$.

Notice that, for a given input x, the value of the sum function $(f + g)(x)$ is found by evaluating $f(x)$ and $g(x)$ individually, and then adding the resulting outputs. In other words, when adding two functions, all we are really doing is adding the corresponding range values for a given domain value. The difference function, product function, and quotient function all behave in a similar way.

VIDEO EXAMPLES

SECTION 9.3

EXAMPLE 1   If $f(x) = 4x^2 + 3x + 2$ and $g(x) = 2x^2 - 5x - 6$, find $(f + g)(2)$, $(f - g)(2)$, $(fg)(2)$, and $\left(\dfrac{f}{g}\right)(2)$.

SOLUTION   To begin, we will evaluate f and g at $x = 2$.

$$f(2) = 4(2)^2 + 3(2) + 2$$
$$= 24$$
$$g(2) = 2(2)^2 - 5(2) - 6$$
$$= -8$$

Therefore,

$$(f + g)(2) = f(2) + g(2)$$
$$= 24 + (-8)$$
$$= 16$$

$$(f - g)(2) = f(2) - g(2)$$
$$= 24 - (-8)$$
$$= 32$$

$$(fg)(2) = f(2)g(2)$$
$$= 24(-8)$$
$$= -192$$

$$\left(\frac{f}{g}\right)(2) = \frac{f(2)}{g(2)}$$
$$= \frac{24}{-8}$$
$$= -3$$

Given formulas for f and g, we can find formulas for the sum, difference, product, and quotient functions by performing the appropriate operation while leaving x as an unknown. We illustrate how this is done in the following example:

EXAMPLE 2   If $f(x) = 4x^2 + 3x + 2$ and $g(x) = 2x^2 - 5x - 6$, write the formulas for the functions $f + g$, $f - g$, fg, and $\frac{f}{g}$.

SOLUTION   The function $f + g$ is defined by

$$(f + g)(x) = f(x) + g(x)$$
$$= (4x^2 + 3x + 2) + (2x^2 - 5x - 6)$$
$$= 6x^2 - 2x - 4$$

The function $f - g$ is defined by

$$(f - g)(x) = f(x) - g(x)$$
$$= (4x^2 + 3x + 2) - (2x^2 - 5x - 6)$$
$$= 4x^2 + 3x + 2 - 2x^2 + 5x + 6$$
$$= 2x^2 + 8x + 8$$

The function fg is defined by

$$(fg)(x) = f(x)g(x)$$
$$= (4x^2 + 3x + 2)(2x^2 - 5x - 6)$$
$$= 8x^4 - 20x^3 - 24x^2 + 6x^3 - 15x^2 - 18x + 4x^2 - 10x - 12$$
$$= 8x^4 - 14x^3 - 35x^2 - 28x - 12$$

The function $\frac{f}{g}$ is defined by

$$\left(\frac{f}{g}\right)(x) = \frac{f(x)}{g(x)}$$
$$= \frac{4x^2 + 3x + 2}{2x^2 - 5x - 6}$$

If we have found the formulas for $f + g$, $f - g$, fg, and $\frac{f}{g}$, then we can, of course, use them to evaluate these functions instead of evaluating f and g individually and then performing the corresponding operation on the outputs. Example 3 illustrates this.

EXAMPLE 3   If f and g are the same functions defined in Example 2, evaluate $(f + g)(2)$ and $(fg)(2)$.

SOLUTION   We use the formulas for $f + g$ and fg found in Example 2:

$$(f + g)(2) = 6(2)^2 - 2(2) - 4$$
$$= 24 - 4 - 4$$
$$= 16$$

$$(fg)(2) = 8(2)^4 - 14(2)^3 - 35(2)^2 - 28(2) - 12$$
$$= 128 - 112 - 140 - 56 - 12$$
$$= -192$$

Notice that these values are in agreement with those we found in Example 1.

Composition of Functions

In addition to the four operations used to combine functions shown so far in this section, there is a fifth way to combine two functions to obtain a new function. It is called *composition of functions*. To illustrate the concept, the definition of training heart rate, in beats per minute, is resting heart rate plus 60% of the difference between maximum heart rate and resting heart rate. If your resting heart rate is 70 beats per minute, then your training heart rate is a function of your maximum heart rate M.

$$T(M) = 70 + 0.6(M - 70) = 70 + 0.6M - 42 = 28 + 0.6M$$

But your maximum heart rate is found by subtracting your age in years from 220. So, if x represents your age in years, then your maximum heart rate is

$$M(x) = 220 - x$$

Therefore, if your resting heart rate is 70 beats per minute and your age in years is x, then your training heart rate can be written as a function of x.

$$T(x) = 28 + 0.6(220 - x)$$

This last line is the composition of functions T and M. We input x into function M, which outputs $M(x)$. Then, we input $M(x)$ into function T, which outputs $T(M(x))$, which is the training heart rate as a function of age x. Here is a diagram, called a function map, of the situation:

Age	Maximum heart rate	Training heart rate

$$x \xrightarrow{\;\;M\;\;} M(x) \xrightarrow{\;\;T\;\;} T(M(x))$$

FIGURE 2

Now let's generalize the preceding ideas into a formal development of composition of functions. To find the composition of two functions f and g, we first require that the range of g have numbers in common with the domain of f. Then the composition of f with g is defined as follows:

> **DEFINITION** *function composition*
>
> If f and g are functions, and if x is in the domain of g and $g(x)$ is in the domain of f, then
>
> $$(f \circ g)(x) = f(g(x))$$

To understand this new function, we begin with a number x, and we operate on it with g, giving us $g(x)$. Then we take $g(x)$ and operate on it with f, giving us $f(g(x))$. The diagrams in Figure 3 illustrate the composition of f with g.

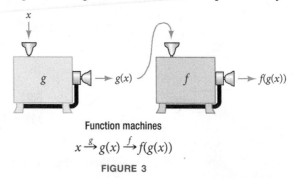

Function machines

$$x \xrightarrow{\;g\;} g(x) \xrightarrow{\;f\;} f(g(x))$$

FIGURE 3

Composition of functions is not commutative. The composition of f with g, $f \circ g$, may therefore be different from the composition of g with f, $g \circ f$.

$$(g \circ f)(x) = g(f(x))$$

The only numbers we can use for the domain of the composition of g with f are numbers in the domain of f, for which $f(x)$ is in the domain of g. The diagrams in Figure 4 illustrate the composition of g with f.

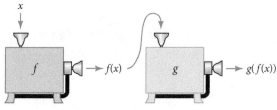

Function machines

$$x \xrightarrow{f} f(x) \xrightarrow{g} g(f(x))$$

FIGURE 4

EXAMPLE 4   If $f(x) = x + 5$ and $g(x) = x^2 - 2x$, find $(f \circ g)(2)$ and $(g \circ f)(2)$.

SOLUTION   To evaluate $(f \circ g)(2)$, we first find $g(2)$.

$$g(2) = (2)^2 - 2(2)$$
$$= 4 - 4$$
$$= 0$$

The output value of 0 from g is now used as an input for f.

$$(f \circ g)(2) = f(g(2))$$
$$= f(0)$$
$$= 0 + 5$$
$$= 5$$

We evaluate $(g \circ f)(2)$ in a similar manner.

Because $f(2) = 2 + 5$
$$= 7$$

we have $(g \circ f)(2) = g(f(2))$
$$= g(7)$$
$$= (7)^2 - 2(7)$$
$$= 49 - 14$$
$$= 35$$

If we repeat the process illustrated in Example 4 but allow x to remain an unknown, then we will find the formulas for the composition functions.

EXAMPLE 5   If $f(x) = x + 5$ and $g(x) = x^2 - 2x$, find $(f \circ g)(x)$ and $(g \circ f)(x)$.

SOLUTION   The composition of f with g is

$$(f \circ g)(x) = f(g(x))$$
$$= f(x^2 - 2x)$$
$$= (x^2 - 2x) + 5$$
$$= x^2 - 2x + 5$$

The composition of g with f is

$$(g \circ f)(x) = g(f(x))$$
$$= g(x + 5)$$
$$= (x + 5)^2 - 2(x + 5)$$
$$= (x^2 + 10x + 25) - 2x - 10$$
$$= x^2 + 8x + 15$$

Now that we have the formulas from Example 5, we could use them to evaluate $f \circ g$ and $g \circ f$. For instance,

$$(f \circ g)(2) = (2)^2 - 2(2) + 5 = 5$$

and

$$(g \circ f)(2) = (2)^2 + 8(2) + 15 = 35$$

which agree with the values we obtained in Example 4.

Using Tables and Graphs

If we are given tables or graphs for two functions, we can still find values for the sum, difference, product, quotient, or composition of the functions even though we may not know their formulas.

EXAMPLE 6   Use the tables shown for functions f and g to find $(f + g)(2)$, $(fg)(1)$, and $(f \circ g)(-2)$.

x	$f(x)$
-2	-3
-1	2
0	6
1	3
2	-1

x	$g(x)$
-2	0
-1	3
0	-4
1	-2
2	5

SOLUTION   From the tables we see that $f(2) = -1$ and $g(2) = 5$. Therefore,

$$(f + g)(2) = f(2) + g(2)$$
$$= -1 + 5$$
$$= 4$$

Also, because $f(1) = 3$ and $g(1) = -2$, we have

$$(fg)(1) = f(1)g(1)$$
$$= 3(-2)$$
$$= -6$$

> **Note**   Be careful not to confuse the composition symbol with a multiplication dot. The notation $f \circ g$ does not mean the product of f and g.

Since $(f \circ g)(-2) = f(g(-2))$, we first find $g(-2) = 0$. We then evaluate f at $x = 0$, because the output from g becomes the input to f. Thus,

$$(f \circ g)(-2) = f(g(-2))$$
$$= f(0)$$
$$= 6$$

EXAMPLE 7   The graphs of functions f and g are shown in Figure 5. Use the graphs to evaluate $(f - g)(-4)$ and $(g \circ f)(1)$.

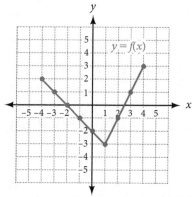 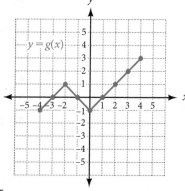

FIGURE 5

SOLUTION From the graphs, we observe that $f(-4) = 2$ and $g(-4) = -1$. Therefore,

$$(f - g)(-4) = f(-4) - g(-4)$$
$$= 2 - (-1)$$
$$= 3$$

Because $f(1) = -3$ and $g(-3) = 0$, we have

$$(g \circ f)(1) = g(f(1))$$
$$= g(-3)$$
$$= 0$$

Getting Ready for Class

After reading through the preceding section, respond in your own words and in complete sentences.

A. How are profit, revenue, and cost related?

B. Explain how you would evaluate the sum function $f + g$ for a given input.

C. For functions f and g, how do you find the composition of f with g?

D. For functions f and g, how do you find the composition of g with f?

Problem Set 9.3

Let $f(x) = 2x + 1$, $g(x) = 4x + 2$, and $h(x) = 4x^2 + 4x + 1$, and find the following.

1. $(f + g)(2)$ **2.** $(f - g)(-1)$ **3.** $(fg)(3)$ **4.** $\left(\dfrac{f}{g}\right)(-3)$

5. $\left(\dfrac{h}{g}\right)(1)$ **6.** $(hg)(1)$ **7.** $(fh)(0)$ **8.** $(h - g)(-4)$

9. $(f + g + h)(2)$ **10.** $(h - f + g)(0)$ **11.** $(h + fg)(3)$ **12.** $(h - fg)(5)$

Let $f(x) = 4x - 3$ and $g(x) = 2x + 5$. Write a formula for each of the following functions.

13. $f + g$ **14.** $f - g$ **15.** $g - f$ **16.** $g + f$

17. fg **18.** $\dfrac{f}{g}$ **19.** $\dfrac{g}{f}$ **20.** ff

If the functions f, g, and h are defined by $f(x) = 3x - 5$, $g(x) = x - 2$ and $h(x) = 3x^2 - 11x + 10$, write a formula for each of the following functions.

21. $g + f$ **22.** $f + h$ **23.** $g + h$ **24.** $f - g$

25. $g - f$ **26.** $h - g$ **27.** fg **28.** gf

29. fh **30.** gh **31.** $\dfrac{h}{f}$ **32.** $\dfrac{h}{g}$

33. $\dfrac{f}{h}$ **34.** $\dfrac{g}{h}$ **35.** $f + g + h$ **36.** $h - g + f$

37. $h + fg$ **38.** $h - fg$

39. If $f(x) = x^2 + 3x$ and $g(x) = 4x - 1$, find

     a. $(f + g)(2)$ by evaluating $f(2)$ and $g(2)$

     b. $(f + g)(x)$

     c. Evaluate your formula from part b at $x = 2$ to verify your answer to part a

40. If $f(x) = 2x - 5$ and $g(x) = 4x^2 + 3$, find

     a. $(f - g)(-1)$ by evaluating $f(-1)$ and $g(-1)$

     b. $(f - g)(x)$

     c. Evaluate your formula from part b at $x = -1$ to verify your answer to part a.

41. If $f(x) = 3x - 2$ and $g(x) = 5x + 4$, find

     a. $(fg)(-2)$

     b. $(fg)(x)$

     c. Evaluate your formula from part b at $x = -2$ to verify your answer to part a.

42. If $f(x) = x^2 - 4$ and $g(x) = x + 2$, find

     a. $\left(\dfrac{f}{g}\right)(3)$ by evaluating $f(3)$ and $g(3)$

     b. $\left(\dfrac{f}{g}\right)(x)$

     c. Evaluate your formula from part b at $x = 3$ to verify your answer to part a.

If $f(x) = 2x + 1$, $g(x) = 4x + 2$, and $h(x) = 4x^2 + 4x + 1$, find the following:

43. $(f \circ g)(-1)$ **44.** $(f \circ h)(-2)$ **45.** $(g \circ h)(1)$ **46.** $(g \circ f)(3)$

47. $(h \circ f)(-3)$ **48.** $(h \circ g)(2)$ **49.** $(g \circ f)(0)$ **50.** $(h \circ f)(0)$

51. Let $f(x) = x^2$ and $g(x) = x + 4$, and find
     a. $(f \circ g)(5)$ **b.** $(g \circ f)(5)$ **c.** $(f \circ g)(x)$ **d.** $(g \circ f)(x)$

52. Let $f(x) = 3 - x$ and $g(x) = x^3 - 1$, and find
     a. $(f \circ g)(0)$ **b.** $(g \circ f)(0)$ **c.** $(f \circ g)(x)$ **d.** $(g \circ f)(x)$

53. Let $f(x) = x^2 + 3x$ and $g(x) = 4x - 1$, and find
     a. $(f \circ g)(0)$ **b.** $(g \circ f)(0)$ **c.** $(f \circ g)(x)$ **d.** $(g \circ f)(x)$

54. Let $f(x) = (x - 2)^2$ and $g(x) = x + 1$, and find the following
     a. $(f \circ g)(-1)$ **b.** $(g \circ f)(-1)$ **c.** $(f \circ g)(x)$ **d.** $(g \circ f)(x)$

For each of the following pairs of functions f and g, show that
$(f \circ g)(x) = (g \circ f)(x) = x$.

55. $f(x) = 5x - 4$ and $g(x) = \dfrac{x + 4}{5}$ **56.** $f(x) = \dfrac{x}{6} - 2$ and $g(x) = 6x + 12$

Use the tables given for functions f and g to find each value in Problems 57–70.

x	-3	-2	-1	0	1	2	3
$f(x)$	4	5	1	-2	-1	0	2

x	-3	-2	-1	0	1	2	3
$g(x)$	3	0	2	-4	-2	1	-1

57. $(f + g)(0)$ **58.** $(g + f)(3)$ **59.** $(g - f)(-2)$ **60.** $(f - g)(1)$

61. $(fg)(-3)$ **62.** $\left(\dfrac{f}{g}\right)(0)$ **63.** $\left(\dfrac{g}{f}\right)(3)$ **64.** $(gf)(2)$

65. $(f \circ g)(-1)$ **66.** $(f \circ g)(-3)$ **67.** $(g \circ f)(2)$ **68.** $(g \circ f)(1)$

69. $(f \circ f)(0)$ **70.** $(g \circ g)(3)$

Use the graphs of $y = f(x)$ and $y = g(x)$ given below to find each value in Problems 71–84.

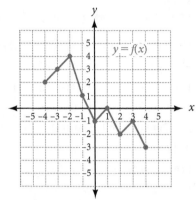

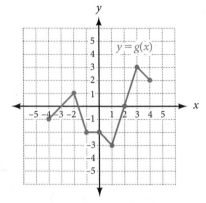

71. $(f - g)(1)$ **72.** $(f + g)(-1)$ **73.** $(g + f)(0)$ **74.** $(g - f)(4)$

75. $(fg)(-3)$ **76.** $\left(\dfrac{f}{g}\right)(3)$ **77.** $\left(\dfrac{g}{f}\right)(-2)$ **78.** $(gf)(2)$

79. $(f \circ g)(0)$ **80.** $(g \circ f)(0)$ **81.** $(g \circ f)(2)$ **82.** $(f \circ g)(-4)$

83. $(f \circ f)(4)$ **84.** $(g \circ g)(-3)$

Applying the Concepts

85. Profit, Revenue, and Cost A company manufactures and sells DVDs. Here are the equations they use in connection with their business.

Number of DVDs sold each day: $n(x) = x$

Selling price for each DVD: $p(x) = 11.5 - 0.05x$

Daily fixed costs: $f(x) = 200$

Daily variable costs: $v(x) = 2x$

Find the following functions.

a. Revenue = $R(x)$ = the product of the number of DVDs sold each day and the selling price of each DVD.

b. Cost = $C(x)$ = the sum of the fixed costs and the variable costs.

c. Profit = $P(x)$ = the difference between revenue and cost.

d. Average cost = $\overline{C}(x)$ = the quotient of cost and the number of DVDs sold each day.

86. **Profit, Revenue, and Cost** A company manufactures and sells CDs for home computers. Here are the equations they use in connection with their business.

Number of CDs sold each day: $n(x) = x$

Selling price for each CD: $p(x) = 3 - \dfrac{1}{300}x$

Daily fixed costs: $f(x) = 200$

Daily variable costs: $v(x) = 2x$

Find the following functions.

a. Revenue = $R(x)$ = the product of the number of CDs sold each day and the selling price of each CD.

b. Cost = $C(x)$ = the sum of the fixed costs and the variable costs.

c. Profit = $P(x)$ = the difference between revenue and cost.

d. Average cost = $\overline{C}(x)$ = the quotient of cost and the number of CDs sold each day.

87. **Training Heart Rate** Recall the heart rate functions discussed earlier in this section. Find the training heart rate function, $T(M)$, for a person with a resting heart rate of 62 beats per minute, then find the following to the nearest whole number.

a. Find the maximum heart rate function, $M(x)$, for a person x years of age.

b. What is the maximum heart rate for a 24-year-old person?

c. What is the training heart rate for a 24-year-old person with a resting heart rate of 62 beats per minute?

d. What is the training heart rate for a 36-year-old person with a resting heart rate of 62 beats per minute?

e. What is the training heart rate for a 48-year-old person with a resting heart rate of 62 beats per minute?

88. **Training Heart Rate** Find the training heart rate function, $T(M)$ for a person with a resting heart rate of 72 beats per minute, then find the following to the nearest whole number.

a. Find the maximum heart rate function, $M(x)$, for a person x years of age.

b. What is the maximum heart rate for a 20-year-old person?

c. What is the training heart rate for a 20-year-old person with a resting heart rate of 72 beats per minute?

d. What is the training heart rate for a 30-year-old person with a resting heart rate of 72 beats per minute?

e. What is the training heart rate for a 40-year-old person with a resting heart rate of 72 beats per minute?

Learning Objectives Assessment

The following problems can be used to help assess if you have successfully met the learning objectives for this section.

89. If $f(x) = 3x - 2$ and $g(x) = 4x + 5$, find $(f + g)(-1)$.

    a. -6 **b.** 3 **c.** -4 **d.** 10

90. If $f(x) = 3x - 2$ and $g(x) = 4x + 5$, find $(f - g)(x)$.

    a. $-x - 7$ **b.** -8 **c.** -7 **d.** $x^2 + 7x$

91. If $f(x) = 3x - 2$ and $g(x) = 4x + 5$, find $(f \circ g)(-2)$.

    a. -3 **b.** 24 **c.** -27 **d.** -11

92. If $f(x) = 3x - 2$ and $g(x) = 4x + 5$, find $(g \circ f)(x)$.

    a. $12x - 3$ **b.** $12x + 13$ **c.** $12x^2 + 7x - 10$ **d.** $12x^2 - 3x$

Getting Ready for the Next Section

Simplify.

93. $2\left(-\dfrac{1}{2}\right)$ **94.** $\dfrac{3 - (-1)}{-3 - 3}$ **95.** $-\dfrac{5 - (-3)}{2 - 6}$ **96.** $3\left(-\dfrac{2}{3}x + 1\right)$

Solve for y.

97. $\dfrac{y - b}{x - 0} = m$ **98.** $2x + 3y = 6$

99. $y - 3 = -2(x + 4)$ **100.** $y + 1 = -\dfrac{2}{3}(x - 3)$

101. If $y = -\dfrac{4}{3}x + 5$, find y when x is 0.

102. If $y = -\dfrac{4}{3}x + 5$, find y when x is 3.

Lines and Linear Functions

Learning Objectives

In this section we will learn how to:

1. Find the slope of a line.

2. Interpret slope as an average rate of change.

3. Write the equation of a line.

4. Graph a linear function.

Introduction

The table and illustrations below show some corresponding temperatures on the Fahrenheit and Celsius temperature scales. For example, water freezes at 32°F and 0°C, and boils at 212°F and 100°C.

Degrees Celsius	Degrees Fahrenheit
0	32
25	77
50	122
75	167
100	212

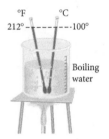

If we plot all the points in the table using the x-axis for temperatures on the Celsius scale and the y-axis for temperatures on the Fahrenheit scale, we see that they line up in a straight line (Figure 1).

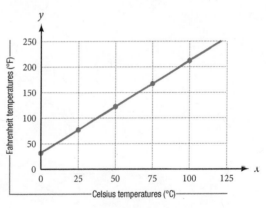

FIGURE 1

The graph shown in Figure 1 is an example of a *linear function*. In this section, we will review the important facts about lines from Chapter 3 and look at linear functions in more detail.

Slope

The slope of a line is a value that allows us to describe the steepness and direction of the line. A line that rises going form left to right has a positive slope. A line that falls going from left to right has a negative slope. A line that neither rises nor falls (a horizontal line) has a slop of zero.

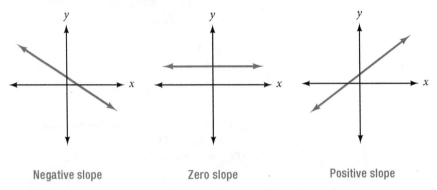

Negative slope   Zero slope   Positive slope

Geometrically, we can define the *slope* of a line as the ratio of the vertical change to the horizontal change encountered when moving from one point to another on the line. The vertical change is sometimes called the *rise*. The horizontal change is called the *run*.

(def) DEFINITION   *slope*

The **slope** of the line passing through the points (x_1, y_1) and (x_2, y_2) is given by

$$\text{Slope} = m = \frac{\text{Rise}}{\text{Run}} = \frac{y_2 - y_1}{x_2 - x_1}$$

Geometric Form   Algebraic Form

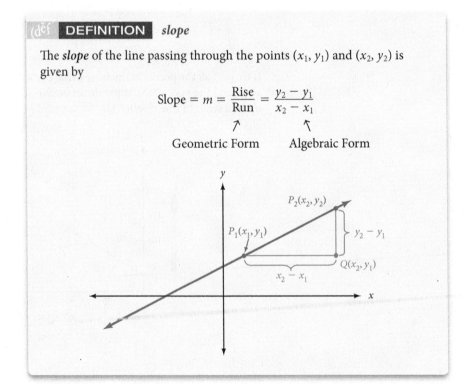

Note The two most common mistakes students make when first working with the formula for the slope of a line are

1. Putting the difference of the *x*-coordinates over the difference of the *y*-coordinates.

2. Subtracting in one order in the numerator and then subtracting in the opposite order in the denominator. You would make this mistake in Example 1 if you wrote $1 - (-3)$ in the numerator and then $-2 - (-5)$ in the denominator.

EXAMPLE 1   Find the slope of the line through $(-2, -3)$ and $(-5, 1)$.

SOLUTION   If we let $(x_1, y_1) = (-2, -3)$ and $(x_2, y_2) = (-5, 1)$, then

$$m = \frac{y_2 - y_1}{x_2 - x_1} = \frac{1 - (-3)}{-5 - (-2)} = \frac{4}{-3} = -\frac{4}{3}$$

Of course, we can also find the slope geometrically using the graph of the line as shown in Figure 2.

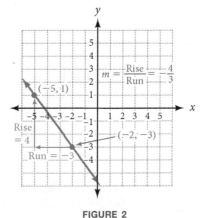

FIGURE 2

We can see the algebraic approach and the geometric approach give the same result.

EXAMPLE 2   Find the slope of the line containing $(3, -1)$ and $(3, 4)$.

SOLUTION   Using the definition for slope, we have

$$m = \frac{-1 - 4}{3 - 3} = \frac{-5}{0}$$

The expression $\frac{-5}{0}$ is undefined. That is, there is no real number to associate with it. In this case, we say the line *has an undefined slope.*

The line in Example 2 is a vertical line. All vertical lines have an undefined slope. (All horizontal lines, as we mentioned earlier, have zero slope.)

Parallel and Perpendicular Lines

In Chapter 3, we introduced the concept of parallel and perpendicular lines. For two lines to be parallel, they must rise or fall at the same rate, which means they have the same slope. Two nonvertical lines are perpendicular if their slopes are negative reciprocals. This means the product of their slopes is -1.

Slope and Rate of Change

So far, the slopes we have worked with represent the ratio of the change in *y* to the corresponding change in *x*, or, on the graph of the line, the slope is the ratio of vertical change to horizontal change in moving from one point on the line to another. However, when our variables represent quantities from the world around us, slope can have additional interpretations.

EXAMPLE 3   On the chart below, find the slope of the line connecting the first point (1955, 0.29) with the last point (2005, 2.93). Explain the significance of the result.

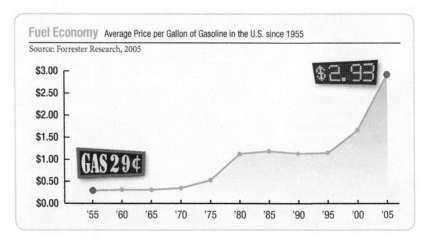

SOLUTION   The slope of the line connecting the first point (1955, 0.29) with the last point (2005, 2.93), is

$$m = \frac{2.93 - 0.29}{2005 - 1955} = \frac{2.64}{50} = 0.0528$$

The units are dollars/year. If we write this in terms of cents we have

$$m = 5.28 \text{ cents/year}$$

which is the average change in the price of a gallon of gasoline over a 50-year period of time.

Slope and Average Speed

EXAMPLE 4   A car is traveling at a constant speed. A graph (Figure 3) of the distance the car has traveled over time is shown below. Use the graph to find the speed of the car.

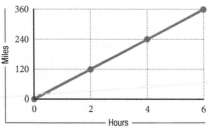

FIGURE 3

SOLUTION   Using the second and third points, we see the rise is $240 - 120 = 120$ miles, and the run is $4 - 2 = 2$ hours. The speed is given by the slope, which is

$$m = \frac{\text{Rise}}{\text{Run}}$$

$$= \frac{120 \text{ miles}}{2 \text{ hours}}$$

$$= 60 \text{ miles per hour}$$

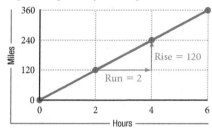

The units of the rise are miles and the units of the run are hours, so the slope will be in units of miles per hour. We see that the slope is simply the change in distance divided by the change in time, which is how we compute the average speed. Since the speed is constant, the slope of the line represents the speed of 60 miles per hour.

Equations of Lines

Recall from Chapter 3 the *slope-intercept form* of the equation of a line.

> **⟨Δ≠Σ⟩ PROPERTY**   *Slope-Intercept Form of the Equation of a Line*
>
> The equation of any line with slope m and y-intercept b is given by
>
> $$y = mx + b$$
>
> Slope y-intercept

When the equation is in this form, the *slope* of the line is always the *coefficient* of x and the y-intercept is always the *constant term*.

EXAMPLE 5   Graph the line $2x + 3y = 6$ using the slope and y-intercept.

SOLUTION   To use the slope-intercept form, we must solve the equation for y in terms of x:

$$2x + 3y = 6$$

$$3y = -2x + 6 \qquad \text{Add } -2x \text{ to both sides}$$

$$y = -\frac{2}{3}x + 2 \qquad \text{Divide by 3}$$

The slope is $m = -\frac{2}{3}$ and the y-intercept is $b = 2$. Therefore, the point $(0, 2)$ is on the graph, and the ratio of rise to run going from $(0, 2)$ to any other point on the line is $-\frac{2}{3}$. If we interpret $-\frac{2}{3}$ as $\frac{-2}{3}$, we can start at $(0, 2)$ and move 2 units down (a rise of -2) and 3 units to the right (a run of 3) to locate another point on the graph. Or, we can interpret $-\frac{2}{3}$ as $\frac{2}{-3}$ and move 2 units up (a rise of 2) and 3 units to the left (a run of -3) from $(0, 2)$ to locate another point. The resulting graph is shown in Figure 4.

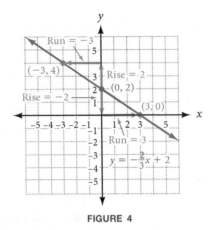

FIGURE 4

EXAMPLE 6   Find the equation of the line with slope $m = 2$ and passing through the point $(1, -3)$.

SOLUTION   We can find the equation using the slope-intercept form. However, because $(1, -3)$ is not on the y-axis, it is not a y-intercept. That is, we cannot assume $b = -3$. But we can use the slope and given point to solve for b.

Using	$m = 2, x = 1,$ and $y = -3$	
in	$y = mx + b$	Slope-intercept form
gives us	$-3 = 2(1) + b$	
	$-3 = 2 + b$	Simplify
	$-5 = b$	Add -2 to both sides

Therefore, the equation of the line is $y = 2x - 5$.

A second useful form of the equation of a line is point-slope form.

> **PROPERTY**   *Point-Slope Form of the Equation of a Line*
>
> The equation of the line through (x_1, y_1) with slope m is given by
> $$y - y_1 = m(x - x_1)$$

This form of the equation of a line is used to find the equation of a line, either given one point on the line and the slope, or given two points on the line.

EXAMPLE 7   Find the equation of the line that passes through the points $(-3, 3)$ and $(3, -1)$.

SOLUTION   We begin by finding the slope of the line:
$$m = \frac{3 - (-1)}{-3 - 3} = \frac{4}{-6} = -\frac{2}{3}$$

Using $(x_1, y_1) = (3, -1)$ and $m = -\frac{2}{3}$ in $y - y_1 = m(x - x_1)$ yields

$$y + 1 = -\frac{2}{3}(x - 3)$$

$$y + 1 = -\frac{2}{3}x + 2 \qquad \text{Multiply out right side}$$

$$y = -\frac{2}{3}x + 1 \qquad \text{Add } -1 \text{ to each side}$$

Note We could have used the point $(-3, 3)$ instead of $(3, -1)$ and obtained the same equation. That is, using $(x_1, y_1) = (-3, 3)$ and $m = -\frac{2}{3}$ in

$$y - y_1 = m(x - x_1)$$

gives us

$$y - 3 = -\frac{2}{3}(x + 3)$$

$$y - 3 = -\frac{2}{3}x - 2$$

$$y = -\frac{2}{3}x + 1$$

which is the same result we obtained using $(3, -1)$.

Figure 5 shows the graph of the line that passes through the points $(-3, 3)$ and $(3, -1)$. As you can see, the slope and y-intercept are $-\frac{2}{3}$ and 1, respectively.

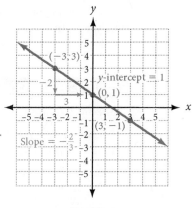

FIGURE 5

The last form of the equation of a line that we will consider in this section is called the *standard form*. It is used mainly to write equations in a form that is free of fractions and is easy to compare with other equations.

[△≠Σ] PROPERTY *Standard Form for the Equation of a Line*

If a, b, and c are integers with $a \geq 0$, then the equation of a line is in standard form when it has the form

$$ax + by = c$$

EXAMPLE 8 Give the equation of the line through $(-1, 4)$ whose graph is perpendicular to the graph of $2x - y = -3$. Write the answer in standard form.

SOLUTION To find the slope of $2x - y = -3$, we solve for y:

$$2x - y = -3$$

$$y = 2x + 3$$

The slope of this line is 2. The line we are interested in is perpendicular to the line with slope 2 and must, therefore, have a slope of $-\frac{1}{2}$.

Using $(x_1, y_1) = (-1, 4)$ and $m = -\frac{1}{2}$, we have

$$y - y_1 = m(x - x_1)$$

$$y - 4 = -\frac{1}{2}(x + 1)$$

Because we want our answer in standard form, we multiply each side by 2.

$$2y - 8 = -1(x + 1)$$

$$2y - 8 = -x - 1$$

$$x + 2y - 8 = -1$$

$$x + 2y = 7$$

The last equation is in standard form.

As a final note, the following summary reminds us that all horizontal lines have equations of the form $y = b$, and slopes of 0. Since they cross the y-axis at b, the y-intercept is b; there is no x-intercept. Vertical lines have an undefined slope, and equations of the form $x = a$. Each will have an x-intercept at a, and no y-intercept. Finally, equations of the form $y = mx$ have graphs that pass through the origin. The slope is always m and both the x-intercept and the y-intercept are 0.

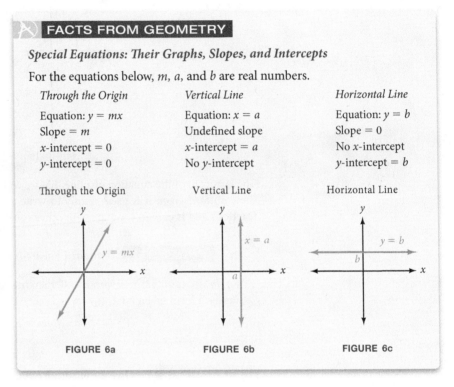

FACTS FROM GEOMETRY

Special Equations: Their Graphs, Slopes, and Intercepts

For the equations below, m, a, and b are real numbers.

Through the Origin	*Vertical Line*	*Horizontal Line*
Equation: $y = mx$	Equation: $x = a$	Equation: $y = b$
Slope $= m$	Undefined slope	Slope $= 0$
x-intercept $= 0$	x-intercept $= a$	No x-intercept
y-intercept $= 0$	No y-intercept	y-intercept $= b$

Through the Origin	Vertical Line	Horizontal Line
FIGURE 6a	FIGURE 6b	FIGURE 6c

We conclude this section by taking another look at the equation of a line from a function perspective.

Linear Functions

Previously, we mentioned the slope-intercept form of a line, $y = mx + b$. As long as the slope is defined (the line is not vertical), the graph of the line will pass the vertical line test. Therefore, every non-vertical line represents a function. This leads us to the following definition.

DEFINITION   *linear function*

A **linear function** is any function that can be expressed in the form

$$f(x) = mx + b$$

The graph of f is a line with slope m passing through the y-axis at $(0, b)$.

EXAMPLE 9   The average price per gallon for gasoline between the years 2002 and 2008 can be modeled by the linear function

$$f(x) = 0.32x + 0.76$$

where x is the number of years from 2000 and $f(x)$ is the average price in dollars per gallon.   (*Source*: U.S. Department of Energy)

a. Graph the function.

b. Evaluate $f(8)$ and explain what it means in practical terms.

c. Based on this model, what would we expect the price of gasoline to be in the year 2020?

SOLUTION

a. The graph, shown in Figure 7, is a line with slope $m = 0.32$ and y-intercept $(0, 0.76)$.

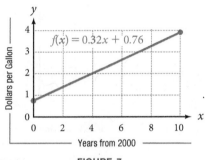

FIGURE 7

b. $f(8) = 0.32(8) + 0.76 = 3.32$

In 2008 (8 years after 2000) the average price of gasoline was $3.32 per gallon.

c. For the year 2020 we use $x = 20$, so

$$f(20) = 0.32(20) + 0.76 = 7.16$$

The expected price of gasoline is $7.16 per gallon.

Getting Ready for Class

After reading through the preceding section, respond in your own words and in complete sentences.

A. Would you rather climb a hill with a slope of $\frac{1}{2}$ or a slope of 3? Explain why.

B. How would you graph the line $y = \frac{1}{2}x + 3$?

C. Describe how you would find the equation of a line if you knew the slope and a point on the line.

D. What is a linear function?

Problem Set 9.4

Find the slope of each of the following lines from the given graph.

1.

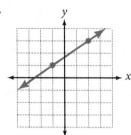

2.

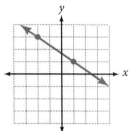

3.

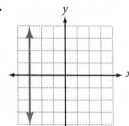

4.

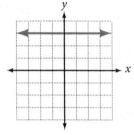

Find the slope of the line through each of the following pairs of points. Then, plot each pair of points, draw a line through them, and indicate the rise and run in the graph in the manner shown in Example 1.

5. $(2, 1), (4, 4)$ **6.** $(3, 1), (5, 6)$ **7.** $(-3, 5), (1, -1)$

8. $(-2, -1), (3, -5)$ **9.** $(-4, 6), (2, 6)$ **10.** $(2, -3), (2, 7)$

Solve for the indicated variable if the line through the two given points has the given slope.

11. $(a, 3)$ and $(2, 6)$, $m = -1$ **12.** $(-4, y)$ and $(-1, 6y)$, $m = 2$

For each of the equations in Problems 13–16, complete the table, and then use the results to find the slope of the graph of the equation.

13. $2x + 3y = 6$ **14.** $3x - 2y = 6$ **15.** $y = \dfrac{2}{3}x - 5$ **16.** $y = -\dfrac{3}{4}x + 2$

x	y
0	
	0

x	y
0	
	0

x	y
0	
3	

x	y
0	
4	

17. **Finding Slope from Intercepts** Graph the line that has an x-intercept of 3 and a y-intercept of -2. What is the slope of this line?

18. **Finding Slope from Intercepts** Graph the line with x-intercept -4 and y-intercept -2. What is the slope of this line?

19. **Finding Slope from Intercepts** A line has an x-intercept of -1 and no y-intercept. What is the slope of this line?

20. **Finding Slope from Intercepts** A line has a y-intercept of 6 and no x-intercept. What is the slope of this line?

21. **Parallel Lines** Find the slope of any line parallel to the line through $(2, 3)$ and $(-8, 1)$.

22. **Parallel Lines** Find the slope of any line parallel to the line through $(2, 5)$ and $(5, -3)$.

23. **Perpendicular Lines** Line l contains the points $(-2, -5)$ and $(1, -3)$. Find the slope of any line perpendicular to l.

24. **Perpendicular Lines** Line l contains the points $(6, -3)$ and $(-2, 7)$. Find the slope of any line perpendicular to l.

25. Determine if each of the following tables could represent ordered pairs from an equation of a line.

a.

x	y
0	5
1	7
2	9
3	11

b.

x	y
-2	-5
0	-2
2	0
4	1

26. The following lines have slope 2, $\frac{1}{2}$, 0, and -1. Match each line to its slope value.

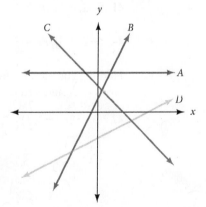

Give the equation of the line with the following slope and y-intercept.

27. $m = -4, b = -3$ **28.** $m = -\dfrac{2}{3}, b = 0$ **29.** $m = 0, b = \dfrac{3}{4}$

30. $m = \dfrac{5}{12}, b = -\dfrac{3}{2}$

Find the slope of a line **a.** parallel and **b.** perpendicular to the given line.

31. $y = 3x - 4$ **32.** $y = -4x + 1$ **33.** $2x + 5y = -11$

34. $3x - 5y = -4$

Give the slope and y-intercept for each of the following equations. Sketch the graph using the slope and y-intercept. Give the slope of any line perpendicular to the given line.

35. $y = 3x - 2$ **36.** $y = 2x + 3$ **37.** $2x - 3y = 12$

38. $4x + 5y = 20$

For each of the following lines, name the slope and y-intercept. Then write the equation of the line in slope-intercept form.

39.

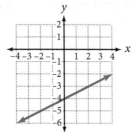

40.

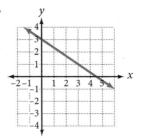

For each of the following problems, the slope and one point on the line are given. In each case, find the equation of that line and write your answer in slope-intercept form.

41. $(-2, -5); m = 2$ **42.** $(-2, 1); m = -\dfrac{1}{2}$ **43.** $\left(-\dfrac{2}{3}, 5\right); m = -3$

44. $(-4, -3), m = \dfrac{1}{6}$ **45.** $(5, 6), m = 0$ **46.** $(-8, -1), m = 0$

Find the equation of the line that passes through each pair of points. Write your answers in standard form.

47. $(3, -2), (-2, 1)$ **48.** $(-6, -2), (-3, -6)$ **49.** $\left(-2, \dfrac{1}{2}\right), \left(-4, \dfrac{1}{3}\right)$

50. $\left(\dfrac{1}{3}, -\dfrac{1}{5}\right), \left(-\dfrac{1}{3}, -1\right)$ **51.** $\left(\dfrac{3}{4}, 2\right), \left(-\dfrac{1}{6}, 2\right)$ **52.** $(5, 3), (5, -1)$

For each of the following lines, name the coordinates of any two points on the line. Then use those two points to find the equation of the line. Write your answer in slope-intercept form.

53.

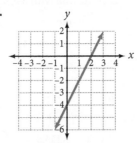

54.

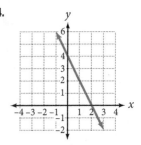

55.

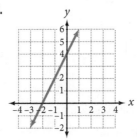

56.

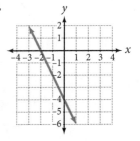

57. The equation $3x - 2y = 10$ is a linear equation in standard form. From this equation, answer the following:

   a. Find the x- and y-intercepts

   b. Find a solution to this equation other than the intercepts in part a.

   c. Write this equation in slope-intercept form

   d. Is the point $(2, 2)$ a solution to the equation?

58. The equation $4x + 3y = 8$ is a linear equation in standard form. From this equation, answer the following:

   a. Find the x- and y-intercepts

   b. Find a solution to this equation other than the intercepts in part a.

   c. Write this equation in slope-intercept form

   d. Is the point $(-3, 2)$ a solution to the equation?

59. Graph each of the following lines. In each case, name the slope, the x-intercept, and the y-intercept.

   a. $y = \dfrac{1}{2}x$ **b.** $x = 3$ **c.** $y = -2$

60. Graph each of the following lines. In each case, name the slope, the x-intercept, and the y-intercept.

   a. $y = -2x$ **b.** $x = 2$ **c.** $y = -4$

For problems 61-66, write the equation of the line in standard form.

61. Find the equation of the line parallel to the graph of $3x - y = 5$ that contains the point $(-1, 4)$.

62. Line l is perpendicular to the graph of the equation $2x - 5y = 10$ and contains the point $(-4, -3)$. Find the equation for l.

63. Give the equation of the line perpendicular to the graph of $y = -4x + 2$ that has an x-intercept of -1.

64. Write the equation of the line parallel to the graph of $7x - 2y = 14$ that has an x-intercept of 5.

65. Find the equation of the line with x-intercept 3 and y-intercept 2.

66. Find the equation of the line with x-intercept 2 and y-intercept 3.

67. Paying Attention to Instructions Work each problem according to the instructions given:

    a. Solve: $-2x + 1 = -3$ **b.** Find x when y is 0: $-2x + y = -3$

    c. Find y when x is 0: $-2x + y = -3$ **d.** Graph: $-2x + y = -3$

    e. Solve for y: $-2x + y = -3$

68. Paying Attention to Instructions Work each problem according to the instructions given:

    a. Solve: $\frac{x}{3} + \frac{1}{4} = 1$ **b.** Find x when y is 0: $\frac{x}{3} + \frac{y}{4} = 1$

    c. Find y when x is 0: $\frac{x}{3} + \frac{y}{4} = 1$ **d.** Graph: $\frac{x}{3} + \frac{y}{4} = 1$

    e. Solve for y: $\frac{x}{3} + \frac{y}{4} = 1$

69. Graph the linear function $f(x) = \frac{1}{2}x + 2$. Then use the graph to evaluate $f(4)$.

70. Graph the linear function $f(x) = -\frac{1}{2}x + 6$. Then use the graph to evaluate $f(4)$.

71. If f is a linear function, and $f(0) = 2$ and $f(6) = 0$, find the equation for f. Write your answer using function notation.

72. If g is a linear function, and $g(-2) = -4$ and $g(4) = 5$, find the equation for g. Write your answer using function notation.

Applying the Concepts

An object is traveling at a constant speed. The distance and time data are shown on the given graph. Use the graph to find the speed of the object.

73.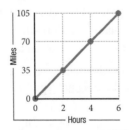

74.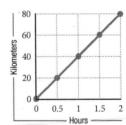

75. **Heating a Block of Ice** A block of ice with an initial temperature of $-20°C$ is heated at a steady rate. The graph shows how the temperature changes as the ice melts to become water and the water boils to become steam and water.

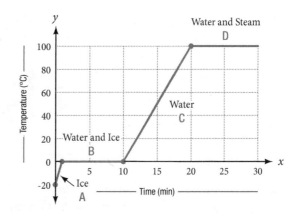

a. How long does it take all the ice to melt?

b. From the time the heat is applied to the block of ice, how long is it before the water boils?

c. Find the slope of the line segment labeled A. What units would you attach to this number?

d. Find the slope of the line segment labeled C. Be sure to attach units to your answer.

e. Is the temperature changing faster during the 1st minute or the 16th minute?

76. **Solar Energy** The graph below shows the annual shipments of solar thermal collectors in the United States. Using the graph below, find the slope of the line connecting the first (1997, 8,000) and last (2006, 20,000) endpoints and then explain in words what the slope represents.

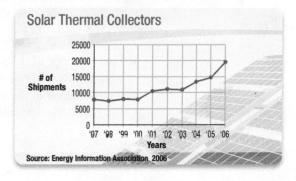

77. Light Bulbs The chart shows a comparison of power usage between incandescent and energy efficient light bulbs. Use the chart to work the following problems involving slope.

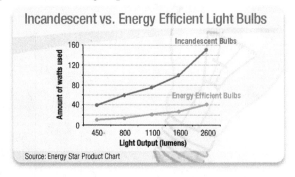

Incandescent vs. Energy Efficient Light Bulbs

Source: Energy Star Product Chart

a. Find the slope of the line for the incandescent bulb from the two endpoints and then explain in words what the slope represents.

b. Find the slope of the line for the energy efficient bulb from the two endpoints and then explain in words what the slope represents.

c. Which light bulb is better? Why?

78. Horse Racing The graph shows the amount of money bet on horse racing from 1985 to 2005. Use the chart to work the following problems involving slope.

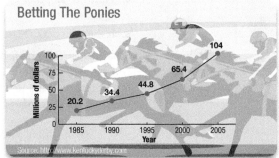

Betting The Ponies

Source: http://www.kentuckyderby.com

a. Find the slope of the line from 1985 to 1990, and then explain in words what the slope represents.

b. Find the slope of the line from 2000 to 2005, and then explain in words what the slope represents.

79. Deriving the Temperature Equation The table below resembles the table from the introduction to this section. The rows of the table give us ordered pairs (C, F).

Degrees Celsius	Degrees Fahrenheit
C	F
0	32
25	77
50	122
75	167
100	212

a. Use any two of the ordered pairs from the table to derive the equation $F = \frac{9}{5}C + 32$.

b. Use the equation from part a to find the Fahrenheit temperature that corresponds to a Celsius temperature of 30°.

80. Maximum Heart Rate The table below gives the maximum heart rate for adults 30, 40, 50, and 60 years old. Each row of the table gives us an ordered pair (A, M).

Age (years)	Maximum Heart Rate (beats per minute)
A	M
30	190
40	180
50	170
60	160

a. Use any two of the ordered pairs from the table to derive the equation $M = 220 - A$, which gives the maximum heart rate M for an adult whose age is A.

b. Use the equation from part a to find the maximum heart rate for a 25-year-old adult.

81. Length of a Spring The linear function $L(x) = 0.03x + 12$ gives the length of a spring, $L(x)$, in centimeters, when a weight of x grams is added to the spring.

a. What is the normal length of the spring with no weight attached?

b. What will be the length of the spring if 200 grams of weight is attached?

c. How much weight will cause the spring to double in length?

d. Graph the function for $0 \leq x \leq 500$.

Straight-Line Depreciation Straight-line depreciation is an accounting method used to help spread the cost of new equipment over a number of years. It takes into account both the cost when new and the salvage value, which is the value of the equipment at the time it gets replaced.

82. **Value of a Copy Machine** The linear function $V(t) = -3{,}300t + 18{,}000$, where V is value and t is time in years, can be used to find the value of a large copy machine during the first 5 years of use.

    a. What is the value of the copier after 3 years and 9 months?

    b. What is the salvage value of this copier if it is replaced after 5 years?

    c. State the domain of this function.

    d. Sketch the graph of this function.

    e. What is the range of this function?

    f. After how many years will the copier be worth only $10,000?

83. **Spring Length** The table below shows the data from the table in the introduction to this chapter, where w is the weight applied to a spring and s is the amount the spring stretches as a result of that weight. Each row of the table gives us an ordered pair (w, s).

Weight (pounds)	Stretch (cm)
w	s
2	2.8
4	5.6
6	8.4
8	11.2

    a. Use any two ordered pairs from the table to find an equation of the linear function $s = f(w)$.

    b. Use your equation to find the amount by which the spring will stretch if 11 pounds of weight is added to the spring.

84. **Spring Length** The table below gives the length of a spring after various weights are added onto the spring. Each row of the table gives us an ordered pair (W, L).

Weight (pounds)	Length of Spring (cm)
W	L
0.5	5.95
1	7.3
1.5	8.65
2	10

    a. Use any two ordered pairs from the table to find an equation of the linear function $L = f(w)$.

    b. What is the normal length of the spring (with no weight attached)?

85. **Textbook Cost** To produce this textbook, suppose the publisher spent $125,000 for typesetting and $6.50 per book for printing and binding. The total cost to produce and print n books can be written as

$$C(n) = 125,000 + 6.5n$$

a. Suppose the number of books printed in the first printing is 10,000. What is the total cost?

b. If the average cost is the total cost divided by the number of books printed, find the average cost of producing 10,000 textbooks.

c. Find the cost to produce one more textbook when you have already produced 10,000 textbooks.

86. **Exercise Heart Rate** In an aerobics class, the instructor indicates that her students' exercise heart rate is 60% of their maximum heart rate, where maximum heart rate is 220 minus their age.

a. Determine the equation that gives exercise heart rate E as a function of age A.

b. Use the equation to find the exercise heart rate of a 22-year-old student.

c. Sketch the graph of the function for students from 18 to 80 years of age.

Learning Objectives Assessment

The following problems can be used to help assess if you have successfully met the learning objectives for this section.

87. Find the slope of the line passing through the points $(4, 5)$ and $(-2, -5)$.

a. $\dfrac{3}{5}$ b. $\dfrac{5}{3}$ c. $-\dfrac{3}{5}$ d. $-\dfrac{5}{3}$

88. At 9:00 a.m. the temperature was 65°F, and by 3:00 p.m. the temperature had risen to 89°F. Which of the following gives the average rate at which the temperature is increasing?

a. 24°F   b. 6 hours   c. 4°F/hr   d. 0.25°F/hr

89. Use the point-slope form to find the equation of the line passing through $(-2, 3)$ and $(1, -1)$.

a. $y + 1 = -\dfrac{3}{4}(x - 1)$ b. $y + 2 = -\dfrac{3}{4}(x - 3)$

c. $y + 2 = -\dfrac{4}{3}(x - 3)$ d. $y + 1 = -\dfrac{4}{3}(x - 1)$

90. In graphing the linear function $f(x) = \dfrac{2}{5}x - 1$, which of the following correctly describes how to locate a second point on the graph?

a. From $(0, -1)$, go up 5 units and right 2 units.

b. From $(-1, 0)$, go up 5 units and right 2 units.

c. From $(0, -1)$, go up 2 units and right 5 units.

d. From $(-1, 0)$, go up 2 units and right 5 units.

Getting Ready for the Next Section

Simplify.

91. $16(3.5)^2$ **92.** $\dfrac{2{,}400}{100}$ **93.** $\dfrac{180}{45}$ **94.** $4(2)(4)^2$

95. $\dfrac{0.0005(200)}{(0.25)^2}$ **96.** $\dfrac{0.2(0.5)^2}{100}$

97. If $y = Kx$, find K if $x = 5$ and $y = 15$.

98. If $d = Kt^2$, find K if $t = 2$ and $d = 64$.

99. If $P = \dfrac{K}{V}$, find K if $P = 48$ and $V = 50$.

100. If $y = Kxz^2$, find K if $x = 5$, $z = 3$, and $y = 180$.

Learning Objectives

In this section we will learn how to:

1. Solve a direct variation problem.

2. Solve an inverse variation problem.

3. Solve problems involving joint or combined variations.

4. Solve applied problems involving variation.

Introduction

If you are a runner and you average t minutes for every mile you run during one of your workouts, then your speed s in miles per hour is given by the equation and graph shown here. The graph (Figure 1) is shown in the first quadrant only because both t and s are positive.

$$s = \frac{60}{t}$$

Input	Output
t	s
4	15
6	10
8	7.5
10	6
12	5
14	4.3

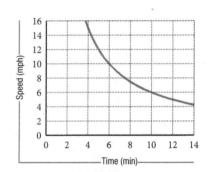

FIGURE 1

You know intuitively that as your average time per mile t increases, your speed s decreases. Likewise, lowering your time per mile will increase your speed. The equation and Figure 1 also show this to be true: Increasing t decreases s, and decreasing t increases s. Quantities that are connected in this way are said to *vary inversely* with each other. Inverse variation is one of the topics we will study in this section.

There are two main types of variation: *direct variation* and *inverse variation*. Variation problems are most common in the sciences, particularly in chemistry and physics.

Direct Variation

When we say the variable y *varies directly* with the variable x, we mean that the relationship can be written in symbols as $y = Kx$, where K is a nonzero constant called the *constant of variation* (or *proportionality constant*).

Another way of saying y varies directly with x is to say y is *directly proportional* to x.

Study the following list. It gives the mathematical equivalent of some direct variation statements.

Verbal Phrase	Algebraic Equation
y varies directly with x.	$y = Kx$
s varies directly with the square of t.	$s = Kt^2$
y is directly proportional to the cube of z.	$y = Kz^3$
u is directly proportional to the square root of v.	$u = K\sqrt{v}$

VIDEO EXAMPLES

SECTION 9.5

EXAMPLE 1   If y varies directly with x, and y is 15 when x is 5, find y when x is 7.

SOLUTION   The first part of the sentence gives us the general relationship between x and y. The equation equivalent to the statement "y varies directly with x" is

$$y = Kx$$

The second part of the sentence in our example gives us the information necessary to evaluate the constant K:

When $y = 15$

and $x = 5$

the equation $y = Kx$

becomes $15 = K \cdot 5$

or $K = 3$

The equation can now be written specifically as

$$y = 3x$$

We can now determine the value asked for in the third part of the sentence. Letting $x = 7$, we have

$$y = 3 \cdot 7$$
$$y = 21$$

Notice that the equation $y = 3x$ from Example 1 is a linear equation. The graph of $y = 3x$ is a line with slope $m = 3$ passing through the origin.

In general, the direct variation $y = Kx$ represents a linear function whose graph is a line that passes through the origin. The variation constant K is the slope of this line, or the rate of change in y with respect to x.

The reverse is also true. Any linear function having a y-intercept of 0 will be a direct variation with K given by the slope.

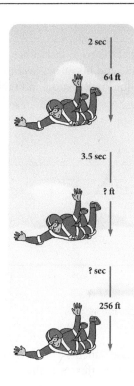

2 sec

64 ft

3.5 sec

? ft

? sec

256 ft

EXAMPLE 2   A skydiver jumps from a plane. Like any object that falls toward earth, the distance the skydiver falls is directly proportional to the square of the time he has been falling, until he reaches his terminal velocity. If the skydiver falls 64 feet in the first 2 seconds of the jump, then

a. How far will he have fallen after 3.5 seconds?
b. Graph the relationship between distance and time.
c. How long will it take him to fall 256 feet?

SOLUTION   We let t represent the time the skydiver has been falling, then we can let $d(t)$ represent the distance he has fallen.

a. Since $d(t)$ is directly proportional to the square of t, we have the general function that describes this situation:

$$d(t) = Kt^2$$

Next, we use the fact that $d(2) = 64$ to find K.

$$64 = K(2)^2$$

$$K = 16$$

The specific equation that describes this situation is

$$d(t) = 16t^2$$

To find how far a skydiver will fall after 3.5 seconds, we find $d(3.5)$,

$$d(3.5) = 16(3.5)^2$$

$$d(3.5) = 196$$

A skydiver will fall 196 feet after 3.5 seconds.

b. To graph this equation, we use a table:

Input	Output
t	$d(t)$
0	0
1	16
2	64
3	144
4	256
5	400

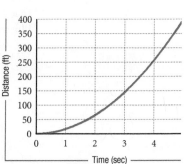

FIGURE 2

c. From the table or the graph (Figure 2), we see that it will take 4 seconds for the skydiver to fall 256 feet.

Inverse Variation

From the introduction to this section, we know that the relationship between the number of minutes t it takes a person to run a mile and his or her average speed in miles per hour s can be described with the following equation and table, and with Figure 3.

$$s = \frac{60}{t}$$

Input	Output
t	s
4	15
6	10
8	7.5
10	6
12	5
14	4.3

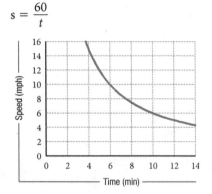

FIGURE 3

If t decreases, then s will increase, and if t increases, then s will decrease. The variable s is *inversely proportional* to the variable t. In this case, the *constant of proportionality* is 60.

Another example of inverse variation can be found in photography. If you are familiar with the terminology and mechanics associated with photography, you know that the f-stop for a particular lens will increase as the aperture (the maximum diameter of the opening of the lens) decreases. In mathematics, we say that f-stop and aperture vary inversely with each other. The following diagram illustrates this relationship.

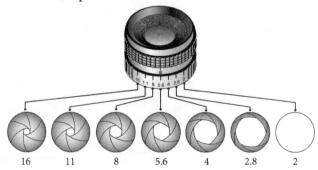

If f is the f-stop and d is the aperture, then their relationship can be written

$$f = \frac{K}{d}$$

In this case, K is the constant of proportionality. (Those of you familiar with photography know that K is also the focal length of the camera lens.)

We generalize this discussion of inverse variation as follows: If y varies inversely with x, then

$$y = K\frac{1}{x} \qquad \text{or} \qquad y = \frac{K}{x}$$

We can also say y is inversely proportional to x. The constant K is again called the constant of variation or proportionality constant.

Verbal Phrase	Algebraic Equation
y is inversely proportional to x.	$y = \dfrac{K}{x}$
s varies inversely with the square of t.	$s = \dfrac{K}{t^2}$
y is inversely proportional to x^4.	$y = \dfrac{K}{x^4}$
z varies inversely with the cube root of t.	$z = \dfrac{K}{\sqrt[3]{t}}$

EXAMPLE 3   The volume of a gas is inversely proportional to the pressure of the gas on its container. If a pressure of 48 pounds per square inch corresponds to a volume of 50 cubic feet, what pressure is needed to produce a volume of 100 cubic feet?

SOLUTION   We can represent volume with V and pressure with P:

$$V = \frac{K}{P}$$

Using $P = 48$ and $V = 50$, we have

$$50 = \frac{K}{48}$$

$$K = 50(48)$$

$$K = 2{,}400$$

The equation that describes the relationship between P and V is

$$V = \frac{2{,}400}{P}$$

Here is a graph of this relationship.

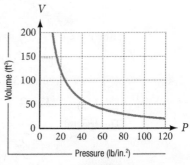

FIGURE 4

Note   The relationship between pressure and volume as given in this example is known as Boyle's law and applies to situations such as those encountered in a piston-cylinder arrangement. It was Robert Boyle (1627–1691) who, in 1662, published the results of some of his experiments that showed, among other things, that the volume of a gas decreases as the pressure increases. This is an example of inverse variation.

Substituting $V = 100$ into our last equation, we get

$$100 = \frac{2{,}400}{P}$$

$$100P = 2{,}400$$

$$P = \frac{2{,}400}{100}$$

$$P = 24$$

A volume of 100 cubic feet is produced by a pressure of 24 pounds per square inch.

Joint Variation and Other Variation Combinations

Many times relationships among different quantities are described in terms of more than two variables. If the variable y varies directly with *two* other variables, say x and z, then we say y varies *jointly* with x and z. In addition to *joint variation*, there are many other combinations of direct and inverse variation involving more than two variables.

The following table is a list of some variation statements and their equivalent mathematical forms:

Verbal Phrase	Algebraic Equation
y varies jointly with x and z.	$y = Kxz$
z varies jointly with r and the square of s.	$z = Krs^2$
V is directly proportional to T and inversely proportional to P.	$V = \dfrac{KT}{P}$
F varies jointly with m_1 and m_2 and inversely with the square of r.	$F = \dfrac{Km_1 m_2}{r^2}$

EXAMPLE 4 y varies jointly with x and the square of z. When x is 5 and z is 3, y is 180. Find y when x is 2 and z is 4.

SOLUTION   The general equation is given by

$$y = Kxz^2$$

Substituting $x = 5$, $z = 3$, and $y = 180$, we have

$$180 = K(5)(3)^2$$

$$180 = 45K$$

$$K = 4$$

The specific equation is

$$y = 4xz^2$$

When $x = 2$ and $z = 4$, the last equation becomes

$$y = 4(2)(4)^2$$

$$y = 128$$

EXAMPLE 5 In electricity, the resistance of a cable is directly proportional to its length and inversely proportional to the square of the diameter. If a 100-foot cable 0.5 inch in diameter has a resistance of 0.2 ohm, what will be the resistance of a cable made from the same material if it is 200 feet long with a diameter of 0.25 inch?

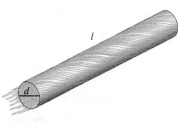

SOLUTION Let R = resistance, l = length, and d = diameter. The equation is

$$R = \frac{Kl}{d^2}$$

When $R = 0.2$, $l = 100$, and $d = 0.5$, the equation becomes

$$0.2 = \frac{K(100)}{(0.5)^2}$$

or

$$K = 0.0005$$

Using this value of K in our original equation, the result is

$$R = \frac{0.0005l}{d^2}$$

When $l = 200$ and $d = 0.25$, the equation becomes

$$R = \frac{0.0005(200)}{(0.25)^2}$$

$$R = 1.6 \text{ ohms}$$

Getting Ready for Class

After reading through the preceding section, respond in your own words and in complete sentences.

A. Give an example of a direct variation statement, and then translate it into symbols.

B. Translate the equation $y = \frac{K}{x}$ into words.

C. For the inverse variation equation $y = \frac{3}{x}$ what happens to the values of y as x gets larger?

D. How are direct variation statements and linear equations in two variables related?

Problem Set 9.5

For the following problems, determine whether the equation represents a direct, inverse, or joint variation, and identify the constant of variation, K.

1. $y = \dfrac{3}{x}$

2. $y = 12x$

3. $C = 2\pi r$

4. $L = \dfrac{4}{d^2}$

5. $A = \dfrac{1}{2}bh$

6. $A = \pi r^2$

7. $S = 0.5\sqrt{d}$

8. $F = \dfrac{m_1 m_2}{9}$

Express each of the following sentences symbolically as an equation.

9. z is directly proportional to the square root of x.

10. y varies inversely with the cube of r.

11. F varies directly with the square of m and inversely with d.

12. p is jointly proportional to C and the square of t.

13. A varies jointly with h and the sum of a and b.

14. m varies directly with d and inversely with the square root of l.

For the following problems, y varies directly with x.

15. If y is 10 when x is 2, find y when x is 6.

16. If y is -32 when x is 4, find x when y is -40.

For the following problems, r is inversely proportional to s.

17. If r is -3 when s is 4, find r when s is 2.

18. If r is 8 when s is 3, find s when r is 48.

For the following problems, d varies directly with the square of r.

19. If $d = 10$ when $r = 5$, find d when $r = 10$.

20. If $d = 12$ when $r = 6$, find d when $r = 9$.

For the following problems, y varies inversely with the square of x.

21. If $y = 45$ when $x = 3$, find y when x is 5.

22. If $y = 12$ when $x = 2$, find y when x is 6.

For the following problems, z varies jointly with x and the square of y.

23. If z is 54 when x and y are 3, find z when $x = 2$ and $y = 4$.

24. If z is 27 when $x = 6$ and $y = 3$, find x when $z = 50$ and $y = 4$.

For the following problems, I varies inversely with the cube of w.

25. If $I = 32$ when $w = \dfrac{1}{2}$, find I when $w = \dfrac{1}{3}$.

26. If $I = \dfrac{1}{25}$ when $w = 5$, find I when $w = 10$.

For the following problems, z varies jointly with y and the square of x.

27. If $z = 72$ when $x = 3$ and $y = 2$, find z when $x = 5$ and $y = 3$.

28. If $z = 240$ when $x = 4$ and $y = 5$, find z when $x = 6$ and $y = 3$.

29. If $x = 1$ when $z = 25$ and $y = 5$, find x when $z = 160$ and $y = 8$.

30. If $x = 4$ when $z = 96$ and $y = 2$, find x when $z = 108$ and $y = 1$.

For the following problems, F varies directly with m and inversely with the square of d.

31. If $F = 150$ when $m = 240$ and $d = 8$, find F when $m = 360$ and $d = 3$.

32. If $F = 72$ when $m = 50$ and $d = 5$, find F when $m = 80$ and $d = 6$.

33. If $d = 5$ when $F = 24$ and $m = 20$, find d when $F = 18.75$ and $m = 40$.

34. If $d = 4$ when $F = 75$ and $m = 20$, find d when $F = 200$ and $m = 120$.

Applying the Concepts

35. Length of a Spring The length a spring stretches is directly proportional to the force applied. If a force of 5 pounds stretches a spring 7 inches, how much force is necessary to stretch the same spring 10 inches?

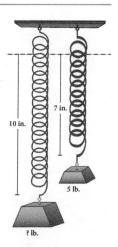

36. Weight and Surface Area The weight of a certain material varies directly with the surface area of that material. If 8 square feet weighs half a pound, how much will 10 square feet weigh?

37. Pressure and Temperature The temperature of a gas varies directly with its pressure. A temperature of 200 K produces a pressure of 50 pounds per square inch.

  a. Find the equation that relates pressure and temperature.

  b. Graph the equation from part *a* in the first quadrant only.

  c. What pressure will the gas have at 280 K?

38. Circumference and Diameter The circumference of a wheel is directly proportional to its diameter. A wheel has a circumference of 8.5 feet and a diameter of 2.7 feet.

  a. Find the equation that relates circumference and diameter.

  b. Graph the equation from part *a* in the first quadrant only.

  c. What is the circumference of a wheel that has a diameter of 11.3 feet?

39. Volume and Pressure The volume of a gas is inversely proportional to the pressure. If a pressure of 36 pounds per square inch corresponds to a volume of 25 cubic feet, what pressure is needed to produce a volume of 75 cubic feet?

40. Wave Frequency The frequency of an electromagnetic wave varies inversely with the wavelength. If a wavelength of 200 meters has a frequency of 800 kilocycles per second, what frequency will be associated with a wavelength of 500 meters?

41. f-Stop and Aperture Diameter The relative aperture, or *f*-stop, for a camera lens is inversely proportional to the diameter of the aperture. An *f*-stop of 2 corresponds to an aperture diameter of 40 millimeters for the lens on an automatic camera.

   a. Find the equation that relates *f*-stop and diameter.
   b. Graph the equation from part *a* in the first quadrant only.
   c. What is the *f*-stop of this camera when the aperture diameter is 10 millimeters?

42. f-Stop and Aperture Diameter The relative aperture, or *f*-stop, for a camera lens is inversely proportional to the diameter of the aperture. An *f*-stop of 2.8 corresponds to an aperture diameter of 75 millimeters for a certain telephoto lens.

   a. Find the equation that relates *f*-stop and diameter.
   b. Graph the equation from part a. in the first quadrant only.
   c. What aperture diameter corresponds to an *f*-stop of 5.6?

43. Surface Area of a Cylinder The surface area of a hollow cylinder varies jointly with the height and radius of the cylinder. If a cylinder with radius 3 inches and height 5 inches has a surface area of 94 square inches, what is the surface area of a cylinder with radius 2 inches and height 8 inches?

44. Capacity of a Cylinder The capacity of a cylinder varies jointly with its height and the square of its radius. If a cylinder with a radius of 3 centimeters and a height of 6 centimeters has a capacity of 169.56 cubic centimeters, what will be the capacity of a cylinder with radius 4 centimeters and height 9 centimeters?

45. Electrical Resistance The resistance of a wire varies directly with its length and inversely with the square of its diameter. If 100 feet of wire with diameter 0.01 inch has a resistance of 10 ohms, what is the resistance of 60 feet of the same type of wire if its diameter is 0.02 inch?

46. Volume and Temperature The volume of a gas varies directly with its temperature and inversely with the pressure. If the volume of a certain gas is 30 cubic feet at a temperature of 300 K and a pressure of 20 pounds per square inch, what is the volume of the same gas at 340 K when the pressure is 30 pounds per square inch?

47. Period of a Pendulum The time it takes for a pendulum to complete one period varies directly with the square root of the length of the pendulum. A 100-centimeter pendulum takes 2.1 seconds to complete one period.

   a. Find the equation that relates period and pendulum length.
   b. Graph the equation from part *a* in quadrant I only.
   c. How long does it take to complete one period if the pendulum hangs 225 centimeters?

48. Intensity of Light Table 4 gives the intensity of light that falls on a surface at various distances from a 100-watt light bulb. Construct a bar chart from the information in Table 4.

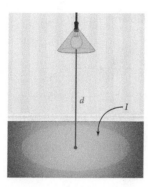

TABLE 4	Light intensity from a 100-watt light bulb
Distance Above Surface (ft)	Intensity (lumens/sq ft)
1	120.0
2	30.0
3	13.3
4	7.5
5	4.8
6	3.3

Learning Objectives Assessment

The following problems can be used to help assess if you have successfully met the learning objectives for this section.

49. If y varies directly with the square of x, and y is 450 when x is 5, find y when x is 3.

  a. 270   **b.** 750   **c.** 1,250   **d.** 162

50. If z is inversely proportional to p, and z is 36 when p is 4, find z when p is 6.

  a. 144   **b.** 9   **c.** 54   **d.** 24

51. If d varies jointly with r and the square root of x, and d is 36 when r is 6 and x is 4, find d when r is 5 and x is 9.

  a. 45   **b.** 180   **c.** 22.5   **d.** 6

52. The water temperature in a lake varies inversely with the depth. If the temperature is 10°C at a depth of 200 meters, what is the temperature at a depth of 250 meters?

  a. 16°C   **b.** 6.5°C   **c.** 8°C   **d.** 12.5°C

Maintaining Your Skills

The problems that follow review some of the more important skills you have learned in previous sections and chapters.

Solve the following equations.

53. $x - 5 = 7$ **54.** $3y = -4$ **55.** $5 - \dfrac{4}{7}a = -11$

56. $\dfrac{1}{5}x - \dfrac{1}{2} - \dfrac{1}{10}x + \dfrac{2}{5} = \dfrac{3}{10}x + \dfrac{1}{2}$

57. $5(x - 1) - 2(2x + 3) = 5x - 4$

58. $0.07 - 0.02(3x + 1) = -0.04x + 0.01$

Solve for the indicated variable.

59. $P = 2l + 2w$ for w **60.** $A = \dfrac{1}{2}h(b + B)$ for B

Solve the following inequalities. Write the solution set using interval notation, then graph the solution set.

61. $-5t \le 30$ **62.** $5 - \dfrac{3}{2}x > -1$

63. $1.6x - 2 < 0.8x + 2.8$ **64.** $3(2y + 4) \ge 5(y - 8)$

Solve the following equations.

65. $\left| \dfrac{1}{4}x - 1 \right| = \dfrac{1}{2}$ **66.** $\left| \dfrac{2}{3}a + 4 \right| = 6$

67. $|3 - 2x| + 5 = 2$ **68.** $5 = |3y + 6| - 4$

Chapter 9 Summary

Relations and Functions [9.1]

1. The relation

$$\{(8, 1), (6, 1), (-3, 0)\}$$

is also a function because no ordered pairs have the same first coordinates. The domain is $\{-3, 6, 8\}$ and the range is $\{0, 1\}$.

A *relation* is any set of ordered pairs. The set of all first coordinates is called the *domain* of the relation, and the set of all second coordinates is the *range* of the relation.

A *function* is a rule that pairs each element in one set, called the *domain,* with exactly one element from a second set, called the *range.* A function is a relation in which no two different ordered pairs have the same first coordinates.

Vertical Line Test [9.1]

2. The graph of $x = y^2$ shown in Figure 2 in Section 9.1 fails the vertical line test. It is not the graph of a function.

If a vertical line crosses the graph of a relation in more than one place, the relation cannot be a function. If no vertical line can be found that crosses the graph in more than one place, the relation must be a function.

Function Notation [9.2]

3. If $f(x) = 5x - 3$ then
$$f(0) = 5(0) - 3$$
$$= -3$$
$$f(1) = 5(1) - 3$$
$$= 2$$
$$f(-2) = 5(-2) - 3$$
$$= -13$$
$$f(a) = 5a - 3$$

The alternative notation for y is $f(x)$. It is read "f of x" and can be used instead of the variable y when working with functions. The notation y and the notation $f(x)$ are equivalent; that is, $y = f(x)$.

Algebra with Functions [9.3]

4. If $f(x) = 3x - 1$ and $g(x) = 4x + 2$, then
$$(f + g)(0) = f(0) + g(0)$$
$$= -1 + 2$$
$$= 1$$
and
$$(f + g)(x) = f(x) + g(x)$$
$$= (3x - 1) + (4x + 2)$$
$$= 7x + 1$$

If f and g are any two functions with a common domain, then:

$(f + g)(x) = f(x) + g(x)$ The function $f + g$ is the sum of the functions f and g.

$(f - g)(x) = f(x) - g(x)$ The function $f - g$ is the difference of the functions f and g.

$(fg)(x) = f(x)g(x)$ The function fg is the product of the functions f and g.

$\dfrac{f}{g}(x) = \dfrac{f(x)}{g(x)}$ The function $\dfrac{f}{g}$ is the quotient of the functions f and g, where $g(x) \neq 0$

Composition of Functions [9.3]

5. If $f(x) = 3x - 1$ and $g(x) = 4x + 2$, then

$$\begin{aligned}
(f \circ g)(0) &= f(g(0)) \\
&= f(2) \\
&= 5
\end{aligned}$$

and

$$\begin{aligned}
(f \circ g)(x) &= f(g(x)) \\
&= f(4x + 2) \\
&= 3(4x + 2) - 1 \\
&= 12x + 5
\end{aligned}$$

If f and g are two functions for which the range of each has numbers in common with the domain of the other, then we have the following definitions:

The composition of f with g: $(f \circ g)(x) = f[g(x)]$

The composition of g with f: $(g \circ f)(x) = g[f(x)]$

The Slope of a Line [9.4]

6. The equation $3x + 2y = 6$ is an example of a linear equation in two variables.

The *slope* of the line containing points (x_1, y_1) and (x_2, y_2) is given by

$$\text{Slope} = m = \frac{\text{Rise}}{\text{Run}} = \frac{y_2 - y_1}{x_2 - x_1}$$

Horizontal lines have 0 slope, and vertical lines have an undefined slope. Parallel lines have equal slopes, and perpendicular lines have slopes that are negative reciprocals.

The Slope-Intercept Form of a Line [9.4]

7. The equation of the line with slope 5 and y-intercept 3 is

$$y = 5x + 3$$

The equation of a line with slope m and y-intercept b is given by

$$y = mx + b$$

The Point-Slope Form of a Line [9.4]

8. The equation of the line through $(3, 2)$ with slope -4 is

$$y - 2 = -4(x - 3)$$

which can be simplified to

$$y = -4x + 14$$

The equation of the line through (x_1, y_1) that has slope m can be written as

$$y - y_1 = m(x - x_1)$$

Linear Function [9.4]

9. The function $f(x) = 2x - 3$ is a linear function. The graph of f is a line with slope $m = 2$ and y-intercept $(0, -3)$.

A *linear function* is any function that can be expressed in the form $f(x) = mx + b$. The graph of f is a line with slope m passing through the y-axis at $(0, b)$.

Variation [9.5]

10. If y varies directly with x, then
$$y = Kx$$
Then if y is 18 when x is 6,
$$18 = K \cdot 6$$
or
$$K = 3$$
So the equation can be written more specifically as
$$y = 3x$$
If we want to know what y is when x is 4, we simply substitute:
$$y = 3 \cdot 4$$
$$y = 12$$

If y *varies directly* with x (y is directly proportional to x), then
$$y = Kx$$
If y *varies inversely* with x (y is inversely proportional to x), then
$$y = \frac{K}{x}$$
If z *varies jointly* with x and y (z is directly proportional to both x and y), then
$$z = Kxy$$
In each case, K is called the *constant of variation*.

COMMON MISTAKE

1. When graphing ordered pairs, the most common mistake is to associate the first coordinate with the y-axis and the second with the x-axis. If you make this mistake you would graph (3, 1) by going up 3 and to the right 1, which is just the reverse of what you should do. Remember, the first coordinate is always associated with the horizontal axis, and the second coordinate is always associated with the vertical axis.

2. The two most common mistakes students make when first working with the formula for the slope of a line are the following:
   a. Putting the difference of the x-coordinates over the difference of the y-coordinates.
   b. Subtracting in one order in the numerator and then subtracting in the opposite order in the denominator.

3. When graphing linear inequalities in two variables, remember to graph the boundary with a broken line when the inequality symbol is $<$ or $>$. The only time you use a solid line for the boundary is when the inequality symbol is $\leq$ or $\geq$.

Chapter 9 Test

State the domain and range for the following relations, and indicate which relations are also functions. [9.1]

1. $\{(-2, 0), (-3, 0), (-2, 1)\}$ **2.** $y = x^2 - 9$

Let $f(x) = x - 2$, $g(x) = 3x + 4$ and $h(x) = 3x^2 - 2x - 8$, and find the following. [9.2, 9.3]

3. $f(3) + g(2)$ **4.** $h(x) - g(x)$ **5.** $(f \circ g)(2)$ **6.** $(g \circ h)(x)$

For each of the following lines, identify the x-intercept, y-intercept, and slope, and sketch the graph. [9.4]

7. $2x + y = 6$ **8.** $y = -2x - 3$ **9.** $y = \dfrac{3}{2}x + 4$ **10.** $x = -2$

Find the equation for each line. [9.4]

11. Give the equation of the line through $(-3, 2)$ and $(4, -1)$.

12. Give the equation of the vertical line through $(4, -7)$.

13. Line l contains the point $(5, -3)$ and has a graph parallel to the graph of $2x - 5y = 10$. Find the equation for l.

14. Line l contains the point $(-1, -2)$ and has a graph perpendicular to the graph of $y = 3x - 1$. Find the equation for l.

15. Give the equation of the linear function whose graph passes through $(-1, 3)$ and has slope $m = 2$.

Solve the following variation problems. [9.5]

16. Direct Variation Quantity y varies directly with the square of x. If y is 50 when x is 5, find y when x is 3.

17. Joint Variation Quantity z varies jointly with x and the cube of y. If z is 15 when x is 5 and y is 2, find z when x is 2 and y is 3.

18. Maximum Load The maximum load (L) a horizontal beam can safely hold varies jointly with the width (w) and the square of the depth (d) and inversely with the length (l). If a 10-foot beam with width 3 feet and depth 4 feet will safely hold up to 800 pounds, how many pounds will a 12-foot beam with width 3 feet and depth 4 feet hold?

Roots and Rational Exponents

iStockphoto.com © trait2lumiere

Ecology and conservation are topics that interest most college students. If our rivers and oceans are to be preserved for future generations, we need to work to eliminate pollution from our waters. If a river is flowing at 1 meter per second and a pollutant is entering the river at a constant rate, the shape of the pollution plume can often be modeled by the simple equation

$$y = \sqrt{x}$$

The following table and graph were produced from the equation.

Width of a Pollutant Plume

Distance from Source (meters)	Width of Plume (meters)
x	y
0	0
1	1
4	2
9	3
16	4

To visualize how the graph models the pollutant plume, imagine that the river is flowing from left to right, parallel to the x-axis, with the x-axis as one of its banks. The pollutant is entering the river from the bank at $(0, 0)$.

By modeling pollution with mathematics, we can use our knowledge of mathematics to help control and eliminate pollution.

Think about the most successful people you have met or heard about. What are the qualities they tend to have in common? One of these qualities usually involves making a resolute commitment. If you are not firmly committed to something, then you will tend to give less than your full effort. Consider this quote from Faust by Johann Wolfgang Von Goethe:

> *Until one is committed, there is hesitancy, the chance to draw back, always ineffectiveness. Concerning all acts of initiative and creation, there is one elementary truth the ignorance of which kills countless ideas and splendid plans: that the moment one definitely commits oneself, then providence moves too. All sorts of things occur to help one that would never otherwise have occurred. A whole stream of events issues from the decision, raising in one's favor all manner of unforeseen incidents, meetings and material assistance which no man could have dreamed would have come his way. Whatever you can do or dream you can, begin it. Boldness has genius, power and magic in it.*

Successful people do not give up easily. They forge ahead, even when confronted by difficulties or when the odds seem stacked against them.

Take a moment to reflect on your own life experiences. When have you been the most successful? Can you think of a time when providence has moved in your favor, perhaps unexpectedly?

Learning Objectives

In this section, we will learn how to:

1. Find the square root of a number.

2. Find the nth root of a number.

3. Graph a simple root function.

4. Find the domain for a root function.

Introduction

In Chapter 1, we developed notation (exponents) to give us the square, cube, or any other power of a number. For instance, if we wanted the square of 3, we wrote $3^2 = 9$. If we wanted the cube of 3, we wrote $3^3 = 27$. In this section, we will develop notation that will take us in the reverse direction, that is, from the square of a number, say 25, back to the original number, 5.

Figure 1 shows a square in which each of the four sides is 1 inch long. To find the square of the length of the diagonal c, we apply the Pythagorean theorem:

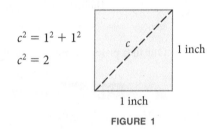

$$c^2 = 1^2 + 1^2$$
$$c^2 = 2$$

1 inch

FIGURE 1

Note The Pythagoreans, whose motto was "All is number," believed everything in the world was constructed from whole numbers. The discovery that $\sqrt{2}$ is an irrational number (which cannot be expressed as a ratio of whole numbers) was a terrible shock to their society and endangered their beliefs. Therefore, it was kept as a closely guarded secret. According to legend, Hippasus was murdered for divulging this secret.

Because we know that c is positive and that its square is 2, we call c the *positive square root* of 2, and we write $c = \sqrt{2}$. This leads us to the following definition.

> **DEFINITION** *positive square root*
>
> If x is a nonnegative real number, then the expression $\sqrt{x}$ is called the *positive square root* of x and is such that
>
> $$(\sqrt{x})^2 = x$$
>
> *In words:* $\sqrt{x}$ is the positive number we square to get x.
> **Note:** $\sqrt{x}$ is sometimes referred to as the *principal square root* of x.

The negative square root of x, denoted as $-\sqrt{x}$, is the negative number we square to get x.

VIDEO EXAMPLES

SECTION 10.1

EXAMPLE 1 The positive square root of 64 is 8 because 8 is the positive number with the property $8^2 = 64$. The negative square root of 64 is -8 because -8 is the negative number whose square is 64. We can summarize both these facts by saying

$$\sqrt{64} = 8 \qquad \text{and} \qquad -\sqrt{64} = -8$$

It is a common mistake to assume that an expression like $\sqrt{25}$ indicates both square roots, 5 and -5. The expression $\sqrt{25}$ indicates only the positive square root of 25, which is 5. If we want the negative square root, we must use a negative sign: $-\sqrt{25} = -5$.

The higher roots, cube roots, fourth roots, and so on, are defined by definitions similar to that of square roots.

DEFINITION

If x is a real number and n is a positive integer, then

Positive square root of x, $\sqrt{x}$, is such that $(\sqrt{x})^2 = x$ $x \geq 0$

Cube root of x, $\sqrt[3]{x}$, is such that $(\sqrt[3]{x})^3 = x$

Positive fourth root of x, $\sqrt[4]{x}$, is such that $(\sqrt[4]{x})^4 = x$ $x \geq 0$

Fifth root of x, $\sqrt[5]{x}$, is such that $(\sqrt[5]{x})^5 = x$

The nth root of x, $\sqrt[n]{x}$, is such that $(\sqrt[n]{x})^n = x$ $x \geq 0$ if n is even

Note We have restricted the even roots in this definition to nonnegative numbers. Even roots of negative numbers exist, but are not represented by real numbers. That is, $\sqrt{-4}$ is not a real number because there is no real number whose square is -4.

Our first property for radicals is a direct result of the previous definition.

PROPERTY   *Property 1 for Radicals*

If a is a real number and n is a positive integer, then

$$(\sqrt[n]{a})^n = a, \ a \geq 0 \text{ if } n \text{ is even}$$

EXAMPLES   Use Property 1 to simplify each expression.

2. $(\sqrt{3})^2 = 3$

3. $(\sqrt[3]{-11})^3 = -11$

4. $(\sqrt[5]{2y})^5 = 2y$

Notation An expression like $\sqrt[3]{8}$ that involves a root is called a *radical expression*. In the expression $\sqrt[3]{8}$, the ^{3} is called the *index*, the $\sqrt{}$ is the *radical sign*, and 8 is called the *radicand*. The index of a radical must be a positive integer greater than 1. If no index is written, it is assumed to be 2.

The following is a table of the most common roots used in this book. Any of the roots that are unfamiliar should be memorized.

Square Roots		Cube Roots	Fourth Roots
$\sqrt{0} = 0$	$\sqrt{49} = 7$	$\sqrt[3]{0} = 0$	$\sqrt[4]{0} = 0$
$\sqrt{1} = 1$	$\sqrt{64} = 8$	$\sqrt[3]{1} = 1$	$\sqrt[4]{1} = 1$
$\sqrt{4} = 2$	$\sqrt{81} = 9$	$\sqrt[3]{8} = 2$	$\sqrt[4]{16} = 2$
$\sqrt{9} = 3$	$\sqrt{100} = 10$	$\sqrt[3]{27} = 3$	$\sqrt[4]{81} = 3$
$\sqrt{16} = 4$	$\sqrt{121} = 11$	$\sqrt[3]{64} = 4$	
$\sqrt{25} = 5$	$\sqrt{144} = 12$	$\sqrt[3]{125} = 5$	
$\sqrt{36} = 6$	$\sqrt{169} = 13$		

Roots and Negative Numbers

When dealing with negative numbers and radicals, the only restriction concerns negative numbers under even roots. We can have negative signs in front of radicals and negative numbers under odd roots and still obtain real numbers. Here are some examples to help clarify this. In the last section of this chapter, we will see how to deal with square roots of negative numbers.

EXAMPLES   Simplify each expression, if possible.

5. $\sqrt[3]{-8} = -2$ because $(-2)^3 = -8$.

6. $\sqrt{-4}$ is not a real number because there is no real number whose square is -4.

7. $\sqrt[5]{-32} = -2$ because $(-2)^5 = -32$.

8. $\sqrt[4]{-81}$ is not a real number because there is no real number we can raise to the fourth power and obtain -81.

When there is a negative sign in front of a radical, we can simply interpret the negative as indicating the "opposite of" a value, as shown in the next two examples.

EXAMPLES   Simplify each expression, if possible.

9. $-\sqrt{25} = -(\sqrt{25})$

$\qquad = -(5)$

$\qquad = -5$

10. $-\sqrt[3]{-64} = -(\sqrt[3]{-64})$

$\qquad\quad = -(-4)$

$\qquad\quad = 4$

Variables Under a Radical

From the preceding examples, it is clear that we must be careful that we do not try to take an even root of a negative number. For this reason, we will assume that all variables appearing under a radical sign represent nonnegative numbers.

EXAMPLES   Assume all variables represent nonnegative numbers, and simplify each expression as much as possible.

11. $\sqrt{25a^4b^6} = 5a^2b^3$ because $(5a^2b^3)^2 = 25a^4b^6$.

12. $\sqrt[3]{x^6y^{12}} = x^2y^4$ because $(x^2y^4)^3 = x^6y^{12}$.

13. $\sqrt[4]{81r^8s^{20}} = 3r^2s^5$ because $(3r^2s^5)^4 = 81r^8s^{20}$.

The Spiral of Roots

⊿ FACTS FROM GEOMETRY   *The Pythagorean Theorem (Again)*

Now that we have had some experience working with square roots, we can rewrite the Pythagorean theorem using a square root. If triangle ABC is a right triangle with $C=90°$, then the length of the longest side is the *positive square root* of the sum of the squares of the other two sides (see Figure 2).

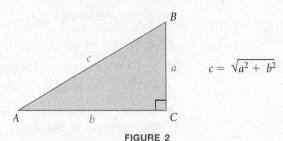

$$c = \sqrt{a^2 + b^2}$$

FIGURE 2

In the introduction to this section, we showed how the Pythagorean theorem can be used to represent $\sqrt{2}$ geometrically as the length of the diagonal of a square. In a similar manner, the Pythagorean theorem can be used to construct the attractive spiral shown in Figure 3.

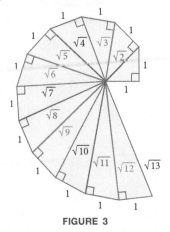

FIGURE 3

This spiral is called the Spiral of Roots because each of the diagonals is the positive square root of one of the positive integers. To construct the spiral, we begin by drawing two line segments, each of length 1, at right angles to each other. Then we use the Pythagorean theorem to find the length of the diagonal. Figure 4 illustrates this procedure.

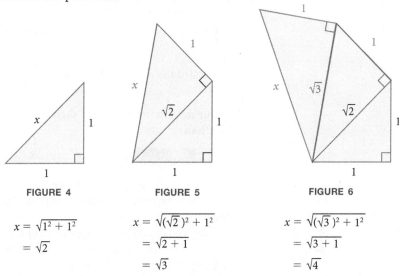

| FIGURE 4 | FIGURE 5 | FIGURE 6 |

$$x = \sqrt{1^2 + 1^2}$$
$$= \sqrt{2}$$

$$x = \sqrt{(\sqrt{2})^2 + 1^2}$$
$$= \sqrt{2 + 1}$$
$$= \sqrt{3}$$

$$x = \sqrt{(\sqrt{3})^2 + 1^2}$$
$$= \sqrt{3 + 1}$$
$$= \sqrt{4}$$

Next, we construct a second triangle by connecting a line segment of length 1 to the end of the first diagonal so that the angle formed is a right angle. We find the length of the second diagonal using the Pythagorean theorem. Figure 5 illustrates this procedure. Continuing to draw new triangles by connecting line segments of length 1 to the end of each new diagonal, so that the angle formed is a right angle, the spiral of roots begins to appear (Figure 6).

USING TECHNOLOGY

As our preceding discussion indicates, the length of each diagonal in the spiral of roots is used to calculate the length of the next diagonal. The $\boxed{\text{ANS}}$ key on a graphing calculator can be used effectively in a situation like this. To begin, we store the number 1 in the variable ANS. Next, we key in the formula used to produce each diagonal using ANS for the variable. After that, it is simply a matter of pressing $\boxed{\text{ENTER}}$, as many times as we like, to produce the lengths of as many diagonals as we like. Here is a summary of what we do:

Enter This	Display Shows
1 $\boxed{\text{ENTER}}$	1.000
$\sqrt{\quad}$ (ANS^2 + 1) $\boxed{\text{ENTER}}$	1.414
$\boxed{\text{ENTER}}$	1.732
$\boxed{\text{ENTER}}$	2.000
$\boxed{\text{ENTER}}$	2.236

If you continue to press the $\boxed{\text{ENTER}}$ key, you will produce decimal approximations for as many of the diagonals in the spiral of roots as you like.

Root Functions

If we use a root as the formula for a function, the result is called a *root function*. Here is the definition.

> **(def) DEFINITION**   *root function*
>
> For any positive integer n, the function given by
> $$f(x) = \sqrt[n]{x}$$
> is called the **nth root function**.

In our next example we will sketch the graph of the square root and cube root functions.

EXAMPLE 14   Graph $f(x) = \sqrt{x}$ and $g(x) = \sqrt[3]{x}$.

SOLUTION   The graphs are shown in Figures 7 and 8. Notice that the graph of $f(x) = \sqrt{x}$ appears in the first quadrant only, because in the equation $y = \sqrt{x}$, x and y cannot be negative.

The graph of $g(x) = \sqrt[3]{x}$ appears in Quadrants 1 and 3 because the cube root of a positive number is also a positive number, and the cube root of a negative number is a negative number. That is, when x is positive, y will be positive, and when x is negative, y will be negative.

The graphs of both equations will contain the origin, because $y = 0$ when $x = 0$ in both equations.

x	$y = f(x)$
-4	Not real
-1	Not real
0	0
1	1
4	2
9	3
16	4

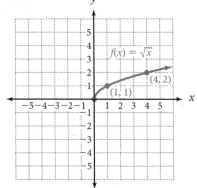

FIGURE 7

x	$y = g(x)$
-27	-3
-8	-2
-1	-1
0	0
1	1
8	2
27	3

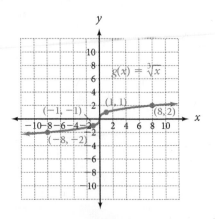

FIGURE 8

Domain of a Root Function

As we observed in Example 14, the square root function $y = \sqrt{x}$ will only give real number outputs if $x \geq 0$, but with the cube root function $y = \sqrt[3]{x}$, x can be any real number. This leads us to the following property:

◺≠Σ   PROPERTY   *Domain of a Root Function*

The domain of $f(x) = \sqrt[n]{x}$ is

Set-Builder Notation	Interval Notation	
$\{x \mid x \geq 0\}$	$[0, \infty)$	if n is even
$\{x \mid x$ is any real number$\}$	$(-\infty, \infty)$	if n is odd

---

EXAMPLES

15. The domain of $f(x) = \sqrt{x}$ is $[0, \infty)$.

16. The domain of $f(x) = \sqrt[3]{x} + 3$ is $(-\infty, \infty)$.

If the radical contains some expression involving x, we must make sure the radicand represents a nonnegative number if the index of the radical is even. We illustrate how this is done in our last example.

EXAMPLE 17   Find the domain for $f(x) = \sqrt{x + 2}$.

SOLUTION   The value of the radicand, $x + 2$, must be nonnegative. We can set up an appropriate inequality and solve for x.

$$\text{Radicand} \geq 0$$

$$x + 2 \geq 0$$

$$x \geq -2$$

The domain is $\{x \mid x \geq -2\}$.

Getting Ready for Class

After reading through the preceding section, respond in your own words and in complete sentences.

A. Every real number has two square roots. Explain the notation we use to tell them apart. Use the square roots of 3 for examples.

B. Explain why the square root of -4 is not a real number.

C. Explain why $\left(\sqrt[10]{2} \right)^{10} = 2$.

D. When can the radicand of a root function be negative?

Problem Set 10.1

Find each of the following roots, if possible.

1. $\sqrt{144}$ **2.** $-\sqrt{144}$ **3.** $\sqrt{-144}$ **4.** $\sqrt{-49}$

5. $-\sqrt{49}$ **6.** $\sqrt{49}$ **7.** $\sqrt[3]{-27}$ **8.** $-\sqrt[3]{27}$

9. $-\sqrt[3]{-27}$ **10.** $\sqrt[4]{16}$ **11.** $-\sqrt[4]{16}$ **12.** $\sqrt[4]{-16}$

13. $\sqrt{0.04}$ **14.** $\sqrt{0.81}$ **15.** $\sqrt[3]{0.008}$ **16.** $\sqrt[3]{0.125}$

17. $\sqrt{\dfrac{1}{36}}$ **18.** $\sqrt{\dfrac{9}{25}}$ **19.** $\sqrt[3]{\dfrac{1}{8}}$ **20.** $\sqrt[3]{\dfrac{27}{64}}$

Use Property 1 for radicals to simplify each expression. Assume all variables represent nonnegative numbers.

21. $(\sqrt{5})^2$ **22.** $(\sqrt{8})^2$ **23.** $(\sqrt[3]{2})^3$ **24.** $(\sqrt[3]{-6})^3$

25. $(\sqrt[4]{10})^4$ **26.** $(\sqrt[5]{16})^5$ **27.** $(\sqrt{7x})^2$ **28.** $(\sqrt[3]{4a^2})^3$

Simplify each expression. Assume all variables represent nonnegative numbers.

29. $\sqrt{36a^8}$ **30.** $\sqrt{49a^{10}}$ **31.** $\sqrt[3]{27a^{12}}$ **32.** $\sqrt[3]{8a^{15}}$

33. $\sqrt[3]{x^3y^6}$ **34.** $\sqrt[3]{x^6y^3}$ **35.** $\sqrt[5]{32x^{10}y^5}$ **36.** $\sqrt[5]{32x^5y^{10}}$

37. $\sqrt[4]{16a^{12}b^{20}}$ **38.** $\sqrt[4]{81a^{24}b^8}$

Simplify. Assume all variables are nonnegative.

39. a. $\sqrt{25}$ **b.** $\sqrt{0.25}$ **c.** $\sqrt{2500}$ **d.** $\sqrt{0.0025}$

40. a. $\sqrt[3]{8}$ **b.** $\sqrt[3]{0.008}$ **c.** $\sqrt[3]{8,000}$ **d.** $\sqrt[3]{8 \times 10^{-6}}$

41. a. $\sqrt{16a^4b^8}$ **b.** $\sqrt[4]{16a^4b^8}$

42. a. $\sqrt[3]{64x^6y^{18}}$ **b.** $\sqrt[6]{64x^6y^{18}}$

Graph each root function.

43. $f(x) = 2\sqrt{x}$ **44.** $f(x) = -2\sqrt{x}$ **45.** $f(x) = \sqrt{x} - 2$

46. $f(x) = \sqrt{x} + 2$ **47.** $f(x) = \sqrt{x - 2}$ **48.** $f(x) = \sqrt{x + 2}$

49. $f(x) = 3\sqrt[3]{x}$ **50.** $f(x) = -3\sqrt[3]{x}$ **51.** $f(x) = \sqrt[3]{x} + 3$

52. $f(x) = \sqrt[3]{x} - 3$ **53.** $f(x) = \sqrt[3]{x + 3}$ **54.** $f(x) = \sqrt[3]{x - 3}$

Find the domain for each function.

55. $f(x) = \sqrt{x + 3}$ **56.** $f(x) = \sqrt{x - 3}$

57. $f(x) = \sqrt{x} + 3$ **58.** $f(x) = \sqrt{3x}$

59. $f(x) = \sqrt{2x - 10}$ **60.** $f(x) = \sqrt{3x + 6}$

61. $f(x) = \sqrt{5 - x}$ **62.** $f(x) = \sqrt{8 - x}$

63. $f(x) = \sqrt[3]{x + 4}$ **64.** $f(x) = \sqrt[3]{x - 4}$

65. $f(x) = \sqrt[3]{4x}$ **66.** $f(x) = \sqrt[3]{x - 4}$

Applying the Concepts

67. Chemistry Figure 9 shows part of a model of a magnesium oxide (MgO) crystal. Each corner of the square is at the center of one oxygen ion (O^{2-}), and the center of the middle ion is at the center of the square. The radius for each oxygen ion is 150 picometers (pm), and the radius for each magnesium ion (Mg^{2+}) is 60 picometers.

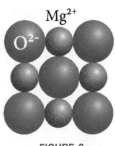

FIGURE 9

a. Find the length of the side of the square. Write your answer in picometers.

b. Find the length of the diagonal of the square. Write your answer in picometers.

c. If 1 meter is 10^{12} picometers, give the length of the diagonal of the square in meters.

68. Geometry The length of each side of the cube shown in Figure 10 is 1 inch.

a. Find the length of the diagonal CH.

b. Find the length of the diagonal CF.

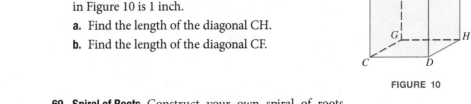

FIGURE 10

69. Spiral of Roots Construct your own spiral of roots by using a ruler. Draw the first triangle by using two 1-inch lines. The first diagonal will have a length of $\sqrt{2}$ inches. Each new triangle will be formed by drawing a 1-inch line segment at the end of the previous diagonal so the angle formed is 90°.

70. Spiral of Roots Construct a spiral of roots by using line segments of length 2 inches. The length of the first diagonal will be $2\sqrt{2}$ inches. The length of the second diagonal will be $2\sqrt{3}$ inches.

Learning Objectives Assessment

The following problems can be used to help assess if you have successfully met the learning objectives for this section.

71. Find: $-\sqrt{64}$.

    a. 8   **b.** -8 **c.** -4 **d.** Not a real number

72. Simplify: $\sqrt[3]{-64}$.

    a. -4 **b.** -8 **c.** 4   **d.** Not a real number

73. Which point lies on the graph of $f(x) = \sqrt{x+4}$?

    a. $(4, 2)$ **b.** $(0, 4)$ **c.** $(-3, 1)$ **d.** $(-5, 1)$

74. Find the domain of $f(x) = \sqrt{x+4}$.

    a. $\{x \mid x \geq 4\}$ **b.** $\{x \mid x \geq -4\}$ **c.** $\{x \mid x \geq 0\}$ **d.** $\{x \mid x \text{ is any real number}\}$

Getting Ready for the Next Section

Simplify. Assume all variables represent positive real numbers.

75. $\sqrt{25}$ **76.** $\sqrt{4}$ **77.** $\sqrt{16x^4y^2}$ **78.** $\sqrt{4x^6y^8}$

79. $\sqrt[3]{27}$ **80.** $\sqrt[3]{-8}$ **81.** $\sqrt[3]{8a^3b^3}$ **82.** $\sqrt[3]{64a^6b^3}$

83. -5^2 **84.** $(-5)^2$ **85.** 5^{-2} **86.** $\left(\dfrac{1}{5}\right)^{-2}$

87. $x^2 \cdot x^5$ **88.** $(x^2)^5$ **89.** $\dfrac{x^5}{x^2}$ **90.** $\left(\dfrac{x^2}{y^5}\right)^3$

Learning Objectives

In this section, we will learn how to:

1. Write a root using a rational exponent.
2. Write a rational exponent in radical notation.
3. Use rational exponents to simplify roots.
4. Simplify expressions containing rational exponents.

Introduction

We will now develop a second kind of notation involving exponents that will allow us to designate square roots, cube roots, and so on in another way.

Consider the equation $x = 8^{1/3}$. Although we have not encountered fractional exponents before, let's assume that all the properties of exponents hold in this case. Cubing both sides of the equation, we have

$$x^3 = (8^{1/3})^3$$
$$x^3 = 8^{(1/3)(3)}$$
$$x^3 = 8^1$$
$$x^3 = 8$$

The last line tells us that x is the number whose cube is 8. It must be true, then, that x is the cube root of 8, $x = \sqrt[3]{8}$. Because we started with $x = 8^{1/3}$, it follows that

$$8^{1/3} = \sqrt[3]{8}$$

It seems reasonable, then, to define fractional exponents as indicating roots. Here is the formal definition.

> ### (def) DEFINITION
>
> If x is a real number and n is a positive integer greater than 1, then
> $$x^{1/n} = \sqrt[n]{x} \qquad (x \geq 0 \text{ when } n \text{ is even})$$
> *In words:* The quantity $x^{1/n}$ is the nth root of x.

With this definition, we have a way of representing roots with exponents. Here are some examples.

VIDEO EXAMPLES

SECTION 10.2

EXAMPLES Write each expression as a root and then simplify, if possible.

1. $8^{1/3} = \sqrt[3]{8} = 2$

2. $36^{1/2} = \sqrt{36} = 6$

3. $-25^{1/2} = -\sqrt{25} = -5$

4. $(-25)^{1/2} = \sqrt{-25}$, which is not a real number

5. $\left(\dfrac{4}{9}\right)^{1/2} = \sqrt{\dfrac{4}{9}} = \dfrac{2}{3}$

The properties of exponents developed in Chapter 1 were applied to integer exponents only. We will now extend these properties to include rational exponents also. We do so without proof.

△≠Σ PROPERTY *Properties of Exponents*

If a and b are real numbers and r and s are rational numbers, and a and b are nonnegative whenever r and s indicate even roots, then

1. $a^r \cdot a^s = a^{r+s}$ **4.** $a^{-r} = \dfrac{1}{a^r}$ $(a \neq 0)$

2. $(a^r)^s = a^{rs}$ **5.** $\left(\dfrac{a}{b}\right)^r = \dfrac{a^r}{b^r}$ $(b \neq 0)$

3. $(ab)^r = a^r b^r$ **6.** $\dfrac{a^r}{a^s} = a^{r-s}$ $(a \neq 0)$

Sometimes rational exponents can simplify our work with radicals. Here are Examples 12 and 13 from Section 10.1 again, but this time we will work them using rational exponents.

EXAMPLES   Write each radical with a rational exponent, then simplify.

6. $\sqrt[3]{x^6 y^{12}} = (x^6 y^{12})^{1/3}$

$\qquad\qquad = (x^6)^{1/3}(y^{12})^{1/3}$

$\qquad\qquad = x^2 y^4$

7. $\sqrt[4]{81 r^8 s^{20}} = (81 r^8 s^{20})^{1/4}$

$\qquad\qquad = 81^{1/4}(r^8)^{1/4}(s^{20})^{1/4}$

$\qquad\qquad = 3r^2 s^5$

So far, the numerators of all the rational exponents we have encountered have been 1. The next theorem extends the work we can do with rational exponents to rational exponents with numerators other than 1.

We can extend our properties of exponents with the following theorem.

△≠Σ THEOREM *Theorem 7.1*

If a is a nonnegative real number, m is an integer, and n is a positive integer, then

$$a^{m/n} = (a^{1/n})^m = (\sqrt[n]{a})^m \quad \text{and} \quad a^{m/n} = (a^m)^{1/n} = \sqrt[n]{a^m}$$

With rational exponents, the numerator always represents a power and the denominator represents the index of a root.

Proof We can prove Theorem 7.1 using the properties of exponents. Because $m/n = m(1/n)$, we have

$$a^{m/n} = a^{m(1/n)} \qquad\qquad a^{m/n} = a^{(1/n)(m)}$$

$$\qquad = (a^m)^{1/n} \qquad\qquad\qquad = (a^{1/n})^m$$

$$\qquad = \sqrt[n]{a^m} \qquad\qquad\qquad\quad = (\sqrt[n]{a})^m$$

Here are some examples that illustrate how we use this theorem.

EXAMPLES   Simplify as much as possible.

Note With a negative rational exponent, the negative sign must always be associated with the power, as the index of a root cannot be negative.

8. $8^{2/3} = (8^{1/3})^2$ Theorem 7.1

$= (\sqrt[3]{8})^2$ Definition of fractional exponents

$= 2^2$ The cube root of 8 is 2

$= 4$ The square of 2 is 4

9. $25^{(3/2)} = (25^{1/2})^3$ Theorem 7.1

$= (\sqrt{25})^3$ Definition of fractional exponents

$= 5^3$ The square root of 25 is 5

$= 125$ The cube of 5 is 125

10. $9^{-3/2} = (9^{1/2})^{-3}$ Theorem 7.1

$= (\sqrt{9})^{-3}$ Definition of fractional exponents

$= 3^{-3}$ The square root of 9 is 3

$= \dfrac{1}{3^3}$ Property 4 for exponents

$= \dfrac{1}{27}$ The cube of 3 is 27

11. $\left(\dfrac{27}{8}\right)^{-4/3} = \left[\left(\dfrac{27}{8}\right)^{1/3}\right]^{-4}$ Theorem 7.1

$= \left[\sqrt[3]{\dfrac{27}{8}}\right]^{-4}$ Definition of fractional exponents

$= \left(\dfrac{3}{2}\right)^{-4}$ Evaluate the cube root

$= \left(\dfrac{2}{3}\right)^4$ Property 4 for exponents

$= \dfrac{16}{81}$ The fourth power of $\frac{2}{3}$ is $\frac{16}{81}$

USING TECHNOLOGY   *Graphing Calculators—A Word of Caution*

Some graphing calculators give surprising results when evaluating expressions such as $(-8)^{2/3}$. As you know from reading this section, the expression $(-8)^{2/3}$ simplifies to 4, either by taking the cube root first and then squaring the result, or by squaring the base first and then taking the cube root of the result. Here are three different ways to evaluate this expression on your calculator:

1. $(-8)\wedge(2/3)$ To evaluate $(-8)^{2/3}$
2. $((-8)\wedge 2)\wedge(1/3)$ To evaluate $((-8)^2)^{1/3}$
3. $((-8)\wedge(1/3))\wedge 2$ To evaluate $((-8)^{1/3})^2$

Note any differences in the results.

Next, graph each of the following functions, one at a time.

1. $Y_1 = X^{2/3}$ **2.** $Y_2 = (X^2)^{1/3}$ **3.** $Y_3 = (X^{1/3})^2$

The correct graph is shown in Figure 1. Note which of your graphs match the correct graph.

Different calculators evaluate exponential expressions in different ways. You should use the method (or methods) that gave you the correct graph.

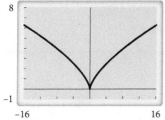

FIGURE 1

The following examples show the application of the properties of exponents to rational exponents.

EXAMPLES Assume all variables represent positive quantities, and simplify as much as possible.

12. $x^{1/3} \cdot x^{5/6} = x^{1/3 + 5/6}$ Property 1 for exponents

$= x^{2/6 + 5/6}$ LCD is 6

$= x^{7/6}$ Add fractions

13. $(y^{2/3})^{3/4} = y^{(2/3)(3/4)}$ Property 2 for exponents

$= y^{1/2}$ Multiply fractions: $\frac{2}{3} \cdot \frac{3}{4} = \frac{6}{12} = \frac{1}{2}$

14. $\dfrac{z^{1/3}}{z^{1/4}} = z^{1/3 - 1/4}$ Property 6 for exponents

$= z^{4/12 - 3/12}$ LCD is 12

$= z^{1/12}$ Subtract fractions

15. $\left(\dfrac{a^{-1/3}}{b^{1/2}} \right)^6 = \dfrac{(a^{-1/3})^6}{(b^{1/2})^6}$ Property 5 for exponents

$= \dfrac{a^{-2}}{b^3}$ Property 2 for exponents

$= \dfrac{1}{a^2 b^3}$ Property 4 for exponents

16. $\dfrac{(x^{-3}y^{1/2})^4}{x^{10}y^{3/2}} = \dfrac{(x^{-3})^4(y^{1/2})^4}{x^{10}y^{3/2}}$ Property 3 for exponents

$= \dfrac{x^{-12}y^2}{x^{10}y^{3/2}}$ Property 2 for exponents

$= x^{-22}y^{1/2}$ Property 6 for exponents

$= \dfrac{y^{1/2}}{x^{22}}$ Property 4 for exponents

Getting Ready for Class

After reading through the preceding section, respond in your own words and in complete sentences.

A. What does $5^{1/2}$ represent?

B. Explain why $9^{1/2}$ and $(-9)^{1/2}$ give different results.

C. For the expression $a^{m/n}$, explain the significance of the numerator m and the significance of the denominator n in the exponent.

D. Why must we interpret $8^{-2/3}$ as $8^{(-2)/3}$ and not $8^{2/(-3)}$?

Use the definition of rational exponents to write each of the following with the appropriate root. Then simplify.

1. $36^{1/2}$ **2.** $49^{1/2}$ **3.** $-9^{1/2}$ **4.** $-16^{1/2}$

5. $8^{1/3}$ **6.** $-8^{1/3}$ **7.** $(-8)^{1/3}$ **8.** $-27^{1/3}$

9. $32^{1/5}$ **10.** $81^{1/4}$ **11.** $\left(\dfrac{81}{25}\right)^{1/2}$ **12.** $\left(\dfrac{9}{16}\right)^{1/2}$

13. $\left(\dfrac{64}{125}\right)^{1/3}$ **14.** $\left(\dfrac{8}{27}\right)^{1/3}$

Use the definition of rational exponents to write each radical expression using a rational exponent.

15. $\sqrt{5}$ **16.** $\sqrt{2}$ **17.** $\sqrt{3x}$ **18.** $\sqrt{11ab}$

19. $\sqrt[3]{9}$ **20.** $\sqrt[3]{15}$ **21.** $\sqrt[3]{4x^2}$ **22.** $\sqrt[3]{10bc}$

Use Theorem 7.1 to simplify each of the following as much as possible.

23. $27^{2/3}$ **24.** $8^{4/3}$ **25.** $25^{3/2}$ **26.** $9^{3/2}$

27. $16^{3/4}$ **28.** $81^{3/4}$

Simplify each expression. Remember, negative exponents give reciprocals.

29. $27^{-1/3}$ **30.** $9^{-1/2}$ **31.** $81^{-3/4}$ **32.** $4^{-3/2}$

33. $\left(\dfrac{25}{36}\right)^{-1/2}$ **34.** $\left(\dfrac{16}{49}\right)^{-1/2}$ **35.** $\left(\dfrac{81}{16}\right)^{-3/4}$ **36.** $\left(\dfrac{27}{8}\right)^{-2/3}$

37. $16^{1/2} + 27^{1/3}$ **38.** $25^{1/2} + 100^{1/2}$ **39.** $8^{-2/3} + 4^{-1/2}$ **40.** $49^{-1/2} + 25^{-1/2}$

Use the properties of exponents to simplify each of the following as much as possible. Assume all bases are positive.

41. $x^{3/5} \cdot x^{1/5}$ **42.** $x^{3/4} \cdot x^{5/4}$ **43.** $y^{1/2} \cdot y^{1/4}$ **44.** $y^{2/3} \cdot y^{3/5}$

45. $(a^{3/4})^{4/3}$ **46.** $(a^{2/3})^{3/4}$ **47.** $\dfrac{x^{1/5}}{x^{3/5}}$ **48.** $\dfrac{x^{2/7}}{x^{5/7}}$

49. $\dfrac{x^{5/6}}{x^{2/3}}$ **50.** $\dfrac{x^{7/8}}{x^{8/7}}$ **51.** $(x^{3/5}y^{5/6}z^{1/3})^{3/5}$ **52.** $(x^{3/4}y^{1/8}z^{5/6})^{4/5}$

53. $\dfrac{a^{3/4}b^2}{a^{7/8}b^{1/4}}$ **54.** $\dfrac{a^{1/3}b^4}{a^{3/5}b^{1/3}}$ **55.** $\dfrac{(y^{2/3})^{3/4}}{(y^{1/3})^{3/5}}$ **56.** $\dfrac{(y^{5/4})^{2/5}}{(y^{1/4})^{4/3}}$

57. $\dfrac{x \cdot x^{2/3}}{(x^{5/6})^3}$ **58.** $\dfrac{x^3 \cdot x^{1/4}}{(x^{2/5})^2}$ **59.** $\left(\dfrac{a^{-1/4}}{b^{1/2}}\right)^8$ **60.** $\left(\dfrac{a^{-1/5}}{b^{1/3}}\right)^{15}$

Use rational exponents to simplify each expression. Assume all variables represent nonnegative numbers.

61. $\sqrt{25a^6}$ **62.** $\sqrt{64b^8}$ **63.** $\sqrt{x^2y^{10}}$ **64.** $\sqrt{x^4y^{12}}$

65. $\sqrt[3]{27b^9}$ **66.** $\sqrt[3]{8a^{15}}$ **67.** $\sqrt[3]{x^6y^{21}}$ **68.** $\sqrt[3]{x^3y^{18}}$

69. $\sqrt[4]{81a^8b^{20}}$ **70.** $\sqrt[5]{32a^{10}b^{20}}$

71. Show that the expression $(a^{1/2} + b^{1/2})^2$ is not equal to $a + b$ by replacing a with 9 and b with 4 in both expressions and then simplifying each.

72. Show that the statement $(a^2 + b^2)^{1/2} = a + b$ is not, in general, true by replacing a with 3 and b with 4 and then simplifying both sides.

73. You may have noticed, if you have been using a calculator to find roots, that you can find the fourth root of a number by pressing the square root button twice. Written in symbols, this fact looks like this:

$$\sqrt{\sqrt{a}} = \sqrt[4]{a} \qquad (a \geq 0)$$

Show that this statement is true by rewriting each side with exponents instead of radical notation and then simplifying the left side.

74. Show that the statement is true by rewriting each side with exponents instead of radical notation and then simplifying the left side.

$$\sqrt[3]{\sqrt{a}} = \sqrt[6]{a} \qquad (a \geq 0)$$

Applying the Concepts

75. Maximum Speed The maximum speed (v) that an automobile can travel around a curve of radius r without skidding is given by the equation

$$v = \left(\frac{5r}{2}\right)^{1/2}$$

where v is in miles per hour and r is measured in feet. What is the maximum speed a car can travel around a curve with a radius of 250 feet without skidding?

76. Relativity The equation

$$L = \left(1 - \frac{v^2}{c^2}\right)^{1/2}$$

gives the relativistic length of a 1-foot ruler traveling with velocity v. Find L if

$$\frac{v}{c} = \frac{3}{5}$$

Learning Objectives Assessment

The following problems can be used to help assess if you have successfully met the learning objectives for this section.

77. Write $\sqrt{8x}$ using a rational exponent.

    a. $(8x)^{1/2}$ **b.** $8x^{1/2}$ **c.** $(8x)^2$ **d.** $8x^2$

78. Write $-8^{2/3}$ as a root.

    a. $-\sqrt[3]{8^2}$ **b.** $\left(\sqrt[3]{-8}\right)^2$ **c.** $\left(\sqrt{-8}\right)^3$ **d.** $-\sqrt{8^3}$

79. Simplify $\sqrt{64x^6y^{12}}$ using rational exponents.

    a. $4x^3y^6$ **b.** $8x^3y^6$ **c.** $4x^2y^4$ **d.** $8x^2y^4$

80. Simplify: $y^{1/2} \cdot y^{2/3}$.

    a. $y^{1/3}$ **b.** $y^{7/6}$ **c.** $y^{3/5}$ **d.** $y^{-1/6}$

Getting Ready for the Next Section

Simplify. Assume all variables represent positive real numbers.

81. $\sqrt{6^2}$ **82.** $\sqrt{3^2}$ **83.** $\sqrt{(5y)^2}$ **84.** $\sqrt{(8x^3)^2}$

85. $\sqrt[3]{2^3}$ **86.** $\sqrt[3]{(-5)^3}$

Fill in the blank.

87. $50 = \underline{\hspace{1cm}} \cdot 2$ **88.** $12 = \underline{\hspace{1cm}} \cdot 3$

89. $48x^4y^3 = \underline{\hspace{1cm}} \cdot y$ **90.** $40a^5b^4 = \underline{\hspace{1cm}} \cdot 5a^2b$

91. $12x^7y^6 = \underline{\hspace{1cm}} \cdot 3x$ **92.** $54a^6b^2c^4 = \underline{\hspace{1cm}} \cdot 2b^2c$

SPOTLIGHT ON SUCCESS   *Instructor Octabio*

*The best thing about the future
is that it comes one day at a time.*
—Abraham Lincoln

For my family, education was always the way to go. Education would move us ahead, but the path through education was not always clear. My parents had immigrated to this country and had not had the opportunity to continue in education. Luckily, with the help of school counselors and the A.V.I.D. (Advancement Via Individual Determination) program in our school district, my older sister and brother were able to get into some of their top colleges. Later, with A.V.I.D. and the guidance of my siblings, I was able to take the right courses and was lucky enough to be accepted at my dream university.

Math has been my favorite subject ever since I can remember. When I got to higher level math classes, however, I struggled more than I had with previous levels of math. This struggle initially stopped me from enjoying the class, but as my understanding grew, I became more and more interested in seeing how things connected. I have found these connections at all levels of mathematics. These connections continue to be a source of satisfaction for me.

Learning Objectives

In this section, we will learn how to:

1. Simplify a radical expression by writing it as a product.
2. Simplify a radical expression by writing it as a quotient.
3. Simplify fractions containing radicals.
4. Simplify nth roots of nth powers.

Introduction

In this section, we will use radical notation instead of rational exponents. We will begin by stating two more properties of radicals. Following this, we will give a definition for simplified form for radical expressions. The examples in this section show how we use the properties of radicals to write radical expressions in simplified form.

Here are the next two properties of radicals. For these two properties, we will assume a and b are nonnegative real numbers whenever n is an even number.

> **[Δ≠Σ] PROPERTY** *Property 2 for Radicals*
>
> $$\sqrt[n]{ab} = \sqrt[n]{a}\sqrt[n]{b}$$
>
> *In words:* The nth root of a product is the product of the nth roots.
>
> **Proof of Property 2**
>
> $$\sqrt[n]{ab} = (ab)^{1/n} \qquad \text{Definition of fractional exponents}$$
> $$= a^{1/n}b^{1/n} \qquad \text{Exponents distribute over products}$$
> $$= \sqrt[n]{a}\sqrt[n]{b} \qquad \text{Definition of fractional exponents}$$

Note There is not a property for radicals that says the nth root of a sum is the sum of the nth roots. That is,

$$\sqrt[n]{a+b} \neq \sqrt[n]{a} + \sqrt[n]{b}$$

> **[Δ≠Σ] PROPERTY** *Property 3 for Radicals*
>
> $$\sqrt[n]{\frac{a}{b}} = \frac{\sqrt[n]{a}}{\sqrt[n]{b}} \qquad (b \neq 0)$$
>
> *In words:* The nth root of a quotient is the quotient of the nth roots.

The proof of Property 3 is similar to the proof of Property 2.

These two properties of radicals allow us to change the form of and simplify radical expressions without changing their value.

> **RULE** *Simplified Form for Radical Expressions*
>
> A radical expression is in *simplified form* if
>
> 1. None of the factors of the radicand (the quantity under the radical sign) can be written as powers greater than or equal to the index—that is, no perfect squares can be factors of the quantity under a square root sign, no perfect cubes can be factors of what is under a cube root sign, and so forth.
> 2. There are no fractions under the radical sign.
> 3. There are no radicals in the denominator.

Satisfying the first condition for simplified form actually amounts to taking as much out from under the radical sign as possible. The following examples illustrate the first condition for simplified form.

EXAMPLE 1   Write $\sqrt{50}$ in simplified form.

SOLUTION   This radical expression does not meet the first condition for simplified form because the radicand contains a perfect square. The largest perfect square that divides 50 is 25. We write 50 as $25 \cdot 2$ and apply Property 2 for radicals:

$$\sqrt{50} = \sqrt{25 \cdot 2} \qquad 50 = 25 \cdot 2$$
$$= \sqrt{25}\sqrt{2} \qquad \text{Property 2}$$
$$= 5\sqrt{2} \qquad \sqrt{25} = 5$$

We have taken as much as possible out from under the radical sign—in this case, factoring 25 from 50 and then writing $\sqrt{25}$ as 5.

EXAMPLE 2   Write $\sqrt[3]{24}$ in simplified form.

SOLUTION   Once again, our expression does not meet the first condition for simplified form because 24 contains a perfect cube. We write 24 as $8 \cdot 3$ and simplify as we did in Example 1.

$$\sqrt[3]{24} = \sqrt[3]{8 \cdot 3} \qquad 24 = 8 \cdot 3$$
$$= \sqrt[3]{8}\sqrt[3]{3} \qquad \text{Property 2}$$
$$= 2\sqrt[3]{3} \qquad \sqrt[3]{8} = 2$$

Note   In Example 2, we do not want to write 24 as $4 \cdot 6$, because the problem involves a cube root, not a square root. Neither 4 nor 6 are perfect cubes.

As we progress through this chapter you will see more and more expressions that involve the product of a number and a radical. Here are some examples:

$$3\sqrt{2} \qquad \frac{1}{2}\sqrt{5} \qquad 5\sqrt[3]{7} \qquad 3x\sqrt{2x} \qquad 2a^2b\sqrt[3]{5a}$$

All of these are products. The first expression $3\sqrt{2}$ is the product of 3 and $\sqrt{2}$. That is,

$$3\sqrt{2} = 3 \cdot \sqrt{2}$$

The 3 and the $\sqrt{2}$ are not stuck together in some mysterious way. The expression $3\sqrt{2}$ is simply the product of two numbers, one of which is rational, and the other is irrational.

EXAMPLE 3   Write in simplified form: $\sqrt{48x^4y^3}$, where $x, y \geq 0$

SOLUTION   The largest perfect square that is a factor of the radicand is $16x^4y^2$. Applying Property 2, we have

$$\sqrt{48x^4y^3} = \sqrt{16x^4y^2 \cdot 3y}$$
$$= \sqrt{16x^4y^2}\sqrt{3y}$$
$$= 4x^2y\sqrt{3y}$$

EXAMPLE 4   Write $\sqrt[3]{40a^5b^4}$ in simplified form.

SOLUTION   We now want to factor the largest perfect cube from the radicand. We write $40a^5b^4$ as $8a^3b^3 \cdot 5a^2b$ and proceed as in previous examples.

$$\sqrt[3]{40a^5b^4} = \sqrt[3]{8a^3b^3 \cdot 5a^2b}$$
$$= \sqrt[3]{8a^3b^3}\sqrt[3]{5a^2b}$$
$$= 2ab\sqrt[3]{5a^2b}$$

Fractions and Radical Expressions

We now consider some examples that involve fractions and simplified form for radicals.

EXAMPLE 5   Simplify each expression.

a. $\dfrac{\sqrt{12}}{6}$ **b.** $\dfrac{5\sqrt{18}}{15}$ **c.** $\dfrac{6 + \sqrt{8}}{2}$ **d.** $\dfrac{-1 + \sqrt{45}}{2}$

SOLUTION   These expressions are not yet simplified because they do not meet the first condition for simplified form. In each case, we simplify the radical first, then we factor and reduce to lowest terms.

a. $\dfrac{\sqrt{12}}{6} = \dfrac{2\sqrt{3}}{6}$ $\quad$ Simplify the radical

$\qquad\qquad\qquad\qquad$ $\sqrt{12} = \sqrt{4 \cdot 3} = \sqrt{4}\sqrt{3} = 2\sqrt{3}$

$\qquad\quad = \dfrac{2\sqrt{3}}{2 \cdot 3}$ $\quad$ Factor denominator

$\qquad\quad = \dfrac{\sqrt{3}}{3}$ $\quad$ Divide out common factors

b. $\dfrac{5\sqrt{18}}{15} = \dfrac{5 \cdot 3\sqrt{2}}{15}$ $\quad$ $\sqrt{18} = \sqrt{9 \cdot 2} = \sqrt{9}\sqrt{2} = 3\sqrt{2}$

$\qquad\quad = \dfrac{5 \cdot 3\sqrt{2}}{3 \cdot 5}$ $\quad$ Factor denominator

$\qquad\quad = \sqrt{2}$ $\quad$ Divide out common factors

c. $\dfrac{6 + \sqrt{8}}{2} = \dfrac{6 + 2\sqrt{2}}{2}$ $\quad$ $\sqrt{8} = \sqrt{4 \cdot 2} = \sqrt{4}\sqrt{2} = 2\sqrt{2}$

$\qquad\quad = \dfrac{2(3 + \sqrt{2})}{2}$ $\quad$ Factor numerator

$\qquad\quad = 3 + \sqrt{2}$ $\quad$ Divide out common factors

d. $\dfrac{-1 + \sqrt{45}}{2} = \dfrac{-1 + 3\sqrt{5}}{2}$ $\quad$ $\sqrt{45} = \sqrt{9 \cdot 5} = \sqrt{9}\sqrt{5} = 3\sqrt{5}$

This expression cannot be simplified further because $-1 + 3\sqrt{5}$ and 2 have no factors in common.

Note   In Example 5d, we cannot combine $-1 + 3\sqrt{5}$ in the numerator. That is,

$$-1 + 3\sqrt{5} \neq 2\sqrt{5}$$

The reason is that -1 and $3\sqrt{5}$ are not similar terms. We will define similar terms for radicals in the next section.

> **EXAMPLE 6** Simplify: $\sqrt{\dfrac{3}{4}}$.

SOLUTION In this case, we want to eliminate the fraction under the radical sign in order to satisfy condition 2 for simplified form. Applying Property 3 for radicals, we have

$$\sqrt{\dfrac{3}{4}} = \dfrac{\sqrt{3}}{\sqrt{4}} \qquad \text{Property 3}$$

$$= \dfrac{\sqrt{3}}{2} \qquad \sqrt{4} = 2$$

The last expression is now simplified because it satisfies all three conditions for simplified form.

> **EXAMPLE 7** Simplify: $\sqrt[3]{\dfrac{40}{27y^3}}$.

SOLUTION As we did in Example 6, we use Property 3 to avoid having a fraction under the radical sign. Then we simplify each radical.

$$\sqrt[3]{\dfrac{40}{27y^3}} = \dfrac{\sqrt[3]{40}}{\sqrt[3]{27y^3}} \qquad \text{Property 3}$$

$$= \dfrac{\sqrt[3]{8}\sqrt[3]{5}}{3y} \qquad \text{Property 2; } \sqrt[3]{27y^3} = 3y$$

$$= \dfrac{2\sqrt[3]{5}}{3y} \qquad \sqrt[3]{8} = 2$$

> **EXAMPLE 8** Simplify: $\dfrac{\sqrt{10}}{\sqrt{2}}$.

SOLUTION Neither $\sqrt{10}$ nor $\sqrt{2}$ can be simplified. But because of the radical in the denominator, this expression does not meet the third condition for simplified form.

Notice both radicands contain a common factor. By using Property 3 for radicals we can write the expression as a single radical, which will then allow us to reduce the resulting fraction.

$$\dfrac{\sqrt{10}}{\sqrt{2}} = \sqrt{\dfrac{10}{2}} \qquad \text{Property 3}$$

$$= \sqrt{5} \qquad \text{Reduce}$$

The Golden Ratio

In Section 7.1, we used the Pythagorean theorem to show that the diagonal of a square had a length of $\sqrt{2}$. Associating numbers, such as $\sqrt{2}$, with the diagonal of a square or rectangle allows us to analyze some interesting items from geometry. One particularly interesting geometric object is shown in Figure 1.

The Golden Rectangle

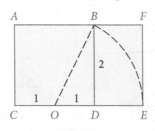

FIGURE 1

Its origins can be traced back over 2,000 years to the Greek civilization that produced Pythagoras, Socrates, Plato, Aristotle, and Euclid. The most important mathematical work to come from that Greek civilization was Euclid's *Elements,* an elegantly written summary of all that was known about geometry at that time in history. Euclid's *Elements,* according to Howard Eves, an authority on the history of mathematics, exercised a greater influence on scientific thinking than any other work. Here is how we construct a golden rectangle from a square of side 2, using the same method that Euclid used in his *Elements.*

Constructing a Golden Rectangle From a Square of Side 2

Step 1: Draw a square with a side of length 2. Connect the midpoint of side *CD* to corner *B.* (Note that we have labeled the midpoint of segment *CD* with the letter *O.*)

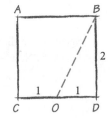

Step 2: Drop the diagonal from step 1 down so it aligns with side *CD.*

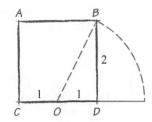

Step 3: Form rectangle *ACEF.* This is a golden rectangle.

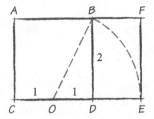

All golden rectangles are constructed from squares. Every golden rectangle, no matter how large or small it is, will have the same shape. To associate a number with the shape of the golden rectangle, we use the ratio of its length to its width. This ratio is called the *golden ratio.*

To calculate the golden ratio, we must first find the length of the diagonal we used to construct the golden rectangle. Figure 2 shows the golden rectangle we constructed from a square of side 2. The length of the diagonal OB is found by applying the Pythagorean theorem to triangle OBD.

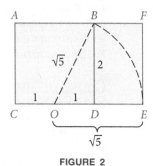

FIGURE 2

The length of segment OE is equal to the length of diagonal OB; both are $\sqrt{5}$. Because the distance from C to O is 1, the length CE of the golden rectangle is $1 + \sqrt{5}$. Now we can find the golden ratio:

$$\text{Golden ratio} = \frac{\text{length}}{\text{width}} = \frac{CE}{EF} = \frac{1 + \sqrt{5}}{2}$$

EXAMPLE 9   Construct a golden rectangle from a square of side 4. Then show that the ratio of the length to the width is the golden ratio $\frac{1+\sqrt{5}}{2}$.

SOLUTION   Figure 3 shows the golden rectangle constructed from a square of side 4. The length of the diagonal OB is found from the Pythagorean theorem.

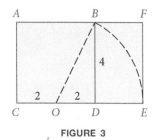

FIGURE 3

$$OB = \sqrt{2^2 + 4^2}$$
$$= \sqrt{4 + 16}$$
$$= \sqrt{20}$$
$$= 2\sqrt{5}$$

The ratio of the length to the width for the rectangle is the golden ratio.

$$\text{Golden ratio} = \frac{CE}{EF}$$
$$= \frac{2 + OE}{4}$$
$$= \frac{2 + OB}{4}$$
$$= \frac{2 + 2\sqrt{5}}{4}$$
$$= \frac{2(1 + \sqrt{5})}{2 \cdot 2}$$
$$= \frac{1 + \sqrt{5}}{2}$$

As you can see, showing that the ratio of length to width in this rectangle is the golden ratio depends on our ability to write $\sqrt{20}$ as $2\sqrt{5}$ and our ability to reduce to lowest terms by factoring and then dividing out the common factor 2 from the numerator and denominator.

Square Root of a Perfect Square

So far in this chapter, we have assumed that all our variables are nonnegative when they appear under a square root symbol. There are times, however, when this is not the case.

Consider $\sqrt{x^2}$, where x is allowed to represent any real number. Let's evaluate this expression for $x = 3$ and $x = -3$.

$$\text{If} \quad x = 3 \qquad\qquad \text{If} \quad x = -3$$

$$\text{then } \sqrt{3^2} = \sqrt{9} = 3 \qquad \text{then } \sqrt{(-3)^2} = \sqrt{9} = 3$$

Whether we operate on 3 or -3, the result is the same: Both expressions simplify to 3. When we used $x = 3$, the result is equal to our value of x. But when we used $x = -3$, the result is the opposite of our x value. The other operation we have worked with in the past that produces the same result is absolute value. That is,

$$|3| = 3 \qquad \text{and} \qquad |-3| = 3$$

This leads us to the fourth property.

> **PROPERTY** *Property 4 for Square Roots*
>
> If a is a real number, then $\sqrt{a^2} = |a|$.

The result of this discussion and Property 4 is simply this:

If we know a is positive, then $\sqrt{a^2} = a$.

If we know a is negative, then $\sqrt{a^2} = -a$.

If we don't know if a is positive or negative, then $\sqrt{a^2} = |a|$.

EXAMPLES Simplify each expression. Do *not* assume the variables represent positive numbers.

10. $\sqrt{9x^2} = \sqrt{9}\sqrt{x^2}$ Property 2

$\qquad = 3|x|$ Property 4

11. $\sqrt{x^3} = \sqrt{x^2}\sqrt{x}$ Property 2

$\qquad = |x|\sqrt{x}$ Property 4

12. $\sqrt{x^2 - 6x + 9} = \sqrt{(x - 3)^2} = |x - 3|$

13. $\sqrt{x^3 - 5x^2} = \sqrt{x^2(x - 5)} = |x|\sqrt{x - 5}$

nth Root of an nth Power

As you can see, we must use absolute value symbols when we take a square root of a perfect square, unless we know the base of the perfect square is a positive number. The same idea holds for higher even roots, but not for odd roots. With odd roots, no absolute value symbols are necessary.

■ **EXAMPLES**   Simplify each expression.

14 $\sqrt[3]{2^3} = \sqrt[3]{8} = 2$

15. $\sqrt[3]{(-2)^3} = \sqrt[3]{-8} = -2$

We can extend this discussion to all roots as follows:

△≠∑ **PROPERTY**   *Property 4 for Radicals*

If a is a real number, then

$$\sqrt[n]{a^n} = |a| \qquad \text{if} \qquad n \text{ is even}$$

$$\sqrt[n]{a^n} = a \qquad \text{if} \qquad n \text{ is odd}$$

■ **EXAMPLES**   Simplify each expression. Do *not* assume the variables represent positive numbers.

16. $\sqrt[3]{(x+2)^3} = x + 2$

17. $\sqrt[3]{-64y^3} = -4y$

18. $\sqrt[4]{81b^4} = 3|b|$

19. $\sqrt[5]{32x^5} = 2x$

Getting Ready for Class

After reading through the preceding section, respond in your own words and in complete sentences.

A. Explain why this statement is false: "The square root of a sum is the sum of the square roots."

B. What is simplified form for an expression that contains a square root?

C. Describe two different ways we used Property 3 for radicals in this section.

D. Why is it not necessarily true that $\sqrt{a^2} = a$?

Use Property 2 for radicals to write each of the following expressions in simplified form. Assume all variables represent positive numbers.

1. $\sqrt{8}$ **2.** $\sqrt{32}$ **3.** $\sqrt{98}$ **4.** $\sqrt{75}$

5. $\sqrt{288}$ **6.** $\sqrt{128}$ **7.** $\sqrt{80}$ **8.** $\sqrt{200}$

9. $\sqrt{48}$ **10.** $\sqrt{27}$ **11.** $\sqrt{675}$ **12.** $\sqrt{972}$

13. $\sqrt[3]{54}$ **14.** $\sqrt[3]{24}$ **15.** $\sqrt[3]{128}$ **16.** $\sqrt[3]{162}$

17. $\sqrt[3]{432}$ **18.** $\sqrt[3]{1,536}$ **19.** $\sqrt[5]{64}$ **20.** $\sqrt[4]{48}$

21. $\sqrt{18x^3}$ **22.** $\sqrt{27x^5}$ **23.** $\sqrt[4]{32y^7}$ **24.** $\sqrt[5]{32y^7}$

25. $\sqrt[3]{40x^4y^7}$ **26.** $\sqrt[3]{128x^6y^2}$ **27.** $\sqrt{48a^2b^3c^4}$ **28.** $\sqrt{72a^4b^3c^2}$

29. $\sqrt[3]{48a^2b^3c^4}$ **30.** $\sqrt[3]{72a^4b^3c^2}$ **31.** $\sqrt[5]{64x^8y^{12}}$ **32.** $\sqrt[4]{32x^9y^{10}}$

33. $\sqrt[5]{243x^7y^{10}z^5}$ **34.** $\sqrt[5]{64x^8y^4z^{11}}$

Substitute the given numbers into the expression $\sqrt{b^2 - 4ac}$, and then simplify, if possible.

35. $a = 2, b = -6, c = 3$ **36.** $a = 6, b = 7, c = -5$

37. $a = 1, b = 2, c = 6$ **38.** $a = 2, b = 5, c = 3$

39. $a = \dfrac{1}{2}, b = -\dfrac{1}{2}, c = -\dfrac{5}{4}$ **40.** $a = \dfrac{7}{4}, b = -\dfrac{3}{4}, c = -2$

Simplify each expression using Property 2 for radicals.

41. $\dfrac{\sqrt{20}}{4}$ **42.** $\dfrac{3\sqrt{20}}{15}$ **43.** $\dfrac{\sqrt{12}}{4}$ **44.** $\dfrac{2\sqrt{32}}{8}$

45. $\dfrac{4 + \sqrt{12}}{2}$ **46.** $\dfrac{2 + \sqrt{9}}{5}$ **47.** $\dfrac{9 + \sqrt{27}}{3}$ **48.** $\dfrac{-6 - \sqrt{64}}{2}$

49. $\dfrac{10 + \sqrt{75}}{5}$ **50.** $\dfrac{-6 + \sqrt{45}}{3}$ **51.** $\dfrac{-2 - \sqrt{27}}{6}$ **52.** $\dfrac{12 - \sqrt{12}}{6}$

53. $\dfrac{-4 - \sqrt{8}}{2}$ **54.** $\dfrac{6 - \sqrt{48}}{8}$

Use Property 3 for radicals to simplify each expression. Assume all variables represent positive numbers.

55. $\sqrt{\dfrac{7}{25}}$ **56.** $\sqrt{\dfrac{13}{64}}$ **57.** $\sqrt{\dfrac{5x}{36}}$ **58.** $\sqrt{\dfrac{3ab}{16}}$

59. $\sqrt[3]{\dfrac{3}{64}}$ **60.** $\sqrt[3]{\dfrac{5}{8}}$ **61.** $\sqrt[3]{\dfrac{2a}{b^3}}$ **62.** $\sqrt[3]{\dfrac{11x^2}{27}}$

63. $\sqrt[4]{\dfrac{9}{16}}$ **64.** $\sqrt[5]{\dfrac{3y^3}{32}}$ **65.** $\dfrac{\sqrt{15}}{\sqrt{3}}$ **66.** $\dfrac{\sqrt{30}}{\sqrt{5}}$

67. $\dfrac{\sqrt[3]{12}}{\sqrt[3]{4}}$ **68.** $\dfrac{\sqrt[3]{18}}{\sqrt[3]{2}}$

Simplify each expression. Assume all variables represent positive numbers.

69. $\sqrt{\dfrac{12x^2}{25}}$ **70.** $\sqrt{\dfrac{5ab^4}{36}}$ **71.** $\sqrt{\dfrac{3x^3}{4y^6}}$ **72.** $\sqrt{\dfrac{28a^7}{9b^2}}$

73. $\sqrt[3]{\dfrac{15b^4}{8a^3}}$ **74.** $\sqrt[3]{\dfrac{81x^2y^5}{64z^3}}$ **75.** $\sqrt[4]{\dfrac{9x^6y^{10}}{16z^8}}$ **76.** $\sqrt[4]{\dfrac{48a^3b^9}{625c^{12}}}$

Simplify each expression. Do *not* assume the variables represent positive numbers.

77. $\sqrt{25x^2}$ **78.** $\sqrt{49x^2}$ **79.** $\sqrt{27x^3y^2}$ **80.** $\sqrt{40x^3y^2}$

81. $\sqrt{x^2 - 10x + 25}$ **82.** $\sqrt{x^2 - 16x + 64}$

83. $\sqrt{4x^2 + 12x + 9}$ **84.** $\sqrt{16x^2 + 40x + 25}$

85. $\sqrt{4a^4 + 16a^3 + 16a^2}$ **86.** $\sqrt{9a^4 + 18a^3 + 9a^2}$

87. $\sqrt{4x^3 - 8x^2}$ **88.** $\sqrt{18x^3 - 9x^2}$

89. Show that the statement $\sqrt{a + b} = \sqrt{a} + \sqrt{b}$ is not true by replacing a with 9 and b with 16 and simplifying both sides.

90. Find a pair of values for a and b that will make the statement $\sqrt{a + b} = \sqrt{a} + \sqrt{b}$ true.

Applying the Concepts

91. Diagonal Distance The distance d between opposite corners of a rectangular room with length l and width w is given by

$$d = \sqrt{l^2 + w^2}$$

How far is it between opposite corners of a living room that measures 10 by 15 feet?

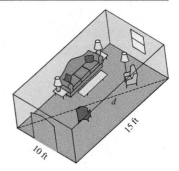

92. Distance to the Horizon If you are at a point k miles above the surface of the Earth, the distance you can see, in miles, is approximated by the equation $d = \sqrt{8000k + k^2}$.

  a. How far can you see from a point that is 1 mile above the surface of the Earth?

  b. How far can you see from a point that is 2 miles above the surface of the Earth?

  c. How far can you see from a point that is 3 miles above the surface of the Earth?

93. Isosceles Right Triangles A triangle is isosceles if it has two equal sides, and a triangle is a right triangle if it has a right angle in it. Sketch an isosceles right triangle, and find the ratio of the hypotenuse to a leg.

94. Equilateral Triangles A triangle is equilateral if it has three equal sides. The triangle in the figure is equilateral with each side of length $2x$. Find the ratio of the height to a side.

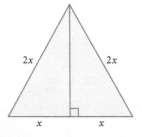

95. Pyramids The following solid is called a regular square pyramid because its base is a square and all eight edges are the same length, 5. It is also true that the vertex, V, is directly above the center of the base.

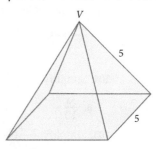

    a. Find the ratio of a diagonal of the base to the length of a side.

    b. Find the ratio of the area of the base to the diagonal of the base.

    c. Find the ratio of the area of the base to the perimeter of the base.

96. Pyramids Refer to this diagram of a square pyramid. Find the ratio of the height h of the pyramid to the slant height a.

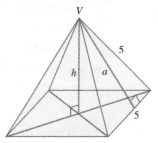

97. Golden Ratio The golden ratio is the ratio of the length to the width in any golden rectangle. The exact value of this number is $\frac{1+\sqrt{5}}{2}$. Use a calculator to find a decimal approximation to this number and round it to the nearest thousandth.

98. Golden Ratio The reciprocal of the golden ratio is $\frac{2}{1+\sqrt{5}}$. Find a decimal approximation to this number that is accurate to the nearest thousandth.

99. Golden Rectangle Construct a golden rectangle from a square of side 8. Then show that the ratio of the length to the width is the golden ratio $\frac{1+\sqrt{5}}{2}$.

100. Golden Rectangle Construct a golden rectangle from a square of side 10. Then show that the ratio of the length to the width is the golden ratio $\frac{1+\sqrt{5}}{2}$.

101. Golden Rectangle To show that all golden rectangles have the same ratio of length to width, construct a golden rectangle from a square of side $2x$. Then show that the ratio of the length to the width is the golden ratio.

102. Golden Rectangle To show that all golden rectangles have the same ratio of length to width, construct a golden rectangle from a square of side x. Then show that the ratio of the length to the width is the golden ratio.

Learning Objectives Assessment

The following problems can be used to help assess if you have successfully met the learning objectives for this section.

103. Simplify: $\sqrt{48}$.

    a. $2\sqrt{12}$ **b.** $4\sqrt{3}$ **c.** $2\sqrt{6}$ **d.** $24\sqrt{2}$

104. Simplify: $\sqrt{\dfrac{27x^2}{100}}$. Assume x is a positive number.

    a. $\dfrac{3x}{10}$ **b.** $\dfrac{3x\sqrt{3}}{10}$ **c.** $\dfrac{9x\sqrt{3}}{10}$ **d.** $\dfrac{3x\sqrt{x}}{5\sqrt{2}}$

105. Simplify: $\dfrac{2+\sqrt{48}}{6}$.

    a. $\dfrac{1+2\sqrt{3}}{3}$ **b.** $\sqrt{3}$ **c.** $\dfrac{1+\sqrt{6}}{3}$ **d.** $\dfrac{1+4\sqrt{3}}{3}$

106. Simplify $\sqrt{(x-4)^2}$ for any real number x.

    a. $x-4$ **b.** $x+4$ **c.** $|x|-4$ **d.** $|x-4|$

Getting Ready for the Next Section

Simplify the following.

107. $5x - 4x + 6x$ **108.** $12x + 8x - 7x$

109. $35xy^2 - 8xy^2$ **110.** $20a^2b + 33a^2b$

111. $\dfrac{1}{2}x + \dfrac{1}{3}x$ **112.** $\dfrac{2}{3}x + \dfrac{5}{8}x$

Write in simplified form for radicals.

113. $\sqrt{18}$ **114.** $\sqrt{8}$

115. $\sqrt{75xy^3}$ **116.** $\sqrt{12xy}$

117. $\sqrt[3]{8a^4b^2}$ **118.** $\sqrt[3]{27ab^2}$

Addition and Subtraction of Radical Expressions

10.4

Learning Objectives

In this section, we will learn how to:

1. Identify similar radicals.
2. Combine similar radicals.

Introduction

In Chapter 1, we found we could add similar terms when combining polynomials. The same idea applies to addition and subtraction of radical expressions.

> **DEFINITION** *similar radicals*
>
> Two radicals are said to be *similar radicals* if they have the same index and the same radicand.

The expressions $5\sqrt[3]{7}$ and $-8\sqrt[3]{7}$ are similar since they both have an index of 3 and a radicand of 7. The expressions $3\sqrt[4]{5}$ and $7\sqrt[3]{5}$ are not similar because they have different indices, and the expressions $2\sqrt[5]{8}$ and $3\sqrt[5]{9}$ are not similar because the radicands are not the same.

We add and subtract radical expressions in the same way we add and subtract polynomials — by combining similar terms under the distributive property.

EXAMPLE 1   Combine: $5\sqrt{3} - 4\sqrt{3} + 6\sqrt{3}$.

SOLUTION   All three radicals are similar. We apply the distributive property to get

$$5\sqrt{3} - 4\sqrt{3} + 6\sqrt{3} = (5 - 4 + 6)\sqrt{3}$$
$$= 7\sqrt{3}$$

EXAMPLE 2   Simplify: $7\sqrt{5} + 2\sqrt{7} - \sqrt{5} + 5\sqrt{7}$.

SOLUTION   First, we group pairs of similar radicals. Then we combine terms in each group using the distributive property.

$$7\sqrt{5} + 2\sqrt{7} - \sqrt{5} + 5\sqrt{7} = (7\sqrt{5} - \sqrt{5}) + (2\sqrt{7} + 5\sqrt{7})$$
$$= (7 - 1)\sqrt{5} + (2 + 5)\sqrt{7}$$
$$= 6\sqrt{5} + 7\sqrt{7}$$

We cannot simplify any further because $6\sqrt{5}$ and $7\sqrt{7}$ are not similar radicals. They have different radicands and so they cannot be combined.

EXAMPLE 3   Combine: $3\sqrt{8} + 5\sqrt{18}$.

SOLUTION The two radicals do not seem to be similar. We must write each in simplified form before applying the distributive property.

$$
\begin{aligned}
3\sqrt{8} + 5\sqrt{18} &= 3\sqrt{4 \cdot 2} + 5\sqrt{9 \cdot 2} \\
&= 3\sqrt{4}\,\sqrt{2} + 5\sqrt{9}\,\sqrt{2} \\
&= 3 \cdot 2\,\sqrt{2} + 5 \cdot 3\,\sqrt{2} \\
&= 6\,\sqrt{2} + 15\,\sqrt{2} \\
&= (6 + 15)\,\sqrt{2} \\
&= 21\,\sqrt{2}
\end{aligned}
$$

The result of Example 3 can be generalized to the following rule for sums and differences of radical expressions.

> **RULE**
>
> To add or subtract radical expressions, put each in simplified form and apply the distributive property, if possible. We can only add similar radicals. We must write each expression in simplified form for radicals before we can tell if the radicals are similar.

EXAMPLE 4   Combine $7\sqrt{75xy^3} - 4y\sqrt{12xy}$, where $x, y \geq 0$.

SOLUTION We write each expression in simplified form and combine similar radicals:

$$
\begin{aligned}
7\sqrt{75xy^3} - 4y\sqrt{12xy} &= 7\sqrt{25y^2}\,\sqrt{3xy} - 4y\sqrt{4}\,\sqrt{3xy} \\
&= 7 \cdot 5y\sqrt{3xy} - 4y \cdot 2\sqrt{3xy} \\
&= 35y\sqrt{3xy} - 8y\sqrt{3xy} \\
&= (35y - 8y)\sqrt{3xy} \\
&= 27y\sqrt{3xy}
\end{aligned}
$$

EXAMPLE 5   Combine: $10\sqrt[3]{8a^4b^2} + 11a\sqrt[3]{27ab^2}$.

SOLUTION Writing each radical in simplified form and combining similar terms, we have

$$
\begin{aligned}
10\sqrt[3]{8a^4b^2} + 11a\sqrt[3]{27ab^2} &= 10\sqrt[3]{8a^3}\,\sqrt[3]{ab^2} + 11a\sqrt[3]{27}\,\sqrt[3]{ab^2} \\
&= 10 \cdot 2a\sqrt[3]{ab^2} + 11a \cdot 3\sqrt[3]{ab^2} \\
&= 20a\sqrt[3]{ab^2} + 33a\sqrt[3]{ab^2} \\
&= 53a\sqrt[3]{ab^2}
\end{aligned}
$$

EXAMPLE 6   Combine: $\dfrac{\sqrt{3}}{2} + \dfrac{\sqrt{12}}{6}$.

SOLUTION   We begin by writing the second term in simplified form.

$$\dfrac{\sqrt{3}}{2} + \dfrac{\sqrt{12}}{6} = \dfrac{\sqrt{3}}{2} + \dfrac{\sqrt{4}\sqrt{3}}{6}$$

$$= \dfrac{\sqrt{3}}{2} + \dfrac{2\sqrt{3}}{6}$$

$$= \dfrac{\sqrt{3}}{2} + \dfrac{\sqrt{3}}{3}$$

$$= \dfrac{1}{2}\sqrt{3} + \dfrac{1}{3}\sqrt{3}$$

$$= \left(\dfrac{1}{2} + \dfrac{1}{3}\right)\sqrt{3}$$

$$= \dfrac{5}{6}\sqrt{3}$$

$$= \dfrac{5\sqrt{3}}{6}$$

EXAMPLE 7   Simplify: $3x\sqrt{54} - 4y\sqrt{24}$.

SOLUTION   First, we simplify each radical expression.

$$3x\sqrt{54} - 4y\sqrt{24} = 3x\sqrt{9}\sqrt{6} - 4y\sqrt{4}\sqrt{6}$$

$$= 9x\sqrt{6} - 8y\sqrt{6}$$

Although the two expressions contain similar radicals, they are not similar terms because of the different variable factors. They cannot be combined, though we can still apply the distributive property to factor out the similar radical.

$$9x\sqrt{6} - 8y\sqrt{6} = (9x - 8y)\sqrt{6}$$

Getting Ready for Class

After reading through the preceding section, respond in your own words and in complete sentences.

A. What are similar radicals?

B. When can we add two radical expressions?

C. What is the first step when adding or subtracting expressions containing radicals?

D. Explain why $2 + 4\sqrt{5} \neq 6\sqrt{5}$.

Problem Set 10.4

Simplify the following expressions by combining similar radicals. Assume any variables under an even root are nonnegative.

1. $3\sqrt{5} + 4\sqrt{5}$

2. $6\sqrt{3} - 5\sqrt{3}$

3. $3x\sqrt{7} - 4x\sqrt{7}$

4. $6y\sqrt{a} + 7y\sqrt{a}$

5. $5\sqrt[3]{10} - 4\sqrt[3]{10}$

6. $6\sqrt[4]{2} + 9\sqrt[4]{2}$

7. $8\sqrt[5]{6} - 2\sqrt[5]{6} + 3\sqrt[5]{6}$

8. $7\sqrt[6]{7} - \sqrt[6]{7} + 4\sqrt[6]{7}$

9. $3x\sqrt{2} - 4x\sqrt{2} + x\sqrt{2}$

10. $5x\sqrt{6} - 3x\sqrt{6} - 2x\sqrt{6}$

11. $4\sqrt{2} + \sqrt{3} + 3\sqrt{2} + 2\sqrt{3}$

12. $\sqrt{5} - 2\sqrt{6} + 9\sqrt{5} + 6\sqrt{6}$

13. $6\sqrt{x} - 5\sqrt{y} - 4\sqrt{x} - 7\sqrt{y}$

14. $\sqrt[3]{2a} + 2\sqrt[3]{2a} + 8\sqrt[3]{3b} - 7\sqrt[3]{2a}$

15. $5\sqrt{3} + 4\sqrt[3]{3} + \sqrt{3} - 3\sqrt[3]{3}$

16. $3\sqrt[3]{2} - \sqrt{2} - 6\sqrt[3]{2} + 9\sqrt{2}$

17. $\sqrt{20} - \sqrt{80} + \sqrt{45}$

18. $\sqrt{8} - \sqrt{32} - \sqrt{18}$

19. $4\sqrt{8} - 2\sqrt{50} - 5\sqrt{72}$

20. $\sqrt{48} - 3\sqrt{27} + 2\sqrt{75}$

21. $5x\sqrt{8} + 3\sqrt{32x^2} - 5\sqrt{50x^2}$

22. $2\sqrt{50x^2} - 8x\sqrt{18} - 3\sqrt{72x^2}$

23. $5\sqrt[3]{16} - 4\sqrt[3]{54}$

24. $\sqrt[3]{81} + 3\sqrt[3]{24}$

25. $\sqrt[3]{x^4y^2} + 7x\sqrt[3]{xy^2}$

26. $2\sqrt[3]{x^8y^6} - 3y^2\sqrt[3]{8x^8}$

27. $5a^2\sqrt{27ab^3} - 6b\sqrt{12a^5b}$

28. $9a\sqrt{20a^3b^2} + 7b\sqrt{45a^5}$

29. $b\sqrt[3]{24a^5b} + 3a\sqrt[3]{81a^2b^4}$

30. $7\sqrt[3]{a^4b^3c^2} - 6ab\sqrt[3]{ac^2}$

31. $5x\sqrt[4]{3y^5} + y\sqrt[4]{243x^4y} + \sqrt[4]{48x^4y^5}$

32. $x\sqrt[4]{5xy^8} + y\sqrt[4]{405x^5y^4} + y^2\sqrt[4]{80x^5}$

33. $\dfrac{\sqrt{3}}{2} + \dfrac{\sqrt{27}}{2}$

34. $\dfrac{\sqrt{5}}{3} - \dfrac{\sqrt{20}}{3}$

35. $\sqrt{\dfrac{5}{36}} + \dfrac{\sqrt{45}}{6}$

36. $\sqrt{\dfrac{18}{25}} - \dfrac{\sqrt{8}}{5}$

37. $\dfrac{\sqrt{x}}{3} - \dfrac{\sqrt{x}}{2}$

38. $\dfrac{3\sqrt{a}}{5} + \dfrac{\sqrt{a}}{3}$

39. $\dfrac{\sqrt{18}}{6} + \sqrt{\dfrac{2}{9}}$

40. $\dfrac{\sqrt{12}}{6} + \sqrt{\dfrac{3}{16}}$

41. $2x\sqrt{8} + 3y\sqrt{50}$

42. $4a\sqrt{12} - 3b\sqrt{27}$

43. $2\sqrt[3]{16x^3} - \sqrt[3]{54}$

44. $\sqrt[3]{125x^3y} + 2\sqrt[3]{8y^4}$

45. Use a calculator to find a decimal approximation for $\sqrt{2} + \sqrt{3}$ and for $\sqrt{5}$.

46. Use a calculator to find decimal approximations for $\sqrt{7} - \sqrt{5}$ and $\sqrt{2}$.

47. Use a calculator to find a decimal approximation for $\sqrt{8} + \sqrt{18}$. Is it equal to the decimal approximation for $\sqrt{26}$ or $\sqrt{50}$?

48. Use a calculator to find a decimal approximation for $\sqrt{3} + \sqrt{12}$. Is it equal to the decimal approximation for $\sqrt{15}$ or $\sqrt{27}$?

Each of the following statements is false. Correct the right side of each one to make the statement true.

49. $3\sqrt{2x} + 5\sqrt{2x} = 8\sqrt{4x}$

50. $5\sqrt{3} - 7\sqrt{3} = -2\sqrt{9}$

51. $\sqrt{9 + 16} = 3 + 4$

52. $\sqrt{36 + 64} = 6 + 8$

Learning Objectives Assessment

The following problems can be used to help assess if you have successfully met the learning objectives for this section.

53. Which pair of radicals are similar?

    a. $4x\sqrt[3]{5}, \frac{1}{2}x\sqrt[3]{5}$ **b.** $4x\sqrt[3]{5}, 2\sqrt[3]{5y}$ **c.** $4\sqrt{5}, 2\sqrt[3]{5}$ **d.** $4x\sqrt{2}, x\sqrt{3}$

54. Combine: $\sqrt{48} + \sqrt{75}$.

    a. $\sqrt{123}$ **b.** $9\sqrt{6}$ **c.** $41\sqrt{3}$ **d.** $9\sqrt{3}$

Getting Ready for the Next Section

Simplify the following.

55. $3 \cdot 2$ **56.** $5 \cdot 7$

57. $(x + y)(4x - y)$ **58.** $(2x + y)(x - y)$

59. $(x + 3)^2$ **60.** $(3x - 2y)^2$

61. $(x - 2)(x + 2)$ **62.** $(2x + 5)(2x - 5)$

Simplify the following expressions.

63. $2\sqrt{18}$ **64.** $5\sqrt{36}$

65. $(\sqrt{6})^2$ **66.** $(\sqrt{2})^2$

67. $(3\sqrt{x})^2$ **68.** $(2\sqrt{y})^2$

Learning Objectives

In this section, we will learn how to:

1. Multiply radicals.
2. Simplify products involving radicals.
3. Divide radicals.
4. Rationalize the denominator.

Introduction

In Section 7.3, we introduced the golden rectangle. An example of a golden rectangle is shown in Figure 1.

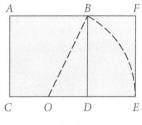

FIGURE 1

By now you know that, in any golden rectangle constructed from a square (of any size), the ratio of the length to the width will be

$$\frac{1 + \sqrt{5}}{2}$$

which we call the golden ratio. What is interesting is that the smaller rectangle on the right, *BFED*, shown in Figure 1, is also a golden rectangle. We will use the mathematics developed in this section to confirm this fact.

In this section, we will look at multiplication and division of expressions that contain radicals. As you will see, multiplication of expressions that contain radicals is very similar to multiplication of polynomials. The division problems in this section are an extension of the work we did previously in Section 7.3.

Multiplication of Radical Expressions

EXAMPLE 1   Multiply $(3\sqrt{5})(2\sqrt{7})$.

SOLUTION   We can rearrange the order and grouping of the numbers in this product by applying the commutative and associative properties. Following this, we apply Property 2 for radicals and multiply:

$$(3\sqrt{5})(2\sqrt{7}) = (3 \cdot 2)(\sqrt{5}\sqrt{7}) \qquad \text{Communicative and associative properties}$$

$$= (3 \cdot 2)(\sqrt{5 \cdot 7}) \qquad \text{Property 2 for radicals}$$

$$= 6\sqrt{35} \qquad \text{Multiplication}$$

In practice, it is not necessary to show the first two steps.

EXAMPLE 2   Multiply $\sqrt{3}(2\sqrt{6} - 5\sqrt{12})$.

SOLUTION   Applying the distributive property, we have

$$\sqrt{3}(2\sqrt{6} - 5\sqrt{12}) = \sqrt{3} \cdot 2\sqrt{6} - \sqrt{3} \cdot 5\sqrt{12}$$
$$= 2\sqrt{18} - 5\sqrt{36}$$

Writing each radical in simplified form gives

$$2\sqrt{18} - 5\sqrt{36} = 2\sqrt{9}\sqrt{2} - 5\sqrt{36}$$
$$= 2 \cdot 3\sqrt{2} - 5 \cdot 6$$
$$= 6\sqrt{2} - 30$$

EXAMPLE 3   Multiply $(\sqrt{3} + \sqrt{5})(4\sqrt{3} - \sqrt{5})$.

SOLUTION   The same principle that applies when multiplying two binomials applies to this product. We must multiply each term in the first expression by each term in the second one. Any convenient method can be used. Let's use the FOIL method.

$$\underset{FOIL}{(\sqrt{3} + \sqrt{5})(4\sqrt{3} - \sqrt{5}) = \sqrt{3} \cdot 4\sqrt{3} - \sqrt{3} \cdot \sqrt{5} + \sqrt{5} \cdot 4\sqrt{3} - \sqrt{5} \cdot \sqrt{5}}$$
$$= 4 \cdot 3 - \sqrt{15} + 4\sqrt{15} - 5$$
$$= 12 + 3\sqrt{15} - 5$$
$$= 7 + 3\sqrt{15}$$

EXAMPLE 4   Expand and simplify $(\sqrt{x} + 3)^2$.

SOLUTION 1   We can write this problem as a multiplication problem and proceed as we did in Example 3:

$$(\sqrt{x} + 3)^2 = (\sqrt{x} + 3)(\sqrt{x} + 3)$$

$$\underset{FOIL}{= \sqrt{x} \cdot \sqrt{x} + 3\sqrt{x} + 3\sqrt{x} + 3 \cdot 3}$$
$$= x + 3\sqrt{x} + 3\sqrt{x} + 9$$
$$= x + 6\sqrt{x} + 9$$

SOLUTION 2   We can obtain the same result by applying the formula for the square of a sum: $(a + b)^2 = a^2 + 2ab + b^2$.

$$(\sqrt{x} + 3)^2 = (\sqrt{x})^2 + 2(\sqrt{x})(3) + 3^2$$
$$= x + 6\sqrt{x} + 9$$

EXAMPLE 5   Expand $(3\sqrt{x} - 2\sqrt{y})^2$ and simplify the result.

SOLUTION   Let's apply the formula for the square of a difference, $(a - b)^2 = a^2 - 2ab + b^2$.

$$(3\sqrt{x} - 2\sqrt{y})^2 = (3\sqrt{x})^2 - 2(3\sqrt{x})(2\sqrt{y}) + (2\sqrt{y})^2$$
$$= 9x - 12\sqrt{xy} + 4y$$

EXAMPLE 6 Expand and simplify $(\sqrt{x+2} - 1)^2$.

SOLUTION Applying the formula $(a - b)^2 = a^2 - 2ab + b^2$, we have

$$(\sqrt{x+2} - 1)^2 = (\sqrt{x+2})^2 - 2\sqrt{x+2}(1) + 1^2$$
$$= x + 2 - 2\sqrt{x+2} + 1$$
$$= x + 3 - 2\sqrt{x+2}$$

EXAMPLE 7 Multiply $(\sqrt{6} + \sqrt{2})(\sqrt{6} - \sqrt{2})$.

SOLUTION We notice the product is of the form $(a + b)(a - b)$, which always gives the difference of two squares, $a^2 - b^2$:

$$(\sqrt{6} + \sqrt{2})(\sqrt{6} - \sqrt{2}) = (\sqrt{6})^2 - (\sqrt{2})^2$$
$$= 6 - 2$$
$$= 4$$

In Example 7, the two expressions $(\sqrt{6} + \sqrt{2})$ and $(\sqrt{6} - \sqrt{2})$ are called *conjugates*. In general, the conjugate of $\sqrt{a} + \sqrt{b}$ is $\sqrt{a} - \sqrt{b}$. If a and b are positive rational numbers, multiplying conjugates of this form always produces a rational number. That is, if a and b are positive rational numbers, then

$$(\sqrt{a} + \sqrt{b})(\sqrt{a} - \sqrt{b}) = \sqrt{a}\sqrt{a} - \sqrt{a}\sqrt{b} + \sqrt{a}\sqrt{b} - \sqrt{b}\sqrt{b}$$
$$= a - \sqrt{ab} + \sqrt{ab} - b$$
$$= a - b$$

which is rational if a and b are positive rational numbers. Later in this section, we will see how the conjugate can be used to simplify certain quotients containing radicals.

Division of Radical Expressions

EXAMPLE 8 Divide: $\dfrac{6\sqrt{14}}{2\sqrt{7}}$.

SOLUTION We begin by writing the expression as a product of two fractions. Then we can use Property 3 to simplify the fraction containing the radicals.

$$\frac{6\sqrt{14}}{2\sqrt{7}} = \frac{6}{2} \cdot \frac{\sqrt{14}}{\sqrt{7}}$$

$$= \frac{6}{2} \cdot \sqrt{\frac{14}{7}} \quad \text{Property 3}$$

$$= 3\sqrt{2} \quad \text{Reduce}$$

EXAMPLE 9   Divide: $\dfrac{3\sqrt{60}}{4\sqrt{3}}$.

SOLUTION   Following our process from the previous example, we have

$$\frac{3\sqrt{60}}{4\sqrt{3}} = \frac{3}{4} \cdot \frac{\sqrt{60}}{\sqrt{3}}$$

$$= \frac{3}{4} \cdot \sqrt{20}$$

Now we simplify the remaining radical expression and reduce if possible.

$$\frac{3\sqrt{20}}{4} = \frac{3 \cdot 2\sqrt{5}}{2 \cdot 2} \qquad \sqrt{20} = \sqrt{4}\sqrt{5} = 2\sqrt{5}$$

$$= \frac{3\sqrt{5}}{2} \qquad \text{Reduce}$$

Rationalizing the Denominator

Next we look at some examples that involve radicals in quotients. When simplifying these expressions, our motivation is to satisfy the second and third conditions for simplified form for radicals that we introduced in Section 7.3.

EXAMPLE 10   Write $\sqrt{\dfrac{5}{6}}$ in simplified form.

SOLUTION   Using Property 3 for radicals, we have

$$\sqrt{\frac{5}{6}} = \frac{\sqrt{5}}{\sqrt{6}}$$

Note The phrase "rationalizing the denominator" is used because we have changed the denominator from $\sqrt{6}$, which is an irrational number, into $\sqrt{36} = 6$, which is a rational number.

The resulting expression satisfies the second condition for simplified form because neither radical contains a fraction. It does, however, violate Condition 3 because it has a radical in the denominator. Getting rid of the radical in the denominator is called *rationalizing the denominator* and is accomplished by turning the radicand in the denominator into a perfect square. In this case, we can do this by multiplying the numerator and denominator by $\sqrt{6}$:

$$\frac{\sqrt{5}}{\sqrt{6}} = \frac{\sqrt{5}}{\sqrt{6}} \cdot \frac{\sqrt{6}}{\sqrt{6}} \qquad \text{Equivalent fraction}$$

$$= \frac{\sqrt{30}}{\sqrt{36}} \qquad \text{Property 2 for radicals}$$

$$= \frac{\sqrt{30}}{6}$$

EXAMPLES   Rationalize the denominator.

11. $\dfrac{4}{\sqrt{3}} = \dfrac{4}{\sqrt{3}} \cdot \dfrac{\sqrt{3}}{\sqrt{3}}$

$$= \frac{4\sqrt{3}}{\sqrt{3^2}}$$

$$= \frac{4\sqrt{3}}{3}$$

12. $\dfrac{2\sqrt{3x}}{\sqrt{5y}} = \dfrac{2\sqrt{3x}}{\sqrt{5y}} \cdot \dfrac{\sqrt{5y}}{\sqrt{5y}}$

$$= \frac{2\sqrt{15xy}}{\sqrt{(5y)^2}}$$

$$= \frac{2\sqrt{15xy}}{5y}$$

When the denominator involves a cube root, we must multiply by a radical that will produce a perfect cube under the cube root sign in the denominator, as Example 13 illustrates.

EXAMPLE 13 Rationalize the denominator in $\dfrac{7}{\sqrt[3]{4}}$.

SOLUTION Because $4 = 2^2$, we can multiply both numerator and denominator by $\sqrt[3]{2}$ and obtain $\sqrt[3]{2^3}$ in the denominator.

$$\frac{7}{\sqrt[3]{4}} = \frac{7}{\sqrt[3]{2^2}}$$

$$= \frac{7}{\sqrt[3]{2^2}} \cdot \frac{\sqrt[3]{2}}{\sqrt[3]{2}}$$

$$= \frac{7\sqrt[3]{2}}{\sqrt[3]{2^3}}$$

$$= \frac{7\sqrt[3]{2}}{2}$$

EXAMPLE 14 Simplify: $\sqrt{\dfrac{12x^5y^3}{5z}}$. Assume all variables represent positive numbers.

SOLUTION We use Property 3 to write the numerator and denominator as two separate radicals:

$$\sqrt{\frac{12x^5y^3}{5z}} = \frac{\sqrt{12x^5y^3}}{\sqrt{5z}}$$

Simplifying the numerator, we have

$$\frac{\sqrt{12x^5y^3}}{\sqrt{5z}} = \frac{\sqrt{4x^4y^2}\sqrt{3xy}}{\sqrt{5z}}$$

$$= \frac{2x^2y\sqrt{3xy}}{\sqrt{5z}}$$

To rationalize the denominator, we multiply the numerator and denominator by $\sqrt{5z}$:

$$\frac{2x^2y\sqrt{3xy}}{\sqrt{5z}} \cdot \frac{\sqrt{5z}}{\sqrt{5z}} = \frac{2x^2y\sqrt{15xyz}}{\sqrt{(5z)^2}}$$

$$= \frac{2x^2y\sqrt{15xyz}}{5z}$$

EXAMPLE 15 Rationalize the denominator: $\dfrac{6}{\sqrt{5} - \sqrt{3}}$.

SOLUTION Because the product of two conjugates is a rational number, we multiply the numerator and denominator by the conjugate of the denominator.

$$\frac{6}{\sqrt{5} - \sqrt{3}} = \frac{6}{\sqrt{5} - \sqrt{3}} \cdot \frac{(\sqrt{5} + \sqrt{3})}{(\sqrt{5} + \sqrt{3})}$$

$$= \frac{6\sqrt{5} + 6\sqrt{3}}{(\sqrt{5})^2 - (\sqrt{3})^2}$$

$$= \frac{6\sqrt{5} + 6\sqrt{3}}{5 - 3}$$

$$= \frac{6\sqrt{5} + 6\sqrt{3}}{2}$$

The numerator and denominator of this last expression have a factor of 2 in common.

We can reduce to lowest terms by factoring 2 from the numerator and then dividing both the numerator and denominator by 2:

$$= \frac{2(3\sqrt{5} + 3\sqrt{3})}{2}$$

$$= 3\sqrt{5} + 3\sqrt{3}$$

EXAMPLE 16   Rationalize the denominator: $\dfrac{\sqrt{5} - 2}{\sqrt{5} + 2}$.

SOLUTION   To rationalize the denominator, we multiply the numerator and denominator by the conjugate of the denominator:

$$\frac{\sqrt{5} - 2}{\sqrt{5} + 2} = \frac{\sqrt{5} - 2}{\sqrt{5} + 2} \cdot \frac{(\sqrt{5} - 2)}{(\sqrt{5} - 2)}$$

$$= \frac{5 - 2\sqrt{5} - 2\sqrt{5} + 4}{(\sqrt{5})^2 - 2^2}$$

$$= \frac{9 - 4\sqrt{5}}{5 - 4}$$

$$= \frac{9 - 4\sqrt{5}}{1}$$

$$= 9 - 4\sqrt{5}$$

Applications

EXAMPLE 17   A golden rectangle constructed from a square of side 2 is shown in Figure 2. Show that the smaller rectangle *BDEF* is also a golden rectangle by finding the ratio of its length to its width.

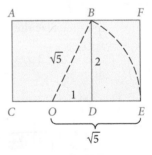

FIGURE 2

SOLUTION   First, find expressions for the length and width of the smaller rectangle.

$$\text{Length} = EF = 2$$

$$\text{Width} = DE = \sqrt{5} - 1$$

Next, we find the ratio of length to width.

$$\text{Ratio of length to width} = \frac{EF}{DE} = \frac{2}{\sqrt{5} - 1}$$

To show that the small rectangle is a golden rectangle, we must show that the ratio of length to width is the golden ratio. We do so by rationalizing the denominator.

$$\frac{2}{\sqrt{5}-1} = \frac{2}{\sqrt{5}-1} \cdot \frac{\sqrt{5}+1}{\sqrt{5}+1}$$

$$= \frac{2(\sqrt{5}+1)}{5-1}$$

$$= \frac{2(\sqrt{5}+1)}{4}$$

$$= \frac{\sqrt{5}+1}{2} \qquad \text{Divide out common factor 2}$$

Because addition is commutative, this last expression is the golden ratio. Therefore, the small rectangle in Figure 2 is a golden rectangle.

Getting Ready for Class

After reading through the preceding section, respond in your own words and in complete sentences.

A. Explain why $(\sqrt{5} + \sqrt{2})^2 \neq 5 + 2$.

B. What are conjugates?

C. What result is guaranteed when multiplying radical expressions that are conjugates?

D. How is rationalizing the denominator for $\frac{3}{\sqrt{5}-2}$ different than for $\frac{3}{\sqrt{5}}$?

Problem Set 10.5

Assume all expressions appearing under a square root symbol represent positive numbers throughout this problem set.

Multiply.

1. $\sqrt{6}\sqrt{3}$　　　　　　　　　　　**2.** $\sqrt{6}\sqrt{2}$

3. $(2\sqrt{3})(5\sqrt{7})$　　　　　　　　**4.** $(3\sqrt{5})(2\sqrt{7})$

5. $(4\sqrt{6})(2\sqrt{15})(3\sqrt{10})$　　**6.** $(4\sqrt{35})(2\sqrt{21})(5\sqrt{15})$

7. $(3\sqrt[3]{3})(6\sqrt[3]{9})$　　　　　　**8.** $(2\sqrt[3]{2})(6\sqrt[3]{4})$

9. $\sqrt{3}(\sqrt{2} - 3\sqrt{3})$　　　　　**10.** $\sqrt{2}(5\sqrt{3} + 4\sqrt{2})$

11. $6\sqrt[3]{4}(2\sqrt[3]{2} + 1)$　　　　**12.** $7\sqrt[3]{5}(3\sqrt[3]{25} - 2)$

13. $(\sqrt{3} + \sqrt{2})(3\sqrt{3} - \sqrt{2})$　**14.** $(\sqrt{5} - \sqrt{2})(3\sqrt{5} + 2\sqrt{2})$

15. $(\sqrt{x} + 5)(\sqrt{x} - 3)$　　　　**16.** $(\sqrt{x} + 4)(\sqrt{x} + 2)$

17. $(3\sqrt{6} + 4\sqrt{2})(\sqrt{6} + 2\sqrt{2})$　**18.** $(\sqrt{7} - 3\sqrt{3})(2\sqrt{7} - 4\sqrt{3})$

19. $(\sqrt{3} + 4)^2$　　　　　　　　**20.** $(\sqrt{5} - 2)^2$

21. $(\sqrt{x} - 3)^2$　　　　　　　　**22.** $(\sqrt{x} + 4)^2$

23. $(2\sqrt{a} - 3\sqrt{b})^2$　　　　　**24.** $(5\sqrt{a} - 2\sqrt{b})^2$

25. $(\sqrt{x - 4} + 2)^2$　　　　　　**26.** $(\sqrt{x - 3} + 2)^2$

27. $(\sqrt{x - 5} - 3)^2$　　　　　　**28.** $(\sqrt{x - 3} - 4)^2$

29. $(\sqrt{3} - \sqrt{2})(\sqrt{3} + \sqrt{2})$　**30.** $(\sqrt{5} - \sqrt{2})(\sqrt{5} + \sqrt{2})$

31. $(\sqrt{a} + 7)(\sqrt{a} - 7)$　　　　**32.** $(\sqrt{a} + 5)(\sqrt{a} - 5)$

33. $(5 - \sqrt{x})(5 + \sqrt{x})$　　　　**34.** $(3 - \sqrt{x})(3 + \sqrt{x})$

35. $(\sqrt{x - 4} + 2)(\sqrt{x - 4} - 2)$　**36.** $(\sqrt{x + 3} + 5)(\sqrt{x + 3} - 5)$

37. $(\sqrt{3} + 1)^3$　　　　　　　　**38.** $(\sqrt{5} - 2)^3$

Divide.

39. $\dfrac{\sqrt{30}}{\sqrt{6}}$　　**40.** $\dfrac{\sqrt{21}}{\sqrt{3}}$　　**41.** $\dfrac{6\sqrt{10}}{3\sqrt{2}}$　　**42.** $\dfrac{8\sqrt{15}}{2\sqrt{5}}$

43. $\dfrac{\sqrt[3]{12}}{\sqrt[3]{3}}$　　**44.** $\dfrac{\sqrt[3]{60}}{\sqrt[3]{4}}$　　**45.** $\dfrac{2\sqrt[3]{18}}{12\sqrt[3]{9}}$　　**46.** $\dfrac{4\sqrt[3]{42}}{10\sqrt[3]{6}}$

47. $\dfrac{3x\sqrt{24}}{9\sqrt{2}}$　　**48.** $\dfrac{5\sqrt{54x^2}}{35\sqrt{3}}$　　**49.** $\dfrac{11\sqrt{40ab^3}}{2\sqrt{5ab}}$　　**50.** $\dfrac{3\sqrt{120x^2y^3}}{4x\sqrt{6y}}$

Rationalize the denominator in each of the following expressions.

51. $\dfrac{2}{\sqrt{3}}$　　**52.** $\dfrac{3}{\sqrt{2}}$　　**53.** $\dfrac{5}{\sqrt{6}}$　　**54.** $\dfrac{7}{\sqrt{5}}$

55. $\sqrt{\dfrac{1}{2}}$　　**56.** $\sqrt{\dfrac{1}{3}}$　　**57.** $\sqrt{\dfrac{1}{5}}$　　**58.** $\sqrt{\dfrac{1}{6}}$

59. $\dfrac{4}{\sqrt[3]{2}}$　　**60.** $\dfrac{5}{\sqrt[3]{3}}$　　**61.** $\dfrac{2}{\sqrt[3]{9}}$　　**62.** $\dfrac{3}{\sqrt[3]{4}}$

63. $\sqrt[4]{\dfrac{3}{2x^2}}$　　**64.** $\sqrt[4]{\dfrac{5}{3x^2}}$　　**65.** $\sqrt[4]{\dfrac{8}{y}}$　　**66.** $\sqrt[4]{\dfrac{27}{y}}$

67. $\sqrt[3]{\dfrac{4x}{3y}}$　　**68.** $\sqrt[3]{\dfrac{7x}{6y}}$　　**69.** $\sqrt[3]{\dfrac{2x}{9y}}$　　**70.** $\sqrt[3]{\dfrac{5x}{4y}}$

Write each of the following in simplified form.

71. $\sqrt{\dfrac{27x^3}{5y}}$

72. $\sqrt{\dfrac{12x^5}{7y}}$

73. $\sqrt{\dfrac{75x^3y^2}{2z}}$

74. $\sqrt{\dfrac{50x^2y^3}{3z}}$

Rationalize the denominator.

75. a. $\dfrac{1}{\sqrt{2}}$ **b.** $\dfrac{1}{\sqrt[3]{2}}$ **c.** $\dfrac{1}{\sqrt[4]{2}}$

76. a. $\dfrac{1}{\sqrt{3}}$ **b.** $\dfrac{1}{\sqrt[3]{9}}$ **c.** $\dfrac{1}{\sqrt[4]{27}}$

Simplify the following expressions by combining similar radicals. Assume any variables under an even root are positive.

77. $\dfrac{\sqrt{2}}{2} + \dfrac{1}{\sqrt{2}}$

78. $\dfrac{\sqrt{3}}{3} + \dfrac{1}{\sqrt{3}}$

79. $\dfrac{\sqrt{5}}{3} + \dfrac{1}{\sqrt{5}}$

80. $\dfrac{\sqrt{6}}{2} + \dfrac{1}{\sqrt{6}}$

81. $\sqrt{x} - \dfrac{1}{\sqrt{x}}$

82. $\sqrt{x} + \dfrac{1}{\sqrt{x}}$

83. $\dfrac{\sqrt{18}}{6} + \sqrt{\dfrac{1}{2}} + \dfrac{\sqrt{2}}{2}$

84. $\dfrac{\sqrt{12}}{6} + \sqrt{\dfrac{1}{3}} + \dfrac{\sqrt{3}}{3}$

85. $\sqrt{6} - \sqrt{\dfrac{2}{3}} + \sqrt{\dfrac{1}{6}}$

86. $\sqrt{15} - \sqrt{\dfrac{3}{5}} + \sqrt{\dfrac{5}{3}}$

87. $\sqrt[3]{25} + \dfrac{3}{\sqrt[3]{5}}$

88. $\sqrt[4]{8} + \dfrac{1}{\sqrt[4]{2}}$

Rationalize the denominator in each of the following.

89. $\dfrac{\sqrt{2}}{\sqrt{6} - \sqrt{2}}$

90. $\dfrac{\sqrt{5}}{\sqrt{5} + \sqrt{3}}$

91. $\dfrac{\sqrt{5}}{\sqrt{5} + 1}$

92. $\dfrac{\sqrt{7}}{\sqrt{7} - 1}$

93. $\dfrac{\sqrt{x}}{\sqrt{x} - 3}$

94. $\dfrac{\sqrt{x}}{\sqrt{x} + 2}$

95. $\dfrac{\sqrt{5}}{2\sqrt{5} - 3}$

96. $\dfrac{\sqrt{7}}{3\sqrt{7} - 2}$

97. $\dfrac{3}{\sqrt{x} - \sqrt{y}}$

98. $\dfrac{2}{\sqrt{x} + \sqrt{y}}$

99. $\dfrac{\sqrt{6} + \sqrt{2}}{\sqrt{6} - \sqrt{2}}$

100. $\dfrac{\sqrt{5} - \sqrt{3}}{\sqrt{5} + \sqrt{3}}$

101. $\dfrac{\sqrt{7} - 2}{\sqrt{7} + 2}$

102. $\dfrac{\sqrt{11} + 3}{\sqrt{11} - 3}$

103. Paying Attention to Instructions Work each problem according to the instructions given.

 a. Add: $(\sqrt{x} + 2) + (\sqrt{x} - 2)$ **b.** Multiply: $(\sqrt{x} + 2)(\sqrt{x} - 2)$

 c. Square: $(\sqrt{x} + 2)^2$ **d.** Divide: $\dfrac{\sqrt{x} + 2}{\sqrt{x} - 2}$

104. Paying Attention to Instructions Work each problem according to the instructions given.

 a. Add: $(5 + \sqrt{2}) + (5 - \sqrt{2})$ **b.** Multiply: $(5 + \sqrt{2})(5 - \sqrt{2})$

 c. Square: $(5 + \sqrt{2})^2$ **d.** Divide: $\dfrac{5 + \sqrt{2}}{5 - \sqrt{2}}$

105. Paying Attention to Instructions Work each problem according to the instructions given.

    a. Add: $\sqrt{2} + (\sqrt{6} + \sqrt{2})$ **b.** Multiply: $\sqrt{2}(\sqrt{6} + \sqrt{2})$

    c. Divide: $\dfrac{\sqrt{6} + \sqrt{2}}{\sqrt{2}}$ **d.** Divide: $\dfrac{\sqrt{2}}{\sqrt{6} + \sqrt{2}}$

106. Paying Attention to Instructions Work each problem according to the instructions given.

    a. Add: $\left(\dfrac{1 + \sqrt{5}}{2}\right) + \left(\dfrac{1 - \sqrt{5}}{2}\right)$ **b.** Multiply: $\left(\dfrac{1 + \sqrt{5}}{2}\right)\left(\dfrac{1 - \sqrt{5}}{2}\right)$

107. Show that the product below is 5:

$$(\sqrt[3]{2} + \sqrt[3]{3})(\sqrt[3]{4} - \sqrt[3]{6} + \sqrt[3]{9})$$

108. Show that the product below is $x + 8$:

$$(\sqrt[3]{x} + 2)(\sqrt[3]{x^2} - 2\sqrt[3]{x} + 4)$$

Each of the following statements below is false. Correct the right side of each one to make it true.

109. $5(2\sqrt{3}) = 10\sqrt{15}$ **110.** $3(2\sqrt{x}) = 6\sqrt{3x}$ **111.** $(\sqrt{x} + 3)^2 = x + 9$

112. $(\sqrt{x} - 7)^2 = x - 49$ **113.** $(5\sqrt{3})^2 = 15$ **114.** $(3\sqrt{5})^2 = 15$

Applying the Concepts

115. Gravity If an object is dropped from the top of a 100-foot building, the amount of time t (in seconds) that it takes for the object to be h feet from the ground is given by the formula

$$t = \frac{\sqrt{100 - h}}{4}$$

How long does it take before the object is 50 feet from the ground? How long does it take to reach the ground? (When it is on the ground, h is 0.)

116. Radius of a Sphere The radius r of a sphere with volume V can be found by using the formula

$$r = \sqrt[3]{\frac{3V}{4\pi}}$$

Volume

Find the radius of a sphere with volume 9 cubic feet. Write your answer in simplified form. $\left(\text{Use } \frac{22}{7} \text{ for } \pi.\right)$

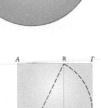

117. Golden Rectangle Rectangle $ACEF$ in Figure 3 is a golden rectangle. If side AC is 6 inches, show that the smaller rectangle $BDEF$ is also a golden rectangle.

118. Golden Rectangle Rectangle $ACEF$ in Figure 3 is a golden rectangle. If side AC is 1 inch, show that the smaller rectangle $BDEF$ is also a golden rectangle.

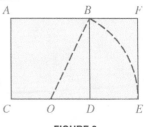

FIGURE 3

119. Golden Rectangle If side AC in Figure 3 is $2x$, show that rectangle $BDEF$ is a golden rectangle.

120. Golden Rectangle If side AC in Figure 3 is x, show that rectangle $BDEF$ is a golden rectangle.

Learning Objectives Assessment

The following problems can be used to help assess if you have successfully met the learning objectives for this section.

121. Multiply: $(3\sqrt{6})(4\sqrt{10})$.

    a. $24\sqrt{15}$ **b.** $7\sqrt{60}$ **c.** $12\sqrt{15}$ **d.** 48

122. Multiply: $(\sqrt{3} + \sqrt{7})^2$.

    a. 10   **b.** $10 + 2\sqrt{21}$ **c.** $12\sqrt{21}$ **d.** $2\sqrt{3} + 2\sqrt{7}$

123. Divide: $\dfrac{8\sqrt{12}}{12\sqrt{2}}$.

    a. $\dfrac{2\sqrt{6}}{3}$ **b.** 4   **c.** $\dfrac{8}{\sqrt{2}}$ **d.** $\dfrac{\sqrt{10}}{4}$

124. Rationalize the denominator: $\dfrac{3}{\sqrt[3]{2}}$.

    a. $\dfrac{3\sqrt[3]{2}}{2}$ **b.** $\dfrac{27}{2}$ **c.** $\dfrac{3\sqrt[3]{4}}{2}$ **d.** $\dfrac{3\sqrt{2}}{2}$

Getting Ready for the Next Section

Simplify.

125. $(t + 5)^2$ **126.** $(x - 4)^2$ **127.** $\sqrt{x} \cdot \sqrt{x}$ **128.** $\sqrt{3x} \cdot \sqrt{3x}$

Solve.

129. $3x + 4 = 5^2$ **130.** $4x - 7 = 3^2$

131. $t^2 + 7t + 12 = 0$ **132.** $x^2 - 3x - 10 = 0$

133. $t^2 + 10t + 25 = t + 7$ **134.** $x^2 - 4x + 4 = x - 2$

135. $(x + 4)^2 = x + 6$ **136.** $(x - 6)^2 = x - 4$

137. Is $x = 7$ a solution to $\sqrt{3x + 4} = 5$?

138. Is $x = 4$ a solution to $\sqrt{4x - 7} = -3$?

139. Is $t = -6$ a solution to $t + 5 = \sqrt{t + 7}$?

140. Is $t = -3$ a solution to $t + 5 = \sqrt{t + 7}$?

Learning Objectives

In this section, we will learn how to:

1. Solve equations containing square roots.
2. Identify extraneous solutions when squaring both sides of an equation.
3. Solve equations involving nth roots.
4. Solve equations containing rational exponents.

Introduction

This section is concerned with solving equations that involve one or more radicals. The first step in solving an equation that contains a radical is to eliminate the radical from the equation. To do so, we need an additional property.

>   **PROPERTY**   *Squaring Property of Equality*
>
> If both sides of an equation are squared, the solutions to the original equation are solutions to the resulting equation.

We will never lose solutions to our equations by squaring both sides. We may, however, introduce *extraneous solutions*. Extraneous solutions satisfy the equation obtained by squaring both sides of the original equation, but do not satisfy the original equation.

We know that if two real numbers a and b are equal, then so are their squares:

$$\text{If} \qquad a = b$$
$$\text{then} \qquad a^2 = b^2$$

On the other hand, extraneous solutions are introduced when we square opposites. That is, even though opposites are not equal, their squares are. For example,

$$5 = -5 \qquad \text{A false statement}$$
$$(5)^2 = (-5)^2 \qquad \text{Square both sides}$$
$$25 = 25 \qquad \text{A true statement}$$

We are free to square both sides of an equation any time it is convenient. We must be aware, however, that doing so may introduce extraneous solutions. We must, therefore, check all our solutions in the original equation if at any time we square both sides of the original equation.

VIDEO EXAMPLES

SECTION 10.6

EXAMPLE 1   Solve for x: $\sqrt{3x + 4} = 5$.

SOLUTION   We square both sides and proceed as usual:

$$\sqrt{3x + 4} = 5$$
$$(\sqrt{3x + 4})^2 = 5^2$$
$$3x + 4 = 25$$
$$3x = 21$$
$$x = 7$$

Checking $x = 7$ in the original equation, we have

$$\sqrt{3(7) + 4} \stackrel{?}{=} 5$$

$$\sqrt{21 + 4} \stackrel{?}{=} 5$$

$$\sqrt{25} \stackrel{?}{=} 5$$

$$5 = 5$$

The solution $x = 7$ satisfies the original equation.

EXAMPLE 2   Solve: $\sqrt{4x - 7} = -3$.

SOLUTION   Squaring both sides, we have

$$\sqrt{4x - 7} = -3$$

$$(\sqrt{4x - 7})^2 = (-3)^2$$

$$4x - 7 = 9$$

$$4x = 16$$

$$x = 4$$

Checking $x = 4$ in the original equation gives

$$\sqrt{4(4) - 7} \stackrel{?}{=} -3$$

$$\sqrt{16 - 7} \stackrel{?}{=} -3$$

$$\sqrt{9} \stackrel{?}{=} -3$$

$$3 = -3 \qquad \text{A false statement}$$

The solution $x = 4$ produces a false statement when checked in the original equation. Because $x = 4$ was the only possible solution, there is no solution to the original equation. The possible solution $x = 4$ is an extraneous solution. It satisfies the equation obtained by squaring both sides of the original equation, but does not satisfy the original equation. In this case, the solution set is $\varnothing$.

Note   The fact that there is no solution to the equation in Example 2 was obvious to begin with. Notice that the left side of the equation is the positive square root of $4x - 7$, which must be a positive number or 0. The right side of the equation is -3. Because we cannot have a number that is either positive or zero equal to a negative number, there is no solution to the equation.

EXAMPLE 3   Solve: $\sqrt{5x - 1} + 3 = 7$.

SOLUTION   We must isolate the radical on the left side of the equation. If we attempt to square both sides without doing so, the resulting equation will also contain a radical. Adding -3 to both sides, we have

$$\sqrt{5x - 1} + 3 = 7$$

$$\sqrt{5x - 1} = 4$$

We can now square both sides and proceed as usual:

$$(\sqrt{5x - 1})^2 = 4^2$$

$$5x - 1 = 16$$

$$5x = 17$$

$$x = \frac{17}{5}$$

Checking $x = \dfrac{17}{5}$, we have

$$\sqrt{5\left(\dfrac{17}{5}\right) - 1} + 3 \stackrel{?}{=} 7$$

$$\sqrt{17 - 1} + 3 \stackrel{?}{=} 7$$

$$\sqrt{16} + 3 \stackrel{?}{=} 7$$

$$4 + 3 \stackrel{?}{=} 7$$

$$7 = 7$$

EXAMPLE 4   Solve: $t + 5 = \sqrt{t + 7}$.

SOLUTION   This time, squaring both sides of the equation results in a quadratic equation:

$$(t + 5)^2 = (\sqrt{t + 7})^2 \qquad \text{Square both sides}$$

$$t^2 + 10t + 25 = t + 7$$

$$t^2 + 9t + 18 = 0 \qquad \text{Standard form}$$

$$(t + 3)(t + 6) = 0 \qquad \text{Factor the left side}$$

$$t + 3 = 0 \quad \text{or} \quad t + 6 = 0 \qquad \text{Set factors equal to 0}$$

$$t = -3 \qquad\qquad t = -6$$

We must check each solution in the original equation:

Check $t = -3$	Check $t = -6$
$-3 + 5 \stackrel{?}{=} \sqrt{-3 + 7}$	$-6 + 5 \stackrel{?}{=} \sqrt{-6 + 7}$
$2 \stackrel{?}{=} \sqrt{4}$	$-1 \stackrel{?}{=} \sqrt{1}$
$2 = 2$ A true statement	$-1 = 1$ A false statement

Because $t = -6$ does not check, our only solution is $t = -3$.

EXAMPLE 5   Solve: $\sqrt{x - 3} = \sqrt{x} - 3$.

SOLUTION   We begin by squaring both sides. Note carefully what happens when we square the right side of the equation, and compare the square of the right side with the square of the left side. You must convince yourself that these results are correct. (The note in the margin will help if you are having trouble convincing yourself that what is written below is true.)

$$(\sqrt{x - 3})^2 = (\sqrt{x} - 3)^2$$

$$x - 3 = x - 6\sqrt{x} + 9$$

Now we still have a radical in our equation, so we will have to square both sides again. Before we do, though, let's isolate the remaining radical.

$$x - 3 = x - 6\sqrt{x} + 9$$

$$-3 = -6\sqrt{x} + 9 \qquad \text{Add } -x \text{ to each side}$$

$$-12 = -6\sqrt{x} \qquad \text{Add } -9 \text{ to each side}$$

$$2 = \sqrt{x} \qquad \text{Divide each side by } -6$$

$$4 = x \qquad \text{Square each side}$$

Note   It is very important that you realize that the square of $(\sqrt{x} - 3)$ is not $x + 9$. Remember, when we square a difference with two terms, we use the formula

$$(a - b)^2 = a^2 - 2ab + b^2$$

Applying this formula to $(\sqrt{x} - 3)^2$ we have

$$(\sqrt{x} - 3)^2 =$$
$$(\sqrt{x})^2 - 2(\sqrt{x})(3) + 3^2$$
$$= x - 6\sqrt{x} + 9$$

Our only possible solution is $x = 4$, which we check in our original equation as follows:

$$\sqrt{4 - 3} \stackrel{?}{=} \sqrt{4} - 3$$
$$\sqrt{1} \stackrel{?}{=} 2 - 3$$
$$1 = -1 \qquad \text{A false statement}$$

Substituting 4 for x in the original equation yields a false statement. Because 4 was our only possible solution, there is no solution to our equation.

Here is another example of an equation for which we must apply our squaring property twice before all radicals are eliminated.

EXAMPLE 6   Solve: $\sqrt{x + 1} = 1 - \sqrt{2x}$.

SOLUTION   This equation has two separate terms involving radical signs. Squaring both sides gives

$$x + 1 = 1 - 2\sqrt{2x} + 2x$$
$$-x = -2\sqrt{2x} \qquad \text{Add } -2x \text{ and } -1 \text{ to both sides}$$
$$x^2 = 4(2x) \qquad \text{Square both sides}$$
$$x^2 - 8x = 0 \qquad \text{Standard form}$$

Our equation is a quadratic equation in standard form. To solve for x, we factor the left side and set each factor equal to 0:

$$x(x - 8) = 0 \qquad \text{Factor left side}$$
$$x = 0 \quad \text{or} \quad x - 8 = 0$$
$$x = 8 \qquad \text{Set factors equal to 0}$$

Because we squared both sides of our equation, we have the possibility that one or both of the solutions are extraneous. We must check each one in the original equation:

Check $x = 8$	Check $x = 0$
$\sqrt{8 + 1} \stackrel{?}{=} 1 - \sqrt{2 \cdot 8}$	$\sqrt{0 + 1} \stackrel{?}{=} 1 - \sqrt{2 \cdot 0}$
$\sqrt{9} \stackrel{?}{=} 1 - \sqrt{16}$	$\sqrt{1} \stackrel{?}{=} 1 - \sqrt{0}$
$3 \stackrel{?}{=} 1 - 4$	$1 \stackrel{?}{=} 1 - 0$
$3 = -3$ A false statement	$1 = 1$ A true statement

Because $x = 8$ does not check, it is an extraneous solution. Our only solution is $x = 0$.

EXAMPLE 7　Solve: $\sqrt{x+1} = \sqrt{x+2} - 1$.

SOLUTION　Squaring both sides we have

$$(\sqrt{x+1})^2 = (\sqrt{x+2} - 1)^2$$
$$x + 1 = x + 2 - 2\sqrt{x+2} + 1$$

Once again, we are left with a radical in our equation. Before we square each side again, we must isolate the radical on the right side of the equation.

$x + 1 = x + 3 - 2\sqrt{x+2}$	Simplify the right side
$1 = 3 - 2\sqrt{x+2}$	Add $-x$ to each side
$-2 = -2\sqrt{x+2}$	Add -3 to each side
$1 = \sqrt{x+2}$	Divide each side by -2
$1 = x + 2$	Square both sides
$-1 = x$	Add -2 to each side

Checking our only possible solution, $x = -1$, in our original equation, we have

$$\sqrt{-1+1} \overset{?}{=} \sqrt{-1+2} - 1$$
$$\sqrt{0} \overset{?}{=} \sqrt{1} - 1$$
$$0 \overset{?}{=} 1 - 1$$
$$0 = 0 \qquad \text{A true statement}$$

Our solution checks.

It is also possible to raise both sides of an equation to powers greater than 2. We only need to check for extraneous solutions when we raise both sides of an equation to an even power. Raising both sides of an equation to an odd power will not produce extraneous solutions.

EXAMPLE 8　Solve: $\sqrt[3]{4x+5} = 3$.

SOLUTION　Cubing both sides, we have

$$(\sqrt[3]{4x+5})^3 = 3^3$$
$$4x + 5 = 27$$
$$4x = 22$$
$$x = \frac{22}{4}$$
$$x = \frac{11}{2}$$

We do not need to check $x = \frac{11}{2}$ because we raised both sides to an odd power.

EXAMPLE 9   Solve: $(x + 3)^{2/3} = 4$.

SOLUTION   We begin by writing the rational exponent as a radical.

$$(x + 3)^{2/3} = \sqrt[3]{(x + 3)^2}$$

Now we cube both sides to eliminate the cube root.

$$\sqrt[3]{(x + 3)^2} = 4$$

$$\left(\sqrt[3]{(x + 3)^2}\right)^3 = 4^3 \qquad\qquad \text{Cube both sides}$$

$$(x + 3)^2 = 64$$

$$x^2 + 6x + 9 = 64 \qquad\qquad \text{FOIL}$$

$$x^2 + 6x - 55 = 0 \qquad\qquad \text{Standard form}$$

$$(x + 11)(x - 5) = 0 \qquad\qquad \text{Factor left side}$$

$$x + 11 = 0 \quad \text{ or } \quad x - 5 = 0$$

$$x = -11 \qquad\qquad x = 5$$

Because we raised both sides to an odd power, we do not need to check our solutions.

Getting Ready for Class

After reading through the preceding section, respond in your own words and in complete sentences.

A. What is the squaring property of equality?

B. Under what conditions do we obtain extraneous solutions to equations that contain radical expressions?

C. If we have raised both sides of an equation to a power, when is it not necessary to check for extraneous solutions?

D. When will you need to apply the squaring property of equality twice in the process of solving an equation containing radicals?

Solve each of the following equations.

1. $\sqrt{2x+1} = 3$ 2. $\sqrt{3x+1} = 4$ 3. $\sqrt{4x+1} = -5$

4. $\sqrt{6x+1} = -5$ 5. $\sqrt{2y-1} = 3$ 6. $\sqrt{3y-1} = 2$

7. $\sqrt{5x-7} = -1$ 8. $\sqrt{8x+3} = -6$ 9. $\sqrt{2x-3} - 2 = 4$

10. $\sqrt{3x+1} - 4 = 1$ 11. $\sqrt{4a+1} + 3 = 2$ 12. $\sqrt{5a-3} + 6 = 2$

13. $\sqrt[4]{3x+1} = 2$ 14. $\sqrt[4]{4x+1} = 3$ 15. $\sqrt[3]{2x-5} = 1$

16. $\sqrt[3]{5x+7} = 2$ 17. $\sqrt[3]{3a+5} = -3$ 18. $\sqrt[3]{2a+7} = -2$

19. $\sqrt{y-3} = y-3$ 20. $\sqrt{y+3} = y-3$ 21. $\sqrt{a+2} = a+2$

22. $\sqrt{a+10} = a-2$ 23. $\sqrt{2x+4} = \sqrt{1-x}$

24. $\sqrt{3x+4} = -\sqrt{2x+3}$ 25. $\sqrt{4a+7} = -\sqrt{a+2}$

26. $\sqrt{7a-1} = \sqrt{2a+4}$ 27. $\sqrt[4]{5x-8} = \sqrt[4]{4x-1}$

28. $\sqrt[4]{6x+7} = \sqrt[4]{x+2}$ 29. $x+1 = \sqrt{5x+1}$

30. $x-1 = \sqrt{6x+1}$ 31. $t+5 = \sqrt{2t+9}$

32. $t+7 = \sqrt{2t+13}$ 33. $\sqrt{y-8} = \sqrt{8-y}$

34. $\sqrt{2y+5} = \sqrt{5y+2}$ 35. $\sqrt[3]{3x+5} = \sqrt[3]{5-2x}$

36. $\sqrt[3]{4x+9} = \sqrt[3]{3-2x}$

The following equations will require that you square both sides twice before all the radicals are eliminated. Solve each equation using the methods shown in Examples 5, 6, and 7.

37. $\sqrt{x-8} = \sqrt{x} - 2$ 38. $\sqrt{x+3} = \sqrt{x} - 3$

39. $\sqrt{x+1} = \sqrt{x} + 1$ 40. $\sqrt{x-1} = \sqrt{x} - 1$

41. $\sqrt{x+8} = \sqrt{x-4} + 2$ 42. $\sqrt{x+5} = \sqrt{x-3} + 2$

43. $\sqrt{x-5} - 3 = \sqrt{x-8}$ 44. $\sqrt{x-3} - 4 = \sqrt{x-3}$

45. Solve each equation.

   a. $\sqrt{y} - 4 = 6$ b. $\sqrt{y-4} = 6$

   c. $\sqrt{y} - 4 = -6$ d. $\sqrt{y-4} = y-6$

46. Solve each equation.

   a. $\sqrt{2y} + 15 = 7$ b. $\sqrt{2y+15} = 7$

   c. $\sqrt{2y+15} = y$ d. $\sqrt{2y+15} = y+6$

47. Solve each equation.

   a. $x - 3 = 0$ b. $\sqrt{x} - 3 = 0$

   c. $\sqrt{x-3} = 0$ d. $\sqrt{x} + 3 = 0$

   e. $\sqrt{x} + 3 = 5$ f. $\sqrt{x} + 3 = -5$

   g. $x - 3 = \sqrt{5-x}$

48. Solve each equation.

   a. $x - 2 = 0$ b. $\sqrt{x} - 2 = 0$ c. $\sqrt{x} + 2 = 0$

   d. $\sqrt{x+2} = 0$ e. $\sqrt{x} + 2 = 7$ f. $x - 2 = \sqrt{2x-1}$

Solve each of the following equations by writing the rational exponent as a radical.

49. $(5x - 1)^{1/2} = 3$

50. $(2x - 5)^{1/2} = 7$

51. $(4x + 1)^{1/3} = 2$

52. $(3x + 4)^{1/3} = -5$

53. $(x + 2)^{2/3} = 1$

54. $(x - 4)^{2/3} = 4$

Applying the Concepts

55. Solving a Formula Solve the following formula for h:

$$t = \frac{\sqrt{100 - h}}{4}$$

56. Solving a Formula Solve the following formula for h:

$$t = \sqrt{\frac{2h - 40t}{g}}$$

57. Pendulum Clock The length of time (T) in seconds it takes the pendulum of a clock to swing through one complete cycle is given by the formula

$$T = 2\pi\sqrt{\frac{L}{32}}$$

where L is the length, in feet, of the pendulum, and π is approximately $\frac{22}{7}$. How long must the pendulum be if one complete cycle takes 2 seconds?

58. Pollution A long straight river, 100 meters wide, is flowing at 1 meter per second. A pollutant is entering the river at a constant rate from one of its banks. As the pollutant disperses in the water, it forms a plume that is modeled by the equation $y = \sqrt{x}$. Use this information to answer the following questions.

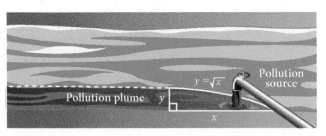

a. How wide is the plume 25 meters down river from the source of the pollution?

b. How wide is the plume 100 meters down river from the source of the pollution?

c. How far down river from the source of the pollution does the plume reach halfway across the river?

d. How far down the river from the source of the pollution does the plume reach the other side of the river?

Learning Objectives Assessment

The following problems can be used to help assess if you have successfully met the learning objectives for this section.

59. Solve: $\sqrt{3x - 2} - 3 = 1$.

    a. $\varnothing$ **b.** $\dfrac{4}{3}$ **c.** -2 **d.** 6

60. Solve: $\sqrt{2x + 5} + 1 = 0$.

    a. -2 **b.** $\varnothing$ **c.** -3 **d.** $-\dfrac{9}{2}$

61. Solve: $\sqrt[3]{2x - 3} = -4$.

    a. $\dfrac{19}{2}$ **b.** $\varnothing$ **c.** $\dfrac{67}{2}$ **d.** $-\dfrac{61}{2}$

62. Solve: $(2x + 1)^{1/2} = 9$.

    a. 1   **b.** 40   **c.** $\varnothing$ **d.** 4

Getting Ready for the Next Section

Simplify.

63. $\sqrt{25}$ **64.** $\sqrt{49}$ **65.** $\sqrt{12}$ **66.** $\sqrt{50}$

67. $(-1)^{15}$ **68.** $(-1)^{20}$ **69.** $(-1)^{50}$ **70.** $(-1)^5$

Solve.

71. $3x = 12$ **72.** $4 = 8y$ **73.** $4x - 3 = 5$ **74.** $7 = 2y - 1$

Perform the indicated operation.

75. $(3 + 4x) + (7 - 6x)$ **76.** $(2 - 5x) + (-1 + 7x)$

77. $(7 + 3x) - (5 + 6x)$ **78.** $(5 - 2x) - (9 - 4x)$

79. $(3 - 4x)(2 + 5x)$ **80.** $(8 + x)(7 - 3x)$

81. $2x(4 - 6x)$ **82.** $3x(7 + 2x)$

83. $(2 + 3x)^2$ **84.** $(3 + 5x)^2$

85. $(2 - 3x)(2 + 3x)$ **86.** $(4 - 5x)(4 + 5x)$

Learning Objectives

In this section, we will learn how to:

1. Write the square root of a negative number as a pure imaginary number.
2. Simplify powers of i.
3. Add and subtract complex numbers.
4. Multiply and divide complex numbers.

Introduction

The equation $x^2 = -1$ has no real number solutions because the square of a real number is always nonnegative. We have been unable to work with square roots of negative numbers like $\sqrt{-25}$ and $\sqrt{-16}$ for the same reason. Complex numbers allow us to expand our work with radicals to include square roots of negative numbers and to solve equations like $x^2 = -9$ and $x^2 = -64$.

Imaginary Numbers

Our work with complex numbers begins with the following definition.

> **(déf) DEFINITION** *the number i*
>
> The **number i** is such that $i = \sqrt{-1}$ (which is the same as saying $i^2 = -1$).

Note The first use of the term "imaginary number" was by René Descartes in his work *La Géométrie*, published in 1637. A century later, Leonhard Euler introduced the use of i to represent $\sqrt{-1}$ in 1777.

The number i, called the *imaginary unit*, is not a real number. It is what we call a *pure imaginary number*. In general, a pure imaginary number is the product of a real number, b, and the imaginary unit i.

> **(déf) DEFINITION** *pure imaginary number*
>
> A **pure imaginary number** is any number that can be expressed in the form bi, where b is a real number and i is the imaginary unit.

Some examples of pure imaginary numbers are

$$3i \qquad -\frac{2}{7}i \qquad \sqrt{5}i$$

Because of the way we have defined i, we can use it to simplify square roots of negative numbers.

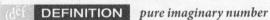

> **⟨Δ≠Σ⟩ *Square Roots of Negative Numbers***
>
> If b is a positive number, then $\sqrt{-b}$ can always be written as the pure imaginary number $i\sqrt{b}$. That is,
>
> $$\sqrt{-b} = i\sqrt{b} \qquad \text{if } b \text{ is a positive number}$$

To justify our rule, we simply square the quantity $i\sqrt{b}$ to obtain $-b$. This is what it looks like when we do so:

$$(i\sqrt{b})^2 = i^2 \cdot (\sqrt{b})^2$$
$$= -1 \cdot b$$
$$= -b$$

Here are some examples that illustrate the use of our new rule.

VIDEO EXAMPLES

SECTION 10.7

EXAMPLES   Write each square root as a pure imaginary number.

1. $\sqrt{-25} = i\sqrt{25} = i \cdot 5 = 5i$

2. $\sqrt{-49} = i\sqrt{49} = i \cdot 7 = 7i$

3. $\sqrt{-12} = i\sqrt{12} = i \cdot 2\sqrt{3} = 2i\sqrt{3}$

4. $\sqrt{-17} = i\sqrt{17}$

In Examples 3 and 4, we wrote i before the radical simply to avoid confusion. If we were to write the answer to 3 as $2\sqrt{3}i$, some people would think the i was under the radical sign, but it is not.

Powers of i

If we assume all the properties of exponents hold when the base is i, we can write any power of i as i, -1, $-i$, or 1. Using the fact that $i^2 = -1$, we have

$$i^1 = i$$
$$i^2 = -1$$
$$i^3 = i^2 \cdot i = -1(i) = -i$$
$$i^4 = i^2 \cdot i^2 = -1(-1) = 1$$

Because $i^4 = 1$, i^5 will simplify to i, and we will begin repeating the sequence i, -1, $-i$, 1 as we simplify higher powers of i: Any power of i simplifies to i, -1, $-i$, or 1. The easiest way to simplify higher powers of i is to write them in terms of i^4. For instance, to simplify i^{21}, we would write it as

$$(i^4)^5 \cdot i \qquad \text{because} \qquad 4 \cdot 5 + 1 = 21$$

Then, because $i^4 = 1$, we have

$$(1)^5 \cdot i = 1 \cdot i = i$$

EXAMPLES   Simplify each power of i.

5. $i^{30} = (i^4)^7 \cdot i^2 = (1)^7(-1) = -1$

6. $i^{11} = (i^4)^2 \cdot i^3 = (1)^2 \cdot (-i) = -i$

7. $i^{40} = (i^4)^{10} = (1)^{10} = 1$

Complex Numbers

Next, we consider numbers created by adding a real number and a pure imaginary number. Called *complex numbers*, these numbers are essential in many different fields, including digital signal and image processing, quantum mechanics, electrical engineering, and biology.

> **DEF** **DEFINITION** *complex number*
>
> A *complex number* is any number that can be put in the form
>
> $$a + bi$$
>
> where a and b are real numbers and $i = \sqrt{-1}$. The form $a + bi$ is called *standard form* for complex numbers. The number a is called the *real part* of the complex number. The number b is called the *imaginary part* of the complex number.

Every real number is a complex number, whose imaginary part is 0. For example, 8 can be written as $8 + 0i$. Likewise, every pure imaginary number is a complex number whose real part is 0. For example, $2i$ can be written as $0 + 2i$. The remaining complex numbers, which cannot be classified as either real numbers or pure imaginary numbers, are called *compound numbers*. The diagram below shows all three subsets of the complex numbers, along with examples of the type of numbers that fall into those subsets.

Real Numbers	Compound Numbers	Pure Imaginary Numbers
When $a \neq 0$ and $b = 0$ Examples include: $-10, 0, 1, \sqrt{3}, \frac{5}{8}, \pi$	When neither a nor b is 0 Examples include: $5 + 4i, \frac{1}{3} + 4i, \sqrt{5} - i,$ $-6 + i\sqrt{5}$	When $a = 0$ and $b \neq 0$ Examples include: $-4i, i\sqrt{3}, -5i\sqrt{7}, \frac{3}{4}i$

©2009 James Robert Metz

Note See Section 1.2 for a review of the subsets of real numbers.

Note: The definition for compound numbers is from Jim Metz of Kapiolani Community College in Hawaii. Some textbooks use the phrase *imaginary numbers* to represent both the compound numbers and the pure imaginary numbers. In those books, the pure imaginary numbers are a subset of the imaginary numbers. We like the definition from Mr. Metz because it keeps the three subsets from overlapping.

Equality for Complex Numbers

Two complex numbers are equal if and only if their real parts are equal and their imaginary parts are equal. That is, for real numbers a, b, c, and d,

$$a + bi = c + di \quad \text{if and only if} \quad a = c \quad \text{and} \quad b = d$$

EXAMPLE 8 Find x and y if $3x + 4i = 12 - 8yi$.

SOLUTION Because the two complex numbers are equal, their real parts are equal and their imaginary parts are equal:

$$3x = 12 \quad \text{and} \quad 4 = -8y$$

$$x = 4 \qquad y = -\frac{1}{2}$$

EXAMPLE 9   Find x and y if $(4x - 3) + 7i = 5 + (2y - 1)i$.

SOLUTION   The real parts are $4x - 3$ and 5. The imaginary parts are 7 and $2y - 1$:

$$4x - 3 = 5 \quad \text{and} \quad 7 = 2y - 1$$
$$4x = 8 \qquad\qquad 8 = 2y$$
$$x = 2 \qquad\qquad y = 4$$

Addition and Subtraction of Complex Numbers

To add two complex numbers, add their real parts and their imaginary parts. That is, if a, b, c, and d are real numbers, then

$$(a + bi) + (c + di) = (a + c) + (b + d)i$$

If we assume that the commutative, associative, and distributive properties hold for the number i, then the definition of addition is simply an extension of these properties, allowing us to add complex numbers by combining similar terms.

We define subtraction in a similar manner. If a, b, c, and d are real numbers, then

$$(a + bi) - (c + di) = (a - c) + (b - d)i$$

Notice that we can achieve this same result by simply distributing the negative sign and then combining similar terms.

EXAMPLES   Add or subtract as indicated.

10. $(3 + 4i) + (7 - 6i) = (3 + 7) + (4 - 6)i$

$$= 10 - 2i$$

11. $(7 + 3i) - (5 + 6i) = 7 + 3i - 5 - 6i$

$$= (7 - 5) + (3 - 6)i$$
$$= 2 - 3i$$

12. $(5 - 2i) - (9 - 4i) = 5 - 2i - 9 + 4i$

$$= (5 - 9) + (-2 + 4)i$$
$$= -4 + 2i$$

Multiplication of Complex Numbers

Because complex numbers have the same form as binomials, we find the product of two complex numbers the same way we find the product of two binomials.

EXAMPLE 13   Multiply $(3 - 4i)(2 + 5i)$.

SOLUTION   Multiplying each term in the second complex number by each term in the first, we have

$$\overset{\text{F}}{(3 - 4i)(2 + 5i)} = 3 \cdot 2 + 3 \cdot 5i - 2 \cdot 4i - 4i(5i)$$

$$= 6 + 15i - 8i - 20i^2$$

Combining similar terms and using the fact that $i^2 = -1$, we can simplify as follows:

$$6 + 15i - 8i - 20i^2 = 6 + 7i - 20(-1)$$
$$= 6 + 7i + 20$$
$$= 26 + 7i$$

The product of the complex numbers $3 - 4i$ and $2 + 5i$ is the complex number $26 + 7i$.

EXAMPLE 14   Multiply $2i(4 - 6i)$.

SOLUTION   Applying the distributive property gives us

$$2i(4 - 6i) = 2i \cdot 4 - 2i \cdot 6i$$
$$= 8i - 12i^2$$
$$= 8i - 12(-1)$$
$$= 12 + 8i$$

EXAMPLE 15   Expand $(3 + 5i)^2$.

SOLUTION   We treat this like the square of a binomial. Remember, $(a + b)^2 = a^2 + 2ab + b^2$:

$$(3 + 5i)^2 = 3^2 + 2(3)(5i) + (5i)^2$$
$$= 9 + 30i + 25i^2$$
$$= 9 + 30i - 25$$
$$= -16 + 30i$$

EXAMPLE 16   Multiply $(2 - 3i)(2 + 3i)$.

SOLUTION   This product has the form $(a - b)(a + b)$, which we know results in the difference of two squares, $a^2 - b^2$:

$$(2 - 3i)(2 + 3i) = 2^2 - (3i)^2$$
$$= 4 - 9i^2$$
$$= 4 + 9$$
$$= 13$$

The product of the two complex numbers $2 - 3i$ and $2 + 3i$ is the real number 13. The two complex numbers $2 - 3i$ and $2 + 3i$ are called *complex conjugates*. The fact that their product is a real number is very useful.

> **DEFINITION**   *complex conjugates*
>
> The complex numbers $a + bi$ and $a - bi$ are called *complex conjugates*. One important property they have is that their product is the real number $a^2 + b^2$. Here's why :
>
> $$\begin{aligned}(a + bi)(a - bi) &= a^2 - (bi)^2 \\ &= a^2 - b^2 i^2 \\ &= a^2 - b^2(-1) \\ &= a^2 + b^2\end{aligned}$$

Division With Complex Numbers

The fact that the product of two complex conjugates is a real number is the key to division with complex numbers.

EXAMPLE 17   Divide $\dfrac{2 + i}{3 - 2i}$.

SOLUTION   We want a complex number in standard form that is equivalent to the quotient $\frac{2+i}{3-2i}$. We need to eliminate i from the denominator. Multiplying the numerator and denominator by $3 + 2i$ will give us what we want:

$$\begin{aligned}\frac{2 + i}{3 - 2i} &= \frac{2 + i}{3 - 2i} \cdot \frac{(3 + 2i)}{(3 + 2i)} \\ &= \frac{6 + 4i + 3i + 2i^2}{9 - 4i^2} \\ &= \frac{6 + 7i - 2}{9 + 4} \\ &= \frac{4 + 7i}{13} \\ &= \frac{4}{13} + \frac{7}{13}i\end{aligned}$$

Dividing the complex number $2 + i$ by $3 - 2i$ gives the complex number $\frac{4}{13} + \frac{7}{13}i$.

EXAMPLE 18   Divide $\dfrac{7 - 4i}{2i}$.

SOLUTION   The conjugate of the denominator is $-2i$. Multiplying numerator and denominator by this number, we have

$$\begin{aligned}\frac{7 - 4i}{2i} &= \frac{7 - 4i}{2i} \cdot \frac{-2i}{-2i} \\ &= \frac{-14i + 8i^2}{-4i^2} \\ &= \frac{-14i - 8}{4} \\ &= -\frac{8}{4} - \frac{14i}{4} \\ &= -2 - \frac{7}{2}i\end{aligned}$$

Fractal Geometry

A *fractal* is an infinitely complex pattern that is self-similar across different scales. In other words, a geometric pattern that looks the same under any level of magnification. An example of a fractal, called the Julia Set, is shown in Figure 1.

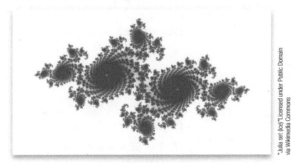

FIGURE 1

Fractals originated in 1918 in a paper published by the French mathematician Gaston Julia, but the subject of fractal geometry did not take off until 1975 with the advent of computers.

Most fractals are generated by taking complex numbers and repeating a simple set of operations on them. For instance, the Mandelbrot Set shown in Figure 2 is created by taking a complex number, squaring it, adding the original number, and then repeating this process many, many times.

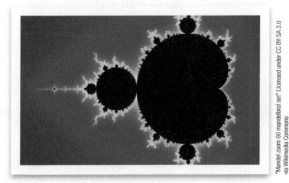

FIGURE 2

Besides their artistic qualities, fractals have applications to biology, geology, economics, music, architecture, fiber optics, image compression, and chaos theory, among others.

Getting Ready for Class

After reading through the preceding section, respond in your own words and in complete sentences.

A. What is the number i?

B. What is a complex number?

C. What kind of number will always result when we multiply complex conjugates?

D. Explain how to divide complex numbers.

Problem Set 10.7

Write the following as pure imaginary numbers in terms of i, and simplify as much as possible.

1. $\sqrt{-36}$ **2.** $\sqrt{-49}$ **3.** $-\sqrt{-25}$ **4.** $-\sqrt{-81}$

5. $\sqrt{-72}$ **6.** $\sqrt{-48}$ **7.** $-\sqrt{-12}$ **8.** $-\sqrt{-75}$

Simplify each power of i.

9. i^{28} **10.** i^{31} **11.** i^{26} **12.** i^{37}

13. i^{75} **14.** i^{42}

Find x and y so each of the following equations is true.

15. $2x + 3yi = 6 - 3i$ **16.** $4x - 2yi = 4 + 8i$

17. $2 - 5i = -x + 10yi$ **18.** $4 + 7i = 6x - 14yi$

19. $2x + 10i = -16 - 2yi$ **20.** $4x - 5i = -2 + 3yi$

21. $(2x - 4) - 3i = 10 - 6yi$ **22.** $(4x - 3) - 2i = 8 + yi$

23. $(7x - 1) + 4i = 2 + (5y + 2)i$ **24.** $(5x + 2) - 7i = 4 + (2y + 1)i$

Add or subtract as indicated.

25. $(2 + 3i) + (3 + 6i)$ **26.** $(4 + i) + (3 + 2i)$

27. $(3 - 5i) + (2 + 4i)$ **28.** $(7 + 2i) + (3 - 4i)$

29. $(5 + 2i) - (3 + 6i)$ **30.** $(6 + 7i) - (4 + i)$

31. $(3 - 5i) - (2 + i)$ **32.** $(7 - 3i) - (4 + 10i)$

33. $[(3 + 2i) - (6 + i)] + (5 + i)$ **34.** $[(4 - 5i) - (2 + i)] + (2 + 5i)$

35. $[(7 - i) - (2 + 4i)] - (6 + 2i)$ **36.** $[(3 - i) - (4 + 7i)] - (3 - 4i)$

37. $(3 + 2i) - [(3 - 4i) - (6 + 2i)]$ **38.** $(7 - 4i) - [(-2 + i) - (3 + 7i)]$

39. $(4 - 9i) + [(2 - 7i) - (4 + 8i)]$ **40.** $(10 - 2i) - [(2 + i) - (3 - i)]$

Find the following products.

41. $3i(4 + 5i)$ **42.** $2i(3 + 4i)$ **43.** $6i(4 - 3i)$

44. $11i(2 - i)$ **45.** $(3 + 2i)(4 + i)$ **46.** $(2 - 4i)(3 + i)$

47. $(4 + 9i)(3 - i)$ **48.** $(5 - 2i)(1 + i)$ **49.** $(-1 + 2i)(6 - 5i)$

50. $(7 + 3i)(-3 - i)$ **51.** $(2 - i)^3$ **52.** $(2 + i)^3$

53. $(2 + 5i)^2$ **54.** $(3 + 2i)^2$ **55.** $(1 - i)^2$

56. $(1 + i)^2$ **57.** $(3 - 4i)^2$ **58.** $(6 - 5i)^2$

59. $(2 + i)(2 - i)$ **60.** $(3 + i)(3 - i)$ **61.** $(6 - 2i)(6 + 2i)$

62. $(5 + 4i)(5 - 4i)$ **63.** $(2 + 3i)(2 - 3i)$ **64.** $(2 - 7i)(2 + 7i)$

65. $(10 + 8i)(10 - 8i)$ **66.** $(11 - 7i)(11 + 7i)$

Simplify.

67. $(2 - 5i)^2 + (3 + i)^2$ **68.** $(4 + 3i)^2 + (5 - i)^2$

69. $(4 + i)(4 - i) - (1 + 2i)^2$ **70.** $(1 + 5i)(1 - 5i) - (3 - 2i)^2$

Find the following quotients. Write all answers in standard form for complex numbers.

71. $\dfrac{2 - 3i}{i}$ **72.** $\dfrac{3 + 4i}{-i}$ **73.** $\dfrac{5 + 2i}{-3i}$

74. $\dfrac{4 - 3i}{2i}$ **75.** $\dfrac{4}{2 - 3i}$ **76.** $\dfrac{3}{4 - 5i}$

77. $\dfrac{6}{-3 + 2i}$ **78.** $\dfrac{-1}{-2 - 5i}$ **79.** $\dfrac{2 + 3i}{2 - 3i}$

80. $\dfrac{4 - 7i}{4 + 7i}$ **81.** $\dfrac{5 + 4i}{3 + 6i}$ **82.** $\dfrac{2 + i}{5 - 6i}$

Applying the Concepts

83. Electric Circuits Complex numbers may be applied to electrical circuits. Electrical engineers use the fact that resistance R to electrical flow of the electrical current I and the voltage V are related by the formula $V = RI$. (Voltage is measured in volts, resistance in ohms, and current in amperes.) Find the resistance to electrical flow in a circuit that has a voltage $V = (80 + 20i)$ volts and current $I = (-6 + 2i)$ amps.

84. Electric Circuits Refer to the information about electrical circuits in Problem 83, and find the current in a circuit that has a resistance of $(4 + 10i)$ ohms and a voltage of $(5 - 7i)$ volts.

Learning Objectives Assessment

The following problems can be used to help assess if you have successfully met the learning objectives for this section.

85. Write $\sqrt{-44}$ as a pure imaginary number.

     a. $-2\sqrt{11}$ **b.** $2\sqrt{11}i$ **c.** $2i\sqrt{11}$ **d.** $11i\sqrt{2}$

86. Simplify: i^{61}.

     a. i **b.** $-i$ **c.** 1 **d.** -1

87. Subtract: $(5 - 3i) - (-7 - 4i)$.

     a. $12 + i$ **b.** $12 - 7i$ **c.** $-2 - 7i$ **d.** $-2 + i$

88. Mulitply: $(2 + i)(8 - 3i)$.

     a. $16 - 3i$ **b.** $13 + 2i$ **c.** 19 **d.** $19 + 2i$

Maintaining Your Skills

Solve each equation.

89. $\dfrac{t}{3} - \dfrac{1}{2} = -1$

90. $\dfrac{x}{x-2} + \dfrac{2}{3} = \dfrac{2}{x-2}$

91. $2 + \dfrac{5}{y} = \dfrac{3}{y^2}$

92. $1 - \dfrac{1}{y} = \dfrac{12}{y^2}$

Solve each application problem.

93. The sum of a number and its reciprocal is $\dfrac{41}{20}$. Find the number.

94. It takes an inlet pipe 8 hours to fill a tank. The drain can empty the tank in 6 hours. If the tank is full and both the inlet pipe and drain are open, how long will it take to drain the tank?

Chapter 10 Summary

Square Roots [10.1]

1. The number 49 has two square roots, 7 and -7. They are written like this:

$$\sqrt{49} = 7 \qquad -\sqrt{49} = -7$$

Every positive real number x has two square roots. The *positive square root* (or *principal square root*) of x is written $\sqrt{x}$, and the *negative square root* of x is written $-\sqrt{x}$. Both the positive and the negative square roots of x are numbers we square to get x; that is,

$$\left. \begin{array}{c} (\sqrt{x})^2 = x \\ \text{and} \qquad (-\sqrt{x})^2 = x \end{array} \right\} \text{ for } x \geq 0$$

Higher Roots [10.1]

2. $\sqrt[3]{8} = 2$

   $\sqrt[3]{-27} = -3$

In the expression $\sqrt[n]{a}$, n is the *index*, a is the *radicand*, and $\sqrt{}$ is the *radical sign*. The expression $\sqrt[n]{a}$ is such that

$$(\sqrt[n]{a})^n = a \qquad a \geq 0 \text{ when } n \text{ is even}$$

Property of Radicals [10.1]

3. $(\sqrt[3]{-13})^3 = -13$

If a is a nonnegative real number whenever n is even, then

1. $(\sqrt[n]{a})^n = a$

Root Functions [10.1]

4. The function $f(x) = \sqrt{x - 6}$ has domain $\{x \mid x \geq 6\}$.

For any positive integer n, the function given by $f(x) = \sqrt[n]{x}$ is called the *nth root function*.

The domain of $f(x) = \sqrt[n]{x}$ is

$$\{x \mid x \geq 0\} \qquad \text{if } n \text{ is even}$$
$$\{x \mid x \text{ is any real number}\} \qquad \text{if } n \text{ is odd}$$

Rational Exponents [10.2]

5. $25^{1/2} = \sqrt{25} = 5$

   $8^{2/3} = (\sqrt[3]{8})^2 = 2^2 = 4$

   $9^{3/2} = (\sqrt{9})^3 = 3^3 = 27$

Rational exponents are used to indicate roots. The relationship between rational exponents and roots is as follows:

$$a^{1/n} = \sqrt[n]{a} \qquad \text{and} \qquad a^{m/n} = (a^{1/n})^m = (a^m)^{1/n}$$

$$a \geq 0 \text{ when } n \text{ is even}$$

Properties of Radicals [10.3]

6. $\sqrt{4\cdot 5} = \sqrt{4}\,\sqrt{5} = 2\sqrt{5}$

$\sqrt{\dfrac{7}{9}} = \dfrac{\sqrt{7}}{\sqrt{9}} = \dfrac{\sqrt{7}}{3}$

$\sqrt{(x-5)^2} = |x-5|$

If a and b are nonnegative real numbers whenever n is even, then

2. $\sqrt[n]{ab} = \sqrt[n]{a}\,\sqrt[n]{b}$

3. $\sqrt[n]{\dfrac{a}{b}} = \dfrac{\sqrt[n]{a}}{\sqrt[n]{b}}$ $(b \neq 0)$

If a is any real number, then

4. $\sqrt[n]{a^n} = |a|$ if n is even

  $\sqrt[n]{a^n} = a$ if n is odd

Simplified Form for Radicals [10.3]

7. $\sqrt{\dfrac{12}{25}} = \dfrac{\sqrt{12}}{\sqrt{25}}$

$= \dfrac{\sqrt{4}\sqrt{3}}{5}$

$= \dfrac{2\sqrt{3}}{5}$

A radical expression is said to be in *simplified form*

1. If there is no factor of the radicand that can be written as a power greater than or equal to the index;
2. If there are no fractions under the radical sign; and
3. If there are no radicals in the denominator.

Addition and Subtraction of Radical Expressions [10.4]

8. $5\sqrt{3} - 7\sqrt{3} = (5-7)\sqrt{3}$

$= -2\sqrt{3}$

$\sqrt{20} + \sqrt{45} = 2\sqrt{5} + 3\sqrt{5}$

$= (2+3)\sqrt{5}$

$= 5\sqrt{5}$

We add and subtract radical expressions by using the distributive property to combine similar radicals. Similar radicals are radicals with the same index and the same radicand.

Multiplication of Radical Expressions [10.5]

9. $(\sqrt{x}+2)(\sqrt{x}+3)$

$= \sqrt{x}\,\sqrt{x} + 3\sqrt{x} + 2\sqrt{x} + 2\cdot 3$

$= x + 5\sqrt{x} + 6$

We multiply radical expressions in the same way that we multiply polynomials. We can use the distributive property and the FOIL method.

Rationalizing the Denominator [10.5]

10. $\dfrac{3}{\sqrt{2}} = \dfrac{3}{\sqrt{2}}\cdot\dfrac{\sqrt{2}}{\sqrt{2}} = \dfrac{3\sqrt{2}}{2}$

$\dfrac{3}{\sqrt{5}-\sqrt{3}} = \dfrac{3}{\sqrt{5}-\sqrt{3}}\cdot\dfrac{\sqrt{5}+\sqrt{3}}{\sqrt{5}+\sqrt{3}}$

$= \dfrac{3\sqrt{5}+3\sqrt{3}}{5-3}$

$= \dfrac{3\sqrt{5}+3\sqrt{3}}{2}$

$\dfrac{2}{\sqrt[3]{25}} = \dfrac{2}{\sqrt[3]{25}}\cdot\dfrac{\sqrt[3]{5}}{\sqrt[3]{5}} = \dfrac{2\sqrt[3]{5}}{5}$

When a fraction contains a square root in the denominator, we rationalize the denominator by multiplying numerator and denominator by

1. The square root itself if there is only one term in the denominator, or
2. The conjugate of the denominator if there are two terms in the denominator.
3. When the denominator involves a cube root, we multiply by a radical that will produce a perfect cube under the cube root sign in the denominator.

Squaring Property of Equality [10.6]

11. $\sqrt{2x+1} = 3$
$(\sqrt{2x+1})^2 = 3^2$
$2x + 1 = 9$
$x = 4$

We may square both sides of an equation any time it is convenient to do so, as long as we check all resulting solutions in the original equation.

Complex Numbers [10.7]

12. $3 + 4i$ is a complex number.

Addition
$(3 + 4i) + (2 - 5i) = 5 - i$

Multiplication
$(3 + 4i)(2 - 5i)$
$= 6 - 15i + 8i - 20i^2$
$= 6 - 7i + 20$
$= 26 - 7i$

Division
$\dfrac{2}{3 + 4i} = \dfrac{2}{3 + 4i} \cdot \dfrac{3 - 4i}{3 - 4i}$

$= \dfrac{6 - 8i}{9 + 16}$

$= \dfrac{6}{25} - \dfrac{8}{25}i$

A *complex number* is any number that can be put in the form

$$a + bi$$

where a and b are real numbers and $i = \sqrt{-1}$. The *real part* of the complex number is a, and b is the *imaginary part*.

If a, b, c, and d are real numbers, then we have the following definitions associated with complex numbers:

1. Equality

$$a + bi = c + di \quad \text{if and only if} \quad a = c \text{ and } b = d$$

2. Addition and subtraction

$$(a + bi) + (c + di) = (a + c) + (b + d)i$$
$$(a + bi) - (c + di) = (a - c) + (b - d)i$$

3. Multiplication

$$(a + bi)(c + di) = (ac - bd) + (ad + bc)i$$

4. Division is similar to rationalizing the denominator.

Chapter 10 Test

Assume all variable bases are positive integers throughout this test.

Simplify each of the following. [10.1]

1. $-\sqrt{81}$ **2.** $\sqrt[3]{-125}$ **3.** $(\sqrt{7})^2$ **4.** $(\sqrt[3]{-15})^3$

5. $\sqrt{49x^8}$ **6.** $\sqrt[5]{32x^{10}y^{20}}$

Graph. [10.1]

7. $f(x) = \sqrt{x-2}$ **8.** $f(x) = \sqrt[3]{x} + 3$

Find the domain of each function. [10.1]

9. $f(x) = \sqrt{9-x}$ **10.** $f(x) = \sqrt[3]{x+7}$

Simplify. [10.2]

11. $27^{-2/3}$ **12.** $\left(\dfrac{25}{49}\right)^{-1/2}$ **13.** $a^{3/4} \cdot a^{-1/3}$

14. $(x^{3/5})^{5/6}$ **15.** $\dfrac{x^{2/3}y^{-3}}{x^{3/4}y^{1/2}}$ **16.** $\dfrac{(36a^8b^4)^{1/2}}{(27a^9b^6)^{1/3}}$

17. Write $\sqrt[3]{2a}$ using a rational exponent. [10.2]

18. Use rational exponents to simplify $\sqrt{36x^6y^{18}}$. [10.2]

Write in simplified form. [10.3]

19. $\sqrt{125x^3y^5}$ **20.** $\sqrt[3]{40x^7y^8}$ **21.** $\sqrt{\dfrac{2}{9}}$ **22.** $\sqrt{\dfrac{12a^4b^3}{25c^6}}$

Combine. [10.4]

23. $3\sqrt{12} - 4\sqrt{27}$ **24.** $\sqrt[3]{24a^3b^3} - 5a\sqrt[3]{3b^3}$

Multiply. [10.5]

25. $(\sqrt{x} + 7)(\sqrt{x} - 4)$ **26.** $(3\sqrt{2} - \sqrt{3})^2$

Rationalize the denominator. [10.5]

27. $\sqrt{\dfrac{5}{6}}$ **28.** $\sqrt[3]{\dfrac{3x}{4y}}$ **29.** $\dfrac{5}{\sqrt{3} - 1}$ **30.** $\dfrac{\sqrt{x} - \sqrt{2}}{\sqrt{x} + \sqrt{2}}$

Solve for x. [10.6]

31. $\sqrt{3x+1} = x - 3$ **32.** $\sqrt[3]{2x+7} = -1$

33. $\sqrt{x+3} = \sqrt{x+4} - 1$

34. Solve for x and y so that the following equation is true [10.7]:
$$(2x + 5) - 4i = 6 - (y - 3)i$$

Perform the indicated operations. [10.7]

35. $(3 + 2i) - [(7 - i) - (4 + 3i)]$ **36.** $(2 - 3i)(4 + 3i)$

37. $(5 - 4i)^2$ **38.** $\dfrac{2 - 3i}{2 + 3i}$

39. Simplify i^{38}. [10.7]

Quadratic Equations and Functions

Fir0002/Flagstaffotos
http://commons.wikimedia.org/wiki/Commons:GNU_Free_Documentation_License,_version_1.2

I f you have been to the circus or the county fair recently, you may have witnessed one of the more spectacular acts, the human cannonball. The human cannonball shown in the photograph will reach a height of 70 feet, and travel a distance of 160 feet, before landing in a safety net. In this chapter, we use this information to derive the function

$$f(x) = -\frac{7}{640}(x - 80)^2 + 70 \quad \text{for } 0 \le x \le 160$$

which describes the path flown by this particular cannonball. The table and graph below were constructed from this equation. The function $f(x)$ is called a *quadratic function*, and its graph is a parabola.

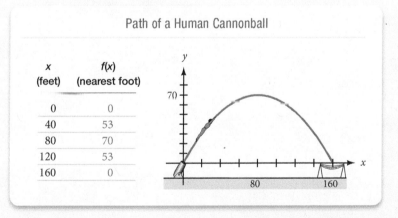

Path of a Human Cannonball

x (feet)	$f(x)$ (nearest foot)
0	0
40	53
80	70
120	53
160	0

All objects that are projected into the air, whether they are basketballs, bullets, arrows, or coins, follow parabolic paths like the one shown in the graph. Studying the material in this chapter will give you a more mathematical hold on the world around you.

Learning Objectives

In this section, we will learn how to:

1. Use the Square Root Property for Equations to solve a quadratic equation.
2. Solve a quadratic equation by completing the square.
3. Solve applied problems involving quadratic equations.

Introduction

If a baseball is dropped from a balcony that is 32 feet high, then the time it takes for the baseball to strike the ground can be found by solving the equation

$$-16t^2 + 32 = 0$$

If, instead, the baseball is thrown upward from the balcony with an initial velocity of 48 feet per second, then we would need to solve the equation

$$-16t^2 + 48t + 32 = 0$$

to find how long it would take for the baseball to hit the ground. Both of these equations are examples of a *quadratic equation*. Quadratic equations are one of the main topics we will study in this chapter. Here is the formal definition.

> **Note** For a quadratic equation written in standard form, the first term ax^2 is called the *quadratic term,* the second term bx is the *linear term,* and the last term c is called the *constant term.*

> **(def) DEFINITION**   *quadratic equation*
>
> Any equation that can be written in the form
>
> $$ax^2 + bx + c = 0$$
>
> where a, b, and c are constants and a is not 0 ($a \neq 0$), is called a ***quadratic equation.*** The form $ax^2 + bx + c = 0$ is called ***standard form*** for quadratic equations.

In Chapter 5 we learned how to solve certain quadratic equations using the Zero-Factor Property and factoring. In this section, we will develop two new methods of solving quadratic equations. The second of these methods is called *completing the square.* Completing the square on a quadratic equation allows us to obtain solutions, regardless of whether the equation can be factored. But before we solve equations by completing the square, we need to learn how to solve equations by taking square roots of both sides.

Square Root Property for Equations

Consider the equation

$$x^2 = 16$$

We could solve it by writing it in standard form, factoring the left side, and proceeding as we did in Chapter 5. We can shorten our work considerably, however, if we simply notice that x must be either the positive square root of 16 or the negative square root of 16. That is,

$$\text{If} \qquad x^2 = 16$$
$$\text{Then} \quad x = \sqrt{16} \quad \text{or} \quad x = -\sqrt{16}$$
$$x = 4 \qquad\qquad x = -4$$

We can generalize this result as follows.

> $\sqrt{\Delta \neq \Sigma}$ **PROPERTY**   *Square Root Property for Equations*
>
> If $a^2 = b$, where b is a real number, then $a = \sqrt{b}$ or $a = -\sqrt{b}$.

Notation   The expression $a = \sqrt{b}$ or $a = -\sqrt{b}$ can be written in shorthand form as $a = \pm\sqrt{b}$. The symbol $\pm$ is read "plus or minus."

VIDEO EXAMPLES

SECTION 11.1

EXAMPLE 1   Solve: $-16t^2 + 32 = 0$.

SOLUTION   To use the Square Root Property for Equations, we must first isolate the quantity that is squared.

$$-16t^2 + 32 = 0$$
$$-16t^2 = -32$$
$$t^2 = 2$$

Now, applying the property, we have

$$t = \pm\sqrt{2}$$

The solution set is $\{-\sqrt{2}, \sqrt{2}\}$.

From the introduction to this section, we now know it would take $\sqrt{2} \approx 1.4$ seconds for the baseball to strike the ground if dropped from a balcony 32 feet high.

We can apply the Square Root Property for Equations to more complicated quadratic equations.

EXAMPLE 2   Solve: $(2x - 3)^2 = 25$.

SOLUTION

$$(2x - 3)^2 = 25$$

$2x - 3 = \pm\sqrt{25}$ Square Root Property for Equations

$2x - 3 = \pm 5$ $\sqrt{25} = 5$

$2x = 3 \pm 5$ Add 3 to both sides

$x = \dfrac{3 \pm 5}{2}$ Divide both sides by 2

The last equation can be written as two separate statements:

$$x = \frac{3 + 5}{2} \quad \text{or} \quad x = \frac{3 - 5}{2}$$
$$= \frac{8}{2} \qquad\qquad = \frac{-2}{2}$$
$$= 4 \qquad\qquad = -1$$

The solution set is $\{-1, 4\}$.

Notice that we could have solved the equation in Example 2 by expanding the left side, writing the resulting equation in standard form, and then factoring. The problem would look like this:

$$(2x - 3)^2 = 25 \qquad \text{Original equation}$$
$$4x^2 - 12x + 9 = 25 \qquad \text{Expand the left side}$$
$$4x^2 - 12x - 16 = 0 \qquad \text{Add } -25 \text{ to each side}$$
$$4(x^2 - 3x - 4) = 0 \qquad \text{Begin factoring}$$
$$4(x - 4)(x + 1) = 0 \qquad \text{Factor completely}$$
$$x - 4 = 0 \quad \text{or} \quad x + 1 = 0 \qquad \text{Set variable factors equal to 0}$$
$$x = 4 \qquad\quad x = -1$$

As you can see, solving the equation by factoring leads to the same two solutions.

EXAMPLE 3 Solve for x: $(3x - 1)^2 = -12$

SOLUTION

$$(3x - 1)^2 = -12$$
$$3x - 1 = \pm\sqrt{-12} \qquad \text{Square Root Property for Equations}$$
$$3x - 1 = \pm 2i\sqrt{3} \qquad \sqrt{-12} = 2i\sqrt{3}$$
$$3x = 1 \pm 2i\sqrt{3} \qquad \text{Add 1 to both sides}$$
$$x = \frac{1}{3} \pm \frac{2\sqrt{3}}{3}i \qquad \text{Divide both sides by 3}$$

The solution set is $\left\{ \dfrac{1}{3} + \dfrac{2\sqrt{3}}{3}i, \dfrac{1}{3} - \dfrac{2\sqrt{3}}{3}i \right\}$.

Note We cannot solve the equation in Example 3 by factoring. If we expand the left side and write the resulting equation in standard form, we have

$$(3x - 1)^2 = -12$$
$$9x^2 - 6x + 1 = -12$$
$$9x^2 - 6x + 13 = 0$$

which is not factorable.

EXAMPLE 4 Solve: $x^2 + 6x + 9 = 12$.

SOLUTION We can solve this equation using the Square Root Property for Equations if we first write the left side as a perfect square.

$$x^2 + 6x + 9 = 12 \qquad \text{Original equation}$$
$$(x + 3)^2 = 12 \qquad \text{Write } x^2 + 6x + 9 \text{ as } (x + 3)^2$$
$$x + 3 = \pm\sqrt{12} \qquad \text{Square Root Property for Equations}$$
$$x + 3 = \pm 2\sqrt{3} \qquad \text{Simplify the radical}$$
$$x = -3 \pm 2\sqrt{3} \qquad \text{Add } -3 \text{ to each side}$$

We have two irrational solutions: $-3 + 2\sqrt{3}$ and $-3 - 2\sqrt{3}$. What is important about this problem, however, is the fact that the equation was easy to solve because the left side was a perfect square trinomial.

Method of Completing the Square

The method of completing the square is simply a way of transforming any quadratic equation into an equation of the form found in the preceding three examples.

The key to understanding the method of completing the square lies in recognizing the relationship between the last two terms of any perfect square trinomial whose leading coefficient is 1.

Consider the formula for the square of a binomial

$$(a + b)^2 = a^2 + 2ab + b^2$$

Replacing a with x, we have

$$(x + b)^2 = x^2 + 2xb + b^2$$

Notice that the coefficient of x in the trinomial, $2b$, is twice the second term in the binomial, and the third term in the trinomial, b^2, is the square of the second term in the binomial. In other words, to be a perfect square trinomial, the third term must be the square of half the coefficient of the second term. So, if we are given

$$x^2 + ax$$

then

$$x^2 + ax + \left(\frac{a}{2}\right)^2$$

will be a perfect square trinomial whose factored form is $\left(x + \frac{a}{2}\right)^2$.

We can use these observations to build our own perfect square trinomials and, in doing so, solve some quadratic equations. The key is to add the term $\left(\frac{1}{2}a\right)^2$ in order to "complete" the perfect square trinomial.

EXAMPLE 5   Solve $x^2 - 6x + 5 = 0$ by completing the square.

SOLUTION   We begin by adding -5 to both sides of the equation. We want just $x^2 - 6x$ on the left side so that we can add on our own third term to get a perfect square trinomial:

$$x^2 - 6x + 5 = 0$$
$$x^2 - 6x \quad\;\; = -5 \qquad \text{Add } -5 \text{ to both sides}$$

The coefficient of x is -6, so we must add $(-6/2)^2 = (-3)^2 = 9$ to both sides in order to complete the perfect square trinomial.

$$x^2 - 6x + 9 = -5 + 9 \qquad \text{Add 9 to both sides}$$
$$(x - 3)^2 = 4 \qquad\quad \text{Factor the left side, simplify the right side}$$

The resulting equation can now be solved using the Square Root Property for Equations.

$$x - 3 = \pm 2$$
$$x = 3 \pm 2 \qquad \text{Add 3 to both sides}$$
$$x = 3 + 2 \quad \text{or} \quad x = 3 - 2$$
$$x = 5 \qquad\qquad\;\; x = 1$$

The two solutions are 5 and 1.

> *Note* The equation in Example 5 can be solved quickly by factoring:
>
> $$x^2 - 6x + 5 = 0$$
> $$(x - 5)(x - 1) = 0$$
> $$x - 5 = 0 \quad \text{or} \quad x - 1 = 0$$
> $$x = 5 \qquad\qquad x = 1$$
>
> The reason we didn't solve it by factoring is we want to practice completing the square on some simple equations.

EXAMPLE 6   Solve by completing the square: $x^2 + 5x - 2 = 0$

SOLUTION   We must begin by adding 2 to both sides. (The left side of the equation, as it is, is not a perfect square, because it does not have the correct constant term. We will simply "move" that term to the other side and use our own constant term.)

$$x^2 + 5x = 2 \qquad \text{Add 2 to each side}$$

We complete the square by adding the square of half the coefficient of the linear term to both sides:

$$x^2 + 5x + \frac{25}{4} = 2 + \frac{25}{4}$$

Half of 5 is $\frac{5}{2}$, the square of which is $\frac{25}{4}$

$$\left(x + \frac{5}{2}\right)^2 = \frac{33}{4}$$

$2 + \frac{25}{4} = \frac{8}{4} + \frac{25}{4} = \frac{33}{4}$

$$x + \frac{5}{2} = \pm\sqrt{\frac{33}{4}}$$

Square Root Property for Equations

$$x + \frac{5}{2} = \pm\frac{\sqrt{33}}{2}$$

Simplify the radical

$$x = -\frac{5}{2} \pm \frac{\sqrt{33}}{2}$$

Add $-\frac{5}{2}$ to both sides

$$x = \frac{-5 \pm \sqrt{33}}{2}$$

The solution set is $\left\{\dfrac{-5 + \sqrt{33}}{2}, \dfrac{-5 - \sqrt{33}}{2}\right\}$.

We can use a calculator to get decimal approximations to these solutions. If $\sqrt{33} \approx 5.74$, then

$$\frac{-5 + 5.74}{2} = 0.37 \quad \text{and} \quad \frac{-5 - 5.74}{2} = -5.37$$

The method we have developed for completing the perfect square trinomial is only valid when the coefficient of the quadratic term is 1. If this is not the case, then we must first modify the equation to obtain a leading coefficient of 1. The next two examples illustrate how this is done.

EXAMPLE 7   Solve: $-16t^2 + 48t + 32 = 0$

SOLUTION   Before we can complete the square, we must have a leading coefficient of 1. We begin by dividing both sides by -16, and then proceeding as before.

$$-16t^2 + 48t + 32 = 0$$
$$t^2 - 3t - 2 = 0$$

Divide both sides by -16

$$t^2 - 3t = 2$$

Add 2 to both sides

$$t^2 - 3t + \frac{9}{4} = 2 + \frac{9}{4}$$

Add $\left(-\frac{3}{2}\right)^2 = \frac{9}{4}$ to both sides

$$\left(t - \frac{3}{2}\right)^2 = \frac{17}{4}$$

Factor the left side, simplify the right side

$$t - \frac{3}{2} = \pm\sqrt{\frac{17}{4}}$$

Square Root Property for Equations

$$t - \frac{3}{2} = \pm\frac{\sqrt{17}}{2}$$

Simplify the radical

$$t = \frac{3}{2} \pm \frac{\sqrt{17}}{2}$$

Add $\frac{3}{2}$ to both sides

$$t = \frac{3 \pm \sqrt{17}}{2}$$

The solutions are $t = \dfrac{3 + \sqrt{17}}{2}$ and $t = \dfrac{3 - \sqrt{17}}{2}$.

As a result of our work in Example 7, we can now see it would take

$$\frac{3 + \sqrt{17}}{2} \approx 3.6 \text{ seconds}$$

for the baseball described in the introduction to this section to strike the ground if it were thrown upward at a speed of 48 feet per second.

EXAMPLE 8   Solve for x: $3x^2 - 8x + 7 = 0$.

SOLUTION

$$3x^2 - 8x + 7 = 0$$

$$3x^2 - 8x = -7 \qquad \text{Add } -7 \text{ to both sides}$$

We cannot complete the square on the left side because the leading coefficient is not 1. We take an extra step and divide both sides by 3

$$\frac{3x^2}{3} - \frac{8x}{3} = -\frac{7}{3}$$

$$x^2 - \frac{8}{3}x = -\frac{7}{3}$$

Half of $\frac{8}{3}$ is $\frac{4}{3}$, the square of which is $\frac{16}{9}$:

$$x^2 - \frac{8}{3}x + \frac{16}{9} = -\frac{7}{3} + \frac{16}{9} \qquad \text{Add } \frac{16}{9} \text{ to both sides}$$

$$\left(x - \frac{4}{3}\right)^2 = -\frac{5}{9} \qquad \text{Factor the left side, simplify right side}$$

$$x - \frac{4}{3} = \pm\sqrt{-\frac{5}{9}} \qquad \text{Square Root Property for Equations}$$

$$x - \frac{4}{3} = \pm\frac{i\sqrt{5}}{3} \qquad \sqrt{-\frac{5}{9}} = \frac{\sqrt{-5}}{3} = \frac{i\sqrt{5}}{3}$$

$$x = \frac{4}{3} \pm \frac{\sqrt{5}}{3}i \qquad \text{Add } \frac{4}{3} \text{ to both sides}$$

The solution set is $\left\{\frac{4}{3} + \frac{\sqrt{5}}{3}i, \frac{4}{3} - \frac{\sqrt{5}}{3}i\right\}$.

HOW TO   *Solve a Quadratic Equation by Completing the Square*

To summarize the method used in the preceding two examples, we list the following steps:

Step 1: Write the equation in the form $ax^2 + bx = c$.

Step 2: If the leading coefficient is not 1, divide both sides by the coefficient so that the resulting equation has a leading coefficient of 1. That is, if $a \neq 1$, then divide both sides by a.

Step 3: Add the square of half the coefficient of the linear term to both sides of the equation.

Step 4: Write the left side of the equation as the square of a binomial, and simplify the right side if possible.

Step 5: Apply the Square Root Property for Equations, and solve as usual.

Applications

We conclude this section with some real-life applications of quadratic equations that can be solved using our two new methods.

EXAMPLE 9   The vertical rise of the Forest Double chair lift at the Northstar at Tahoe Ski Resort is 1,170 feet and the length of the chair lift as 5,750 feet. To the nearest foot, find the horizontal distance covered by a person riding this lift.

SOLUTION   Figure 1 is a model of the Forest Double chair lift. A rider gets on the lift at point A and exits at point B. The length of the lift is AB.

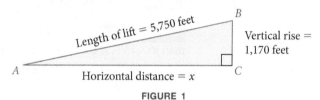

Length of lift = 5,750 feet

Vertical rise = 1,170 feet

Horizontal distance = x

FIGURE 1

To find the horizontal distance covered by a person riding the chair lift, we use the Pythagorean theorem.

$$5,750^2 = x^2 + 1,170^2 \qquad \text{Pythagorean theorem}$$

$$33,062,500 = x^2 + 1,368,900 \qquad \text{Simplify squares}$$

$$x^2 = 33,062,500 - 1,368,900 \qquad \text{Solve for } x^2$$

$$x^2 = 31,693,600 \qquad \text{Simplify the right side}$$

$$x = \sqrt{31,693,600} \qquad \text{Square Root Property for Equations}$$

$$\approx 5,630 \text{ feet} \qquad \text{to the nearest foot}$$

Note   When we use the Square Root Property for Equations in Example 9, we do not need to consider the negative square root because x represents a distance and must be positive.

A rider getting on the lift at point A and riding to point B will cover a horizontal distance of approximately 5,630 feet.

EXAMPLE 10   Two boats leave from an island port at the same time. One travels due north at a speed of twelve miles per hour, and the other travels due west at a speed of 16 miles per hour. How long until the distance between the two boats is 50 miles?

SOLUTION   If we let t represent the time, then the distance traveled by the boat going north is $12t$ and the distance traveled by the boat going west is $16t$. Figure 2 shows a diagram for the problem. We see that the distances traveled by the two boats form the legs of a right triangle. The hypotenuse of the triangle will be the distance between the boats, which is 50 miles.

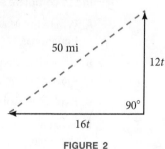

50 mi

$12t$

$90°$

$16t$

FIGURE 2

By the Pythagorean theorem, we have

$$(16t)^2 + (12t)^2 = 50^2 \qquad \text{Pythagorean theorem}$$
$$256t^2 + 144t^2 = 2500 \qquad \text{Simplify squares}$$
$$400t^2 = 2500 \qquad \text{Combine similar terms}$$
$$t^2 = \frac{25}{4} \qquad \text{Divide both sides by 400}$$
$$t = \sqrt{\frac{25}{4}} \qquad \text{Square Root Property for Equations (t must be positive)}$$
$$t = \frac{5}{2} \qquad \text{Simplify the radical}$$

The two boats will be 50 miles apart after 2.5 hours.

EXAMPLE 11   A rectangular cement patio has a length that is 6 feet longer than its width. If the area of the patio is 120 square feet, how wide is the patio?

SOLUTION   We let x represent the width of the patio. The length will then be $x + 6$. Figure 3 illustrates the situation.

x | Area = 120 feet

$x + 6$

FIGURE 3

Since the area is given by the product of the length and the width, we have

$$x(x + 6) = 120$$
$$x^2 + 6x = 120$$

This quadratic equation cannot be solved by factoring (try it), so we use the method of completing the square.

$$x^2 + 6x + 9 = 120 + 9 \qquad \text{Add } \left(\frac{6}{2}\right)^2 = 9 \text{ to both sides}$$
$$(x + 3)^2 = 129 \qquad \text{Factor and simplify}$$
$$x + 3 = \pm\sqrt{129} \qquad \text{Square Root Property for Equations}$$
$$x = -3 \pm \sqrt{129}$$

Because x must be a positive number, the only valid solution is

$$x = -3 + \sqrt{129} \approx 8.4 \text{ feet for the width}$$

Getting Ready for Class

After reading through the preceding section, respond in your own words and in complete sentences.

A. What kind of equation do we solve using the Square Root Property for Equations?

B. What kind of equation do we solve using the method of completing the square?

C. Explain in words how you would complete the square on $x^2 - 16x = 4$.

D. What are the first two steps in solving $2x^2 + 7x - 1 = 0$ by completing the square?

Solve using the Square Root Property for Equations.

1. $x^2 = 25$ **2.** $x^2 = 16$ **3.** $a^2 = -9$ **4.** $a^2 = -49$

5. $y^2 = \dfrac{3}{4}$ **6.** $y^2 = \dfrac{5}{9}$ **7.** $x^2 + 12 = 0$ **8.** $x^2 + 8 = 0$

9. $4a^2 - 45 = 0$ **10.** $9a^2 - 20 = 0$ **11.** $3x^2 + 28 = 0$ **12.** $5x^2 + 18 = 0$

13. $(2y - 1)^2 = 25$ **14.** $(3y + 7)^2 = 1$

15. $(2a + 3)^2 = -9$ **16.** $(3a - 5)^2 = -49$

17. $(5x + 2)^2 = -8$ **18.** $(6x - 7)^2 = -75$

19. $x^2 + 8x + 16 = 27$ **20.** $x^2 - 12x + 36 = 8$

21. $4a^2 - 12a + 9 = -4$ **22.** $9a^2 - 12a + 4 = -9$

Copy each of the following, and fill in the blanks so the left side of each is a perfect square trinomial. That is, complete the square.

23. $x^2 + 12x +$ ___ $= (x +$ ___$)^2$ **24.** $x^2 + 6x +$ ___ $= (x +$ ___$)^2$

25. $x^2 - 4x +$ ___ $= (x -$ ___$)^2$ **26.** $x^2 - 2x +$ ___ $= (x -$ ___$)^2$

27. $a^2 - 10a +$ ___ $= (a -$ ___$)^2$ **28.** $a^2 - 8a +$ ___ $= (a -$ ___$)^2$

29. $x^2 + 5x +$ ___ $= (x +$ ___$)^2$ **30.** $x^2 + 3x +$ ___ $= (x +$ ___$)^2$

31. $y^2 - 7y +$ ___ $= (y -$ ___$)^2$ **32.** $y^2 - y +$ ___ $= (y -$ ___$)^2$

33. $x^2 + \dfrac{1}{2}x +$ ___ $= (x +$ ___$)^2$ **34.** $x^2 - \dfrac{3}{4}x +$ ___ $= (x -$ ___$)^2$

35. $x^2 + \dfrac{2}{3}x +$ ___ $= (x +$ ___$)^2$ **36.** $x^2 - \dfrac{4}{5}x +$ ___ $= (x -$ ___$)^2$

Solve each of the following quadratic equations by completing the square.

37. $x^2 + 4x = 12$ **38.** $x^2 - 2x = 8$ **39.** $x^2 + 12x = -27$

40. $x^2 - 6x = 16$ **41.** $a^2 - 2a + 5 = 0$ **42.** $a^2 + 10a + 22 = 0$

43. $y^2 - 8y + 1 = 0$ **44.** $y^2 + 6y + 19 = 0$ **45.** $x^2 - 5x - 3 = 0$

46. $x^2 - 5x - 2 = 0$ **47.** $2x^2 - 4x - 8 = 0$ **48.** $3x^2 - 9x - 12 = 0$

49. $3t^2 - 8t + 1 = 0$ **50.** $5t^2 + 12t - 1 = 0$ **51.** $4x^2 - 3x + 5 = 0$

52. $7x^2 - 5x + 2 = 0$ **53.** $3x^2 + 4x - 1 = 0$ **54.** $2x^2 + 6x - 1 = 0$

55. $2x^2 - 10x = 11$ **56.** $25x^2 - 20x = 1$ **57.** $4x^2 - 10x + 11 = 0$

58. $4x^2 - 6x + 9 = 0$

59. For the equation $x^2 = -9$
     a. Can it be solved by factoring?   **b.** Solve it.

60. For the equation $x^2 - 10x + 18 = 0$
     a. Can it be solved by factoring?   **b.** Solve it.

61. Solve the equation $x^2 - 6x = 0$
     a. by factoring   **b.** by completing the square

62. Solve the equation $x^2 + ax = 0$
     a. by factoring   **b.** by completing the square

63. Solve the equation $x^2 + 2x = 35$
     a. by factoring   **b.** by completing the square

64. Solve the equation $8x^2 - 10x - 25 = 0$

    a. by factoring   **b.** by completing the square

65. Is $x = -3 + \sqrt{2}$ a solution to $x^2 - 6x = 7$?

66. Is $x = 2 - \sqrt{5}$ a solution to $x^2 - 4x = 1$?

67. Solve each equation.

    a. $5x - 7 = 0$ **b.** $5x - 7 = 8$ **c.** $(5x - 7)^2 = 8$

    d. $\sqrt{5x - 7} = 8$ **e.** $\dfrac{5}{2} - \dfrac{7}{2x} = \dfrac{4}{x}$

68. Solve each equation.

    a. $5x + 11 = 0$ **b.** $5x + 11 = 9$ **c.** $(5x + 11)^2 = 9$

    d. $\sqrt{5x + 11} = 9$ **e.** $\dfrac{5}{3} - \dfrac{11}{3x} = \dfrac{3}{x}$

69. Paying Attention to Instructions Work each problem according to the instructions given.

    a. Factor: $(2x - 3)^2 - 16$.

    b. Simplify: $(2x - 3)^2 - 16$.

    c. Solve: $(2x - 3)^2 - 16 = 0$.

    d. Solve: $(2x - 3)^2 = -16$.

70. Paying Attention to Instructions Work each problem according to the instructions given.

    a. Evaluate: $(3x + 4)^2 + 9$ if $x = -2$.

    b. Simplify: $(3x + 4)^2 + 9$.

    c. Solve: $(3x + 4)^2 + 9 = 0$.

    d. Solve: $(3x + 4)^2 = 9$.

Applying the Concepts

71. Geometry If the length of a side of a square is 1 inch, find the length of a diagonal of the square.

72. Geometry If the length of the shorter sides of a $45° - 45° - 90°$ triangle is x, find the length of the hypotenuse, in terms of x (Figure 4).

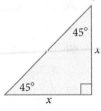

FIGURE 4

73. Chair Lift The Bear Paw Double chair lift at the Northstar at Tahoe Ski Resort is 790 feet long and has a vertical rise of 120 feet. Find the horizontal distance covered by a person riding this lift. Round your answer to the nearest foot.

74. Fermat's Last Theorem As mentioned in a previous chapter, the postage stamp shows Fermat's last theorem, which states that if n is an integer greater than 2, then there are no positive integers x, y, and z that will make the formula $x^n + y^n = z^n$ true. Use the formula $x^n + y^n = z^n$ to

  a. find z if $n = 2$, $x = 6$, and $y = 8$. **b.** find y if $n = 2$, $x = 5$, and $z = 13$.

75. Interest Rate Suppose a deposit of \$3,000 in a savings account that paid an annual interest rate r (compounded yearly) is worth \$3,456 after 2 years. Using the formula $A = P(1 + r)^t$, we have

$$3{,}456 = 3{,}000(1 + r)^2$$

Solve for r to find the annual interest rate.

76. Length of an Escalator An escalator in a department store is made to carry people a horizontal distance of 30 feet and a vertical distance of 20 feet between floors. How long is the escalator? (See Figure 5.)

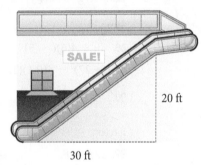

20 ft

30 ft

FIGURE 5

7 ft

FIGURE 6

77. Right Triangle A 25-foot ladder is leaning against a building. The base of the ladder is 7 feet from the side of the building (Figure 6). How high does the ladder reach along the side of the building?

78. Right Triangle Noreen wants to place a 13-foot ramp against the side of her house so the top of the ramp rests on a ledge that is 4 feet above the ground. How far will the base of the ramp be from the house?

79. Distance Two cyclists leave from an intersection at the same time. One travels due north at a speed of 15 miles per hour, and the other travels due east at a speed of 20 miles per hour. How long until the distance between the two cyclists is 70 miles?

80. Distance Two airplanes leave from an airport at the same time. One travels due south at a speed of 480 miles per hour, and the other travels due west at a speed of 360 miles per hour. How long until the distance between the two airplanes is 2700 miles?

81. Rectangle The length of a rectangle is 3 feet more than twice the width. If the area is 25 square feet, find the width of the rectangle.

82. Poster A rectangular poster is 12 inches longer than it is wide. If the area of the poster is 650 square inches, find the dimensions of the poster.

Learning Objectives Assessment

The following problems can be used to help assess if you have successfully met the learning objectives for this section.

83. Solve: $2x^2 - 9 = 0$.

    a. $\pm\dfrac{3\sqrt{2}}{2}$ **b.** $\pm\dfrac{3\sqrt{2}}{2}i$ **c.** $\dfrac{3}{2}$ **d.** $\pm\dfrac{3}{2}$

84. In solving $2x^2 + 6x = 5$ by completing the square, what term should be added to both sides?

    a. 36   **b.** 9   **c.** $\dfrac{9}{4}$ **d.** $\dfrac{3}{2}$

85. Find the length of a diagonal of a rectangle that is 4 meters wide and 5 meters long.

    a. 3 m   **b.** 9 m   **c.** 41 m   **d.** $\sqrt{41}$ m

Getting Ready for the Next Section

Simplify.

86. $49 - 4(6)(-5)$ **87.** $49 - 4(6)(2)$

88. $(-27)^2 - 4(0.1)(1{,}700)$ **89.** $25 - 4(4)(-10)$

90. $-7 + \dfrac{169}{12}$ **91.** $-7 - \dfrac{169}{12}$

Factor.

92. $27t^3 - 8$ **93.** $125t^3 + 1$

Learning Objectives

In this section, we will learn how to:

1. Solve a quadratic equation using the quadratic formula.

2. Solve applied problems involving quadratic equations.

Introduction

As we mentioned in the previous section, the method of completing the square can be used to solve any quadratic equation. We will now take this a step further and solve *every* quadratic equation.

The idea of finding general solutions to different types of equations is threaded throughout the history of mathematics. The general solution for the quadratic equation, which we are about to show you, was first published in Europe in 1145 in a book written by Abraham bar Hiyya Ha-Nasi. It is presented here as a theorem.

$\sqrt{\Delta \neq \Sigma}$ **THEOREM** *The Quadratic Theorem*

For any quadratic equation in the form $ax^2 + bx + c = 0$, $a \neq 0$, the two solutions are

$$x = \frac{-b + \sqrt{b^2 - 4ac}}{2a} \qquad \text{and} \qquad x = \frac{-b - \sqrt{b^2 - 4ac}}{2a}$$

Proof We will prove the quadratic theorem by completing the square on $ax^2 + bx + c = 0$:

$$ax^2 + bx + c = 0$$

$$ax^2 + bx = -c \qquad \text{Add } -c \text{ to both sides}$$

$$x^2 + \frac{b}{a}x = -\frac{c}{a} \qquad \text{Divide both sides by } a$$

To complete the square on the left side, we add the square of $\frac{1}{2}$ of $\frac{b}{a}$ to both sides $\left(\frac{1}{2} \text{ of } \frac{b}{a} \text{ is } \frac{b}{2a}\right)$.

$$x^2 + \frac{b}{a}x + \left(\frac{b}{2a}\right)^2 = -\frac{c}{a} + \left(\frac{b}{2a}\right)^2$$

We now simplify the right side as a separate step. We combine the two terms by writing each with the least common denominator $4a^2$:

$$-\frac{c}{a} + \left(\frac{b}{2a}\right)^2 = -\frac{c}{a} + \frac{b^2}{4a^2} = \frac{4a}{4a}\left(\frac{-c}{a}\right) + \frac{b^2}{4a^2} = \frac{-4ac + b^2}{4a^2}$$

It is convenient to write this last expression as

$$\frac{b^2 - 4ac}{4a^2}$$

Continuing with the proof, we have

$$x^2 + \frac{b}{a}x + \left(\frac{b}{2a}\right)^2 = \frac{b^2 - 4ac}{4a^2}$$

$$\left(x + \frac{b}{2a}\right)^2 = \frac{b^2 - 4ac}{4a^2} \qquad \text{Write left side as a binomial square}$$

$$x + \frac{b}{2a} = \pm\sqrt{\frac{b^2 - 4ac}{4a^2}} \qquad \text{Square Root Property for Equations}$$

$$x + \frac{b}{2a} = \pm\frac{\sqrt{b^2 - 4ac}}{2a} \qquad \text{Simplify the radical}$$

$$x = -\frac{b}{2a} \pm \frac{\sqrt{b^2 - 4ac}}{2a} \qquad \text{Add } -\frac{b}{2a} \text{ to both sides}$$

$$= \frac{-b \pm \sqrt{b^2 - 4ac}}{2a}$$

Our proof is now complete. What we have is this: if our equation is in the form $ax^2 + bx + c = 0$ (standard form), where $a \neq 0$, the two solutions are always given by the formula

$$x = \frac{-b \pm \sqrt{b^2 - 4ac}}{2a}$$

This formula is known as the *quadratic formula*. If we substitute the coefficients a, b, and c of any quadratic equation in standard form into the formula, we need only perform some basic arithmetic to arrive at the solution set.

EXAMPLE 1   Solve $x^2 - 5x - 6 = 0$ by using the quadratic formula.

SOLUTION   To use the quadratic formula, we must make sure the equation is in standard form; identify a, b, and c; substitute them into the formula; and work out the arithmetic.

For the equation $x^2 - 5x - 6 = 0$, $a = 1$, $b = -5$, and $c = -6$:

$$x = \frac{-b \pm \sqrt{b^2 - 4ac}}{2a}$$

$$= \frac{-(-5) \pm \sqrt{(-5)^2 - 4(1)(-6)}}{2(1)}$$

$$= \frac{5 \pm \sqrt{49}}{2}$$

$$= \frac{5 \pm 7}{2}$$

$$x = \frac{5 + 7}{2} \quad \text{or} \quad x = \frac{5 - 7}{2}$$

$$x = \frac{12}{2} \qquad\qquad x = -\frac{2}{2}$$

$$x = 6 \qquad\qquad\quad x = -1$$

The two solutions are 6 and -1.

Note Whenever the solutions to our quadratic equations turn out to be rational numbers, as in Example 1, it means the original equation could have been solved by factoring. (We didn't solve the equation in Example 1 by factoring because we were trying to get some practice with the quadratic formula.)

EXAMPLE 2   Solve for x: $2x^2 = -4x + 3$.

SOLUTION   Before we can identify a, b, and c, we must write the equation in standard form. To do so, we add $4x$ and -3 to each side of the equation:

$$2x^2 = -4x + 3$$

$$2x^2 + 4x - 3 = 0 \qquad \text{Add } 4x \text{ and } -3 \text{ to each side}$$

Now that the equation is in standard form, we see that $a = 2$, $b = 4$, and $c = -3$. Using the quadratic formula we have:

$$x = \frac{-b \pm \sqrt{b^2 - 4ac}}{2a}$$

$$= \frac{-4 \pm \sqrt{4^2 - 4(2)(-3)}}{2(2)}$$

$$= \frac{-4 \pm \sqrt{40}}{4}$$

$$= \frac{-4 \pm 2\sqrt{10}}{4}$$

We can reduce the final expression in the preceding equation to lowest terms by factoring 2 from the numerator and denominator and then dividing it out:

$$x = \frac{2(-2 \pm \sqrt{10})}{2 \cdot 2}$$

$$= \frac{-2 \pm \sqrt{10}}{2}$$

Our two solutions are $\dfrac{-2 + \sqrt{10}}{2}$ and $\dfrac{-2 - \sqrt{10}}{2}$

EXAMPLE 3   Solve: $x^2 - 6x = -7$.

SOLUTION   We begin by writing the equation in standard form:

$$x^2 - 6x = -7$$

$$x^2 - 6x + 7 = 0 \qquad \text{Add 7 to each side}$$

Using $a = 1$, $b = -6$, and $c = 7$ in the quadratic formula

$$x = \frac{-b \pm \sqrt{b^2 - 4ac}}{2a}$$

we have:

$$x = \frac{-(-6) \pm \sqrt{(-6)^2 - 4(1)(7)}}{2(1)}$$

$$= \frac{6 \pm \sqrt{36 - 28}}{2}$$

$$= \frac{6 \pm \sqrt{8}}{2}$$

$$= \frac{6 \pm 2\sqrt{2}}{2}$$

The two terms in the numerator have a 2 in common. We reduce to lowest terms by factoring the 2 from the numerator and then dividing numerator and denominator by 2:

$$x = \frac{2(3 \pm \sqrt{2})}{2}$$

$$= 3 \pm \sqrt{2}$$

The two solutions are $3 + \sqrt{2}$ and $3 - \sqrt{2}$.

EXAMPLE 4   Solve for x: $\frac{1}{10}x^2 - \frac{1}{5}x = -\frac{1}{2}$.

SOLUTION   It will be easier to apply the quadratic formula if we clear the equation of fractions. Multiplying both sides of the equation by the LCD 10 and then writing it in standard form gives us

$$10\left(\frac{1}{10}x^2 - \frac{1}{5}x\right) = \left(-\frac{1}{2}\right)10 \qquad \text{Multiply both sides by 10}$$

$$x^2 - 2x = -5 \qquad \text{Simplify}$$

$$x^2 - 2x + 5 = 0 \qquad \text{Add 5 to both sides}$$

Applying the quadratic formula with $a = 1$, $b = -2$, and $c = 5$, we have:

$$x = \frac{-(-2) \pm \sqrt{(-2)^2 - 4(1)(5)}}{2(1)}$$

$$= \frac{2 \pm \sqrt{-16}}{2}$$

$$= \frac{2 \pm 4i}{2}$$

$$= 1 \pm 2i$$

The two solutions are $1 + 2i$ and $1 - 2i$.

EXAMPLE 5   Solve: $(2x - 3)(2x - 1) = -4$.

SOLUTION   We multiply the binomials on the left side and then add 4 to each side to write the equation in standard form. From there we identify a, b, and c and apply the quadratic formula:

$$(2x - 3)(2x - 1) = -4$$

$$4x^2 - 8x + 3 = -4 \qquad \text{Multiply binomials on left side}$$

$$4x^2 - 8x + 7 = 0 \qquad \text{Add 4 to each side}$$

Placing $a = 4$, $b = -8$, and $c = 7$ in the quadratic formula we have:

$$x = \frac{-(-8) \pm \sqrt{(-8)^2 - 4(4)(7)}}{2(4)}$$

$$= \frac{8 \pm \sqrt{64 - 112}}{8}$$

$$= \frac{8 \pm \sqrt{-48}}{8}$$

$$= \frac{8 \pm 4i\sqrt{3}}{8} \qquad\qquad \sqrt{-48} = i\sqrt{48} = i\sqrt{16}\sqrt{3} = 4i\sqrt{3}$$

$$= \frac{8}{8} \pm \frac{4i\sqrt{3}}{8}$$

$$= 1 \pm \frac{\sqrt{3}}{2}i$$

Although the equation in our next example is not a quadratic equation, we solve it by using both factoring and the quadratic formula.

EXAMPLE 6   Solve: $27t^3 - 8 = 0$.

SOLUTION It would be a mistake to add 8 to each side of this equation and then take the cube root of each side because we would lose two of our solutions. Instead, we factor the left side, and then set the factors equal to 0:

$$27t^3 - 8 = 0$$ Equation in standard form

$$(3t - 2)(9t^2 + 6t + 4) = 0$$ Factor as the difference of two cubes.

$$3t - 2 = 0 \quad \text{or} \quad 9t^2 + 6t + 4 = 0$$ Set each factor equal to 0

The first equation leads to a solution of $t = \frac{2}{3}$. The second equation does not factor, so we use the quadratic formula with $a = 9$, $b = 6$, and $c = 4$:

$$t = \frac{-6 \pm \sqrt{6^2 - 4(9)(4)}}{2(9)}$$

$$= \frac{-6 \pm \sqrt{36 - 144}}{18}$$

$$= \frac{-6 \pm \sqrt{-108}}{18}$$

$$= \frac{-6 \pm 6i\sqrt{3}}{18} \qquad \sqrt{-108} = i\sqrt{36 \cdot 3} = 6i\sqrt{3}$$

$$= -\frac{6}{18} \pm \frac{6i\sqrt{3}}{18}$$

$$= -\frac{1}{3} \pm \frac{\sqrt{3}}{3}i$$

The three solutions to our original equation are

$$\frac{2}{3}, \qquad -\frac{1}{3} + \frac{\sqrt{3}}{3}i, \qquad \text{and} \qquad -\frac{1}{3} - \frac{\sqrt{3}}{3}i$$

Applications

We conclude this section with some applied problems that can be solved using the quadratic formula.

EXAMPLE 7   One leg of a right triangle is 3 centimeters longer than the other leg. If the hypotenuse is 9 centimeters, find the lengths of the two legs. Approximate your answers to the nearest tenth of a centimeter.

SOLUTION We let x represent the length of the shorter leg. Then the longer leg will have length $x + 3$. Figure 1 shows the triangle.

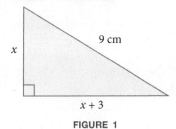

FIGURE 1

From the Pythagorean theorem, we have

$$x^2 + (x + 3)^2 = 9^2 \qquad \text{Pythagorean theorem}$$

$$x^2 + x^2 + 6x + 9 = 81 \qquad \text{Expand } (x + 3)^2$$

$$2x^2 + 6x - 72 = 0 \qquad \text{Standard form}$$

$$x^2 + 3x - 36 = 0 \qquad \text{Divide both sides by 2}$$

This equation cannot be factored, so we use the quadratic formula to solve for x.

$$x = \frac{-3 \pm \sqrt{3^2 - 4(1)(-36)}}{2(1)} \qquad \text{Quadratic formula}$$

$$= \frac{-3 \pm \sqrt{153}}{2} \qquad \text{Simplify}$$

$$= \frac{-3 \pm 3\sqrt{17}}{2} \qquad \sqrt{153} = \sqrt{9}\sqrt{17} = 3\sqrt{17}$$

Using a calculator to approximate $\sqrt{17} \approx 4.1$, the two solutions are $x = 4.7$ or $x = -7.7$. Because x is a length it must be positive. Discarding the negative solution, we find the lengths of the legs are 4.7 centimeters and $4.7 + 3 = 7.7$ centimeters.

EXAMPLE 8   A photographer wants to make a matte for an 8 x 10 inch frame that is the same width on all sides, leaving an open area of 50 square inches. Find the width of the matte. Approximate your answer to the nearest tenth of an inch.

SOLUTION   Figure 2 shows a diagram of the problem, where x represents the width of the matte.

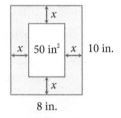

8 in.

FIGURE 2

The inner rectangle will have a width of $8 - 2x$ and a height of $10 - 2x$. Since the area of this rectangle is 50, we have

$$(8 - 2x)(10 - 2x) = 50 \qquad \text{Area equals 50}$$

$$80 - 36x + 4x^2 = 50 \qquad \text{FOIL}$$

$$4x^2 - 36x + 30 = 0 \qquad \text{Standard form}$$

$$2x^2 - 18x + 15 = 0 \qquad \text{Divide both sides by 2}$$

Using the quadratic formula, we have

$$x = \frac{18 \pm \sqrt{(-18)^2 - 4(2)(15)}}{2(2)} \qquad \text{Quadratic formula}$$

$$= \frac{18 \pm \sqrt{204}}{4} \qquad \text{Simplify}$$

$$= \frac{18 \pm 2\sqrt{51}}{4} \qquad \sqrt{204} = \sqrt{4}\sqrt{51} = 2\sqrt{51}$$

$$= \frac{9 \pm \sqrt{51}}{2} \qquad \text{Reduce}$$

Approximating to the nearest tenth of an inch, we obtain $x = 8.1$ or $x = 0.9$. Although both of these values are positive, the width of the matte cannot be 8.1 inches because that exceeds the width of the original frame. Therefore, the photographer should make the matte 0.9 inches wide.

Getting Ready for Class

After reading through the preceding section, respond in your own words and in complete sentences.

A. State the quadratic formula.

B. Explain what the quadratic formula represents.

C. Under what circumstances should the quadratic formula be applied?

D. When would the quadratic formula result in complex solutions?

Problem Set 11.2

Solve each equation using the quadratic formula.

1. $a^2 - 4a + 1 = 0$ **2.** $a^2 + 4a + 1 = 0$ **3.** $2x^2 - x - 5 = 0$

4. $3x^2 + 4x - 1 = 0$ **5.** $12y^2 - 7y = 10$ **6.** $18y^2 + 8 = 51y$

7. $2x + 3 = -2x^2$ **8.** $2x - 3 = 3x^2$ **9.** $4x^2 - 28x + 49 = 0$

10. $9x^2 + 24x + 16 = 0$ **11.** $0.01x^2 + 0.06x - 0.08 = 0$

12. $0.02x^2 - 0.03x + 0.05 = 0$ **13.** $\dfrac{1}{6}x^2 - \dfrac{1}{2}x + \dfrac{1}{3} = 0$

14. $\dfrac{1}{6}x^2 + \dfrac{1}{2}x + \dfrac{1}{3} = 0$ **15.** $\dfrac{x^2}{2} + 1 = \dfrac{2x}{3}$ **16.** $\dfrac{x^2}{2} + \dfrac{2}{3} = -\dfrac{2x}{3}$

17. $\dfrac{2t^2}{3} - t = -\dfrac{1}{6}$ **18.** $\dfrac{t^2}{3} - \dfrac{t}{2} = -\dfrac{3}{2}$ **19.** $\dfrac{1}{2}r^2 = \dfrac{1}{6}r - \dfrac{2}{3}$

20. $\dfrac{1}{4}r^2 = \dfrac{2}{5}r + \dfrac{1}{10}$ **21.** $(x - 3)(x - 5) = 1$ **22.** $(x - 3)(x + 1) = -6$

Multiply both sides of each equation by its LCD. Then solve the resulting equation.

23. $\dfrac{1}{x + 1} - \dfrac{1}{x} = \dfrac{1}{2}$ **24.** $\dfrac{1}{x + 1} + \dfrac{1}{x} = \dfrac{1}{3}$ **25.** $\dfrac{1}{y - 1} + \dfrac{1}{y + 1} = 1$

26. $\dfrac{2}{y + 2} + \dfrac{3}{y - 2} = 1$ **27.** $\dfrac{1}{x + 2} + \dfrac{1}{x + 3} = 1$ **28.** $\dfrac{1}{x + 3} + \dfrac{1}{x + 4} = 1$

29. $\dfrac{6}{r^2 - 1} - \dfrac{1}{2} = \dfrac{1}{r + 1}$ **30.** $2 + \dfrac{5}{r - 1} = \dfrac{12}{(r - 1)^2}$

Solve each equation. In each case you will have three solutions.

31. $x^3 - 8 = 0$ **32.** $x^3 - 27 = 0$ **33.** $8a^3 + 27 = 0$

34. $27a^3 + 8 = 0$ **35.** $125t^3 - 1 = 0$ **36.** $64t^3 + 1 = 0$

Each of the following equations has three solutions. Look for the greatest common factor; then use the quadratic formula to find all solutions.

37. $2x^3 + 2x^2 + 3x = 0$ **38.** $6x^3 - 4x^2 + 6x = 0$ **39.** $3y^4 = 6y^3 - 6y^2$

40. $4y^4 = 16y^3 - 20y^2$ **41.** $6t^5 + 4t^4 = -2t^3$ **42.** $8t^5 + 2t^4 = -10t^3$

43. Which two of the expressions below are equivalent?

    a. $\dfrac{6 + 2\sqrt{3}}{4}$ **b.** $\dfrac{3 + \sqrt{3}}{2}$ **c.** $6 + \dfrac{\sqrt{3}}{2}$

44. Which two of the expressions below are equivalent?

    a. $\dfrac{8 - 4\sqrt{2}}{4}$ **b.** $2 - 4\sqrt{3}$ **c.** $2 - \sqrt{2}$

45. Solve $3x^2 - 5x = 0$

    a. by factoring   **b.** by the quadratic formula

46. Solve $3x^2 + 23x - 70 = 0$

    a. by factoring   **b.** by the quadratic formula

47. Can the equation $x^2 - 4x + 7 = 0$ be solved by factoring? Solve it.

48. Can the equation $x^2 = 5$ be solved by factoring? Solve it.

49. Is $x = -1 + i$ a solution to $x^2 + 2x = -2$?

50. Is $x = 2 + 2i$ a solution to $(x - 2)^2 = -4$?

Solve each equation using an appropriate method (factoring, Square Root Property for Equations, completing the square, or the quadratic formula).

51. $x^2 + 5x + 6 = 0$ **52.** $x^2 + 5x - 6 = 0$ **53.** $2y^2 + 10y = 0$

54. $30x^2 + 40x = 0$ **55.** $4a^2 - 27 = 0$ **56.** $6a^2 + 30 = 0$

57. $y^2 = 5y$ **58.** $50x^2 = 20x$ **59.** $2x^2 + 5x = 6$

60. $3x^2 + 13 = 12x$ **61.** $100x^2 - 200x + 100 = 0$

62. $100x^2 - 600x + 900 = 0$ **63.** $(x + 3)^2 + (x - 8)(x - 1) = 16$

64. $(x - 4)^2 + (x + 2)(x + 1) = 9$ **65.** $\dfrac{x^2}{3} - \dfrac{5x}{6} = \dfrac{1}{2}$

66. $\dfrac{x^2}{6} + \dfrac{5}{6} = -\dfrac{x}{3}$ **67.** $(19y - 31)^2 - 121 = 0$

68. $\left(\dfrac{1}{23}y - \dfrac{1}{13}\right)^2 + \dfrac{1}{16} = 0$

69. Solve each equation using an appropriate method.
   a. $(2x + 3)(2x - 3) = 0$
   b. $(2x + 3)(2x - 3) = 7$
   c. $(2x + 3)^2 = 7$
   d. $2x + 3 = 7x^2$

70. Solve each equation using an appropriate method.
   a. $(3x + 2)(3x - 4) = 0$
   b. $(3x + 2)(3x - 4) = 1$
   c. $(3x + 2)(3x - 4) = -6x$
   d. $3x + 2 = -6x^2$

Applying the Concepts

71. Right Triangle One leg of a right triangle is 2 meters shorter than the other leg. If the hypotenuse is 12 meters, find the lengths of the two legs. Approximate your answers to the nearest tenth of a meter.

72. Geometry A triangle has a height that is 4 feet longer than its base. If the area of the triangle is 18 square feet, find the length of the base and the height. Approximate your answers to the nearest tenth of a foot.

73. Rectangle The length of a rectangle is 5 centimeters less than 4 times its width. If the rectangle has an area of 60 square centimeters, find the dimensions of the rectangle. Approximate your answers to the nearest tenth of a centimeter.

74. Gravel Path A rectangular plot of ground that measures 40 feet by 60 feet is to be used for a garden surrounded by a gravel path (Figure 3). The path will be the same width on all sides. If the area inside the gravel path needs to be 2,000 square feet, find the width of the path. Round your answer to the nearest tenth of a foot.

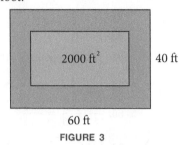

2000 ft^2 40 ft

60 ft

FIGURE 3

75. Area In the following diagram, $ABCD$ is a rectangle with diagonal AC. Find its area.

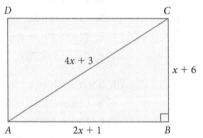

D   C

$4x + 3$

$x + 6$

A $2x + 1$ B

76. Area and Perimeter A total of 160 yards of fencing is to be used to enclose part of a lot that borders on a river. This situation is shown in the following diagram.

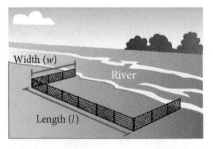

Width (w)

River

Length (l)

a. Write an equation that gives the relationship between the length and width and the 160 yards of fencing.

b. The formula for the area that is enclosed by the fencing and the river is $A = lw$. Solve the equation in part a for l, and then use the result to write the area in terms of w only.

c. Make a table that gives at least five possible values of w and associated area A.

d. From the pattern in your table shown in part c, what is the largest area that can be enclosed by the 160 yards of fencing? (Try some other table values if necessary.)

Learning Objectives Assessment

The following problems can be used to help assess if you have successfully met the learning objectives for this section.

77. Use the quadratic formula to solve: $2x^2 + x = 5$.

   a. $\dfrac{-1 \pm \sqrt{41}}{4}$ **b.** $\dfrac{1 \pm \sqrt{11}}{4}$ **c.** $-\dfrac{1}{4} \pm \dfrac{\sqrt{39}}{4}i$ **d.** $\dfrac{1}{2} \pm \dfrac{3}{2}i$

78. Right Triangle A right triangle has one leg that is 1 inch longer than the shorter leg, and the hypotenuse is 4 inches longer than the shorter leg. Find the length of the shortest leg.

   a. 11.9 inches   **b.** 3 inches   **c.** 8.9 inches   **d.** 7.9 inches

Getting Ready for the Next Section

Find the value of $b^2 - 4ac$ when

79. $a = 1, b = -3, c = -40$ **80.** $a = 2, b = 3, c = 4$

81. $a = 4, b = 12, c = 9$ **82.** $a = -3, b = 8, c = -1$

Solve.

83. $k^2 - 144 = 0$ **84.** $36 - 20k = 0$

Multiply.

85. $(x - 3)(x + 2)$ **86.** $(t - 5)(t + 3)$

87. $(x - 3)(x - 3)$ **88.** $(t - 5)(t + 5)$

Learning Objectives

In this section, we will learn how to:

1. Find the value of the discriminant.

2. Use the discriminant to determine the type of solutions a quadratic equation has.

3. Find a quadratic equation by reversing the factoring method.

4. Find a quadratic equation by reversing the Square Root Property for Equations method.

Introduction

In this section, we will do two things. First, we will define the discriminant and use it to find the kind of solutions a quadratic equation has without solving the equation. Second, we will reverse the Zero-Factor Property or Square Root Property for Equations to build equations from their solutions.

The Discriminant

The quadratic formula

$$x = \frac{-b \pm \sqrt{b^2 - 4ac}}{2a}$$

gives the solutions to any quadratic equation in standard form. There are times, when working with quadratic equations, that it is important only to know what kind of solutions the equation has.

(def) DEFINITION *discriminant*

The expression under the radical in the quadratic formula is called the *discriminant*:

$$\text{Discriminant} = D = b^2 - 4ac$$

The discriminant indicates the number and type of solutions to a quadratic equation, when the original equation has integer coefficients. For example, if we were to use the quadratic formula to solve the equation $2x^2 + 2x + 3 = 0$, we would find the discriminant to be

$$b^2 - 4ac - 2^? \quad 4(2)(3) - -20$$

Because the discriminant appears under a square root symbol, we have the square root of a negative number in the quadratic formula. Our solutions would therefore be complex numbers. Similarly, if the discriminant were 0, the quadratic formula would yield

$$x = \frac{-b \pm \sqrt{0}}{2a} = \frac{-b \pm 0}{2a} = \frac{-b}{2a}$$

and the equation would have one rational solution, the number $\frac{-b}{2a}$.

The following table gives the relationship between the discriminant and the type of solutions to the equation.

For the equation $ax^2 + bx + c = 0$ where a, b, and c are integers and $a \neq 0$:

If the Discriminant b^2-4ac is	Then the Equation Will Have
Negative	Two non-real complex solutions containing i
Zero	One rational solution
A positive number that is also a perfect square	Two rational solutions
A positive number that is not a perfect square	Two irrational solutions

In the first case, when a quadratic equation has non-real complex solutions, they will always be complex conjugates. In the second and third cases, when the discriminant is 0 or a positive perfect square, the solutions are rational numbers. The quadratic equations in these two cases are the ones that can be factored.

VIDEO EXAMPLES

SECTION 11.3

EXAMPLES   For each equation, give the number and kind of solutions.

1. $x^2 - 3x - 40 = 0$

SOLUTION   Using $a = 1$, $b = -3$, and $c = -40$ in $b^2 - 4ac$, we have

$$(-3)^2 - 4(1)(-40) = 9 + 160 = 169.$$

The discriminant is a perfect square. The equation therefore has two rational solutions.

2. $2x^2 - 3x + 4 = 0$

SOLUTION   Using $a = 2$, $b = -3$, and $c = 4$, we have

$$b^2 - 4ac = (-3)^2 - 4(2)(4) = 9 - 32 = -23$$

The discriminant is negative, implying the equation has two complex solutions that contain i.

3. $4x^2 - 12x + 9 = 0$

SOLUTION   Using $a = 4$, $b = -12$, and $c = 9$, the discriminant is

$$b^2 - 4ac = (-12)^2 - 4(4)(9) = 144 - 144 = 0$$

Because the discriminant is 0, the equation will have one rational solution.

4. $x^2 + 6x = 8$

SOLUTION   We must first put the equation in standard form by adding -8 to each side. If we do so, the resulting equation is

$$x^2 + 6x - 8 = 0$$

Now we identify a, b, and c as 1, 6, and -8, respectively:

$$b^2 - 4ac = 6^2 - 4(1)(-8) = 36 + 32 = 68$$

The discriminant is a positive number, but not a perfect square. The equation will therefore have two irrational solutions.

EXAMPLE 5   Find an appropriate k so that the equation $4x^2 - kx = -9$ has exactly one rational solution.

SOLUTION   We begin by writing the equation in standard form:

$$4x^2 - kx + 9 = 0$$

Using $a = 4$, $b = -k$, and $c = 9$, we have

$$b^2 - 4ac = (-k)^2 - 4(4)(9)$$

$$= k^2 - 144$$

An equation has exactly one rational solution when the discriminant is 0. We set the discriminant equal to 0 and solve:

$$k^2 - 144 = 0$$

$$k^2 = 144$$

$$k = \pm 12$$

Choosing k to be 12 or -12 will result in an equation with one rational solution.

Building Equations From Their Solutions

Suppose we are given the two solutions to a quadratic equation, and we would like to work backwards and find what the original equation was. We can do this by reversing the steps of the factoring method or Square Root Property for Equations. Before continuing to the next examples, you may want to refresh your memory on these two methods by reviewing the examples from Sections 5.8 and 8.1.

EXAMPLE 6   Find a quadratic equation that has solutions $x = 3$ and $x = -2$. Write your answer in standard form.

SOLUTION   We can always use the factoring method in reverse to find an equation given the solutions. First, let's write our solutions as equations with 0 on the right side:

If	$x = 3$	First solution
then	$x - 3 = 0$	Add -3 to each side
and if	$x = -2$	Second solution
then	$x + 2 = 0$	Add 2 to each side

The quantities $x - 3$ and $x + 2$ must have been factors in our original equation. Because both $x - 3$ and $x + 2$ are 0, their product must be 0 also. We can therefore write

$$(x - 3)(x + 2) = 0 \quad \text{Zero-factor property}$$

$$x^2 - x - 6 = 0 \quad \text{Multiply out the left side}$$

In standard form, $x^2 - x - 6 = 0$ is a quadratic equation having $x = 3$ and $x = -2$ as solutions.

You may be wondering why the previous example asked us to find "a" quadratic equation instead of find "the" quadratic equation with the given solutions. The reason is that many equations have 3 and -2 as solutions. For example, any constant multiple of $x^2 - x - 6 = 0$, such as $5x^2 - 5x - 30 = 0$, also has 3 and -2 as solutions.

EXAMPLE 7   Find a quadratic equation with solutions $x = -\dfrac{2}{3}$ and $x = \dfrac{4}{5}$. Write your answer in standard form.

SOLUTION   The solution $x = -\frac{2}{3}$ can be rewritten as $3x + 2 = 0$ as follows:

$$x = -\frac{2}{3} \quad \text{The first solution}$$

$$3x = -2 \quad \text{Multiply each side by 3}$$

$$3x + 2 = 0 \quad \text{Add 2 to each side}$$

Similarly, the solution $x = \frac{4}{5}$ can be rewritten as $5x - 4 = 0$:

$$x = \frac{4}{5} \qquad \text{The second solution}$$

$$5x = 4 \qquad \text{Multiply each side by 5}$$

$$5x - 4 = 0 \qquad \text{Add } -4 \text{ to each side}$$

Because both $3x + 2$ and $5x - 4$ are 0, their product is 0 also, giving us the equation we are looking for:

$$(3x + 2)(5x - 4) = 0 \qquad \text{Zero-factor property}$$

$$15x^2 - 2x - 8 = 0 \qquad \text{Multiplication}$$

If the two solutions are identical except for a $\pm$ sign, then another way to find an equation is to reverse the steps of the Square Root Property for Equations method. We illustrate how this is done in the next two examples.

EXAMPLE 8   Find a quadratic equation in standard form with solutions $x = -\sqrt{5}$ and $x = \sqrt{5}$.

SOLUTION   We begin by writing the solutions using a $\pm$ symbol, then squaring both sides to eliminate the radical.

$$x = \pm\sqrt{5}$$

$$x^2 = (\pm\sqrt{5})^2 \qquad \text{Square both sides}$$

$$x^2 = 5 \qquad \text{Simplify}$$

$$x^2 - 5 = 0 \qquad \text{Standard form}$$

Note   The $\pm$ symbol is eliminated when squaring both sides because the square of a positive number and the square of a negative number are both positive.

EXAMPLE 9   Find a quadratic equation with solutions $x = 2 + 3i$ and $x = 2 - 3i$.

SOLUTION   In this case, we isolate the $\pm$ term before squaring both sides in order to eliminate the imaginary unit i.

$$x = 2 \pm 3i$$

$$x - 2 = \pm 3i \qquad \text{Subtract 2 from both sides}$$

$$(x - 2)^2 = (\pm 3i)^2 \qquad \text{Square both sides}$$

$$(x - 2)^2 = -9 \qquad (\pm 3i)^2 = 9i^2 = 9(-1) = -9$$

$$x^2 - 4x + 4 = -9 \qquad \text{FOIL}$$

$$x^2 - 4x + 13 = 0 \qquad \text{Standard form}$$

USING TECHNOLOGY *Graphing Calculators*

Solving Equations

Now that we have explored the relationship between equations and their solutions, we can look at how a graphing calculator can be used in the solution process. To begin, let's solve the equation $x^2 = x + 2$ using techniques from algebra: writing it in standard form, factoring, and then setting each factor equal to 0.

$x^2 - x - 2 = 0$	Standard form
$(x - 2)(x + 1) = 0$	Factor
$x - 2 = 0 \quad \text{or} \quad x + 1 = 0$	Set each factor equal to 0
$x = 2 \quad \text{or} \qquad x = -1$	Solve

Our original equation, $x^2 = x + 2$, has two solutions: $x = 2$ and $x = -1$. To solve the equation using a graphing calculator, we need to associate it with an equation (or equations) in two variables. One way to do this is to associate the left side with the equation $y = x^2$ and the right side of the equation with $y = x + 2$. To do so, we set up the functions list in our calculator this way:

$$Y_1 = X^2$$

$$Y_2 = X + 2$$

Window: X from -5 to 5, Y from -5 to 5

Graphing these functions in this window will produce a graph similar to the one shown in Figure 1.

If we use the Trace feature to find the coordinates of the points of intesection, we find that the two curves intersect at $(-1, 1)$ and $(2, 4)$. We note that the x-coordinates of these two points match the solutions to the equation $x^2 = x + 2$, which we found using algebraic techniques. This makes sense because if two graphs intersect at a point (x, y), then the coordinates of that point satisfy both equations. If a point (x, y) satisfies both $y = x^2$ and $y = x + 2$, then for that particular point, $x^2 = x + 2$. From this, we conclude that the x-coordinates of the points of intersection are solutions to our original equation. Here is a summary of what we have discovered:

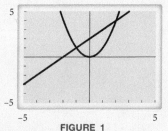

FIGURE 1

Conclusion 1   If the graphs of two functions $y = f(x)$ and $y = g(x)$ intersect in the coordinate plane, then the x-coordinates of the points of intersection are solutions to the equation $f(x) = g(x)$.

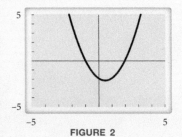

USING TECHNOLOGY   *Graphing Calculators Continued*

A second method of solving our original equation $x^2 = x + 2$ graphically requires the use of one function instead of two. To begin, we write the equation in standard form as $x^2 - x - 2 = 0$. Next, we graph the function $y = x^2 - x - 2$. The x-intercepts of the graph are the points with y-coordinates of 0. They therefore satisfy the equation $0 = x^2 - x - 2$, which is equivalent to our original equation. The graph in Figure 2 shows $Y_1 = X^2 - X - 2$ in a window with X from -5 to 5 and Y from -5 to 5.

Using the Trace feature, we find that the x-intercepts of the graph are $x = -1$ and $x = 2$, which match the solutions to our original equation $x^2 = x + 2$. We can summarize the relationship between solutions to an equation and the intercepts of its associated graph this way:

FIGURE 2

Conclusion 2   If $y = f(x)$ is a function, then any x-intercept on the graph of $y = f(x)$ is a solution to the equation $f(x) = 0$.

Getting Ready for Class

After reading through the preceding section, respond in your own words and in complete sentences.

A. What is the discriminant?

B. What kind of solutions do we get to a quadratic equation when the discriminant is negative?

C. When will a quadratic equation have two rational solutions?

D. Describe two different methods you could use to find a quadratic equation having solutions $x = 4$ and $x = -4$.

Use the discriminant to find the number and kind of solutions for each of the following equations.

1. $x^2 - 6x + 5 = 0$

2. $x^2 - x - 12 = 0$

3. $4x^2 - 4x = -1$

4. $9x^2 + 12x = -4$

5. $x^2 + x - 1 = 0$

6. $x^2 - 2x + 3 = 0$

7. $2y^2 = 3y + 1$

8. $3y^2 = 4y - 2$

9. $x^2 - 9 = 0$

10. $4x^2 - 81 = 0$

11. $5a^2 - 4a = 5$

12. $3a = 4a^2 - 5$

Determine k so that each of the following has exactly one rational solution.

13. $x^2 - kx + 25 = 0$

14. $x^2 + kx + 25 = 0$

15. $x^2 = kx - 36$

16. $x^2 = kx - 49$

17. $4x^2 - 12x + k = 0$

18. $9x^2 + 30x + k = 0$

19. $kx^2 - 40x = 25$

20. $kx^2 - 2x = -1$

21. $3x^2 - kx + 2 = 0$

22. $5x^2 + kx + 1 = 0$

For each of the following problems, find a quadratic equation that has the given solutions. Write your answer in standard form.

23. $x = 5, x = 2$

24. $x = -5, x = -2$

25. $t = -3, t = 6$

26. $t = -4, t = 2$

27. $y = 2, y = -2$

28. $y = 1, y = -1$

29. $x = \dfrac{1}{2}, x = 3$

30. $x = \dfrac{1}{3}, x = 5$

31. $t = -\dfrac{3}{4}, t = 3$

32. $t = -\dfrac{4}{5}, t = 2$

33. $x = 3, x = -3$

34. $x = 5, x = -5$

35. $a = -\dfrac{1}{2}, a = \dfrac{3}{5}$

36. $a = -\dfrac{1}{3}, a = \dfrac{4}{7}$

37. $x = -\dfrac{2}{3}, x = \dfrac{2}{3}$

38. $x = -\dfrac{4}{5}, x = \dfrac{4}{5}$

39. $x = \sqrt{7}, x = -\sqrt{7}$

40. $x = -\sqrt{3}, x = \sqrt{3}$

41. $x = 5i, x = -5i$

42. $x = -2i, x = 2i$

43. $y = 3 + \sqrt{11}, y = 3 - \sqrt{11}$

44. $y = 4 - \sqrt{5}, y = 4 + \sqrt{5}$

45. $t = -6 - \sqrt{2}, t = -6 + \sqrt{2}$

46. $t = -5 + \sqrt{6}, t = -5 - \sqrt{6}$

47. $x = 1 + i, x = 1 - i$

48. $x = 2 + 3i, x = 2 - 3i$

49. $x = -2 - 3i, x = -2 + 3i$

50. $x = -1 + i, x = -1 - i$

51. $x = 7 + i\sqrt{3}, x = 7 - i\sqrt{3}$

52. $x = -8 - i\sqrt{7}, x = -8 + i\sqrt{7}$

53. $x = -3 - 5i\sqrt{2}, x = -3 + 5i\sqrt{2}$

54. $x = 4 + 2i\sqrt{5}, x = 4 - 2i\sqrt{5}$

55. Find a quadratic equation with solutions $x = 1 \pm \sqrt{10}$ using the following method:

   a. Zero-Factor Property

   b. squaring both sides

56. Find a quadratic equation with solutions $x = -8 \pm \sqrt{3}$ using the following method:

   a. Zero-Factor Property

   b. squaring both sides

57. Find a quadratic equation with solutions $x = -2 \pm i\sqrt{2}$ using the following method:

   a. Zero-Factor Property

   b. squaring both sides

58. Find a quadratic equation with solutions $x = 5 \pm 2i\sqrt{3}$ using the following method:

   a. Zero-Factor Property

   b. squaring both sides

Learning Objectives Assessment

The following problems can be used to help assess if you have successfully met the learning objectives for this section.

59. Find the value of the discriminant for the quadratic equation: $2x^2 + 5x = 3$.

   a. 1   **b.** 24   **c.** 7   **d.** 49

60. If a quadratic equation has discriminant $D = 20$, then it will have

   a. two irrational solutions   **b.** two rational solutions

   c. two complex solutions   **d.** one rational solution

61. Find a quadratic equation with solutions $x = \frac{1}{3}$ and $x = 2$.

   a. $3x^2 - 7x + 2 = 0$ **b.** $3x^2 + 7x + 2 = 0$

   c. $x^2 - 3x + 2 = 0$ **d.** $x^2 + 3x - 2 = 0$

62. Find a quadratic equation with solutions $x = 3 + i$ and $x = 3 - i$.

   a. $x^2 - 10 = 0$ **b.** $x^2 + 6x + 10 = 0$

   c. $x^2 - 6x + 8 = 0$ **d.** $x^2 - 6x + 10 = 0$

Getting Ready for the Next Section

Simplify.

63. $(x + 3)^2 - 2(x + 3) - 8$

64. $(x - 2)^2 - 3(x - 2) - 10$

65. $(2a - 3)^2 - 9(2a - 3) + 20$

66. $(3a - 2)^2 + 2(3a - 2) - 3$

67. $2(4a + 2)^2 - 3(4a + 2) - 20$

68. $6(2a + 4)^2 - (2a + 4) - 2$

Solve.

69. $x^2 = \dfrac{1}{4}$

70. $x^2 = -2$

71. $x^3 = \dfrac{1}{8}$

72. $x^3 = -27$

73. $\sqrt{x} = -3$

74. $\sqrt{x} = 2$

75. $\sqrt[3]{x} = -4$

76. $\sqrt[3]{x} = \dfrac{1}{3}$

77. $x + 3 = 4$

78. $x + 3 = -2$

79. $y^2 - 2y - 8 = 0$

80. $y^2 + y - 6 = 0$

81. $4y^2 + 7y - 2 = 0$

82. $6x^2 - 13x - 5 = 0$

SPOTLIGHT ON SUCCESS   *Student Instructor Breylor*

There are three ingredients in the good life: learning, earning and yearning.

—*Christopher Morley*

It can be hard to improve yourself in life, no matter what you are doing. To succeed and prosper, it is helpful to think about Christopher Morley's quote above. I love to learn new things and value what I earn from learning, but sometimes life can get busy and I think, "I know enough. I can slow down." The real key to improvement is perseverance and yearning for more. Training in martial arts is a passion of mine, and it continues to enthuse me to this day. However, obstacles often pop up that can distract me from my training. In the moment, I find it easy to think, "I'll just skip today." Then I ask myself, "Where would that thinking take me?" I strive for improvement, I yearn for it, and skipping a day of learning will not help me reach my goals and earn the success I seek. This thinking relates to all aspects of life, math included. Improvement only happens if someone has a desire to get better, or a yearning for the knowledge to come.

Quadratic Form

Learning Objectives

In this section, we will learn how to:

1. Solve equations that are quadratic in form using substitution.

2. Solve formulas that are quadratic in form.

Introduction

We are now in a position to put our knowledge of quadratic equations to work to solve a variety of equations. In this section, we will solve equations that are not quadratic, but have a structure similar to a quadratic equation. We call this structure *quadratic form*.

> (def) **DEFINITION** *quadratic form*
>
> An equation is *quadratic in form* if it can be written in the standard form
>
> $$a\blacksquare^2 + b\blacksquare + c = 0$$
>
> where $\blacksquare$ is some variable expression and $a \neq 0$.

Here are some examples of equations that are quadratic in form:

$$4x^4 + 7x^2 - 2 = 0 \qquad \blacksquare = x^2$$
$$x^{2/3} - x^{1/3} - 6 = 0 \qquad \blacksquare = x^{1/3}$$
$$(x + 3)^{-2} - 2(x + 3)^{-1} - 8 = 0 \qquad \blacksquare = (x + 3)^{-1}$$

We can solve equations that are quadratic in form using the method of substitution. We assign a new variable to represent the variable quantity from the definition, thus turning the equation into a quadratic. Then we can use any of the methods from the previous two sections to solve the quadratic. Here is an outline of the process.

> 🔍 **HOW TO** *Solve an Equation Quadratic in Form Using Substitution*
>
> **Step 1:** Write the equation in standard quadratic form.
> **Step 2:** Assign a new variable to represent the variable quantity from the middle term.
> **Step 3:** Substitute using the new variable.
> **Step 4:** Solve the resulting quadratic equation for the new variable.
> **Step 5:** Substitute back for the original variable.
> **Step 6:** Solve for the original variable.
> **Step 7:** Check your solutions.

Here are some examples of how this is done:

EXAMPLE 1   Solve: $(x + 3)^2 - 2(x + 3) - 8 = 0$.

SOLUTION   This equation is quadratic in terms of the variable expression $x + 3$. If we let $y = x + 3$, then replacing $x + 3$ with y we have

$$(x + 3)^2 - 2(x + 3) - 8 = 0$$

$$y^2 - 2y - 8 = 0 \qquad \text{Substitute}$$

This is now a quadratic equation in standard form. We can solve this equation by factoring.

$$y^2 - 2y - 8 = 0$$

$$(y - 4)(y + 2) = 0 \qquad \text{Factor}$$

$$y - 4 = 0 \quad \text{or} \quad y + 2 = 0 \quad \text{Zero-factor property}$$

$$y = 4 \qquad\qquad y = -2$$

Because our original equation was written in terms of the variable x, we want our solutions in terms of x also. Replacing y with $x + 3$ and then solving for x, we have

$$x + 3 = 4 \quad \text{or} \quad x + 3 = -2$$

$$x = 1 \quad \text{or} \qquad x = -5$$

The solutions to our original equation are 1 and -5.

Notice, however, that the original equation in Example 1 was quadratic to begin with. In this case, there is another method that works just as well. Let's solve Example 1 again, but this time, let's begin by expanding $(x + 3)^2$ and $2(x + 3)$.

$$(x + 3)^2 - 2(x + 3) - 8 = 0$$

$$x^2 + 6x + 9 - 2x - 6 - 8 = 0 \qquad \text{Multiply}$$

$$x^2 + 4x - 5 = 0 \qquad \text{Combine similar terms}$$

$$(x - 1)(x + 5) = 0 \qquad \text{Factor}$$

$$x - 1 = 0 \quad \text{or} \quad x + 5 = 0 \quad \text{Zero-factor property}$$

$$x = 1 \qquad\qquad x = -5$$

As you can see, either method produces the same result.

EXAMPLE 2   Solve: $4x^4 + 7x^2 = 2$.

SOLUTION   If we write the equation as

$$4(x^2)^2 + 7x^2 - 2 = 0$$

we can see that this equation is quadratic in terms of the expression x^2. We can use the substitution $y = x^2$. Replacing x^2 with y and then solving the resulting equation, we have

$$4(x^2)^2 + 7x^2 - 2 = 0$$

$$4y^2 + 7y - 2 = 0 \qquad \text{Substitute}$$

$$(4y - 1)(y + 2) = 0 \qquad \text{Factor}$$

$$4y - 1 = 0 \quad \text{or} \quad y + 2 = 0 \quad \text{Zero-factor property}$$

$$y = \frac{1}{4} \qquad\qquad y = -2$$

Now we replace y with x^2 to solve for x:

$$x^2 = \frac{1}{4} \qquad \text{or} \quad x^2 = -2$$

$$x = \pm\sqrt{\frac{1}{4}} \quad \text{or} \quad x = \pm\sqrt{-2} \qquad \text{Square Root Property for Equations}$$

$$x = \pm\frac{1}{2} \qquad \text{or} \quad x = \pm i\sqrt{2}$$

The solution set is $\left\{ \frac{1}{2}, -\frac{1}{2}, i\sqrt{2}, -i\sqrt{2} \right\}$.

EXAMPLE 3 Solve: $x + \sqrt{x} - 6 = 0$.

SOLUTION To see that this equation is quadratic in form, we have to notice that $(\sqrt{x})^2 = x$. That is, the equation can be rewritten as

$$(\sqrt{x})^2 + \sqrt{x} - 6 = 0$$

In this case, we let $y = \sqrt{x}$. Replacing $\sqrt{x}$ with y and solving as usual, we have

$$(\sqrt{x})^2 + \sqrt{x} - 6 = 0$$

$$y^2 + y - 6 = 0 \qquad \text{Substitute}$$

$$(y + 3)(y - 2) = 0$$

$$y + 3 = 0 \qquad \text{or} \qquad y - 2 = 0$$

$$y = -3 \qquad\qquad y = 2$$

To find x, we replace y with $\sqrt{x}$ and solve:

$$\sqrt{x} = -3 \quad \text{or} \quad \sqrt{x} = 2$$

$$x = 9 \qquad \text{or} \qquad x = 4 \qquad \text{Square both sides of each equation}$$

Because we squared both sides of each equation, we have the possibility of obtaining extraneous solutions. We have to check both solutions in our original equation.

When	$x = 9$	When	$x = 4$
the equation	$x + \sqrt{x} - 6 = 0$	the equation	$x + \sqrt{x} - 6 = 0$
becomes	$9 + \sqrt{9} - 6 \overset{?}{=} 0$	becomes	$4 + \sqrt{4} - 6 \overset{?}{=} 0$
	$9 + 3 - 6 \overset{?}{=} 0$		$4 + 2 - 6 \overset{?}{=} 0$
	$6 \neq 0$		$0 = 0$
	This means 9 is extraneous		This means 4 is a solution

The only solution to the equation $x + \sqrt{x} - 6 = 0$ is $x = 4$.

We should note here that the two possible solutions, 9 and 4, to the equation in Example 3 can be obtained by another method. Instead of substituting for $\sqrt{x}$, we can isolate it on one side of the equation and then square both sides to clear the equation of radicals.

$$x + \sqrt{x} - 6 = 0$$

$$\sqrt{x} = -x + 6 \qquad \text{Isolate } \sqrt{x}$$

$$x = x^2 - 12x + 36 \qquad \text{Square both sides}$$

$$0 = x^2 - 13x + 36 \qquad \text{Add } -x \text{ to both sides}$$

$$0 = (x - 4)(x - 9) \qquad \text{Factor}$$

$$x - 4 = 0 \quad \text{or} \quad x - 9 = 0$$

$$x = 4 \qquad\qquad x = 9$$

We obtain the same two possible solutions. Because we squared both sides of the equation to find them, we would have to check each one in the original equation. As was the case in Example 3, only $x = 4$ is a solution; $x = 9$ is extraneous.

EXAMPLE 4   Solve: $x^{2/3} - x^{1/3} - 6 = 0$.

SOLUTION   Because $(x^{1/3})^2 = x^{2/3}$, this equation is quadratic in terms of the expression $x^{1/3}$. We substitute $y = x^{1/3}$ and then solve by factoring.

$$(x^{1/3})^2 - x^{1/3} - 6 = 0$$

$$y^2 - y - 6 = 0 \qquad \text{Substitute}$$

$$(y - 3)(y + 2) = 0 \qquad \text{Factor}$$

$$y - 3 = 0 \quad \text{or} \quad y + 2 = 0$$

$$y = 3 \qquad\qquad y = -2$$

Now we substitute back in terms of x and solve for x.

$$x^{1/3} = 3 \qquad \text{or} \qquad x^{1/3} = -2$$

$$\sqrt[3]{x} = 3 \qquad\qquad \sqrt[3]{x} = -2 \qquad \text{Definition of rational exponent}$$

$$x = 3^3 \qquad\qquad x = (-2)^3 \qquad \text{Cube both sides}$$

$$x = 27 \qquad\qquad x = -8$$

The solution set is $\{-8, 27\}$. If you check, you will see that both solutions satisfy the original equation.

EXAMPLE 5   Solve: $6(2x - 1)^{-2} - 7(2x - 1)^{-1} + 2 = 0$.

SOLUTION   We notice that $(2x - 1)^{-2} = \left[(2x - 1)^{-1}\right]^2$, so this equation is quadratic in the expression $(2x - 1)^{-1}$. Substituting $y = (2x - 1)^{-1}$ gives us

$$6\left[(2x - 1)^{-1}\right]^2 - 7(2x - 1)^{-1} + 2 = 0$$

$$6y^2 - 7y + 2 = 0 \qquad \text{Substitute}$$

$$(3y - 2)(2y - 1) = 0 \qquad \text{Factor}$$

$$3y - 2 = 0 \quad \text{or} \quad 2y - 1 = 0$$

$$3y = 2 \qquad\qquad 2y = 1$$

$$y = \frac{2}{3} \qquad\qquad y = \frac{1}{2}$$

Now we replace y with $(2x - 1)^{-1}$ and solve for x, keeping in mind an exponent of -1 indicates the reciprocal.

$$(2x - 1)^{-1} = \frac{2}{3} \quad \text{or} \quad (2x - 1)^{-1} = \frac{1}{2}$$

$$\frac{1}{2x - 1} = \frac{2}{3} \qquad\qquad \frac{1}{2x - 1} = \frac{1}{2} \qquad \text{Reciprocal}$$

$$3 = 4x - 2 \qquad\qquad 2 = 2x - 1 \qquad \text{Cross-multiplication}$$

$$5 = 4x \qquad\qquad\qquad 3 = 2x$$

$$\frac{5}{4} = x \qquad\qquad\qquad \frac{3}{2} = x$$

Because of the negative exponent, the original equation would be undefined if $x = \frac{1}{2}$. This value does not appear as one of our potential solutions, so the solution set is $\left\{ \frac{5}{4}, \frac{3}{2} \right\}$.

Another way to solve the equation in Example 5 is to write the equation as the rational equation

$$\frac{6}{(2x - 1)^2} - \frac{7}{2x - 1} + 2 = 0$$

and then solve it using the methods we introduced in Section 6.5.

EXAMPLE 6   Solve: $x^4 - 8x^2 + 14 = 0$.

SOLUTION   Writing x^4 as $(x^2)^2$, we see that this equation is quadratic in the expression x^2. We can substitute $y = x^2$ to obtain

$$(x^2)^2 - 8x^2 + 14 = 0$$

$$y^2 - 8y + 14 = 0$$

This equation does not factor, so we use the quadratic formula to solve for y.

$$y = \frac{-(-8) \pm \sqrt{(-8)^2 - 4(1)(14)}}{2(1)}$$

$$= \frac{8 \pm \sqrt{8}}{2}$$

$$= \frac{8 \pm 2\sqrt{2}}{2}$$

$$= 4 \pm \sqrt{2}$$

Replacing y with x^2, we can then solve for x by taking a cube root of both sides.

$$x^2 = 4 \pm \sqrt{2}$$

$$x = \pm\sqrt{4 \pm \sqrt{2}}$$

We will not attempt to simplify further. There are four solutions.

$$\sqrt{4 + \sqrt{2}}, \sqrt{4 - \sqrt{2}}, -\sqrt{4 + \sqrt{2}}, -\sqrt{4 - \sqrt{2}}$$

Quadratic Formulas

Recall that a formula is an equation that contains more than one variable. Our last example involves a formula that is quadratic in terms of one of the variables.

EXAMPLE 7   If an object is tossed into the air with an upward velocity of 12 feet per second from the top of a building h feet high, the time it takes for the object to hit the ground below is given by the formula

$$16t^2 - 12t - h = 0$$

Solve this formula for t.

SOLUTION   The formula is in standard form and is quadratic in t. The coefficients a, b, and c that we need to apply to the quadratic formula are $a = 16$, $b = -12$, and $c = -h$. Substituting these quantities into the quadratic formula, we have

$$t = \frac{12 \pm \sqrt{144 - 4(16)(-h)}}{2(16)}$$

$$= \frac{12 \pm \sqrt{144 + 64h}}{32}$$

We can factor the perfect square 16 from the two terms under the radical and simplify our radical somewhat:

$$t = \frac{12 \pm \sqrt{16(9 + 4h)}}{32}$$

$$= \frac{12 \pm 4\sqrt{9 + 4h}}{32}$$

Now we can reduce to lowest terms by factoring a 4 from the numerator and denominator:

$$t = \frac{4(3 \pm \sqrt{9 + 4h})}{4 \cdot 8}$$

$$= \frac{3 \pm \sqrt{9 + 4h}}{8}$$

If we were given a value of h, we would find that one of the solutions to this last formula would be a negative number. Because time is always measured in positive units, we wouldn't use that solution.

USING TECHNOLOGY *Graphing Calculators*

More About Example 1

As we mentioned before, algebraic expressions entered into a graphing calculator do not have to be simplified to be evaluated. This fact also applies to equations. We can graph the equation $y = (x + 3)^2 - 2(x + 3) - 8$ to assist us in solving the equation in Example 1. The graph is shown in Figure 1. Using the Zoom and Trace features at the x-intercepts gives us $x = 1$ and $x = -5$ as the solutions to the equation $0 = (x + 3)^2 - 2(x + 3) - 8$.

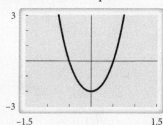

FIGURE 1

More About Example 2

Figure 2 shows the graph of $y = 4x^4 + 7x^2 - 2$. As we expect, the x-intercepts give the real number solutions to the equation $0 = 4x^4 + 7x^2 - 2$. The complex solutions do not appear on the graph.

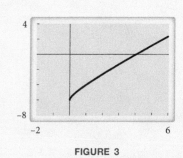

FIGURE 2

More About Example 3

In solving the equation in Example 3, we found that one of the possible solutions was an extraneous solution. If we solve the equation $x + \sqrt{x} - 6 = 0$ by graphing the function $y = x + \sqrt{x} - 6$, we find that the extraneous solution, 9, is not an x-intercept. Figure 3 shows that the only solution to the equation occurs at the x-intercept 4.

FIGURE 3

Getting Ready for Class

After reading through the preceding section, respond in your own words and in complete sentences.

A. What does it mean for an equation to be quadratic in form?

B. What are all the circumstances in solving equations (that we have studied) in which it is necessary to check for extraneous solutions?

C. How would you start to solve the equation $x + \sqrt{x} - 6 = 0$?

D. What substitution would you use the solve $x^{1/2} + x^{1/4} = 12$?

Problem Set 11.4

Solve each equation.

1. $(x - 3)^2 + 3(x - 3) + 2 = 0$

2. $(x + 4)^2 - (x + 4) - 6 = 0$

3. $(2a - 3)^2 - 9(2a - 3) = -20$

4. $(3a - 2)^2 + 2(3a - 2) = 3$

5. $x^4 - 6x^2 - 27 = 0$

6. $x^4 + 2x^2 - 8 = 0$

7. $x^4 + 9x^2 = -20$

8. $x^4 - 11x^2 = -30$

9. $6t^4 = -t^2 + 5$

10. $3t^4 = -2t^2 + 8$

11. $9x^4 - 49 = 0$

12. $25x^4 - 9 = 0$

13. $8x^6 + 7x^3 - 1 = 0$

14. $27x^6 - 26x^3 - 1 = 0$

15. $x^6 - 28x^3 + 27 = 0$

16. $x^6 - 9x^3 + 8 = 0$

17. $t^8 + 81 = 82t^4$

18. $16t^8 + 1 = 17t^4$

19. $x^{-2} - 2x^{-1} - 15 = 0$

20. $8x^{-2} - 6x^{-1} + 1 = 0$

21. $x^{-4} - 14x^{-2} + 45 = 0$

22. $x^{-4} + 7x^{-2} + 12 = 0$

23. $2(x + 4)^{-2} + 5(x + 4)^{-1} - 12 = 0$ **24.** $3(x - 5)^{-2} + 14(x - 5)^{-1} - 5 = 0$

25. $2(4a + 2)^{-2} = 3(4a + 2)^{-1} + 20$ **26.** $6(2a + 4)^{-2} = (2a + 4)^{-1} + 2$

Solve each of the following equations. Remember, if you square both sides of an equation in the process of solving it, you have to check all solutions in the original equation.

27. $x - 7\sqrt{x} + 10 = 0$

28. $x - 6\sqrt{x} + 8 = 0$

29. $t - 2\sqrt{t} - 15 = 0$

30. $t - 3\sqrt{t} - 10 = 0$

31. $(a - 2) - 11\sqrt{a - 2} + 30 = 0$

32. $(a - 3) - 9\sqrt{a - 3} + 20 = 0$

33. $(2x + 1) - 8\sqrt{2x + 1} + 15 = 0$

34. $(2x - 3) - 7\sqrt{2x - 3} + 12 = 0$

35. $6x + 11x^{1/2} = 35$

36. $2x + x^{1/2} = 15$

37. $20x^{2/3} - 3 = 11x^{1/3}$

38. $3x^{2/3} + 4x^{1/3} = 4$

39. $4x^{4/3} - 37x^{2/3} + 9 = 0$

40. $9x^{4/3} - 13x^{2/3} + 4 = 0$

41. $27x^3 + 19x^{3/2} - 8 = 0$

42. $1,000x^3 + 117x^{3/2} - 1 = 0$

43. $12a^{-1} - 8a^{-1/2} + 1 = 0$

44. $4a^{-1} - 11a^{-1/2} - 3 = 0$

Use substitution with the quadratic formula to solve each of the following equations.

45. $x^4 - 8x^2 + 1 = 0$

46. $x^4 - 4x^2 + 1 = 0$

47. $x^4 + 10x^2 + 22 = 0$

48. $2x^4 - 4x^2 - 8 = 0$

49. $x - 2\sqrt{x} - 1 = 0$

50. $x + 4\sqrt{x} - 1 = 0$

51. Solve the formula $16t^2 - vt - h = 0$ for t.

52. Solve the formula $16t^2 + vt + h = 0$ for t.

53. Solve the formula $kx^2 + 8x + 4 = 0$ for x.

54. Solve the formula $k^2x^2 + kx + 4 = 0$ for x.

55. Solve $x^2 + 2xy + y^2 = 0$ for x by using the quadratic formula with $a = 1$, $b = 2y$, and $c = y^2$.

56. Solve $x^2 - 2xy + y^2 = 0$ for x by using the quadratic formula, with $a = 1$, $b = -2y$, $c = y^2$.

Applying the Concepts

For Problems 57 and 58, t is in seconds.

57. Falling Object An object is tossed into the air with an upward velocity of 8 feet per second from the top of a building h feet high. The time it takes for the object to hit the ground below is given by the formula $16t^2 - 8t - h = 0$. Solve this formula for t.

58. Falling Object An object is tossed into the air with an upward velocity of 6 feet per second from the top of a building h feet high. The time it takes for the object to hit the ground below is given by the formula $16t^2 - 6t - h = 0$. Solve this formula for t.

Learning Objectives Assessment

The following problems can be used to help assess if you have successfully met the learning objectives for this section.

59. Solve: $4x^4 + 13x^2 - 12 = 0$.

    a. $\pm 2i, \pm\dfrac{\sqrt{3}}{2}$ **b.** $16, \dfrac{9}{16}$ **c.** $-4, \dfrac{3}{4}$ **d.** $4, -\dfrac{3}{4}$

60. Solve the formula: $-\dfrac{1}{2}gt^2 + vt + h = 0$ for t.

    a. $\pm\dfrac{\sqrt{2gh}}{g}$ **b.** $\sqrt{2h}$ **c.** $\dfrac{v \pm \sqrt{v^2 + 2gh}}{g}$ **d.** $\dfrac{v \pm 2\sqrt{v^2 - 2gh}}{g}$

Getting Ready for the Next Section

Evaluate each function for $x = -2$, $x = -1$, $x = 0$, $x = 1$, and $x = 2$.

61. $f(x) = x^2$ **62.** $f(x) = -x^2$ **63.** $f(x) = 2x^2$

64. $f(x) = \dfrac{1}{2}x^2$ **65.** $f(x) = -\dfrac{1}{4}x^2$ **66.** $f(x) = -4x^2$

67. $f(x) = (x + 2)^2$ **68.** $f(x) = (x - 2)^2$ **69.** $f(x) = x^2 + 2$

70. $f(x) = x^2 - 2$

SPOTLIGHT ON SUCCESS   *Student Instructor Stephanie*

For success, attitude is equally as important as ability.
—Harry F. Banks

Math has always fascinated me. From addition to calculus, I've taken great interest in the material and great pride in my work. Whenever I struggled with concepts, I asked questions and worked problems over and over until they became second nature. I used to assume this was how everyone dealt with concepts they didn't understand. However, in high school, I noticed how easily students got discouraged with mathematics. In my senior year calculus and statistics classes, I was surrounded by bright students who simply gave up on trying to fully understand the material because it seemed confusing or difficult. Even if we shared a similar level of academic ability, the difference between these students' grades and my own reflected a difference in attitude. I noticed many students giving up without really trying to understand the concepts because they lacked confidence and didn't feel they were capable. They began coming to me for help. Though I was glad to help them with the math, I had a greater goal to help them believe they could succeed on their own. Soon the students I tutored gained more understanding and achieved success by simply paying more attention in class and working extra problems outside of class. It was amazing how much improvement I saw in both their confidence levels and their grades. It goes to show that a little extra effort and a positive attitude can truly make a difference.

Quadratic Functions and Transformations

Learning Objectives

In this section, we will learn how to:

1. Graph the basic quadratic function.
2. Identify transformations of a quadratic function.
3. Use transformations to graph a quadratic function.
4. Determine the vertex of a quadratic function written in vertex form.

Introduction

In Example 5 of Section 3.5, we considered the function $h(t) = 32t - 16t^2$, which gave the height of a softball thrown into the air after t seconds for $0 \leq t \leq 2$. In this section, we will explore further these types of functions and their graphs.

Up to now in this chapter, we have been studying quadratic equations. If we take a quadratic equation in standard form and use it instead as the formula for a function, the result is called a *quadratic function*. Here is a formal definition:

> **def** **DEFINITION** *quadratic function*
>
> Any function that can be written in the form
>
> $$f(x) = ax^2 + bx + c$$
>
> where a, b, and c are constants with $a \neq 0$, is called a **quadratic function**. We refer to this form as **standard form**.

The Basic Quadratic Function

The simplest of all quadratic functions results when we let $a = 1$ and $b = c = 0$. We will refer to $f(x) = x^2$ as the *basic quadratic function*. Table 1 gives some ordered pairs for this function, and the corresponding graph is shown in Figure 1. This graph is an example of a *parabola*.

x	$f(x) = x^2$
-3	9
-2	4
-1	1
0	0
1	1
2	4
3	9

TABLE 1

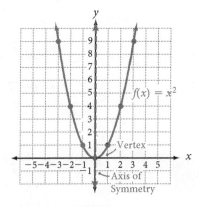

FIGURE 1

From the graph we can see that the domain of this function is the set of all real numbers and the range is $\{y \mid y \geq 0\}$. The point $(0, 0)$ where the parabola changes direction (the lowest point on the parabola) is called the *vertex*.

We also observe that the graph is symmetric about the y-axis, meaning the right half of the graph is a mirror image of the left half. For this reason, the vertical line $x = 0$ passing through the vertex is called the *axis of symmetry*.

All quadratic functions have a graph that is a parabola and a domain that is the set of all real numbers. However, the shape, direction, and position of the parabola can vary as we will see in the following segment.

Transformations

Let's consider quadratic functions of the form $f(x) = ax^2$. In this case, all we are doing is taking each y-value (output) from the basic quadratic function $y = x^2$ and multiplying it by a factor of a. As a result, we can change the shape and direction of the basic parabola. We illustrate how this is done in the next two examples.

VIDEO EXAMPLES

SECTION 11.5

   EXAMPLE 1   Graph: $f(x) = 2x^2$.

SOLUTION   Because $a = 2$, we take each y-coordinate from the basic parabola $y = x^2$ and double it. Table 2 shows how this is done for several values of x. The graph of the basic parabola $y = x^2$ and the graph of $f(x) = 2x^2$ are shown together in Figure 2.

x	$y = x^2$	$f(x) = 2x^2$
-3	9	$2 \cdot 9 = 18$
-2	4	$2 \cdot 4 = 8$
-1	1	$2 \cdot 1 = 2$
0	0	$2 \cdot 0 = 0$
1	1	$2 \cdot 1 = 2$
2	4	$2 \cdot 4 = 8$
3	9	$2 \cdot 9 = 18$

TABLE 2

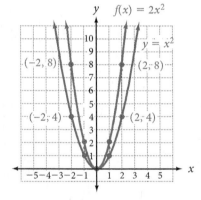

FIGURE 2

Notice that each point on the graph of $f(x) = 2x^2$ is twice the distance from the x-axis as the corresponding point on the basic quadratic. As a result, the graph of $f(x) = 2x^2$ appears narrower than the basic parabola.

EXAMPLE 2   Graph: $f(x) = -\frac{1}{2}x^2$.

SOLUTION   This time $a = -\frac{1}{2}$, so we multiply each y-coordinate from the basic parabola by $-\frac{1}{2}$ (Table 3). Figure 3 shows the graph of the basic quadratic $y = x^2$ and the graph of $f(x) = -\frac{1}{2}x^2$.

x	$y = x^2$	$f(x) = -\frac{1}{2}x^2$
-3	9	$-\frac{1}{2}(9) = -4.5$
-2	4	$-\frac{1}{2}(4) = -2$
-1	1	$-\frac{1}{2}(1) = -0.5$
0	0	$-\frac{1}{2}(0) = 0$
1	1	$-\frac{1}{2}(1) = -0.5$
2	4	$-\frac{1}{2}(4) = -2$
3	9	$-\frac{1}{2}(9) = -4.5$

TABLE 3

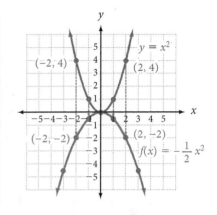

FIGURE 3

Observe that each point on the graph of $f(x) = -\frac{1}{2}x^2$ is half the distance from the x-axis as the corresponding point on the basic quadratic. Also, because of the negative sign, each point is now on the opposite side of the x-axis. As a result, the graph of $f(x) = -\frac{1}{2}x^2$ appears wider than the basic parabola and opens downward instead of upward. The vertex, though still at $(0, 0)$, is now the highest point on the graph.

Here is a formal definition that summarizes our observations from the previous two examples.

(def) DEFINITION   *vertical scaling and reflection*

If $f(x) = ax^2$ and a is any nonzero real number, then for

$|a| \neq 1$ The basic parabola will be *scaled vertically* by a factor of a.

If $|a| > 1$, there is a *vertical expansion* and the graph of $y = ax^2$ will appear narrower than the basic parabola.

If $|a| < 1$, there is a *vertical contraction* and the graph of $y = ax^2$ will appear wider than the basic parabola.

$a < 0$ The basic parabola will be *reflected about the x-axis*. The graph of $y = ax^2$ will open downward instead of upward, and the vertex will be the highest point on the graph.

Next, let's consider quadratic functions of the form $f(x) = (x - h)^2 + k$. As the following examples illustrate, the terms h and k can change the position of the basic parabola on a rectangular coordinate system.

EXAMPLE 3   Graph $f(x) = (x + 2)^2$ and $g(x) = (x - 2)^2$.

SOLUTION   Table 4 shows the results of calculating values of x^2, $(x + 2)^2$, and $(x - 2)^2$ for several values of x. By plotting points, we obtain the three graphs shown in Figure 4.

x	$y = x^2$	$f(x) = (x + 2)^2$	$g(x) = (x - 2)^2$
-5	25	9	49
-4	16	4	36
-3	9	1	25
-2	4	0	16
-1	1	1	9
0	0	4	4
1	1	9	1
2	4	16	0
3	9	25	1
4	16	36	4
5	25	49	9

TABLE 4

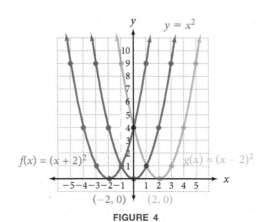

FIGURE 4

Looking at Table 4, notice that in order for the outputs of $f(x) = (x + 2)^2$ to match those of $y = x^2$, we must use x-values that are 2 units less, and with $g(x) = (x - 2)^2$ we must use x-values that are 2 units greater. From Figure 4, we can see that the graph of $f(x) = (x + 2)^2$ is the same shape as $y = x^2$, only shifted 2 units to the left. Likewise, the graph of $g(x) = (x - 2)^2$ is identical to the basic parabola, except shifted 2 units to the right.

EXAMPLE 4   Graph $f(x) = x^2 + 2$ and $g(x) = x^2 - 2$.

SOLUTION In this case, we can obtain values of $f(x)$ and $g(x)$ by adding 2 or subtracting 2 from each y-coordinate of the basic quadratic $y = x^2$. Table 5 shows these calculations for several values of x. The graphs of $y = x^2$, $f(x) = x^2 + 2$, and $g(x) = x^2 - 2$ are shown in Figure 5.

x	$y = x^2$	$f(x) = x^2 + 2$	$g(x) = x^2 - 2$
-3	9	$9 + 2 = 11$	$9 - 2 = 7$
-2	4	$4 + 2 = 6$	$4 - 2 = 2$
-1	1	$1 + 2 = 3$	$1 - 2 = -1$
0	0	$0 + 2 = 2$	$0 - 2 = -2$
1	1	$1 + 2 = 3$	$1 - 2 = -1$
2	4	$4 + 2 = 6$	$4 - 2 = 2$
3	9	$9 + 2 = 11$	$9 - 2 = 7$

TABLE 5

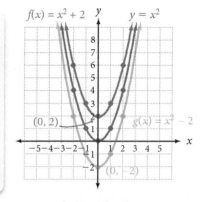

FIGURE 5

As you can see in Figure 5, the graph of $f(x) = x^2 + 2$ is identical to the basic parabola $y = x^2$, only shifted upward 2 units. Likewise, the graph of $g(x) = x^2 - 2$ is identical to the basic parabola, but shifted 2 units downward.

We can summarize our observations from Examples 3 and 4 as follows:

DEFINITION   *horizontal and vertical translation*

If $f(x) = (x - h)^2 + k$, and h and k are real numbers, then h represents a *horizontal translation* and k represents a *vertical translation*. Specifically, if h and k are positive numbers, then

The graph of	is the graph of $y = x^2$ translated
$f(x) = (x - h)^2$	h units to the right
$f(x) = (x + h)^2$	h units to the left
$f(x) = x^2 + k$	k units upward
$f(x) = x^2 - k$	k units downward

It is important to note that of the three types of transformations (vertical scaling, vertical reflection, and translations), only the translations can affect the position of the vertex of the parabola.

In our next example, we tie these concepts together in graphing a quadratic function involving all three types of transformation.

EXAMPLE 5   Graph $f(x) = 5 - 3(x-1)^2$, and state the vertex and range.

SOLUTION Writing the function in the form $f(x) = -3(x-1)^2 + 5$, we see that there is a vertical expansion by a factor of 3 and reflection about the x-axis, a horizontal translation of 1 unit to the right, and a vertical translation of 5 units upward.

The process is shown in Figure 6. We begin by graphing the basic parabola $y = x^2$. Next, we multiply each y-coordinate from the basic parabola by -3 to obtain the graph of $y = -3x^2$. Finally, we shift each point on this new graph 1 unit to the right and 5 units upward.

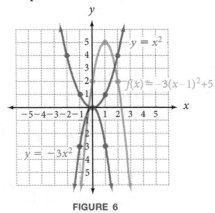

FIGURE 6

From the graph, we can see that the vertex is $(1, 5)$ and the range of the function is $\{y \mid y \leq 5\}$, $(-\infty, 5]$ using interval notation.

Vertex Form

Now that we have a good understanding of transformations, we can give an alternate definition for a quadratic function.

Looking back at Example 5, the vertex ended up at the point $(1, 5)$ because we had to translate the parabola 1 unit to the right and 5 units upward.

$$f(x) = -3\,(x - 1)^2 + 5 \qquad \text{Vertex} = (1, 5)$$

$$\uparrow \qquad \uparrow$$

Shift 1   Shift 5
unit right   units upward

Notice how the coordinates of the vertex appear in the equation of the function. We can generalize this result as follows.

> **DEFINITION**   *vertex form*
>
> Any quadratic function that can be written in the *vertex form* as
>
> $$f(x) = a(x - h)^2 + k$$
>
> where a, h, and k are constants with $a \neq 0$. The vertex of the parabola will be the point (h, k).

EXAMPLE 6   If $f(x) = \frac{2}{3}(x + 4)^2 - 7$, state the vertex, domain, range, and axis of symmetry.

SOLUTION   Writing the function in vertex form as

$$f(x) = \frac{2}{3}(x - (-4))^2 - 7$$

we have $h = -4$ and $k = -7$. Therefore, the vertex is $(-4, -7)$. The domain for any quadratic function is all real numbers. Because the parabola has not been reflected about the x-axis, it opens upward and the vertex will be the lowest point on the graph. Thus, the range is $\{y \mid y \geq -7\}$. Finally, the axis of symmetry is the vertical line passing through the vertex, so it must have the equation $x = -4$.

Getting Ready for Class

After reading through the preceding section, respond in your own words and in complete sentences.

A. What is a parabola?

B. What are the two forms for writing the equation of a quadratic function?

C. How do you know by looking at the equation if the graph of a quadratic function opens upward or downward?

D. Explain how to tell the difference between the horizontal translation and the vertical translation in the equation of a parabola.

Problem Set 11.5

Complete each table using the given function.

1. $f(x) = 3x^2$

x	y
-3	
-2	
-1	
0	
1	
2	
3	

2. $f(x) = \frac{1}{3}x^2$

x	y
-3	
-2	
-1	
0	
1	
2	
3	

3. $f(x) = -\frac{3}{4}x^2$

x	y
-3	
-2	
-1	
0	
1	
2	
3	

4. $f(x) = -\frac{5}{2}x^2$

x	y
-3	
-2	
-1	
0	
1	
2	
3	

5. $f(x) = (x - 3)^2$

x	y
-3	
-2	
-1	
0	
1	
2	
3	

6. $f(x) = (x + 3)^2$

x	y
-3	
-2	
-1	
0	
1	
2	
3	

7. $f(x) = x^2 + 3$

x	y
-3	
-2	
-1	
0	
1	
2	
3	

8. $f(x) = x^2 - 3$

x	y
-3	
-2	
-1	
0	
1	
2	
3	

For each quadratic function, identify any vertical scaling or vertical reflection. Also state if the graph opens upward or downward, and whether the graph would be narrower or wider than the basic parabola $y = x^2$.

9. $f(x) = 4x^2$

10. $f(x) = \frac{1}{4}x^2$

11. $f(x) = -\frac{2}{3}x^2$

12. $f(x) = -\frac{5}{3}x^2$

For each quadratic function, identify any horizontal or vertical translations.

13. $f(x) = x^2 + 4$

14. $f(x) = (x + 4)^2$

15. $f(x) = (x - 1)^2$

16. $f(x) = x^2 - 1$

17. $f(x) = (x - 2)^2 + 5$

18. $f(x) = (x + 5)^2 - 2$

19. $f(x) = 3 - (x + 6)^2$

20. $f(x) = -3 - (x - 4)^2$

For each quadratic function, identify any transformations.

21. $f(x) = 3(x + 5)^2 - 2$

22. $f(x) = \frac{1}{2}(x - 1)^2 - 3$

23. $f(x) = 1 - 4(x - 3)^2$

24. $f(x) = 6 - (x + 4)^2$

Graph each of the following. Use one coordinate system for each problem.

25. a. $y = \frac{1}{2}x^2$ **b.** $y = \frac{1}{2}x^2 - 2$ **c.** $y = \frac{1}{2}x^2 + 2$

26. a. $y = 2x^2$ **b.** $y = 2x^2 - 8$ **c.** $y = 2x^2 + 1$

27. a. $y = -2x^2$ **b.** $y = -2(x - 3)^2$ **c.** $y = -2(x + 3)^2$

28. a. $y = -\frac{1}{2}x^2$ **b.** $y = -\frac{1}{2}(x + 4)^2$ **c.** $y = -\frac{1}{2}(x - 4)^2$

Use transformations to graph each of the following quadratic functions. Begin with the basic parabola $y = x^2$, then graph any vertical scaling and/or reflection, and finally graph any translations. Show all graphs on a single coordinate system (you may find it helpful to use colored pencils).

29. $f(x) = 3x^2$

30. $f(x) = \frac{1}{3}x^2$

31. $f(x) = -\frac{1}{4}x^2$

32. $f(x) = -4x^2$

33. $f(x) = (x - 2)^2 + 4$

34. $f(x) = (x + 1)^2 - 5$

35. $f(x) = -(x - 4)^2$

36. $f(x) = \frac{1}{4}(x - 3)^2$

37. $f(x) = 2x^2 + 6$

38. $f(x) = -3x^2 - 2$

39. $f(x) = \frac{1}{2}(x - 1)^2 - 3$

40. $f(x) = -4(x + 3)^2 + 1$

41. $f(x) = 2 - \frac{3}{2}(x + 4)^2$

42. $f(x) = 4 - \frac{3}{4}(x - 1)^2$

State the vertex for each of the following quadratic functions, and determine if the vertex is the highest or lowest point on the graph. Then state the range of each function.

43. $y = 2(x - 1)^2 + 3$

44. $y = 2(x + 1)^2 - 3$

45. $f(x) = -(x + 2)^2 + 4$

46. $f(x) = -(x - 3)^2 + 1$

47. $g(x) = \frac{1}{2}(x - 2)^2 - 4$

48. $g(x) = \frac{1}{3}(x - 3)^2 - 3$

49. $f(x) = -2(x - 4)^2 - 1$

50. $f(x) = -4(x - 1)^2 + 4$

Find the equation of the quadratic function, $f(x)$, in vertex form, whose graph is shown.

51.

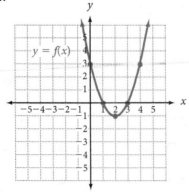

52.

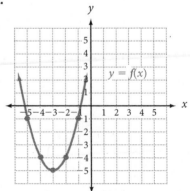

53.

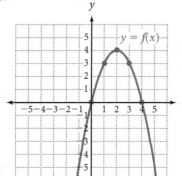

54.

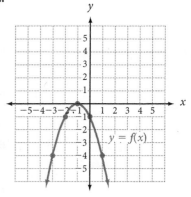

Learning Objectives Assessment

The following problems can be used to help assess if you have successfully met the learning objectives for this section.

55. Which point lies on the graph of the basic quadratic function?

   a. $(4, 2)$ **b.** $(4, -2)$ **c.** $(-2, 4)$ **d.** $(-2, -4)$

56. In the quadratic function $f(x) = 1 - 5(x + 3)^2$, the value 5 represents a

   a. horizontal translation   **b.** vertical translation

   c. vertical contraction   **d.** vertical expansion

57. Which of the following could be the graph of $f(x) = -\frac{1}{2}(x + 1)^2$?

   a.

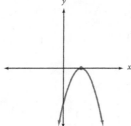

   b.

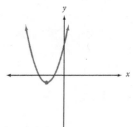

   c.

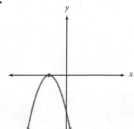

   d.

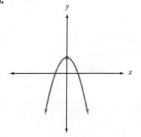

58. State the vertex for the quadratic function $f(x) = \frac{2}{3}(x + 6)^2 + 1$.

   a. $(6, 1)$ **b.** $(-6, 1)$ **c.** $(2, 3)$ **d.** $\frac{2}{3}$

Getting Ready for the Next Section

59. Evaluate $y = 3x^2 - 6x + 1$ for $x = 1$.

60. Evaluate $y = -2x^2 + 6x - 5$ for $x = \frac{3}{2}$.

61. Let $P(x) = -0.1x^2 + 27x - 500$ and find $P(135)$.

62. Let $P(x) = -0.1x^2 + 12x - 400$ and find $P(600)$.

Solve.

63. $0 = a(80)^2 + 70$ **64.** $0 = a(80)^2 + 90$

65. $x^2 - 6x + 5 = 0$ **66.** $x^2 - 3x - 4 = 0$

67. $-x^2 - 2x + 3 = 0$ **68.** $-x^2 + 4x + 12 = 0$

69. $2x^2 - 6x + 5 = 0$ **70.** $x^2 - 4x + 5 = 0$

Fill in the blanks to complete the square.

71. $x^2 - 6x + \square = (x - \square)^2$ **72.** $x^2 - 10x + \square = (x - \square)^2$

73. $y^2 + 2y + \square = (y + \square)^2$ **74.** $y^2 - 12y + \square = (x - \square)^2$

Learning Objectives

In this section, we will learn how to:

1. Find the vertex of a quadratic function written in standard form.
2. Find the *x*-intercepts and *y*-intercept for a quadratic function.
3. Graph a quadratic function using the vertex and intercepts.
4. Convert a quadratic function from standard form into vertex form by completing the square.

Introduction

In this section, we will continue to explore the behavior of quadratic functions and their graphs.

First, let's summarize what we learned in the previous section.

> **Quadratic Functions in Vertex Form**
>
> The graph of $f(x) = a(x - h)^2 + k$, $a \neq 0$, will be a parabola with vertex (h, k).
>
> If $a > 0$, the parabola will open upward and the vertex will be the lowest point on the graph.
>
> If $a < 0$, the parabola will open downward and the vertex will be the highest point on the graph.

If the quadratic function is in standard form, however, we do not yet have a way to identify the vertex easily. We will consider how to do this next.

Finding the Vertex in Standard Form

The vertex for the graph of $f(x) = ax^2 + bx + c$ will always occur when

$$x = -\frac{b}{2a}$$

To see this, we must transform the right side of $f(x) = ax^2 + bx + c$ into an expression that contains x in just one of its terms. This is accomplished by completing the square on the first two terms. Here is what it looks like:

$$f(x) = ax^2 + bx + c$$

$$= a\left(x^2 + \frac{b}{a}x\right) + c$$

$$= a\left[x^2 + \frac{b}{a}x + \left(\frac{b}{2a}\right)^2 - \left(\frac{b}{2a}\right)^2\right] + c$$

$$= a\left[x^2 + \frac{b}{a}x + \left(\frac{b}{2a}\right)^2\right] + c - a\left(\frac{b}{2a}\right)^2$$

$$= a\left(x + \frac{b}{2a}\right)^2 + \frac{4ac}{4a} - \frac{b^2}{4a}$$

$$= a\left(x - \left(-\frac{b}{2a}\right)\right)^2 + \frac{4ac - b^2}{4a}$$

This last line is now expressed in vertex form with

$$h = -\frac{b}{2a} \qquad \text{and} \qquad k = \frac{4ac - b^2}{4a}$$

This leads us to the following result, which we will refer to as the *vertex formula*.

$|\Delta \neq \Sigma$ **PROPERTY**   *vertex formula*

The graph of the quadratic function $f(x) = ax^2 + bx + c$, $a \neq 0$, will be a parabola with

$$\text{vertex} = \left(-\frac{b}{2a}, \frac{4ac - b^2}{4a}\right)$$

VIDEO EXAMPLES

SECTION 11.6

EXAMPLE 1   Find the vertex of $f(x) = 2x^2 - 12x + 23$.

SOLUTION   To find the coordinates of the vertex, we calculate

$$x = -\frac{b}{2a} \qquad\qquad y = \frac{4ac - b^2}{4a}$$

$$= -\frac{(-12)}{2(2)} \qquad\qquad = \frac{4(2)(23) - (-12)^2}{4(2)}$$

$$= \frac{12}{4} \qquad\qquad = \frac{40}{8}$$

$$= 3 \qquad\qquad = 5$$

The vertex is the point $(3, 5)$.

Another way to find the y-coordinate of the vertex, which is often easier, is to simply evaluate the function at the x-coordinate of the vertex. Using this method, we have

$$\text{If} \qquad x = 3$$

$$\text{then} \quad f(3) = 2(3)^2 - 12(3) + 23$$

$$= 18 - 36 + 23$$

$$= 5$$

As you can see, we obtain the same value with either method.

Based on our observations in the previous example, we offer the following alternative formula for finding the vertex from standard form.

$|\Delta \neq \Sigma$ **ALTERNATE PROPERTY**   *vertex formula*

The vertex of the quadratic function $f(x) = ax^2 + bx + c$, $a \neq 0$, is given by

$$\left(-\frac{b}{2a}, f\left(-\frac{b}{2a}\right)\right)$$

Intercepts

Recall that the x-intercepts (if they exist) are the points where a graph intersects the x-axis, and the y-intercept is the point where the graph intersects the y-axis.

EXAMPLE 2   Find any intercepts for $f(x) = -3(x - 1)^2 + 5$.

SOLUTION   To find the x-intercepts, we let $y = 0$ and solve for x. Because the function is in vertex form, this is most easily done using the Square Root Property for Equations.

When $\quad y = 0$

we have $\quad 0 = -3(x - 1)^2 + 5 \qquad$ Replace $f(x)$ with 0

$$-5 = -3(x - 1)^2$$

$$\frac{5}{3} = (x - 1)^2$$

$$\pm\sqrt{\frac{5}{3}} = x - 1 \qquad \text{Square Root Property}$$

$$\pm\frac{\sqrt{15}}{3} = x - 1 \qquad\qquad \sqrt{\frac{5}{3}} = \frac{\sqrt{5}}{\sqrt{3}} \cdot \frac{\sqrt{3}}{\sqrt{3}} = \frac{\sqrt{15}}{3}$$

$$1 \pm \frac{\sqrt{15}}{3} = x$$

Using a calculator, we can approximate these values as $x \approx -0.3$ and $x \approx 2.3$.

To find the y-intercept, we let $x = 0$ and solve for y. This can be done by evaluating the function for $x = 0$.

$$f(0) = -3(0 - 1)^2 + 5$$
$$= -3(1) + 5$$
$$= 2$$

The graph will cross the y-axis at the point $(0, 2)$.

We actually graphed this function in the previous section. Looking at Figure 6 in Section 8.5, you can see that the final graph is consistent with these values.

> **EXAMPLE 3**   Find any intercepts for $f(x) = 3x^2 - 6x + 1$.

SOLUTION To find the x-intercepts, we replace y with 0 and solve for x. The resulting equation does not factor, so we use the quadratic formula.

When $\quad y = 0$

we have $\quad 0 = 3x^2 - 6x + 1$

$$x = \frac{-(-6) \pm \sqrt{(-6)^2 - 4(3)(1)}}{2(3)}$$

$$= \frac{6 \pm \sqrt{24}}{6}$$

$$= \frac{6 \pm 2\sqrt{6}}{6}$$

$$= \frac{3 \pm \sqrt{6}}{3}$$

Approximating with a calculator, we obtain $x \approx 0.2$ and $x \approx 1.8$.

The y-intercept is found by evaluating the function for $x = 0$.

$$f(0) = 3(0)^2 - 6(0) + 1$$

$$= 1$$

Notice in Example 3 that the y-intercept was equal to the constant term in the equation of the function. If the quadratic is in standard form,

$$f(x) = ax^2 + bx + c$$

then for $x = 0$ we have

$$f(0) = a(0)^2 + b(0) + c$$

$$= c$$

So the y-intercept will always be the point $(0, c)$. Here is a summary of the process for finding the intercepts of a quadratic function.

> **HOW TO**   *Find Intercepts of a Quadratic Function*
>
> If the quadratic function is in vertex form, $f(x) = a(x - h)^2 + k$, then
>
> **Step 1:** Find the x-intercepts by solving the equation $a(x - h)^2 + k = 0$ using the Square Root Property for Equations.
> **Step 2:** Evaluate $f(0)$ to find the y-intercept.
>
> If the quadratic function is in standard form, $f(x) = ax^2 + bx + c$, then
>
> **Step 1:** Find the x-intercepts by solving the equation $ax^2 + bx + c = 0$ by factoring or using the quadratic formula.
> **Step 2:** The y-intercept is c.

Graphing Quadratic Functions

We can use the vertex along with the x- and y-intercepts to sketch the graph of any quadratic function.

EXAMPLE 4   Graph: $f(x) = -x^2 - 2x + 3$.

SOLUTION   The y-intercept is 3. To find the x-intercepts, we solve

$$-x^2 - 2x + 3 = 0$$
$$x^2 + 2x - 3 = 0 \qquad \text{Multiply each side by } -1$$
$$(x + 3)(x - 1) = 0$$
$$x = -3 \quad \text{or} \quad x = 1$$

The x-coordinate of the vertex is given by

$$x = -\frac{b}{2a} = -\frac{(-2)}{2(-1)} = -1$$

To find the y-coordinate of the vertex, we evaluate the function at $x = -1$ to get

$$f(-1) = -(-1)^2 - 2(-1) + 3 = -1 + 2 + 3 = 4$$

Our parabola has x-intercepts at -3 and 1, a y-intercept at 3, and a vertex at $(-1, 4)$. Figure 1 shows the graph.

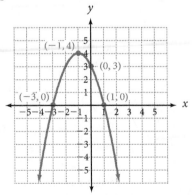

FIGURE 1

EXAMPLE 5   Graph: $f(x) = 3x^2 - 6x + 1$.

SOLUTION   We already found the intercepts for this graph back in Example 3. The y-intercept is the point $(0, 1)$ and the x-intercepts are

$$\frac{3 - \sqrt{6}}{3} \approx 0.2 \quad \text{and} \quad \frac{3 + \sqrt{6}}{3} \approx 1.8$$

All we need now is to find the vertex. Using the formula that gives us the x-coordinate of the vertex, we have

$$x = -\frac{b}{2a} = -\frac{(-6)}{2(3)} = 1$$

Evaluating the function at $x = 1$ gives us the y-coordinate of the vertex.

$$f(1) = 3 \cdot 1^2 - 6 \cdot 1 + 1 = -2$$

Plotting the intercepts along with the vertex $(1, -2)$, we have the graph shown in Figure 2.

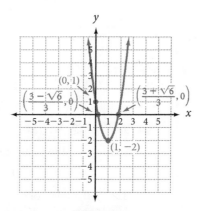

FIGURE 2

EXAMPLE 6   Graph: $f(x) = 2(x + 1)^2 - 3$.

SOLUTION   To find the x-intercepts, we solve

$$2(x + 1)^2 - 3 = 0$$

$$2(x + 1)^2 = 3$$

$$(x + 1)^2 = \frac{3}{2}$$

$$x + 1 = \pm\sqrt{\frac{3}{2}} \qquad \text{Square Root Property for Equations}$$

$$x + 1 = \pm\frac{\sqrt{6}}{2} \qquad \sqrt{\frac{3}{2}} = \frac{\sqrt{3}}{\sqrt{2}} \cdot \frac{\sqrt{2}}{\sqrt{2}} = \frac{\sqrt{6}}{2}$$

$$x = -1 \pm\frac{\sqrt{6}}{2}$$

Using a calculator, we can approximate these values, obtaining $x \approx -2.2$ and $x \approx 0.2$.

For the y-intercept, we evaluate the function at $x = 0$.

$$f(0) = 2(0 + 1)^2 - 3$$

$$= 2(1) - 3$$

$$= -1$$

The vertex is the point $(-1, -3)$. Plotting these points, we have the graph shown in Figure 3.

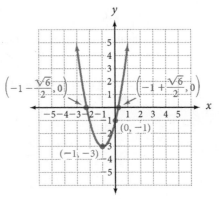

FIGURE 3

EXAMPLE 7   Graph: $f(x) = -2x^2 + 6x - 5$.

SOLUTION   The y-intercept is -5. To find the x-intercepts, we solve

$$-2x^2 + 6x - 5 = 0$$

The left side of this equation does not factor. The discriminant is $b^2 - 4ac = 36 - 4(-2)(-5) = -4$, which indicates that the solutions are complex numbers. This means that our original equation does not have x-intercepts. The graph does not cross the x-axis.

Let's find the vertex. Using our formula for the x-coordinate of the vertex, we have

$$x = -\frac{b}{2a} = -\frac{6}{2(-2)} = \frac{3}{2}$$

To find the y-coordinate, we evaluate $f(x)$ for $x = \frac{3}{2}$:

$$f\left(\frac{3}{2}\right) = -2\left(\frac{3}{2}\right)^2 + 6\left(\frac{3}{2}\right) - 5$$

$$= \frac{-18}{4} + \frac{18}{2} \quad 5$$

$$= \frac{-18 + 36 - 20}{4}$$

$$= -\frac{1}{2}$$

The vertex is $\left(\frac{3}{2}, -\frac{1}{2}\right)$. Because this is only two points so far, we must find at least one more. Let's try $x = 3$:

$$\text{When } x = 3$$

$$f(3) = -2(3)^2 + 6(3) - 5$$

$$= -18 + 18 - 5$$

$$= -5$$

An additional point on the graph is $(3, -5)$. Figure 4 shows the graph.

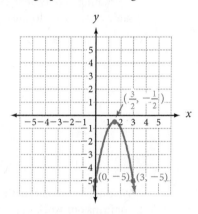

FIGURE 4

Converting Between Forms

We conclude this section by considering how to convert between standard form and vertex form.

To convert vertex form into standard form is a simple matter of squaring the binomial and then simplifying.

EXAMPLE 8   Write $f(x) = -3(x - 1)^2 + 5$ in standard form.

SOLUTION   We FOIL and then simplify.

$$f(x) = -3(x - 1)^2 + 5$$

$$= -3(x^2 - 2x + 1) + 5 \qquad \text{FOIL}$$

$$= -3x^2 + 6x - 3 + 5 \qquad \text{Distribute}$$

$$= -3x^2 + 6x + 2 \qquad \text{Standard form}$$

Now that the quadratic function is in standard form, we can see that the y-intercept is $y = 2$, which agrees with the value we obtained in Example 2.

To convert from standard form into vertex form, we complete the square on the first two terms. Because we are not solving an equation, this process is a little different from the one we followed in Section 8.1. Our last example illustrates how it is done.

EXAMPLE 9   Write $f(x) = -2x^2 + 6x - 5$ in vertex form.

SOLUTION   This is the same function we looked at in Example 7. We cannot complete the square unless the coefficient of x^2 is equal to 1. Instead of dividing by -2, we factor -2 from the first two terms.

$$f(x) = -2x^2 + 6x - 5$$

$$= -2(x^2 - 3x) - 5$$

To create a perfect square trinomial, we must add $\left(-\frac{3}{2}\right)^2 = \frac{9}{4}$. However, to maintain an equivalent expression, we add and subtract $\frac{9}{4}$ so the net result is the same as adding 0 to the right side.

$$f(x) = -2\left(x^2 - 3x + \frac{9}{4} - \frac{9}{4}\right) - 5 \qquad \text{Add and subtract } \tfrac{9}{4}$$

$$= -2\left(x^2 - 3x + \frac{9}{4}\right) - 2\left(-\frac{9}{4}\right) - 5 \qquad \text{Distribute } -2$$

$$= -2\left(x - \frac{3}{2}\right)^2 + \frac{9}{2} - 5 \qquad \text{Factor}$$

$$= -2\left(x - \frac{3}{2}\right)^2 - \frac{1}{2} \qquad \text{Simplify}$$

We now have the function in vertex form, so the vertex will be $\left(\frac{3}{2}, -\frac{1}{2}\right)$, which confirms our work in Example 7.

One advantage of converting a quadratic function from standard form into vertex form is that it allows us to graph the function using transformations instead of plotting points.

For example, we can now see that the graph of the function in Example 7 will be a basic parabola that is vertically expanded by 2, reflected about the x-axis, translated horizontally $\frac{3}{2}$ units to the right, and translated vertically $\frac{1}{2}$ unit downward.

Getting Ready for Class

After reading through the preceding section, respond in your own words and in complete sentences.

A. Explain how to find the vertex of a quadratic function in standard form.

B. In which form is the constant term equal to the y-intercept?

C. What is the best method to use in finding the x-intercepts when the quadratic function is in standard form? In vertex form?

D. How is the process of completing the square in this section different from the one we described in Section 8.1?

For each of the following quadratic functions, find the coordinates of the vertex and indicate whether the vertex is the highest point on the graph or the lowest point on the graph. Then state the range.

1. $f(x) = x^2 - 6x + 5$ **2.** $f(x) = -x^2 + 6x - 5$ **3.** $f(x) = -x^2 + 2x + 8$

4. $f(x) = x^2 - 2x - 8$ **5.** $f(x) = 12 + 4x - x^2$ **6.** $f(x) = -12 - 4x + x^2$

7. $f(x) = -x^2 - 8x$ **8.** $f(x) = x^2 + 8x$ **9.** $f(x) = x^2 - 4$

10. $f(x) = 6 - x^2$ **11.** $f(x) = 3x^2 - 6x + 14$ **12.** $f(x) = 2x^2 + 12x + 13$

13. $f(x) = -4x^2 - 16x - 17$ **14.** $f(x) = -3x^2 - 30x - 73$

15. $f(x) = 4x^2 - 4x + 19$ **16.** $f(x) = 4x^2 + 12x - 1$

For each of the following quadratic functions, give the x-intercepts (if they exist), the y-intercept, and the coordinates of the vertex. Then use these points to sketch the graph. Plot additional points as necessary.

17. $y = x^2 + 2x - 3$ **18.** $y = x^2 - 2x - 3$ **19.** $y = -x^2 - 4x + 5$

20. $y = x^2 + 4x - 5$ **21.** $y = x^2 - 1$ **22.** $y = x^2 - 4$

23. $y = -x^2 + 9$ **24.** $y = -x^2 + 1$ **25.** $f(x) = (x + 1)^2 - 4$

26. $f(x) = (x - 2)^2 - 9$ **27.** $y = 2x^2 - 4x - 6$ **28.** $y = 2x^2 + 4x - 6$

29. $y = x^2 - 2x - 4$ **30.** $y = x^2 - 2x - 2$ **31.** $f(x) = 2 - (x - 3)^2$

32. $f(x) = 3 - (x + 4)^2$ **33.** $y = x^2 - 4x - 4$ **34.** $y = x^2 - 2x + 3$

35. $y = -x^2 + 2x - 5$ **36.** $y = -x^2 + 4x - 2$ **37.** $f(x) = x^2 + 1$

38. $f(x) = x^2 + 4$ **39.** $y = -x^2 - 3$ **40.** $y = -x^2 - 2$

41. $g(x) = 3x^2 + 4x + 1$ **42.** $g(x) = 2x^2 + 4x + 3$

43. $f(x) = 2(x - 1)^2 - 6$ **44.** $f(x) = 3(x + 2)^2 + 3$

45. $f(x) = -3(x + 3)^2 - 1$ **46.** $f(x) = -4(x - 4)^2 + 20$

47. $f(x) = x^2 + 3x$ **48.** $f(x) = x^2 - x$ **49.** $f(x) = 8x - 2x^2$

50. $f(x) = -6x - 3x^2$ **51.** $f(x) = 6x^2 - 7x - 3$ **52.** $f(x) = 8x^2 - 10x + 3$

53. $f(x) = -2x^2 - x + 5$ **54.** $f(x) = 3x^2 - x + 2$ **55.** $f(x) = 3 + 3x^2 - 2x$

56. $f(x) = x + 1 - 4x^2$

Write each of the following quadratic functions in vertex form by completing the square. Then state the vertex.

57. $f(x) = x^2 + 4x$ **58.** $f(x) = x^2 - 6x$

59. $f(x) = -x^2 + 2x$ **60.** $f(x) = -x^2 - 2x$

61. $f(x) = 2x^2 - 8x + 13$ **62.** $f(x) = 3x^2 + 18x + 23$

63. $f(x) = -3x^2 - 3x - 2$ **64.** $f(x) = -2x^2 + 6x + 1$

65. $f(x) = 4x^2 + 8x + 4$ **66.** $f(x) = -5x^2 - 20x - 20$

67. Find a general formula for the x-intercepts of $f(x) = a(x - h)^2 + k$ by replacing $f(x)$ with 0 and solving for x.

68. Find a general formula for the y-intercept of $f(x) = a(x - h)^2 + k$ by evaluating $f(0)$.

Applying the Concepts

69. Use $h(t) = 32t - 16t^2$ to complete the table. Then sketch the graph of the function by plotting points.

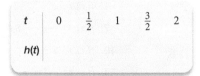

t	0	$\frac{1}{2}$	1	$\frac{3}{2}$	2
$h(t)$					

70. Use $h(t) = 48t - 16t^2$ to complete the table. Then sketch the graph of the function by plotting points.

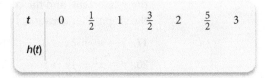

t	0	$\frac{1}{2}$	1	$\frac{3}{2}$	2	$\frac{5}{2}$	3
$h(t)$							

71. Softball Toss Chaudra is tossing a softball into the air with an underhand motion. The function $h(t) = -16t^2 + 64t$ gives the height of the softball t seconds after it is thrown, where $h(t)$ is measured in feet.

a. Use this function to complete the table.

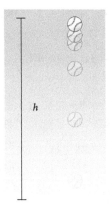

Time (seconds)	Height (feet)
0	
0.5	
1	
1.5	
2	
2.5	
3	
3.5	
4	

b. Sketch the graph of the functions by plotting points.

72. **Model Rocket** A small rocket is projected straight up into the air with a velocity of 128 feet per second. The function $h(t) = -16t^2 + 128t$ gives the height of the rocket t seconds after it is launched, where $h(t)$ is measured in feet.

a. Use this function to complete the table.

Time (seconds)	Height (feet)
0	
1	
2	
3	
4	
5	
6	
7	
8	

b. Sketch the graph of the function by plotting points.

Learning Objectives Assessment

The following problems can be used to help assess if you have successfully met the learning objectives for this section.

73. Find the vertex for $f(x) = 2x^2 + 4x^2 - 1$.

    a. $(0, -1)$ **b.** $(1, 4)$ **c.** $(-1, -3)$ **d.** $(-2, -1)$

74. Find the y-intercept of $f(x) = -(x + 3)^2 + 4$.

    a. -3 **b.** 4 **c.** -5 **d.** 3

75. Which graph could be the correct graph of $f(x) = -x^2 + 4x - 5$?

a.

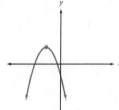

b.

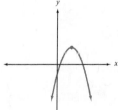

c.

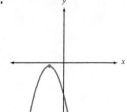

d.

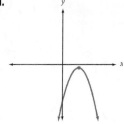

76. Convert $f(x) = 2x^2 + 20x + 38$ into vertex form by completing the square.

   a. $f(x) = 2(x + 10)^2 - 68$ **b.** $f(x) = 2(x - 10)^2 + 68$

   c. $f(x) = 2(x - 5)^2 + 12$ **d.** $f(x) = 2(x + 5)^2 - 12$

Getting Ready for the Next Section

77. Evaluate $f(t) = -16t^2 + 112t$ for $t = 1$ and $t = 3$.

78. Evaluate $f(p) = 1{,}300p - 100p^2$ for $p = 2$ and $p = 5$.

Solve each equation.

79. $-16x^2 + 112x = 0$ **80.** $1{,}300p - 100p^2 = 0$

81. $-16x^2 + 112x = 160$ **82.** $1{,}300p - 100p^2 = 3{,}600$

83. $96 + 80t - 16t^2 = 160$ **84.** $32 + 48t - 16t^2 = 52$

Find the vertex of each parabola.

85. $f(x) = 900x - 300x^2$ **86.** $f(x) = -16x^2 + 96x$

Applications of Quadratic Functions

Learning Objectives

In this section, we will learn how to:

1. Solve applied problems involving projectile motion.
2. Solve applied problems involving profit and revenue.
3. Solve optimization problems.
4. Find the equation of a quadratic function from the graph.

Introduction

An air-powered Stomp Rocket can be propelled over 200 feet using a blast of air. The harder you stomp on the Launch Pad, the farther the rocket flies.

If the rocket is launched straight up into the air with a velocity of 112 feet per second, then the quadratic function

$$h(t) = -16t^2 + 112t$$

gives the height h of the rocket t seconds after it is launched. We can use this formula to find the height of the rocket 3.5 seconds after launch by substituting $t = 3.5$:

$$h(t) = -16(3.5)^2 + 112(3.5) = 196$$

At 3.5 seconds, the rocket reaches a height of 196 feet.

Quadratic functions are good models for many types of real-life situations. We will see how quadratic functions can be used to solve a number of applications in this section.

Projectile Motion

The stomp rocket we just described is an example of *projectile motion*, which refers to the motion of an object that is somehow projected into the air. If gravity is the only force acting on the object, then the following formula can be used to model its height over time.

> **[$\Delta \neq \Sigma$] PROPERTY** *projectile motion formula*
>
> If an object is projected vertically into the air with an initial speed v, in feet per second, from an initial height s, in feet, then the height of the object after t seconds is given by the quadratic function
>
> $$h(t) = -16t^2 + vt + s$$
>
> where h is measured in feet.

EXAMPLE 1   An object is projected into the air from ground level with an initial vertical velocity of 64 feet per second.

a. Find the height of the object after 1.5 seconds.

b. At what times will the object be at a height of 48 feet?

SOLUTION   Substituting $v = 64$ and $s = 0$ into the projectile motion formula, we have

$$h(t) = -16t^2 + 64t$$

which is a quadratic function.

843

a. Substituting $t = 1.5$, we have

$$h(1.5) = -16(1.5)^2 + 64(1.5)$$
$$= 60$$

The object will be 60 feet high after 1.5 seconds.

b. We let $h(t) = 48$ and solve for t:

When $\qquad\qquad\qquad h(t) = 48$
the function $\qquad\qquad h(t) = -16t^2 + 64t$
becomes $\qquad\qquad\quad 48 = -16t^2 + 64t$

We write it in standard form and solve by factoring:

$$16t^2 - 64t + 48 = 0$$
$$t^2 - 4t + 3 = 0 \qquad \text{Divide each side by 16.}$$
$$(t - 1)(t - 3) = 0 \qquad \text{Factor.}$$
$$t - 1 = 0 \quad \text{or} \quad t - 3 = 0$$
$$t = 1 \quad \text{or} \qquad\quad t = 3$$

The object will be 48 feet above the ground after 1 second and again after 3 seconds. That is, it passes 48 feet going up and also coming back down.

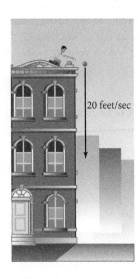

EXAMPLE 2   If an object is thrown downward with an initial velocity of 20 feet per second, the distance $s(t)$, in feet, it travels in t seconds is given by the function $s(t) = 20t + 16t^2$. How long does it take the object to fall 40 feet?

SOLUTION   We let $s(t) = 40$, and solve for t:

When $\qquad\qquad\qquad\qquad\qquad s(t) = 40$

the function $\qquad\qquad\qquad\quad s(t) = 20t + 16t^2$

becomes $\qquad\qquad\qquad\qquad\; 40 = 20t + 16t^2$

or $\qquad\qquad 16t^2 + 20t - 40 = 0$

$$4t^2 + 5t - 10 = 0 \qquad \text{Divide by 4}$$

Using the quadratic formula, we have

$$t = \frac{-5 \pm \sqrt{25 - 4(4)(-10)}}{2(4)}$$

$$= \frac{-5 \pm \sqrt{185}}{8}$$

$$= \frac{-5 + \sqrt{185}}{8} \quad \text{or} \quad t - \frac{-5 - \sqrt{185}}{8}$$

The second solution is impossible because it is a negative number and time t must be positive. It takes

$$t = \frac{-5 + \sqrt{185}}{8} \qquad \text{or approximately} \qquad \frac{-5 + 13.60}{8} \approx 1.08 \text{ seconds}$$

for the object to fall 40 feet.

More About Example 2

We can solve the problem discussed in Example 2 by graphing the function $Y_1 = 20X + 16X^2$ in a window with X from 0 to 2 (because X is taking the place of t and we know t is a positive quantity) and Y from 0 to 50 (because we are looking for X when Y_1 is 40). Graphing Y_1 gives a graph similar to the graph in Figure 1. Using the Zoom and Trace features at $Y_1 = 40$ gives us X = 1.08 to the nearest hundredth, matching the results we obtained by solving the original equation algebraically.

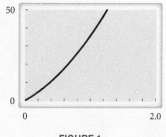

FIGURE 1

EXAMPLE 3   A water balloon is thrown upward with an initial velocity of 40 feet per second from a balcony that is 12 feet off the ground. When will the water balloon strike the ground?

SOLUTION   Substituting $v = 40$ and $s = 12$ into the projectile motion formula, we have

$$h(t) = -16t^2 + 40t + 12$$

When the water balloon strikes the ground, its height will be zero. We substitute $h(t) = 0$ and solve for t.

When	$h(t) = 0$
the function	$h(t) = -16t^2 + 40t + 12$
becomes	$0 = -16t^2 + 40t + 12$
	$0 = 4t^2 - 10t - 3$ Divide both sides by -4

The right side does not factor, so we can use the quadratic formula to solve for t.

$$t = \frac{-(-10) \pm \sqrt{(-10)^2 - 4(4)(-3)}}{2(4)}$$

$$= \frac{10 \pm \sqrt{148}}{8}$$

$$= \frac{10 \pm 2\sqrt{37}}{8} \qquad \sqrt{148} = \sqrt{4 \cdot 37} = 2\sqrt{37}$$

$$= \frac{5 \pm \sqrt{37}}{4} \qquad \text{Reduce}$$

Using a calculator to approximate both values, we obtain $t \approx -0.27$ and $t \approx 2.77$.

The negative value of t is not possible because the time must be positive. Thus, the water balloon will strike the ground after

$$t = \frac{5 + \sqrt{37}}{4} \approx 2.77 \text{ seconds}$$

Revenue, Cost, and Profit

In Chapter 5, we introduced the concepts of profit, revenue, and cost. If you recall, the relationship between the three quantities is known as the profit equation:

$$\text{Profit} = \text{Revenue} - \text{Cost}$$

$$P(x) = R(x) - C(x)$$

The revenue obtained from selling x items is the product of the number of items sold and the price per item, p. That is,

$$\text{Revenue} = (\text{Number of items sold})(\text{Price of each item})$$

$$R = xp$$

EXAMPLE 4   A manufacturer of small calculators knows that the number of calculators she can sell each week is related to the price of the calculators by the equation $x = 1{,}300 - 100p$, where x is the number of calculators and p is the price per calculator. What price should she charge for each calculator if she wants the weekly revenue to be $4,000?

SOLUTION   The formula for total revenue is $R = xp$. Because we want R in terms of p, we substitute $1{,}300 - 100p$ for x in the equation $R = xp$:

$$\begin{aligned} \text{If} \quad & R = xp \\ \text{and} \quad & x = 1{,}300 - 100p \\ \text{then} \quad & R = (1{,}300 - 100p)p \end{aligned}$$

We want to find p when R is 4,000. Substituting for R in the formula gives us

$$4{,}000 = (1{,}300 - 100p)p$$

$$4{,}000 = 1{,}300p - 100p^2$$

This is a quadratic equation. To write it in standard form, we add $100p^2$ and $-1{,}300p$ to each side, giving us

$$100p^2 - 1{,}300p + 4{,}000 = 0$$

$$p^2 - 13p + 40 = 0 \qquad \text{Divide each side by 100}$$

$$(p - 5)(p - 8) = 0$$

$$p - 5 = 0 \quad \text{or} \quad p - 8 = 0$$

$$p = 5 \quad \text{or} \quad p = 8$$

If she sells the calculators for $5 each or for $8 each, she will have a weekly revenue of $4,000.

EXAMPLE 5   A company produces and sells copies of an accounting program for home computers. The total weekly cost (in dollars) to produce x copies of the program is $C(x) = 8x + 500$, and the weekly revenue for selling all x copies of the program is $R(x) = 35x - 0.1x^2$. How many programs must be sold each week for the weekly profit to be $1,200?

SOLUTION   Substituting the given expressions for $R(x)$ and $C(x)$ in the equation $P(x) = R(x) - C(x)$, we have a quadratic function that represents the weekly profit $P(x)$:

$$P(x) = R(x) - C(x)$$
$$= 35x - 0.1x^2 - (8x + 500)$$
$$= 35x - 0.1x^2 - 8x - 500$$
$$= -500 + 27x - 0.1x^2$$

Setting this expression equal to 1,200, we have a quadratic equation to solve that gives us the number of programs x that need to be sold each week to bring in a profit of $1,200:

$$1,200 = -500 + 27x - 0.1x^2$$

We can write this equation in standard form by adding the opposite of each term on the right side of the equation to both sides of the equation. Doing so produces the following equation:

$$0.1x^2 - 27x + 1,700 = 0$$

Applying the quadratic formula to this equation with $a = 0.1$, $b = -27$, and $c = 1,700$, we have

$$x = \frac{27 \pm \sqrt{(-27)^2 - 4(0.1)(1,700)}}{2(0.1)}$$

$$= \frac{27 \pm \sqrt{729 - 680}}{0.2}$$

$$= \frac{27 \pm \sqrt{49}}{0.2}$$

$$= \frac{27 \pm 7}{0.2}$$

Writing this last expression as two separate expressions, we have our two solutions:

$$x = \frac{27 + 7}{0.2} \quad \text{or} \quad x = \frac{27 - 7}{0.2}$$

$$= \frac{34}{0.2} \qquad\qquad = \frac{20}{0.2}$$

$$= 170 \qquad\qquad = 100$$

The weekly profit will be $1,200 if the company produces and sells 100 programs or 170 programs.

What is interesting about this last example is that it has rational solutions, meaning it could have been solved by factoring. But looking back at the equation, factoring does not seem like a reasonable method of solution because the coefficients are either very large or very small. So, there are times when using the quadratic formula is a faster method of solution, even though the equation you are solving is factorable.

USING TECHNOLOGY　*Graphing Calculators*

More About Example 5

To visualize the functions in Example 5, we set up our calculator this way:

$$Y_1 = 35X - .1X^2 \qquad \text{Revenue function}$$

$$Y_2 = 8X + 500 \qquad \text{Cost function}$$

$$Y_3 = Y_1 - Y_2 \qquad \text{Profit function}$$

Window:　X from 0 to 350, Y from 0 to 3,500

Graphing these functions produces graphs similar to the ones shown in Figure 2. The lowest graph is the graph of the profit function. Using the Zoom and Trace features on the lowest graph at $Y_3 = 1,200$ produces two corresponding values of X, 170 and 100, which match the results in Example 5.

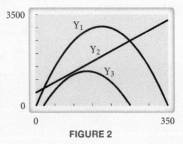

FIGURE 2

Optimization

The term *optimization* refers to the process of finding an optimal solution to some problem. In many cases, the optimal solution will be the maximum value or minimum value for some quantity. For example, a business would be interested in finding the maximum profit or minimum cost.

If the quantity in question is being modeled by a quadratic function, then the maximum or minimum value of the function (the optimal value) will correspond to the vertex.

EXAMPLE 6　For the water balloon described in Example 3, find the maximum height reached by the water balloon, and determine when it reaches this height.

SOLUTION　From Example 3, the function giving the height of the water balloon after t seconds is

$$h(t) = -16t^2 + 40t + 12$$

The graph of $h(t)$ is a parabola that opens downward, so the highest point on the graph is the vertex. Therefore, the vertex represents the point where the water balloon is at its maximum height.

Because the quadratic function is in standard form, we can use the vertex formula to find the coordinates of the vertex.

$$t = -\frac{b}{2a} = -\frac{40}{2(-16)} = \frac{40}{32} = 1.25$$

Now we evaluate the function at 1.25 to find the second coordinate.

$$h(1.25) = -16(1.25)^2 + 40(1.25) + 12$$

$$= 37$$

The vertex is the point (1.25, 37). This means the water balloon will reach a maximum height of 37 feet after 1.25 seconds.

EXAMPLE 7 A company selling copies of an accounting program for home computers finds that it will make a weekly profit of P dollars from selling x copies of the program, according to the equation

$$P(x) = -0.1x^2 + 27x - 500$$

How many copies of the program should it sell to make the largest possible profit, and what is the largest possible profit?

SOLUTION Because the coefficient of x^2 is negative, we know the graph of this parabola will be concave down, meaning that the vertex is the highest point of the curve. We find the vertex by first finding its x-coordinate:

$$x = -\frac{b}{2a} = -\frac{27}{2(-0.1)} = \frac{27}{0.2} = 135$$

This represents the number of programs the company needs to sell each week to make a maximum profit. To find the maximum profit, we substitute 135 for x in the original equation. (A calculator is helpful for these kinds of calculations.)

$$P(135) = -0.1(135)^2 + 27(135) - 500$$

$$= -0.1(18{,}225) + 3{,}645 - 500$$

$$= -1{,}822.5 + 3{,}645 - 500$$

$$= 1{,}322.5$$

The maximum weekly profit is \$1,322.50 and is obtained by selling 135 programs a week.

EXAMPLE 8 An art supply store finds that they can sell x sketch pads each week at p dollars each, according to the equation $x = 900 - 300p$. Graph the revenue equation $R = xp$. Then use the graph to find the price p that will bring in the maximum revenue. Finally, find the maximum revenue.

SOLUTION As it stands, the revenue equation contains three variables. Because we are asked to find the value of p that gives us the maximum value of R, we rewrite the equation using just the variables R and p. Because $x = 900 - 300p$, we have

$$R = xp = (900 - 300p)p$$

The graph of this equation is shown in Figure 3. The graph appears in the first quadrant only, because R and p are both positive quantities.

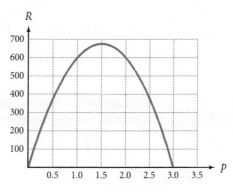

FIGURE 3

From the graph, we see that the maximum value of R occurs when $p = \$1.50$. We can calculate the maximum value of R from the equation:

When $\hspace{6em} p = 1.5$

the equation $\hspace{5em} R = (900 - 300p)p$

becomes $\hspace{5.5em} R = (900 - 300 \cdot 1.5)1.5$

$$= (900 - 450)1.5$$

$$= 450 \cdot 1.5$$

$$= 675$$

The maximum revenue is $675. It is obtained by setting the price of each sketch pad at $p = \$1.50$.

Finding the Equation from the Graph

Before we conclude this section, we will look at a couple of examples of *curve-fitting*, which refers to finding the equation of a graph that meets certain criteria. In our case, we will find the equation of a quadratic function (parabola) given some information about the graph.

EXAMPLE 9   At a past Washington County Fair in Oregon, David Smith, Jr., The Bullet, was shot from a cannon. As a human cannonball, he reached a height of 70 feet before landing in a net 160 feet from the cannon. Sketch the graph of his path, and then find the equation of the graph.

SOLUTION   We assume that the path taken by the human cannonball is a parabola. If the origin of the coordinate system is at the opening of the cannon, then the net that catches him will be at 160 on the x-axis. Figure 4 shows the graph.

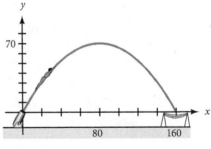

FIGURE 4

Because the curve is a parabola, we know the equation will have the form

$$y = a(x - h)^2 + k$$

Because the vertex of the parabola is at $(80, 70)$, we can fill in two of the three constants in our equation, giving us

$$y = a(x - 80)^2 + 70$$

To find a, we note that the landing point will be (160, 0). Substituting the coordinates of this point into the equation, we solve for a:

$$0 = a(160 - 80)^2 + 70$$

$$0 = a(80)^2 + 70$$

$$0 = 6{,}400a + 70$$

$$a = -\frac{70}{6{,}400} = -\frac{7}{640}$$

The equation that describes the path of the human cannonball is

$$y = -\frac{7}{640}(x - 80)^2 + 70 \quad \text{for} \quad 0 \leq x \leq 160$$

USING TECHNOLOGY *Graphing Calculators*

Graph the equation found in Example 8 on a graphing calculator using the window shown here.

Window: X from 0 to 180, increment 20
         Y from 0 to 80, increment 10

On the TI-84, an increment of 20 for X means Xscl = 20.

EXAMPLE 10 Find the equation of a quadratic function in standard form whose graph passes through the points $(-1, 4)$, $(1, -2)$, and $(2, 1)$.

SOLUTION The standard form for a quadratic function is $y = ax^2 + bx + c$. The three given points will lie on the graph of the function if all three ordered pairs satisfy this equation.

By substituting each pair of values of x and y, we obtain the following:

Using	$x = -1$ and $y = 4$
we have	$4 = a(-1)^2 + b(-1) + c$
	$4 = a - b + c$
Using	$x = 1$ and $y = -2$
we have	$-2 = a(1)^2 + b(1) + c$
	$-2 = a + b + c$
Using	$x = 2$ and $y = 1$
we have	$1 = a(2)^2 + b(2) + c$
	$1 = 4a + 2b + c$

We must find values of a, b, and c that make all three of these equations true. In other words, we must solve the system of equations

$$a - b + c = 4 \qquad (1)$$

$$a + b + c = -2 \qquad (2)$$

$$4a + 2b + c = 1 \qquad (3)$$

Multiplying equation (1) by -1 and adding the result to equation (2) gives us

$$2b = -6$$
$$b = -3$$

If we multiply equation (2) by -1 and add the result to equation (3), we have

$$3a + b = 3$$

Substituting $b = -3$ into this last equation and solving for a gives us $a = 2$. Using $a = 2$ and $b = -3$ in equation (1), (2), or (3) and solving for c results in $c = -1$.

Therefore, the equation of the quadratic function whose graph passes through the three points is

$$y = 2x^2 - 3x - 1$$

Figure 5 shows the three given points and the graph of this function. As you can see, the parabola passes through all of the points.

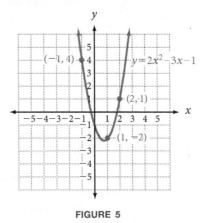

FIGURE 5

Getting Ready for Class

After reading through the preceding section, respond in your own words and in complete sentences.

A. What does projectile motion refer to?

B. State the formulas for revenue and profit.

C. Explain what optimization is.

D. What will be the optimal value for a quadratic function?

1. Find R if $p = 1.5$ and $R = (900 - 300p)p$

2. Find R if $p = 2.5$ and $R = (900 - 300p)p$

3. Find P if $P = -0.1x^2 + 27x + 1,700$ and
   a. $x = 100$ b. $x = 170$

4. Find P if $P = -0.1x^2 + 27x + 1,820$ and
   a. $x = 130$ b. $x = 140$

5. Find h if $h = 16 + 32t - 16t^2$ and
   a. $t = \dfrac{1}{4}$ b. $t = \dfrac{7}{4}$

6. Find h if $h = 64t - 16t^2$ and
   a. $t = 1$ b. $t = 3$

7. **Saint Louis Arch** The shape of the famous "Gateway to the West" arch in Saint Louis can be modeled by a parabola. The equation for one such parabola is:

$$y = -\frac{1}{150}x^2 + \frac{21}{5}x$$

   a. Sketch the graph of the arch's equation on a coordinate axis.

   b. Approximately how far do you have to walk to get from one side of the arch to the other?

8. **Interpreting Graphs** The graph below shows the different paths taken by the human cannonball when his velocity out of the cannon is 50 miles/hour, and his cannon is inclined at varying angles.

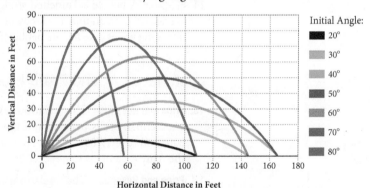

Initial Velocity: 50 miles per hour
Angle: 20°, 30°, 40°, 50°, 60°, 70°, 80°

   a. If his landing net is placed 104 feet from the cannon, at what angle should the cannon be inclined so that he lands in the net?

   b. Approximately where do you think he would land if the cannon was inclined at 45°?

   c. If the cannon was inclined at 45°, approximately what height do you think he would attain?

   d. Do you think there is another angle for which he would travel the same distance he travels at 80°? Give an estimate of that angle.

   e. The fact that every landing point can come from two different paths makes us think that the equations that give us the landing points must be what type of equations?

Projectile Motion Problems

9. **Height of a Bullet**   A bullet is fired into the air with an initial upward velocity of 80 feet per second from the top of a building 96 feet high. The function that gives the height of the bullet at any time t is $h(t) = 96 + 80t - 16t^2$. At what times will the bullet be 192 feet in the air?

10. **Height of an Arrow**   An arrow is shot into the air with an upward velocity of 48 feet per second from a hill 32 feet high. The function that gives the height of the arrow at any time t is $h(t) = 32 + 48t - 16t^2$. Find the times at which the arrow will be 64 feet above the ground.

11. **Velocity and Height** If an object is thrown straight up into the air with an initial velocity of 32 feet per second, then its height h (in feet) above the ground at any time t (in seconds) is given by the function $h(t) = 32t - 16t^2$. Find the times at which the object is on the ground by letting $h(t) = 0$ in the equation and solving for t.

12. **Falling Object** An object is thrown downward with an initial velocity of 5 feet per second. The relationship between the distance s it travels and time t is given by $s = 5t + 16t^2$. How long does it take the object to fall 74 feet?

13. **Coin Toss** A coin is tossed upward with an initial velocity of 32 feet per second from a height of 16 feet above the ground. The function giving the object's height h at any time t is $h(t) = 16 + 32t - 16t^2$. Does the object ever reach a height of 32 feet?

14. **Slingshot** A pebble is launched straight upward using a slingshot. If the pebble is released with an initial velocity of 120 feet per second from a height of 6 feet, how long will it take for the pebble to strike the ground?

Cost, Revenue, and Profit Problems

15. **Price and Revenue**   The relationship between the number of calculators x a company sells per day and the price of each calculator p is given by the equation $x = 1{,}700 - 100p$. At what price should the calculators be sold if the daily revenue is to be $7,000?

16. **Price and Revenue**   The relationship between the number of pencil sharpeners x a company can sell each week and the price of each sharpener p is given by the equation $x = 1{,}800 - 100p$. At what price should the sharpeners be sold if the weekly revenue is to be $7,200?

17. **Revenue** A company manufactures and sells DVDs. The revenue obtained by selling x DVDs is given by the function

$$R(x) = 11.5x - 0.05x^2$$

Find the number of DVDs they must sell to receive $650 in revenue.

18. **Revenue** A software company sells licenses to its office management suite. The revenue obtained by selling x licenses per month is given by the function

$$R(x) = 48x - 0.06x^2$$

Find the number of licenses they must sell each month to receive $7,200 in revenue.

19. **Profit** The total cost (in dollars) for a company to manufacture and sell x items per week is $C = 60x + 300$, whereas the revenue brought in by selling all x items is $R = 100x - 0.5x^2$. How many items must be sold to obtain a weekly profit of $300?

20. **Profit** Suppose a company manufactures and sells x picture frames each month with a total cost of $C = 1,200 + 3.5x$ dollars. If the revenue obtained by selling x frames is $R = 9x - 0.002x^2$, find the number of frames it must sell each month if its monthly profit is to be $2,300.

Optimization Problems

21. **Maximum Profit** A company finds that it can make a profit of P dollars each month by selling x patterns, according to the formula $P(x) = -0.002x^2 + 3.5x - 800$. How many patterns must it sell each month to have a maximum profit? What is the maximum profit?

22. **Maximum Profit** A company selling picture frames finds that it can make a profit of P dollars each month by selling x frames, according to the formula $P(x) = -0.002x^2 + 5.5x - 1,200$. How many frames must it sell each month to have a maximum profit? What is the maximum profit?

23. **Maximum Height** Chaudra is tossing a softball into the air with an underhand motion. The distance of the ball above her hand at any time is given by the function

$$h(t) = 32t - 16t^2 \quad \text{for} \quad 0 \le t \le 2$$

where $h(t)$ is the height of the ball (in feet) and t is the time (in seconds). Find the times at which the ball is in her hand, and the maximum height of the ball.

24. **Maximum Area** Justin wants to fence three sides of a rectangular exercise yard for his dog. The fourth side of the exercise yard will be a side of the house. He has 80 feet of fencing available. Find the dimensions of the exercise yard that will enclose the maximum area.

25. **Maximum Revenue** A company that manufactures typewriter ribbons knows that the number of ribbons x it can sell each week is related to the price p of each ribbon by the equation $x = 1,200 - 100p$. Graph the revenue equation $R = xp$. Then use the graph to find the price p that will bring in the maximum revenue. Finally, find the maximum revenue.

26. **Maximum Revenue** A company that manufactures diskettes for home computers finds that it can sell x diskettes each day at p dollars per diskette, according to the equation $x = 800 - 100p$. Graph the revenue equation $R = xp$. Then use the graph to find the price p that will bring in the maximum revenue. Finally, find the maximum revenue.

27. **Maximum Revenue** The relationship between the number of calculators x a company sells each day and the price p of each calculator is given by the equation $x = 1,700 - 100p$. Graph the revenue equation $R = xp$, and use the graph to find the price p that will bring in the maximum revenue. Then find the maximum revenue.

28. **Maximum Revenue** The relationship between the number x of pencil sharpeners a company sells each week and the price p of each sharpener is given by the equation $x = 1{,}800 - 100p$. Graph the revenue equation $R = xp$, and use the graph to find the price p that will bring in the maximum revenue. Then find the maximum revenue.

29. **Union Dues** A labor union has 10,000 members. For every $10 increase in union dues, membership is decreased by 200 people. If the current dues are $100, what should be the new dues (to the nearest multiple of $10) so income from dues is greatest, and what is that income? *Hint:* Because Income = (membership)(dues), we can let x = the number of $10 increases in dues, and then this will give us income of $y = (10{,}000 - 200x)(100 + 10x)$.

30. **Bookstore Receipts** The owner of a used book store charges $2 for quality paperbacks and usually sells 40 per day. For every 10-cent increase in the price of these paperbacks, he thinks that he will sell two fewer per day. What is the price he should charge (to the nearest 10 cents) for these books to maximize his income, and what would be that income? *Hint:* Let x = the number of 10-cent increases in price.

31. **Jiffy-Lube** The owner of a quick oil-change business charges $20 per oil change and has 40 customers per day. If each increase of $2 results in 2 fewer daily customers, what price should the owner charge (to the nearest $2) for an oil change if the income from this business is to be as great as possible?

32. **Computer Sales** A computer manufacturer charges $2,200 for its basic model and sells 1,500 computers per month at this price. For every $200 increase in price, it is believed that 75 fewer computers will be sold. What price should the company place on its basic model of computer (to the nearest $100) to have the greatest income?

Curve Fitting Problems

33. **Human Cannonball** A human cannonball is shot from a cannon at the county fair. He reaches a height of 60 feet before landing in a net 180 feet from the cannon. Sketch the graph of his path, and then find the equation of the graph.

34. **Human Cannonball** A human cannonball is shot from a cannon at the state fair. He reaches a height of 80 feet before landing in a net 120 feet from the cannon. Sketch the graph of his path, and then find the equation of the graph.

35. **Gateway Arch** The Gateway Arch in St. Louis, Missouri, has a shape that can be approximated using a parabola. The height and width of the arch are both 630 feet. Find the equation for this parabola.

36. **Stone Bridge** The Konitsa Bridge in Epirus, Greece, contains an arch whose shape can be approximated using a parabola. If the arch is 40 meters long and 20 meters high, find the equation for this parabola.

37. **Parabola** Find the equation of the quadratic function, in standard form, passing through the points $(-4, -5)$, $(-1, -8)$, and $(2, 7)$.

38. **Parabola** Find the equation of the quadratic function, in standard form, passing through the points $(-2, -1)$, $(-1, 2)$, and $(1, -4)$.

Learning Objectives Assessment

The following problems can be used to help assess if you have successfully met the learning objectives for this section.

39. **Baseball** A baseball is thrown upward with an initial velocity of 44 feet per second and released from a height of 6 feet. When will the baseball strike the ground?

    a. 2.5 sec   **b.** 2.9 sec   **c.** 3.1 sec   **d.** 2.7 sec

40. **Revenue** The relationship between the number of coffee makers x a company sells each week and the price of each coffee maker p is given by the equation $x = 800 - 40p$. At what price should the coffee makers be sold if the weekly revenue is to be $3,000?

    a. $4, $12   **b.** $9, $15   **c.** $10   **d.** $5, $15

41. **Maximum Height** Find the maximum height of the baseball described in Problem 39.

    a. 36.25 ft   **b.** 30.25 ft   **c.** 41.5 ft   **d.** 44 ft

42. **Human Cannonball** A human cannonball is shot from a cannon at a county fair. He reaches a height of 50 feet before landing in a net 110 feet from the cannon. Find the equation of his path.

    a. $y = -\dfrac{4}{121}(x + 55)^2 + 50$ **b.** $y = -\dfrac{2}{121}(x - 55)^2 + 50$

    c. $y = -\dfrac{5}{11}(x - 110)^2 + 50$ **d.** $y = -\dfrac{4}{11}(x + 110)^2 + 50$

Getting Ready for the Next Section

Solve.

43. $x^2 - 2x - 8 = 0$

44. $x^2 - x - 12 = 0$

45. $6x^2 - x = 2$

46. $3x^2 - 5x = 2$

47. $x^2 - 6x + 9 = 0$

48. $x^2 + 8x + 16 = 0$

Learning Objectives

In this section, we will learn how to:

1. Solve a quadratic inequality.

2. Solve a rational inequality.

Quadratic Inequalities

Quadratic inequalities in one variable are inequalities of the form

$$ax^2 + bx + c < 0 \qquad ax^2 + bx + c > 0$$
$$ax^2 + bx + c \leq 0 \qquad ax^2 + bx + c \geq 0$$

where a, b, and c are constants, with $a \neq 0$. The technique we will use to solve inequalities of this type involves graphing. Suppose, for example, we want to find the solution set for the inequality $x^2 - x - 6 > 0$. We begin by factoring the left side to obtain

$$(x - 3)(x + 2) > 0$$

We have two real numbers $x - 3$ and $x + 2$ whose product $(x - 3)(x + 2)$ is greater than zero. That is, their product is positive. The only way the product can be positive is either if both factors, $(x - 3)$ and $(x + 2)$, are positive or if they are both negative. To help visualize where $x - 3$ is positive and where it is negative, we draw a real number line and label it accordingly:

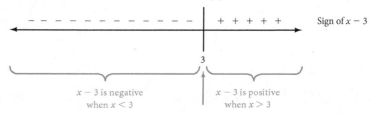

Here is a similar diagram showing where the factor $x + 2$ is positive and where it is negative:

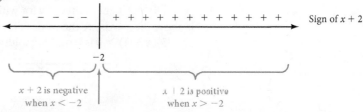

Drawing the two number lines together and eliminating the unnecessary numbers, we have

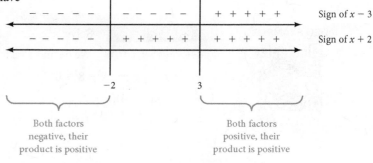

859

We can see from the preceding diagram that the graph of the solution to $x^2 - x - 6 > 0$ is

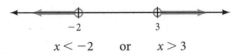

$$x < -2 \qquad \text{or} \qquad x > 3$$

In set-builder notation, we can write the solution set as $\{x \mid x < -2 \text{ or } x > 3\}$. Using interval notation, it would be $(-\infty, -2) \cup (3, \infty)$.

USING TECHNOLOGY   *Graphical Solutions to Quadratic Inequalities*

We can solve the preceding problem by using a graphing calculator to visualize where the product $(x - 3)(x + 2)$ is positive. First, we graph the function $y = (x - 3)(x + 2)$ as shown in Figure 1.

Next, we observe where the graph is above the x-axis. As you can see, the graph is above the x-axis to the right of 3 and to the left of -2, as shown in Figure 2.

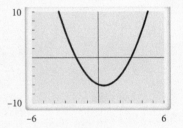

FIGURE 1

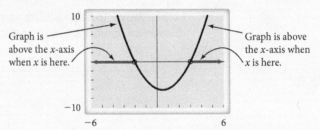

Graph is above the x-axis when x is here.

Graph is above the x-axis when x is here.

FIGURE 2

When the graph is above the x-axis, we have points whose y-coordinates are positive. Because these y-coordinates are the same as the expression $(x - 3)(x + 2)$, the values of x for which the graph of $y = (x - 3)(x + 2)$ is above the x-axis are the values of x for which the inequality $(x - 3)(x + 2) > 0$ is true. Our solution set is therefore

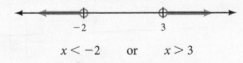

$$x < -2 \qquad \text{or} \qquad x > 3$$

VIDEO EXAMPLES

SECTION 11.8

EXAMPLE 1   Solve: $x^2 - 2x - 8 \le 0$.

ALGEBRAIC SOLUTION   We begin by factoring:

$$x^2 - 2x - 8 \le 0$$

$$(x - 4)(x + 2) \le 0$$

The product $(x - 4)(x + 2)$ is negative or zero. Either one of the factors must equal 0, or the factors must have opposite signs. The product will equal zero if

$$x - 4 = 0 \qquad \text{or} \qquad x + 2 = 0$$
$$x = 4 \qquad\qquad\qquad x = -2$$

We draw a diagram showing where each factor is positive and where each factor is negative:

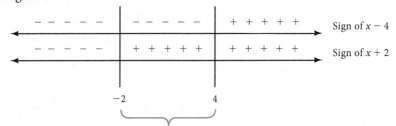

The product will equal zero if $x = -2$ or $x = 4$. From the diagram, we can see that the factors will have opposite signs if x is between -2 and 4. Therefore, the graph of the solution set is

We can write the solution set using set-builder notation or interval notation as

$$\{x \mid -2 \le x \le 4\} \text{ or } [-2, 4]$$

GRAPHICAL SOLUTION   To solve this inequality with a graphing calculator, we graph the function $y = (x - 4)(x + 2)$ and observe where the graph is below the x-axis. These points have negative y-coordinates, which means that the product $(x - 4)(x + 2)$ is negative for these points. Figure 3 shows the graph of $y = (x - 4)$ $(x + 2)$, along with the region on the x-axis where the graph contains points with negative y-coordinates.

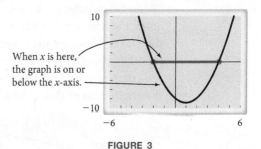

When x is here, the graph is on or below the x-axis.

FIGURE 3

As you can see, the graph is below the x-axis when x is between -2 and 4. Because our original inequality includes the possibility that $(x - 4)(x + 2)$ is 0, we include the endpoints, -2 and 4, with our solution set.

$$\{x \mid -2 \le x \le 4\} \text{ or } [-2, 4]$$

EXAMPLE 2   Solve: $6x^2 - x \geq 2$.

ALGEBRAIC SOLUTION

$$6x^2 - x \geq 2$$

$$6x^2 - x - 2 \geq 0 \qquad \text{Standard form}$$

$$(3x - 2)(2x + 1) \geq 0$$

The product is positive or zero, so the factors must equal zero or agree in sign. For the product to be zero, either

$$3x - 2 = 0 \quad \text{or} \quad 2x + 1 = 0$$

$$x = \frac{2}{3} \qquad\qquad x = -\frac{1}{2}$$

We draw a diagram to see where the factors will agree in sign.

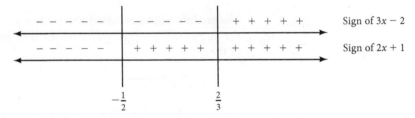

Because the factors agree in sign to the left of $-\frac{1}{2}$ and to the right of $\frac{2}{3}$, the graph of the solution set is

We can write the solution set as

$$\{x \mid x \leq -\frac{1}{2} \text{ or } x \geq \frac{2}{3}\} \quad \text{or} \quad \left(-\infty, -\frac{1}{2}\right] \cup \left[\frac{2}{3}, \infty\right)$$

GRAPHICAL SOLUTION   To solve this inequality with a graphing calculator, we graph the function $y = (3x - 2)(2x + 1)$ and observe where the graph is above the x-axis. These are the points that have positive y-coordinates, which means that the product $(3x - 2)(2x + 1)$ is positive for these points. Figure 4 shows the graph of $y = (3x - 2)(2x + 1)$, along with the regions on the x-axis where the graph is on or above the x-axis.

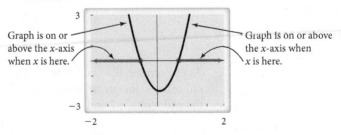

FIGURE 4

To find the points where the graph crosses the x-axis, we need to use either the Trace and Zoom features to zoom in on each point, or the calculator function that finds the intercepts automatically (on the TI-84 this is the root/zero function under the CALC key). Whichever method we use, we will obtain the following result:

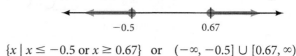

$$\{x \mid x \le -0.5 \text{ or } x \ge 0.67\} \quad \text{or} \quad (-\infty, -0.5] \cup [0.67, \infty)$$

EXAMPLE 3   Solve: $x^2 - 6x + 9 \ge 0$.

ALGEBRAIC SOLUTION

$$x^2 - 6x + 9 \ge 0$$

$$(x - 3)^2 \ge 0$$

This is a special case in which both factors are the same. Because $(x - 3)^2$ is always positive or zero, the solution set is all real numbers. That is, any real number that is used in place of x in the original inequality will produce a true statement.

GRAPHICAL SOLUTION   The graph of $y = (x - 3)^2$ is shown in Figure 5.

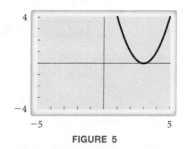

FIGURE 5

Notice that it touches the x-axis at 3 and is above the x-axis everywhere else. This means that every point on the graph has a y-coordinate greater than or equal to 0, no matter what the value of x. The conclusion that we draw from the graph is that the inequality $(x - 3)^2 \ge 0$ is true for all values of x.

Rational Inequalities

Our last two examples involve inequalities that contain rational expressions.

EXAMPLE 4   Solve: $\dfrac{x - 4}{x + 1} \le 0$.

SOLUTION   The inequality indicates that the quotient of $(x - 4)$ and $(x + 1)$ is negative or 0 (less than or equal to 0). We can use the same reasoning we used to solve the first three examples, because quotients are positive or negative under the same conditions that products are positive or negative. The quotient will equal zero if the numerator is zero, which is true if $x = 4$. If $x = -1$, the denominator would be zero, making the expression undefined.

Here is the diagram that shows where each factor is positive and where each factor is negative:

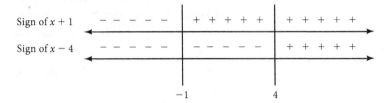

Between -1 and 4, the quotient is negative because the factors have opposite signs. The solution set and its graph are shown here:

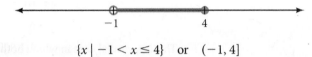

$$\{x \mid -1 < x \leq 4\} \quad \text{or} \quad (-1, 4]$$

Notice that the left endpoint is open—that is, it is not included in the solution set—because $x = -1$ would make the denominator in the original inequality 0. It is important to check all endpoints of solution sets to inequalities that involve rational expressions.

EXAMPLE 5   Solve: $\dfrac{3}{x - 2} - \dfrac{2}{x - 3} > 0$.

SOLUTION   We begin by adding the two rational expressions on the left side. The common denominator is $(x - 2)(x - 3)$:

$$\frac{3}{x - 2} \cdot \frac{(x - 3)}{(x - 3)} - \frac{2}{x - 3} \cdot \frac{(x - 2)}{(x - 2)} > 0$$

$$\frac{3x - 9 - 2x + 4}{(x - 2)(x - 3)} > 0$$

$$\frac{x - 5}{(x - 2)(x - 3)} > 0$$

This time the quotient involves three factors. Here is the diagram that shows the signs of the three factors:

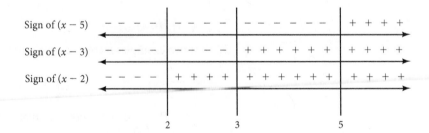

The original inequality indicates that the quotient is positive. For this to happen, either all three factors must be positive, or exactly two factors must be negative. Looking back at the diagram, we see the regions that satisfy these conditions are between 2 and 3 or to the right of 5. Here is our solution set:

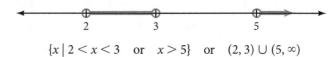

$$\{x \mid 2 < x < 3 \quad \text{or} \quad x > 5\} \quad \text{or} \quad (2, 3) \cup (5, \infty)$$

Getting Ready for Class

After reading through the preceding section, respond in your own words and in complete sentences.

A. What is the first step in solving a quadratic inequality?

B. How do you show that the endpoint of a line segment is not part of the graph of a quadratic inequality?

C. How would you use the graph of $y = ax^2 + bx + c$ to help you solve $ax^2 + bx + c < 0$?

D. How would the solution set to Example 5 be different if the inequality sign was $\geq$ instead of $>$?

Problem Set 11.8

Solve each of the following inequalities, and graph the solution set.

1. $x^2 + x - 6 > 0$ **2.** $x^2 + x - 6 < 0$ **3.** $x^2 - x - 12 \leq 0$

4. $x^2 - x - 12 \geq 0$ **5.** $x^2 + 5x \geq -6$ **6.** $x^2 - 5x > 6$

7. $6x^2 < 5x - 1$ **8.** $4x^2 \geq -5x + 6$ **9.** $x^2 - 9 < 0$

10. $x^2 - 16 \geq 0$ **11.** $4x^2 - 9 \geq 0$ **12.** $9x^2 - 4 < 0$

13. $2x^2 - x - 3 < 0$ **14.** $3x^2 + x - 10 \geq 0$ **15.** $x^2 - 4x + 4 \geq 0$

16. $x^2 - 4x + 4 < 0$ **17.** $x^2 - 10x + 25 < 0$ **18.** $x^2 - 10x + 25 > 0$

19. $(x - 2)(x - 3)(x - 4) > 0$ **20.** $(x - 2)(x - 3)(x - 4) < 0$

21. $(x + 1)(x + 2)(x + 3) \leq 0$ **22.** $(x + 1)(x + 2)(x + 3) \geq 0$

23. $\dfrac{x - 1}{x + 4} \leq 0$ **24.** $\dfrac{x + 4}{x - 1} \leq 0$

25. $\dfrac{3x}{x + 6} - \dfrac{8}{x + 6} < 0$ **26.** $\dfrac{5x}{x + 1} - \dfrac{3}{x + 1} < 0$

27. $\dfrac{4}{x - 6} + 1 > 0$ **28.** $\dfrac{2}{x - 3} + 1 \geq 0$

29. $\dfrac{x - 2}{(x + 3)(x - 4)} < 0$ **30.** $\dfrac{x - 1}{(x + 2)(x - 5)} < 0$

31. $\dfrac{2}{x - 4} - \dfrac{1}{x - 3} > 0$ **32.** $\dfrac{4}{x + 3} - \dfrac{3}{x + 2} > 0$

33. $\dfrac{x + 7}{2x + 12} + \dfrac{6}{x^2 - 36} \leq 0$ **34.** $\dfrac{x + 1}{2x - 2} - \dfrac{2}{x^2 - 1} \leq 0$

35. The graph of $y = x^2 - 4$ is shown in Figure 6. Use the graph to write the solution set for each of the following:

     a. $x^2 - 4 < 0$ **b.** $x^2 - 4 > 0$ **c.** $x^2 - 4 = 0$

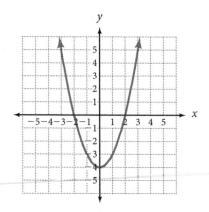

FIGURE 6

36. The graph of $y = 4 - x^2$ is shown in Figure 7. Use the graph to write the solution set for each of the following:

     a. $4 - x^2 < 0$ **b.** $4 - x^2 > 0$ **c.** $4 - x^2 = 0$

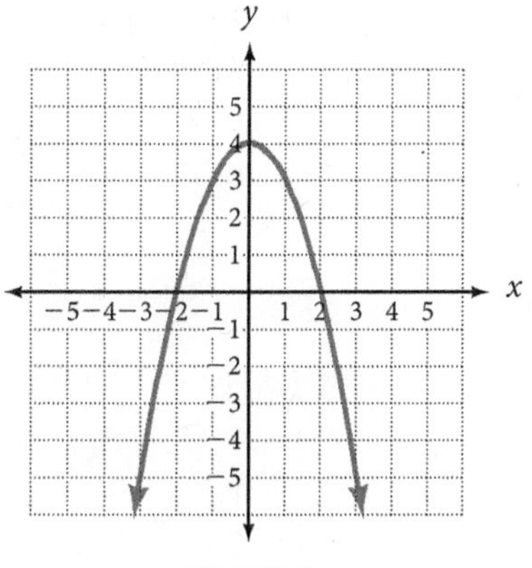

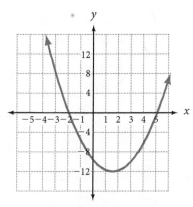

FIGURE 7

37. The graph of $y = x^2 - 3x - 10$ is shown in Figure 8. Use the graph to write the solution set for each of the following:

    a. $x^2 - 3x - 10 < 0$ **b.** $x^2 - 3x - 10 > 0$ **c.** $x^2 - 3x - 10 = 0$

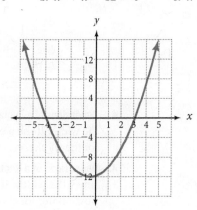

FIGURE 8

38. The graph of $y = x^2 + x - 12$ is shown in Figure 9. Use the graph to write the solution set for each of the following:

    a. $x^2 + x - 12 < 0$ **b.** $x^2 + x - 12 > 0$ **c.** $x^2 + x - 12 = 0$

FIGURE 9

39. The graph of $y = x^3 - 3x^2 - x + 3$ is shown in Figure 10. Use the graph to write the solution set for each of the following:

a. $x^3 - 3x^2 - x + 3 < 0$ **b.** $x^3 - 3x^2 - x + 3 > 0$

c. $x^3 - 3x^2 - x + 3 = 0$

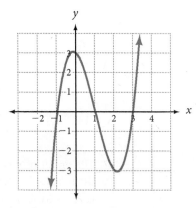

FIGURE 10

40. The graph of $y = x^3 + 4x^2 - 4x - 16$ is shown in Figure 11. Use the graph to write the solution set for each of the following:

a. $x^3 + 4x^2 - 4x - 16 < 0$ **b.** $x^3 + 4x^2 - 4x - 16 > 0$

c. $x^3 + 4x^2 - 4x - 16 = 0$

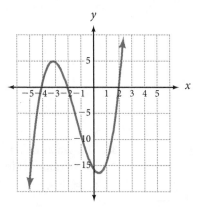

FIGURE 11

Applying the Concepts

41. Dimensions of a Rectangle The length of a rectangle is 3 inches more than twice the width. If the area is to be at least 44 square inches, what are the possibilities for the width?

42. Dimensions of a Rectangle The length of a rectangle is 5 inches less than three times the width. If the area is to be less than 12 square inches, what are the possibilities for the width?

43. Revenue A manufacturer of portable radios knows that the weekly revenue produced by selling x radios is given by the equation $R = 1,300p - 100p^2$, where p is the price of each radio (in dollars). What price should be charged for each radio if the weekly revenue is to be at least $4,000?

44. Revenue A manufacturer of small calculators knows that the weekly revenue produced by selling x calculators is given by the equation $R = 1,700p - 100p^2$, where p is the price of each calculator (in dollars). What price should be charged for each calculator if the revenue is to be at least $7,000 each week?

Learning Objectives Assessment

The following problems can be used to help assess if you have successfully met the learning objectives for this section.

45. Solve: $2x^2 - 3x - 20 < 0$.

    a. $x < -\dfrac{5}{2}$ or $x > 4$ **b.** $x \le -\dfrac{5}{2}$ or $x \ge 4$

    c. $-\dfrac{5}{2} \le x \le 4$ **d.** $-\dfrac{5}{2} < x < 4$

46. Solve: $\dfrac{x - 2}{x + 3} \ge 0$.

    a. $-3 \le x \le 2$ **b.** $-3 < x \le 2$

    c. $x < -3$ or $x \ge 2$ **d.** $x \le -3$ or $x \ge 2$

Maintaining Your Skills

Use a calculator to evaluate, give answers to 4 decimal places

47. $\dfrac{50,000}{32,000}$ **48.** $\dfrac{2.4362}{1.9758} - 1$ **49.** $\dfrac{1}{2}\left(\dfrac{4.5926}{1.3876} - 2\right)$ **50.** $1 + \dfrac{0.06}{12}$

Solve each equation

51. $2\sqrt{3t - 1} = 2$ **52.** $\sqrt{4t + 5} + 7 = 3$

53. $\sqrt{x + 3} = x - 3$ **54.** $\sqrt{x + 3} = \sqrt{x} - 3$

Graph each equation

55. $y = \sqrt[3]{x} - 1$ **56.** $y = \sqrt[3]{x} - 1$

Chapter 11 Summary

The Square Root Property for Equations [11.1]

1. If $(x - 3)^2 = 25$
then $x - 3 = \pm 5$
$x = 3 \pm 5$
$x = 8$ or $x = -2$

If $a^2 = b$, where b is a real number, then

$$a = \sqrt{b} \quad \text{or} \quad a = -\sqrt{b}$$

which can be written as $a = \pm\sqrt{b}$.

To Solve a Quadratic Equation by Completing the Square [11.1]

2. Solve: $x^2 - 6x - 6 = 0$
$x^2 - 6x = 6$
$x^2 - 6x + 9 = 6 + 9$
$(x - 3)^2 = 15$
$x - 3 = \pm\sqrt{15}$
$x = 3 \pm \sqrt{15}$

Step 1: Write the equation in the form $ax^2 + bx = c$.
Step 2: If $a \neq 1$, divide through by the constant a so the coefficient of x^2 is 1.
Step 3: Complete the square on the left side by adding the square of $\frac{1}{2}$ the coefficient of x to both sides.
Step 4: Write the left side of the equation as the square of a binomial. Simplify the right side if possible.
Step 5: Apply the square root property for equations, and solve as usual.

The Quadratic Theorem [11.2]

3. If $2x^2 + 3x - 4 = 0$, then

$$x = \frac{-3 \pm \sqrt{9 - 4(2)(-4)}}{2(2)}$$

$$= \frac{-3 \pm \sqrt{41}}{4}$$

For any quadratic equation in the form $ax^2 + bx + c = 0$, $a \neq 0$, the two solutions are

$$x = \frac{-b \pm \sqrt{b^2 - 4ac}}{2a}$$

This last equation is known as the *quadratic formula*.

The Discriminant [11.3]

4. The discriminant for
$x^2 + 6x + 9 = 0$
is $D = 36 - 4(1)(9) = 0$, which
means the equation has one rational solution.

The expression $b^2 - 4ac$ that appears under the radical sign in the quadratic formula is known as the *discriminant*.

We can classify the solutions to $ax^2 + bx + c = 0$ as follows:

The solutions are	When the discriminant is
Two complex numbers containing i	Negative
One rational number	Zero
Two rational numbers	A positive perfect square
Two irrational numbers	A positive number, but not a perfect square

Equations Quadratic in Form [11.4]

5. The equation $x^4 - x^2 - 12 = 0$ is quadratic in x^2. Letting $y = x^2$ we have

$$y^2 - y - 12 = 0$$
$$(y - 4)(y + 3) = 0$$
$$y = 4 \quad \text{or} \quad y = -3$$

Resubstituting x^2 for y, we have

$$x^2 = 4 \qquad \text{or} \qquad x^2 = -3$$
$$x = \pm 2 \qquad \text{or} \qquad x = \pm i\sqrt{3}$$

There are a variety of equations whose form is quadratic. We solve most of them by making a substitution so the equation becomes quadratic, and then solving the equation by factoring or the quadratic formula. For example,

The equation	is quadratic in
$(2x - 3)^2 + 5(2x - 3) - 6 = 0$	$2x - 3$
$4x^4 - 7x^2 - 2 = 0$	x^2
$2x - 7\sqrt{x} + 3 = 0$	$\sqrt{x}$

Transformations [11.5]

6. The graph of $f(x) = -2(x + 1)^2 + 3$ is the graph of $y = x^2$, but with a vertical expansion by a factor of 2, an x-axis reflection, a horizontal translation of 1 unit left, and a vertical translation of 3 units upward.

The graph of $f(x) = ax^2$, $a \neq 0$, will be a
     vertical expansion of $y = x^2$ if $|a| > 1$
     vertical contraction of $y = x^2$ if $|a| < 1$
     x-axis reflection of $y = x^2$ if $a < 0$

The graph of $f(x) = (x - h)^2$ is the graph of $y = x^2$ translated h units to the right.

The graph of $f(x) = (x + h)^2$ is the graph of $y = x^2$ translated h units to the left.

The graph of $f(x) = x^2 + k$ is the graph of $y = x^2$ translated k units upward.

The graph of $f(x) = x^2 - k$ is the graph of $y = x^2$ translated k units downward.

Vertex Form [11.6]

7. The vertex of the function $f(x) = -2(x + 1)^2 + 3$ is the point $(-1, 3)$, which is the highest point on the graph.

The graph of the function
$$f(x) = a(x - h)^2 + k, \, a \neq 0$$
is a parabola with vertex (h, k).

If $a > 0$, the parabola opens upward and the vertex is the lowest point on the graph.

If $a < 0$, the parabola opens downward and the vertex is the highest point on the graph.

Graphing Quadratic Functions in Standard Form [11.6]

8. The graph of $y = x^2 - 4$ will be a parabola. It will cross the x-axis at 2 and -2, and the vertex will be $(0, -4)$.

The graph of any function of the form
$$f(x) = ax^2 + bx + c \qquad a \neq 0$$
is a *parabola*. The graph opens upward if $a > 0$ and opens downward if $a < 0$. The *vertex* is the point
$$\left(-\frac{b}{2a}, f\left(-\frac{b}{2a}\right)\right)$$

Projectile Motion [11.7]

9. If a baseball is thrown upward with an initial velocity of 48 feet per second and released from a height of 4 feet, then its height after t seconds is given by

$$h(t) = -16t^2 + 48t + 4$$

The vertex represents the highest point reached by the baseball, which is 40 feet after 1.5 seconds.

If an object is projected vertically into the air with an initial speed v, in feet per second, from an initial height s, in feet, then the height of the object after t seconds is given by the quadratic function

$$h(t) = -16t^2 + vt + s$$

where h is measured in feet.

Profit, Cost, and Revenue [11.7]

10. An art supply store can sell x paint sets each week at p dollars each according to the equation $x = 700 - 20p$. The revenue is

$$R = xp$$
$$= (700 - 20p)p$$

For the revenue to be $6,000, we solve

$$700p - 20p^2 = 6{,}000$$
$$20p^2 - 700p + 6{,}000 = 0$$
$$p^2 - 35p + 300 = 0$$
$$(p - 15)(p - 20) = 0$$
$$p = 15 \quad \text{or} \quad p = 20$$

The relationship between profit, cost, and revenue is given by

$$\text{Profit} = \text{Revenue} - \text{Cost}$$

$$P(x) = R(x) - C(x)$$

If x items are sold and p is the selling price of each item, then

$$R = xp$$

Quadratic Inequalities [11.8]

11. Solve: $x^2 - 2x - 8 > 0$.

We factor and draw the sign diagram:

$$(x - 4)(x + 2) > 0$$

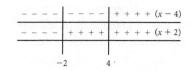

The solution is $x < -2$ or $x > 4$.

We solve quadratic inequalities by manipulating the inequality to get 0 on the right side and then factoring the left side. We then make a diagram that indicates where the factors are positive and where they are negative. From this sign diagram and the original inequality we graph the appropriate solution set.

Solve each equation. [11.1, 11.2]

1. $(2x + 4)^2 = 25$ **2.** $(2x - 6)^2 = -8$ **3.** $y^2 - 10y + 25 = -4$

4. $(y + 1)(y - 3) = -6$ **5.** $8t^3 - 125 = 0$ **6.** $\dfrac{1}{a + 2} - \dfrac{1}{3} = \dfrac{1}{a}$

7. Solve the formula $64(1 + r)^2 = A$ for r. [11.1]

8. Solve $x^2 - 4x = -2$ by completing the square. [11.1]

9. Find k so that $kx^2 = 12x - 4$ has one rational solution. [11.3]

10. Use the discriminant to identify the number and kind of solutions to $2x^2 - 5x = 7$. [11.3]

Find equations that have the given solutions. [11.3]

11. $x = 5, x = -\dfrac{2}{3}$ **12.** $x = 2i, x = -2i$

Solve each equation. [11.4]

13. $4x^4 - 7x^2 - 2 = 0$ **14.** $(2t + 1)^2 - 5(2t + 1) + 6 = 0$

15. $2t - 7\sqrt{t} + 3 = 0$

16. Projectile Motion An object is tossed into the air with an upward velocity of 14 feet per second from the top of a building h feet high. The time it takes for the object to hit the ground below is given by the formula $16t^2 - 14t - h = 0$. Solve this formula for t. [11.4]

Sketch the graph of each of the following functions. Find any intercepts and give the coordinates of the vertex in each case. [11.5, 11.6]

17. $f(x) = 3 - (x + 2)^2$ **18.** $f(x) = 2(x - 1)^2 - 3$

19. $f(x) = x^2 - 2x - 3$ **20.** $f(x) = -x^2 + 2x + 8$

21. Projectile Motion An object projected upward with an initial velocity of 32 feet per second will rise and fall according to the equation $s(t) = 32t - 16t^2$, where s is its distance above the ground at time t. At what times will the object be 12 feet above the ground? [11.7]

20. Revenue The total weekly cost for a company to make x ceramic coffee cups is given by the formula $C(x) = 2x + 100$. If the weekly revenue from selling all x cups is $R(x) = 25x - 0.2x^2$, how many cups must it sell a week to make a profit of $200 a week? [11.7]

23. Profit Find the maximum weekly profit for a company with weekly costs of $C = 5x + 100$ and weekly revenue of $R = 25x - 0.1x^2$. [11.7]

Graph each of the following inequalities. [11.8]

24. $x^2 - x - 6 \leq 0$ **25.** $2x^2 + 5x > 3$

Exponential and Logarithmic Functions

Chapter Outline

iStockphoto.com © ZoneCreative

I f you have had any problems with or had testing done on your thyroid gland, then you may have come in contact with radioactive iodine-131. Like all radio-active elements, iodine-131 decays naturally. The half-life of iodine-131 is 8 days, which means that every 8 days a sample of iodine-131 will decrease to half of its original amount. The following table and graph show what happens to a 1,600-microgram sample of iodine-131 over time.

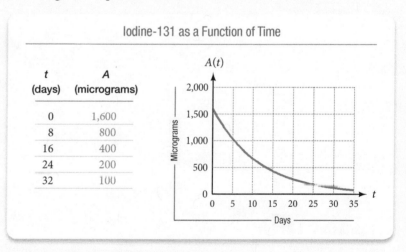

Iodine-131 as a Function of Time

t (days)	A (micrograms)
0	1,600
8	800
16	400
24	200
32	100

The function represented by the information in the table and graph is

$$A(t) = 1,600 \cdot \frac{1}{2}^{\,t/8}$$

It is one of the types of functions we will study in this chapter.

Learning Objectives

In this section, we will learn how to:

1. Evaluate an exponential function.
2. Sketch the graph of an exponential function.
3. Solve problems involving compound interest.
4. Graph the natural exponential function.

Introduction

To obtain an intuitive idea of how exponential functions behave, we can consider the heights attained by a bouncing ball. When a ball used in the game of racquetball is dropped from any height, the first bounce will reach a height that is $\frac{2}{3}$ of the original height. The second bounce will reach $\frac{2}{3}$ of the height of the first bounce, and so on, as shown in Figure 1.

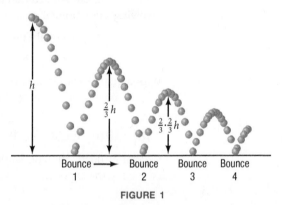

FIGURE 1

If the ball is initially dropped from a height of 1 meter, then during the first bounce it will reach a height of $\frac{2}{3}$ meter. The height of the second bounce will reach $\frac{2}{3}$ of the height reached on the first bounce. The maximum height of any bounce is $\frac{2}{3}$ of the height of the previous bounce.

Initial height: $h = 1$

Bounce 1: $\quad h = \frac{2}{3}(1) = \frac{2}{3}$

Bounce 2: $\quad h = \frac{2}{3}\left(\frac{2}{3}\right) = \left(\frac{2}{3}\right)^2$

Bounce 3: $\quad h = \frac{2}{3}\left(\frac{2}{3}\right)^2 = \left(\frac{2}{3}\right)^3$

Bounce 4: $\quad h = \frac{2}{3}\left(\frac{2}{3}\right)^3 = \left(\frac{2}{3}\right)^4$

$\vdots \qquad\qquad\qquad \vdots$

Bounce n: $\quad h = \frac{2}{3}\left(\frac{2}{3}\right)^{n-1} = \left(\frac{2}{3}\right)^n$

This last equation is exponential in form. In fact, this relationship can be expressed in function notation as

$$h(n) = \left(\frac{2}{3}\right)^n$$

Because the variable is an exponent, we call this an *exponential function*. We classify all exponential functions together with the following definition.

> **(def) DEFINITION** *exponential function*
>
> An *exponential function* is any function that can be written in the form
>
> $$f(x) = b^x$$
>
> where b is a positive real number other than 1. The constant b is called the *base*.

Each of the following is an exponential function:

$$f(x) = 2^x \qquad y = 3^x \qquad f(x) = \left(\frac{1}{4}\right)^x$$

Notice the fundamental difference between an exponential function and a function involving a polynomial, such as a quadratic function.

Exponential Function	Quadratic function
$f(x) = 2^x$	$f(x) = x^2$

With a quadratic function, we have a constant exponent on a variable base. With the exponential function, the base is a constant and the exponent is a variable.

Evaluating Exponential Functions

We can evaluate an exponential function by substituting values for x and then evaluating the exponent.

EXAMPLE 1   If $f(x) = 2^x$, then

$$f(0) = 2^0 = 1$$

$$f(3) = 2^3 = 8$$

$$f(-2) = 2^{-2} = \frac{1}{2^2} = \frac{1}{4}$$

$$f\left(\frac{1}{2}\right) = 2^{1/2} = \sqrt{2} \approx 1.4$$

$$f\left(-\frac{3}{4}\right) = 2^{-3/4} = \frac{1}{2^{3/4}} = \frac{1}{\sqrt[4]{2^3}} \approx 0.6$$

$$f(\sqrt{5}) = 2^{\sqrt{5}} \approx 2^{2.24} \approx 4.7$$

With the last three values we used a calculator to obtain an approximation.

As you can see in Example 1, we can use any real number as the input for an exponential function. All exponential functions have a domain that is the set of all real numbers.

In the introduction to this chapter, we indicated that the half-life of iodine-131 is 8 days, which means that every 8 days a sample of iodine-131 will decrease to half of its original amount. If we start with A_0 micrograms of iodine-131, then after t days the sample will contain

$$A(t) = A_0 \cdot \left(\frac{1}{2}\right)^{t/8}$$

micrograms of iodine-131. This is an exponential function with a base of $\frac{1}{2}$.

EXAMPLE 2   A patient is administered a 1,200-microgram dose of iodine-131. How much iodine-131 will be in the patient's system after 10 days, and after 16 days?

SOLUTION   The initial amount of iodine-131 is $A_0 = 1{,}200$, so the function that gives the amount left in the patient's system after t days is

$$A(t) = 1{,}200 \cdot \left(\frac{1}{2}\right)^{t/8}$$

After 10 days, the amount left in the patient's system is

$$A(10) = 1{,}200 \cdot \left(\frac{1}{2}\right)^{10/8} = 1{,}200 \cdot \left(\frac{1}{2}\right)^{1.25} \approx 504.5 \text{ micrograms}$$

After 16 days, the amount left in the patient's system is

$$A(16) = 1{,}200 \cdot \left(\frac{1}{2}\right)^{16/8} = 1{,}200 \cdot \left(\frac{1}{2}\right)^{2} = 300 \text{ micrograms}$$

Graphs of Exponential Functions

We now turn our attention to the graphs of exponential functions.

EXAMPLE 3   Sketch the graph of the exponential function $f(x) = 2^x$.

SOLUTION   First we make a table of ordered pairs by choosing convenient values of x (see Example 1 for reference). Graphing the ordered pairs given in the table and connecting them with a smooth curve, we have the graph of $y = 2^x$ shown in Figure 2.

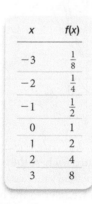

x	$f(x)$
-3	$\frac{1}{8}$
-2	$\frac{1}{4}$
-1	$\frac{1}{2}$
0	1
1	2
2	4
3	8

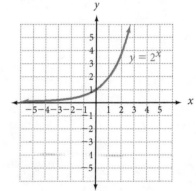

FIGURE 2

As you can see from Figure 2, the range of the function is $\{y \mid y > 0\}$. Notice that the graph does not cross the x-axis. It *approaches* the x-axis — in fact, we can get it as close to the x-axis as we want without it actually intersecting the x-axis. For the graph of $y = 2^x$ to intersect the x-axis, we would have to find a value of x that would make $2^x = 0$. Because no such value of x exists, the graph of $y = 2^x$ cannot intersect the x-axis. The graph has a horizontal asymptote at the x-axis, which we can express as the line $y = 0$.

Although the graph does not have an x-intercept, it does have a y-intercept of 1.

EXAMPLE 4   Sketch the graph of $f(x) = \left(\dfrac{1}{3}\right)^x$.

SOLUTION   The table beside Figure 3 gives some ordered pairs that satisfy the equation. Using the ordered pairs from the table, we have the graph shown in Figure 3.

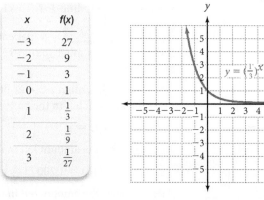

x	f(x)
−3	27
−2	9
−1	3
0	1
1	$\frac{1}{3}$
2	$\frac{1}{9}$
3	$\frac{1}{27}$

FIGURE 3

Once again, the range of the function is $\{y \mid y > 0\}$ and the graph has a horizontal asymptote at $y = 0$. The y-intercept is 1. There is no x-intercept.

Figures 4 and 5 show some families of exponential curves to help you become more familiar with them on an intuitive level.

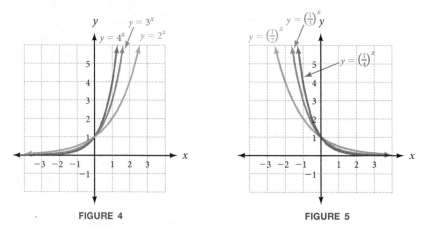

FIGURE 4   **FIGURE 5**

The graphs in Figure 4, where the base b is larger than 1, are examples of *exponential growth*. As x increases, y increases very rapidly. If the base b is less than 1, such as in Figure 5, then we refer to the behavior as *exponential decay*. As x increases, y decreases towards 0.

Here is a summary of the behavior of the graph for an exponential function.

> **RULE** *Graphs of Exponential Functions*
>
> The graph of the $f(x) = b^x$, for $b > 0$ and $b \neq 1$, has the following:
>
> $$\text{domain} = \text{all real numbers}$$
> $$\text{range} = \{y \mid y > 0\}$$
> $$y\text{-intercept} = (0, 1)$$
> $$\text{horizontal asymptote at } y = 0$$
>
> If $b > 1$ the graph represents exponential growth, and if $b < 1$ the graph represents exponential decay.

EXAMPLE 5 Sketch the graph of $f(x) = 3 - 2^x$, and then state the range of the function.

SOLUTION We can use transformations to sketch the graph. Figure 2 in Example 3 shows the graph of $y = 2^x$. To obtain the graph of $f(x) = 3 - 2^x$, we do the following:

1. reflect the graph of $y = 2^x$ about the x-axis

2. translate the result upward 3 units.

Figure 6 shows all the steps and the final graph.

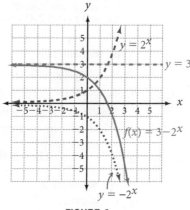

FIGURE 6

Notice that, as a result of the vertical translation, the horizontal asymptote is the line $y = 3$. The range is $\{y \mid y < 3\}$.

Compound Interest

Among the many applications of exponential functions are the applications having to do with interest-bearing accounts. Suppose you invest P dollars (this is referred to as the *principal*) in an account that earns an annual interest rate r, and that your interest is calculated n times each year. Then with each calculation the rate applied will be $\frac{r}{n}$.

So, after the first interest period, your new balance will be

$$\text{Balance} = \text{Principal} + \text{Interest}$$

$$= P + \left(\frac{r}{n}\right)P$$

$$= \left(1 + \frac{r}{n}\right)P$$

In other words, at each calculation your previous balance is multiplied by a factor of

$$\left(1 + \frac{r}{n}\right)$$

If you leave your money in the account for t years and do not make any withdrawals, then we have the following.

⟨Δ≠Σ⟩   *Compound Interest*

If P dollars are deposited in an account with annual interest rate r, compounded n times per year, then the amount of money in the account after t years is given by the formula

$$A(t) = P\left(1 + \frac{r}{n}\right)^{nt}$$

EXAMPLE 6   Suppose you deposit $500 in an account with an annual interest rate of 2.4%. Find the amount of money in your account after 5 years if the interest is compounded:

a. semiannually

b. quarterly

c. monthly

SOLUTION   First, we note that $P = 500$, $r = 0.024$, and $t = 5$. Substituting these values into the compound interest formula gives us

$$A(5) = 500\left(1 + \frac{0.024}{n}\right)^{n \cdot 5}$$

All we need to do is determine the correct value of n and then perform the calculation.

a. Semiannually means twice each year, so $n = 2$:

$$A(5) = 500\left(1 + \frac{0.024}{2}\right)^{2(5)} = 500(1.012)^{10} \approx \$563.35$$

b. Quarterly means four times each year, so now $n = 4$.

$$A(5) = 500\left(1 + \frac{0.024}{4}\right)^{4(5)} = 500(1.006)^{20} \approx \$563.55$$

c. There are 12 months in a year, so we use $n = 12$.

$$A(5) = 500\left(1 + \frac{0.024}{12}\right)^{12(5)} = 500(1.002)^{60} \approx \$563.68$$

As you can see in Example 6, we earn more money by compounding interest more frequently. This is because our interest begins earning its own interest earlier in the year.

What would happen if we let the number of compounding periods become larger and larger, so that we compounded the interest every week, then every day, then every hour, then every second, and so on? If we take this as far as it can go, we end up compounding the interest every moment. When this happens, we have an account with interest that is compounded continuously.

To see how this affects our compound interest formula, we let $x = \frac{n}{r}$, giving us

$$A(t) = P\left(1 + \frac{r}{n}\right)^{nt}$$

$$= P\left(1 + \frac{1}{x}\right)^{xrt}$$

$$= P\left[\left(1 + \frac{1}{x}\right)^{x}\right]^{rt}$$

Table 1 shows values of the expression

$$\left(1 + \frac{1}{x}\right)^{x}$$

as n, and thus x, increases.

x	$\left(1 + \frac{1}{x}\right)^{x}$
1	2
10	2.59374
100	2.70481
1,000	2.71692
10,000	2.71815
100,000	2.71827

TABLE 1

Notice the values in the right column seem to be approaching some specific number. This number is denoted as e. The number e is a number like π. It is irrational and occurs in many formulas that describe the world around us. Like π, it can be approximated with a decimal number. Whereas π is approximately 3.1416, e is approximately 2.7183.

Replacing the expression $\left(1 + \frac{1}{x}\right)^{x}$ with e in our compound interest formula leads us to the following.

Continuously Compounded Interest

If P dollars are deposited in an account with annual interest rate r, compounded continuously, then the amount of money in the account after t years is given by the formula

$$A(t) = Pe^{rt}$$

EXAMPLE 7   Suppose you deposit $500 in an account with an annual interest rate of 2.4% compounded continuously. Find an equation that gives the amount of money in the account after t years. Then find the amount of money in the account after 5 years.

SOLUTION   Because the interest is compounded continuously, we use the formula $A(t) = Pe^{rt}$. Substituting $P = 500$ and $r = 0.024$ into this formula, we have

$$A(t) = 500e^{0.024t}$$

After 5 years, this account will contain

$$A(5) = 500e^{0.024 \cdot 5} = 500e^{0.12} \approx \$563.75$$

to the nearest cent.

The Natural Exponential Function

Because e is a positive number, we can use it as the base of an exponential function, giving us $f(x) = e^x$. This is called the *natural exponential* function.

The table below shows some values of the natural exponential function. The graph is shown in Figure 7. Notice that this graph is another example of exponential growth.

x	$f(x) = e^x$
-2	$f(-2) = e^{-2} = \frac{1}{e^2} \approx 0.135$
-1	$f(-1) = e^{-1} = \frac{1}{e} \approx 0.368$
0	$f(0) = e^0 = 1$
1	$f(1) = e^1 = e \approx 2.72$
2	$f(2) = e^2 \approx 7.39$
3	$f(3) = e^3 \approx 20.09$

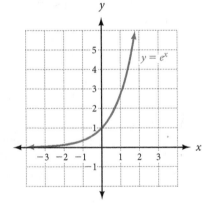

FIGURE 7

Getting Ready for Class

After reading through the preceding section, respond in your own words and in complete sentences.

A. What is an exponential function?

B. In an exponential function, explain why the base b cannot equal 1. (What kind of function would you get if the base was equal to 1?)

C. What characteristics do the graphs of $y = 2^x$ and $y = \left(\frac{1}{2}\right)^x$ have in common?

D. What is meant by continuously compounded interest?

Let $f(x) = 3^x$ and $g(x) = \left(\frac{1}{2}\right)^x$, and evaluate each of the following.

1. $g(0)$ **2.** $f(0)$ **3.** $g(-1)$ **4.** $g(-4)$

5. $f(-3)$ **6.** $f(-1)$ **7.** $f(2) + g(-2)$ **8.** $f(2) - g(-2)$

Let $f(x) = 4^x$ and $g(x) = \left(\frac{1}{3}\right)^x$. Evaluate each of the following.

9. $f(-1) + g(1)$ **10.** $f(2) + g(-2)$ **11.** $\dfrac{f(-2)}{g(1)}$ **12.** $f(3) - f(2)$

Let $f(x) = 2^x$. Use a calculator to approximate each of the following. Round to the nearest hundredth.

13. $f\left(\frac{1}{3}\right)$ **14.** $f(\sqrt{3})$ **15.** $f(-\sqrt{7})$ **16.** $f\left(-\frac{3}{2}\right)$

Let $f(x) = e^x$. Use a calculator to approximate each of the following. Round to the nearest hundredth. (If your calculator does not have an e^x key, use $e \approx 2.7183$.)

17. $f(3)$ **18.** $f(-3)$ **19.** $f(-0.5)$ **20.** $f(1.5)$

21. $f\left(\frac{1}{5}\right)$ **22.** $f\left(\frac{5}{3}\right)$ **23.** $f(\pi)$ **24.** $f(e)$

Graph each of the following functions.

25. $y = 4^x$ **26.** $y = 3^x$ **27.** $y = \left(\frac{1}{2}\right)^x$ **28.** $y = \left(\frac{1}{4}\right)^x$

29. $y = \left(\frac{1}{3}\right)^{-x}$ **30.** $y = \left(\frac{1}{2}\right)^{-x}$ **31.** $y = e^x$ **32.** $y = e^{-x}$

Use transformations to graph each function. Then state the horizontal asymptote and the range.

33. $y = 2^{x+1}$ **34.** $y = 2^{x-3}$ **35.** $y = 3^x + 2$ **36.** $y = 3^x - 1$

37. $y = -2^x$ **38.** $y = -e^x$ **39.** $y = 2e^x$ **40.** $y = \frac{1}{2} \cdot 3^x$

41. $y = 4 - 2^x$ **42.** $y = -1 - 3^x$ **43.** $y = e^x + 2$ **44.** $y = -e^x + 2$

Graph each of the following functions on the same coordinate system for positive values of x only.

45. $y = 2x, y = x^2, y = 2^x$ **46.** $y = 3x, y = x^3, y = 3^x$

47. On a graphing calculator, graph the family of curves $y = b^x$, $b = 2, 4, 6, 8$.

48. On a graphing calculator, graph the family of curves $y = b^x$, $b = \frac{1}{2}, \frac{1}{4}, \frac{1}{6}, \frac{1}{8}$.

Applying the Concepts

49. Bouncing Ball Suppose the ball mentioned in the introduction to this section is dropped from a height of 6 feet above the ground. Find an exponential equation that gives the height h the ball will attain during the nth bounce. How high will it bounce on the fifth bounce?

50. **Bouncing Ball** A golf ball is manufactured so that if it is dropped from A feet above the ground onto a hard surface, the maximum height of each bounce will be one half of the height of the previous bounce. Find an exponential equation that gives the height h the ball will attain during the nth bounce. If the ball is dropped from 10 feet above the ground onto a hard surface, how high will it bounce on the eighth bounce?

51. **Cost of Freon** Automobiles built before 1993 use Freon in their air conditioners. The federal government now prohibits the manufacture of Freon. Because the supply of Freon is decreasing, the price per pound is increasing exponentially. Current estimates put the formula for the price per pound of Freon at $p(t) = 17.6(1.25)^t$, where t is the number of years since 2000. Find the price of Freon in 2000 and 2010. How much will Freon cost in the year 2025?

52. **Airline Travel** The number of airline passengers in 1990 was 466 million. The number of passengers traveling by airplane each year has increased exponentially according to the model, $P(t) = 466 \cdot 1.035^t$, where t is the number of years since 1990 (U.S. Census Bureau).

    a. How many passengers traveled in 2010?

    b. How many passengers will travel in 2025?

53. **Bacteria Growth** Suppose it takes 12 hours for a certain strain of bacteria to reproduce by dividing in half. If 50 bacteria are present to begin with, then the total number present after x days will be $f(x) = 50 \cdot 4^x$. Find the total number present after 1 day, 2 days, and 3 days.

54. **Bacteria Growth** Suppose it takes 1 day for a certain strain of bacteria to reproduce by dividing in half. If 100 bacteria are present to begin with, then the total number present after x days will be $f(x) = 100 \cdot 2^x$. Find the total number present after 1 day, 2 days, 3 days, and 4 days. How many days must elapse before over 100,000 bacteria are present?

55. **Cost Increase** The cost of a can of Coca Cola in 1960 was $0.10. The exponential function that models the cost of a Coca Cola by year is given below, where t is the number of years since 1960.

    $$C(t) = 0.10e^{0.0576t}$$

    a. What was the expected cost of a can of Coca Cola in 2000?

    b. What was the expected cost of a can of Coca Cola in 2015?

    c. What is the expected cost of a can of Coca Cola in 2050?

56. **Bacteria Decay** You are conducting a biology experiment and begin with 5,000,000 cells, but some of those cells are dying each minute. The rate of death of the cells is modeled by the function $A(t) = A_0 \cdot e^{-0.598t}$, where A_0 is the original number of cells, t is time in minutes, and A is the number of cells remaining after t minutes.

    a. How may cells remain after 5 minutes?

    b. How many cells remain after 10 minutes?

    c. How many cells remain after 20 minutes?

57. **Compound Interest** Suppose you deposit $1,200 in an account with an annual interest rate of 6% compounded quarterly.

    a. Find an equation that gives the amount of money in the account after t years.

    b. Find the amount of money in the account after 8 years.

    c. If the interest were compounded continuously, how much money would the account contain after 8 years?

58. **Compound Interest** Suppose you deposit $500 in an account with an annual interest rate of 8% compounded monthly.

    a. Find an equation that gives the amount of money in the account after t years.

    b. Find the amount of money in the account after 5 years.

    c. If the interest were compounded continuously, how much money would the account contain after 5 years?

59. **Compound Interest** Valerie invests $10,000 in a CD earning 1.5% annual interest. If the CD matures in 5 years, what will be its value if interest is compounded:

    a. quarterly

    b. monthly

    c. continuously

60. **Compound Interest** Daniel purchases a U.S. Savings Bond for $100 that earns 0.5% annual interest. How much will the bond be worth in 30 years if the interest is compounded:

    a. semi-annually

    b. monthly

    c. continuously

61. **Compound Interest** Mark has $2,500 he wants to invest in an interest earning account for 4 years. One bank offers 1.4% annual interest, compounded quarterly. Another bank offers 1.35% annual interest, compounded continuously. Which is the better deal?

62. **Compound Interest** Ashley deposits $800 in a savings account that earns 2% annual interest, compounded continuously. At the end of two years whe withdraws $500. What is the balance in her account after an additional 2 years pass?

63. **Value of a Painting** A painting is purchased as an investment for $150. If the painting's value doubles every 3 years, then its value is given by the function

$$V(t) = 150 \cdot 2^{t/3} \text{ for } t \geq 0$$

where t is the number of years since it was purchased, and $V(t)$ is its value (in dollars) at that time. Graph this function.

64. **Value of a Painting** A painting is purchased as an investment for $125. If the painting's value doubles every 5 years, then its value is given by the function

$$V(t) = 125 \cdot 2^{t/5} \text{ for } t \geq 0$$

where t is the number of years since it was purchased, and $V(t)$ is its value (in dollars) at that time. Graph this function.

65. **Bankruptcy Model** The model for the number of bankruptcies filed under the Bankruptcy Reform Act is $B(t) = 0.798 \cdot 1.164^t$, where t is the number of years since 1994 and B is the number of bankruptcies filed in terms of millions. (*Source*: Administrative Office of the U.S. Courts, Statistical Tables for the Federal Judiciary)

    a. What is the expected number of bankruptcy filings in 2030?

    b. Graph this function for $0 \leq t \leq 40$.

66. **Health Care** In 1990, $699 billion were spent on health care expenditures. The amount of money, E, in billions spent on health care expenditures can be estimated using the function $E(t) = 78.16(1.11)^t$, where t is time in years since 1970.   (*Source*: U.S. Census Bureau)

    a. What are the expected health care expenditures in 2020, 2025, and 2030?

    b. Graph this function for $0 \leq t \leq 60$.

Declining-Balance Depreciation The declining-balance method of depreciation is an accounting method businesses use to deduct most of the cost of new equipment during the first few years of purchase. Unlike other methods, the declining-balance formula does not consider salvage value.

67. **Value of a Crane** The function

$$V(t) = 450{,}000 \, (1 - 0.30)^t,$$

   where V is value and t is time in years, can be used to find the value of a crane for the first 6 years of use.

    a. What is the value of the crane after 3 years and 6 months?

    b. State the domain of this function.

    c. Sketch the graph of this function.

    d. State the range of this function.

    e. After how many years will the crane be worth only $85,000?

68. **Value of a Printing Press** The function $V(t) = 375{,}000(1 - 0.25)^t$, where V is value and t is time in years, can be used to find the value of a printing press during the first 7 years of use.

    a. What is the value of the printing press after 4 years and 9 months?

    b. State the domain of this function.

    c. Sketch the graph of this function.

    d. State the range of this function.

    e. After how many years will the printing press be worth only $65,000?

69. **Getting Close to e** Use a calculator to complete the following table.

x	$(1 + x)^{1/x}$
1	
0.5	
0.1	
0.01	
0.001	
0.0001	
0.00001	

What number does the expression $(1 + x)^{1/x}$ seem to approach as x gets closer and closer to zero?

70. Getting Close to e Use a calculator to complete the following table.

x	$\left(1 + \frac{1}{x}\right)^x$
1	
10	
50	
100	
500	
1,000	
10,000	
1,000,000	

What number does the expression $\left(1 + \frac{1}{x}\right)^x$ seem to approach as x gets larger and larger?

Learning Objectives Assessment

The following problems can be used to help assess if you have successfully met the learning objectives for this section.

71. Evaluate $f(-2)$ if $f(x) = \left(\frac{1}{2}\right)^x$.

a. -1 **b.** $\frac{1}{4}$ **c.** 4 **d.** $-\frac{1}{4}$

72. Which function has the graph shown in Figure 8?

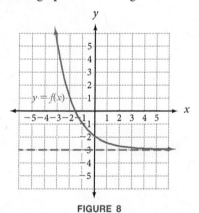

FIGURE 8

a. $f(x) = 2^x - 3$ **b.** $f(x) = \left(\frac{1}{2}\right)^x - 3$

c. $f(x) = \left(\frac{1}{2}\right)^{x-3}$ **d.** $f(x) = 2^{x-3}$

73. If $600 is invested in an account earning 3.5% annual interest compounded monthly, how much is in the account after 8 years?

    a. $650.98   **b.** $793.88   **c.** $792.91   **d.** $793.55

74. Which point is on the graph of $f(x) = e^x$?

    a. $(0, 2.7183)$ **b.** $(3, 8.1548)$

    c. $(-1, -2.7183)$ **d.** $(-2, 0.1353)$

Getting Ready for the Next Section

Solve each equation for y.

75. $x = 2y - 3$ **76.** $x = \dfrac{y + 7}{5}$

77. $x = y^2 - 3$ **78.** $x = (y + 4)^3$

79. $x = \dfrac{y - 4}{y - 2}$ **80.** $x = \dfrac{y + 5}{y - 3}$

81. $x = \sqrt{y - 3}$ **82.** $x = \sqrt{y} + 5$

Learning Objectives

In this section, we will learn how to:

1. Find the Inverse of a function as a set of ordered pairs.

2. Graph the inverse of a function.

3. Find the equation of an inverse function.

4. Use the horizontal line test to identify a one-to-one function.

5. Use composition to identify functions that are inverses.

Introduction

The following diagram (Figure 1) shows the route Justin takes to school. He leaves his home and drives 3 miles east, and then turns left and drives 2 miles north. When he leaves school to drive home, he drives the same two segments, but in the reverse order and the opposite direction; that is, he drives 2 miles south, turns right, and drives 3 miles west. When he arrives home from school, he is right where he started. His route home "undoes" his route to school, leaving him where he began.

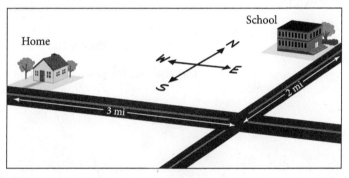

FIGURE 1

The relationship between a function and its inverse function is similar to the relationship between Justin's route from home to school and his route from school to home. The purpose of an inverse function is to undo, or reverse, whatever action the function performed. In other words, if a function contains the ordered pair (a, b), then the inverse should reverse this and contain the ordered pair (b, a). Since the function "turns a into b," the inverse should "turn b back into a."

This leads us to the following definition.

(def) DEFINITION *inverse of a relation*

The ***inverse of a relation*** R is obtained by interchanging the components of each ordered pair contained in R.

VIDEO EXAMPLES

SECTION 12.2

EXAMPLE 1 Find the inverse of the function given by
$f = \{(1, 4), (2, 5), (3, 6), (4, 7)\}$.

SOLUTION The inverse of f is obtained by reversing the order of the coordinates in each ordered pair in f. The inverse of f is the relation given by

$$g = \{(4, 1), (5, 2), (6, 3), (7, 4)\}$$

Looking at Example 1, it is obvious that the domain of f is now the range of g, and the range of f is now the domain of g. With inverses, the domain and range simply switch roles.

Suppose a function f is defined with an equation instead of a list of ordered pairs. We can obtain the equation of the inverse of f by interchanging the role of x and y in the equation for f.

EXAMPLE 2   If the function f is defined by $f(x) = 2x - 3$, find the equation that represents the inverse of f.

SOLUTION   Because the inverse of f is obtained by interchanging the components of all the ordered pairs belonging to f, every value of x takes on the role of a y-value, and every value of y assumes the role of an x-value. We simply exchange x and y in the equation $y = 2x - 3$ to get the formula for the inverse of f:

$$x = 2y - 3$$

We now solve this equation for y in terms of x:

$$x + 3 = 2y$$
$$\frac{x + 3}{2} = y$$
$$y = \frac{x + 3}{2}$$

The last line gives the equation that defines the inverse of f.

Let's compare the graphs of f and its inverse from Example 2. (See Figure 2.)

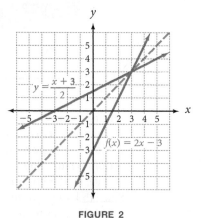

FIGURE 2

The graphs of f and its inverse have symmetry about the line $y = x$. This is a reasonable result since the one function was obtained from the other by interchanging x and y in the equation. The ordered pairs (a, b) and (b, a) always have symmetry about the line $y = x$. This gives us the following property.

PROPERTY   *graph of an inverse relation*

The graph of the inverse of a relation can be found by reflecting the graph of the original relation about the line $y = x$.

EXAMPLE 3   Graph the function $y = x^2 - 2$ and its inverse. Give the equation for the inverse.

SOLUTION   We can obtain the graph of the inverse of $y = x^2 - 2$ by graphing $y = x^2 - 2$ by the usual methods, and then reflecting the graph about the line $y = x$.

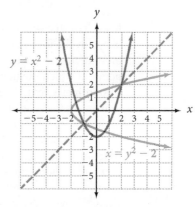

FIGURE 3

The equation that corresponds to the inverse of $y = x^2 - 2$ is obtained by interchanging x and y to get $x = y^2 - 2$.

We can solve the equation $x = y^2 - 2$ for y in terms of x as follows:

$$x = y^2 - 2$$
$$x + 2 = y^2$$
$$y = \pm\sqrt{x + 2}$$

Comparing the graphs in Figures 2 and 3, we observe that the inverse of a function is not always a function. In Example 2, both f and its inverse have graphs that are nonvertical straight lines and therefore both represent functions. In Example 3, the inverse of function f is not a function, since a vertical line crosses it in more than one place.

One-to-One Functions

We can distinguish between those functions with inverses that are also functions and those functions with inverses that are not functions with the following definition.

> **(def) DEFINITION**   *one-to-one functions*
>
> A function is a *one-to-one function* if every element in the range comes from exactly one element in the domain.

This definition indicates that a one-to-one function will yield a set of ordered pairs in which no two different ordered pairs have the same second coordinates. For example, the function

$$f = \{(2, 3), (-1, 3), (5, 8)\}$$

is not one-to-one because the element 3 in the range comes from both 2 and -1 in the domain.

On the other hand, the function

$$g = \{(5, 7), (3, -1), (4, 2)\}$$

is a one-to-one function because every element in the range comes from only one element in the domain.

Horizontal Line Test

If we have the graph of a function, we can determine if the function is one-to-one with the following test. If a horizontal line crosses the graph of a function in more than one place, then the function is not a one-to-one function because the points at which the horizontal line crosses the graph will be points with the same y-coordinates, but different x-coordinates. Therefore, the function will have an element in the range (the y-coordinate) that comes from more than one element in the domain (the x-coordinates).

Of the functions we have covered previously, all the (non-horizontal) linear functions and exponential functions are one-to-one functions because no horizontal lines can be found that will cross their graphs in more than one place.

Functions Whose Inverses Are Also Functions

Because one-to-one functions do not repeat second coordinates, when we reverse the components of the ordered pairs in a one-to-one function, we obtain a relation in which no two ordered pairs have the same first coordinate — by definition, this relation must be a function. In other words, every one-to-one function has an inverse that is itself a function. Because of this, we can use function notation to represent that inverse.

> ⟦Δ≠Σ⟧   *Inverse Function Notation*
>
> If $f(x)$ is a one-to-one function, then the inverse of f is also a function and can be denoted by $f^{-1}(x)$.

Note The notation f^{-1} does not represent the reciprocal of f. That is, the -1 in this notation is not an exponent. The notation f^{-1} is defined as representing the inverse function for a one-to-one function.

To illustrate, in Example 2 we found that the inverse of $f(x) = 2x - 3$ was the function $y = \frac{x+3}{2}$. We can write this inverse function with inverse function notation as

$$f^{-1}(x) = \frac{x + 3}{2}$$

On the other hand, the inverse of the function in Example 2 is not itself a function, so we do not use the notation $f^{-1}(x)$ to represent it.

 EXAMPLE 4   Find the inverse of $g(x) = \dfrac{x - 4}{x - 2}$.

SOLUTION   To find the inverse for g, we begin by replacing $g(x)$ with y to obtain

$$y = \frac{x - 4}{x - 2} \qquad \text{The original function}$$

To find an equation for the inverse, we exchange x and y.

$$x = \frac{y - 4}{y - 2} \qquad \text{The inverse of the original function}$$

To solve for y, we first multiply each side by $y - 2$ to obtain

$$x(y - 2) = y - 4$$

$$xy - 2x = y - 4 \qquad \text{Distributive property}$$

$$xy - y = 2x - 4 \qquad \text{Collect all terms containing } y \text{ on the left side}$$

$$y(x - 1) = 2x - 4 \qquad \text{Factor } y \text{ from each term on the left side}$$

$$y = \frac{2x - 4}{x - 1} \qquad \text{Divide each side by } x - 1$$

Because our original function is one-to-one, as verified by the graph in Figure 4, its inverse is also a function. Therefore, we can use inverse function notation to write

$$g^{-1}(x) = \frac{2x - 4}{x - 1}$$

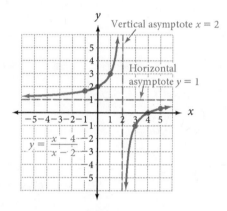

FIGURE 4

Graphing the Inverse Function

EXAMPLE 5   Graph the function $y = 2^x$ and its inverse $x = 2^y$.

SOLUTION   We graphed $y = 2^x$ in the preceding section. We simply reflect its graph about the line $y = x$ to obtain the graph of its inverse $x = 2^y$.

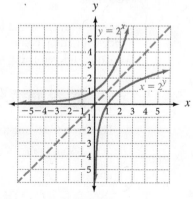

FIGURE 5

As you can see from the graph, $x = 2^y$ is a function. We do not have the mathematical tools to solve this equation for y, however. Therefore, we are unable to use the inverse function notation to represent this function. In the next section, we will give a definition that solves this problem. For now, we simply leave the equation as $x = 2^y$.

Inverses and Composition

One of the most powerful applications of an inverse function occurs when we perform function composition with a function and its inverse. Consider the following example.

EXAMPLE 6   Given $f(x) = 2x - 3$ and $f^{-1}(x) = \dfrac{x + 3}{2}$, find $(f^{-1} \circ f)(x)$ and $(f \circ f^{-1})(x)$.

SOLUTION

$$(f^{-1} \circ f)(x) = f^{-1}[f(x)]$$

$$= f^{-1}(2x - 3)$$

$$= \frac{2x - 3 + 3}{2}$$

$$= \frac{2x}{2}$$

$$= x$$

$$(f \circ f^{-1})(x) = f[f^{-1}(x)]$$

$$= f\left(\frac{x + 3}{2}\right)$$

$$= 2\left(\frac{x + 3}{2}\right) - 3$$

$$= x + 3 - 3$$

$$= x$$

Notice that in both cases the result is x, which was our input into both composition functions.

Because a function and its inverse "undo" each other, when we use them together under function composition the second function reverses whatever the first function did, returning us to our original value.

PROPERTY   *Composition of Inverses*

For any one-to-one function $f(x)$ and its inverse function $f^{-1}(x)$,

$$(f \circ f^{-1})(x) = x \qquad \text{for all } x \text{ in the domain of } f^{-1}(x)$$

and

$$(f^{-1} \circ f)(x) = x \qquad \text{for all } x \text{ in the domain of } f(x)$$

We can use this property to identify functions that are inverses of each other. Given functions $f(x)$ and $g(x)$, if $(f \circ g)(x) = x$ and $(g \circ f)(x) = x$, then f and g *must* be inverses. That is, $g(x) = f^{-1}(x)$ and $f(x) = g^{-1}(x)$.

EXAMPLE 7   Show that $f(x) = \dfrac{x}{x+2}$ and $g(x) = \dfrac{2x}{1-x}$ are inverses.

SOLUTION   We must show $(f \circ g)(x) = x$ and $(g \circ f)(x) = x$.

$$(f \circ g)(x) = f[g(x)]$$

$$= f\left(\frac{2x}{1-x}\right)$$

$$= \frac{\dfrac{2x}{1-x}}{\dfrac{2x}{1-x} + 2}$$

$$= \frac{2x}{2x + 2(1-x)} \qquad \text{Multiply numerator and}$$
$$\phantom{= \frac{2x}{2x + 2(1-x)}} \qquad \text{denominator by } 1-x$$

$$= \frac{2x}{2x + 2 - 2x}$$

$$= \frac{2x}{2}$$

$$= x$$

Also,

$$(g \circ f)(x) = g[f(x)]$$

$$= g\left(\frac{x}{x+2}\right)$$

$$= \frac{2\left(\dfrac{x}{x+2}\right)}{1 - \dfrac{x}{x+2}}$$

$$= \frac{2x}{x+2-x} \qquad \text{Multiply numerator and}$$
$$\phantom{= \frac{2x}{x+2-x}} \qquad \text{denominator by } x+2$$

$$= \frac{2x}{2}$$

$$= x$$

Because both compositions simplify to x, the functions must be inverses.

Functions, Relations, and Inverses—A Summary

Here is a summary of some of the things we know about functions, relations, and their inverses:

1. Every function is a relation, but not every relation is a function.

2. Every function has an inverse, but only one-to-one functions have inverses that are also functions.

3. The domain of a function is the range of its inverse, and the range of a function is the domain of its inverse.

4. If $f(x)$ is a one-to-one function, then we can use the notation $f^{-1}(x)$ to represent its inverse function.

5. The graph of a function and its inverse have symmetry about the line $y = x$.

6. If (a, b) belongs to the function f, then the point (b, a) belongs to its inverse.

7. For a function $f(x)$ and its inverse function $f^{-1}(x)$, $(f \circ f^{-1})(x) = x$ and $(f^{-1} \circ f)(x) = x$.

Getting Ready for Class

After reading through the preceding section, respond in your own words and in complete sentences.

A. What is the inverse of a function?

B. What is the relationship between the graph of a function and the graph of its inverse?

C. Explain why only one-to-one functions have inverses that are also functions.

D. Describe the vertical line test, and explain the difference between the vertical line test and the horizontal line test.

Find the inverse of each function, and then determine whether the inverse itself is a function or not.

1. $\{(1, 0), (2, 1), (3, 2), (4, 3)\}$ **2.** $\{(-2, 3), (-1, 2), (0, 1), (1, -1)\}$

3. $\{(-4, 3), (-2, -1), (1, 3), (3, -2)\}$ **4.** $\{(5, 1), (5, -1), (6, 2), (6, -2)\}$

5. $\{(-3, 4), (0, 4), (3, 4)\}$ **6.** $\{(-3, -3), (0, 0), (3, 3)\}$

For each of the following relations, sketch the graph of the relation and its inverse, and write an equation for the inverse.

7. $y = 2x - 1$ **8.** $y = 3x + 1$ **9.** $y = x^2 - 3$

10. $y = x^2 + 1$ **11.** $y = x^2 - 2x - 3$ **12.** $y = x^2 + 2x - 3$

13. $y = 3^x$ **14.** $y = \left(\dfrac{1}{2}\right)^x$ **15.** $y = 4$

16. $y = -2$ **17.** $y = \dfrac{1}{2}x^3$ **18.** $y = x^3 - 2$

19. $y = \dfrac{1}{2}x + 2$ **20.** $y = \dfrac{1}{3}x - 1$ **21.** $y = \sqrt{x + 2}$

22. $y = \sqrt{x} + 2$

Determine if the following functions are one-to-one.

23.

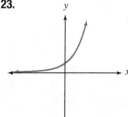

24.

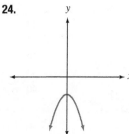

25.

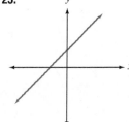

26.

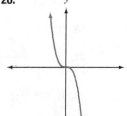

27.

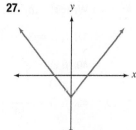

28.

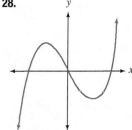

29.

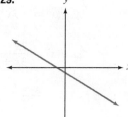

30.

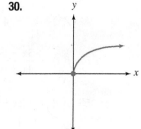

31.

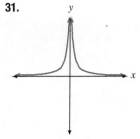

32.

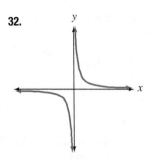

Could the following tables of values represent ordered pairs from one-to-one functions? Explain your answer.

33.

x	y
−2	5
−1	4
0	3
1	4
2	5

34.

x	y
1.5	0.1
2.0	0.2
2.5	0.3
3.0	0.4
3.5	0.5

35.

x	y
0	63
10	35
20	16
30	7
40	4

36.

x	y
0	1
2.5	−1
5	1
7.5	−1
10	1

For each of the following one-to-one functions, find the equation of the inverse. Write the inverse using the notation $f^{-1}(x)$.

37. $f(x) = 3x - 1$ **38.** $f(x) = 2x - 5$ **39.** $f(x) = x^3$

40. $f(x) = x^3 - 2$ **41.** $f(x) = \dfrac{x-3}{x-1}$ **42.** $f(x) = \dfrac{x-2}{x-3}$

43. $f(x) = \dfrac{x-3}{4}$ **44.** $f(x) = \dfrac{x+7}{2}$ **45.** $f(x) = \dfrac{1}{2}x - 3$

46. $f(x) = \dfrac{1}{3}x + 1$ **47.** $f(x) = \dfrac{2}{3}x - 3$ **48.** $f(x) = -\dfrac{1}{2}x + 4$

49. $f(x) = x^3 - 4$ **50.** $f(x) = -3x^3 + 2$ **51.** $f(x) = \dfrac{4x-3}{2x+1}$

52. $f(x) = \dfrac{3x-5}{4x+3}$ **53.** $f(x) = \dfrac{2x+1}{3x+1}$ **54.** $f(x) = \dfrac{3x+2}{5x+1}$

55. If $f(x) = 3x - 2$, then $f^{-1}(x) = \dfrac{x+2}{3}$. Use these two functions to find

   a. $f(2)$ **b.** $f^{-1}(2)$ **c.** $f[f^{-1}(2)]$

   d. $f^{-1}[f(2)]$ **e.** $(f \circ f^{-1})(x)$ **f.** $(f^{-1} \circ f)(x)$

56. If $f(x) = \dfrac{1}{2}x + 5$, then $f^{-1}(x) = 2x - 10$. Use these two functions to find

  a. $f(-4)$ **b.** $f^{-1}(-4)$ **c.** $f[f^{-1}(-4)]$

  d. $f^{-1}[f(-4)]$ **e.** $(f \circ f^{-1})(x)$ **f.** $(f^{-1} \circ f)(x)$

57. Let $f(x) = \dfrac{1}{x}$, and find $f^{-1}(x)$.

58. Let $f(x) = \dfrac{a}{x}$, and find $f^{-1}(x)$. (a is a real number constant.)

Sketch the graph of the inverse of each function.

59.

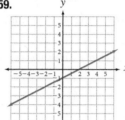

60.

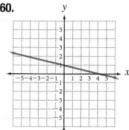

61.

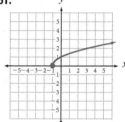

62.

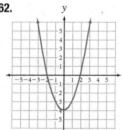

63.

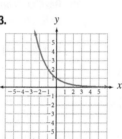

64.

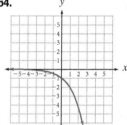

65.

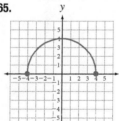

66.

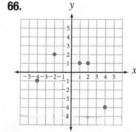

Use function composition to show that each pair of functions are inverses. That is, show $(f \circ g)(x) = x$ and $(g \circ f)(x) = x$.

67. $f(x) = 3x + 4, g(x) = \dfrac{x - 4}{3}$ **68.** $f(x) = \dfrac{1}{3}x + 2, g(x) = 3x - 6$

69. $f(x) = \sqrt{x + 4}, g(x) = x^2 - 4$ **70.** $f(x) = x^3 + 5, g(x) = \sqrt[3]{x - 5}$
  $(x \geq 0)$

71. $f(x) = \dfrac{1}{x + 1}, g(x) = \dfrac{1 - x}{x}$ **72.** $f(x) = \dfrac{x + 2}{x - 3}, g(x) = \dfrac{3x + 2}{x - 1}$

Applying the Concepts

Inverse Functions in Words Inverses may also be found by *inverse reasoning*. For example, to find the inverse of $f(x) = 3x + 2$, first list, in order, the operations done to variable x:

Step 1: Multiply by 3.
Step 2: Add 2.

Then, to find the inverse, simply apply the inverse operations, in reverse order, to the variable x. That is:

Step 3:   Subtract 2.
Step 4:   Divide by 3.

The inverse function then becomes $f^{-1}(x) = \frac{x-2}{3}$.

73. Use this method of "inverse reasoning" to find the inverse of the *function* $f(x) = \frac{x}{7} - 2$.

74. Inverse Functions in Words Use *inverse reasoning* to find the following inverses:

a. $f(x) = 2x + 7$

b. $f(x) = \sqrt{x} - 9$

c. $f(x) = x^3 - 4$

d. $f(x) = \sqrt{x^3 - 4}$

75. Reading Tables Evaluate each of the following functions using the functions defined by Tables 1 and 2.

a. $f[g(-3)]$ **b.** $g[f(-6)]$ **c.** $g[f(2)]$

d. $f[g(3)]$ **e.** $f[g(-2)]$ **f.** $g[f(3)]$

What can you conclude about the relationship between functions f and g?

TABLE 1	
x	$f(x)$
-6	3
2	-3
3	-2
6	4

TABLE 2	
x	$g(x)$
-3	2
-2	3
3	-6
4	6

76. Reading Tables Use the functions defined in Tables 1 and 2 in Problem 75 to answer the following questions.

a. What are the domain and range of f?

b. What are the domain and range of g?

c. How are the domain and range of f related to the domain and range of g?

d. Is f a one-to-one function?

e. Is g a one-to-one function?

77. **Social Security** A function that models the billions of dollars of Social Security payment (as shown in the chart) per year is $s(t) = 16t + 249.4$, where t is time in years since 1990 (U.S. Census Bureau).

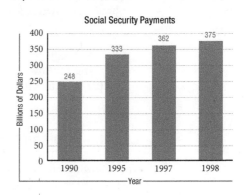

Social Security Payments

a. Use the model to estimate the amount of Social Security payments to be paid in 2020.

b. Write the inverse of the function.

c. Using the inverse function, estimate the year in which payments will reach $1 trillion.

78. **Families** The function for the percentage of one-parent families (as shown in the following chart) is $f(x) = 0.417x + 24$, when x is the time in years since 1990. *(Source:* U.S. Census Bureau)

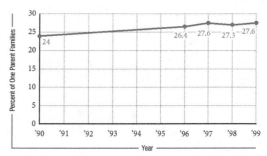

a. Use the function to predict the percentage of families with one parent in the year 2020.

b. Determine the inverse of the function, and estimate the year in which approximately 50% of the families are one-parent families.

79. **Speed** The fastest type of plane, a rocket plane, can travel at a speed of 4,520 miles per hour. The function $f(m) = \frac{22m}{15}$ converts miles per hour, m, to feet per second. *(Source:* World Book Encyclopedia)

a. Use the function to convert the speed of the rocket plane to feet per second.

b. Write the inverse of the function.

c. Using the inverse function, convert 2 feet per second to miles per hour.

80. **Speed** A Lockheed SR-71A airplane set a world record (as reported by Air Force Armament Museum in 1996) with an absolute speed record of 2,193.167 miles per hour. The function $s(h) = 0.4468424h$ converts miles per hour, h, to meters per second, s.

    a. What is the absolute speed of the Lockheed SR-71A in meters per second?

    b. What is the inverse of this function?

    c. Using the inverse function, determine the speed of an airplane in miles per hour that flies 150 meters per second.

Learning Objectives Assessment

The following problems can be used to help assess if you have successfully met the learning objectives for this section.

81. If $(2, -5)$ is an element of function f, which ordered pair is an element of the inverse of f?

    a. $(-2, 5)$ **b.** $(-5, 2)$ **c.** $(-2, -5)$ **d.** $(2, 5)$

82. Graph the inverse of the function shown in the figure below.

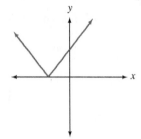

  a.

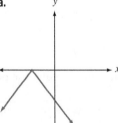

  b.

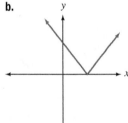

  c.

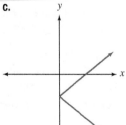

  d.

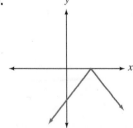

83. If $f(x) = 4x + 12$, find $f^{-1}(x)$.

 a. $f^{-1}(x) = \dfrac{1}{4}x - 3$ **b.** $f^{-1}(x) = \dfrac{1}{4}x - 12$

 c. $f^{-1}(x) = \dfrac{1}{4x + 12}$ **d.** $f^{-1}(x) = 4y + 12$

84. Which of the following is a one-to-one function?

 a. 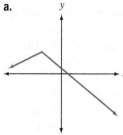   **b.**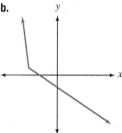

 c. 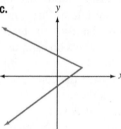   **d.**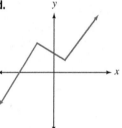

85. Which of the following would help prove that f and g are inverse functions?

 a. $g(f(x)) = x$ **b.** $f(g(x)) = 1$

 c. $f(x) = -g(x)$ **d.** $g(x) = \dfrac{1}{f(x)}$

Getting Ready for the Next Section

Simplify.

86. 3^{-2} **87.** 2^3

Solve.

88. $2 = 3x$ **89.** $3 = 5x$ **90.** $4 = x^3$ **91.** $12 = x^2$

Fill in the boxes to make each statement true.

92. $8 = 2^{\square}$ **93.** $27 = 3^{\square}$

94. $10,000 = 10^{\square}$ **95.** $1,000 = 10^{\square}$

96. $81 = 3^{\square}$ **97.** $81 = 9^{\square}$

98. $6 = 6^{\square}$ **99.** $1 = 5^{\square}$

SPOTLIGHT ON SUCCESS *Student Instructor Shelby*

The price of success is hard work, dedication to the job at hand, and the determination that whether we win or lose, we have applied the best of ourselves to the task at hand.
— *Vince Lombardi*

My earliest memory of math is from elementary school, having to continuously take the division and times tables test because I couldn't finish it in the allotted time. I have never been naturally gifted at math, but I enjoy a challenge. I wouldn't allow my setbacks to stop me from succeeding in my classes. As a high school freshman I struggled in my geometry class, and as a senior, I thrived in my AP Calculus class. The difference in those short four years was the effort I put in, as well as having great teachers, who provided the necessary knowledge and support along the way.

However, to continue to thrive in math, I had to realize that my success wasn't solely in the hands of the teacher. I saw students fail classes taught by some of the best teachers on campus. It all stemmed from the personal goals each student held. There were multiple times when I told myself, "You can do this. You can learn the concepts." I'm not sure I would have moved past prealgebra without those personal words of encouragement.

Having confidence in yourself is necessary to be successful in all aspects of life. It's easy to give up on something that doesn't come naturally, but the reward of achieving something you thought to be impossible is worth the hardship.

Logarithms and Logarithmic Functions

Learning Objectives

In this section, we will learn how to:

1. Write an exponential expression in logarithmic form.
2. Write a logarithmic expression in exponential form.
3. Evaluate a logarithm.
4. Graph a logarithmic function.

Introduction

In March 2011, a major earthquake occurred off the coast of Japan. The sudden displacement of water in the Pacific Ocean caused a large tsunami, resulting in massive destruction and loss of life. The USGS (United States Geological Survey) reported the strength of the quake by indicating that it measured 9.0 on the Richter scale. For comparison, Table 1 gives the Richter magnitude of a number of other earthquakes.

Although the size of the numbers in the table do not seem to be very different, the intensity of the earthquakes they measure can be very different. For example, the 2004 earthquake off the coast of Northern Sumatra was 10 times stronger than the 1985 earthquake in Mexico City. The reason behind this is that the Richter scale is a *logarithmic scale*.

TABLE 1 Earthquakes

Year	Earthquake	Richter Magnitude
1985	Mexico City	8.1
1994	Northridge	6.6
2004	Northern Sumatra	9.1
2008	Eastern Sichuan, China	7.9
2010	Haiti	7.0
2011	Honshu, Japan	9.0

In this section, we start our work with logarithms, which will give you an understanding of the Richter scale. Let's begin.

In Section 12.1 we introduced exponential functions

$$f(x) = b^x \qquad b > 0, b \neq 1$$

From our work in that section, we know that the graph of an exponential function for any base will pass the horizontal line test. This means that exponential function are one-to-one and have an inverse that is also a function.

To find the inverse, we exchange x and y:

Exponential function   Inverse function
$$y = b^x \qquad \longrightarrow \qquad x = b^y$$

To isolate the y in the equation on the right, we must define a new notation.

> **(def) DEFINITION**   *logarithm*
>
> The expression $y = \log_b x$ is read "y is the logarithm to the base b of x" and is equivalent to the expression
>
> $$x = b^y \qquad b > 0, b \neq 1$$
>
> In words, we say "$\log_b x$ is the exponent we raise b to in order to get x."

Notation   When an expression is in the form $x = b^y$, it is said to be in *exponential form*. On the other hand, if an expression is in the form $y = \log_b x$, it is said to be in *logarithmic form*.

Here are some equivalent statements written in both forms.

Exponential Form		Logarithmic Form
$8 = 2^3$	$\Leftrightarrow$	$\log_2 8 = 3$
$25 = 5^2$	$\Leftrightarrow$	$\log_5 25 = 2$
$0.1 = 10^{-1}$	$\Leftrightarrow$	$\log_{10} 0.1 = -1$
$\frac{1}{8} = 2^{-3}$	$\Leftrightarrow$	$\log_2 \frac{1}{8} = -3$
$r = z^s$	$\Leftrightarrow$	$\log_z r = s$

Evaluating Logarithms

One of the most important things to remember about logarithms is that a logarithm always represents an exponent. To evaluate a logarithm means to find the exponent that it represents. We illustrate this with the following examples.

EXAMPLE 1   Evaluate: $\log_3 9$.

SOLUTION   We must find the exponent of 3 that will result in 9.

$$3^? = 9$$

Since the correct exponent is 2, we have $\log_3 9 = 2$.

EXAMPLES

Note   Remember that a rational exponent can be used to represent a root. We used this fact in Examples 5 and 6:

$$5 = \sqrt{25} = 25^{1/2}$$
$$\frac{1}{4} = \frac{1}{\sqrt[3]{64}} = 64^{-1/3}$$

	To find	We ask	And get		
2.	$\log_2 \frac{1}{8}$	$2^? = \frac{1}{8}$	$? = -3$	so	$\log_2 \frac{1}{8} = -3$
3.	$\log_7 7$	$7^? = 7$	$? = 1$	so	$\log_7 7 = 1$
4.	$\log_9 1$	$9^? = 1$	$? = 0$	so	$\log_9 1 = 0$
5.	$\log_{25} 5$	$25^? = 5$	$? = \frac{1}{2}$	so	$\log_{25} 5 = \frac{1}{2}$
6.	$\log_{64} \frac{1}{4}$	$64^? = \frac{1}{4}$	$? = -\frac{1}{3}$	so	$\log_{64} \frac{1}{4} = -\frac{1}{3}$

EXAMPLE 7   Find: $\log_8 16$.

SOLUTION   We must find an exponent y such that

$$8^y = 16$$

Because $8 = 2^3$ and $16 = 2^4$, we have

$$16 = (\sqrt[3]{8})^4 = 8^{4/3}$$

Therefore $\log_8 16 = \dfrac{4}{3}$.

Logarithmic Functions

Earlier in this section we found that the inverse of the exponential function $f(x) = b^x$ is given by the equation $x = b^y$. Using the logarithmic form of this equation now allows us to make the following definition.

> **(def) DEFINITION**   *logarithmic function*
>
> A *logarithmic function* is any function that can be written in the form
>
> $$f(x) = \log_b x$$
>
> where b is a positive real number other than 1.

We also state the following property, which summarizes the relationship between exponential functions and logarithmic functions.

> **[Δ≠Σ] PROPERTY**
>
> For a given base b ($b > 0$, $b \neq 1$), the exponential function with base b and the logarithmic function with base b are inverses. That is,
>
> $$\text{if} \quad f(x) = b^x \quad \text{then} \quad f^{-1}(x) = \log_b x$$

The exponential function $y = b^x$ has a domain of all real numbers and a range of all positive real numbers. Because they are inverses, the roles will be reversed for the logarithmic function. That is, the function $y = \log_b x$ has a domain of all positive real numbers and a range of all real numbers. It is important to keep in mind that the input to a basic logarithmic function must be a positive number.

Graphing Logarithmic Functions

One way to graph a logarithmic function is to use the graph of an exponential function and the fact that the graphs of inverse functions have symmetry about the line $y = x$. Here's an example to illustrate.

EXAMPLE 8   Graph: $f(x) = \log_2 x$.

SOLUTION   The logarithmic function $y = \log_2 x$ is the inverse of the exponential function $y = 2^x$. The graph of $y = 2^x$ was given in Figure 2 of Section 12.1. We simply reflect the graph of $y = 2^x$ about the line $y = x$ to get the graph of $f(x) = \log_2 x$. (See Figure 1.)

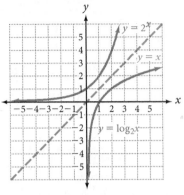

FIGURE 1

It is apparent from the graph that $y = \log_2 x$ is a function, because no vertical line will cross its graph in more than one place. Note also that the graph of $y = \log_2 x$ appears to the right of the y-axis, indicating that the domain consists of positive values of x only. There is an x-intercept at the point $(1, 0)$.

Finally, we can see in Figure 1 that the graph of the logarithmic function approaches the y-axis but never intersects it. This means the logarithmic function has a vertical asymptote at $x = 0$.

Here is a summary of the behavior of the graph of a logarithmic function.

> ### $|\Delta \neq \Sigma|$ *Graphs of Logarithmic Functions*
>
> The graph of $f(x) = \log_b x$, for $b > 0$ and $b \neq 1$, has the following:
>
> > domain = $\{x \mid x > 0\}$
> > range = all real numbers
> > x-intercept = $(1, 0)$
> > vertical asymptote at $x = 0$

Another way to graph a logarithmic function that is more direct (not requiring we graph an exponential function first) is to simply write the equation for the function in exponential form and then make a table of ordered pairs. We illustrate this procedure in our next example.

 EXAMPLE 9   Graph: $f(x) = \log_{1/2} x$.

SOLUTION   Writing the equation $y = \log_{1/2} x$ in exponential form, we have

$$x = \left(\frac{1}{2}\right)^y$$

We can now choose values of y and evaluate the exponent to get the corresponding values of x.

y	$x = \left(\frac{1}{2}\right)^y$	x	Solutions
-2	$x = \left(\frac{1}{2}\right)^{-2}$	4	$(4, -2)$
-1	$x = \left(\frac{1}{2}\right)^{-1}$	2	$(2, -1)$
0	$x = \left(\frac{1}{2}\right)^{0}$	1	$(1, 0)$
1	$x = \left(\frac{1}{2}\right)^{1}$	$\frac{1}{2}$	$\left(\frac{1}{2}, 1\right)$
2	$x = \left(\frac{1}{2}\right)^{2}$	$\frac{1}{4}$	$\left(\frac{1}{4}, 2\right)$

Plotting these points gives us the graph shown in Figure 2.

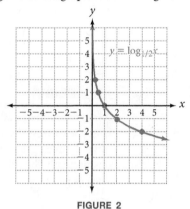

FIGURE 2

This graph represents the inverse of the exponential decay function $y = \left(\frac{1}{2}\right)^x$.

EXAMPLE 10   Find the domain of $f(x) = \log_4 (3 - x)$.

SOLUTION   Because a logarithmic function is only defined for a positive value, we need the expression $3 - x$ to be positive. We can express this as an inequality and solve for x.

$$3 - x > 0 \qquad \text{\small 3 - x must be positive}$$

$$-x > -3 \qquad \text{\small Subtract 3 from both sides}$$

$$x < 3 \qquad \text{\small Multiply both sides by } -1$$

The domain is $\{x \mid x < 3\}$.

EXAMPLE 11   Sketch the graph of $f(x) = \log_2 (x + 4)$ and state the vertical asymptote.

SOLUTION   We can use transformations to sketch the graph. The graph of $y = \log_2 x$ is shown in Figure 1. To obtain the graph of $f(x) = \log_2 (x + 4)$, we must translate this graph 4 units to the left. Figure 3 shows how this is done.

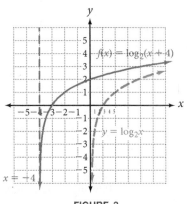

FIGURE 3

As you can see, the vertical asymptote translates 4 units to the left as well, and has the equation $x = -4$. ▨

Application

As we mentioned in the introduction to this section, one application of logarithms is in measuring the magnitude of an earthquake. If an earthquake has a shock wave T times greater than the smallest shock wave that can be measured on a seismograph, then the magnitude M of the earthquake, as measured on the Richter scale, is given by the formula

$$M = \log_{10} T$$

(When we talk about the size of a shock wave, we are talking about its amplitude. The amplitude of a wave is half the difference between its highest point and its lowest point.)

To illustrate the discussion, an earthquake that produces a shock wave that is 10,000 times greater than the smallest shock wave measurable on a seismograph will have a magnitude M on the Richter scale of

$$M = \log_{10} 10,000 = 4$$

▨ **EXAMPLE 12**   If an earthquake has a magnitude of $M = 5$ on the Richter scale, what can you say about the size of its shock wave?

SOLUTION   To answer this question, we put $M = 5$ into the formula $M = \log_{10} T$ to obtain

$$5 = \log_{10} T$$

Writing this expression in exponential form, we have

$$T = 10^5 = 100,000$$

We can say that an earthquake that measures 5 on the Richter scale has a shock wave 100,000 times greater than the smallest shock wave measurable on a seismograph. ▨

From Example 12 and the discussion that preceded it, we find that an earthquake of magnitude 5 has a shock wave that is 10 times greater than an earthquake of magnitude 4, because 100,000 is 10 times 10,000.

Getting Ready for Class

After reading through the preceding section, respond in your own words and in complete sentences.

A. What is a logarithm?

B. What is the relationship between $y = 2^x$ and $y = \log_2 x$? How are their graphs related?

C. Will the graph of $y = \log_b x$ ever appear in the second or third quadrants? Explain why or why not.

D. Explain why $\log_2 0 = x$ has no solution for x.

Write each of the following expressions in logarithmic form.

1. $2^4 = 16$ **2.** $3^2 = 9$ **3.** $125 = 5^3$ **4.** $16 = 4^2$

5. $0.01 = 10^{-2}$ **6.** $0.001 = 10^{-3}$ **7.** $2^{-5} = \dfrac{1}{32}$ **8.** $4^{-2} = \dfrac{1}{16}$

9. $\left(\dfrac{1}{2}\right)^{-3} = 8$ **10.** $\left(\dfrac{1}{3}\right)^{-2} = 9$ **11.** $27 = 3^3$ **12.** $81 = 3^4$

Write each of the following expressions in exponential form.

13. $\log_{10} 100 = 2$ **14.** $\log_2 8 = 3$ **15.** $\log_2 64 = 6$

16. $\log_2 32 = 5$ **17.** $\log_8 1 = 0$ **18.** $\log_9 9 = 1$

19. $\log_{10} 0.001 = -3$ **20.** $\log_{10} 0.0001 = -4$ **21.** $\log_6 36 = 2$

22. $\log_7 49 = 2$ **23.** $\log_5 \dfrac{1}{25} = -2$ **24.** $\log_3 \dfrac{1}{81} = -4$

Evaluate each of the following.

25. $\log_2 16$ **26.** $\log_3 27$ **27.** $\log_{10} 1{,}000$ **28.** $\log_{10} 10{,}000$

29. $\log_3 3$ **30.** $\log_4 4$ **31.** $\log_5 1$ **32.** $\log_{10} 1$

33. $\log_8 \dfrac{1}{8}$ **34.** $\log_3 \dfrac{1}{3}$ **35.** $\log_4 \dfrac{1}{16}$ **36.** $\log_2 \dfrac{1}{32}$

37. $\log_{10} 0.01$ **38.** $\log_{10} 0.0001$ **39.** $\log_{16} 4$ **40.** $\log_{81} 9$

41. $\log_{64} 4$ **42.** $\log_{16} 2$ **43.** $\log_{25} 125$ **44.** $\log_9 27$

45. $\log_4 8$ **46.** $\log_{100} 1000$ **47.** $\log_{32} 16$ **48.** $\log_{64} 16$

Sketch the graph of each of the following logarithmic functions.

49. $y = \log_3 x$ **50.** $y = \log_{1/2} x$ **51.** $y = \log_{1/3} x$ **52.** $y = \log_4 x$

53. $y = \log_5 x$ **54.** $y = \log_{1/5} x$ **55.** $y = \log_{10} x$ **56.** $y = \log_{1/4} x$

Fore each function $y = f(x)$, state the inverse function $y = f^{-1}(x)$.

57. $f(x) = \log_4 x$ **58.** $f(x) = \log_{1/5} x$ **59.** $f(x) = \left(\dfrac{1}{8}\right)^x$ **60.** $f(x) = 10^x$

Find the domain of each logarithmic function.

61. $f(x) = \log_9 x$ **62.** $f(x) = \log_{1/9} x$

63. $f(x) = \log_5 (x + 6)$ **64.** $f(x) = \log_2 (x - 5)$

65. $f(x) = \log_3 (1 - x)$ **66.** $f(x) = \log_{1/3} (4 - x)$

67. $f(x) = \log_{1/2} (2x + 3)$ **68.** $f(x) = \log_{10} (3x - 2)$

Use transformations to sketch the graph of each function. Then state the vertical asymptote.

69. $f(x) = \log_2 (x - 3)$ **70.** $f(x) = \log_3 (x + 2)$

71. $f(x) = 3 + \log_2 x$ **72.** $f(x) = -2 + \log_3 x$

73. $f(x) = -2 \log_4 x$ **74.** $f(x) = -\dfrac{1}{2} \log_5 x$

Each of the following graphs has an equation of the form $y = b^x$ or $y = \log_b x$. Find the equation for each graph.

75.

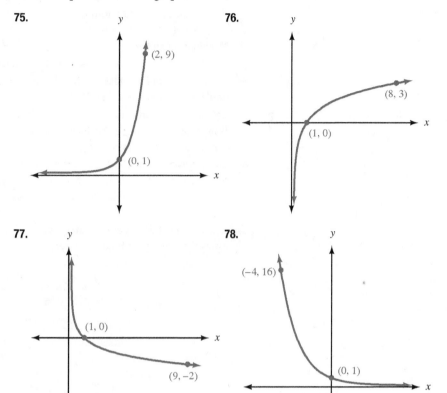

76.

77.

78.

Applying the Concepts

79. Metric System The metric system uses logical and systematic prefixes for multiplication. For instance, to multiply a unit by 100, the prefix "hecto" is applied, so a hectometer is equal to 100 meters. For each of the prefixes in the following table find the logarithm, base 10, of the multiplying factor.

Prefix	Multiplying Factor	$\log_{10}$ (Multiplying Factor)
Nano	0.000 000 001	
Micro	0.000 001	
Deci	0.1	
Giga	1,000,000,000	
Peta	1,000,000,000,000,000	

80. **Domain and Range** Use the graphs of $y = 2^x$ and $y = \log_2 x$ shown in Figure 1 of this section to find the domain and range for each function. Explain how the domain and range found for $y = 2^x$ relate to the domain and range found for $y = \log_2 x$.

81. **Magnitude of an Earthquake** Find the magnitude M of an earthquake with a shock wave that measures $T = 100$ on a seismograph.

82. **Magnitude of an Earthquake** Find the magnitude M of an earthquake with a shock wave that measures $T = 100,000$ on a seismograph.

83. **Shock Wave** If an earthquake has a magnitude of 8 on the Richter scale, how many times greater is its shock wave than the smallest shock wave measurable on a seismograph?

84. **Shock Wave** If the 1999 Colombia earthquake had a magnitude of 6 on the Richter scale, how many times greater was its shock wave than the smallest shock wave measurable on a seismograph?

Earthquake The table below categorizes earthquake by the magnitude and identifies the average annual occurrence.

Earthquakes		
Descriptor	Magnitude	Average Annual Occurrence
Great	≥ 8.0	1
Major	$7 - 7.9$	18
Strong	$6 - 6.9$	120
Moderate	$5 - 5.9$	800
Light	$4 - 4.9$	6,200
Minor	$3 - 3.9$	49,000
Very Minor	$2 - 2.9$	1,000 per day
Very Minor	$1 - 1.9$	8,000 per day

Source: USGS National Earthquake Information.

85. What is the average number of earthquakes that occur per year when the number of times the associated shockwave is greater than the smallest measurable shockwave, T, is 1,000,000?

86. What is the average number of earthquakes that occur per year when $T = 1,000,000$ or greater?

Learning Objectives Assessment

The following problems can be used to help assess if you have successfully met the learning objectives for this section.

87. Write $5^x = 100$ in logarithmic form.

   a. $\log_5 100 = x$ **b.** $\log_{100} 5 = x$ **c.** $\log_x 5 = 100$ **d.** $\log_5 x = 100$

88. Write $\log_{1/3} 81 = -4$ in exponential form.

   a. $(-4)^{1/3} = 81$ **b.** $\frac{1}{3}(81) = -4$ **c.** $81^{1/3} = -4$ **d.** $\left(\frac{1}{3}\right)^{-4} = 81$

89. Evaluate: $\log_6 \dfrac{1}{36}$.

   a. -2 **b.** $-\dfrac{1}{2}$ **c.** 2 **d.** $\dfrac{1}{2}$

90. Graph: $f(x) = \log_6 x$.

  a.

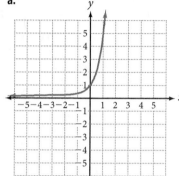

  b.

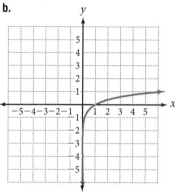

  c.

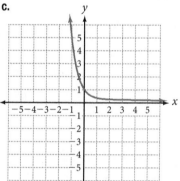

  d.

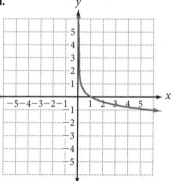

Getting Ready for the Next Section

Simplify.

91. $8^{2/3}$

92. $27^{2/3}$

Solve.

93. $(x + 2)(x) = 2^3$

94. $(x + 3)(x) = 2^2$

95. $\dfrac{x - 2}{x + 1} = 9$

96. $\dfrac{x + 1}{x - 4} = 25$

Write in exponential form.

97. $\log_2 [(x + 2)(x)] = 3$

98. $\log_4 [x(x - 6)] = 2$

99. $\log_3 \left(\dfrac{x - 2}{x + 1} \right) = 4$

100. $\log_3 \left(\dfrac{x - 1}{x - 4} \right) = 2$

Learning Objectives

In this section, we will learn how to:

1. Use properties of logarithms to evaluate logarithms.
2. Use properties of logarithms to expand a logarithm.
3. Use properties of logarithms to consolidate logarithmic expressions.

Introduction

If we search for a definition of the word *decibel*, we find the following: A unit used to express relative difference in power or intensity, usually between two acoustic or electric signals, equal to ten times the common logarithm of the ratio of the two levels.

Decibels	Comparable to
10	A light whisper
20	Quiet conversation
30	Normal conversation
40	Light traffic
50	Typewriter, loud conversation
60	Noisy office
70	Normal traffic, quiet train
80	Rock music, subway
90	Heavy traffic, thunder
100	Jet plane at takeoff

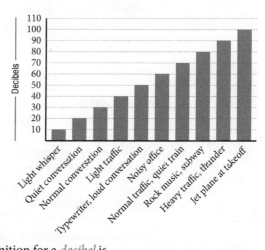

The precise definition for a *decibel* is

$$D = 10 \log_{10}\left(\frac{I}{I_0}\right)$$

where I is the intensity of the sound being measured, and I_0 is the intensity of the least audible sound. (Sound intensity is related to the amplitude of the sound wave that models the sound and is given in units of watts per meter^2.) In this section, we will see that the preceding formula can also be written as

$$D = 10(\log_{10} I - \log_{10} I_0)$$

The rules we use to rewrite expressions containing logarithms are called the *properties of logarithms.* There are seven of them.

Seven Properties of Logarithms

From our work in the previous section, we know that

$$\text{because} \quad b^0 = 1, \text{ we have} \quad \log_b 1 = 0$$

and

$$\text{because} \quad b^1 = b, \text{ we have} \quad \log_b b = 1$$

This leads us to our first two properties of logarithms. All seven properties assume b is a positive number other than 1.

 **PROPERTY**   *Property 1*

$$\log_b 1 = 0$$

In words: The logarithm of 1 is equal to 0.

 **PROPERTY**   *Property 2*

$$\log_b b = 1$$

In words: The logarithm of the base is equal to 1.

If you recall from Section 12.2, if $y = f(x)$ is a one-to-one function, then it has an inverse function $f^{-1}(x)$ and

$$(f \circ f^{-1})(x) = f(f^{-1}(x)) = x$$

and

$$(f^{-1} \circ f)(x) = f^{-1}(f(x)) = x$$

Because $f(x) = b^x$ is one-to-one and $f^{-1}(x) = \log_b x$, substituting these functions into the above properties of inverses gives us the following.

 **PROPERTY**   *Property 3*

$$b^{\log_b x} = x \quad (x > 0)$$

In words: A base raised to a logarithm of the same base "undo" each other.

PROPERTY   *Property 4*

$$\log_b(b^x) = x$$

In words: The logarithm of an exponential function of the same base "undo" each other.

VIDEO EXAMPLES

SECTION 12.4

EXAMPLES

1. $\log_{\sqrt{2}} 1 = 0$ Property 1

2. $\log_5 5 = 1$ Property 2

3. $\log_{10} 10^4 = 4$ Property 4

4. $17^{\log_{17} 2} = 2$ Property 3

EXAMPLE 5   Simplify: $\log_4 (\log_5 5)$.

SOLUTION   Because $\log_5 5 = 1$ (see Example 2), we have

$$\log_4 (\log_5 5) = \log_4 (1) \quad \text{Property 2}$$
$$= 0 \quad \text{Property 1}$$

EXAMPLE 6   Simplify: $\sqrt{6} \log_3 3^{\sqrt{2x}}$.

SOLUTION   By Property 4, we have

$$\sqrt{6} \log_3 3^{\sqrt{2x}} = \sqrt{6}(\sqrt{2x})$$
$$= \sqrt{12x}$$
$$= 2\sqrt{3x}$$

For our last three properties, x and y are both positive real numbers and r is any real number.

Note   The reason logarithms were invented in the early 1600s was because of these properties, which allow products, quotients, and powers to be performed using addition, subtraction, and multiplication.

PROPERTY   *Property 5*

$$\log_b(xy) = \log_b x + \log_b y$$

In words: The logarithm of a **product** is the **sum** of the logarithms.

PROPERTY   *Property 6*

$$\log_b\left(\frac{x}{y}\right) = \log_b x - \log_b y$$

In words: The logarithm of a **quotient** is the **difference** of the logarithms.

PROPERTY   *Property 7*

$$\log_b x^r = r \log_b x$$

In words: The logarithm of a number raised to a *power* is the *product* of the power and the logarithm of the number.

Proof of Property 5   To prove Property 5, we simply apply Property 3 and our knowledge of exponents:

$$b^{\log_b xy} = xy = (b^{\log_b x})(b^{\log_b y}) = b^{\log_b x + \log_b y}$$

Because the first and last expressions are equal and the bases are the same, the exponents $\log_b xy$ and $\log_b x + \log_b y$ must be equal. Therefore,

$$\log_b xy = \log_b x + \log_b y$$

The proofs of Properties 6 and 7 proceed in much the same manner, so we will omit them here. The examples that follow show how these last three properties can be used.

EXAMPLE 7   Simplify: $\log_5 \left(25 \cdot 5^{\sqrt{3}}\right)$.

SOLUTION   We must use Property 5 first, which will then allow us to use Property 4.

$$\log_5 \left(25 \cdot 5^{\sqrt{3}}\right) = \log_5 25 + \log_5 5^{\sqrt{3}} \qquad \text{Property 5}$$

$$= \log_5 25 + \sqrt{3} \qquad \text{Property 4}$$

$$= 2 + \sqrt{3} \qquad \log_5 25 = 2$$

EXAMPLE 8   Expand, using the properties of logarithms: $\log_5 \dfrac{3xy}{z}$

SOLUTION   Applying Property 6, we can write the quotient of $3xy$ and z in terms of a difference:

$$\log_5 \frac{3xy}{z} = \log_5 3xy - \log_5 z$$

Now we can apply Property 5 to the product $3xy$, writing it in terms of addition:

$$\log_5 \frac{3xy}{z} = \log_5 3 + \log_5 x + \log_5 y - \log_5 z$$

EXAMPLE 9   Expand, using the properties of logarithms:

$$\log_2 \frac{x^4}{\sqrt{y} \cdot z^3}$$

SOLUTION   We write $\sqrt{y}$ as $y^{1/2}$ and apply the properties:

$$\log_2 \frac{x^4}{\sqrt{y} \cdot z^3} = \log_2 \frac{x^4}{y^{1/2} z^3} \qquad \sqrt{y} = y^{1/2}$$

$$= \log_2 x^4 - \log_2(y^{1/2} \cdot z^3) \qquad \text{Property 6}$$

$$= \log_2 x^4 - (\log_2 y^{1/2} + \log_2 z^3) \qquad \text{Property 5}$$

$$= \log_2 x^4 - \log_2 y^{1/2} - \log_2 z^3 \qquad \begin{array}{l}\text{Remove parentheses}\\\text{and distribute } -1\end{array}$$

$$= 4 \log_2 x - \frac{1}{2} \log_2 y - 3 \log_2 z \qquad \text{Property 7}$$

EXAMPLE 10   Expand, using the properties of logarithms:

$$\log_4 \frac{(x+2)^3}{4x}$$

SOLUTION   We begin with Property 6 to write the quotient as a difference.

$$\log_4 \frac{(x+2)^3}{4x} = \log_4 (x+2)^3 - \log_4 (4x) \qquad \text{Property 6}$$

$$= 3 \log_4 (x+2) - \log_4 (4x) \qquad \text{Property 7}$$

$$= 3 \log_4 (x+2) - [\log_4 4 + \log_4 x] \qquad \text{Property 5}$$

$$= 3 \log_4 (x+2) - [1 + \log_4 x] \qquad \text{Property 2}$$

$$= 3 \log_4 (x+2) - 1 - \log_4 x \qquad \text{Distribute the } -1$$

⚠ COMMON MISTAKES

In Example 10, it is very tempting for students to want to further expand $\log_4 (x+2)$ as $\log_4 x + \log_4 2$. However, these two expressions are not equal! There is no property allowing us to expand the logarithm of a sum or difference. Because this is such a common mistake, we offer the following caution.

$$\log_b (x+y) \neq \log_b x + \log_b y$$

$$\log_b (x-y) \neq \log_b x - \log_b y$$

Next, we consider some examples where we consolidate an expression containing multiple logarithms into a single logarithm. It is important to understand that in order to consolidate logarithms using Property 5 or Property 6, the logarithms must have the same base and have a coefficient of 1.

EXAMPLE 11   Evaluate: $\log_6 30 - \log_6 5$.

SOLUTION   This problem is very difficult if we leave the logarithms separate, because we do not know the exponents they represent. That is,

$$6^? = 30 \quad \text{and} \quad 6^? = 5$$

do not have simple answers. However, we can use Property 6 to consolidate the expression into a single logarithm.

$$\log_6 30 - \log_6 5 = \log_6 \left(\frac{30}{5} \right) \qquad \text{Property 6}$$

$$= \log_6 6 \qquad \frac{30}{5} = 6$$

$$= 1 \qquad \text{Property 2}$$

EXAMPLE 12   Write as a single logarithm:

$$2 \log_{10} a + 3 \log_{10} b - \frac{1}{3} \log_{10} c$$

SOLUTION   Notice all three logarithms have the same base. We begin by applying Property 7 to write each coefficient as an exponent.

$$2 \log_{10} a + 3 \log_{10} b - \frac{1}{3} \log_{10} c = \log_{10} a^2 + \log_{10} b^3 - \log_{10} c^{1/3} \qquad \text{Property 7}$$

$$= \log_{10} (a^2 \cdot b^3) - \log_{10} c^{1/3} \qquad \text{Property 5}$$

$$= \log_{10} \frac{a^2 b^3}{c^{1/3}} \qquad \text{Property 6}$$

$$= \log_{10} \frac{a^2 b^3}{\sqrt[3]{c}} \qquad c^{1/3} = \sqrt[3]{c}$$

Getting Ready for Class

After reading through the preceding section, respond in your own words and in complete sentences.

A. Explain why the following statement is false: "The logarithm of a product is the product of the logarithms."

B. Explain the difference between $\log_b m + \log_b n$ and $\log_b(m + n)$. Are they equivalent?

C. Is $\log_b (a \cdot b^x) = ax$? Explain why or why not.

D. What conditions must be met in order to combine logarithms using Property 5 or Property 6?

Evaluate each expression by using the properties of logarithms.

1. $\log_{17} 1$ **2.** $\log_{17} 17$ **3.** $4 \log_9 9$ **4.** $9 \log_4 1$

5. $8^{\log_8 3}$ **6.** $5^{\log_5 10}$ **7.** $\log_2 2^{\sqrt{2}}$ **8.** $\log_3 3^{\sqrt{6}}$

9. $3 \log_7 7^4$ **10.** $\sqrt{5} \log_{11} 11^{\sqrt{5}}$ **11.** $6^{2 \log_6 9}$ **12.** $4^{3 \log_4 3}$

13. $\log_9 81^2$ **14.** $\log_{10} 0.1^5$ **15.** $\log_3 (\log_2 8)$ **16.** $\log_5 (\log_{32} 2)$

17. $\log_{1/2} (\log_3 81)$ **18.** $\log_9 (\log_8 2)$ **19.** $\log_3 (\log_6 6)$ **20.** $\log_5 (\log_3 3)$

21. $\log_4 [\log_2(\log_2 16)]$ **22.** $\log_4 [\log_3(\log_2 8)]$

Use the properties of logarithms given in this section to expand each expression as much as possible.

23. $\log_3 4x$ **24.** $\log_2 5x$ **25.** $\log_6 \dfrac{5}{x}$ **26.** $\log_3 \dfrac{x}{5}$

27. $\log_2 y^5$ **28.** $\log_7 y^3$ **29.** $\log_9 \sqrt[3]{z}$ **30.** $\log_8 \sqrt{z}$

31. $\log_6 x^2 y^4$ **32.** $\log_{10} x^2 y^4$ **33.** $\log_5 (\sqrt{x} \cdot y^4)$ **34.** $\log_8 \sqrt[3]{x y^6}$

35. $\log_b \dfrac{xy}{z}$ **36.** $\log_b \dfrac{3x}{y}$ **37.** $\log_{10} \dfrac{4}{xy}$ **38.** $\log_{10} \dfrac{5}{4y}$

39. $\log_{10} \dfrac{x^2 y}{\sqrt{z}}$ **40.** $\log_{10} \dfrac{\sqrt{x} \cdot y}{z^3}$ **41.** $\log_{10} \dfrac{x^3 \sqrt{y}}{z^4}$ **42.** $\log_{10} \dfrac{x^4 \sqrt[3]{y}}{\sqrt{z}}$

43. $\log_b \sqrt[3]{\dfrac{x^2 y}{z^4}}$ **44.** $\log_b \sqrt[4]{\dfrac{x^4 y^3}{z^5}}$ **45.** $\log_3 \sqrt[3]{\dfrac{x^2 y}{z^6}}$ **46.** $\log_8 \sqrt[4]{\dfrac{x^5 y^6}{z^3}}$

47. $\log_a \dfrac{4x^5}{9a^2}$ **48.** $\log_b \dfrac{16b^2}{25y^3}$ **49.** $\log_4 x^2(x+2)$ **50.** $\log_5 y(y-3)^3$

51. $\log_b (5b^7)$ **52.** $\log_b (3b^4)$ **53.** $\log_8 (8x^9)$ **54.** $\log_{10} (10y^2)$

55. $\log_2 8(x-1)^5$ **56.** $\log_3 9(x+4)^8$ **57.** $\log_6 \dfrac{x^2 z^3}{\sqrt{x+z}}$ **58.** $\log_7 \dfrac{\sqrt{x-y}}{xy^4}$

59. $\log_9 \sqrt{\dfrac{x+3}{x-3}}$ **60.** $\log_{11} \sqrt[3]{\dfrac{x+y}{x-y}}$

Evaluate each expression by first writing the expression as a single logarithm.

61. $\log_6 3 + \log_6 12$ **62.** $\log_{10} 25 + \log_{10} 40$ **63.** $\log_5 50 - \log_5 2$

64. $\log_2 48 - \log_2 3$ **65.** $\log_4 100 - 2 \log_4 5$ **66.** $2 \log_2 6 - \log_2 9$

Write each expression as a single logarithm.

67. $\log_b x + \log_b z$ **68.** $\log_b x - \log_b z$

69. $2 \log_3 x - 3 \log_3 y$ **70.** $4 \log_2 x + 5 \log_2 y$

71. $\dfrac{1}{2} \log_{10} x + \dfrac{1}{3} \log_{10} y$ **72.** $\dfrac{1}{3} \log_{10} x - \dfrac{1}{4} \log_{10} y$

73. $3 \log_2 x + \dfrac{1}{2} \log_2 y - \log_2 z$ **74.** $2 \log_3 x + 3 \log_3 y - \log_3 z$

75. $\dfrac{1}{2} \log_2 x - 3 \log_2 y - 4 \log_2 z$ **76.** $3 \log_{10} x - \log_{10} y - \log_{10} z$

77. $\dfrac{3}{2} \log_{10} x - \dfrac{3}{4} \log_{10} y - \dfrac{4}{5} \log_{10} z$ **78.** $3 \log_{10} x - \dfrac{4}{3} \log_{10} y - 5 \log_{10} z$

79. $\dfrac{1}{2} \log_5 x + \dfrac{2}{3} \log_5 y - 4 \log_5 z$ **80.** $\dfrac{1}{4} \log_7 x + 5 \log_7 y - \dfrac{1}{3} \log_7 z$

81. $2\log_b x + 3\log_b (x - 10)$ **82.** $3\log_b y + 2\log_b (y + 8)$

83. $4\log_6 x + 5\log_6 z - 2\log_6 (y + z)$ **84.** $9\log_7 y + \log_7 z - 3\log_7 (x - y)$

85. $\log_3(x^2 - 16) - 2\log_3(x + 4)$ **86.** $\log_4(x^2 - x - 6) - \log_4(x^2 - 9)$

Applying the Concepts

87. Decibel Formula Use the properties of logarithms to rewrite the decibel formula $D = 10 \log_{10}\left(\dfrac{I}{I_0}\right)$ as

$$D = 10(\log_{10} I - \log_{10} I_0).$$

88. Decibel Formula In the decibel formula $D = 10 \log_{10}\left(\dfrac{I}{I_0}\right)$, the threshold of hearing, I_0, is

$$I_0 = 10^{-12} \text{ watts/meter}^2$$

Substitute 10^{-12} for I_0 in the decibel formula, then show that it simplifies to

$$D = 10(\log_{10} I + 12)$$

89. Finding Logarithms If $\log_{10} 8 = 0.903$ and $\log_{10} 5 = 0.699$, find the following without using a calculator.

    a. $\log_{10} 40$ **b.** $\log_{10} 320$ **c.** $\log_{10} 1{,}600$

90. Matching Match each expression in the first column with an equivalent expression in the second column:

    a. $\log_2(ab)$ **i.** b

    b. $\log_2\left(\dfrac{a}{b}\right)$ **ii.** 2

    c. $\log_5 a^b$ **iii.** $\log_2 a + \log_2 b$

    d. $\log_a b^a$ **iv.** $\log_2 a - \log_2 b$

    e. $\log_a a^b$ **v.** $a \log_a b$

    f. $\log_3 9$ **vi.** $b \log_5 a$

91. Henderson–Hasselbalch Formula Doctors use the Henderson–Hasselbalch formula to calculate the pH of a person's blood. pH is a measure of the acidity and/or the alkalinity of a solution. This formula is represented as

$$\text{pH} = 6.1 + \log_{10}\left(\dfrac{x}{y}\right)$$

where x is the base concentration and y is the acidic concentration. Rewrite the Henderson–Hasselbalch formula so that the logarithm of a quotient is not involved.

92. Food Processing The formula $M = 0.21(\log_{10} a - \log_{10} b)$ is used in the food processing industry to find the number of minutes M of heat processing a certain food should undergo at 250°F to reduce the probability of survival of *Clostridium botulinum* spores. The letter a represents the number of spores per can before heating, and b represents the number of spores per can after heating. Find M if $a = 1$ and $b = 10^{-12}$. Then find M using the same values for a and b in the formula $M = 0.21 \log_{10} \frac{a}{b}$.

93. Acoustic Powers The formula $N = \log_{10} \frac{P_1}{P_2}$ is used in radio electronics to find the ratio of the acoustic powers of two electric circuits in terms of their electric powers. Find N if P_1 is 100 and P_2 is 1. Then use the same two values of P_1 and P_2 to find N in the formula $N = \log_{10} P_1 - \log_{10} P_2$.

Learning Objectives Assessment

The following problems can be used to help assess if you have successfully met the learning objectives for this section.

94. Evaluate: $\log_2 72 - \log_2 9$.

    a. 3   **b.** 8   **c.** 126   **d.** 63

95. Use properties of logarithms to expand $\log_{10} \frac{xy}{z^3}$.

    a. $\log_{10} x + \log_{10} y - 3\log_{10} z$ **b.** $\log_{10} x - \log_{10} y + 3\log_{10} z$

    c. $3\log_{10} xy - \log_{10} z$ **d.** $x + y - 3z$

96. Write $3\log_4 x - 5\log_4 y$ as a single logarithm.

    a. $\log_4 \left(\frac{x}{y}\right)^{15}$ **b.** $\log_4 (x^3 y^5)$ **c.** $\frac{\log_4 x^3}{\log_4 y^5}$ **d.** $\log_4 \frac{x^3}{y^5}$

Getting Ready for the Next Section

Simplify.

97. 5^0 **98.** 4^1 **99.** $\log_3 3$ **100.** $\log_5 5$

101. $\log_b b^4$ **102.** $\log_a a^k$

Learning Objectives

In this section, we will learn how to:

1. Find a common logarithm.

2. Find a natural logarithm.

3. Simplify expressions involving common or natural logarithms.

4. Change a logarithm from one base to another.

Introduction

Acid rain was first discovered in the 1960s by Gene Likens and his research team who studied the damage caused by acid rain to Hubbard Brook in New Hampshire. Acid rain is rain with a pH of 5.6 and below. As you will see as you work your way through this section, pH is defined in terms of common logarithms — one of the topics we present in this section. So, when you are finished with this section, you will have a more detailed knowledge of pH and acid rain.

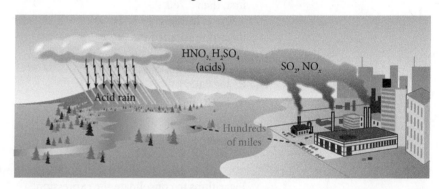

Two kinds of logarithms occur more frequently than other logarithms. Logarithms with a base of 10 are very common because our number system is a base-10 number system. For this reason, we call base-10 logarithms *common logarithms*.

> **(déf) DEFINITION** *common logarithms*
>
> A *common logarithm* is a logarithm with a base of 10. Because common logarithms are used so frequently, it is customary, in order to save time, to omit notating the base. That is,
>
> $$\log_{10} x = \log x$$
>
> When the base is not shown, it is assumed to be 10.

Common Logarithms

Common logarithms of powers of 10 are simple to evaluate. We need only recognize that $\log 10 = \log_{10} 10$ and apply Property 4 of logarithms.

$$\begin{array}{lll}
\log 1{,}000 & = \log_{10} 10^3 & = 3 \\
\log 100 & = \log_{10} 10^2 & = 2 \\
\log 10 & = \log_{10} 10^1 & = 1 \\
\log 1 & = \log_{10} 10^0 & = 0 \\
\log 0.1 & = \log_{10} 10^{-1} & = -1 \\
\log 0.01 & = \log_{10} 10^{-2} & = -2 \\
\log 0.001 & = \log_{10} 10^{-3} & = -3
\end{array}$$

To find common logarithms of numbers that are not powers of 10, we use a calculator with a $\boxed{\text{LOG}}$ key.

VIDEO EXAMPLES

SECTION 12.5

EXAMPLE 1   Use a calculator to approximate log 2,760.

SOLUTION

$$\log 2{,}760 \approx 3.4409$$

To work this problem on a scientific calculator, we simply enter the number 2,760 and press the key labeled $\boxed{\text{LOG}}$. On a graphing calculator we press the $\boxed{\text{LOG}}$ key first, then 2,760.

The 3 in the answer is called the *characteristic*, and the decimal part of the logarithm is called the *mantissa*.

EXAMPLES

2. $\log 0.0391 \approx -1.4078$

3. $\log 0.00523 \approx -2.2815$

4. $\log 9.99 \approx 0.9996$

EXAMPLE 5   Write $\log x - 2\log (x + 1)$ as a single logarithm.

SOLUTION   Because the base of both logarithms is 10, we can use the properties of logarithms to consolidate the expression.

$$\log x - 2\log (x + 1) = \log x - \log (x + 1)^2 \qquad \text{Property 7}$$

$$= \log \frac{x}{(x + 1)^2} \qquad \text{Property 6}$$

EXAMPLE 6   Expand: $\log 10x^5$.

SOLUTION

$$\log 10x^5 = \log 10 + \log x^5 \qquad \text{Property 5}$$

$$= 1 + \log x^5 \qquad \log 10 = \log_{10} 10 = 1$$

$$= 1 + 5\log x \qquad \text{Property 7}$$

In Section 12.3, we found that the magnitude M of an earthquake that produces a shock wave T times larger than the smallest shock wave that can be measured on a seismograph is given by the formula

$$M = \log_{10} T$$

We can rewrite this formula using our shorthand notation for common logarithms as

$$M = \log T$$

Richter Scale

6.6

EXAMPLE 7   The San Fernando earthquake of 1971 measured 6.6 on the Richter scale. The shockwave for the San Francisco earthquake of 1906 was estimated to be 50 times larger than the shockwave for the San Fernando earthquake. Based on this information, find the magnitude of the 1906 San Francisco earthquake.

SOLUTION If we assume T represents the relative size of the shockwave for the 1971 earthquake, then the size of the shockwave for the 1906 earthquake would be $50T$. Therefore, the magnitude of the San Francisco earthquake was

$$M = \log(50T) \qquad \text{Formula}$$
$$= \log 50 + \log T \qquad \text{Property 5}$$
$$= \log 50 + 6.6 \qquad \log T = 6.6$$
$$\approx 1.7 + 6.6 \qquad \log 50 \approx 1.7$$
$$= 8.3$$

In chemistry, the pH of a solution is the measure of the acidity of the solution. The definition for pH involves common logarithms. Here it is:

$$pH = -\log[H^+]$$

where $[H^+]$ is the concentration of the hydrogen ion in moles per liter. The range for pH is from 0 to 14. Pure water, a neutral solution, has a pH of 7. An acidic solution, such as vinegar, will have a pH less than 7, and an alkaline solution, such as ammonia, has a pH above 7.

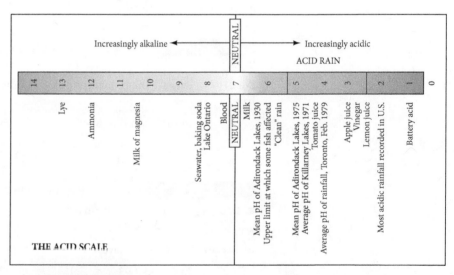

THE ACID SCALE

EXAMPLE 8   The concentration of the hydrogen ion in a sample of acid rain known to kill fish is 3.2×10^{-5} mole per liter. Find the pH of this acid rain to the nearest tenth.

SOLUTION   Substituting 3.2×10^{-5} for $[H^+]$ in the formula $pH = -\log[H^+]$, we have

$$pH = -\log[3.2 \times 10^{-5}] \qquad \text{Substitution}$$
$$\approx -(-4.5) \qquad \text{Evaluate the logarithm}$$
$$\approx 4.5 \qquad \text{Simplify}$$

Natural Logarithms

Note The notation $\ln x$ is short for "logarithm naturale of x," which is the language that was used in the 17th century.

> **DEFINITION** *natural logarithms*
>
> A *natural logarithm* is a logarithm with a base of e. The natural logarithm of x is denoted by $\ln x$. That is,
>
> $$\ln x = \log_e x$$

We can assume that all our properties of exponents and logarithms hold for expressions with a base of e, because e is a real number. Here are some examples intended to make you more familiar with the number e and natural logarithms.

EXAMPLE 9 Simplify each of the following expressions.

a. $e^0 = 1$

b. $e^1 = e$

c. $\ln e = 1$ Property 2

d. $\ln 1 = 0$ Property 1

e. $\ln e^3 = 3$ Property 4

f. $\ln e^{-4} = -4$ Property 4

g. $\ln e^t = t$ Property 4

EXAMPLE 10 Use the properties of logarithms to expand the expression $\ln Ae^{5t}$.

SOLUTION Because the properties of logarithms hold for natural logarithms, we have

$$\ln Ae^{5t} = \ln A + \ln e^{5t} \qquad \text{Property 5}$$
$$= \ln A + 5t \qquad \text{Property 4}$$

EXAMPLE 11 If $\ln 2 = 0.6931$ and $\ln 3 = 1.0986$, find

a. $\ln 6$ **b.** $\ln 0.5$ **c.** $\ln 8$

SOLUTION

a. Because $6 = 2 \cdot 3$, we have

$$\ln 6 = \ln 2 \cdot 3$$
$$= \ln 2 + \ln 3$$
$$= 0.6931 + 1.0986$$
$$= 1.7917$$

b. Writing 0.5 as $\frac{1}{2}$ and applying Property 6 for logarithms gives us

$$\ln 0.5 = \ln \frac{1}{2}$$
$$= \ln 1 - \ln 2$$
$$= 0 - 0.6931$$
$$= -0.6931$$

c. Writing 8 as 2^3 and applying Property 7 for logarithms, we have

$$\ln 8 = \ln 2^3$$
$$= 3 \ln 2$$
$$= 3(0.6931)$$
$$= 2.0793$$

Most calculators will only compute common logarithms and natural logarithms. If we need to approximate a logarithm with a base other than 10 or e, say $\log_8 24$, then we can use the gollowing formula to change one base to another.

> ### Change of Base Formula
>
> If a and b are both positive numbers other than 1, and if $x > 0$, then
>
> $$\log_a x = \frac{\log_b x}{\log_b a}$$
>
> $\qquad\qquad\uparrow\qquad\quad\uparrow$
> $\qquad\qquad$Base a $\quad$ Base b

The logarithm on the left side has a base of a, and both logarithms on the right side have a base of b. This allows us to change from base a to any other base b that is a positive number other than 1. Here is a proof.

Proof We begin by writing the identity (Property 3 for logarithms)

$$a^{\log_a x} = x$$

Taking the logarithm base b of both sides and writing the exponent $\log_a x$ as a coefficient, we have

$$\log_b \left(a^{\log_a x}\right) = \log_b (x)$$
$$\log_a x \cdot \log_b a = \log_b x$$

Dividing both sides by $\log_b a$, we have the desired result:

$$\frac{\log_a x \cdot \log_b a}{\log_b a} = \frac{\log_b x}{\log_b a}$$
$$\log_a x = \frac{\log_b x}{\log_b a}$$

Our last example illustrates the use of this property.

EXAMPLE 12   Find: $\log_8 24$.

SOLUTION   Because we do not have base-8 logarithms on our calculators, we can change this expression to an equivalent expression that contains only base-10 logarithms:

$$\log_8 24 = \frac{\log 24}{\log 8} \qquad \text{Change of base formula}$$

Don't be confused. We did not just drop the base, we changed to base 10. We could have written the last line like this:

$$\log_8 24 = \frac{\log_{10} 24}{\log_{10} 8}$$

From our calculators, we write

$$\log_8 24 \approx \frac{1.3802}{0.9031}$$

$$\approx 1.5283$$

Getting Ready for Class

After reading through the preceding section, respond in your own words and in complete sentences.

A. What is a common logarithm?

B. What is a natural logarithm?

C. What is the change of base formula used for?

D. Explain how you would approximate $\log_2 5$.

Evaluate the following logarithms.

1. $\log 1$ **2.** $\ln 1$ **3.** $\ln e$ **4.** $\log 10$

5. $\log 10{,}000$ **6.** $\log 0.001$ **7.** $\ln e^5$ **8.** $\ln e^{-3}$

9. $\log \sqrt{1000}$ **10.** $\log \sqrt[3]{10{,}000}$ **11.** $\ln \dfrac{1}{e^3}$ **12.** $\ln \sqrt{e}$

Approximate the following logarithms. Round your answers to four decimal places.

13. $\log 378$ **14.** $\log 37.8$ **15.** $\ln 345$ **16.** $\ln 10$

17. $\log 0.4260$ **18.** $\log 0.00971$ **19.** $\ln 0.345$ **20.** $\ln 0.0345$

Simplify each of the following expressions.

21. $\ln e^x$ **22.** $\ln e^y$ **23.** $\log 10^x$ **24.** $\log 10^z$

25. $10^{\log 3x}$ **26.** $e^{\ln 2y}$ **27.** $e^{4\ln x}$ **28.** $10^{5\log y}$

Use the properties of logarithms to expand each of the following expressions.

29. $\ln 10e^{3t}$ **30.** $\ln 10e^{4t}$ **31.** $\ln Ae^{-2t}$

32. $\ln Ae^{-3t}$ **33.** $\log [100(1.01)^{3t}]$ **34.** $\log \left[\dfrac{1}{10} (1.5)^{t+2} \right]$

35. $\ln (Pe^{rt})$ **36.** $\ln \left(\dfrac{1}{2} e^{-kt} \right)$ **37.** $-\log (4.2 \times 10^{-3})$

38. $-\log (5.7 \times 10^{-10})$

Write each expression as a single logarithm.

39. $\log x + \log (x - 2)$ **40.** $\log (x + 3) - \log (x - 1)$

41. $\ln (x + 1) - \ln (x + 4)$ **42.** $\ln x + \ln (x - 3)$

43. $2\log x - 5\log y$ **44.** $3\ln x + 4\ln z$

If $\ln 2 = 0.6931$, $\ln 3 = 1.0986$, and $\ln 5 = 1.6094$, find each of the following.

45. $\ln 15$ **46.** $\ln 10$ **47.** $\ln \dfrac{1}{3}$ **48.** $\ln \dfrac{1}{5}$

49. $\ln 9$ **50.** $\ln 25$ **51.** $\ln 16$ **52.** $\ln 81$

53. Graph: $f(x) = \log x$. **54.** Graph: $f(x) = \ln x$.

Use the change-of-base property and a calculator to find a decimal approximation to each of the following logarithms. Round your answers to four decimal places.

55. $\log_8 16$ **56.** $\log_9 27$ **57.** $\log_{16} 8$ **58.** $\log_{27} 9$

59. $\log_7 15$ **60.** $\log_3 12$ **61.** $\log_{15} 7$ **62.** $\log_{12} 3$

63. $\log_8 240$ **64.** $\log_6 180$ **65.** $\log_4 321$ **66.** $\log_5 462$

Applying the Concepts

67. **Atomic Bomb Tests** The formula for determining the magnitude, M, of an earthquake on the Richter scale is $M = \log_{10} T$, where T is the number of times the shockwave is greater than the smallest measurable shockwave. The Bikini Atoll in the Pacific Ocean was used as a location for atomic bomb tests by the United States government in the 1950s. One such test resulted in an earthquake. If the 1906 San Francisco earthquake of estimated magnitude 8.3 had a shockwave that was approximately 2,000 times greater, find the magnitude of the earthquake caused by this test.

68. **Atomic Bomb Tests** Today's nuclear weapons are 1,000 times more powerful than the atomic bombs tested in the Bikini Atoll mentioned in Problem 67. Determine the Richter scale measurement of a nuclear test today.

69. **Earthquake** The chart below is a partial listing of earthquakes that were recorded in Canada during one year. Complete the chart by computing the magnitude on the Richter Scale, M.

Location	Date	Magnitude M	Shockwave T
Moresby Island	Jan. 23		1.00×10^4
Vancouver Island	Apr. 30		1.99×10^5
Quebec City	June 29		1.58×10^3
Mould Bay	Nov. 13		1.58×10^5
St. Lawrence	Dec. 14		5.01×10^3

Source: National Resources Canada, National Earthquake Hazards Program.

70. **Memory** A class of students take a test on the mathematics concept of solving quadratic equations. That class agrees to take a similar form of the test each month for the next 6 months to test their memory of the topic since instruction. The function of the average score earned each month on the test is $m(x) = 75 - 5 \ln(x + 1)$, where x represents time in months. Complete the table to indicate the average score earned by the class at each month.

Time, x	Score, m
0	
1	
2	
3	
4	
5	
6	

Use the formula $pH = -\log[H^+]$, where $[H^+]$ is the concentration of the hydrogen ion in moles per liter, to solve problems 71-72.

71. **pH** Find the pH of orange juice if the concentration of the hydrogen ion in the juice is $[H^+] = 6.50 \times 10^{-4}$.

72. **pH** Find the pH of milk if the concentration of the hydrogen ions in milk is $[H^+] = 1.88 \times 10^{-6}$.

Learning Objectives Assessment

The following problems can be used to help assess if you have successfully met the learning objectives for this section.

73. Find: log 0.001.

    a. −6.9   **b.** 3   **c.** −2   **d.** −3

74. Approximate: ln 100.

    a. 271.8   **b.** 2.7   **c.** 2   **d.** 4.6

75. Use the properties of logarithms to expand $\ln 50e^{0.6t}$.

    a. $\ln 50 + 0.6t$ **b.** $50 + 0.6t$ **c.** $30t$ **d.** $0.6t(\ln 50)$

76. Approximate: $\log_{13} 31$.

    a. 1.3388   **b.** 0.7469   **c.** 34.5322   **d.** 0.1147

Getting Ready for the Next Section

Solve.

77. $5(2x + 1) = 12$ **78.** $4(3x - 2) = 21$

Use a calculator to evaluate, give answers to 4 decimal places.

79. $\dfrac{100{,}000}{32{,}000}$ **80.** $\dfrac{1.4982}{6.5681} + 3$

81. $\dfrac{1}{2}\left(\dfrac{-0.6931}{1.4289} + 3\right)$ **82.** $1 + \dfrac{0.04}{52}$

Use the power rule to rewrite the following logarithms.

83. $\log 1.05^{t}$ **84.** $\log 1.033^{t}$

Use identities to simplify.

85. $\ln e^{0.05t}$ **86.** $\ln e^{-0.000121t}$

Use a calculator to find each of the following. Write your answer in scientific notation with the first number in each answer rounded to the nearest tenth.

87. $10^{-5.6}$ **88.** $10^{-4.1}$

Divide and round to the nearest whole number.

89. $\dfrac{2.00 \times 10^{8}}{3.96 \times 10^{6}}$ **90.** $\dfrac{3.25 \times 10^{12}}{1.72 \times 10^{10}}$

Learning Objectives

In this section, we will learn how to:

1. Solve an exponential equation.

2. Solve a logarithmic equation.

3. Solve applications involving exponential and logarithmic equations.

Introduction

For items involved in exponential growth, the time it takes for a quantity to double is called the *doubling time*. For example, if you invest $5,000 in an account that pays 5% annual interest, compounded quarterly, you may want to know how long it will take for your money to double in value. You can find this doubling time if you can solve the equation

$$10{,}000 = 5{,}000 \, (1.0125)^{4t}$$

You will see, as you progress through this section, logarithms are the key to solving equations of this type.

Exponential Equations

The equation mentioned above is an example of an *exponential equation*. An exponential equation is simply an equation that contains one or more exponential functions.

One way to solve an exponential equation is to isolate the exponential function, and then write the equation in logarithmic form. The following example shows how this is done.

VIDEO EXAMPLES

SECTION 12.6

> **EXAMPLE 1**   Solve: $5^x = 12$.
>
> SOLUTION   The exponential function, 5^x, is already isolated on the left side. We solve for x by writing the equation in logarithmic form.
>
> $$5^x = 12 \qquad \text{Original equation}$$
>
> $$x = \log_5 12 \qquad \text{Logarithmic form}$$

The solution is the number $\log_5 12$. If we want to approximate this value, we can use the change of base formula.

$$\log_5 12 = \frac{\log 12}{\log 5}$$

$$\approx 1.5440$$

A second method for solving exponential equations involves taking a logarithm of both sides by applying the following property.

> **PROPERTY**
>
> If x and y are positive real numbers and $x = y$, then for any base b ($b > 0$, $b \neq 1$):
>
> $$\log_b x = \log_b y$$

Here is how the previous example would look if we solved the equation using this second method.

EXAMPLE 2   Use the second method for solving exponential equations to solve $5^x = 12$.

SOLUTION   Because 5^x and 12 are equal, we have

$$5^x = 12$$

$$\log 5^x = \log 12 \qquad \text{Apply the property}$$

$$x \log 5 = \log 12 \qquad \text{Property 7}$$

$$x = \frac{\log 12}{\log 5} \qquad \text{Divide both sides by log 5}$$

$$\approx 1.5440 \qquad \text{Approximate}$$

As you can see, we obtain the same result.

HOW TO   *Solve an Exponential Equation*

Step 1: Isolate the exponential function.

Method 1

   Step 2: Write the equation in logarithmic form.

   Step 3: Isolate the variable.

   Step 4: If necessary, use the change of base formula to approximate the logarithm.

Method 2

   Step 2: Take a logarithm of both sides.

   Step 3: Apply Property 7 for logarithms (or Property 4 if the bases are the same).

   Step 4: Isolate the variable.

EXAMPLE 3   Solve: $25^{2x+1} = 15$.

SOLUTION   The exponential function, 25^{2x+1}, is already isolated.

Method 1:

$$25^{2x+1} = 15$$

$$2x + 1 = \log_{25} 15 \qquad \text{Logarithmic form}$$

$$2x = \log_{25} 15 - 1 \qquad \text{Subtract 1 from both sides}$$

$$x = \frac{1}{2}(\log_{25} 15 - 1) \qquad \text{Multiply both sides by } \frac{1}{2}$$

$$x = \frac{1}{2}\left(\frac{\log 15}{\log 25} - 1\right) \qquad \text{Change of base formula}$$

$$\approx \frac{1}{2}(0.8413 - 1)$$

$$\approx -0.079$$

Method 2:

$$25^{2x+1} = 15$$

$$\log 25^{2x+1} = \log 15 \qquad \text{Take the log of both sides}$$

$$(2x + 1)\log 25 = \log 15 \qquad \text{Property 7}$$

$$2x + 1 = \frac{\log 15}{\log 25} \qquad \text{Divide by log 25}$$

$$2x = \frac{\log 15}{\log 25} - 1 \qquad \text{Add } -1 \text{ to both sides}$$

$$x = \frac{1}{2}\left(\frac{\log 15}{\log 25} - 1\right) \qquad \text{Multiply both sides by } \tfrac{1}{2}$$

$$\approx \frac{1}{2}(0.8413 - 1)$$

$$\approx -0.079$$

USING TECHNOLOGY *Graphing Calculators*

We can evaluate many logarithmic expressions on a graphing calculator by using the fact that logarithmic functions and exponential functions are inverses.

EXAMPLE 4 Evaluate the logarithmic expression $\log_3 7$ from the graph of an exponential function.

SOLUTION First, we let $\log_3 7 = x$. Next, we write this expression in exponential form as $3^x = 7$. We can solve this equation graphically by finding the intersection of the graphs $Y_1 = 3^x$ and $Y_2 = 7$, as shown in Figure 1.

Using the calculator, we find the two graphs intersect at $(1.77, 7)$. Therefore, $\log_3 7 = 1.77$ to the nearest hundredth. We can check our work by evaluating the expression $3^{1.77}$ on our calculator with the key strokes

$$3 \boxed{\wedge} 1.77 \boxed{\text{ENTER}}$$

The result is 6.99 to the nearest hundredth, which seems reasonable since 1.77 is accurate to the nearest hundredth. To get a result closer to 7, we would need to find the intersection of the two graphs more accurately.

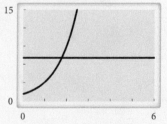

FIGURE 1

Applications of Exponential Equations

If you invest P dollars in an account with an annual interest rate r that is compounded n times a year, then t years later the amount of money in that account will be

$$A = P\left(1 + \frac{r}{n}\right)^{nt}$$

EXAMPLE 5   How long does it take for \$5,000 to double if it is deposited in an account that yields 5% interest compounded once a year?

SOLUTION   Substituting $P = 5{,}000$, $r = 0.05$, $n = 1$, and $A = 10{,}000$ into our formula, we have

$$10{,}000 = 5{,}000(1 + 0.05)^t$$

$$10{,}000 = 5{,}000(1.05)^t$$

$$2 = (1.05)^t \qquad\qquad \text{Divide by 5,000}$$

This is an exponential equation. We solve by taking the logarithm of both sides (Method 2):

$$\log 2 = \log(1.05)^t$$

$$= t \log 1.05$$

Dividing both sides by $\log 1.05$, we have

$$t = \frac{\log 2}{\log 1.05}$$

$$\approx 14.2$$

It takes a little over 14 years for \$5,000 to double if it earns 5% interest per year, compounded once a year.

EXAMPLE 6   Suppose that the population in a small city is 32,000 in the beginning of 2010 and that the city council assumes that the population size t years later can be estimated by the equation

$$P = 32{,}000e^{0.05t}$$

Approximately when will the city have a population of 50,000?

SOLUTION   We substitute 50,000 for P in the equation and solve for t:

$$50{,}000 = 32{,}000e^{0.05t}$$

$$1.5625 = e^{0.05t} \qquad\qquad \text{Divide both sides by 32,000}$$

To solve this equation for t, we can take the natural logarithm of each side:

Note   In Example 6, because the base of the logarithm and the base of the exponential function are both e, we can use Property 4 for logarithms to simplify the right side of the equation instead of Property 7.

$$\ln 1.5625 = \ln e^{0.05t}$$

$$= 0.05t \qquad\qquad \text{Property 4}$$

$$t = \frac{\ln 1.5625}{0.05} \qquad\qquad \text{Divide each side by 0.05}$$

$$\approx 8.93 \text{ years}$$

We can estimate that the population will reach 50,000 toward the end of 2018.

Logarithmic Equations

Now we will turn our attention to solving *logarithmic equations*, which are equations containing one or more logarithmic functions.

> **HOW TO** *Solve Logarithmic Equations*
>
> **Step 1:** Isolate the logarithmic function. If necessary, combine logarithms using Property 5 or Property 6.
>
> **Step 2:** Write the equation in exponential form.
>
> **Step 3:** Isolate the variable.
>
> **Step 4:** Check for extraneous solutions.

EXAMPLE 7   Solve: $\log_3 x = -2$.

SOLUTION   In exponential form, the equation looks like this:

$$x = 3^{-2}$$

or

$$x = \frac{1}{9}$$

The solution is $\frac{1}{9}$.

EXAMPLE 8   Solve: $\log_x 4 = 3$.

SOLUTION   Again, we use the definition of logarithms to write the expression in exponential form:

$$4 = x^3$$

Taking the cube root of both sides, we have

$$\sqrt[3]{4} = \sqrt[3]{x^3}$$

$$x = \sqrt[3]{4}$$

The solution set is $\{\sqrt[3]{4}\}$.

EXAMPLE 9   Solve: $\log x = 3.8774$.

SOLUTION

$$\log x = 3.8774$$

$$x = 10^{3.8774} \qquad \text{Exponential form}$$

$$\approx 7{,}540 \qquad \text{Approximate}$$

In the specific circumstance where the logarithm is a common logarithm, the solution 7,540 is called the *antilogarithm*, or just *antilog*, of 3.8774. That is, 7,540 is the number whose logarithm is 3.8774.

If more than one logarithmic function appears in the equation, we may be able to use a property to combine the logarithms as long as they have the same base.

EXAMPLE 10   Solve: $\log_2(x + 2) + \log_2 x = 3$.

SOLUTION   Applying Property 5 to the left side of the equation allows us to write it as a single logarithm:

$$\log_2(x + 2) + \log_2 x = 3$$

$$\log_2[(x + 2)(x)] = 3$$

The last line can be written in exponential form using the definition of logarithms:

$$(x + 2)(x) = 2^3$$

Solve as usual:

$$x^2 + 2x = 8$$

$$x^2 + 2x - 8 = 0$$

$$(x + 4)(x - 2) = 0$$

$$x + 4 = 0 \quad \text{or} \quad x - 2 = 0$$

$$x = -4 \qquad\qquad x = 2$$

In a previous section, we noted the fact that x in the expression $y = \log_b x$ cannot be a negative number. Because substitution of $x = -4$ into the original equation gives

$$\log_2(-2) + \log_2(-4) = 3$$

which contains logarithms of negative numbers, we cannot use -4 as a solution. It is an extraneous solution. The solution set is $\{2\}$.

Notice that we obtained an extraneous solution in Example 10. Extraneous solutions can occur whenever we use Properties 5, 6, or 7 for logarithms to help solve a logarithmic equation. As a result, it is a good idea to check for extraneous solutions when solving any logarithmic equation.

EXAMPLE 11   Solve: $\ln(3x + 7) = \ln(2x + 5)$.

SOLUTION   First we get both logarithms on the same side of the equation, and then combine them using Property 6.

$$\ln(3x + 7) = \ln(2x + 5)$$

$\ln(3x + 7) - \ln(2x + 5) = 0$	Subtract $\ln(2x + 5)$ from both sides
$\ln \dfrac{3x + 7}{2x + 5} = 0$	Property 6
$\log_e \dfrac{3x + 7}{2x + 5} = 0$	ln means $\log_e$
$\dfrac{3x + 7}{2x + 5} = e^0$	Exponential form
$\dfrac{3x + 7}{2x + 5} = 1$	$e^0 = 1$
$3x + 7 = 2x + 5$	Multiply both sides by $2x + 5$
$x + 7 = 5$	Subtract $2x$ from both sides
$x = -2$	

Now we check to see if $x = -2$ is an extraneous solution. Replacing x with -2 in the original equation gives us

$$\ln (3(-2) + 7) \stackrel{?}{=} \ln (2(-2) + 5)$$
$$\ln (-6 + 7) \stackrel{?}{=} \ln (-4 + 5)$$
$$\ln 1 = \ln 1$$
$$0 = 0 \qquad \text{A true statement}$$

Therefore, $x = -2$ is a solution to the equation.

Note We do not discard $x = -2$ as a solution simply because it is negative. As you can see, both logarithms end up being evaluated at a positive number (1) which is in their domain.

Applications of Logarithmic Equations

In the previous section we introduced the formula for pH of a solution:

$$pH = -\log [H^+]$$

where $[H^+]$ is the concentration of the hydrogen ion in moles per liter.

EXAMPLE 12 Normal rainwater has a pH of 5.6. What is the concentration of the hydrogen ion in normal rainwater?

SOLUTION Substituting 5.6 for pH in the formula $pH = -\log[H^+]$, we have

$$5.6 = -\log[H^+] \qquad \text{Substitution}$$
$$\log[H^+] = -5.6 \qquad \text{Isolate the logarithm}$$
$$[H^+] = 10^{-5.6} \qquad \text{Write in exponential form}$$
$$\approx 2.5 \times 10^{-6} \text{ moles per liter} \qquad \text{Answer in scientific notation}$$

Getting Ready for Class

After reading through the preceding section, respond in your own words and in complete sentences.

A. What is an exponential equation?

B. How do logarithms help you solve exponential equations?

C. Describe the process for solving a logarithmic equation.

D. What can cause extraneous solutions when solving a logarithmic equation?

Problem Set 12.6

Solve each exponential equation. Use a calculator to write the answer in decimal form accurate to four decimal places.

1. $3^x = 5$ **2.** $4^x = 3$ **3.** $5^x = 3$ **4.** $3^x = 4$

5. $5^{-x} = 12$ **6.** $7^{-x} = 8$ **7.** $12^{-x} = 5$ **8.** $8^{-x} = 7$

9. $8^{x+1} = 4$ **10.** $9^{x+1} = 3$ **11.** $4^{x-1} = 4$ **12.** $3^{x-1} = 9$

13. $3^{2x+1} = 2$ **14.** $2^{2x+1} = 3$ **15.** $3^{1-2x} = 2$ **16.** $2^{1-2x} = 3$

17. $15^{3x-4} = 10$ **18.** $10^{3x-4} = 15$ **19.** $6^{5-2x} = 4$ **20.** $9^{7-3x} = 5$

21. $3^{-4x} = 81$ **22.** $2^{5x} = \dfrac{1}{16}$ **23.** $5^{3x-2} = 15$ **24.** $7^{4x+3} = 200$

25. $100e^{3t} = 250$ **26.** $150e^{0.065t} = 400$

27. $1200\left(1 + \dfrac{0.072}{4}\right)^{4t} = 25000$ **28.** $2700\left(1 + \dfrac{0.086}{12}\right)^{12t} = 10000$

29. $50e^{-0.0742t} = 32$ **30.** $19e^{-0.000243t} = 12$

Solve each logarithmic equation.

31. $\log_3 x = 2$ **32.** $\log_4 x = 3$ **33.** $\log_5 x = -3$ **34.** $\log_2 x = -4$

35. $\log_x 4 = 2$ **36.** $\log_x 16 = 4$ **37.** $\log_x 5 = 3$ **38.** $\log_x 8 = 2$

39. $\log_x 36 = 2$ **40.** $\log_5 x = -2$ **41.** $\log_8 x = -2$ **42.** $\log_x \dfrac{1}{25} = 2$

43. $\log x = 1$ **44.** $\log x = -1$ **45.** $\log x = -2$

46. $\log x = 4$ **47.** $\ln x = -1$ **48.** $\ln x = 4$

49. $\log x = 10$ **50.** $\log x = 20$ **51.** $\log x = -20$

52. $\log x = -10$ **53.** $\log x = \log_2 8$ **54.** $\log x = \log_3 9$

Solve each logarithmic equation. Use a calculator to write the answer in decimal form.

55. $\log x = 2.8802$ **56.** $\log x = 4.8802$ **57.** $\log x = -2.1198$

58. $\log x = -3.1198$ **59.** $\ln x = 3.1553$ **60.** $\ln x = 5.5911$

61. $\ln x = -5.3497$ **62.** $\ln x = -1.5670$

Solve each of the following logarithmic equations. Be sure to check for any extraneous solutions.

63. $\log_2 x + \log_2 3 = 1$ **64.** $\log_3 x + \log_3 3 = 1$

65. $\log_3 x - \log_3 2 = 2$ **66.** $\log_3 x + \log_3 2 = 2$

67. $\log_3 x + \log_3(x - 2) = 1$ **68.** $\log_6 x + \log_6(x - 1) = 1$

69. $\log_3(x + 3) - \log_3(x - 1) = 1$ **70.** $\log_4(x - 2) - \log_4(x + 1) = 1$

71. $\log_2 x + \log_2(x - 2) = 3$ **72.** $\log_4 x + \log_4(x + 6) = 2$

73. $\log_8 x + \log_8(x - 3) = \dfrac{2}{3}$ **74.** $\log_{27} x + \log_{27}(x + 8) = \dfrac{2}{3}$

75. $\log_3(x + 2) - \log_3 x = 1$ **76.** $\log_2(x + 3) - \log_2(x - 3) = 2$

77. $\log_2(x + 1) + \log_2(x + 2) = 1$

78. $\log_3 x + \log_3(x + 6) = 3$

79. $\log_9\sqrt{x} + \log_9\sqrt{2x + 3} = \dfrac{1}{2}$

80. $\log_8\sqrt{x} + \log_8\sqrt{5x + 2} = \dfrac{2}{3}$

81. $4 \log_3 x - \log_3 x^2 = 6$

82. $9 \log_4 x - \log_4 x^3 = 12$

83. $\log_5 \sqrt{x} + \log_5 \sqrt{6x + 5} = 1$

84. $\log_2 \sqrt{x} + \log_2 \sqrt{6x + 5} = 1$

85. $\log x = 2 \log 5$

86. $\log x = -\log 4$

87. $\ln x = -3 \ln 2$

88. $\ln x = 5 \ln 3$

Applying the Concepts

89. Compound Interest How long will it take for $500 to double if it is invested at 6% annual interest compounded 2 times a year?

90. Compound Interest How long will it take for $500 to double if it is invested at 6% annual interest compounded 12 times a year?

91. Compound Interest How long will it take for $1,000 to triple if it is invested at 12% annual interest compounded 6 times a year?

92. Compound Interest How long will it take for $1,000 to become $4,000 if it is invested at 12% annual interest compounded 6 times a year?

93. Doubling Time How long does it take for an amount of money P to double itself if it is invested at 8% interest compounded 4 times a year?

94. Tripling Time How long does it take for an amount of money P to triple itself if it is invested at 8% interest compounded 4 times a year?

95. Tripling Time If a $25 investment is worth $75 today, how long ago must that $25 have been invested at 6% interest compounded twice a year?

96. Doubling Time If a $25 investment is worth $50 today, how long ago must that $25 have been invested at 6% interest compounded twice a year?

Recall from Section 12.1 that if P dollars are invested in an account with annual interest rate r, compounded continuously, then the amount of money in the account after t years is given by the formula

$$A(t) = Pe^{rt}$$

97. Continuously Compounded Interest Repeat Problem 89 if the interest is compounded continuously.

98. Continuously Compounded Interest Repeat Problem 92 if the interest is compounded continuously.

99. Continuously Compounded Interest How long will it take $500 to triple if it is invested at 6% annual interest, compounded continuously?

100. Continuously Compounded Interest How long will it take $500 to triple if it is invested at 12% annual interest, compounded continuously?

101. Continuously Compounded Interest How long will it take for $1,000 to be worth $2,500 at 8% interest, compounded continuously?

102. Continuously Compounded Interest How long will it take for $1,000 to be worth $5,000 at 8% interest, compounded continuously?

103. **Exponential Decay** Twinkies on the shelf of a convenience store lose their fresh tastiness over time. We say that the taste quality is 1 when the Twinkies are first put on the shelf at the store, and that the quality of tastiness declines according to the function $Q(t) = 0.85^t$ (t in days). Determine when the taste quality will be one half of its original value.

104. **Henderson–Hasselbalch Formula** Doctors use the Henderson–Hasselbalch formula to calculate the pH of a person's blood. pH is a measure of the acidity and/or the alkalinity of a solution. This formula is represented as

$$pH = 6.1 + \log_{10}\left(\frac{x}{y}\right)$$

where x is the base concentration and y is the acidic concentration. If most people have a blood pH of 7.4, use the Henderson–Hasselbalch formula to find the ratio of $\frac{x}{y}$ for an average person.

105. **University Enrollment** The percentage of students enrolled in a university who are between the ages of 25 and 34 can be modeled by the formula $s = 5\ln x$, where s is the percentage of students and x is the number of years since 1989. Predict the year in which approximately 20% of students will enroll in a university who are between the ages of 25 and 34.

106. **Earthquake** On January 6, 2001, an earthquake with a magnitude of 7.7 on the Richter Scale hit southern India (*National Earthquake Information Center*). By what factor was this earthquake's shockwave greater than the smallest measurable shockwave?

The Richter Scale Find the relative size T of the shock wave of earthquakes with the following magnitudes, as measured on the Richter scale.

107. 5.5   108. 6.6   109. 8.3   110. 8.7

111. **pH** Find the concentration of hydrogen ions in a glass of wine if the pH is 4.75.

112. **pH** Find the concentration of hydrogen ions in a bottle of vinegar if the pH is 5.75.

113. **Exponential Growth** Suppose that the population in a small city is 32,000 at the beginning of 2005 and that the city council assumes that the population size t years later can be estimated by the equation

$$P(t) = 32{,}000e^{0.05t}$$

Approximately when will the city have a population of 80,000?

114. **Exponential Growth** Suppose the population of a city is given by the equation

$$P(t) = 100{,}000e^{0.05t}$$

where t is the number of years from the present time. How large is the population now? (*Now* corresponds to a certain value of t. Once you realize what that value of t is, the problem becomes very simple.)

115. **Airline Travel** The number of airline passengers in 1990 was 466 million. The number of passengers traveling by airplane each year has increased exponentially according to the model, $P(t) = 466 \cdot 1.035^t$, where t is the number of years since 1990 (U.S. Census Bureau). In what year is it predicted that 1.9 billion passengers will travel by airline?

116. **Bankruptcy Model** In 1997, there were a total of 1,316,999 bankruptcies filed under the Bankruptcy Reform Act. The model for the number of bankruptcies filed is $B(t) = 0.798 \cdot 1.164^t$, where t is the number of years since 1994 and B is the number of bankruptcies filed in terms of millions (Administrative Office of the U.S. Courts, *Statistical Tables for the Federal Judiciary*). In what year is it predicted that 50 million bankruptcies will be filed?

117. **Health Care** In 1990, $699 billion was spent on health care expenditures. The amount of money, E, in billions spent on health care expenditures can be estimated using the function $E(t) = 78.16(1.11)^t$, where t is time in years since 1970 (*U.S. Census Bureau*). In what year is it estimated that $40 trillion will be spent on health care expenditures?

118. **Value of a Car** As a car ages, its value decreases. The value of a particular car with an original purchase price of $25,600 is modeled by the function $c(t) = 25,600(1 - 0.22)^t$, where c is the value at time t (Kelly Blue Book). How old is the car when its value is $10,000?

119. **Carbon Dating** Scientists use Carbon-14 dating to find the age of fossils and other artifacts. The amount of Carbon-14 in an organism will yield information concerning its age. A formula used in Carbon-14 dating is $A(t) = A_0 \cdot 2^{-t/5600}$, where A_0 is the amount of carbon originally in the organism, t is time in years, and A is the amount of carbon remaining after t years. Determine the number of years since an organism died if it originally contained 1,000 gram of Carbon-14 and it currently contains 600 gram of Carbon-14.

120. **Online Banking Use** The number of households using online banking services has increased from 754,000 in 1995 to 12,980,000 in 2000. The formula $H(t) = 0.76e^{0.55t}$ models the number of households, H, in millions when time is t years since 1995 according to the Home Banking Report. According to this model, in what year did 50,000,000 households use online banking services?

Depreciation The annual rate of depreciation r on a car that is purchased for P dollars and is worth W dollars t years later can be found from the formula.

$$\log(1 - r) = \frac{1}{t} \log \frac{W}{P}$$

121. Find the annual rate of depreciation on a car that is purchased for $9,000 and sold 5 years later for $4,500.

122. Find the annual rate of depreciation on a car that is purchased for $9,000 and sold 4 years later for $3,000.

Two cars depreciate in value according to the following depreciation tables. In each case, find the annual rate of depreciation.

123.

Age in Years	Value in Dollars
New	7,550
5	5,750

124.

Age in Years	Value in Dollars
New	7,550
3	5,750

Learning Objectives Assessment

The following problems can be used to help assess if you have successfully met the learning objectives for this section.

125. Solve: $3^{2x-9} = 30$.

    a. 6.05   **b.** 9.5   **c.** 2.89   **d.** 5

126. Solve: $\log_5 x + \log_5 (x + 4) = 1$.

    a. $\{-2 \pm \sqrt{5}\}$ **b.** $\left\{ \dfrac{1}{2} \right\}$ **c.** $\{1\}$ **d.** $\{-5, 1\}$

127. Cost Increase The cost of a can of Coca Cola in 1960 was \$0.10. The function that models the cost of a Coca Cola by year is $C(t) = 0.10e^{0.0576t}$, where t is the number of years since 1960. In what year was it expected that a can of Coca Cola would cost \$1.00?

    a. 1985   **b.** 1977   **c.** 1993   **d.** 2000

Maintaining Your Skills

The following problems review material we covered in Section 8.5.

Find the vertex for each of the following parabolas, and then indicate if it is the highest or lowest point on the graph.

128. $y = 2x^2 + 8x - 15$ **129.** $y = 3x^2 - 9x - 10$

130. $y = 12x - 4x^2$ **131.** $y = 18x - 6x^2$

132. Maximum Height An object is projected into the air with an initial upward velocity of 64 feet per second. Its height h at any time t is given by the formula $h = 64t - 16t^2$. Find the time at which the object reaches its maximum height. Then, find the maximum height.

133. Maximum Height An object is projected into the air with an initial upward velocity of 64 feet per second from the top of a building 40 feet high. If the height h of the object t seconds after it is projected into the air is $h = 40 + 64t - 16t^2$, find the time at which the object reaches its maximum height. Then, find the maximum height it attains.

Chapter 12 Summary

Exponential Functions [12.1]

1. For the exponential function
$f(x) = 2^x$,
$$f(0) = 2^0 = 1$$
$$f(1) = 2^1 = 2$$
$$f(2) = 2^2 = 4$$
$$f(3) = 2^3 = 8$$

Any function of the form

$$f(x) = b^x$$

where $b > 0$ and $b \neq 1$, is an *exponential function*. The domain is the set of all real numbers and the range is $\{y \mid y > 0\}$. The graph has a horizontal asymptote at $y = 0$.

Compound Interest [12.1]

2. If \$500 is invested at 3% annual interest compounded quarterly, then after 2 years the balance in the account will be

$$A(4) = 500\left(1 + \frac{0.03}{4}\right)^{4(2)}$$

$$\approx \$530.80$$

If P dollars are deposited in an account with annual interest rate r, compounded n times per year, then the amount of money in the account after t years is given by

$$A(t) = P\left(1 + \frac{r}{n}\right)^{nt}$$

If the interest is compounded continuously, then the formula used is

$$A(t) = Pe^{rt}$$

One-to-One Functions [12.2]

3. The function $f(x) = x^2$ is not one-to-one because 9, which is in the range, comes from both 3 and -3 in the domain.

A function is a *one-to-one function* if every element in the range comes from exactly one element in the domain.

Inverse Functions [12.2]

4. The inverse of $f(x) = 2x - 3$ is

$$f^{-1}(x) = \frac{x + 3}{2}$$

The *inverse* of a function is obtained by reversing the order of the coordinates of the ordered pairs belonging to the function. Only one-to-one functions have inverses that are also functions.

Definition of Logarithms [12.3]

5. The definition allows us to write expressions like
$$y = \log_3 27$$
equivalently in exponential form as
$$3^y = 27$$
which makes it apparent that y is 3.

If b is a positive number not equal to 1, then the expression

$$y = \log_b x$$

is equivalent to $x = b^y$; that is, in the expression $y = \log_b x$, y is the exponent to which we raise b in order to get x. Expressions written in the form $y = \log_b x$ are said to be in *logarithmic form*. Expressions like $x = b^y$ are in *exponential form*.

Logarithmic Functions [12.3]

6. The function $y = \log_2 x$ is the inverse of the exponential function $y = 2^x$.

Any function of the form

$$f(x) = \log_b x$$

where $b > 0$ and $b \neq 1$, is a *logarithmic function*. The domain is $\{x \mid x > 0\}$ and the range is the set of all real numbers. The graph has a vertical asymptote at $x = 0$.

The logarithmic function with base b and the exponential function with base b are inverse functions.

Properties of Logarithms [12.4]

7. We can rewrite the expression

$$\log_{10} \frac{45^6}{273}$$

using the properties of logarithms, as

$$6 \log_{10} 45 - \log_{10} 273$$

If x, y, and b are positive real numbers, $b \neq 1$, and r is any real number, then:

1. $\log_b 1 = 0$

2. $\log_b b = 1$

3. $b^{\log_b x} = x$

4. $\log_b b^x = x$

5. $\log_b (xy) = \log_b x + \log_b y$

6. $\log_b \left(\dfrac{x}{y} \right) = \log_b x - \log_b y$

7. $\log_b x^r = r \log_b x$

Common Logarithms [12.5]

8. $\log_{10} 10{,}000 = \log 10{,}000$
$= \log 10^4$
$= 4$

Common logarithms are logarithms with a base of 10. To save time in writing, we omit the base when working with common logarithms; that is,

$$\log x = \log_{10} x$$

Natural Logarithms [12.5]

9. $\ln e = 1$
$\ln 1 = 0$

Natural logarithms, written *ln x*, are logarithms with a base of e, where the number e is an irrational number (like the number π). A decimal approximation for e is 2.7183. All the properties of exponents and logarithms hold when the base is e.

$$\ln x = \log_e x$$

Change of Base [12.5]

10. $\log_6 475 = \dfrac{\log 475}{\log 6}$

$\approx \dfrac{2.6767}{0.7782}$

≈ 3.44

If x, a, and b are positive real numbers, $a \neq 1$ and $b \neq 1$, then

$$\log_a x = \frac{\log_b x}{\log_b a}$$

Exponential Equations [12.6]

11.
$$10e^{2x} = 50$$
$$e^{2x} = 5$$
$$\ln(e^{2x}) = \ln(5)$$
$$2x = \ln 5$$
$$x = \frac{1}{2}\ln 5 \approx 0.8047$$

To solve an exponential equation, we isolate the exponential function. Then we either write the equation in logarithmic form or take a logarithm of both sides.

Logarithmic Equations [12.6]

12. $\log_2 x + \log_2 (x - 2) = 3$
$$\log_2 x(x - 2) = 3$$
$$x^2 - 2x = 2^3$$
$$x^2 - 2x - 8 = 0$$
$$(x - 4)(x + 2) = 0$$
$$x = 4, -2$$
$x = -2$ is extraneous, so the only solution is $x = 4$.

To solve a logarithmic equation, we first isolate the logarithmic function, and then write the equation in exponential form. If it is necessary to use properties of logarithms, then we should check for extraneous solutions.

> **COMMON MISTAKE**
>
> The most common mistakes that occur with logarithms come from trying to apply the properties of logarithms to situations in which they don't apply. For example, a very common mistake looks like this:
>
> $$\frac{\log 3}{\log 2} = \log 3 - \log 2 \qquad \text{Mistake}$$
>
> This is not a property of logarithms. To write the equation $\log 3 - \log 2$, we would have to start with
>
> $$\log \frac{3}{2} \qquad NOT \qquad \frac{\log 3}{\log 2}$$
>
> There is a difference.

Chapter 12 Test

Graph each exponential function. [12.1]

1. $f(x) = 2^x$

2. $g(x) = 3^{-x}$

3. Graph the relation $y = x^2 - 2$, and then graph the inverse of the relation. [9.2]

4. Graph the function $f(x) = 2x - 3$ and its inverse. Then find the equation for $f^{-1}(x)$. [9.2]

Graph each of the following. [12.3]

5. $y = \log_2 x$

6. $y = \log_{1/2} x$

Evaluate each of the following. [12.3, 12.5]

7. $\log_7 \dfrac{1}{49}$

8. $\log_8 4$

9. $\log 23{,}400$

10. $\ln 0.0462$

Use the properties of logarithms to expand each expression. [12.4]

11. $\log_2 \dfrac{8x^2}{y}$

12. $\log \dfrac{\sqrt{x}}{(y^4)\sqrt[5]{z}}$

Write each expression as a single logarithm. [12.4]

13. $2\log_3 x - \dfrac{1}{2}\log_3 y$

14. $\dfrac{1}{3}\log x - \log y - 2\log z$

Use the change of base formula to find each logarithm. [12.5]

15. $\log_9 100$

16. $\log_{100} 0.9$

Use a calculator to find x. [12.6]

17. $\log x = 4.8476$

18. $\log x = -2.6478$

Solve for x. [12.6]

19. $\log_4 x = 3$

20. $\log_x 5 = 2$

21. $5 = 3^x$

22. $4^{2x-1} = 8$

23. $\log_5 x - \log_5 3 = 1$

24. $\log_2 x + \log_2 (x - 7) = 3$

25. pH Find the pH of a solution in which $[\text{H}^+] = 6.6 \times 10^{-7}$. [12.5]

26. Compound Interest If $400 is deposited in an account that earns 10% annual interest compounded twice a year, how much money will be in the account after 5 years? [12.1]

27. Depreciation If a car depreciates in value 20% per year for the first 5 years after it is purchased for P_0 dollars, then its value after t years will be $V(t) = P_0(1 - r)^t$ for $0 \le t \le 5$. To the nearest dollar, find the value of a car 4 years after it is purchased for $18,000. [12.1]

28. Compound Interest How long will it take $600 to become $1,800 if the $600 is deposited in an account that earns 8% annual interest compounded 4 times a year? [12.6]

Sequences and Series

13

iStockphoto.com © Dangubic

Suppose you run up a balance of \$1,000 on a credit card that charges 1.65% interest each month (i.e., an annual rate of 19.8%). If you stop using the card and make the minimum payment of \$20 each month, how long will it take you to pay off the balance on the card? The answer can be found by using the formula

$$U_n = (1.0165)U_{n-1} - 20$$

where U_n stands for the current unpaid balance on the card, and U_{n-1} is the previous month's balance. The table and figure were created from this formula and a graphing calculator. As you can see from the table, the balance on the credit card decreases very little each month.

Monthly Credit Card Balances

Previous Balance U_{n-1}	Monthly Interest Rate	Payment Number n	Monthly Payment	New Balance U_n
\$1,000.00	1.65%	1	\$20	\$996.00
\$996.00	1.65%	2	\$20	\$992.94
\$992.94	1.65%	3	\$20	\$989.32
\$989.32	1.65%	4	\$20	\$985.64
\$985.64	1.65%	5	\$20	\$981.90

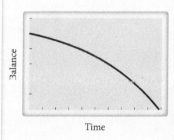

The formula for U_n is called a recursion formula, and the values of U_n it generates

$$1,000.00, \ 996.00, \ 992.94, \ 989.94, \ 989.32, \ 985.32$$

form a sequence. In this chapter, we will learn about different types of sequences and explore some of their applications.

Sequences

Learning Objectives

In this section, we will learn how to:

1. Use the nth term to find terms of a sequence.
2. Find terms of a sequence using a recursion formula.
3. Find a formula for the general term of a sequence.

Introduction

Informally, a sequence is simply a list of numbers that have been placed in a particular order. Many of the sequences in this chapter will be familiar to you on an intuitive level because you have worked with them for some time now. Here are some of those sequences:

The sequence of odd numbers

$$1, 3, 5, 7,\ldots$$

The sequence of even numbers

$$2, 4, 6, 8,\ldots$$

The sequence of squares

$$1^2, 2^2, 3^2, 4^2,\ldots = 1, 4, 9, 16,\ldots$$

The numbers in each of these sequences can be found from formulas that define functions. For example, the sequence of even numbers can be found from the function

$$f(x) = 2x$$

by finding $f(1), f(2), f(3), f(4)$, and so forth. This gives us justification for the formal definition of a sequence.

> ### DEFINITION *sequence*
>
> A *sequence* is a function whose domain is the set of positive integers 1, 2, 3, 4,... .

As you can see, sequences are simply functions with a specific domain. If we want to form a sequence from the function $f(x) = 3x + 5$, we simply find $f(1), f(2), f(3)$, $f(4)$, and so on. Doing so gives us the sequence

$$8, 11, 14, 17,\ldots$$

because $f(1) = 3(1) + 5 = 8$, $f(2) = 3(2) + 5 = 11$, $f(3) = 3(3) + 5 = 14$, and $f(4) = 3(4) + 5 = 17$. Notice that the terms of the sequence are just the outputs from the function written in order.

Notation   Because the domain for a sequence is always the set $\{1, 2, 3,\ldots\}$, we can simplify the notation we use to represent the terms of a sequence. Using the letter a instead of f, and subscripts instead of numbers enclosed by parentheses, we can represent the sequence from the previous discussion as follows:

$$a_n = 3n + 5$$

Instead of $f(1)$, we write a_1 for the *first term* of the sequence.
Instead of $f(2)$, we write a_2 for the *second term* of the sequence.
Instead of $f(3)$, we write a_3 for the *third term* of the sequence.
Instead of $f(4)$, we write a_4 for the *fourth term* of the sequence.
Instead of $f(n)$, we write a_n for the *nth term* of the sequence.

The nth term is also called the *general term* of the sequence. The general term is used to define the other terms of the sequence. That is, if we are given the formula for the general term a_n, we can find any other term in the sequence. The following examples illustrate.

VIDEO EXAMPLES

SECTION 13.1

EXAMPLE 1   Find the first four terms of the sequence whose general term is given by $a_n = 2n - 1$.

SOLUTION   The subscript notation a_n works the same way function notation works. To find the first, second, third, and fourth terms of this sequence, we simply substitute 1, 2, 3, and 4 for n in the formula $2n - 1$:

If   the general term is $a_n = 2n - 1$

then   the first term is $a_1 = 2(1) - 1 = 1$

the second term is $a_2 = 2(2) - 1 = 3$

the third term is $a_3 = 2(3) - 1 = 5$

the fourth term is $a_4 = 2(4) - 1 = 7$

The first four terms of this sequence are the odd numbers 1, 3, 5, and 7. The whole sequence can be written as

$$1, 3, 5, 7, \ldots, 2n - 1, \ldots$$

Because each term in this sequence is greater than the preceding term, we say the sequence is an *increasing sequence*.

EXAMPLE 2   Write the first four terms of the sequence defined by

$$a_n = \frac{1}{n + 1}$$

SOLUTION   Replacing n with 1, 2, 3, and 4, we have, respectively, the first four terms:

$$\text{First term} = a_1 = \frac{1}{1 + 1} = \frac{1}{2}$$

$$\text{Second term} = a_2 = \frac{1}{2 + 1} = \frac{1}{3}$$

$$\text{Third term} = a_3 = \frac{1}{3 + 1} = \frac{1}{4}$$

$$\text{Fourth term} = a_4 = \frac{1}{4 + 1} = \frac{1}{5}$$

The sequence defined by

$$a_n = \frac{1}{n+1}$$

can be written as

$$\frac{1}{2}, \frac{1}{3}, \frac{1}{4}, \frac{1}{5}, \ldots, \frac{1}{n+1}, \ldots$$

Because each term in the sequence is less than the term preceding it, the sequence is said to be a *decreasing sequence*.

EXAMPLE 3   Find the fifth and sixth terms of the sequence whose general term is given by

$$a_n = \frac{(-1)^n}{n^2}$$

SOLUTION   For the fifth term, we replace n with 5. For the sixth term, we replace n with 6:

$$\text{Fifth term} = a_5 = \frac{(-1)^5}{5^2} = \frac{-1}{25}$$

$$\text{Sixth term} = a_6 = \frac{(-1)^6}{6^2} = \frac{1}{36}$$

The sequence in Example 3 can be written as

$$-1, \frac{1}{4}, -\frac{1}{9}, \frac{1}{16}, \ldots, \frac{(-1)^n}{n^2}, \ldots$$

Because the terms alternate in sign — if one term is positive, then the next term is negative — we call this an *alternating sequence*. The first three examples all illustrate how we work with a sequence in which we are given a formula for the general term.

USING TECHNOLOGY   *Finding Sequences on a Graphing Calculator*

Method 1: Using a Table

We can use the table function on a graphing calculator to view the terms of a sequence. To view the terms of the sequence $a_n = 3n + 5$, we set $Y_1 = 3X + 5$. Then we use the table setup feature on the calculator to set the table minimum to 1, and the table increment to 1 also. Here is the setup and result for a TI-84.

Table Setup	Y Variables Setup	Resulting Table	
		X	Y
Table minimum = 1	$Y_1 = 3X + 5$		
Table increment = 1		1	8
Independent variable: Auto		2	11
Dependent variable: Auto		3	14
		4	17
		5	20

To find any particular term of a sequence, we change the independent variable setting to Ask, and then input the number of the term of the sequence we want to find. For example, if we want term a_{100}, then we input 100 for the independent variable, and the table gives us the value of 305 for that term.

USING TECHNOLOGY   *Finding Sequences on a Graphing Calculator Continued*

Method 2: Using the Built-in seq(Command

Using this method, first find the seq(command. On a TI-84 it is found in the $\boxed{\text{LIST}}$ OPS menu. To find terms a_1 through a_7 for $a_n = 3n + 5$, we first bring up the seq(command on our calculator, then we input the following four items, in order, separated by commas: 3X+5, X, 1, 7. Then we close the parentheses. Our screen will look like this:

$$\text{seq}(3X+5, X, 1, 7)$$

Pressing $\boxed{\text{ENTER}}$ displays the first five terms of the sequence. Pressing the right arrow key repeatedly brings the remaining members of the sequence into view.

Method 3: Using the Built-in Seq Mode

Press the $\boxed{\text{MODE}}$ key on your TI-84 and then select Seq (it's next to Func Par and Pol). Go to the Y variables list and set nMin $=1$ and $u(n) = 3n+5$. Then go to the $\boxed{\text{TBLSET}}$ key to set up your table like the one shown in Method 1. Pressing $\boxed{\text{TABLE}}$ will display the sequence you have defined.

Recursion Formulas

Let's go back to one of the first sequences we looked at in this section:

$$8, 11, 14, 17,\ldots$$

Each term in the sequence can be found by simply substituting positive integers for n in the formula $a_n = 3n + 5$. Another way to look at this sequence, however, is to notice that each term can be found by adding 3 to the preceding term; so, we could give all the terms of this sequence by simply saying

Start with 8, and then add 3 to each term to get the next term.

The same idea, expressed in symbols, looks like this:

$$a_1 = 8 \quad \text{and} \quad a_n = a_{n-1} + 3 \quad \text{for } n > 1$$

This formula is called a *recursion formula* because each term is written recursively, meaning defined in relation to the term or terms that precede it.

EXAMPLE 4   Write the first four terms of the sequence given recursively by

$$a_1 = 4 \quad \text{and} \quad a_n = 5a_{n-1} \quad \text{for } n > 1$$

SOLUTION   The formula tells us to start the sequence with the number 4, and then multiply each term by 5 to get the next term. Therefore,

$$a_1 = 4$$
$$a_2 = 5a_1 = 5(4) = 20$$
$$a_3 = 5a_2 = 5(20) = 100$$
$$a_4 = 5a_3 = 5(100) = 500$$

The sequence is 4, 20, 100, 500,....

Recursion Formulas on a Graphing Calculator

We can use a TI-84 graphing calculator to view the sequence defined recursively as

$$a_1 = 8, \, a_n = a_{n-1} + 3$$

First, put your TI-84 calculator in sequence mode by pressing the $\boxed{\text{MODE}}$ key, and then selecting Seq (it's next to Func Par and Pol). Go to the Y variables list and set $n\text{Min} = 1$, $u(n) = u(n-1)+3$, and $u(n\text{Min}) = 8$. (The u is above the 7, and the n is on the $\boxed{\text{X, T, } \theta, n}$ and is automatically displayed if that key is pressed when the calculator is in the Seq mode.) Pressing $\boxed{\text{TABLE}}$ will display the sequence you have defined.

Finding the General Term

In the first four examples, we found some terms of a sequence after being given the general term. In the next two examples, we will do the reverse. That is, given some terms of a sequence, we will find a formula for the general term.

EXAMPLE 5 Find a formula for the nth term of the sequence 2, 8, 18, 32,….

SOLUTION Solving a problem like this involves some guessing. Looking over the first four terms, we see each is twice a perfect square:

$$2 = 2(1)$$
$$8 = 2(4)$$
$$18 = 2(9)$$
$$32 = 2(16)$$

If we write each square with an exponent of 2, the formula for the nth term becomes obvious:

$$a_1 = 2 \quad = 2(1)^2$$
$$a_2 = 8 \quad = 2(2)^2$$
$$a_3 = 18 = 2(3)^2$$
$$a_4 = 32 = 2(4)^2$$
$$\vdots$$
$$a_n = 2(n)^2 = 2n^2$$

The general term of the sequence 2, 8, 18, 32,…is $a_n = 2n^2$.

EXAMPLE 6   Find the general term for the sequence $2, \dfrac{3}{8}, \dfrac{4}{27}, \dfrac{5}{64}, \ldots$.

SOLUTION   The first term can be written as $\frac{2}{1}$. The denominators are all perfect cubes. The numerators are all 1 more than the base of the cubes in the denominators:

$$a_1 = \frac{2}{1} = \frac{1+1}{1^3}$$

$$a_2 = \frac{3}{8} = \frac{2+1}{2^3}$$

$$a_3 = \frac{4}{27} = \frac{3+1}{3^3}$$

$$a_4 = \frac{5}{64} = \frac{4+1}{4^3}$$

Observing this pattern, we recognize the general term to be

$$a_n = \frac{n+1}{n^3}$$

Note   Finding the *n*th term of a sequence from the first few terms is not always automatic. That is, it sometimes takes awhile to recognize the pattern. Don't be afraid to guess at the formula for the general term. Many times, an incorrect guess leads to the correct formula.

Getting Ready for Class

After reading through the preceding section, respond in your own words and in complete sentences.

A. How are subscripts used to denote the terms of a sequence?

B. What is the relationship between the subscripts used to denote the terms of a sequence and function notation?

C. What is a decreasing sequence?

D. What is meant by a recursion formula for a sequence?

Write the first five terms of the sequences with the following general terms.

1. $a_n = 3n + 1$

2. $a_n = 2n + 3$

3. $a_n = 4n - 1$

4. $a_n = n + 4$

5. $a_n = n$

6. $a_n = -n$

7. $a_n = n^2 + 3$

8. $a_n = n^3 + 1$

9. $a_n = \dfrac{n}{n + 3}$

10. $a_n = \dfrac{n + 1}{n + 2}$

11. $a_n = \dfrac{1}{n^2}$

12. $a_n = \dfrac{1}{n^3}$

13. $a_n = 2^n$

14. $a_n = 3^{-n}$

15. $a_n = 1 + \dfrac{1}{n}$

16. $a_n = n - \dfrac{1}{n}$

17. $a_n = (-2)^n$

18. $a_n = (-3)^n$

19. $a_n = 4 + (-1)^n$

20. $a_n = 10 + (-2)^n$

21. $a_n = (-1)^{n+1} \cdot \dfrac{n}{2n - 1}$

22. $a_n = (-1)^n \cdot \dfrac{2n + 1}{2n - 1}$

23. $a_n = n^2 \cdot 2^{-n}$

24. $a_n = n^n$

25. If $a_n = n^2 + 2n$, find a_8.

26. If $a_n = 3n - n^2$, find a_{10}.

27. If $a_n = \dfrac{(-1)^n}{2n + 3}$, find a_{100}.

28. If $a_n = \dfrac{(-1)^{n+1}}{2^n - 3}$, find a_{12}.

Write the first five terms of the sequences defined by the following recursion formulas.

29. $a_1 = 3$ $a_n = -3a_{n-1}$ $n > 1$

30. $a_1 = 3$ $a_n = a_{n-1} - 3$ $n > 1$

31. $a_1 = 1$ $a_n = 2a_{n-1} + 3$ $n > 1$

32. $a_1 = 1$ $a_n = a_{n-1} + n$ $n > 1$

33. $a_1 = 2$ $a_n = 2a_{n-1} - 1$ $n > 1$

34. $a_1 = -4$ $a_n = -2a_{n-1}$ $n > 1$

35. $a_1 = 5$ $a_n = 3a_{n-1} - 4$ $n > 1$

36. $a_1 = -3$ $a_n = -2a_{n-1} + 5$ $n > 1$

37. $a_1 = 4$ $a_n = 2a_{n-1} - a_1$ $n > 1$

38. $a_1 = -3$ $a_n = -2a_{n-1} - n$ $n > 1$

Determine a formula for the general term for each of the following sequences.

39. 4, 8, 12, 16, 20,…

40. 7, 10, 13, 16,…

41. 1, 4, 9, 16,…

42. 3, 12, 27, 48,…

43. 4, 8, 16, 32,…

44. $-2, 4, -8, 16,…$

45. $\dfrac{1}{4}, \dfrac{1}{8}, \dfrac{1}{16}, \dfrac{1}{32},…$

46. $\dfrac{1}{4}, \dfrac{2}{9}, \dfrac{3}{16}, \dfrac{4}{25},…$

47. 5, 8, 11, 14,…

48. 7, 5, 3, 1,…

49. $-2, -6, -10, -14,…$

50. $-2, 2, -2, 2,…$

51. $1, -2, 4, -8,…$

52. $-1, 3, -9, 27,…$

53. $\log_2 3, \log_3 4, \log_4 5, \log_5 6,…$

54. $0, \dfrac{3}{5}, \dfrac{8}{10}, \dfrac{15}{17},…$

Applying the Concepts

55. Salary Increase The entry level salary for a teacher is $28,000 with 4% increases after every year of service.

    a. Write a sequence for this teacher's salary for the first 5 years.

    b. Find the general term of the sequence in part *a*.

56. Holiday Account To save money for holiday presents, a person deposits $5 in a savings account on January 1, and then deposits an additional $5 every week thereafter until Christmas.

    a. Write a sequence for the money in that savings account for the first 10 weeks of the year.

    b. Write the general term of the sequence in part *a*.

    c. If there are 50 weeks from January 1 to Christmas, how much money will be available for spending on Christmas presents?

57. Akaka Falls If a boulder fell from the top of Akaka Falls in Hawaii, the distance, in feet, the boulder would fall in each consecutive second would be modeled by a sequence whose general term is $a_n = 32n - 16$, where n represents the number of seconds.

    a. Write a sequence for the first 5 seconds the boulder falls.

    b. What is the total distance the boulder fell in 5 seconds?

    c. If Akaka Falls is approximately 420 feet high, will the boulder hit the ground within 5 seconds?

58. Polygons The formula for the sum of the interior angles of a polygon with n sides is $a_n = 180°(n - 2)$.

    a. Write a sequence to represent the sum of the interior angles of a polygon with 3, 4, 5, and 6 sides.

    b. What would be the sum of the interior angles of a polygon with 20 sides?

    c. What happens when $n = 2$ to indicate that a polygon cannot be formed with only two sides?

59. **Pendulum** A pendulum swings 10 feet left to right on its first swing. On each swing following the first, the pendulum swings $\frac{4}{5}$ of the previous swing.

   a. Write a sequence for the distance traveled by the pendulum on the first, second, and third swing.

   b. Write a general term for the sequence, where n represents the number of the swing.

   c. How far will the pendulum swing on its tenth swing? (Round to the nearest hundredth.)

Learning Objectives Assessment

The following problems can be used to help assess if you have successfully met the learning objectives for this section.

60. Find the fifth term of the sequence $a_n = (-1)^n(n^2 - 2)$.

   a. 23   **b.** -14 **c.** -23 **d.** 14

61. Find the fifth term of the sequence defined by the recursion formula $a_1 = 6, a_n = 2a_{n-1} + 1 \ (n > 1)$.

   a. 6   **b.** 11   **c.** 111   **d.** 223

62. Find the general term for the sequence 2, 5, 10, 17, 26,....

   a. $a_n = 3n - 1$ **b.** $a_n = n^2 + 1$

   c. $a_n = 4n - 2$ **d.** $a_n = 2n^2$

Getting Ready for the Next Section

Simplify.

63. $-2 + 6 + 4 + 22$ 64. $9 - 27 + 81 - 243$

65. $-8 + 16 - 32 + 64$ 66. $-4 + 8 - 16 + 32 - 64$

67. $(1 - 3) + (4 - 3) + (9 - 3) + (16 - 3)$

68. $(1 - 3) + (9 + 1) + (16 + 1) + (25 + 1) + (36 + 1)$

69. $-\frac{1}{3} + \frac{1}{9} - \frac{1}{27} + \frac{1}{81}$ 70. $\frac{1}{2} + \frac{2}{3} + \frac{3}{4} + \frac{4}{5}$

71. $\frac{1}{3} + \frac{1}{2} + \frac{3}{5} + \frac{2}{3}$ 72. $\frac{1}{16} + \frac{1}{32} + \frac{1}{64}$

SPOTLIGHT ON SUCCESS   *Student Instructor Claire*

"With ideas it is like with dizzy heights you climb: At first they cause you discomfort and you are anxious to get down, distrustful of your own powers; but soon the remoteness of the turmoil of life and the inspiring influence of the altitude calm your blood; your step gets firm and sure and you begin to look - for dizzier heights."
— Nikola Tesla

I think one of the most overwhelming things about college is that nothing really prepares you for how difficult it can be, not just academically, but personally, professionally, financially, socially, in every way you can imagine. College forces you to grapple with unimaginable challenges, which is both the beauty and the beast of it. For me, college was a period of extraordinary transformation, in ways that were often uncomfortable and confusing. It was a time of intense freedom and exploration but also of stress and uncertainty.

The real struggle as a college student is figuring out how to succeed academically amidst all that chaos. What ultimately worked best for me was to think big picture. I would ask myself what I wanted out of each class and out of college as a whole. It's so easy to look at an assignment and say, "I'd much rather take a nap than do this," especially when you're already mentally and physically drained. However, it's much easier to make the productive choice if you say, "Would I rather take a nap right now or get an A in this class? Would I rather watch this TV show or get into my top grad school?"

It's worth it to give as much time and energy as you can to academic pursuits because there will always be more to learn. That's the exciting and daunting thing about intellectual growth; there is no end point, no limit to how high you can climb. Once you learn how to manage your resources and get out of your own way, the possibilities are endless.

Learning Objectives

In this section, we will learn how to:

1. Evaluate a series expressed in summation notation.

2. Write a series using summation notation.

Introduction

There is an interesting relationship between the sequence of odd numbers and the sequence of squares that is found by adding the terms in the sequence of odd numbers.

$$
\begin{aligned}
1 &= 1 \\
1 + 3 &= 4 \\
1 + 3 + 5 &= 9 \\
1 + 3 + 5 + 7 &= 16
\end{aligned}
$$

When we add the terms of a sequence, the result is called a series.

> (dēf) **DEFINITION** *series*
>
> The sum of a number of terms in a sequence is called a *series*.

A sequence can be finite or infinite, depending on whether the sequence ends with a particular term or continues indefinitely. For example,

$$1, 3, 5, 7, 9$$

is a finite sequence, but

$$1, 3, 5, \ldots$$

is an infinite sequence. Associated with each of the preceding sequences is a series found by adding the terms of the sequence:

$$1 + 3 + 5 + 7 + 9 \qquad \text{Finite series}$$

$$1 + 3 + 5 + \ldots \qquad \text{Infinite series}$$

Summation Notation

In this section, we will consider only finite series. We can introduce a new kind of notation here that is a compact way of indicating a finite series. The notation is called *summation notation*, or *sigma notation* because it is written using the Greek letter sigma. The expression

$$\sum_{i=1}^{4} (8i - 10)$$

is an example of summation notation. This expression is used to indicate the sum of the first through the fourth terms of the sequence $a_i = 8i - 10$. That is,

Note The Greek letter sigma Σ is a capital S, which was chosen as a reminder that a series is a *sum*.

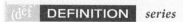

$$
\sum_{i=1}^{4} (8i - 10) = \quad a_1 \quad + \quad a_2 \quad + \quad a_3 \quad + \quad a_4
$$
$$
= (8 \cdot 1 - 10) + (8 \cdot 2 - 10) + (8 \cdot 3 - 10) + (8 \cdot 4 - 10)
$$
$$
= -2 + 6 + 14 + 22
$$
$$
= 40
$$

The letter i as used here is called the *index of summation*, or just *index* for short.

Here are some examples illustrating the use of summation notation.

EXAMPLE 1   Expand and simplify: $\displaystyle\sum_{i=1}^{5}(i^2 - 1)$.

SOLUTION   We replace i in the expression $i^2 - 1$ with all consecutive integers from 1 up to 5, including 1 and 5:

$$\sum_{i=1}^{5}(i^2 - 1) = (1^2 - 1) + (2^2 - 1) + (3^2 - 1) + (4^2 - 1) + (5^2 - 1)$$
$$= 0 + 3 + 8 + 15 + 24$$
$$= 50$$

EXAMPLE 2   Expand and simplify: $\displaystyle\sum_{i=3}^{6}(-2)^i$.

SOLUTION   We replace i in the expression $(-2)^i$ with the consecutive integers beginning at 3 and ending at 6:

$$\sum_{i=3}^{6}(-2)^i = (-2)^3 + (-2)^4 + (-2)^5 + (-2)^6$$
$$= -8 + 16 + (-32) + 64$$
$$= 40$$

USING TECHNOLOGY   *Evaluating a Series on a Graphing Calculator*

A TI-84 graphing calculator has a built-in sum(command that, when used with the seq(command, allows us to add the terms of a series. Let's repeat Example 1 using our graphing calculator. First, we go to $\boxed{\text{LIST}}$ and select MATH. The fifth option in that list is sum(, which we select. Then we go to $\boxed{\text{LIST}}$ again and select OPS. From that list we select seq(. Next we enter X^2−1, X, 1, 5, and then we close both sets of parentheses. Our screen shows the following:

sum(seq(X^2−1, X, 1, 5))   which will give us $\displaystyle\sum_{i=1}^{5}(i^2 - 1)$

When we press $\boxed{\text{ENTER}}$ the calculator displays 50, which is the same result we obtained in Example 1.

EXAMPLE 3   Expand: $\displaystyle\sum_{i=2}^{5}(x^i - 3)$.

SOLUTION   We must be careful not to confuse the letter x with i. The index i is the quantity we replace by the consecutive integers from 2 to 5, not x:

$$\sum_{i=2}^{5}(x^i - 3) = (x^2 - 3) + (x^3 - 3) + (x^4 - 3) + (x^5 - 3).$$

Because we were only asked to expand, but not simplify, the series, we leave our answer in this form.

In the first three examples, we were given an expression with summation notation and asked to expand it. The next examples in this section illustrate how we can write a series as an expression involving summation notation.

EXAMPLE 4   Write with summation notation: $1 + 3 + 5 + 7 + 9$.

SOLUTION   A formula that gives us the terms of this sum is

$$a_i = 2i - 1$$

where i ranges from 1 up to and including 5. Notice we are using the subscript i in exactly the same way we used the subscript n in the previous section — to indicate the general term. Writing the sum

$$1 + 3 + 5 + 7 + 9$$

with summation notation looks like this:

$$\sum_{i=1}^{5} (2i - 1)$$

EXAMPLE 5   Write with summation notation: $3 + 12 + 27 + 48$.

SOLUTION   We need a formula, in terms of i, that will give each term in the sum. Writing the sum as

$$3 \cdot 1^2 + 3 \cdot 2^2 + 3 \cdot 3^2 + 3 \cdot 4^2$$

we see the formula

$$a_i = 3 \cdot i^2$$

where i ranges from 1 up to and including 4. Using this formula and summation notation, we can represent the sum

$$3 + 12 + 27 + 48$$

as

$$\sum_{i=1}^{4} 3i^2$$

EXAMPLE 6   Write with summation notation:

$$\frac{x+3}{x^3} + \frac{x+4}{x^4} + \frac{x+5}{x^5} + \frac{x+6}{x^6}$$

SOLUTION   A formula that gives each of these terms is

$$a_i = \frac{x+i}{x^i}$$

where i assumes all integer values between 3 and 6, including 3 and 6. The sum can be written as

$$\sum_{i=3}^{6} \frac{x+i}{x^i}$$

Getting Ready for Class

After reading through the preceding section, respond in your own words and in complete sentences.

A. What is the difference between a sequence and a series?

B. What does the symbol Σ stand for?

C. Explain what the 1 and 4 indicate in the series $\sum_{i=1}^{4} (2i + 3)$.

D. Determine for what values of n the series $\sum_{i=1}^{n} (-1)^i$ will be equal to 0. Explain your answer.

Expand and simplify each of the following.

1. $\displaystyle\sum_{i=1}^{4}(2i+4)$ **2.** $\displaystyle\sum_{i=1}^{5}(2i+4)$ **3.** $\displaystyle\sum_{i=2}^{3}(i^2-1)$ **4.** $\displaystyle\sum_{i=3}^{6}(i^2+1)$

5. $\displaystyle\sum_{i=1}^{4}(i^2-3)$ **6.** $\displaystyle\sum_{i=2}^{6}(2i^2+1)$ **7.** $\displaystyle\sum_{i=1}^{4}\frac{i}{1+i}$ **8.** $\displaystyle\sum_{i=1}^{3}\frac{i^2}{2i-1}$

9. $\displaystyle\sum_{i=1}^{4}(-3)^i$ **10.** $\displaystyle\sum_{i=1}^{4}\left(-\frac{1}{3}\right)^i$ **11.** $\displaystyle\sum_{i=3}^{6}(-2)^i$ **12.** $\displaystyle\sum_{i=4}^{6}\left(-\frac{1}{2}\right)^i$

13. $\displaystyle\sum_{i=2}^{6}(-2)^i$ **14.** $\displaystyle\sum_{i=2}^{5}(-3)^i$ **15.** $\displaystyle\sum_{i=1}^{5}\left(-\frac{1}{2}\right)^i$ **16.** $\displaystyle\sum_{i=3}^{6}\left(-\frac{1}{3}\right)^i$

17. $\displaystyle\sum_{i=2}^{5}\frac{i-1}{i+1}$ **18.** $\displaystyle\sum_{i=2}^{4}\frac{i^2-1}{i^2+1}$

Expand the following. Do not simplify.

19. $\displaystyle\sum_{i=1}^{5}(x+i)$ **20.** $\displaystyle\sum_{i=2}^{7}(x+1)^i$ **21.** $\displaystyle\sum_{i=1}^{4}(x-2)^i$ **22.** $\displaystyle\sum_{i=2}^{5}\left(x+\frac{1}{i}\right)^2$

23. $\displaystyle\sum_{i=1}^{5}\frac{x+i}{x-1}$ **24.** $\displaystyle\sum_{i=1}^{6}\frac{x-3i}{x+3i}$ **25.** $\displaystyle\sum_{i=3}^{8}(x+i)^i$ **26.** $\displaystyle\sum_{i=1}^{5}(x+i)^{i+1}$

27. $\displaystyle\sum_{i=3}^{6}(x-2i)^{i+3}$ **28.** $\displaystyle\sum_{i=5}^{8}\left(\frac{x-i}{x+i}\right)^{2i}$

Write each of the following sums with summation notation. Do not calculate the sum. Use i as the index of summation. (*Note*: Other answers are possible.)

29. $2+4+8+16$ **30.** $3+5+7+9+11$

31. $4+8+16+32+64$ **32.** $3+8+15+24$

33. $5+9+13+17+21$ **34.** $3-6+12-24+48$

35. $-4+8-16+32$ **36.** $15+24+35+48+63$

37. $\dfrac{3}{4}+\dfrac{4}{5}+\dfrac{5}{6}+\dfrac{6}{7}+\dfrac{7}{8}$ **38.** $\dfrac{1}{2}+\dfrac{2}{3}+\dfrac{3}{4}+\dfrac{4}{5}$

39. $\dfrac{1}{3}+\dfrac{2}{5}+\dfrac{3}{7}+\dfrac{4}{9}$ **40.** $\dfrac{3}{1}+\dfrac{5}{3}+\dfrac{7}{5}+\dfrac{9}{7}$

41. $(x-2)^6+(x-2)^7+(x-2)^8+(x-2)^9$

42. $(x+1)^3+(x+2)^4+(x+3)^5+(x+4)^6+(x+5)^7$

43. $\left(1+\dfrac{1}{x}\right)^2+\left(1+\dfrac{2}{x}\right)^3+\left(1+\dfrac{3}{x}\right)^4+\left(1+\dfrac{4}{x}\right)^5$

44. $\dfrac{x-1}{x+2}+\dfrac{x-2}{x+4}+\dfrac{x-3}{x+6}+\dfrac{x-4}{x+8}+\dfrac{x-5}{x+10}$

45. $\dfrac{x}{x+3}+\dfrac{x}{x+4}+\dfrac{x}{x+5}$ **46.** $\dfrac{x-3}{x^3}+\dfrac{x-4}{x^4}+\dfrac{x-5}{x^5}+\dfrac{x-6}{x^6}$

47. $x^2(x+2)+x^3(x+3)+x^4(x+4)$ **48.** $x(x+2)^2+x(x+3)^3+x(x+4)^4$

49. Repeating Decimals Any repeating, nonterminating decimal may be viewed as a series. For instance, $\frac{2}{3} = 0.6 + 0.06 + 0.006 + 0.0006 + \cdots$. Write the following fractions as series.

a. $\dfrac{1}{3}$

b. $\dfrac{2}{9}$

c. $\dfrac{3}{11}$

50. Repeating Decimals Refer to the previous exercise, and express the following repeating decimals as fractions.

a. $0.55555\ldots$

b. $1.33333\ldots$

c. $0.29292929\ldots$

Applying the Concepts

51. Skydiving A skydiver jumps from a plane and falls 16 feet the first second, 48 feet the second second, and 80 feet the third second. If he continues to fall in the same manner, how far will he fall the seventh second? What is the distance he falls in 7 seconds?

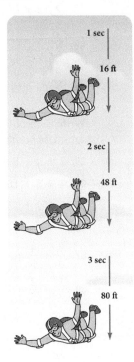

52. Bacterial Growth After 1 day, a colony of 50 bacteria reproduces to become 200 bacteria. After 2 days, they reproduce to become 800 bacteria. If they continue to reproduce at this rate, how many bacteria will be present after 4 days?

Start   1 day   2 days

53. **Akaka Falls** In Section 10.1, when a boulder fell from the top of Akaka Falls in Hawaii, the sequence generated during the first 5 seconds the boulder fell was 16, 48, 80, 112, and 144.

   a. Write a finite series that represents the sum of this sequence.

   b. The general term of this sequence was given as $a_n = 32n - 16$. Write the series produced in part **a** in summation notation.

54. **Pendulum** A pendulum swings 12 feet left to right on its first swing, and on each swing following the first, swings $\frac{3}{4}$ of the previous swing. The distance the pendulum traveled in 5 seconds can be expressed in summation notation

$$\sum_{i=1}^{5} 12\left(\frac{3}{4}\right)^{i-1}$$

Expand the summation notation and simplify. Round your final answer to the nearest tenth.

Learning Objectives Assessment

The following problems can be used to help assess if you have successfully met the learning objectives for this section.

55. Expand and simplify: $\displaystyle\sum_{i=3}^{5} (i^2 - 2i)$.

   a. 15   b. 26   c. 360   d. 3, 8, 15

56. Write $\frac{1}{2} + \frac{1}{4} + \frac{1}{8} + \frac{1}{16} + \frac{1}{32}$ using summation notation.

   a. $\displaystyle\sum_{i=1}^{16} \frac{1}{2i}$ b. $\displaystyle\sum_{i=2}^{32} \frac{1}{i}$

   c. $\displaystyle\sum_{i=1}^{5} \frac{1}{2^i}$ d. $\displaystyle\sum_{i=\frac{1}{2}}^{\frac{1}{32}} \frac{1}{2^i}$

Getting Ready for the Next Section

Simplify.

57. $2 + 9(8)$

58. $\frac{1}{2} + 9\left(\frac{1}{2}\right)$

59. $\frac{10}{2}\left(\frac{1}{2} + 5\right)$

60. $\frac{10}{2}(2 + 74)$

61. $3 + (n - 1)2$

62. $7 + (n - 1)3$

Solve each system of equations.

63. $x + 2y = 7$
    $x + 7y = 17$

64. $x + 3y = 14$
    $x + 9y = 32$

Learning Objectives

In this section, we will learn how to:

1. Identify an arithmetic sequence.
2. Find the common difference for an arithmetic sequence.
3. Find a formula for the general term of an arithmetic sequence.
4. Find the nth partial sum for an arithmetic sequence.

Introduction

In this and the following section, we will investigate two major types of sequences—arithmetic sequences and geometric sequences.

> **(def) DEFINITION** *arithmetic sequence*
>
> An *arithmetic sequence* is a sequence of numbers in which each term is obtained from the preceding term by adding the same amount each time. An arithmetic sequence is also called an *arithmetic progression.*

The sequence

$$2, 6, 10, 14,\ldots$$

is an example of an arithmetic sequence, because each term is obtained from the preceding term by adding 4 each time. The amount we add each time—in this case, 4—is called the *common difference*, because it can be obtained by subtracting any two consecutive terms. The common difference is denoted by d, and given by $d = a_n - a_{n-1}$ for any $n > 1$.

VIDEO EXAMPLES

SECTION 13.3

 EXAMPLE 1 Give the common difference d for the arithmetic sequence 4, 10, 16, 22,…

SOLUTION Because each term can be obtained from the preceding term by adding 6, the common difference is 6. That is, $d = 6$.

EXAMPLE 2 Give the common difference for 100, 93, 86, 79,….

SOLUTION The common difference in this case is $d = -7$, since adding -7 to any term always produces the next consecutive term.

EXAMPLE 3 Give the common difference for $\frac{1}{2}, 1, \frac{3}{2}, 2,\ldots$.

SOLUTION The common difference is $d = \frac{1}{2}$.

The General Term

The general term a_n of an arithmetic progression can always be written in terms of the first term a_1 and the common difference d. Consider the sequence from Example 1:

$$4, 10, 16, 22,\ldots$$

We can write each number in terms of the first term 4 and the common difference 6:

$$4, \qquad 4 + (1 \cdot 6), \qquad 4 + (2 \cdot 6), \qquad 4 + (3 \cdot 6),\ldots$$

$$a_1, \qquad\quad a_2, \qquad\qquad\quad a_3, \qquad\qquad\quad a_4,\ldots$$

Observing the relationship between the subscript on the terms in the second line and the coefficients of the 6's in the first line, we write the general term for the sequence as

$$a_n = 4 + (n - 1)6$$

We generalize this result to obtain the general term of any arithmetic sequence.

[Δ≠Σ] *Arithmetic Sequences*

The *general term* of an arithmetic progression with first term a_1 and common difference d is given by

$$a_n = a_1 + (n - 1)d$$

EXAMPLE 4   Find the general term for the sequence

$$7, 10, 13, 16,\ldots$$

SOLUTION   The first term is $a_1 = 7$, and the common difference is $d = 3$. Substituting these numbers into the formula given earlier, we have

$$a_n = 7 + (n - 1)3$$

which we can simplify, if we choose, to

$$a_n = 7 + 3n - 3$$

$$= 3n + 4$$

EXAMPLE 5   Find the general term of the arithmetic progression whose third term a_3 is 7 and whose eighth term a_8 is 17.

SOLUTION   According to the formula for the general term, the third term can be written as $a_3 = a_1 + 2d$, and the eighth term can be written as $a_8 = a_1 + 7d$. Because these terms are also equal to 7 and 17, respectively, we can write

$$a_3 = a_1 + 2d = 7$$

$$a_8 = a_1 + 7d = 17$$

To find a_1 and d, we simply solve the system:

$$a_1 + 2d = 7$$

$$a_1 + 7d = 17$$

We add the opposite of the top equation to the bottom equation. The result is

$$5d = 10$$

$$d = 2$$

To find a_1, we simply substitute 2 for d in either of the original equations and get

$$a_1 = 3$$

The general term for this progression is

$$a_n = 3 + (n - 1)2$$

which we can simplify to

$$a_n = 2n + 1$$

Looking at the simplified formulas in Examples 4 and 5, notice that we obtained a linear function in both cases. This is true in general. An arithmetic sequence can always be expressed as a linear function with slope given by d.

Arithmetic Series

The sum of the first n terms of an arithmetic sequence is denoted by S_n. The following theorem gives the formula for finding S_n, which is sometimes called the *nth partial sum*.

[$\Delta \neq \Sigma$]   THEOREM   13.3

The sum of the first n terms of an arithmetic sequence whose first term is a_1 and whose nth term is a_n is given by

$$S_n = \sum_{i=1}^{n} (a_1 + (i - 1)d) = \frac{n}{2}(a_1 + a_n)$$

Proof   We can write S_n in expanded form as

$$S_n = a_1 + [a_1 + d] + [a_1 + 2d] + \cdots + [a_1 + (n - 1)d]$$

We can arrive at this same series by starting with the last term a_n and subtracting d each time. Writing S_n this way, we have

$$S_n = a_n + [a_n - d] + [a_n - 2d] + \cdots + [a_n - (n - 1)d]$$

If we add the preceding two expressions term by term, we have

$$2S_n = (a_1 + a_n) + (a_1 + a_n) + (a_1 + a_n) + \cdots + (a_1 + a_n)$$

$$2S_n = n(a_1 + a_n)$$

$$S_n = \frac{n}{2}(a_1 + a_n)$$

EXAMPLE 6   Find the sum of the first 10 terms of the arithmetic progression 2, 10, 18, 26,....

SOLUTION   The first term is 2, and the common difference is 8. The tenth term is

$$a_{10} = 2 + 8(10 - 1)$$

$$= 2 + 72$$

$$= 74$$

Substituting $n = 10$, $a_1 = 2$, and $a_{10} = 74$ into the formula

$$S_n = \frac{n}{2}(a_1 + a_n)$$

we have

$$S_{10} = \frac{10}{2}(2 + 74)$$

$$= 5(76)$$

$$= 380$$

The sum of the first 10 terms is 380.

Getting Ready for Class

After reading through the preceding section, respond in your own words and in complete sentences.

A. Explain how to determine if a sequence is arithmetic.

B. What is a common difference?

C. Suppose the value of a_5 is given. What other possible pieces of information could be given to have enough information to obtain the first 10 terms of the sequence?

D. Explain the formula $a_n = a_1 + (n - 1)d$ in words so that someone who wanted to find the nth term of an arithmetic sequence could do so from your description.

Determine which of the following sequences are arithmetic progressions. For those that are arithmetic progressions, identify the common difference d.

1. 1, 2, 3, 4,...   **2.** 4, 6, 8, 10,...   **3.** 1, 2, 4, 7,...   **4.** 1, 2, 4, 8,...

5. 50, 45, 40,...   **6.** $1, \frac{1}{2}, \frac{1}{4}, \frac{1}{8}$,...   **7.** 1, 4, 9, 16,...   **8.** 5, 7, 9, 11,...

9. $\frac{1}{3}, 1, \frac{5}{3}, \frac{7}{3}$,...   **10.** 5, 11, 17,...

Each of the following problems refers to arithmetic sequences.

11. If $a_1 = 3$ and $d = 4$, find a_n and a_{24}.

12. If $a_1 = 5$ and $d = 10$, find a_n and a_{100}.

13. If $a_1 = 6$ and $d = -2$, find a_{10} and S_{10}.

14. If $a_1 = 7$ and $d = -1$, find a_{24} and S_{24}.

15. If $a_6 = 17$ and $a_{12} = 29$, find a_1, the common difference d, and then find a_{30}.

16. If $a_5 = 23$ and $a_{10} = 48$, find a_1, the common difference d, and then find a_{40}.

17. If the third term is 16 and the eighth term is 26, find the first term, the common difference, and then find a_{20} and S_{20}.

18. If the third term is 16 and the eighth term is 51, find the first term, the common difference, and then find a_{50} and S_{50}.

19. If $a_1 = 3$ and $d = 4$, find a_{20} and S_{20}.

20. If $a_1 = 40$ and $d = -5$, find a_{25} and S_{25}.

21. If $a_4 = 14$ and $a_{10} = 32$, find a_{40} and S_{40}.

22. If $a_7 = 0$ and $a_{11} = -\frac{8}{3}$, find a_{61} and S_{61}.

23. If $a_6 = -17$ and $S_6 = -12$, find a_1 and d.

24. If $a_{10} = 12$ and $S_{10} = 40$, find a_1 and d.

25. Find a_{85} for the sequence 14, 11, 8, 5,...

26. Find S_{100} for the sequence $-32, -25, -18, -11$,...

27. If $S_{20} = 80$ and $a_1 = -4$, find d and a_{39}.

28. If $S_{24} = 60$ and $a_1 = 4$, find d and a_{116}.

29. Find the sum of the first 100 terms of the sequence 5, 9, 13, 17,....

30. Find the sum of the first 50 terms of the sequence 8, 11, 14, 17,....

31. Find a_{35} for the sequence 12, 7, 2, -3,....

32. Find a_{45} for the sequence 25, 20, 15, 10,....

33. Find the tenth term and the sum of the first 10 terms of the sequence $\frac{1}{2}, 1, \frac{3}{2}, 2$,....

34. Find the 15th term and the sum of the first 15 terms of the sequence $-\frac{1}{3}, 0, \frac{1}{3}, \frac{2}{3}$,....

Applying the Concepts

Straight-Line Depreciation Recall from a previous section that straight-line depreciation is an accounting method used to help spread the cost of new equipment over a number of years. The value at any time during the life of the machine can be found with a linear equation in two variables. For income tax purposes, however, it is the value at the end of the year that is most important, and for this reason sequences can be used.

35. **Value of a Copy Machine** A large copy machine sells for $18,000 when it is new. Its value decreases $3,300 each year after that. We can use an arithmetic sequence to find the value of the machine at the end of each year. If we let a_0 represent the value when it is purchased, then a_1 is the value after 1 year, a_2 is the value after 2 years, and so on.

   a. Write the first 5 terms of the sequence.

   b. What is the common difference?

   c. Construct a line graph for the first 5 terms of the sequence.

   d. Use the line graph to estimate the value of the copy machine 2.5 years after it is purchased.

   e. Write the sequence from part a using a recursive formula.

36. **Value of a Forklift** An electric forklift sells for $125,000 when new. Each year after that, it decreases $16,500 in value.

   a. Write an arithmetic sequence that gives the value of the forklift at the end of each of the first 5 years after it is purchased.

   b. What is the common difference for this sequence?

   c. Construct a line graph for this sequence.

   d. Use the line graph to estimate the value of the forklift 3.5 years after it is purchased.

   e. Write the sequence from part a using a recursive formula.

37. **Distance** A rocket travels vertically 1,500 feet in its first second of flight, and then about 40 feet less each succeeding second. Use these estimates to answer the following questions.

   a. Write a sequence of the vertical distance traveled by a rocket in each of its first 6 seconds.

   b. Is the sequence in part a an arithmetic sequence? Explain why or why not.

   c. What is the general term of the sequence in part a?

38. **Depreciation** Suppose an automobile sells for N dollars new, and then depreciates 40% each year.

   a. Write a sequence for the value of this automobile (in terms of N) for each year.

   b. What is the general term of the sequence in part a?

   c. Is the sequence in part a an arithmetic sequence? Explain why it is or is not.

39. Triangular Numbers The first four triangular numbers are 1, 3, 6, 10, . . ., and are illustrated in the following diagram.

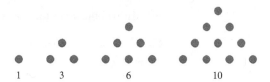

1   3   6   10

a. Write a sequence of the first 15 triangular numbers.

b. Write the recursive general term for the sequence of triangular numbers.

c. Is the sequence of triangular numbers an arithmetic sequence? Explain why it is or is not.

40. Arithmetic Means Three (or more) arithmetic means between two numbers may be found by forming an arithmetic sequence using the original two numbers and the arithmetic means. For example, three arithmetic means between 10 and 34 may be found by examining the sequence 10, a, b, c, 34. For the sequence to be arithmetic, the common difference must be 6; therefore, $a = 16$, $b = 22$, and $c = 28$. Use this idea to answer the following questions.

a. Find four arithmetic means between 10 and 35.

b. Find three arithmetic means between 2 and 62.

c. Find five arithmetic means between 4 and 28.

41. Paratroopers At the Ft. Campbell Army Base, soldiers in the 101st Airborne Division are trained to be paratroopers. A paratrooper's free fall drop per second can be modeled by an arithmetic sequence whose first term is 16 feet and whose common difference is 32 feet.

a. Write the general term for this arithmetic progression.

b. How far would a paratrooper fall during the tenth second of free fall?

c. Using the sum formula for an arithmetic sequence, what would be the total distance a paratrooper fell during 10 seconds of free fall?

42. College Fund When Jack's first grandchild, Kayla, was born, he decided to establish a college fund for her. On Kayla's first birthday, Jack deposited $1,000 into an account and decided that each year on her birthday he would deposit an amount $500 more than the previous year, through her 18th birthday.

a. Write a sequence to represent the amount Jack deposited on her 1st through 5th birthdays. Does this sequence represent an arithmetic progression? If so, what is the common difference?

b. How much will Jack deposit on Kayla's 18th birthday?

c. What would be the total amount (excluding any interest earned) Jack has saved for Kayla's college fund by her 18th birthday?

Learning Objectives Assessment

The following problems can be used to help assess if you have successfully met the learning objectives for this section.

43. Which of the following is an arithmetic sequence?

   a. $7, 4, 1, -2,...$ **b.** $2, 4, 8, 16,...$

   c. $\dfrac{1}{2}, \dfrac{1}{4}, \dfrac{1}{6}, \dfrac{1}{8},....$ **d.** $1, 1.1, 1.11, 1.111,...$

44. What is the common difference for the sequence $90, 80, 70, 60,...$?

   a. 10 **b.** $\dfrac{15}{2}$ **c.** 30 **d.** -10

45. Find the tenth term for the arithmetic sequence $15, 21, 27,....$

   a. 81 **b.** 75 **c.** 60 **d.** 69

46. Find the sum of the first 20 terms of the arithmetic sequence with $a_1 = 5$ and $d = 2.5$.

   a. 57.5 **b.** 600 **c.** 575 **d.** 150

Getting Ready for the Next Section

Simplify.

47. $\dfrac{1}{8}\left(\dfrac{1}{2}\right)$

48. $\dfrac{1}{4}\left(\dfrac{1}{2}\right)$

49. $\dfrac{3\sqrt{3}}{3}$

50. $\dfrac{3}{\sqrt{3}}$

51. $2 \cdot 2^{n-1}$

52. $3 \cdot 3^{n-1}$

53. $\dfrac{ar^6}{ar^3}$

54. $\dfrac{ar^7}{ar^4}$

55. $\dfrac{\dfrac{1}{5}}{1-\dfrac{1}{2}}$

56. $\dfrac{\dfrac{9}{10}}{1-\dfrac{1}{10}}$

57. $\dfrac{3[(-2)^8 - 1]}{-2-1}$

58. $\dfrac{4\left[\left(\dfrac{1}{2}\right)^6 - 1\right]}{\dfrac{1}{2} - 1}$

Learning Objectives

In this section, we will learn how to:

1. Identify a geometric sequence.

2. Find the common ratio for a geometric sequence.

3. Find the general term for a geometric sequence.

4. Find the sum for a finite or infinite geometric series.

Introduction

This section is concerned with the second major classification of sequences, called geometric sequences. The problems in this section are similar to the problems in the preceding section.

> **DEFINITION** *geometric sequence*
>
> A sequence of numbers in which each term is obtained from the previous term by multiplying by the same amount each time is called a *geometric sequence.* Geometric sequences are also called *geometric progressions.*

The sequence

$$3, 6, 12, 24,\ldots$$

is an example of a geometric progression. Each term is obtained from the previous term by multiplying by 2. The amount by which we multiply each time — in this case, 2 — is called the *common ratio*. The common ratio, denoted by r, is found by taking the ratio of any two consecutive terms $r = \frac{a_n}{a_{n-1}}$ for any $n > 1$.

VIDEO EXAMPLES

SECTION 13.4

 EXAMPLE 1   Find the common ratio for the geometric progression.

$$\frac{1}{2}, \frac{1}{4}, \frac{1}{8}, \frac{1}{16},\ldots$$

SOLUTION Because each term can be obtained from the term before it by multiplying by $\frac{1}{2}$, the common ratio is $\frac{1}{2}$. That is, $r = \frac{1}{2}$.

 EXAMPLE 2   Find the common ratio for $\sqrt{3}, 3, 3\sqrt{3}, 9,\ldots$

SOLUTION   If we take the ratio of the third term to the second term, we have

$$\frac{3\sqrt{3}}{3} = \sqrt{3}$$

The common ratio is $r = \sqrt{3}$.

> *Geometric Sequences*
>
> The *general term* a_n of a geometric sequence with first term a_1 and common ratio r is given by
>
> $$a_n = a_1 r^{n-1}$$

To see how we arrive at this formula, consider the following geometric progression whose common ratio is 3:

$$2, 6, 18, 54,\ldots$$

We can write each number in the sequence in terms of the first term 2 and the common ratio 3:

$$2\cdot3^0, \quad 2\cdot3^1, \quad 2\cdot3^2, \quad 2\cdot3^3,\ldots$$
$$a_1, \qquad a_2, \qquad a_3, \qquad a_4,\ldots$$

Observing the relationship between the two preceding lines, we find we can write the general term of this progression as

$$a_n = 2 \cdot 3^{n-1}$$

Because the first term can be designated by a_1 and the common ratio by r, the formula

$$a_n = 2 \cdot 3^{n-1}$$

coincides with the formula

$$a_n = a_1 r^{n-1}$$

EXAMPLE 3   Find the general term for the geometric progression

$$5, 10, 20, \ . \ . \ .$$

SOLUTION   The first term is $a_1 = 5$, and the common ratio is $r = 2$. Using these values in the formula

$$a_n = a_1 r^{n-1}$$

we have

$$a_n = 5 \cdot 2^{n-1}$$

EXAMPLE 4   Find the tenth term of the sequence $3, \dfrac{3}{2}, \dfrac{3}{4}, \dfrac{3}{8},\ldots.$

SOLUTION   The sequence is a geometric progression with first term $a_1 = 3$ and common ratio $r = \frac{1}{2}$. The tenth term is

$$a_{10} = 3\left(\frac{1}{2}\right)^9 = \frac{3}{512}$$

EXAMPLE 5   Find the general term for the geometric progression whose fourth term is 16 and whose seventh term is 128.

SOLUTION   The fourth term can be written as $a_4 = a_1 r^3$, and the seventh term can be written as $a_7 = a_1 r^6$.

$$a_4 = a_1 r^3 = 16$$
$$a_7 = a_1 r^6 = 128$$

We can solve for r by using the ratio $\frac{a_7}{a_4}$.

$$\frac{a_7}{a_4} = \frac{a_1 r^6}{a_1 r^3} = \frac{128}{16}$$
$$r^3 = 8$$
$$r = 2$$

The common ratio is 2. To find the first term, we substitute $r = 2$ into either of the original two equations. The result is

$$a_1 = 2$$

The general term for this progression is

$$a_n = 2 \cdot 2^{n-1}$$

which we can simplify by adding exponents, because the bases are equal:

$$a_n = 2^n$$

Finite Geometric Series

As was the case in the preceding section, the sum of the first n terms of a geometric progression is denoted by S_n, which is called the **nth partial sum** of the progression.

> ⎰Δ≠Σ   **THEOREM**   *13.4*
>
> The sum of the first n terms of a geometric progression with first term a_1 and common ratio r is given by the formula
>
> $$S_n = \sum_{i=1}^{n} a_1 r^{i-1} = \frac{a_1(r^n - 1)}{r - 1}$$

Proof   We can write the sum of the first n terms in expanded form:

$$S_n = a_1 + a_1 r + a_1 r^2 + \cdots + a_1 r^{n-1} \tag{1}$$

Then multiplying both sides by r, we have

$$r S_n = a_1 r + a_1 r^2 + a_1 r^3 + \cdots + a_1 r^n \tag{2}$$

If we subtract the left side of equation (1) from the left side of equation (2) and do the same for the right sides, we end up with

$$r S_n - S_n = a_1 r^n - a_1$$

We factor S_n from both terms on the left side and a_1 from both terms on the right side of this equation:

$$S_n(r - 1) = a_1(r^n - 1)$$

Dividing both sides by $r - 1$ gives the desired result:

$$S_n = \frac{a_1(r^n - 1)}{r - 1}$$

EXAMPLE 6   Find the sum of the first 10 terms of the geometric progression 5, 15, 45, 135,….

SOLUTION   The first term is $a_1 = 5$, and the common ratio is $r = 3$. Substituting these values into the formula for S_{10}, we have the sum of the first 10 terms of the sequence:

$$S_{10} = \frac{5(3^{10} - 1)}{3 - 1}$$

$$= \frac{5(3^{10} - 1)}{2}$$

The answer can be left in this form. A calculator will give the result as 147,620.

Infinite Geometric Series

Suppose the common ratio for a geometric sequence is a number whose absolute value is less than 1—for instance, $\frac{1}{2}$. The sum of the first n terms is given by the formula

$$S_n = \frac{a_1\left[\left(\frac{1}{2}\right)^n - 1\right]}{\frac{1}{2} - 1}$$

As n becomes larger and larger, the term $\left(\frac{1}{2}\right)^n$ will become closer and closer to 0. That is, for $n = 10, 20,$ and 30, we have the following approximations:

$$\left(\frac{1}{2}\right)^{10} \approx 0.001$$

$$\left(\frac{1}{2}\right)^{20} \approx 0.000001$$

$$\left(\frac{1}{2}\right)^{30} \approx 0.000000001$$

so that for large values of n, there is little difference between the expression

$$\frac{a_1(r^n - 1)}{r - 1}$$

and the expression

$$\frac{a_1(0 - 1)}{r - 1} = \frac{-a_1}{r - 1} = \frac{a_1}{1 - r} \qquad \text{if} \qquad |r| < 1$$

In fact, the sum of the terms of a geometric sequence in which $|r| < 1$ actually becomes the expression

$$\frac{a_1}{1 - r}$$

as n approaches infinity. To summarize, we have the following:

 The Sum of an Infinite Geometric Sequence

If a geometric sequence has first term a_1 and common ratio r such that $|r| < 1$, then the following is called an *infinite geometric series*:

$$S = \sum_{i=0}^{\infty} a_1 r^i = a_1 + a_1 r + a_1 r^2 + a_1 r^3 + \cdots$$

Its sum is given by the formula

$$S = \frac{a_1}{1 - r}$$

EXAMPLE 7   Find the sum of the infinite geometric series

$$\frac{1}{5} + \frac{1}{10} + \frac{1}{20} + \frac{1}{40} + \cdots$$

SOLUTION   The first term is $a_1 = \frac{1}{5}$, and the common ratio is $r = \frac{1}{2}$, which has an absolute value less than 1. Therefore, the sum of this series is

$$S = \frac{a_1}{1 - r} = \frac{\frac{1}{5}}{1 - \frac{1}{2}} = \frac{\frac{1}{5}}{\frac{1}{2}} = \frac{2}{5}$$

EXAMPLE 8 Show that 0.999…is equal to 1.

SOLUTION We begin by writing 0.999…as an infinite geometric series:

$$0.999\ldots = 0.9 + 0.09 + 0.009 + 0.0009 + \cdots$$

$$= \frac{9}{10} + \frac{9}{100} + \frac{9}{1,000} + \frac{9}{10,000} + \cdots$$

$$= \frac{9}{10} + \frac{9}{10}\left(\frac{1}{10}\right) + \frac{9}{10}\left(\frac{1}{10}\right)^2 + \frac{9}{10}\left(\frac{1}{10}\right)^3 + \cdots$$

As the last line indicates, we have an infinite geometric series with $a_1 = \frac{9}{10}$ and $r = \frac{1}{10}$. The sum of this series is given by

$$S = \frac{a_1}{1 - r} = \frac{\frac{9}{10}}{1 - \frac{1}{10}} = \frac{\frac{9}{10}}{\frac{9}{10}} = 1$$

Getting Ready for Class

After reading through the preceding section, respond in your own words and in complete sentences.

A. What is a common ratio?

B. Explain the formula $a_n = a_1 r^{n-1}$ in words so that someone who wanted to find the nth term of a geometric sequence could do so from your description.

C. When is the sum of an infinite geometric series a finite number?

D. Explain how a repeating decimal can be represented as an infinite geometric series.

Problem Set 13.4

Identify those sequences that are geometric progressions. For those that are geometric, give the common ratio r.

1. $1, 5, 25, 125,...$

2. $6, 12, 24, 48,...$

3. $\dfrac{1}{2}, \dfrac{1}{6}, \dfrac{1}{18}, \dfrac{1}{54},...$

4. $5, 10, 15, 20,...$

5. $4, 9, 16, 25,...$

6. $-1, \dfrac{1}{3}, -\dfrac{1}{9}, \dfrac{1}{27},...$

7. $-2, 4, -8, 16,...$

8. $1, 8, 27, 64,...$

9. $4, 6, 8, 10,...$

10. $1, -3, 9, -27,...$

Each of the following problems gives some information about a specific geometric progression.

11. If $a_1 = 4$ and $r = 3$, find a_n.

12. If $a_1 = 5$ and $r = 2$, find a_n.

13. If $a_1 = -2$ and $r = -\dfrac{1}{2}$, find a_6.

14. If $a_1 = 25$ and $r = -\dfrac{1}{5}$, find a_6.

15. If $a_1 = 3$ and $r = -1$, find a_{20}.

16. If $a_1 = -3$ and $r = -1$, find a_{20}.

17. If $a_1 = 10$ and $r = 2$, find S_{10}.

18. If $a_1 = 8$ and $r = 3$, find S_5.

19. If $a_1 = 1$ and $r = -1$, find S_{20}.

20. If $a_1 = 1$ and $r = -1$, find S_{21}.

21. Find a_8 for $\dfrac{1}{5}, \dfrac{1}{10}, \dfrac{1}{20},...$

22. Find a_8 for $\dfrac{1}{2}, \dfrac{1}{10}, \dfrac{1}{50},...$

23. Find S_5 for $-\dfrac{1}{2}, -\dfrac{1}{4}, -\dfrac{1}{8},...$

24. Find S_6 for $-\dfrac{1}{2}, 1, -2,...$

25. Find a_{10} and S_{10} for $\sqrt{2}, 2, 2\sqrt{2},...$

26. Find a_8 and S_8 for $\sqrt{3}, 3, 3\sqrt{3},...$

27. Find a_6 and S_6 for $100, 10, 1,...$

28. Find a_6 and S_6 for $100, -10, 1,...$

29. If $a_4 = 40$ and $a_6 = 160$, find r.

30. If $a_5 = \dfrac{1}{8}$ and $a_8 = \dfrac{1}{64}$, find r.

31. Given the sequence $-3, 6, -12, 24,...$, find a_8 and S_8.

32. Given the sequence $4, 2, 1, \frac{1}{2},...$, find a_9 and S_9.

33. Given $a_7 = 13$ and $a_{10} = 104$, find r.

34. Given $a_5 = -12$ and $a_8 = 324$, find r.

Find the sum of each infinite geometric series.

35. $\dfrac{1}{2} + \dfrac{1}{4} + \dfrac{1}{8} + \cdots$

36. $\dfrac{1}{3} + \dfrac{1}{9} + \dfrac{1}{27} + \cdots$

37. $4 + 2 + 1 + \cdots$

38. $8 + 4 + 2 + \cdots$

39. $2 + 1 + \dfrac{1}{2} + \cdots$

40. $3 + 1 + \dfrac{1}{3} + \cdots$

41. $\dfrac{4}{3} - \dfrac{2}{3} + \dfrac{1}{3} + \cdots$

42. $6 - 4 + \dfrac{8}{3} + \cdots$

43. $\dfrac{2}{5} + \dfrac{4}{25} + \dfrac{8}{125} + \cdots$

44. $\dfrac{3}{4} + \dfrac{9}{16} + \dfrac{27}{64} + \cdots$

45. $\dfrac{3}{4} + \dfrac{1}{4} + \dfrac{1}{12} + \cdots$

46. $\dfrac{5}{3} + \dfrac{1}{3} + \dfrac{1}{15} + \cdots$

47. Show that 0.444… is the same as $\dfrac{4}{9}$.

48. Show that 0.333…is the same as $\dfrac{1}{3}$.

49. Show that 0.272727…is the same as $\dfrac{3}{11}$.

50. Show that 0.545454…is the same as $\dfrac{6}{11}$.

Applying the Concepts

Declining-Balance Depreciation The declining-balance method of depreciation is an accounting method businesses use to deduct most of the cost of new equipment during the first few years of purchase. The value at any time during the life of the machine can be found with an exponential equation in two variables. For income tax purposes, however, it is the value at the end of the year that is most important, and for this reason sequences can be used.

51. Value of a Crane A construction crane sells for $450,000 if purchased new. After that, the value decreases by 30% each year. We can use a geometric sequence to find the value of the crane at the end of each year. If we let a_0 represent the value when it is purchased, then a_1 is the value after 1 year, a_2 is the value after 2 years, and so on.

   a. Write the first five terms of the sequence.

   b. What is the common ratio?

   c. Construct a line graph for the first five terms of the sequence.

   d. Use the line graph to estimate the value of the crane 3.5 years after it is purchased.

   e. Write the sequence from part *a* using a recursive formula.

52. Value of a Printing Press A large printing press sells for $375,000 when it is new. After that, its value decreases 25% each year.

   a. Write a geometric sequence that gives the value of the press at the end of each of the first 5 years after it is purchased.

   b. What is the common ratio for this sequence?

   c. Construct a line graph for this sequence.

   d. Use the line graph to estimate the value of the printing press 1.5 years after it is purchased.

   e. Write the sequence from part *a* using a recursive formula.

53. Adding Terms Given the geometric series

$$\frac{1}{3} + \frac{1}{9} + \frac{1}{27} + \cdots$$

   a. Find the sum of all the terms.

   b. Find the sum of the first six terms.

   c. Find the sum of all but the first six terms.

54. Bouncing Ball A ball is dropped from a height of 20 feet. Each time it bounces it returns to $\frac{7}{8}$ of the height it fell from. If the ball is allowed to bounce an infinite number of times, find the total vertical distance that the ball travels.

55. Stacking Paper Assume that a thin sheet of paper is 0.002 inch thick. The paper is torn in half, and the two halves placed together.

   a. How thick is the pile of torn paper?

   b. The pile of paper is torn in half again, and then the two halves placed together and torn in half again. The paper is large enough so this process may be performed a total of 5 times. How thick is the pile of torn paper?

   c. Refer to the tearing and piling process described in part *b* Assuming that somehow the original paper is large enough, how thick is the pile of torn paper if 25 tears are made?

56. Pendulum A pendulum swings 15 feet left to right on its first swing. On each swing following the first, the pendulum swings $\frac{4}{5}$ of the previous swing.

   a. Write the general term for this geometric sequence.

   b. If the pendulum is allowed to swing an infinite number of times, what is the total distance the pendulum will travel?

57. Salary Increases After completing her MBA degree, an accounting firm offered Jane a job with a starting salary of $60,000, with a guaranteed annual raise of 7% of her previous year's salary.

   a. Write a finite sequence to represent Jane's first 5 years of income with this company. (Round each calculation to the nearest dollar.)

   b. Write the general term for this geometric sequence.

   c. Find the sum of Jane's income for the first 10 years with the company. Round to the nearest dollar.

Learning Objectives Assessment

The following problems can be used to help assess if you have successfully met the learning objectives for this section.

58. Which of the following is a geometric sequence?

   a. $7, 4, 1, -2, \ldots$ **b.** $2, 4, 8, 16, \ldots$

   c. $\frac{1}{2}, \frac{1}{4}, \frac{1}{6}, \frac{1}{8}, \ldots$ **d.** $1, 1.1, 1.11, 1.111, \ldots$

59. What is the common ratio for the sequence $5, 0.5, 0.05, 0.005, \ldots$?

   a. 0.1 **b.** 10 **c.** -10 **d.** -0.1

60. Find a_6 for the geometric sequence $64, 96, 144, \ldots$.

   a. 729 **b.** 224 **c.** 486 **d.** 324

61. Find the sum of the infinite geometric series $64, -16, 4, -1, \ldots$.

   a. $\dfrac{64}{5}$ **b.** $\dfrac{256}{3}$ **c.** 51 **d.** $\dfrac{256}{5}$

Getting Ready for the Next Section

Simplify.

62. $(x + y)^0$

63. $(x + y)^1$

Expand and multiply.

64. $(x + y)^2$

65. $(x + y)^3$

Simplify.

66. $\dfrac{6 \cdot 5 \cdot 4 \cdot 3 \cdot 2 \cdot 1}{(2 \cdot 1)(4 \cdot 3 \cdot 2 \cdot 1)}$

67. $\dfrac{7 \cdot 6 \cdot 5 \cdot 4 \cdot 3 \cdot 2 \cdot 1}{(5 \cdot 4 \cdot 3 \cdot 2 \cdot 1)(2 \cdot 1)}$

SPOTLIGHT ON SUCCESS *Student Instructor Nathan*

Keep steadily before you the fact that all true success depends at last upon yourself.
—Theodore T. Hunger

Math has always come fairly easily for me and is the academic subject I have enjoyed most. I knew I wanted to attend Cal Poly San Luis Obispo for its high job placement and prestige, but I had no idea what I wanted to study. I decided to major in Mathematics because it is so universal but not so specialized or concentrated that I would get stuck in a field that I did not enjoy. I felt that if I kept studying math and its related fields, I would set myself up to be successful later in life, as math is the foundation for engineering, physics, and other science related fields. I have not looked back on my decision. I know it will be a degree that I am proud to have achieved.

I appreciate the consistency that math offers in its problems and in its solutions. I like that math can be simplified into smaller easier-to-understand parts, and its answers are almost always definite. It provides challenges that I enjoy solving, like completing a puzzle piece by piece. In the end, I am able to enjoy the success I have put together for myself.

Learning Objectives

In this section, we will learn how to:

1. Expand the power of a binomial using Pascal's Triangle.
2. Evaluate a factorial.
3. Use the Binomial Theorem to find a given term in a binomial expansion.

Introduction

The purpose of this section is to write the expansion of expressions of the form $(x + y)^n$, where n is any positive integer. If n is small, it is not too difficult to find the expansion using multiplication.

EXAMPLE 1 Expand: $(x + y)^3$.

SOLUTION We write the expression as a product and then multiply.

$$(x + y)^3 = (x + y)(x + y)(x + y)$$

$$= (x^2 + 2xy + y^2)(x + y) \qquad \text{FOIL}$$
$$= x^3 + x^2y + 2x^2y + 2xy^2 + xy^2 + y^3 \qquad \text{Multiply}$$
$$= x^3 + 3x^2y + 3xy^2 + y^3 \qquad \text{Combine like terms}$$

As n becomes larger, however, this process becomes very tedious and time consuming. For example, imagine multiplying ten factors of $(x + y)$ in order to expand $(x + y)^{10}$.

Pascal's Triangle

It turns out there is a convenient formula that will allow us to expand a binomial power much more efficiently. To write the formula, we must generalize the information in the following chart:

$$(x + y)^0 = \qquad\qquad\qquad 1$$
$$(x + y)^1 = \qquad\qquad\quad x \quad + \quad y$$
$$(x + y)^2 = \qquad\qquad x^2 \;+\; 2xy \;+\; y^2$$
$$(x + y)^3 = \qquad\quad x^3 \;+\; 3x^2y \;+\; 3xy^2 \;+\; y^3$$
$$(x + y)^4 = \quad x^4 \;+\; 4x^3y \;+\; 6x^2y^2 \;+\; 4xy^3 \;+\; y^4$$
$$(x + y)^5 = x^5 \;+\; 5x^4y \;+\; 10x^3y^2 \;+\; 10x^2y^3 \;+\; 5xy^4 \;+\; y^5$$

Note The polynomials to the right have been found by expanding the binomials on the left—we just haven't shown the work.

There are a number of similarities to notice among the polynomials on the right. Here is a list:

1. The number of terms in each polynomial is one greater than the exponent on the binomial at the left.

2. In each polynomial, the sequence of exponents on the variable x decreases to 0 from the exponent on the binomial at the left. (The exponent 0 is not shown, since $x^0 = 1$.)

3. In each polynomial, the exponents on the variable y increase from 0 to the exponent on the binomial at the left. (Because $y^0 = 1$, it is not shown in the first term.)

4. The sum of the exponents on the variables in any single term is equal to the exponent on the binomial at the left.

5. The coefficients of the first and last terms are both equal to 1.

The pattern in the coefficients of the polynomials on the right can best be seen by writing the right side again without the variables. It looks like this:

row 0						1					
row 1					1		1				
row 2				1		2		1			
row 3			1		3		3		1		
row 4		1		4		6		4		1	
row 5	1		5		10		10		5		1

This triangle-shaped array of coefficients is called *Pascal's Triangle*. Each row begins and ends with the number 1. Each internal entry in the triangular array is obtained by adding the two numbers above it. If we were to continue Pascal's Triangle, the next two rows would be

```
row 5         1      5      10      10       5      1
                \ + / \ + / \ + /  \ + /  \ + /
row 6         1      6      15      20      15      6      1
                \ + / \ + / \ + /  \ + /  \ + /  \ + /
row 7      1      7      21      35      35      21      7      1
```

The coefficients for the terms in the expansion of $(x + y)^n$ are given in the nth row of Pascal's Triangle, where we count rows beginning with 0.

Pascal's Triangle is named after Blaise Pascal, a seventeenth century mathematician and philosopher. However, we now know the triangle had been discovered as early as the eleventh century by both the Persians and the Chinese. Figure 1 shows a version of the triangle by Yang Hui from 1261.

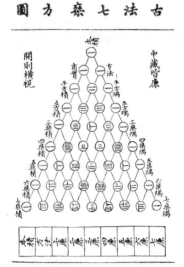

"Yanghui triangle" by Yáng Huī, ca. 1238–1298) - [1]
Licensed under Public Domain via Wikimedia Commons

FIGURE 1

EXAMPLE 2   Expand: $(3x + 2y)^4$.

SOLUTION   First, we find the expansion of $(a + b)^4$. There are 5 terms in the expansion. The powers of a will decrease from 4 and the powers of b will increase from 0. The coefficients can be found in the fourth row of Pascal's Triangle, which are 1, 4, 6, 4, 1. This gives us

$$(a + b)^4 = 1a^4b^0 + 4a^3b^1 + 6a^2b^2 + 4a^1b^3 + 1a^0b^4$$

Now, we simplify $a^0 = b^0 = 1$ and then substitute $a = 3x$ and $b = 2y$.

$$(3x + 2y)^4 = 1(3x)^4 \cdot (1) + 4(3x)^3(2y) + 6(3x)^2(2y)^2 + 4(3x)(2y)^3 + (1) \cdot 1(2y)^4$$

To simplify, we first evaluate each exponent, and the perform all of the multiplications within each term.

$$(3x + 2y)^4 = 1(81x^4)(1) + 4(27x^3)(2y) + 6(9x^2)(4y^2) + 4(3x)(8y^3) + 1(1)(16y^4)$$
$$= 81x^4 + 216x^3y + 216x^2y^2 + 96xy^3 + 16y^4$$

Factorial Notation

There is an alternative method of finding these coefficients that does not involve Pascal's Triangle. The alternative method involves *factorial notation*.

DEFINITION *n!*

The expression **n!** is read "*n* factorial" and is the product of all the consecutive integers from *n* down to 1. For example,

$$1! = 1$$

$$2! = 2 \cdot 1 = 2$$

$$3! = 3 \cdot 2 \cdot 1 = 6$$

$$4! = 4 \cdot 3 \cdot 2 \cdot 1 = 24$$

$$5! = 5 \cdot 4 \cdot 3 \cdot 2 \cdot 1 = 120$$

As a special case, we define $0! = 1$.

We use factorial notation to define binomial coefficients. The following formula comes from probability theory, and is used to count the number of combinations of *r* items selected from *n* items.

DEFINITION *binomial coefficient*

The expression $_nC_r$, sometimes written as $\binom{n}{r}$, is called a ***binomial coefficient*** and is defined by

$$_nC_r = \binom{n}{r} = \frac{n!}{r!(n-r)!}$$

EXAMPLE 3   Calculate the following binomial coefficients:

$$_7C_5, \binom{6}{2}, {_3C_0}$$

SOLUTION   We simply apply the definition for binomial coefficients:

$$_7C_5 = \frac{7!}{5!(7-5)!}$$

$$= \frac{7!}{5! \cdot 2!}$$

$$= \frac{7 \cdot 6 \cdot 5 \cdot 4 \cdot 3 \cdot 2 \cdot 1}{(5 \cdot 4 \cdot 3 \cdot 2 \cdot 1)(2 \cdot 1)}$$

$$= \frac{42}{2}$$

$$= 21$$

$$\binom{6}{2} = \frac{6!}{2!(6-2)!}$$

$$= \frac{6!}{2! \cdot 4!}$$

$$= \frac{6 \cdot 5 \cdot 4 \cdot 3 \cdot 2 \cdot 1}{(2 \cdot 1)(4 \cdot 3 \cdot 2 \cdot 1)}$$

$$= \frac{30}{2}$$

$$= 15$$

$$_3C_0 = \frac{3!}{0!(3-0)!}$$

$$= \frac{3!}{0! \cdot 3!}$$

$$= \frac{3 \cdot 2 \cdot 1}{(1)(3 \cdot 2 \cdot 1)}$$

$$= 1$$

> **USING TECHNOLOGY** *Binomial Coefficients on a Calculator*
>
> Because the binomial coefficient formula is also used for statistics, many scientific and graphing calculators have this formula built-in.
>
> For instance, on a TI-84 graphing calculator we can find $_7C_5$ using the $_nC_r$ command. First input a 7, then press $\boxed{\text{MATH}}$ followed by the left arrow key. Select the $_nC_r$ command and then input a 5. Our screen will look like this:
>
> $$7 \ _nC_r \ 5$$
>
> Pressing $\boxed{\text{ENTER}}$ gives us a result of 21, which agrees with our answer in Example 3.

If we were to calculate all the binomial coefficients in the following array, we would find they match exactly with the numbers in Pascal's Triangle. That is why they are called binomial coefficients — because they are the coefficients of the expansion of $(x + y)^n$. The value $_nC_r = \binom{n}{r}$ will be the number in Pascal's Triangle located in position r of row n, where rows are counted beginning with 0, and position is counted in a given row from the left and also beginning with 0 (See Figure 2).

Row 0					1				
Row 1				1		1			
Row 2			1		2		1		
Row 3		1		3		3		1	
Row 4	1		4		6		4		1	$_4C_2 = 6$
	0		1		2		3		4

Position

FIGURE 2

Using the new notation to represent the entries in Pascal's Triangle, we can summarize everything we have noticed about the expansion of binomial powers of the form $(x + y)^n$.

EXAMPLE 4   Expand $(x - 2)^3$.

SOLUTION   Applying the binomial coefficient formula, we have

$$(x - 2)^3 = \binom{3}{0} x^3(-2)^0 + \binom{3}{1} x^2(-2)^1 + \binom{3}{2} x^1(-2)^2 + \binom{3}{3} x^0(-2)^3$$

The coefficients

$$\binom{3}{0}, \binom{3}{1}, \binom{3}{2}, \text{ and } \binom{3}{3}$$

can be found in the third row of Pascal's Triangle. They are 1, 3, 3, and 1:

$$(x - 2)^3 = 1x^3(-2)^0 + 3x^2(-2)^1 + 3x^1(-2)^2 + 1x^0(-2)^3$$
$$= x^3 - 6x^2 + 12x - 8$$

EXAMPLE 5   Write the first three terms in the expansion of $(x + 5)^9$.

SOLUTION   The coefficients of the first three terms are

$$_9C_0, _9C_1, \text{ and } _9C_2$$

which we calculate as follows:

$$_9C_0 = \frac{9!}{0! \cdot 9!} = \frac{9 \cdot 8 \cdot 7 \cdot 6 \cdot 5 \cdot 4 \cdot 3 \cdot 2 \cdot 1}{(1)(9 \cdot 8 \cdot 7 \cdot 6 \cdot 5 \cdot 4 \cdot 3 \cdot 2 \cdot 1)} = \frac{1}{1} = 1$$

$$_9C_1 = \frac{9!}{1! \cdot 8!} = \frac{9 \cdot 8 \cdot 7 \cdot 6 \cdot 5 \cdot 4 \cdot 3 \cdot 2 \cdot 1}{(1)(8 \cdot 7 \cdot 6 \cdot 5 \cdot 4 \cdot 3 \cdot 2 \cdot 1)} = \frac{9}{1} = 9$$

$$_9C_2 = \frac{9!}{2! \cdot 7!} = \frac{9 \cdot 8 \cdot 7 \cdot 6 \cdot 5 \cdot 4 \cdot 3 \cdot 2 \cdot 1}{(2 \cdot 1)(7 \cdot 6 \cdot 5 \cdot 4 \cdot 3 \cdot 2 \cdot 1)} = \frac{72}{2} = 36$$

We write the first three terms:

$$(x + 5)^9 = 1 \cdot x^9 + 9 \cdot x^8(5) + 36x^7(5)^2 + \cdots$$
$$= x^9 + 45x^8 + 900x^7 + \cdots$$

The Binomial Theorem

If we look at each term in the expansion of $(x + y)^n$ as a term in a sequence, a_1, a_2, a_3, . . . , we can write

$$a_1 = \binom{n}{0} x^n y^0 \qquad = _nC_0 x^n y^0$$

$$a_2 = \binom{n}{1} x^{n-1} y^1 \qquad = _nC_1 x^{n-1} y^1$$

$$a_3 = \binom{n}{2} x^{n-2} y^2 \qquad = _nC_2 x^{n-2} y^2$$

$$a_4 = \binom{n}{3} x^{n-3} y^3 \qquad = _nC_3 x^{n-3} y^3 \quad \text{and so on}$$

To write the formula for the general term, we simply notice that the number used for the binomial coefficient and appearing in the exponents of the variables is always 1 less than the term number. This observation allows us to write the following:

   The General Term of a Binomial Expansion

The kth term in the expansion of $(x + y)^n$ is

$$a_k = \binom{n}{k-1} x^{n-(k-1)} y^{k-1}$$

Then the expansion of $(x + y)^n$ can be treated as a finite series

$$(x + y)^n = a_1 + a_2 + a_3 + \ldots + a_{n+1}$$

Using summation notation, we can express this series as

$$(x + y)^n = \sum_{k=1}^{n+1} a_k$$

To simplify the summation notation and general term formula, we let $r = k - 1$.

Then r will take on the values $0, 1, 2, \ldots, n$. This leads us to the following theorem:

 THEOREM   *Binomial Theorem*

If n is a positive integer, then

$$(x + y)^n = \sum_{r=0}^{n} \binom{n}{r} x^{n-r} y^r = \sum_{r=0}^{n} {}_nC_r \, x^{n-r} y^r$$

EXAMPLE 6   Find the fifth term in the expansion of $(2x - 3y)^{12}$.

SOLUTION   Applying the general term formula with $k = 5$, we have

$$a_5 = \binom{12}{5-1} (2x)^{12-(5-1)}(-3y)^{5-1}$$

$$= \binom{12}{4} (2x)^8 (-3y)^4$$

$$= \frac{12!}{4! \cdot 8!} (2x)^8 (-3y)^4$$

Notice that once we have one of the exponents, the other exponent and the denominator of the coefficient are determined: The two exponents add to 12 and match the numbers in the denominator of the coefficient.

Making the calculations from the preceding formula, we have

$$a_5 = 495(256x^8)(81y^4)$$

$$= 10{,}264{,}320x^8 y^4$$

Getting Ready for Class

After reading through the preceding section, respond in your own words and in complete sentences.

A. What is Pascal's Triangle?

B. Why is $\binom{n}{0} = 1$ for any natural number?

C. State the Binomial Theorem.

D. When is the Binomial Theorem more efficient than using Pascal's Triangle to expand a binomial raised to a whole-number exponent?

Use Pascal's Triangle to expand each of the following.

1. $(x + 2)^4$ **2.** $(x - 2)^5$ **3.** $(x + y)^6$ **4.** $(x - 1)^6$

5. $(2x + 1)^5$ **6.** $(2x - 1)^4$ **7.** $(x - 2y)^5$ **8.** $(2x + y)^5$

9. $(3x - 2)^4$ **10.** $(2x - 3)^4$ **11.** $(4x - 3y)^3$ **12.** $(3x - 4y)^3$

13. $(x^2 + 2)^4$ **14.** $(x^2 - 3)^3$ **15.** $(x^2 + y^2)^3$ **16.** $(x^2 - 3y)^4$

17. $(2x + 3y)^4$ **18.** $(2x - 1)^5$ **19.** $\left(\dfrac{x}{2} + \dfrac{y}{3}\right)^3$ **20.** $\left(\dfrac{x}{3} - \dfrac{y}{2}\right)^4$

21. $\left(\dfrac{x}{2} - 4\right)^3$ **22.** $\left(\dfrac{x}{3} + 6\right)^3$ **23.** $\left(\dfrac{x}{3} + \dfrac{y}{2}\right)^4$ **24.** $\left(\dfrac{x}{2} - \dfrac{y}{3}\right)^4$

Evaluate the factorial.

25. $6!$ **26.** $9!$ **27.** $10!$ **28.** $12!$

Find each of the following binomial coefficients.

29. $\begin{pmatrix} 10 \\ 0 \end{pmatrix}$ **30.** $\begin{pmatrix} 10 \\ 10 \end{pmatrix}$ **31.** $_8C_1$ **32.** $_8C_7$

33. $\begin{pmatrix} 15 \\ 11 \end{pmatrix}$ **34.** $\begin{pmatrix} 11 \\ 4 \end{pmatrix}$ **35.** $_{20}C_7$ **36.** $_{30}C_{25}$

Use the Binomial Theorem to write the first four terms in the expansion of the following.

37. $(x + 2)^9$ **38.** $(x - 2)^9$ **39.** $(x - y)^{10}$ **40.** $(x + 2y)^{10}$

41. $(x + 3)^{25}$ **42.** $(x - 1)^{40}$ **43.** $(x - 2)^{60}$ **44.** $\left(x + \dfrac{1}{2}\right)^{30}$

45. $(x - y)^{18}$ **46.** $(x - 2y)^{65}$

Use the Binomial Theorem to write the first three terms in the expansion of each of the following.

47. $(x + 1)^{15}$ **48.** $(x - 1)^{15}$ **49.** $(x - y)^{12}$ **50.** $(x + y)^{12}$

51. $(x + 2)^{20}$ **52.** $(x - 2)^{20}$

Use the Binomial Theorem to write the first two terms in the expansion of each of the following.

53. $(x + 2)^{100}$ **54.** $(x - 2)^{50}$ **55.** $(x + y)^{50}$ **56.** $(x - y)^{100}$

Use the Binomial Theorem for Problems 57-68.

57. Find the ninth term in the expansion of $(2x + 3y)^{12}$.

58. Find the sixth term in the expansion of $(2x + 3y)^{12}$.

59. Find the fifth term of $(x - 2)^{10}$.

60. Find the fifth term of $(2x - 1)^{10}$.

61. Find the sixth term in the expansion of $(x - 2)^{12}$.

62. Find the ninth term in the expansion of $(7x - 1)^{10}$.

63. Find the third term in the expansion of $(x - 3y)^{25}$.

64. Find the 24th term in the expansion of $(2x - y)^{26}$.

65. Write the formula for the 12th term of $(2x + 5y)^{20}$. Do not simplify.

66. Write the formula for the eighth term of $(2x + 5y)^{20}$. Do not simplify.

67. Write the first three terms of the expansion of $(x^2y - 3)^{10}$.

68. Write the first three terms of the expansion of $\left(x - \dfrac{1}{x}\right)^{50}$.

Applying the Concepts

69. Probability The third term in the expansion of $\left(\frac{1}{2} + \frac{1}{2}\right)^7$ will give the probability that in a family with 7 children, 5 will be boys and 2 will be girls. Find the third term.

70. Probability The fourth term in the expansion of $\left(\frac{1}{2} + \frac{1}{2}\right)^8$ will give the probability that in a family with 8 children, 3 will be boys and 5 will be girls. Find the fourth term.

Learning Objectives Assessment

The following problems can be used to help assess if you have successfully met the learning objectives for this section.

71. Use Pascal's Triangle to expand $(x - 2y)^4$.

    a. $x^4 + 4x^3y + 6x^2y^2 + 4xy^3 + y^4$

    b. $x^4 - 8x^3y + 24x^2y^2 - 32xy^3 + 16y^4$

    c. $x^4 + 16y^4$

    d. $x^4 - 8x^3y - 12x^2y^2 - 8xy^3 - 2y^4$

72. Find $\dbinom{10}{6}$.

    a. $\dfrac{5}{3}$ **b.** 5,040   **c.** 210   **d.** 151,200

73. Find the fourth term in the expansion of $(3x - 2y)^7$.

    a. $-22{,}680x^4y^3$ **b.** $35x^4y^3$

    c. $15{,}120x^3y^4$ **d.** $-210x^3y^4$

Maintaining Your Skills

Solve each equation. Write your answers to the nearest hundredth.

74. $5^x = 7$ **75.** $10^x = 15$ **76.** $8^{2x-1} = 16$ **77.** $9^{3x-1} = 27$

78. Compound Interest How long will it take $400 to double if it is invested in an account with an annual interest rate of 10% compounded four times a year?

79. Compound Interest How long will it take $200 to become $800 if it is invested in an account with an annual interest rate of 8% compounded four times a year?

Find each of the following to the nearest hundredth.

80. $\log_4 20$ **81.** $\log_7 21$ **82.** $\ln 576$ **83.** $\ln 5{,}760$

84. Solve the formula $A = 10e^{5t}$ for t.   **85.** Solve the formula $A = Pe^{-5t}$ for t.

Chapter 13 Summary

EXAMPLES

1. In the sequence $a_n = 2n - 1$,
$$a_1 = 2(1) - 1 = 1$$
$$a_2 = 2(2) - 1 = 3$$
$$a_3 = 2(3) - 1 = 5$$
resulting in $1, 3, 5,\ldots$

Sequences [13.1]

A sequence is a function whose domain is the set of positive integers. The terms of a sequence are denoted by

$$a_1, a_2, a_3,\ldots, a_n,\ldots$$

where a_1 (read "a sub 1") is the first term, a_2 the second term, and a_n the nth or general term.

---

2. $\displaystyle\sum_{i=3}^{6}(-2)^i$

$$= (-2)^3 + (-2)^4 + (-2)^5 + (-2)^6$$
$$= -8 + 16 + (-32) + 64$$
$$= 40$$

Summation Notation [13.2]

The notation

$$\sum_{i=1}^{n} a_i = a_1 + a_2 + a_3 + \cdots + a_n$$

is called summation notation or sigma notation. The letter i as used here is called the index of summation or just index.

---

3. For the sequence $3, 7, 11, 15,\ldots$,
$a_1 = 3$ and $d = 4$. The general term is
$$a_n = 3 + (n - 1)4$$
$$= 4n - 1$$
Using this formula to find the tenth term, we have
$$a_{10} = 4(10) - 1 = 39$$
The sum of the first 10 terms is
$$S_{10} = \frac{10}{2}(3 + 39) = 210$$

Arithmetic Sequences [13.3]

An arithmetic sequence is a sequence in which each term comes from the preceding term by adding a constant amount each time. If the first term of an arithmetic sequence is a_1 and the amount we add each time (called the common difference) is d, then the nth term of the progression is given by

$$a_n = a_1 + (n - 1)d$$

The sum of the first n terms of an arithmetic sequence is

$$S_n = \frac{n}{2}(a_1 + a_n)$$

S_n is called the nth partial sum.

---

4. For the geometric progression
$3, 6, 12, 24,\ldots, a_1 = 3$ and $r = 2$.
The general term is

$$a_n = 3 \cdot 2^{n-1}$$

The sum of the first 10 terms is
$$S_{10} = \frac{3(2^{10} - 1)}{2 - 1} = 3{,}069$$

Geometric Sequences [13.4]

A geometric sequence is a sequence of numbers in which each term comes from the previous term by multiplying by a constant amount each time. The constant by which we multiply each term to get the next term is called the common ratio. If the first term of a geometric sequence is a_1 and the common ratio is r, then the formula that gives the general term a_n is

$$a_n = a_1 r^{n-1}$$

The sum of the first n terms of a geometric sequence is given by the formula

$$S_n = \frac{a_1(r^n - 1)}{r - 1}$$

The Sum of an Infinite Geometric Series [13.4]

5. The sum of the series

$$\frac{1}{3} + \frac{1}{6} + \frac{1}{12} + \cdots$$

is

$$S = \frac{\frac{1}{3}}{1 - \frac{1}{2}} = \frac{\frac{1}{3}}{\frac{1}{2}} = \frac{2}{3}$$

If a geometric sequence has first term a_1 and common ratio r such that $|r| < 1$, then the following is called an infinite geometric series:

$$S = \sum_{i=0}^{\infty} a_1 r^i = a_1 + a_1 r + a_1 r^2 + a_1 r^3 + \cdots$$

Its sum is given by the formula

$$S = \frac{a_1}{1 - r}$$

Factorials [13.5]

The notation $n!$ is called n factorial and is defined to be the product of each consecutive integer from n down to 1. That is,

$$0! = 1 \qquad \text{(By definition)}$$
$$1! = 1$$
$$2! = 2 \cdot 1$$
$$3! = 3 \cdot 2 \cdot 1$$
$$4! = 4 \cdot 3 \cdot 2 \cdot 1$$

and so on.

Binomial Coefficients [13.5]

6. $\dbinom{7}{3} = \dfrac{7!}{3!(7-3)!}$

$$= \frac{7!}{3! \cdot 4!}$$

$$= \frac{7 \cdot 6 \cdot 5 \cdot 4 \cdot 3 \cdot 2 \cdot 1}{(3 \cdot 2 \cdot 1)(4 \cdot 3 \cdot 2 \cdot 1)}$$

$$= 35$$

The notation $\dbinom{n}{r}$, or $_nC_r$, is called a binomial coefficient and is defined by

$$_nC_r = \binom{n}{r} = \frac{n!}{r!(n-r)!}$$

Binomial coefficients can be found by using the formula above or by Pascal's Triangle, which is

```
            1
          1   1
        1   2   1
      1   3   3   1
    1   4   6   4   1
  1   5   10  10  5   1
```

and so on.

Binomial Theorem [13.5]

7. $(x + 2)^4$

$= x^4 + 4x^3 \cdot 2 + 6x^2 \cdot 2^2 + 4x \cdot 2^3 + 2^4$

$= x^4 + 8x^3 + 24x^2 + 32x + 16$

If n is a positive integer, then the formula for expanding $(x + y)^n$ is given by

$$(x + y)^n = \sum_{r=0}^{n} \binom{n}{r} x^{n-r} y^r = \sum_{r=0}^{n} {}_nC_r \, x^{n-r} y^r$$

Write the first five terms of the sequences with the following general terms or recursive formulas. [10.1]

1. $a_n = 3n - 5$

2. $a_1 = 3, a_n = a_{n-1} + 4, n > 1$

3. $a_n = n^2 + 1$

4. $a_n = 2n^3$

5. $a_n = \dfrac{n+1}{n^2}$

6. $a_1 = 4, a_n = -2a_{n-1}, n > 1$

Give the general term for each sequence. [10.1]

7. $6, 10, 14, 18, \ldots$

8. $1, 2, 4, 8, \ldots$

9. $\dfrac{1}{2}, \dfrac{1}{4}, \dfrac{1}{8}, \dfrac{1}{16}, \ldots$

10. $-3, 9, -27, 81, \ldots$

11. Expand and simplify each of the following. [10.2]

a. $\displaystyle\sum_{i=1}^{5}(5i + 3)$

b. $\displaystyle\sum_{i=3}^{5}(2^i - 1)$

c. $\displaystyle\sum_{i=2}^{6}(i^2 + 2i)$

12. Find the first term of an arithmetic progression if $a_5 = 11$ and $a_9 = 19$. [10.3]

13. Find the second term of a geometric progression for which $a_3 = 18$ and $a_5 = 162$. [10.4]

Find the sum of the first 10 terms of the following arithmetic progressions. [10.3]

14. $5, 11, 17, \ldots$

15. $25, 20, 15, \ldots$

16. Write a formula for the sum of the first 50 terms of the geometric progression $3, 6, 12, \ldots$ [10.4]

17. Find the sum of $\dfrac{1}{2} + \dfrac{1}{6} + \dfrac{1}{18} + \dfrac{1}{54} + \cdots$. [10.4]

Use Pascal's Triangle to expand each of the following. [10.5]

18. $(x - 3)^4$

19. $(2x - 1)^5$

Find each binomial coefficient. [10.5]

20. $\dbinom{12}{9}$

21. $_{15}C_5$

22. Find the first 3 terms in the expansion of $(x - 1)^{20}$. [10.5]

23. Find the sixth term in $(2x - 3y)^8$. [10.5]

Conic Sections

Chapter Outline

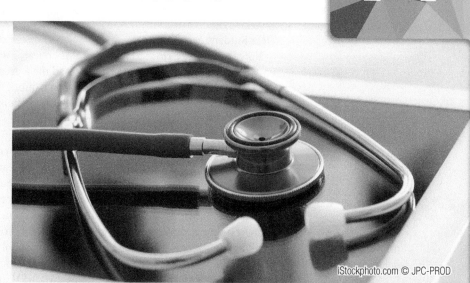

iStockphoto.com © JPC-PROD

One of the curves we will study in this chapter has interesting reflective properties. Figure 1(A) shows how you can draw one of these curves (an ellipse) using thumbtacks, string, pencil, and paper. Elliptical surfaces will reflect sound waves that originate at one focus through the other focus. This property of ellipses allows doctors to treat patients with kidney stones using a procedure called lithotripsy. A lithotripter is an elliptical device that creates sound waves that crush the kidney stone into small pieces, without surgery. The sound wave originates at one focus of the lithotripter. The energy from it reflects off the surface of the lithotripter and converges at the other focus, where the kidney stone is positioned. Below (Figure 1(B)) is a cross-section of a lithotripter, with a patient positioned so the kidney stone is at the other focus.

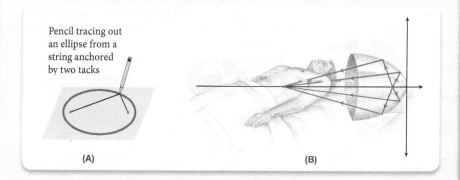

Pencil tracing out an ellipse from a string anchored by two tacks

(A)

(B)

By studying the conic sections in this chapter, you will be better equipped to understand some of the more technical equipment that exists in the world outside of class.

Dear Student,

Now that you are close to finishing this course, I want to pass on a couple of things that have helped me a great deal with my career. I'll introduce each one with a quote:

Do something for the person you will be 5 years from now.

I have always made sure that I arranged my life so that I was doing something for the person I would be 5 years later. For example, when I was 20 years old, I was in college. I imagined that the person I would be as a 25-year-old, would want to have a college degree, so I made sure I stayed in school. That's all there is to this. It is not a hard, rigid philosophy. It is a soft, behind the scenes, foundation. It does not include ideas such as "Five years from now I'm going to graduate at the top of my class from the best college in the country." Instead, you think, "five years from now I will have a college degree, or I will still be in school working towards it."

This philosophy led to a community college teaching job, writing textbooks, doing videos with the textbooks, then to MathTV and the book you are reading right now. Along the way there were many other options and directions that I didn't take, but all the choices I made were due to keeping the person I would be in 5 years in mind.

It's easier to ride a horse in the direction it is going.

I started my college career thinking that I would become a dentist. I enrolled in all the courses that were required for dental school. When I completed the courses, I applied to a number of dental schools, but wasn't accepted. I kept going to school, and applied again the next year, again, without success. My life was not going in the direction of dental school, even though I had worked hard to put it in that direction. So I did a little inventory of the classes I had taken and the grades I earned, and realized that I was doing well in mathematics. My life was actually going in that direction so I decided to see where that would take me. It was a good decision.

It is a good idea to work hard toward your goals, but it is also a good idea to take inventory every now and then to be sure you are headed in the direction that is best for you.

I wish you good luck with the rest of your college years, and with whatever you decide you want to do as a career.

Pat McKeague

Learning Objectives

In this section, we will learn how to:

1. Find the distance between two points in the plane.

2. Find the equation of a circle given the center and radius.

3. Determine the center and radius of a circle from its equation.

4. Sketch the graph of a circle.

Introduction

Conic sections include ellipses, circles, hyperbolas, and parabolas. They are called conic sections because each can be found by slicing a cone with a plane as shown in Figure 1.

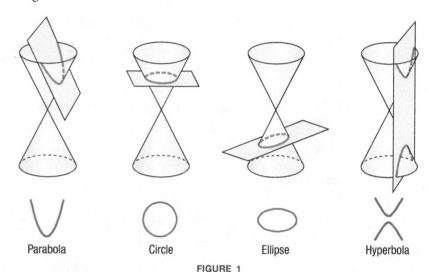

Parabola   Circle   Ellipse   Hyperbola

FIGURE 1

The Distance Formula

We begin our work with conic sections by studying circles. Before we find the general equation of a circle, we must first derive what is known as the *distance formula*. Suppose (x_1, y_1) and (x_2, y_2) are any two points in the first quadrant. (Actually, we could choose the two points to be anywhere on the coordinate plane. It is just more convenient to have them in the first quadrant.) We can name the points P_1 and P_2, respectively, and draw the diagram shown in Figure 2.

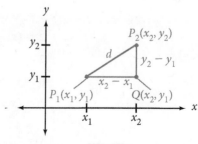

FIGURE 2

Notice the coordinates of point Q. The x-coordinate is x_2 because Q is directly below point P_2. The y-coordinate of Q is y_1 because Q is directly across from point P_1. It is evident from the diagram that the length of P_2Q is $y_2 - y_1$ and the length of P_1Q is $x_2 - x_1$. Using the Pythagorean theorem, we have

$$(P_1P_2)^2 = (P_1Q)^2 + (P_2Q)^2$$

or

$$d^2 = (x_2 - x_1)^2 + (y_2 - y_1)^2$$

Taking the square root of both sides, we have

$$d = \sqrt{(x_2 - x_1)^2 + (y_2 - y_1)^2}$$

We know this is the positive square root, because d is the distance from P_1 to P_2 and must therefore be positive. This formula is called the *distance formula*.

> **FORMULA**   *Distance Formula*
>
> If (x_1, y_1) and (x_2, y_2) are any two points in the coordinate plane, then the distance between them is given by
>
> $$d = \sqrt{(x_2 - x_1)^2 + (y_2 - y_1)^2}$$

EXAMPLE 1   Find the distance between $(3, 5)$ and $(2, -1)$.

SOLUTION   If we let $(3, 5)$ be (x_1, y_1) and $(2, -1)$ be (x_2, y_2) and apply the distance formula, we have

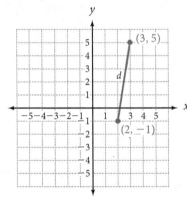

$$d = \sqrt{(2 - 3)^2 + (-1 - 5)^2}$$

$$= \sqrt{(-1)^2 + (-6)^2}$$

$$= \sqrt{1 + 36}$$

$$= \sqrt{37}$$

FIGURE 3

EXAMPLE 2   Find x if the distance from $(x, 5)$ to $(3, 4)$ is $\sqrt{2}$.

SOLUTION   Using the distance formula, we have

$\sqrt{2} = \sqrt{(x - 3)^2 + (5 - 4)^2}$	Distance formula
$2 = (x - 3)^2 + 1^2$	Square each side
$2 = x^2 - 6x + 9 + 1$	Expand $(x - 3)^2$
$0 = x^2 - 6x + 8$	Simplify
$0 = (x - 4)(x - 2)$	Factor
$x = 4 \quad$ or $\quad x = 2$	Set factors equal to 0

The two solutions are 4 and 2, which indicates that two points, $(4, 5)$ and $(2, 5)$, are $\sqrt{2}$ units from $(3, 4)$.

Circles

Because of their perfect symmetry, circles have been used for thousands of years in many disciplines, including art, science, and religion. The photograph on the left is of Stonehenge, a 4,500-year-old site in England. The arrangement of the stones is based on a circular plan that is thought to have both religious and astronomical significance. More recently, the design shown in the photo on the right began appearing in agricultural fields in England in the 1990s. Whoever made these designs chose the circle as their basic shape.

© Masterfile

© Masterfile

We can model circles very easily in algebra by using equations that are based on the distance formula.

> ### THEOREM   *Circle Theorem*
>
> The *equation of the circle* with center at (h, k) and radius r is given by
> $$(x - h)^2 + (y - k)^2 = r^2$$

Proof   By definition, all points on the circle are a distance r from the center (h, k). If we let (x, y) represent any point on the circle, then (x, y) is r units from (h, k). Applying the distance formula, we have

$$r = \sqrt{(x - h)^2 + (y - k)^2}$$

Squaring both sides of this equation gives the equation of the circle:

$$(x - h)^2 + (y - k)^2 = r^2$$

We can use the circle theorem to find the equation of a circle, given its center and radius, or to find its center and radius, given the equation.

EXAMPLE 3   Find the equation of the circle with center at $(-3, 2)$ having a radius of 5.

SOLUTION   We have $(h, k) = (-3, 2)$ and $r = 5$. Applying our theorem for the equation of a circle yields

$$[x - (-3)]^2 + (y - 2)^2 = 5^2$$
$$(x + 3)^2 + (y - 2)^2 = 25$$

EXAMPLE 4   Give the equation of the circle with radius 3 whose center is at the origin.

SOLUTION   The coordinates of the center are $(0, 0)$, and the radius is 3. The equation must be

$$(x - 0)^2 + (y - 0)^2 = 3^2$$
$$x^2 + y^2 = 9$$

We can see from Example 4 that the equation of any circle with its center at the origin and radius r will be

$$x^2 + y^2 = r^2$$

EXAMPLE 5   Find the center and radius, and sketch the graph of the circle whose equation is

$$(x - 1)^2 + (y + 3)^2 = 4$$

SOLUTION   Writing the equation in the form

$$(x - h)^2 + (y - k)^2 = r^2$$

we have

$$(x - 1)^2 + [y - (-3)]^2 = 2^2$$

The center is at $(1, -3)$, and the radius is 2. The graph is shown in Figure 4.

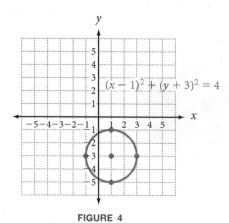

$$(x - 1)^2 + (y + 3)^2 = 4$$

FIGURE 4

EXAMPLE 6   Sketch the graph of $x^2 + y^2 = 9$.

SOLUTION   Because the equation can be written in the form

$$(x - 0)^2 + (y - 0)^2 = 3^2$$

it must have its center at $(0, 0)$ and a radius of 3. The graph is shown in Figure 5.

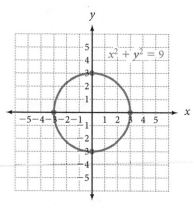

$$x^2 + y^2 = 9$$

FIGURE 5

EXAMPLE 7   Sketch the graph of $x^2 + y^2 + 6x - 4y - 12 = 0$.

SOLUTION   To sketch the graph, we must find the center and radius of our circle. We can do so easily if the equation is in standard form. That is, if it has the form

$$(x - h)^2 + (y - k)^2 = r^2$$

To put our equation in standard form, we start by using the addition property of equality to group all the constant terms together on the right side of the equation.

In this case, we add 12 to each side of the equation. We do this because we are going to add our own constants later to complete the square.

$$x^2 + y^2 + 6x - 4y = 12$$

Next, we group all the terms containing x together and all terms containing y together, and we leave some space at the end of each group for the numbers we will add when we complete the square on each group.

$$x^2 + 6x \qquad + y^2 - 4y \qquad = 12$$

To complete the square on x, we add 9 to each side of the equation. To complete the square on y, we add 4 to each side of the equation.

$$x^2 + 6x + 9 + y^2 - 4y + 4 = 12 + 9 + 4$$

The first three terms on the left side can be written as $(x + 3)^2$. Likewise, the last three terms on the left side can be factored as $(y - 2)^2$. The right side simplifies to 25.

$$(x + 3)^2 + (y - 2)^2 = 25$$

Writing 25 as 5^2, we have our equation in standard form.

$$(x + 3)^2 + (y - 2)^2 = 5^2$$

From this last line, it is apparent that the center is at $(-3, 2)$ and the radius is 5. Using this information, we create the graph shown in Figure 6.

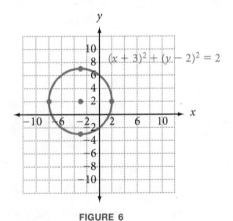

FIGURE 6

Getting Ready for Class

After reading through the preceding section, respond in your own words and in complete sentences.

A. Describe the distance formula in words, as if you were explaining to someone how they should go about finding the distance between two points.

B. What is the mathematical definition of a circle?

C. How are the distance formula and the equation of a circle related?

D. When graphing a circle from its equation, why is completing the square sometimes useful?

Problem Set 14.1

Find the distance between the following points.

1. $(3, 7)$ and $(6, 3)$ **2.** $(4, 7)$ and $(8, 1)$

3. $(0, 9)$ and $(5, 0)$ **4.** $(-3, 0)$ and $(0, 4)$

5. $(3, -5)$ and $(-2, 1)$ **6.** $(-8, 9)$ and $(-3, -2)$

7. $(-1, -2)$ and $(-10, 5)$ **8.** $(-3, -8)$ and $(-1, 6)$

9. Find x so the distance between $(x, 2)$ and $(1, 5)$ is $\sqrt{13}$.

10. Find x so the distance between $(-2, 3)$ and $(x, 1)$ is 3.

11. Find x so the distance between $(x, 5)$ and $(3, 9)$ is 5.

12. Find y so the distance between $(-4, y)$ and $(2, 1)$ is 8.

13. Find x so the distance between $(x, 4)$ and $(2x + 1, 6)$ is 6.

14. Find y so the distance between $(3, y)$ and $(7, 3y - 1)$ is 6.

Write the equation of the circle with the given center and radius.

15. Center $(3, -2)$; $r = 3$ **16.** Center $(-2, 4)$; $r = 1$

17. Center $(-5, -1)$; $r = \sqrt{5}$ **18.** Center $(-7, -6)$; $r = \sqrt{3}$

19. Center $(0, -5)$; $r = 1$ **20.** Center $(0, -1)$; $r = 7$

21. Center $(0, 0)$; $r = 2$ **22.** Center $(0, 0)$; $r = 5$

Give the center and radius, and sketch the graph of each of the following circles.

23. $x^2 + y^2 = 4$ **24.** $x^2 + y^2 = 16$

25. $(x - 1)^2 + (y - 3)^2 = 25$ **26.** $(x - 4)^2 + (y - 1)^2 = 36$

27. $(x + 2)^2 + (y - 4)^2 = 8$ **28.** $(x - 3)^2 + (y + 1)^2 = 12$

29. $(x + 2)^2 + (y - 4)^2 = 17$ **30.** $x^2 + (y + 2)^2 = 11$

31. $x^2 + y^2 + 2x - 4y = 4$ **32.** $x^2 + y^2 - 4x + 2y = 11$

33. $x^2 + y^2 - 6y = 7$ **34.** $x^2 + y^2 - 4y = 5$

35. $x^2 + y^2 + 2x = 1$ **36.** $x^2 + y^2 + 10x = 0$

37. $x^2 + y^2 - 4x - 6y = -4$ **38.** $x^2 + y^2 - 4x + 2y = 4$

39. $x^2 + y^2 + 2x + y = \dfrac{11}{4}$ **40.** $x^2 + y^2 - 6x - y = -\dfrac{1}{4}$

41. $4x^2 + 4y^2 - 4x + 8y = 11$ **42.** $36x^2 + 36y^2 - 24x - 12y = 31$

Each of the following circles passes through the origin. In each case, find the equation.

43.

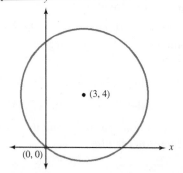

44.

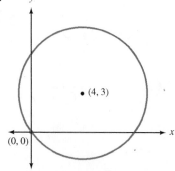

45. Find the equations of circles A, B, and C in the following diagram. The three points are the centers of the three circles.

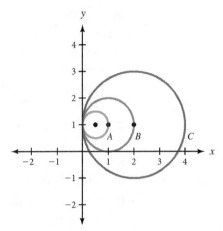

46. Each of the following circles passes through the origin. The centers are as shown. Find the equation of each circle.

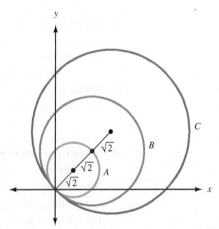

47. Find the equation of the circle with center at the origin that contains the point $(3, 4)$.

48. Find the equation of the circle with center at the origin that contains the point $(-5, 12)$.

49. Find the equation of the circle with center at the origin and x-intercepts 3 and -3.

50. Find the equation of the circle with y-intercepts 4 and -4 and center at the origin.

51. A circle with center at $(-1, 3)$ passes through the point $(4, 3)$. Find the equation.

52. A circle with center at $(2, 5)$ passes through the point $(-1, 4)$. Find the equation.

53. Find the equation of the circle with center at $(-2, 5)$, which passes through the point $(1, -3)$.

54. Find the equation of the circle with center at $(4, -1)$, which passes through the point $(6, -5)$.

55. Find the equation of the circle with center on the y-axis and y-intercepts at -2 and 6.

56. Find the equation of the circle with center on the x-axis and x-intercepts at -8 and 2.

57. Find the circumference and area of the circle $x^2 + (y - 3)^2 = 18$. Leave your answer in terms of π.

58. Find the circumference and area of the circle $(x + 2)^2 + (y + 6)^2 = 12$. Leave your answer in terms of π.

59. Find the circumference and area of the circle $x^2 + y^2 + 4x + 2y = 20$. Leave your answer in terms of π.

60. Find the circumference and area of the circle $x^2 + y^2 - 6x + 2y = 6$. Leave your answer in terms of π.

Applying the Concepts

61. **Search Area** A 3-year-old child has wandered away from home. The police have decided to search a circular area with a radius of 6 blocks. The child turns up at his grandmother's house, 5 blocks East and 3 blocks North of home. Was he found within the search area?

62. **Placing a Bubble Fountain** A circular garden pond with a diameter of 12 feet is to have a bubble fountain. The water from the bubble fountain falls in a circular pattern with a radius of 1.5 feet. If the center of the bubble fountain is placed 4 feet West and 3 feet North of the center of the pond, will all the water from the fountain fall inside the pond? What is the farthest distance from the center of the pond that water from the fountain will fall?

63. **Ferris Wheel** A giant Ferris wheel has a diameter of 240 feet and sits 12 feet above the ground. As shown in the diagram below, the wheel is 500 feet from the entrance to the park. The xy-coordinate system containing the wheel has its origin on the ground at the center of the entrance. Write an equation that models the shape of the wheel.

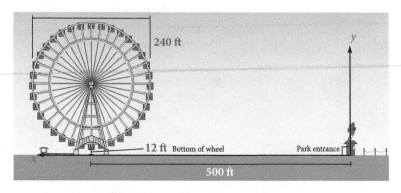

64. Magic Rings A magician is holding two rings that seem to lie in the same plane and intersect in two points. Each ring is 10 inches in diameter.

a. Find the equation of each ring if a coordinate system is placed with its origin at the center of the first ring and the X-axis contains the center of the second ring.

b. Find the equation of each ring if a coordinate system is placed with its origin at the center of the second ring and the x-axis contains the center of the first ring.

Learning Objectives Assessment

The following problems can be used to help assess if you have successfully met the learning objectives for this section.

65. Find the distance between the points $(5, -1)$ and $(2, 4)$.

    a. $3\sqrt{2}$ **b.** 4 **c.** $\sqrt{58}$ **d.** $\sqrt{34}$

66. Find the equation of the circle with center $(1, -2)$ and radius 4.

    a. $x^2 - 2y^2 = 16$ **b.** $(x + 2)^2 - (y - 1)^2 = 4$

    c. $(x - 1)^2 + (y + 2)^2 = 16$ **d.** $(x + 1)^2 + (y - 2)^2 = 4$

67. Find the center of the circle $x^2 + y^2 + 4y = 5$.

    a. $(0, -2)$ **b.** $(0, 2)$ **c.** $(0, 0)$ **d.** $(2, 0)$

68. Graph the circle $(x - 2)^2 + (y + 1)^2 = 3$.

a.

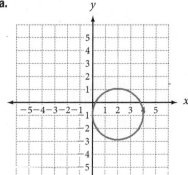

b.

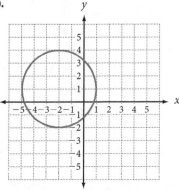

c.

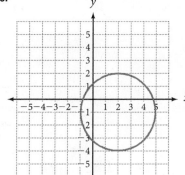

d.

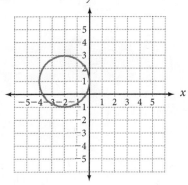

Getting Ready for the Next Section

Solve for p.

69. $4p = 12$

70. $4p = -8$

71. $4p = -1$

72. $4p = \dfrac{1}{2}$

Find the vertex for each quadratic function.

73. $y = 3(x - 4)^2 + 1$

74. $y = -2(x + 3)^2 - 5$

Sketch the graph of each function.

75. $y = 2x^2$

76. $y = -x^2$

77. $y = 2(x - 1)^2 - 3$

78. $y = -(x + 1)^2 + 2$

Learning Objectives

In this section, we will learn how to:

1. Graph a parabola.
2. Find the vertex for a parabola.
3. Find the focus for a parabola.

Introduction

In Chapter 8 we introduced the parabola as the graph of a quadratic function. In this section we will revisit the parabola, but from the context of a conic section.

As with all the conic sections, the parabola has a reflective property that makes it very useful in many modern devices, such as satellite television dishes. Satellite dishes are built in the shape of parabolas, because a parabola will reflect the incoming signal waves through a common point, called the *focus* (Figure 1).

FIGURE 1

Graphing Parabolas

If we position the parabola on a coordinate system with its vertex at the origin, and let p represent the coordinate of the focus, then we have the following.

⟮Δ≠Σ⟯ *Parabolas*

The graph of the equation

$$x^2 = 4py$$

will be a *parabola* with vertex at the origin and *focus* $(0, p)$. The *axis of symmetry* is $x = 0$ (the y-axis). If $p > 0$, the parabola opens upward, and if $p < 0$, the parabola opens downward.

The graph of the equation

$$y^2 = 4px$$

will be a *parabola* with vertex at the origin and *focus* $(p, 0)$. The *axis of symmetry* is $y = 0$ (the x-axis). If $p > 0$, the parabola opens to the right, and if $p < 0$, the parabola opens to the left.

 EXAMPLE 1 Graph $x^2 = 8y$ and state the focus.

SOLUTION The vertex is the origin. To find additional points on the graph, we can isolate the variable y and then substitute values for x.

$$8y = x^2$$

$$y = \frac{x^2}{8}$$

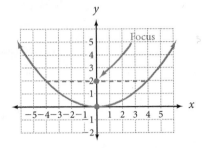

FIGURE 2

The graph is shown in Figure 2. To find the focus, we notice that the coefficent of y is equal to $4p$. Therefore

$$4p = 8$$

$$p = 2$$

The focus is the point $(0, 2)$ (see Figure 2). The focus will always lie on the axis of symmetry.

The length of the dashed line segment shown in Figure 2 is called the *focal width*. It tells us how wide the parabola is at the focus. Notice that the length of this segment is 8 units, which coincides with the coefficient of y in the equation from Example 1. This leads us to the following definition.

> **def** **DEFINITION**   *focal width*
>
> For any parabola, the *focal width* is the distance across the parabola, measured through the focus and perpendicular to the axis of symmetry. Its value is given by
>
> $$\text{focal width} = |4p|$$

The focal width gives us a convenient way of graphing a parabola more easily, as the following example illustrates.

EXAMPLE 2   Graph $y^2 = -3x$ and state the focus.

SOLUTION   The vertex is $(0, 0)$. Because the squared variable is y, the axis of symmetry is the x-axis. To find p, we have

$$4p = -3$$

$$p = -\frac{3}{4}$$

The focus is the point $\left(-\frac{3}{4}, 0\right)$. The focal width is $|-3| = 3$. The graph is shown in Figure 3. Notice how we have used the focal width to locate two other points on the graph.

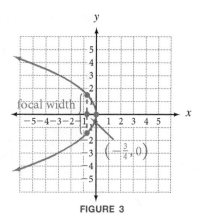

FIGURE 3

Translated Parabolas

From our work in Chapter 8, we know the graph of the equation $y = \frac{1}{4}(x - 1)^2 + 2$ is a parabola with vertex $(1, 2)$. If we isolate the squared binomial, we have

$$\frac{1}{4}(x - 1)^2 + 2 = y$$

$$\frac{1}{4}(x - 1)^2 = y - 2$$

$$(x - 1)^2 = 4(y - 2)$$

This is now expressed in the form $x^2 = 4py$, except that the vertex is no longer located at the origin because the terms subtracted from x and y represent translations. As you can see in Figure 4, the graph of $(x - 1)^2 = 4(y - 2)$ is identical to the graph of $x^2 = 4y$, except that it has been translated horizontally 1 unit to the right and vertically 2 units upward.

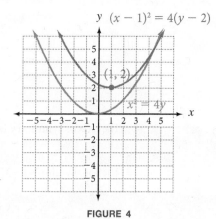

FIGURE 4

We summarize the information above with the following.

> ⎰Δ≠Σ **RULE**   *Parabolas with Vertex at (h, k)*
>
> The graphs of the equations
>
> $$(x - h)^2 = 4p(y - k) \quad \text{and} \quad (y - k)^2 = 4p(x - h)$$
>
> will be *parabolas with their vertex at (h, k)*. The graph of the first equation will have an axis of symmetry $x = h$ and the focus will be the point $(h, p + k)$. The graph of the second equation will have an axis of symmetry $y = k$ and the focus will be the point $(p + h, k)$. In either case, the focal width is $|\, 4p\,|$.

EXAMPLE 3   Graph: $(y + 3)^2 = -3(x - 2)$.

SOLUTION   If we write the equation in the form

$$(y - (-3))^2 = -3(x - 2)$$

then we see that $h = 2$ and $k = -3$. The vertex will be the point $(2, -3)$. Also, $4p = -3$, so $p = -\frac{3}{4}$. The graph will be identical to the parabola shown in Figure 3, except that there is a horizontal translation 2 units to the right and a vertical translation of 3 units downward. The graph is shown in Figure 5.

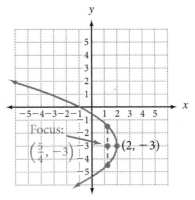

FIGURE 5

The axis of symmetry is $y = -3$ and the focus is the point

$$\left(-\tfrac{3}{4} + 2, -3\right) = \left(\tfrac{5}{4}, -3\right)$$

The focal width is $|-3| = 3$, the same as it was in Example 2.

EXAMPLE 4   Graph the parabola $y^2 - x - 4y - 2 = 0$.

SOLUTION   To identify the vertex and focus, we must complete the square on y. To begin, we rearrange the terms so that those containing y are together, and any other terms are on the other side of the equal sign. Doing so gives us the following equation:

$$y^2 - 4y = x + 2$$

To complete the square on y, we add 4 to each side of the equation. Then we can factor each side to obtain standard form.

$$y^2 - 4y + 4 = x + 2 + 4 \qquad \text{Add 4 to both sides}$$

$$(y - 2)^2 = x + 6 \qquad \text{Factor the left side}$$

$$(y - 2)^2 = 1(x + 6) \qquad \text{Factor the right side}$$

The graph is a parabola with vertex $(-6, 2)$. The axis of symmetry is $y = 2$. To find the focus, we have

$$4p = 1$$

$$p = \frac{1}{4}$$

The focus is the point $\left(\frac{1}{4} + (-6), 2\right) = \left(-\frac{23}{4}, 2\right)$ and the focal width is 1. The graph is shown in Figure 6.

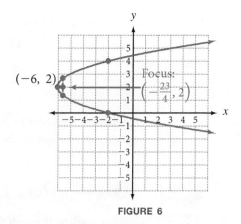

FIGURE 6

We can find extra points on the graph as necessary by choosing values for one variable and then solving for the other. For example, if $x = -2$, then

$$(y - 2)^2 = 1(-2 + 6)$$

$$(y - 2)^2 = 4$$

$$y - 2 = \pm 2$$

$$y = 2 \pm 2$$

$$y = 4 \text{ or } 0$$

The points $(-2, 4)$ and $(-2, 0)$ also lie on the graph (see Figure 6).

Application

As we mentioned in the introduction to this section, parabolas have many practical uses in the real world because of their reflective property.

EXAMPLE 5   A satellite television company uses a parabolic dish to collect the signal from their satellite. The dish is 10 inches deep and measures 30 inches across. The receiver for the dish will be located at the focus. How far from the base of the dish should the receiver be placed?

SOLUTION   We assume the vertex is positioned at the origin and use the equation $x^2 = 4py$. Based on the dimensions of the dish, the point (15, 10) must lie on the graph of the parabola (see Figure 7).

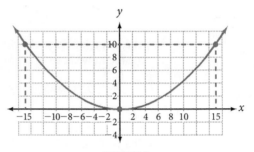

FIGURE 7

Substituting $x = 15$ and $y = 10$, we can solve for p.

$$15^2 = 4p(10)$$

$$215 = 40p$$

$$5.625 = p$$

The focus is the point (0, 5.625). This means the receiver should be placed 5.625 inches from the base of the dish.

Getting Ready for Class

After reading through the preceding section, respond in your own words and in complete sentences.

A. How can you tell the difference between the equation of a parabola with a horizontal axis of symmetry and the equation of a parabola with a vertical axis of symmetry?

B. How do we find the coordinates of the focus for a parabola?

C. What is the focal width for a parabola?

D. Explain how to use the focal width to help sketch the graph of a parabola.

Graph each of the following parabolas. State the coordinates of the focus.

1. $x^2 = 4y$ **2.** $x^2 = -6y$ **3.** $x^2 = y$

4. $x^2 = -y$ **5.** $x^2 = -\dfrac{1}{2}y$ **6.** $x^2 = \dfrac{1}{4}y$

7. $y^2 = -2x$ **8.** $y^2 = 8x$ **9.** $y^2 = -x$

10. $y^2 = x$ **11.** $y^2 = \dfrac{1}{3}x$ **12.** $y^2 = -\dfrac{1}{2}x$

Graph the parabola. In each case, label the coordinates of the vertex and focus.

13. $(x + 1)^2 = 2(y + 3)$ **14.** $(x + 2)^2 = -10(y + 4)$

15. $(x - 4)^2 = -(y - 2)$ **16.** $(x - 3)^2 = (y - 5)$

17. $(x + 2)^2 = -\dfrac{1}{3}(y - 1)$ **18.** $(x - 2)^2 = \dfrac{1}{4}(y + 3)$

19. $(y - 1)^2 = 3(x - 2)$ **20.** $(y + 2)^2 = 4(x + 5)$

21. $(y + 3)^2 = x - 3$ **22.** $(y + 1)^2 = -(x - 4)$

23. $(y - 2)^2 = -\dfrac{1}{3}(x - 5)$ **24.** $(y - 4)^2 = -\dfrac{1}{2}(x + 3)$

25. $x^2 - 4x - y + 1 = 0$ **26.** $x^2 - 4x + y - 3 = 0$

27. $x^2 + 2x + 8y - 23 = 0$ **28.** $x^2 + 4x - 10y - 6 = 0$

29. $y^2 - x + 4y + 7 = 0$ **30.** $y^2 + x - 6y + 5 = 0$

31. $y^2 + 6x - 2y + 7 = 0$ **32.** $y^2 - 9x + 4y + 22 = 0$

Applying the Concepts

33. Telescope A parabolic mirror for a telescope measures 10 inches across and 1 inch deep. If a lens is to be located at the focus, how far from the base of the mirror should the lens be placed?

34. Headlamp The reflector for a car headlamp is in the shape of a parabolic dish measuring 16 centimeters across and 10 centimeters deep. If the bulb is located at the focus of the parabola, how far from the base of the reflector should the bulb be placed?

35. Satellite Dish The parabolic dish for a satellite television company is 24 inches across and 12 inches deep. If the signal receiver is located at the focus of the parabola, how far should it be placed from the base of the dish?

36. Telescope The primary mirror for the telescope at the Keck Observatory is a parabolic dish that is 10 meters across and has a focal length of 17.5 meters (which means the focus is located 17.5 meters from the base of the mirror). What is the depth of the mirror (see Figure 8)?

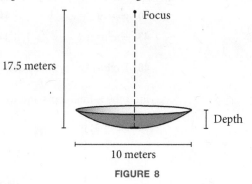

FIGURE 8

Learning Objectives Assessment

The following problems can be used to help assess if you have successfully met the learning objectives for this section.

37. Graph: $y^2 = -7x$.

a.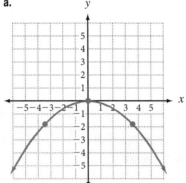

b.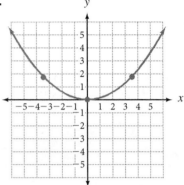

c.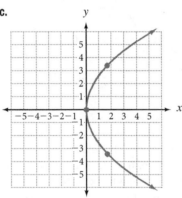

d.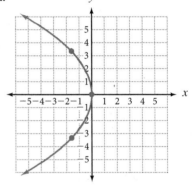

38. State the vertex for the parabola $y^2 - 2x - 6y + 5 = 0$.

   a. $(-2, 3)$ **b.** $(2, -3)$ **c.** $(0, 0)$ **d.** $(3, -2)$

39. Find the coordinates of the focus for the parabola $x^2 = -5y$.

   a. $(0, 0)$ **b.** $(0, -5)$ **c.** $\left(-\dfrac{5}{4}, 0\right)$ **d.** $\left(0, -\dfrac{5}{4}\right)$

Getting Ready for the Next Section

Solve.

40. $y^2 = 9$ **41.** $x^2 = 25$ **42.** $-y^2 = 4$

43. $-x^2 = 16$ **44.** $-x^2 = 9$ **45.** $y^2 = 100$

46. Divide $4x^2 + 9y^2$ by 36.   **47.** Divide $25x^2 + 4y^2$ by 100.

Find the x-intercepts and the y-intercepts

48. $3x - 4y = 12$ **49.** $y = 3x^2 + 5x - 2$

50. If $\dfrac{x^2}{25} + \dfrac{y^2}{9} = 1$, find y when x is 3.   **51.** If $\dfrac{x^2}{25} + \dfrac{y^2}{9} = 1$, find y when x is -4.

Learning Objectives

In this section, we will learn how to:

1. Graph an ellipse.
2. Graph a hyperbola.
3. Find the center for an ellipse or hyperbola.
4. Find the vertices of an ellipse or hyperbola.

Introduction

The photograph below shows Halley's comet as it passed close to earth in 1986. Like the planets in our solar system, it orbits the sun in an elliptical path. While it takes the earth 1 year to complete one orbit around the sun, it takes Halley's comet 76 years. The first known sighting of Halley's comet was in 239 B.C. Its most famous appearance occurred in 1066 A.D., when it was seen at the Battle of Hastings.

NASA

This section is concerned with the last of the two conic sections, which are ellipses and hyperbolas. To begin, we will consider only those graphs that are centered about the origin.

Ellipses

Suppose we want to graph the equation

$$\frac{x^2}{25} + \frac{y^2}{9} = 1$$

We can find the y-intercepts by letting $x = 0$, and we can find the x-intercepts by letting $y = 0$:

When $x = 0$ When $y = 0$

$$\frac{0^2}{25} + \frac{y^2}{9} = 1 \qquad\qquad \frac{x^2}{25} + \frac{0^2}{9} = 1$$

$$y^2 = 9 \qquad\qquad\qquad x^2 = 25$$

$$y = \pm 3 \qquad\qquad\qquad x = \pm 5$$

The graph crosses the y-axis at $(0, 3)$ and $(0, -3)$ and the x-axis at $(5, 0)$ and $(-5, 0)$. Graphing these points and then connecting them with a smooth curve gives the graph shown in Figure 1.

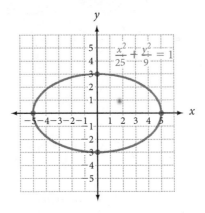

We can find other ordered pairs on the graph by substituting in values for x (or y) and then solving for y (or x). For example, if we let $x = 3$, then

$$\frac{3^2}{25} + \frac{y^2}{9} = 1$$

$$\frac{9}{25} + \frac{y^2}{9} = 1$$

$$0.36 + \frac{y^2}{9} = 1$$

$$\frac{y^2}{9} = 0.64 \qquad \text{Add } -0.36 \text{ to each side}$$

$$y^2 = 5.76 \qquad \text{Multiply each side by 9}$$

$$y = \pm 2.4 \qquad \text{Square root of each side}$$

This would give us the two ordered pairs $(3, -2.4)$ and $(3, 2.4)$.

A graph of the type shown in Figure 1 is called an *ellipse*. If we were to find some other ordered pairs that satisfy our original equation, we would find that their graphs lie on the ellipse. Also, the coordinates of any point on the ellipse will satisfy the equation. We can generalize these results as follows.

> *Note* The vertices are always the two points on the ellipse that are furthest from each other.

The Ellipse

The graph of any equation of the form

$$\frac{x^2}{a^2} + \frac{y^2}{b^2} = 1 \qquad \text{Standard form}$$

will be an *ellipse* centered at the origin. The ellipse will cross the x-axis at $(a, 0)$ and $(-a, 0)$. It will cross the y-axis at $(0, b)$ and $(0, -b)$. When a and b are equal, the ellipse will be a circle.

If $a^2 > b^2$, then the x-intercepts, $(\pm a, 0)$, are called the **vertices** and the y-intercepts, $(0, \pm b)$, are called the **co-vertices**. If $b^2 > a^2$, then the vertices are the points $(0, \pm b)$ and the co-vertices are the points $(\pm a, 0)$.

The most convenient way to graph an ellipse is to locate the intercepts (vertices and co-vertices).

EXAMPLE 1   Sketch the graph of $4x^2 + 9y^2 = 36$.

SOLUTION   To write the equation in the form

$$\frac{x^2}{a^2} + \frac{y^2}{b^2} = 1$$

we must divide both sides by 36:

$$\frac{4x^2}{36} + \frac{9y^2}{36} = \frac{36}{36}$$

$$\frac{x^2}{9} + \frac{y^2}{4} = 1$$

The graph crosses the x-axis at $(3, 0)$, $(-3, 0)$ and the y-axis at $(0, 2)$, $(0, -2)$. (See Figure 2.) The vertices are the points $(\pm 3, 0)$, and the co-vertices are the points $(0, \pm 2)$.

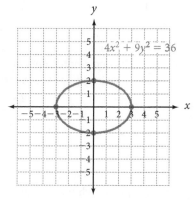

FIGURE 2

Hyperbolas

The photo below shows Europa, one of Jupiter's moons, as it was photographed by the Galileo space probe in the late 1990s. To speed up the trip from Earth to Jupiter—nearly a billion miles—Galileo made use of the *slingshot effect*. This involves flying a hyperbolic path very close to a planet, so that gravity can be used to gain velocity as the space probe hooks around the planet (Figure 3).

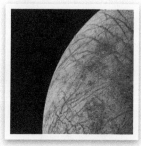

NASA

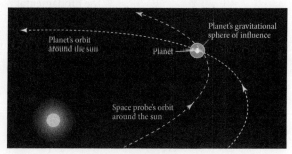

FIGURE 3

Consider the equation

$$\frac{x^2}{9} - \frac{y^2}{4} = 1$$

If we were to find a number of ordered pairs that are solutions to the equation and connect their graphs with a smooth curve, we would have Figure 4.

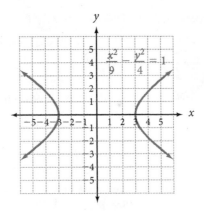

FIGURE 4

This graph is an example of a *hyperbola*. Notice that the graph has x-intercepts at $(3, 0)$ and $(-3, 0)$. These intercepts are the vertices for the hyperbola. The graph has no y-intercepts and hence does not cross the y-axis. We can show this by substituting $x = 0$ into the equation

$$\frac{0^2}{9} - \frac{y^2}{4} = 1 \qquad \text{Substitute 0 for } x$$

$$-\frac{y^2}{4} = 1 \qquad \text{Simplify left side}$$

$$y^2 = -4 \qquad \text{Multiply each side by } -4$$

for which there is no real solution.

We want to produce reasonable sketches of hyperbolas without having to build extensive tables. We can produce the graphs we are after by using what is called the *fundamental rectangle*. The hyperbola is the only conic section whose graph has a pair of asymptotes, and the position of these asymptotes is determined by the fundamental rectangle.

The shape of the fundamental rectangle is based on the square roots of the denominators of the two variable terms. For the hyperbola shown in Figure 4, the sides of the fundamental rectangle will pass through the points $(\pm 3, 0)$ and $(0, \pm 2)$. The asymptotes will be the lines passing through the opposite corners of the fundamental rectangle, as shown in Figure 5.

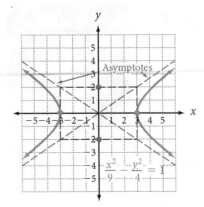

FIGURE 5

Notice that both asymptotes pass through the origin, and that their slopes are $\frac{2}{3}$ and $-\frac{2}{3}$. Thus, the equations of the asymptotes are

$$y = \frac{2}{3}x \quad \text{and} \quad y = -\frac{2}{3}x$$

The further we get from the origin, the closer the hyperbola is to these lines.

EXAMPLE 2 Graph the equation $\frac{y^2}{9} - \frac{x^2}{16} = 1$.

SOLUTION In this case the y-intercepts are 3 and -3, and there are no x-intercepts. The vertices are the points $(0, \pm 3)$. The sides of the fundamental rectangle used to draw the asymptotes must pass through 3 and -3 on the y-axis, and 4 and -4 on the x-axis. Figure 6 shows the fundamental rectangle, the asymptotes, and the hyperbola.

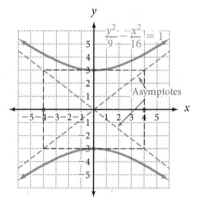

FIGURE 6

Here is a summary of what we have for hyperbolas.

Hyberbolas Centered at the Origin

The graph of the equation

$$\frac{x^2}{a^2} - \frac{y^2}{b^2} = 1$$

will be a *hyperbola centered at the origin.* The graph will have *x-intercepts (vertices)* at $(\pm a, 0)$.

The graph of the equation

$$\frac{y^2}{b^2} - \frac{x^2}{a^2} = 1$$

will be a *hyperbola centered at the origin.* The graph will have *y-intercepts (vertices)* at $(0, \pm b)$.

As an aid in sketching either of these equations, the asymptotes can be found by drawing lines through opposite corners of the fundamental rectangle whose sides pass through $(\pm a, 0)$ and $(0, \pm b)$. The asymptotes are given by the lines

$$y = \frac{b}{a}x \quad \text{and} \quad y = -\frac{b}{a}x$$

Ellipses and Hyperbolas not Centered at the Origin

Consider the equation

$$\frac{(x-4)^2}{9} + \frac{(y-1)^2}{4} = 1$$

The terms subtracted from x and y in the grouping symbols represent translations. The graph of this equation will be identical to the ellipse

$$\frac{x^2}{9} + \frac{y^2}{4} = 1$$

whose graph is shown in Figure 2, except translated 4 units to the right and translated vertically upward 1 unit. This means the center of the ellipse will be shifted from the origin to the point (4, 1). Figure 7 shows the resulting graph.

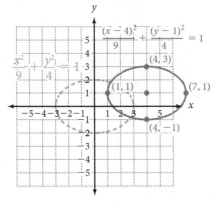

FIGURE 7

Note that the horizontal distance from the center to the vertices is 3—the square root of the denominator of the $(x-4)^2$ term. Likewise, the vertical distance from the center to the co-vertices is 2—the square root of the denominator of the $(y-1)^2$ term.

We summarize the information above with the following:

△≠Σ   *An Ellipse with Center at (h, k)*

The graph of the equation

$$\frac{(x-h)^2}{a^2} + \frac{(y-k)^2}{b^2} = 1$$

will be an *ellipse with center at (h, k)*. The vertices and co-vertices of the ellipse will be at the points $(h + a, k)$, $(h - a, k)$, $(h, k + b)$, and $(h, k - b)$.

EXAMPLE 3   Graph the ellipse: $x^2 + 9y^2 + 4x - 54y + 76 = 0$

SOLUTION   To identify the coordinates of the center, we must complete the square on x and also on y. To begin, we rearrange the terms so that those containing x are together, those containing y are together, and the constant term is on the other side of the equal sign. Doing so gives us the following equation:

$$x^2 + 4x \quad + 9y^2 - 54y \quad = -76$$

Before we can complete the square on y, we must factor 9 from each term containing y:

$$x^2 + 4x \quad + 9(y^2 - 6y \quad) = -76$$

To complete the square on x, we add 4 to each side of the equation. To complete the square on y, we add 9 inside the parentheses. This increases the left side of the equation by 81 since each term within the parentheses is multiplied by 9. Therefore, we must add 81 to the right side of the equation also.

$$x^2 + 4x + 4 + 9(y^2 - 6y + 9) = -76 + 4 + 81$$

$$(x + 2)^2 + 9(y - 3)^2 = 9$$

To obtain standard form, we divide each term on both sides by 9:

$$\frac{(x + 2)^2}{9} + \frac{9(y - 3)^2}{9} = \frac{9}{9}$$

$$\frac{(x + 2)^2}{9} + \frac{(y - 3)^2}{1} = 1$$

The graph is an ellipse with center at $(-2, 3)$, as shown in Figure 8. The vertices are the points located 3 units to the left and right of the center at $(-5, 3)$, and $(1, 3)$. The co-vertices are located 2 units above and below the center at $(-2, 4)$ and $(-2, 2)$.

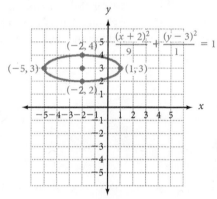

FIGURE 8

The ideas associated with graphing hyperbolas whose centers are not at the origin parallel the ideas just presented about graphing ellipses whose centers have been moved off the origin.

$|\triangle \neq \Sigma|$ *Hyperbolas with Centers at (h, k)*

The graphs of the equations

$$\frac{(x - h)^2}{a^2} - \frac{(y - k)^2}{b^2} = 1 \quad \text{and} \quad \frac{(y - k)^2}{b^2} - \frac{(x - h)^2}{a^2} = 1$$

will be *hyperbolas with their centers at (h, k)*. The vertices of the graph of the first equation will be at the points $(h + a, k)$ and $(h - a, k)$, and the vertices for the graph of the second equation will be at $(h, k + b)$ and $(h, k - b)$. In either case, the asymptotes can be found by connecting opposite corners of the fundamental rectangle that contains the four points $(h + a, k)$, $(h - a, k)$, $(h, k + b)$, and $(h, k - b)$.

EXAMPLE 4   Graph the hyperbola: $4x^2 - y^2 + 4y - 20 = 0$

SOLUTION   To identify the coordinates of the center of the hyperbola, we need to complete the square on y. (Because there is no linear term in x, we do not need to complete the square on x. The x-coordinate of the center will be $x = 0$.)

$$4x^2 - y^2 + 4y - 20 = 0$$

$$4x^2 - y^2 + 4y = 20 \qquad \text{Add 20 to each side}$$

$$4x^2 - 1(y^2 - 4y) = 20 \qquad \text{Factor } -1 \text{ from each term containing } y$$

To complete the square on y, we add 4 to the terms inside the parentheses. Doing so adds -4 to the left side of the equation because everything inside the parentheses is multiplied by -1. To keep from changing the equation we must add -4 to the right side also.

$$4x^2 - 1(y^2 - 4y + 4) = 20 - 4 \qquad \text{Add } -4 \text{ to each side}$$

$$4x^2 - 1(y - 2)^2 = 16 \qquad y^2 - 4y + 4 = (y - 2)^2$$

$$\frac{4x^2}{16} - \frac{(y - 2)^2}{16} = \frac{16}{16} \qquad \text{Divide each side by 16}$$

$$\frac{x^2}{4} - \frac{(y - 2)^2}{16} = 1 \qquad \text{Simplify each term}$$

This is the equation of a hyperbola with center at $(0, 2)$. The graph opens to the right and left as shown in Figure 9. The vertices are located 2 units to the left and right of the center at $(-2, 2)$ and $(2, 2)$.

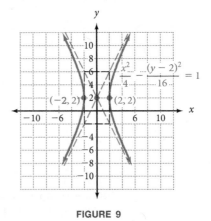

FIGURE 9

Getting Ready for Class

After reading through the preceding section, respond in your own words and in complete sentences.

A. How do we find the x-intercepts of a graph from the equation?

B. What is an ellipse?

C. How can you tell by looking at an equation if its graph will be an ellipse or a hyperbola?

D. How do we know if the graph of a hyperbola will open to the left and right, or open upward and downward?

Graph each of the following ellipses. Be sure to label both the x- and y-intercepts.

1. $\dfrac{x^2}{9} + \dfrac{y^2}{16} = 1$　　　**2.** $\dfrac{x^2}{25} + \dfrac{y^2}{4} = 1$　　　**3.** $\dfrac{x^2}{16} + \dfrac{y^2}{9} = 1$

4. $\dfrac{x^2}{4} + \dfrac{y^2}{25} = 1$　　　**5.** $\dfrac{x^2}{3} + \dfrac{y^2}{4} = 1$　　　**6.** $\dfrac{x^2}{4} + \dfrac{y^2}{3} = 1$

7. $4x^2 + 25y^2 = 100$　　　**8.** $4x^2 + 9y^2 = 36$　　　**9.** $x^2 + 8y^2 = 16$

10. $12x^2 + y^2 = 36$

Graph each of the following hyperbolas. Show the intercepts and the asymptotes in each case.

11. $\dfrac{x^2}{9} - \dfrac{y^2}{16} = 1$　　　**12.** $\dfrac{x^2}{25} - \dfrac{y^2}{4} = 1$　　　**13.** $\dfrac{x^2}{16} - \dfrac{y^2}{9} = 1$

14. $\dfrac{x^2}{4} - \dfrac{y^2}{25} = 1$　　　**15.** $\dfrac{y^2}{9} - \dfrac{x^2}{16} = 1$　　　**16.** $\dfrac{y^2}{25} - \dfrac{x^2}{4} = 1$

17. $\dfrac{y^2}{36} - \dfrac{x^2}{4} = 1$　　　**18.** $\dfrac{y^2}{4} - \dfrac{x^2}{36} = 1$　　　**19.** $x^2 - 4y^2 = 4$

20. $y^2 - 4x^2 = 4$　　　**21.** $16y^2 - 9x^2 = 144$　　　**22.** $4y^2 - 25x^2 = 100$

Find the x- and y-intercepts, if they exist, for each of the following. Do not graph.

23. $0.4x^2 + 0.9y^2 = 3.6$　　**24.** $1.6x^2 + 0.9y^2 = 14.4$　　**25.** $\dfrac{x^2}{0.04} - \dfrac{y^2}{0.09} = 1$

26. $\dfrac{y^2}{0.16} - \dfrac{x^2}{0.25} = 1$　　**27.** $\dfrac{25x^2}{9} + \dfrac{25y^2}{4} = 1$　　**28.** $\dfrac{16x^2}{9} + \dfrac{16y^2}{25} = 1$

Graph each of the following ellipses. In each case, label the coordinates of the center and the vertices.

29. $\dfrac{(x - 4)^2}{4} + \dfrac{(y - 2)^2}{9} = 1$　　　　**30.** $\dfrac{(x - 2)^2}{4} + \dfrac{(y - 4)^2}{9} = 1$

31. $4x^2 + y^2 - 4y - 12 = 0$　　　　**32.** $4x^2 + y^2 - 24x - 4y + 36 = 0$

33. $x^2 + 9y^2 + 4x - 54y + 76 = 0$　　　**34.** $4x^2 + y^2 - 16x + 2y + 13 = 0$

Graph each of the following hyperbolas. In each case, label the coordinates of the center and the vertices and show the asymptotes.

35. $\dfrac{(x - 2)^2}{16} - \dfrac{y^2}{4} = 1$　　　　**36.** $\dfrac{(y - 2)^2}{16} - \dfrac{x^2}{4} = 1$

37. $9y^2 - x^2 - 4x + 54y + 68 = 0$　　**38.** $4x^2 - y^2 - 24x + 4y + 28 = 0$

39. $4y^2 - 9x^2 - 16y + 72x - 164 = 0$　　**40.** $4x^2 - y^2 - 16x - 2y + 11 = 0$

41. Find x when $y = 4$ in the equation $\dfrac{x^2}{25} + \dfrac{y^2}{16} = 1$.

42. Find x when $y = 3$ in the equation $\dfrac{x^2}{25} + \dfrac{y^2}{16} = 1$.

43. Find y when $x = -3$ in the equation $\dfrac{x^2}{9} + \dfrac{y^2}{16} = 1$.

44. Find y when $x = -2$ in the equation $\dfrac{x^2}{9} + \dfrac{y^2}{16} = 1$.

45. The line segment connecting the vertices of an ellipse is called the *major axis* of the ellipse. Give the length of the major axis of the ellipse you graphed in Problem 3.

46. The line segment connecting the co-vertices of an ellipse is called the *minor axis* of the ellipse. Give the length of the minor axis of the ellipse you graphed in Problem 3.

Applying the Concepts

Some of the problems that follow use the major and minor axes mentioned in Problems 45 and 46. The diagram below shows the minor axis and the major axis for an ellipse.

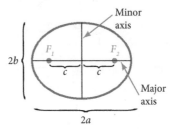

For an ellipse in which $a^2 > b^2$, the length of the major axis is $2a$ and the length of the minor axis is $2b$ (these are the same a and b that appear in the general equation of an ellipse). Each of the points F_1 and F_2 shown above on the major axis is a *focus* of the ellipse. If the distance from the center of the ellipse to each focus is c, then it is always true that $a^2 = b^2 + c^2$. You will need this information for some of the problems that follow.

47. The Colosseum The Colosseum in Rome seated 50,000 spectators around a central elliptical arena. The base of the Colosseum measured 615 feet long and 510 feet wide. Write an equation for the elliptical shape of the Colosseum. Assume the ellipse is centered at the origin and that the major axis is horizontal.

48. Archway A new theme park is planning an archway at its main entrance. The arch is to be in the form of a semi-ellipse (half of an ellipse) with the major axis as the span. If the span is to be 40 feet and the height at the center is to be 10 feet, what is the equation of the ellipse? How far left and right of center could a 6-foot man walk upright under the arch? Assume the ellipse is centered at the origin and that the major axis is horizontal.

© GoogleEarth

49. The Ellipse President's Park, located between the White House and the Washington Monument in Washington, DC, is also called The Ellipse. The park is enclosed by an elliptical path with major axis 458 meters and minor axis 390 meters. What is the equation for the path around The Ellipse? Assume the ellipse is centered at the origin and that the major axis is horizontal.

50. Garden Trellis John is planning to build an arched trellis for the entrance to his botanical garden. If the arch is to be in the shape of the upper half of an ellipse that is 6 feet wide at the base and 9 feet high, what is the equation for the ellipse? Assume the ellipse is centered at the origin and that the major axis is vertical.

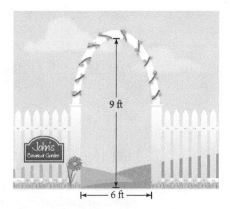

51. Elliptical Pool Table A children's science museum plans to build an elliptical pool table to demonstrate that a ball rolled from a particular point (focus) will always go into a hole located at another particular point (the other focus). The focus needs to be 1 foot from the vertex of the ellipse. If the table is to be 8 feet long, how wide should it be? *Hint:* The distance from the center to each focus point is represented by c and is found by using the equation $a^2 = b^2 + c^2$.

52. Entering the Zoo A zoo is planning a new entrance. Visitors are to be "funneled" into the zoo between two tall brick fences. The bases of the fences will be in the shape of a hyperbola. The narrowest passage East and West between the fences will be 24 feet. The total North–South distance of the fences is to be 50 feet. Write an equation for the hyperbolic shape of the fences if the center of the hyperbola is to be placed at the origin of the coordinate system and the vertices are on the x-axis.

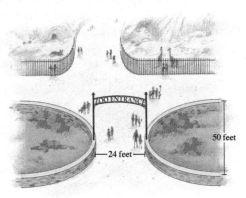

Learning Objectives Assessment

The following problems can be used to help assess if you have successfully met the learning objectives for this section.

53. Graph the ellipse $\dfrac{x^2}{4} + \dfrac{y^2}{6} = 1$.

a.

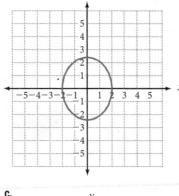

b.

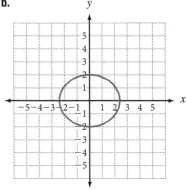

c.

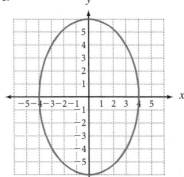

d.

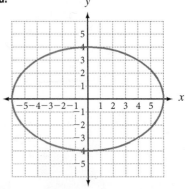

54. Graph the hyperbola $\dfrac{x^2}{9} - \dfrac{y^2}{4} = 1$.

a.

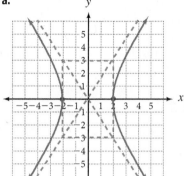

b.

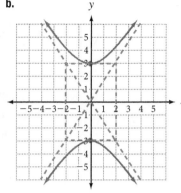

c.

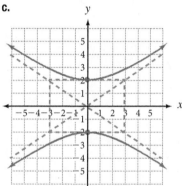

d.

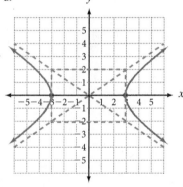

55. State the center of the ellipse $x^2 + 4y^2 + 2x - 24y + 33 = 0$.

    a. $(1, -3)$ **b.** $(-1, 3)$ **c.** $(2, -6)$ **d.** $(-2, 6)$

56. Find the vertices of the hyperbola $(y - 1)^2 - (x + 2)^2 = 4$.

    a. $(0, -1), (4, -1)$ **b.** $(2, -3), (2, 1)$

    c. $(-2, -1), (-2, 3)$ **d.** $(-4, 1), (0, 1)$

Getting Ready for the Next Section

57. Which of the following are solutions to $x^2 + y^2 < 16$?

$$(0, 0) \quad (4, 0) \quad (0, 5)$$

58. Which of the following are solutions to $y \geq x^2 - 16$?

$$(0, 0) \quad (-2, 0) \quad (0, -2)$$

Expand and Multiply.

59. $(2y + 4)^2$ **60.** $(y + 3)^2$

61. Solve $x - 2y = 4$ for x.   **62.** Solve $2x + 3y = 6$ for y.

Simplify.

63. $x^2 - 2(x^2 - 3)$

64. $x^2 + (x^2 - 4)$

Factor.

65. $5y^2 + 16y + 12$

66. $3x^2 + 17x - 28$

Solve.

67. $y^2 = 4$

68. $x^2 = 25$

69. $-x^2 + 6 = 2$

70. $5y^2 + 16y + 12 = 0$

Learning Objectives

In this section, we will learn how to:

1. Graph the solution set for a second-degree inequality.

2. Solve a system of nonlinear equations using the substitution method.

3. Solve a system of nonlinear equations using the addition method.

4. Graph the solution set for a system of nonlinear inequalities.

Introduction

In Section 3.4, we graphed linear inequalities by first graphing the boundary and then choosing a test point not on the boundary to determine the region used for the solution set. The problems in this section are very similar. We will use the same general methods for graphing the inequalities in this section that we used in Section 3.4.

Second-Degree Inequalities

| EXAMPLE 1 | Graph $x^2 + y^2 < 16$.

SOLUTION The boundary is $x^2 + y^2 = 16$, which is a circle with center at the origin and a radius of 4. Because the inequality sign is $<$, the boundary is not included in the solution set and must therefore be represented with a broken line. The graph of the boundary is shown in Figure 1.

The solution set for $x^2 + y^2 < 16$ is either the region inside the circle or the region outside the circle. To see which region represents the solution set, we choose a convenient point not on the boundary and test it in the original inequality. The origin $(0, 0)$ is a convenient point. Because the origin satisfies the inequality $x^2 + y^2 < 16$, all points in the same region will also satisfy the inequality. Therefore, we shade the region inside the circle. The graph of the solution set is shown in Figure 2.

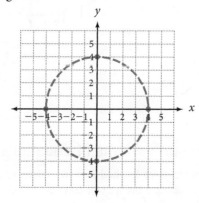

FIGURE 1

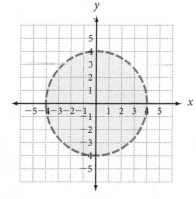

FIGURE 2

EXAMPLE 2   Graph the inequality $y \le x^2 - 2$.

SOLUTION   The parabola $y = x^2 - 2$ is the boundary and is included in the solution set. Using $(0, 0)$ as the test point, we see that $0 \le 0^2 - 2$ is a false statement, which means that the region containing $(0, 0)$ is not in the solution set. Therefore, we shade the region to the outside of the parabola, as shown in Figure 3.

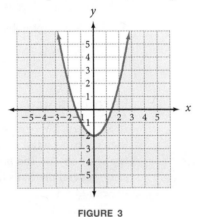

FIGURE 3

EXAMPLE 3   Graph $4y^2 - 9x^2 < 36$.

SOLUTION   The boundary is the hyperbola $4y^2 - 9x^2 = 36$, which we can write in standard form as

$$\frac{y^2}{9} - \frac{x^2}{4} = 1$$

It is not included in the solution set. Testing $(0, 0)$ in the original inequality yields a true statement, which means that the region containing the origin is the solution set. (See Figure 4.)

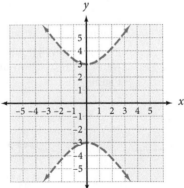

FIGURE 4

Nonlinear Systems of Equations

In Chapter 4 we learned how to solve systems of linear equations in two and three variables. Now we will consider systems of equations that are not linear. We will rely once again on the addition method and substitution method that was introduced back in Section 4.1.

EXAMPLE 4   Solve the system.

$$x^2 + y^2 = 4$$
$$x - 2y = 4$$

SOLUTION In this case, the substitution method is the most convenient. Solving the second equation for x in terms of y, we have

$$x - 2y = 4$$

$$x = 2y + 4$$

We now substitute $2y + 4$ for x in the first equation in our original system and proceed to solve for y:

$$(2y + 4)^2 + y^2 = 4$$

$$4y^2 + 16y + 16 + y^2 = 4 \qquad \text{Expand } (2y + 4)^2$$

$$5y^2 + 16y + 16 = 4 \qquad \text{Simplify left side}$$

$$5y^2 + 16y + 12 = 0 \qquad \text{Add } -4 \text{ to each side}$$

$$(5y + 6)(y + 2) = 0 \qquad \text{Factor}$$

$$5y + 6 = 0 \quad \text{or} \quad y + 2 = 0 \qquad \text{Set factors equal to 0}$$

$$y = -\frac{6}{5} \quad \text{or} \qquad y = -2 \qquad \text{Solve}$$

These are the y-coordinates of the two solutions to the system. Substituting $y = -\frac{6}{5}$ into $x - 2y = 4$ and solving for x gives us $x = \frac{8}{5}$. Using $y = -2$ in the same equation yields $x = 0$. The two solutions to our system are $\left(\frac{8}{5}, -\frac{6}{5}\right)$ and $(0, -2)$. Although graphing the system is not necessary, it does help us visualize the situation. (See Figure 5.)

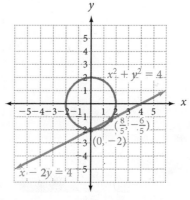

FIGURE 5

EXAMPLE 5 Solve the system.

$$16x^2 - 4y^2 = 64$$

$$x^2 + y^2 = 9$$

SOLUTION Because each equation is of the second degree in both x and y, it is easier to solve this system by eliminating one of the variables by addition. To eliminate y, we multiply the bottom equation by 4 and add the result to the top equation:

$$16x^2 - 4y^2 = 64$$
$$\underline{4x^2 + 4y^2 = 36}$$
$$20x^2 = 100$$

$$x^2 = 5$$

$$x = \pm\sqrt{5}$$

The x-coordinates of the points of intersection are $\sqrt{5}$ and $-\sqrt{5}$. We substitute each back into the second equation in the original system and solve for y:

When $$x = \sqrt{5}$$

$$(\sqrt{5})^2 + y^2 = 9$$

$$5 + y^2 = 9$$

$$y^2 = 4$$

$$y = \pm 2$$

When $$x = -\sqrt{5}$$

$$(-\sqrt{5})^2 + y^2 = 9$$

$$5 + y^2 = 9$$

$$y^2 = 4$$

$$y = \pm 2$$

The four points of intersection are $(-\sqrt{5},\ 2)$, $(-\sqrt{5},\ -2)$, $(\sqrt{5},\ 2)$, and $(\sqrt{5},\ -2)$. Graphically the situation is as shown in Figure 6.

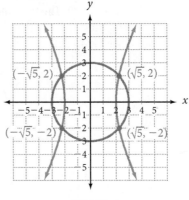

FIGURE 6

EXAMPLE 6   Solve the system.

$$x^2 - 2y = 2$$

$$y = x^2 - 3$$

SOLUTION   We can solve this system using the substitution method. Replacing y in the first equation with $x^2 - 3$ from the second equation, we have

$$x^2 - 2(x^2 - 3) = 2$$

$$-x^2 + 6 = 2$$

$$x^2 = 4$$

$$x = \pm 2$$

Using either $+2$ or -2 in the equation $y = x^2 - 3$ gives us $y = 1$. The system has two solutions: $(2, 1)$ and $(-2, 1)$.

EXAMPLE 7 The sum of the squares of two numbers is 34. The difference of their squares is 16. Find the two numbers.

SOLUTION Let x and y be the two numbers. The sum of their squares is $x^2 + y^2$, and the difference of their squares is $x^2 - y^2$. (We can assume here that x^2 is the larger number.) The system of equations that describes the situation is

$$x^2 + y^2 = 34$$
$$x^2 - y^2 = 16$$

We can eliminate y by simply adding the two equations. The result of doing so is

$$2x^2 = 50$$
$$x^2 = 25$$
$$x = \pm 5$$

Substituting $x = 5$ into either equation in the system gives $y = \pm 3$. Using $x = -5$ gives the same results, $y = \pm 3$. The four pairs of numbers that are solutions to the original problem are

$$(5, 3) \qquad (-5, 3) \qquad (5, -3) \qquad (-5, -3)$$

Systems of Nonlinear Inequalities

We now turn our attention to systems of inequalities. To solve a system of inequalities by graphing, we simply graph each inequality on the same set of axes. The solution set for the system is the region common to both graphs — the intersection of the individual solution sets.

EXAMPLE 8 Graph the solution set for the system

$$x^2 + y^2 \le 9$$
$$\frac{x^2}{4} + \frac{y^2}{25} \ge 1$$

SOLUTION The boundary for the top inequality is a circle with center at the origin and a radius of 3. The solution set includes the boundary and the region inside the boundary. The boundary for the second inequality is an ellipse. In this case, the solution set includes the boundary and the region outside the boundary. (See Figure 7.)

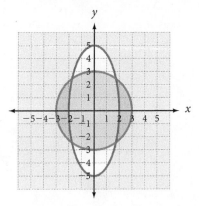

FIGURE 7

The solution set for the system is the intersection of the two individual solution sets, which consists of the two small regions inside the circle but outside the ellipse, and the portions of the boundaries that enclose these regions. Figure 8 shows the graph of the solution set, where we have kept the original boundaries as dashed curves for reference.

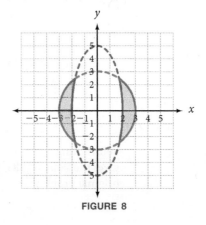

FIGURE 8

Getting Ready for Class

After reading through the preceding section, respond in your own words and in complete sentences.

A. What is the significance of a broken line when graphing inequalities?

B. Describe, in words, the set of points described by $(x - 3)^2 + (y - 2)^2 < 9$.

C. When solving nonlinear systems of equations whose graphs are a line and a circle, how many possible solutions can you expect?

D. When solving nonlinear systems of equations whose graphs are both circles, how many possible solutions can you expect?

Graph each of the following second-degree inequalities.

1. $x^2 + y^2 \le 49$

2. $x^2 + y^2 < 49$

3. $(x - 2)^2 + (y + 3)^2 < 16$

4. $(x + 3)^2 + (y - 2)^2 \ge 25$

5. $y < x^2 - 6x + 7$

6. $y \ge x^2 + 2x - 8$

7. $\dfrac{x^2}{25} - \dfrac{y^2}{9} \ge 1$

8. $\dfrac{x^2}{25} - \dfrac{y^2}{9} \le 1$

9. $4x^2 + 25y^2 \le 100$

10. $25x^2 - 4y^2 > 100$

11. $\dfrac{(x + 2)^2}{25} + \dfrac{(y - 1)^2}{9} \le 1$

12. $\dfrac{(x - 1)^2}{16} - \dfrac{(y + 1)^2}{16} < 1$

13. $16x^2 - 9y^2 \ge 144$

14. $16y^2 - 9x^2 < 144$

15. $9x^2 + 4y^2 + 36x - 8y + 4 < 0$

16. $9x^2 - 4y^2 + 36x + 8y \ge 4$

17. $9y^2 - x^2 + 18y + 2x > 1$

18. $x^2 + y^2 - 6x - 4y \le 12$

Solve each of the following systems of equations.

19. $x^2 + y^2 = 9$
$2x + y = 3$

20. $x^2 + y^2 = 9$
$x + 2y = 3$

21. $x^2 + y^2 = 16$
$x + 2y = 8$

22. $x^2 + y^2 = 16$
$x - 2y = 8$

23. $x^2 + y^2 = 25$
$x^2 - y^2 = 25$

24. $x^2 + y^2 = 4$
$2x^2 - y^2 = 5$

25. $x^2 + y^2 = 9$
$y = x^2 - 3$

26. $x^2 + y^2 = 4$
$y = x^2 - 2$

27. $x^2 + y^2 = 16$
$x = y^2 - 4$

28. $x^2 + y^2 = 1$
$x = y^2 - 1$

29. $3x + 2y = 10$
$y = x^2 - 5$

30. $4x + 2y = 10$
$y = x^2 - 10$

31. $y = x^2 + 2x - 3$
$y = -x + 1$

32. $y = -x^2 - 2x + 3$
$y = x - 1$

33. $x = y^2 - 6y + 5$
$x = y - 5$

34. $x = y^2 - 2y - 4$
$x = y - 4$

35. $4x^2 - 9y^2 = 36$
$4x^2 + 9y^2 = 36$

36. $4x^2 + 25y^2 = 100$
$4x^2 - 25y^2 = 100$

37. $x - y = 4$
$x^2 + y^2 = 16$

38. $x + y = 2$
$x^2 - y^2 = 4$

39. $2x^2 - y = 1$
$x^2 + y = 7$

40. $x^2 + y^2 = 52$
$y = x + 2$

41. $y = x^2 - 3$
$y = x^2 - 2x - 1$

42. $y = 8 - 2x^2$
$y = x^2 - 1$

43. $4x^2 + 5y^2 = 40$
$4x^2 - 5y^2 = 40$

44. $x + 2y^2 = -4$
$3x - 4y^2 = -3$

Graph the solution sets to the following systems of nonlinear inequalities.

45. $x^2 + y^2 < 9$
$\quad\quad y \geq x^2 - 1$

46. $x^2 + y^2 \leq 16$
$\quad\quad y < x^2 + 2$

47. $\dfrac{x^2}{9} + \dfrac{y^2}{25} \leq 1$
$\quad\quad \dfrac{x^2}{4} - \dfrac{y^2}{9} > 1$

48. $\dfrac{x^2}{4} + \dfrac{y^2}{16} \geq 1$
$\quad\quad \dfrac{x^2}{9} - \dfrac{y^2}{25} < 1$

49. $4x^2 + 9y^2 \leq 36$
$\quad\quad y > x^2 + 2$

50. $9x^2 + 4y^2 \geq 36$
$\quad\quad y < x^2 + 1$

51. $x^2 + y^2 \leq 3$
$\quad\quad y^2 \leq 4x$

52. $x^2 + y^2 < 4$
$\quad\quad y^2 \geq 2x$

53. $\quad x + y \leq 3$
$\quad\quad y^2 + 4x > 0$

54. $\quad x - y > 3$
$\quad\quad x^2 + 2y \leq 0$

55. $x^2 - y^2 \leq 4$
$\quad\quad y \geq 0$

56. $y^2 - x^2 \geq 4$
$\quad\quad x \leq 0$

57. $x^2 - 4y \leq 0$
$\quad\quad y^2 - 4x \leq 0$

58. $x^2 - y^2 \geq 1$
$\quad\quad x + y^2 \leq 0$

59. $\quad x^2 + y^2 \leq 25$
$\quad\quad \dfrac{x^2}{9} - \dfrac{y^2}{16} > 1$

60. $\dfrac{x^2}{16} + \dfrac{y^2}{25} < 1$
$\quad\quad \dfrac{y^2}{4} - \dfrac{x^2}{1} \geq 1$

61. $\quad x + y \leq 2$
$\quad\quad y > x^2$

62. $\dfrac{x^2}{9} + \dfrac{y^2}{16} \leq 1$
$\quad\quad \dfrac{x^2}{16} + \dfrac{y^2}{9} > 1$

Applying the Concepts

63. Number Problem The sum of the squares of two numbers is 89. The difference of their squares is 39. Find the numbers.

64. Number Problem The difference of the squares of two numbers is 35. The sum of their squares is 37. Find the numbers.

65. Consider the equations for the three circles below. They are are

Circle A $\qquad\qquad$ Circle B $\qquad\qquad$ Circle C

$(x + 8)^2 + y^2 = 64$ $\qquad$ $x^2 + y^2 = 64$ $\qquad$ $(x - 8)^2 + y^2 = 64$

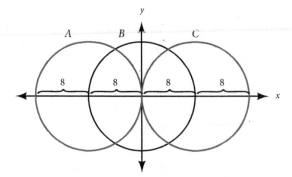

a. Find the points of intersection of circles A and B.

b. Find the points of intersection of circles B and C.

66. A magician is holding two rings that seem to lie in the same plane and intersect in two points. Each ring is 10 inches in diameter. If a coordinate system is placed with its origin at the center of the first ring and the x-axis contains the center of the second ring, then the equations are as follows:

First Ring	Second Ring
$x^2 + y^2 = 25$	$(x - 5)^2 + y^2 = 25$

Find the points of intersection of the two rings.

Learning Objectives Assessment

The following problems can be used to help assess if you have successfully met the learning objectives for this section.

67. Graph: $x^2 + y^2 > 16$.

a.

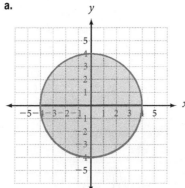

b.

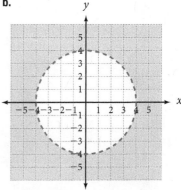

c.

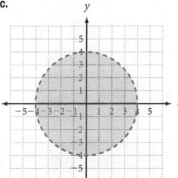

d.

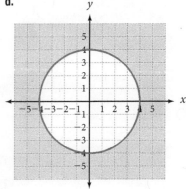

68. Use substitution to solve the system of equations:

$$4x^2 + y^2 = 16$$
$$2x + y = 4$$

a. $\{(-4, 0), (0, -2)\}$ **b.** $\{(-4, 0), (0, 2)\}$

c. $\{(2, 0), (0, -4)\}$ **d.** $\{(2, 0), (0, 4)\}$

69. Use the addition method to solve the system of equations:

$$4x^2 + y^2 = 16$$
$$x^2 - y^2 = 4$$

a. $\{(2, 0)\}$ **b.** $\{(0, 4)\}$

c. $\{(0, -4), (0, 4)\}$ **d.** $\{(-2, 0), (2, 0)\}$

70. Graph the solution set for the system of inequalities:

$$x^2 + y^2 \geq 9$$
$$x^2 - y^2 \leq 4$$

a.

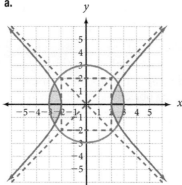

b.

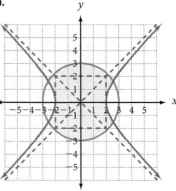

c.

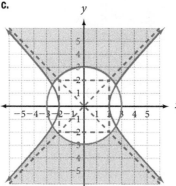

d.

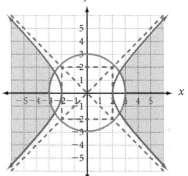

Maintaining Your Skills

Expand and simplify.

71. $(x + 2)^4$ **72.** $(x - 2)^4$ **73.** $(2x + y)^3$ **74.** $(x - 2y)^3$

75. Find the first two terms in the expansion of $(x + 3)^{50}$.

76. Find the first two terms in the expansion of $(x - y)^{75}$.

Chapter 14 Summary

Distance Formula [14.1]

1. The distance between $(5, 2)$ and $(-1, 1)$ is
$$d = \sqrt{(5 + 1)^2 + (2 - 1)^2} = \sqrt{37}$$

The distance between the two points (x_1, y_1) and (x_2, y_2) is given by the formula
$$d = \sqrt{(x_2 - x_1)^2 + (y_2 - y_1)^2}$$

The Circle [14.1]

2. The graph of the circle $(x - 3)^2 + (y + 2)^2 = 25$ will have its center at $(3, -2)$ and the radius will be 5.

The graph of any equation of the form
$$(x - h)^2 + (y - k)^2 = r^2$$

will be a circle having its center at (h, k) and a radius of r.

The Parabola [14.2]

3. The parabola $y^2 = 12x$ has the vertex $(0, 0)$ and focus $(3, 0)$. The focal width is 12. The parabola will open to the right.

The graph of an equation that can be put into either of the forms
$$x^2 = 4py \quad \text{or} \quad y^2 = 4px$$

will be a parabola with vertex at $(0, 0)$ and focal width equal to $|4p|$. The focus for the first equation will be at $(0, p)$, and the focus for the second equation will be at $(p, 0)$.

The Ellipse [14.3]

4. The ellipse $\frac{x^2}{9} + \frac{y^2}{4} = 1$ will cross the x-axis at 3 and -3 and will cross the y-axis at 2 and -2.

Any equation that can be put in the form
$$\frac{x^2}{a^2} + \frac{y^2}{b^2} = 1$$

will have an ellipse for its graph. The x-intercepts will be at a and $-a$, and the y-intercepts will be at b and $-b$.

The Hyperbola [14.3]

5. The hyperbola $\frac{x^2}{4} - \frac{y^2}{9} = 1$ will cross the x-axis at 2 and -2. It will not cross the y-axis.

The graph of an equation that can be put in either of the forms
$$\frac{x^2}{a^2} - \frac{y^2}{b^2} = 1 \quad \text{or} \quad \frac{y^2}{b^2} - \frac{x^2}{a^2} = 1$$

will be a hyperbola. The x-intercepts, for the first equation, will be at a and $-a$. The y-intercepts, for the second equation, will be at b and $-b$. Two straight lines, called *asymptotes*, are associated with the graph of every hyperbola. Although the asymptotes are not part of the hyperbola, they are useful in sketching the graph.

Second-Degree Inequalities in Two Variables [14.4]

6. The graph of the inequality

$$x^2 + y^2 < 9$$

is all points inside the circle with center at the origin and radius 3. The circle itself is not part of the solution and therefore is shown with a broken curve.

We graph second-degree inequalities in two variables in much the same way that we graphed linear inequalities; that is, we begin by graphing the boundary, using a solid curve if the boundary is included in the solution (this happens when the inequality symbol is $\geq$ or $\leq$) or a broken curve if the boundary is not included in the solution (when the inequality symbol is $>$ or $<$). After we have graphed the boundary, we choose a test point that is not on the boundary and try it in the original inequality. A true statement indicates we are in the region of the solution. A false statement indicates we are not in the region of the solution. Then we shade the region that contains solutions.

Systems of Nonlinear Equations [14.4]

7. We can solve the system

$$x^2 + y^2 = 4$$
$$x = 2y + 4$$

by substituting $2y + 4$ from the second equation for x in the first equation:

$$(2y + 4)^2 + y^2 = 4$$
$$4y^2 + 16y + 16 + y^2 = 4$$
$$5y^2 + 16y + 12 = 0$$
$$(5y + 6)(y + 2) = 0$$
$$y = -\frac{6}{5} \quad \text{or} \quad y = -2$$

Substituting these values of y into the second equation in our system gives $x = \frac{8}{5}$ and $x = 0$. The solutions are $\left(\frac{8}{5}, -\frac{6}{5}\right)$ and $(0, -2)$.

A system of nonlinear equations is two or more equations, at least one of which is not linear, considered at the same time. The solution set for the system consists of all ordered pairs that satisfy all of the equations. In most cases we use the substitution method to solve these systems; however, the addition method can be used if like variables are raised to the same power in two equations. It is sometimes helpful to graph each equation in the system on the same set of axes to anticipate the number and approximate positions of the solutions.

1. Find x so that $(x, 2)$ is $2\sqrt{5}$ units from $(-1, 4)$. [14.1]

2. Give the equation of the circle with center at $(-2, 4)$ and radius 3. [14.1]

3. Give the equation of the circle with center at the origin that contains the point $(-3, -4)$. [14.1]

4. Find the center and radius of the circle $x^2 + y^2 - 10x + 6y = 5$. [14.1]

Graph each of the following. [14.1- 14.3]

5. $4x^2 - y^2 = 16$

6. $\dfrac{x^2}{25} + \dfrac{y^2}{4} = 1$

7. $x^2 + y^2 = 16$

8. $y^2 = 6x$

9. $9x^2 + 4y^2 - 72x - 16y + 124 = 0$

10. $(x - 1)^2 + (y + 3)^2 = 4$

11. $\dfrac{(y - 1)^2}{4} - \dfrac{(x - 3)^2}{1} = 1$

12. $x^2 + 4x + 4y + 8 = 0$

Graph the solution set to each inequality. [14.4]

13. $(x - 2)^2 + (y + 1)^2 \le 9$

14. $9x^2 - 4y^2 < 36$

Solve the following systems. [14.4]

15. $x^2 + y^2 = 25$
    $2x + y = 5$

16. $x^2 + y^2 = 16$
    $y = x^2 - 4$

Graph the solution set to each system of inequalities. [14.4]

17. $\dfrac{x^2}{16} + \dfrac{y^2}{9} \le 1$
    $y^2 - x^2 < 1$

18. $(x + 2)^2 + y^2 < 9$
    $y^2 + 4x \le 0$

Appendix: Synthetic Division

Learning Objectives

In this section, we will learn how to:

1. Divide polynomials using synthetic division.

Synthetic division is a short form of long division with polynomials. We will consider synthetic division only for those cases in which the divisor is of the form $x + k$, where k is a constant.

Let's begin by looking over an example of long division with polynomials.

$$
\begin{array}{r}
3x^2 - 2x + 4 \\
x + 3 \overline{)\, 3x^3 + 7x^2 - 2x - 4} \\
\underline{3x^3 + 9x^2} \\
-2x^2 - 2x \\
\underline{-2x^2 - 6x} \\
4x - 4 \\
\underline{4x + 12} \\
-16
\end{array}
$$

We can rewrite the problem without showing the variable since the variable is written in descending powers and similar terms are in alignment. It looks like this:

$$
\begin{array}{r}
3 \quad -2 \quad 4 \\
1 + 3 \overline{)\, 3 \quad 7 \quad -2 \quad -4} \\
\underline{(3) + 9} \\
-2 \;\; (-2) \\
\underline{(-2) \; -6} \\
4 \;\; (-4) \\
\underline{(4) \quad 12} \\
-16
\end{array}
$$

We have used parentheses to enclose the numbers that are repetitions of the numbers above them. We can compress the problem by eliminating all repetitions except the first one:

$$
\begin{array}{r}
3 \quad -2 \quad 4 \\
1 + 3 \overline{)\, 3 \quad 7 \quad -2 \quad -4} \\
\underline{9 \quad -6 \quad 12} \\
3 \quad -2 \quad 4 \; -16
\end{array}
$$

The top line is the same as the first three terms of the bottom line, so we eliminate the top line. Also, the 1 that was the coefficient of x in the original problem can be eliminated since we will consider only division problems where the divisor is of the form $x + k$.

The following is the most compact form of the original division problem:

$$
\begin{array}{r}
+3 \overline{)\, 3 \quad 7 \quad -2 \quad -4} \\
\underline{9 \quad -6 \quad 12} \\
3 \quad -2 \quad 4 \; -16
\end{array}
$$

If we check over the problem, we find that the first term in the bottom row is exactly the same as the first term in the top row—and it always will be in problems of this type. Also, the last three terms in the bottom row come from multiplication by $+3$ and then subtraction. We can get an equivalent result by multiplying by -3 and adding. The problem would then look like this:

$$
\begin{array}{r|rrrr}
-3 & 3 & 7 & -2 & -4 \\
 & \downarrow & -9 & 6 & -12 \\
\hline
 & 3 & -2 & 4 & \boxed{-16}
\end{array}
$$

We have used the brackets $\rfloor$ and $\llcorner$ to separate the divisor and the remainder. This last expression is synthetic division. It is an easy process to remember. Simply change the sign of the constant term in the divisor, then bring down the first term of the dividend. The process is then just a series of multiplications and additions, as indicated in the following diagram by the arrows:

The last term of the bottom row is always the remainder. The numbers to the left of this term are the coefficients of the terms for the quotient.

Here are some additional examples of synthetic division with polynomials.

EXAMPLE 1   Divide $x^4 - 2x^3 + 4x^2 - 6x + 2$ by $x - 2$.

SOLUTION   To begin, we change the sign of the constant term in the divisor to get $+2$ and write this on the left, followed by the coefficients of the dividend. Next, we bring the left-most coefficient straight down. Here is how it looks:

$$
\begin{array}{r|rrrrr}
+2 & 1 & -2 & 4 & -6 & 2 \\
 & \downarrow & & & & \\
\hline
 & 1 & & & &
\end{array}
$$

Now we multiply the 1 in the bottom line by 2, and write the result below the next coefficient. Then we add to obtain 0.

$$
\begin{array}{r|rrrrr}
+2 & 1 & -2 & 4 & -6 & 2 \\
 & \downarrow & 2 & & & \\
\hline
 & 1 & 0 & & &
\end{array}
$$

We repeat this procedure with each new number in the bottom row. Here is the result in individual steps:

$$
\begin{array}{r|rrrrr}
+2 & 1 & -2 & 4 & -6 & 2 \\
 & \downarrow & 2 & 0 & & \\
\hline
 & 1 & 0 & 4 & &
\end{array}
$$

$$
\begin{array}{r|rrrrr}
+2 & 1 & -2 & 4 & -6 & 2 \\
 & \downarrow & 2 & 0 & 8 & \\
\hline
 & 1 & 0 & 4 & 2 &
\end{array}
$$

$$
\begin{array}{r|rrrrr}
+2 & 1 & -2 & 4 & -6 & 2 \\
 & \downarrow & 2 & 0 & 8 & 4 \\
\hline
 & 1 & 0 & 4 & 2 & \boxed{6}
\end{array}
$$

From the last line we have the answer. The first term in the quotient will always have a degree that is one less than the degree of the leading term in the dividend. In this case, the quotient will begin with an x^3 term.

$$1x^3 + 0x^2 + 4x + 2 + \frac{6}{x-2}$$

Further simplifying the result, we get:

$$x^3 + 4x + 2 + \frac{6}{x-2}$$

EXAMPLE 2   Divide: $\dfrac{3x^3 - 4x + 5}{x+4}$.

SOLUTION   Since we cannot skip any powers of the variable in the dividend $3x^3 - 4x + 5$, we rewrite it as $3x^3 + 0x^2 - 4x + 5$ and proceed as we did in Example 1:

$$
\begin{array}{r|rrrr}
-4 & 3 & 0 & -4 & 5 \\
   & \downarrow & -12 & 48 & -176 \\
\hline
   & 3 & -12 & 44 & \boxed{-171}
\end{array}
$$

From the synthetic division, we have

$$\frac{3x^3 - 4x + 5}{x+4} = 3x^2 - 12x + 44 + \frac{-171}{x+4}$$

EXAMPLE 3   Divide: $\dfrac{x^3 - 1}{x-1}$.

SOLUTION   Writing the numerator as $x^3 + 0x^2 + 0x - 1$ and using synthetic division, we have

$$
\begin{array}{r|rrrr}
+1 & 1 & 0 & 0 & -1 \\
   & \downarrow & 1 & 1 & 1 \\
\hline
   & 1 & 1 & 1 & \boxed{0}
\end{array}
$$

which indicates

$$\frac{x^3 - 1}{x-1} = x^2 + x + 1$$

Getting Ready for Class

After reading through the preceding section, respond in your own words and in complete sentences.

A. When can synthetic division be used?

B. How do we know what power of the variable the quotient begins with?

C. What number goes in the top left bracket?

D. How do we handle missing powers of the variable in the dividend?

Divide using the long division method.

1. $\dfrac{x^2 - 5x - 7}{x + 2}$

2. $\dfrac{x^2 + 4x - 8}{x - 3}$

3. $\dfrac{2x^3 - 3x^2 - 4x + 5}{x + 1}$

4. $\dfrac{3x^3 - 5x^2 + 2x - 1}{x - 2}$

5. $\dfrac{a^4 - 2a + 5}{a - 2}$

6. $\dfrac{a^4 + a^3 - 1}{a + 2}$

7. $\dfrac{y^4 - 16}{y - 2}$

8. $\dfrac{y^4 - 81}{y - 3}$

Divide using synthetic division.

9. $\dfrac{x^2 - 5x + 6}{x + 2}$

10. $\dfrac{x^2 + 8x - 12}{x - 3}$

11. $\dfrac{3x^2 - 4x + 1}{x - 1}$

12. $\dfrac{4x^2 - 2x - 6}{x + 1}$

13. $\dfrac{x^3 + 2x^2 + 3x + 4}{x - 2}$

14. $\dfrac{x^3 - 2x^2 - 3x - 4}{x - 2}$

15. $\dfrac{3x^3 - x^2 + 2x + 5}{x - 3}$

16. $\dfrac{2x^3 - 5x^2 + x + 2}{x - 2}$

17. $\dfrac{2x^3 + x - 3}{x - 1}$

18. $\dfrac{3x^3 - 2x + 1}{x - 5}$

19. $\dfrac{x^4 + 2x^2 + 1}{x + 4}$

20. $\dfrac{x^4 - 3x^2 + 1}{x - 4}$

21. $\dfrac{x^5 - 2x^4 + x^3 - 3x^2 - x + 1}{x - 2}$

22. $\dfrac{2x^5 - 3x^4 + x^3 - x^2 + 2x + 1}{x + 2}$

23. $\dfrac{x^2 + x + 1}{x - 1}$

24. $\dfrac{x^2 + x + 1}{x + 1}$

25. $\dfrac{x^4 - 1}{x + 1}$

26. $\dfrac{x^4 + 1}{x - 1}$

27. $\dfrac{x^3 - 1}{x - 1}$

28. $\dfrac{x^3 - 1}{x + 1}$

Applying the Concepts

29. The Remainder Theorem Find $P(-2)$ if $P(x) = x^2 - 5x + 6$. Compare it with the remainder in Problem 9.

30. The Remainder Theorem The remainder theorem of algebra states that if a polynomial, $P(x)$, is divided by $x - a$, then the remainder is $P(a)$. Verify the remainder theorem by showing that when $P(x) = x^2 - x + 3$ is divided by $x - 2$ the remainder is 5, and that $P(2) = 5$.

Learning Objectives Assessment

The following problems can be used to help assess if you have successfully met the learning objectives for this section.

31. Use synthetic division to divide $\dfrac{x^3 + 8}{x + 2}$.

   a. $x^2 + 4$ **b.** $x^2 - 2x + 4$

   c. $x^2 + 2x - 4 + \dfrac{16}{x + 2}$ **d.** $x^2 + 2x + 4$

32. Divide $\dfrac{x^2 - x + 6}{x + 2}$ using synthetic division.

   a. $x + 1 + \dfrac{8}{x + 2}$ **b.** $x - 1 + \dfrac{8}{x + 2}$

   c. $-2x + 3$ **d.** $x^2 + 2$

Chapter 1

PROBLEM SET 1.1

1. $x + 5$ **3.** $5y$ **5.** $5(y - 16)$ **7.** $\frac{x}{3}$ **9.** 9
11. 49 **13.** 8 **15.** 64 **17.** 16 **19.** 100
21. 121 **23.** 11 **25.** 16 **27.** 17 **29.** 42
31. 30 **33.** 30 **35.** 24 **37.** 80 **39.** 27
41. 35 **43.** 13 **45.** 4 **47.** 37 **49.** 37 **51.** 16
53. 16 **55.** 81 **57.** 41 **59.** 345 **61.** 2,345
63. 2 **65.** 148 **67.** 36 **69.** 36 **71.** 58
73. 62 **75.** 100 **77.** 9 **79.** 18 **81.** 8
83. 12 **85.** 18 **87.** 42 **89.** 53
91. 4 inches; 1 square inch
93. 4.5 inches; 1.125 square inches
95. 10.25 centimeters; 5 square centimeters
97. 10 **99.** 420 **101.** About 224 chips
103. Less than 95g **105. a.** 1,680 mg **b.** 209 mg
107.

Calories Burned by 150-Pound Person	
Activity	Calories Burned in 1 Hour
Bicycling	374
Bowling	265
Handball	680
Jogging	680
Skiing	544

109. 93.5 square inches, 39 inches **111.** d **113.** a **115.** b

PROBLEM SET 1.2

1-8.

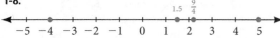

9. 0, 1 **11.** $-3, -2.5, 0, 1, \frac{3}{2}$ **13.** All
15. $-10, -8, -2, 9$ **17.** π **19.** T **21.** F
23. F **25.** T **27.** $-10, 10$ **29.** $-\frac{3}{4}, \frac{3}{4}$
31. $-\frac{11}{2}, \frac{11}{2}$ **33.** 3, 3 **35.** $\frac{2}{5}, \frac{2}{5}$ **37.** $-x, |x|$
39. < **41.** > **43.** > **45.** > **47.** 6
49. 22 **51.** 3 **53.** 7 **55.** 3 **57.** $-8, -2$
59. $-64°F; -54°F$ **61.** $-15°F$ **63.** -100 feet; -105 feet
65. 1,387 calories **67.** 654 more calories
69. a. 93 million **b.** False **c.** True **71.** c **73.** a

PROBLEM SET 1.3

1. $3 + 5 = 8, 3 + (-5) = -2, -3 + 5 = 2, -3 + (-5) = -8$
3. $15 + 20 = 35, 15 + (-20) = -5, -15 + 20 = 5,$
$-15 + (-20) = -35$
5. 3 **7.** -7 **9.** -14 **11.** -3 **13.** -25
15. -12 **17.** -19 **19.** -25 **21.** -8 **23.** -4
25. 6 **27.** 6 **29.** 8 **31.** -4 **33.** -14 **35.** -17
37. 4 **39.** 3 **41.** 15 **43.** -8 **45.** 12
47. $5 + 9 = 14$ **49.** $[-7 + (-5)] + 4 = -8$
51. $[-2 + (-3)] + 10 = 5$ **53.** $4 + x$ **55.** $-8 + x$
57. $[x + (-2)] + 3$ **59.** 3 **61.** -3 **63.** 23, 28
65. 30, 35 **67.** 0, -5 **69.** $-12, -18$ **71.** $-4, -8$

73. Yes **75.** $-12 + 4$ **77.** $10 + (-6) + (-8) = -\$4$
79. $-30 + 40 = 10$ **81.** \$2,000 **83.** 2006, \$500
85. c

PROBLEM SET 1.4

1. -3 **3.** -6 **5.** 0 **7.** -10 **9.** -16 **11.** -12
13. -7 **15.** 35 **17.** 0 **19.** -4 **21.** 4
23. -24 **25.** -28 **27.** 25 **29.** 4 **31.** 7
33. 17 **35.** 8 **37.** 4 **39.** 18 **41.** 10 **43.** 17
45. 1 **47.** 1 **49.** 27 **51.** -26 **53.** -2
55. 68 **57.** $-7 - 4 = -11$ **59.** $12 - (-8) = 20$
61. $-5 - (-7) = 2$ **63.** $[4 + (-5)] - 17 = -18$
65. $8 - 5 = 3$ **67.** $-8 - 5 = -13$ **69.** $8 - (-5) = 13$
71. $x - 6$ **73.** $-4 - x$ **75.** $(x + 12) - 5$
77. 10 **79.** -2 **81.** $1,500 - 730 = \$770$
83. $-35 + 15 - 20 = -\$40$ **85.** $73 + 10 - 8, 75°F$
87. \$4,500, \$3,950, \$3,400, \$2,850, \$2,300; yes
89. **b.** 12 inches

Day	Plant Height (inches)
0	0
2	1
4	3
6	6
8	13
10	23

91. a. Yes, the hundreds place **b.** 8,400 **c.** 29,800 **93.** a

PROBLEM SET 1.5

1. -42 **3.** -16 **5.** 3 **7.** 121 **9.** 6 **11.** -60
13. 24 **15.** 49 **17.** -27 **19.** -2 **21.** -3
23. $-\frac{1}{3}$ **25.** 3 **27.** $\frac{1}{7}$ **29.** 0 **31.** 9
33. -15 **35.** -36 **37.** $-\frac{1}{4}$ **39.** $\frac{3}{5}$ **41.** $-\frac{5}{3}$
43. -2 **45.** 6 **47.** 10 **49.** 9 **51.** 45 **53.** 14
55. -2 **57.** -3 **59.** Undefined **61.** Undefined
63. 5 **65.** $-\frac{7}{3}$ **67.** -1 **69.** 216 **71.** -2
73. -18 **75.** 29 **77.** 38 **79.** -7 **81.** $\frac{15}{17}$
83. $-\frac{32}{17}$ **85.** $\frac{1}{3}$ **87.** -5 **89.** 37 **91.** 80
93. 1 **95.** 1 **97.** -2 **99.** $\frac{9}{7}$ **101.** $\frac{16}{11}$
103. -1 **105. a.** 25 **b.** -25 **c.** -25 **d.** -25 **e.** 25
107. -25 **109.** -26 **111.** 3 **113.** -10 **115.** -3
117. -8 **119.** $3x - 11$ **121.** 14 **123.** 8
125. -80 **127.** -24 **129.** 1°F **131.** \$350
133. Drops 3.5°F each hour
135. a. \$20,000 **b.** \$50,000
c. Yes, the projected revenue for 5,000 email addresses is \$10,000, which is \$5,000 more than the list costs.
137. 465 calories **139.** a **141.** b

PROBLEM SET 1.6

1. Composite, $2^4 \cdot 3$ **3.** Prime
5. Composite, $3 \cdot 11 \cdot 31$ **7.** $2^4 \cdot 3^2$ **9.** $2 \cdot 19$
11. $3 \cdot 5 \cdot 7$ **13.** $2^2 \cdot 3^2 \cdot 5$ **15.** $5 \cdot 7 \cdot 11$ **17.** 11^2
19. $2^2 \cdot 3 \cdot 5 \cdot 7$ **21.** $2^2 \cdot 5 \cdot 31$ **23.** $\frac{7}{11}$ **25.** $\frac{5}{7}$
27. $\frac{11}{13}$ **29.** $\frac{14}{15}$ **31.** $\frac{5}{9}$ **33.** $\frac{5}{8}$

35. $3 \cdot 8 + 3 \cdot 7 + 3 \cdot 5 = 24 + 21 + 15 = 60 = 2^2 \cdot 3 \cdot 5$
37. $\frac{18}{24}$ **39.** $\frac{12}{24}$ **41.** $\frac{15}{24}$ **43.** $\frac{36}{60}$ **45.** $\frac{22}{60}$
47. $<$ **49.** $<$ **51.** $\frac{8}{15}$ **53.** $\frac{3}{2}$ **55.** $\frac{5}{4}$ **57.** 1
59. 1 **61.** 1 **63.** $\frac{9}{16}$ **65.** $\frac{8}{27}$ **67.** $\frac{1}{10,000}$
69. $-\frac{10}{21}$ **71.** -4 **73.** 1 **75.** $\frac{9}{16}$ **77.** x
79. $\frac{16}{15}$ **81.** $\frac{4}{3}$ **83.** $-\frac{8}{13}$ **85.** -1 **87.** 1
89. a. 10 **b.** 0 **c.** -100 **d.** -20 **93.** $-\frac{1}{4}$
95. $\frac{1}{2}$ **97.** $\frac{x-1}{3}$ **99.** $\frac{3}{2}$ **101.** $\frac{x+6}{2}$
103. $-\frac{3}{5}$ **105.** $\frac{10}{a}$

107.

First Number a	Second Number b	The Sum of a and b $a+b$
$\frac{1}{2}$	$\frac{1}{3}$	$\frac{5}{6}$
$\frac{1}{3}$	$\frac{1}{4}$	$\frac{7}{12}$
$\frac{1}{4}$	$\frac{1}{5}$	$\frac{9}{20}$
$\frac{1}{5}$	$\frac{1}{6}$	$\frac{11}{30}$

109.

First Number a	Second Number b	The Sum of a and b $a+b$
$\frac{1}{12}$	$\frac{1}{2}$	$\frac{7}{12}$
$\frac{1}{12}$	$\frac{1}{3}$	$\frac{5}{12}$
$\frac{1}{12}$	$\frac{1}{4}$	$\frac{1}{3}$
$\frac{1}{12}$	$\frac{1}{6}$	$\frac{1}{4}$

111. $\frac{7}{9}$ **113.** $\frac{7}{3}$ **115.** $\frac{1}{4}$ **117.** $\frac{7}{6}$ **119.** $\frac{19}{24}$ **121.** $\frac{13}{60}$
123. $\frac{29}{35}$ **125.** $\frac{949}{1,260}$ **127.** $\frac{13}{420}$ **129.** $\frac{41}{24}$ **131.** $\frac{5}{4}$
133. $-\frac{3}{2}$ **135.** $\frac{3}{2}$ **137.** $\frac{160}{63}$ **139.** $\frac{5}{8}$ **141.** $-\frac{2}{3}$
143. $\frac{7}{3}$ **145.** $\frac{1}{125}$ **147.** $\frac{3}{2}$ ft $= 1\frac{1}{2}$ ft **149.** $\frac{11}{5}$ cm $= 2\frac{1}{5}$ cm
151. 14 blankets **153.** 48 bags **155.** 6 eighth-teaspoons
157. 28 half-pint cartons **159.** $\frac{9}{2}$ pints $= 4\frac{1}{2}$ pints
161. \$1,325 **163.** $\frac{2}{5}$

165.

Grade	# of Students	Fraction of Students
A	5	$\frac{1}{8}$
B	8	$\frac{1}{5}$
C	20	$\frac{1}{2}$
below C	7	$\frac{7}{40}$
Total	40	1

167. 10 lots **169.** b **171.** c **173.** a

PROBLEM SET 1.7
1. Commutative **3.** Multiplicative inverse
5. Commutative **7.** Distributive
9. Commutative, associative
11. Commutative, associative
13. Commutative **15.** Commutative, associative
17. Commutative **19.** Additive inverse
21. $3x + 6$ **23.** $9a + 9b$ **25.** 0 **27.** 0
29. 10 **31.** $(4 + 2) + x = 6 + x$
33. $x + (2 + 7) = x + 9$ **35.** $(3 \cdot 5)x = 15x$
37. $(-9 \cdot 6)y = -54y$ **39.** $\left(\frac{1}{2} \cdot 3\right)a = \frac{3}{2}a$
41. $\left(-\frac{1}{3} \cdot 3\right)x = -x$ **43.** $\left(\frac{1}{2} \cdot 2\right)y = y$
45. $\left(-\frac{3}{4} \cdot \frac{4}{3}\right)x = -x$ **47.** $\left[-\frac{6}{5}\left(-\frac{5}{6}\right)\right]a = a$
49. $8x + 16$ **50.** $5x + 15$ **51.** $8x - 16$ **53.** $4y + 4$
55. $18x + 15$ **57.** $-6a - 14$ **59.** $-54y + 72$
61. $x + 2$ **63.** $12x + 18y$ **65.** $12a - 8b$
67. $3x + 2y$ **69.** $-4a - 8$ **71.** $-\frac{3}{2}x + 3$
73. $5x + 6$ **75.** $3x - 20$ **77.** $3 + x$ **79.** $-3x + 7y$
81. 1 **83.** $4a + 25$ **85.** $6x + 12$ **87.** $14x + 38$
89. $-6x + 8$ **91.** $-15x - 30$ **93.** 81 **95.** $\frac{9}{4}$
97. $2x + 1$ **99.** $6x - 3$ **101.** $5x + 10$ **103.** $6x + 5$
105. $5x + 6$ **107.** $6m - 5$ **109.** $7 + 3x$
111. $3x - 2y$ **113.** $\frac{2}{3}x - 2$ **115.** $-2x + y$
117. $0.09x + 180$ **119.** $0.12x + 60$ **121.** $a + 1$
123. $1 - a$ **125.** No
127. Answers may vary. $8 \div 4 \neq 4 \div 8$
129. $4(2 + 3) = 20$
$(4 \cdot 2) + (4 \cdot 3) = 20$ **131.** a

CHAPTER 1 TEST
1. 144 **2.** 64 **3.** 2 **4.** 10 **5.** $-3, 2$
6. $-3, -\frac{1}{2}, 2$ **7.** $6 + (-9) = -3$ **8.** $-5 - (-12) = 7$
9. $6 \cdot (-7) = -42$ **10.** $32 \div (-8) = -4$ **11.** 13
12. 1 **13.** -13 **14.** -10 **15.** -7 **16.** 62
17. 2 **18.** -6 **19.** $2^2 \cdot 3 \cdot 5 \cdot 11$ **20.** $3^3 \cdot 5^2 \cdot 7$
21. $\frac{11}{24}$ **22.** $\frac{5+6}{y} = \frac{11}{y}$ **23.** d **24.** e **25.** a
26. c **27.** $3x + 12$ **28.** $-15y$ **29.** $-10x + 15$
30. $2x + 4$

Chapter 2

PROBLEM SET 2.1
1. $-3x$ **3.** $-a$ **5.** $12x$ **7.** $6a$ **9.** $6x - 3$
11. $7a + 5$ **13.** $5x - 5$ **15.** $4a + 2$ **17.** $-9x - 2$
19. $12a + 3$ **21.** $10x - 1$ **23.** $21y + 6$ **25.** $-6x + 8$
27. $-2a + 3$ **29.** $-4x + 26$ **31.** $4y - 16$
33. $-6x - 1$ **35.** $2x - 12$ **37.** $10a + 33$
39. $4x - 9$ **41.** $7y - 39$ **43.** $-19x - 14$ **45.** 5
47. -9 **49.** 4 **51.** 4 **53.** -37 **55.** -41
57. 64 **59.** 64 **61.** 144 **63.** 144 **65.** 3
67. 0 **69.** 15 **71.** 6
73. a.

n	1	2	3	4
$3n$	3	6	9	12

b.

n	1	2	3	4
n^3	1	8	27	64

75. 1, 4, 7, 10, . . .   **77.** 0, 1, 4, 9, . . .   **79.** $-6y + 4$
81. $0.17x$ **83.** $2x$ **85.** $5x - 4$ **87.** $7x - 5$
89. $-2x - 9$ **91.** $7x + 2$ **93.** $-7x + 6$ **95.** $7x$
97. $-y$ **99.** $10y$ **101.** $0.17x + 180$ **103.** $0.22x + 60$
105. 49   **107.** 40   **109. a.** $42°F$ **b.** $28°F$ **c.** $-14°F$
111. a. \$37.50 **b.** \$40.00 **c.** \$42.50   **113.** c   **115.** c
117. 12   **119.** -3 **121.** -9.7 **123.** $-\frac{5}{4}$ **125.** 53
127. $a - 12$ **129.** 7

PROBLEM SET 2.2

1. Yes   **3.** No   **5. a.** No **b.** Yes   **7.a.** Yes **b.** No
9. 11   **11.** 4   **13.** $-\frac{3}{4}$ **15.** -5.8 **17.** -17 **19.** $-\frac{1}{8}$
21. -4 **23.** -3.6 **25.** 1   **27.** $-\frac{7}{45}$ **29.** 3
31. $\frac{11}{8}$ **33.** 21   **35.** 7   **37.** 3.5   **39.** 22
41. -2 **43.** -16 **45.** -3 **47.** 10   **49.** -12
51. 4   **53.** 2   **55.** -5 **57.** -1 **59.** -3 **61.** 8
63. -8 **65.** 2   **67.** 11   **69.** -5.8
71. a. 6% **b.** 5% **c.** 2% **d.** 75%   **73.** a   **75.** c
77. $-y$ **79.** a **81.** -6 **83.** $\frac{1}{2}$ **85.** 6   **87.** -2
89. -18 **91.** $-\frac{6}{5}$ **93.** $3x$

PROBLEM SET 2.3

1. 2   **3.** 4   **5.** $-\frac{1}{2}$ **7.** -2 **9.** 3   **11.** 4
13. 0   **15.** 0   **17.** 6   **19.** -50 **21.** $\frac{3}{2}$ **23.** 12
25. -3 **27.** 32   **29.** -8 **31.** $\frac{1}{2}$ **33.** 4   **35.** 8
37. -4 **39.** 4   **41.** -15 **43.** $-\frac{1}{2}$ **45.** 3   **47.** 1
49. $\frac{1}{4}$ **51.** -3 **53.** 3   **55.** 2   **57.** $-\frac{3}{2}$ **59.** 1
61. -2 **63.** 3   **65.** -2 **67.** -1 **69.** 2   **71.** -4
73. -2 **75.** 0   **77.** 1   **79.** $\frac{1}{2}$
81. a. $\frac{3}{2}$ **b.** 1 **c.** $-\frac{3}{2}$ **d.** -4 **e.** $\frac{8}{5}$ **83.** 200 tickets
85. \$1,390.85 per month   **87.** d   **89.** 2   **91.** 6
93. 3,000   **95.** $3x - 11$ **97.** $0.09x + 180$
99. $-6y + 4$ **101.** $4x - 11$ **103.** $5x$ **105.** $0.17x$

PROBLEM SET 2.4

1. 1   **3.** 6   **5.** 2   **7.** -1 **9.** $\frac{3}{4}$ **11.** 3
13. $\frac{3}{4}$ **15.** 2   **17.** 2   **19.** 11   **21.** -2 **23.** -6
25. 20   **27.** -2 **29.** $-\frac{1}{3}$ **31.** 8   **33.** 7
35. 0   **37.** $\frac{3}{7}$ **39.** 1   **41.** $-\frac{50}{3}$ **43.** $-\frac{11}{4}$ **45.** $-\frac{3}{2}$
47. 7   **49.** $\frac{3}{4}$ **51.** 6   **53.** 75   **55.** 6
57. 4,000   **59.** 700   **61.** 8   **63.** 8
65. $\varnothing$, contradiction   **67.** $\frac{5}{3}$
69. All real numbers, identity   **71.** $\varnothing$, contradiction
73. a. $\frac{5}{4} = 1.25$ **b.** $\frac{15}{2} = 7.5$ **c.** $6x + 20$ **d.** 15
  e. $4x - 20$ **f.** $\frac{45}{2} = 22.5$
75. a   **77.** c   **79.** 14   **81.** -3 **83.** $\frac{1}{4}$ **85.** $\frac{1}{3}$
87. $-\frac{3}{2}x + 3$

PROBLEM SET 2.5

1. 100 feet   **3.** 0   **5.** 2   **7.** 15   **9.** 10   **11.** -2
13. 1   **15. a.** 2 **b.** 4   **17. a.** 5 **b.** 18   **19.** $l = \frac{A}{w}$
21. $h = \frac{V}{lw}$ **23.** $a = P - b - c$ **25.** $x = 3y - 1$
27. $y = 3x + 6$ **29.** $y = -\frac{2}{3}x + 2$ **31.** $y = -2x - 5$
33. $y = -\frac{2}{3}x + 1$ **35.** $w = \frac{P - 2l}{2}$ **37.** $v = \frac{h - 16t^2}{t}$
39. $h = \frac{A - \pi r^2}{2\pi r}$

41. a. $y = \frac{3}{5}x + 1$ **b.** $y = \frac{1}{2}x + 2$ **c.** $y = 4x + 3$
43. $y = \frac{3}{7}x - 3$ **45.** $y = 2x + 8$ **47.** 10   **49.** 240
51. 25%   **53.** 35%   **55.** 64   **57.** 2,000
59. $T = 35$; The temperature is 35°F at an altitude of 10,000 feet.
61. 4,000   **63.** $A = \frac{T - 70}{-0.0035} = \frac{70 - T}{0.0035}$ **65.** 100°C; yes
67. 20°C; yes   **69.** $C = \frac{5}{9}(F - 32)$ **71.** 4°F over
73. 44 meters   **75.** $\frac{3}{2}$ or 1.5 inches
77. 56.52 cubic centimeters   **79.** 132 feet   **81.** 60%
83. 26.5%   **85.** a   **87.** The sum of 4 and 1.
89. The difference of 6 and 2.
91. The difference of a number and 15.
93. Four times the difference of a number and 3
95. $2(6 + 3)$ **97.** $2(5) + 3$ **99.** $x + 5$ **101.** $5(x + 7)$

PROBLEM SET 2.6

1. $x + 5 = 14$ **3.** $\frac{x}{3} = x + 2$ **5.** $2(x - 9) + 5 = 11$
7. $\frac{1}{2}(x + 5) = 3(x - 5)$ **9.** 8   **11.** 5   **13.** -1
15. 3 and 5   **17.** 6 and 14   **19.** Shelly is 39; Michele is 36
21. Evan is 11; Cody is 22   **23.** Barney is 27; Fred is 31
25. Lacy is 16; Jack is 32   **27.** Patrick is 18; Pat is 38
29. $s = 9$ inches   **31.** $s = 15$ feet
33. 11 feet, 18 feet, 33 feet   **35.** 26 feet, 13 feet, 14 feet
37. $l = 11$ inches; $w = 6$ inches
39. $l = 25$ inches; $w = 9$ inches
41. $l = 15$ feet; $w = 3$ feet   **43.** 9 dimes; 14 quarters
45. 12 quarters; 27 nickels   **47.** 8 nickels; 17 dimes
49. 7 nickels; 10 dimes; 12 quarters
51. 3 nickels; 9 dimes; 6 quarters
53. c   **55.** d   **57.** $5x$ **59.** $1.075x$ **61.** $0.09x + 180$
63. 6,000   **65.** 30

PROBLEM SET 2.7

1. 5 and 6   **3.** -5 and -4 **5.** 13 and 15
7. 52 and 54   **9.** -16 and -14 **11.** 17, 19, and 21
13. 42, 44, and 46
15. \$4,000 invested at 8%, \$6,000 invested at 9%
17. \$700 invested at 10%, \$1,200 invested at 12%
19. \$500 at 8%, \$1,000 at 9%, \$1,500 at 10%
21. 12 liters of each
23. 15 gallons of 10% solution, 10 gallons of 5% solution
25. 32 pounds of \$9.50 beans, 8 pounds of \$12.00 beans
27. 45°, 45°, 90°   **29.** 22.5°, 45°, 112.5°
31. 80°, 60°, 40°   **33.** 16 adult and 22 children's tickets
35. 16 minutes   **37.** 39 hours
39. They are in offices 7329 and 7331.
41. Kendra is 8 years old and Marissa is 10 years old.
43. Jeff   **45.** \$10.38   **47.** $l = 12$ meters; $w = 10$ meters
49. 59°, 60°, 61°   **51.** \$54.00   **53.** Yes
55. a   **57.** a   **59. a.** 9 **b.** 3 **c.** -9 **d.** -3
61. a. -8 **b.** 8 **c.** 8 **d.** -8 **63.** -2.3125 **65.** $\frac{10}{3}$

PROBLEM SET 2.8

1. $\{x \mid x < 12\}$
3. $\{a \mid a \le 12\}$
5. $\{x \mid x > 13\}$
7. $\{y \mid y \ge 4\}$

9. $\{x \mid x > 9\}$

11. $\{x \mid x < 2\}$

13. $\{a \mid a \le 5\}$

15. $\{x \mid x > 15\}$

17. $\{x \mid x < -3\}$

19. $\{x \mid x \le 6\}$

21. $\{x \mid x \ge -50\}$

23. $\{y \mid y < -6\}$

25. $\{x \mid x < 6\}$ **27.** $\{y \mid y \ge -5\}$ **29.** $\{x \mid x < 3\}$
31. $\{x \mid x \le 18\}$ **33.** $\{a \mid a < -20\}$ **35.** $\{y \mid y < 25\}$
37. $\{a \mid a \le 3\}$ **39.** $\left\{x \mid x \ge \frac{15}{2}\right\}$ **41.** $\{x \mid x < -1\}$
43. $\{y \mid y \ge -2\}$ **45.** $\{x \mid x < -1\}$ **47.** $\{m \mid m \le -6\}$
49. $\{x \mid x \le -5\}$ **51.** $y < -\frac{3}{2}x + 3$ **53.** $y < \frac{2}{5}x - 2$
55. $y \le \frac{3}{7}x + 3$ **57.** $y \le \frac{1}{2}x + 1$
59. a. 3 **b.** 2 **c.** No **d.** $\{x \mid x > 2\}$
61. $x < 3$ **63.** $x \le 3$ **65.** At least 291
67. $\{x \mid x < 2\}$ **69.** $\left\{x \mid x > -\frac{8}{3}\right\}$
71. $x \ge 6$; the width is at least 6 meters.
73. $x > 6$; the shortest side is even and greater than 6 inches.
75. b **77.** 8 **79.** 24 **81.** 25% **83.** 10%
85. 80 **87.** 400 **89.** -5 **91.** 5 **93.** 7
95. 9 **97.** 6 **99.** $2x - 3$ **101.** $-3, 0, 2$

CHAPTER 2 TEST
1. $-y + 1$ **2.** $4x - 1$ **3.** $2y + 4$ **4.** $x - 22$
5. -3 **6.** -4

7. a.

n	$(n + 2)^2$
1	9
2	16
3	25
4	36

b.

n	$n^2 + 2$
1	3
2	6
3	11
4	18

8. $x = 3$ **9.** $y = -5$
10. $x = 1$ **11.** $x = 4$ **12.** $x = 1$ **13.** $x = 55$
14. $t = -3$ **15.** $x = \frac{10}{4} = \frac{5}{2}$ **16.** $x = (0.40)(56)$
17. $720 = 0.24x$ **18.** -1 **19.** 8 **20.** $y = -\frac{1}{3}x + 2$
21. $a = \frac{x^2 - v^2}{2d}$ **22.** Becca is 18, and Paul is 36.
23. The width is 20 cm, and the length is 55 cm.
24. 6 nickels, 14 dimes
25. \$700 at 6%, \$1,200 at 12%
26. $\{x \mid x > 10\}$
27. $\{y \mid y \ge -4\}$
28. $\{x \mid x > -4\}$
29. $\{n \mid n \le -2\}$

Chapter 3

PROBLEM SET 3.1
1. QI **3.** QII **5.** QI **7.** QI **9.** QII
11. QI **13.** QIII **15.** Not in a quadrant
17. Not in a quadrant

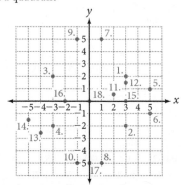

19. $(-4, 4)$ **21.** $(-4, 2)$ **23.** $(-3, 0)$ **25.** $(2, -2)$
27. $(-5, -5)$ **29.** Yes **31.** No **33.** Yes **35.** No
37. Yes **39.** No **41.** No **43.** No
45.

47.

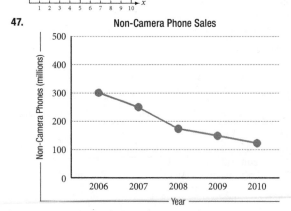

49. a. $(5, 40), (10, 80), (20, 160)$, Answers may vary
   b. \$320 **c.** 30 hours
   d. No, if she works 35 hours, she should be paid \$280.
51. $(1995, 44.8), (2000, 65.4), (2005, 104), (2010, 112.7),$
   $(2015, 137.9)$
53. $A = (2, 2), B = (2, 5), C = (7, 5)$
55. c **57.** d **59. a.** 10 **b.** -5 **c.** -4 **d.** -2
61. a. 2 **b.** $\frac{5}{3}$ **c.** 4 **d.** -11 **63.** $y = 3x + 5$
65. $y = \frac{2}{3}x - 2$

PROBLEM SET 3.2
1. $(0, -2)$ **3.** $(1, 5), (0, -2)$, and $(-2, -16)$

5. $(2, -2)$ **7.** $(3, 0)$ and $(3, -3)$ **9.** $(0, 6), (3, 0), (6, -6)$

11. $(0, 3), (4, 0), (-4, 6)$ **13.** $(1, 1), \left(\frac{3}{4}, 0\right), (5, 17)$

15. $(2, 13), (1, 6), (0, -1)$ **17.** $(-5, 4), (-5, -3), (-5, 0)$

19.

x	y
1	3
-3	-9
4	12
6	18

21.

x	y
2	3
3	2
5	0
9	-4

23.

x	y
2	0
3	2
1	-2
-3	-10

25.

x	y
0	-1
-1	-7
-3	-19
$\frac{3}{2}$	8

27. $(0, 4), (2, 2), (4, 0)$

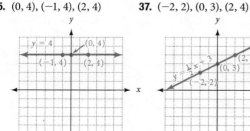

29. $(0, 0), (-2, -4), (2, 4)$

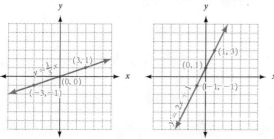

31. $(-3, -1), (0, 0), (3, 1)$

33. $(0, 1), (-1, -1), (1, 3)$

35. $(0, 4), (-1, 4), (2, 4)$

37. $(-2, 2), (0, 3), (2, 4)$

39. $(-3, 3), (0, 1), (3, -1)$

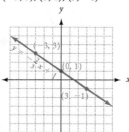

41. $(-1, 5), (0, 3), (1, 1)$

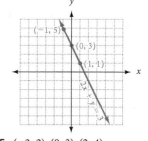

43. $(0, 3), (2, 0), (4, -3)$

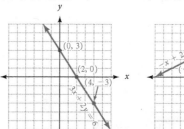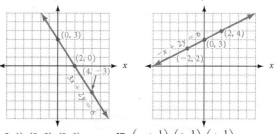

45. $(-2, 2), (0, 3), (2, 4)$

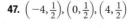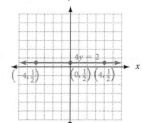

46. $(-3, 1), (0, 2), (3, 3)$

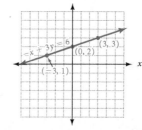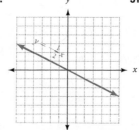

47. $\left(-4, \frac{1}{2}\right), \left(0, \frac{1}{2}\right), \left(4, \frac{1}{2}\right)$

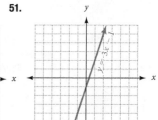

49.

51.

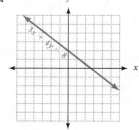

53.

55.

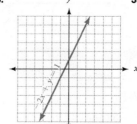

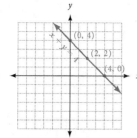

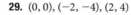

57.

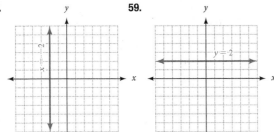

59.

61.

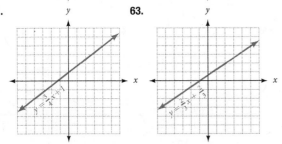

63.

79. d   **81.** c   **83. a.** 2   **b.** 3
85. a. −4   **b.** 2   **87. a.** 6   **b.** 2

PROBLEM SET 3.3

1.   **3.**

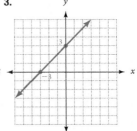
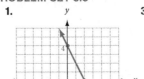

5.   **7.**

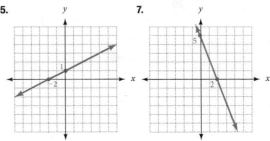

65.

Equation	H, V, and/or O
$x = 3$	V
$y = 3$	H
$y = 3x$	O
$y = 0$	O, H

9.   **11.**

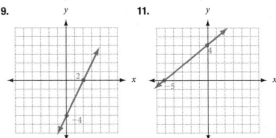

67.

Equation	H, V, and/or O
$x = -\frac{3}{5}$	V
$y = -\frac{3}{5}$	H
$y = -\frac{3}{5}x$	O
$x = 0$	O, V

13.   **15.**

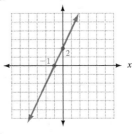

69.

x	y
−4	−3
−2	−2
0	−1
2	0
6	2

71. a. $\frac{5}{2}$ **b.** 5   **c.** 2
d.

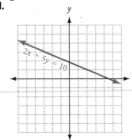

17.   **19.**

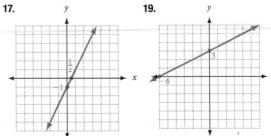

e. $y = -\frac{2}{5}x + 2$

73. 12 inches
75. a. Yes
    b. No, she should earn $108 for working 9 hours.
    c. No, she should earn $84 for working 7 hours.
    d. Yes
77. a. $375,000   **b.** At the end of 6 years.
    c. No, the crane will be worth $195,000 after 9 years.
    d. $600,000

21.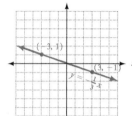

23.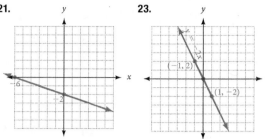

47.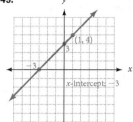

49.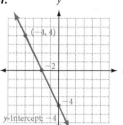

25.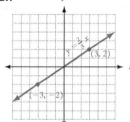

27.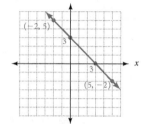

51.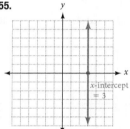

x-intercept $= 3$;
y-intercept $= 3$

29.

Equation	x-intercept	y-intercept
$3x + 4y = 12$	4	3
$3x + 4y = 4$	$\frac{4}{3}$	1
$3x + 4y = 3$	1	$\frac{3}{4}$
$3x + 4y = 2$	$\frac{2}{3}$	$\frac{1}{2}$

31.

Equation	x-intercept	y-intercept
$x - 3y = 2$	2	$-\frac{2}{3}$
$y = \frac{1}{3}x - \frac{2}{3}$	2	$-\frac{2}{3}$
$x - 3y = 0$	0	0
$y = \frac{1}{3}x$	0	0

53.

x	y
-2	1
0	-1
-1	0
1	-2

55.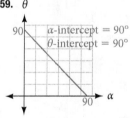

33. 5   **35.** $-\frac{2}{3}$ **37.** 4   **39.** $\frac{1}{2}$

41. a. 0   **b.** $-\frac{3}{2}$ **c.** 1

d.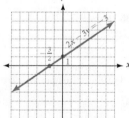

e. $y = \frac{2}{3}x + 1$

43. x-intercept $= 3$; y-intercept $= 5$
44. x-intercept $= -5$; y-intercept $= 2$
45. x-intercept $= -1$; y-intercept $= -3$

57.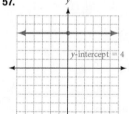

59. θ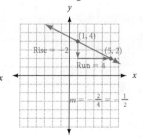

α-intercept $= 90°$
θ-intercept $= 90°$

61. d   **63.** b   **65. a.** $-\frac{5}{7}$ **b.** $-\frac{5}{7}$
67. a. $-\frac{5}{7}$ **b.** $-\frac{5}{7}$

PROBLEM SET 3.4

1. Slope $= \frac{3}{2}$

3. Slope $= -\frac{1}{2}$

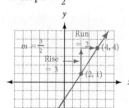

5. Slope = $\frac{5}{3}$

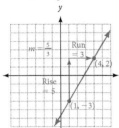

7. Slope = $\frac{5}{4}$

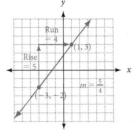

9. Slope = $-\frac{2}{3}$

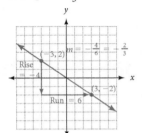

11. Slope = 3

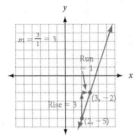

13. Undefined slope

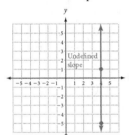

15. Slope = 0

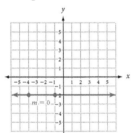

17. Slope = $\frac{1}{3}$

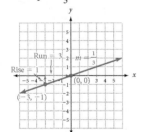

19. Slope = 3 **21.** Slope = 2

23.

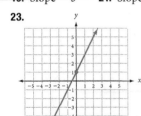

25.

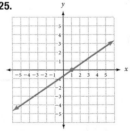

27.

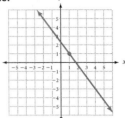

29.

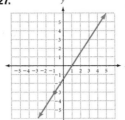

31.

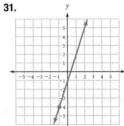

32.

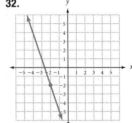

33.

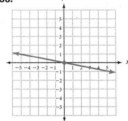

35. Slope = $\frac{2}{3}$ **37.** Slope = $-\frac{1}{2}$

39. Slope = 2; y-intercept = -3

41. Slope = $\frac{1}{2}$; y-intercept = 1

43.

Equation	Slope
$x = 3$	Undefined
$y = 3$	0
$y = 3x$	3

45.

Equation	Slope
$y = -\frac{2}{3}$	0
$x = -\frac{2}{3}$	Undefined
$y = -\frac{2}{3}x$	$-\frac{2}{3}$

47. a. $\frac{2}{3}$ **b.** $-\frac{3}{2}$ **49. a.** $-\frac{1}{4}$ **b.** 4 **51. a.** 2 **b.** $-\frac{1}{2}$

53. a. 0 **b.** No slope **55.** Parallel

57. Perpendicular **59.** Perpendicular **61.** 6

63. a. Slopes: A, 3.3; B, 3.1; C, 5.3; D, 1.9

b. The annual production of garbage in the U.S. increased at a rate of 3.3 million tons per year from 1960 to 1970.

65. a. Slopes: A, -50; B, -75; C, -25

b. Non-camera phones sales decreased at a rate of 75 million phones per year between 2007 and 2008.

67. a **69.** d **71.** $y = 2x + 4$

73. $y = -2x + 3$ **75.** $y = \frac{4}{5}x - 4$

PROBLEM SET 3.5

1. $m = 5, b = -3$ **3.** $m = -\frac{2}{3}, b = \frac{7}{3}$

5. $m = 1, b = 9$ **7.** $m = \frac{1}{2}, b = -\frac{5}{2}$ **9.** $m = -2, b = \frac{1}{4}$

11. $m = 3, b = 0$ **13.** $m = 0, b = -10$ **35.** $m = \frac{4}{5}; b = -4$ **37.** $m = -\frac{2}{5}; b = -2$

15.
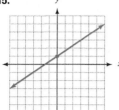

17.
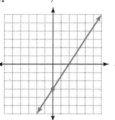

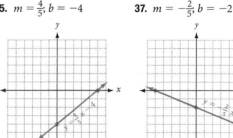

39. $y = \frac{2}{3}x + 1$ **41.** $y = \frac{3}{2}x - 1$ **43.** $y = -\frac{2}{3}x + 3$

45. $y = 2x - 4$ **47.** $m = 3, b = 3, y = 3x + 3$

49. $m = \frac{1}{4}, b = -1, y = \frac{1}{4}x - 1$ **51.** $2x - y = 1$

53. $x + 3y = -11$ **55.** $3x - 5y = -36$

57. $4x + 3y = 16$ **59. a.** $y = 3x - 1$ **b.** $y = -\frac{1}{3}x + \frac{7}{3}$

61. a. $y = -\frac{1}{2}x - 3$ **b.** $y = 2x + 7$

63. a. $y = -\frac{2}{3}x + 6$ **b.** $y = \frac{3}{2}x - \frac{1}{2}$

65. $y = 2$ **67.** $y = 5$

69. a. $-\frac{5}{2}$ **b.** $y = 2x + 6$ **c.** 6   **d.** 2

19.
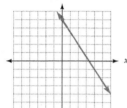

21.
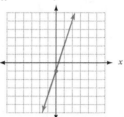

e.
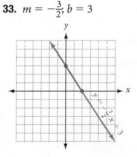

23.
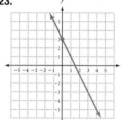

25.
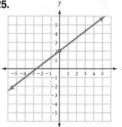

71. a. $\$6,000$ **b.** 3 years   **c.** slope $= -3,000$
     d. $\$3,000$ **e.** $V = -3,000t + 21,000$

73. c   **75.** c

77. $y = -2x + 1$ **79.** $y = \frac{1}{2}x + 1$ **81.** $y = -\frac{3}{2}x - 1$

83. $\frac{5}{4}$ **85.** -1 **87.** 0

27.
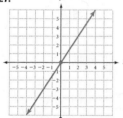

29. $m = 2; b = 4$
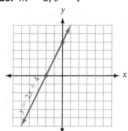

PROBLEM SET 3.6

1. $2x - y = 1$ **3.** $x + 2y = -2$ **5.** $3x - 2y = 12$

7. $3x + y = 1$ **9.** $2x + 3y = 12$ **11.** $x - 5y = 5$

13. $y = 3$ **15.** $3x - 2y = 0$ **17.** $y = x - 2$

19. $y = 2x - 3$ **21.** $y = \frac{4}{3}x + 2$ **23.** $y = -\frac{2}{3}x - 3$

25. $y = -\frac{3}{2}x + 3$ **27.** $x = -1$ **29.** $y = 1$

31. $y = -\frac{2}{3}x + 2$ **33.** $y = -\frac{5}{2}x - 5$ **35.** $x = 3$

37. a. $y = 3$ **b.** $x = -2$ **39. a.** $y = 2$ **b.** $x = 6$

41. a. $2x - y = 7$ **b.** $x + 2y = 1$

43. a. $x + 3y = -13$ **b.** $3x - y = -9$

45. a. $3x + 4y = 20$ **b.** $4x - 3y = -15$

47. a. $2x - 3y = 2$ **b.** $3x + 2y = 3$

49. a. $y = 2$ **b.** $x = 4$

51. a. $0°C$ **b.** $m = \frac{5}{9}$ **c.** $y = \frac{5}{9}x - \frac{160}{9}$ **d.** $100°C$

53. b

31. $m = -3; b = 3$
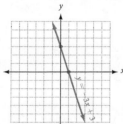

33. $m = -\frac{3}{2}, b = 3$

55.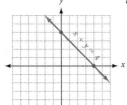

57.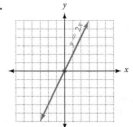

59.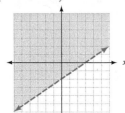

PROBLEM SET 3.7

1.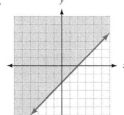

3.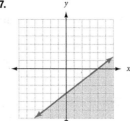

5.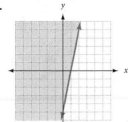

7.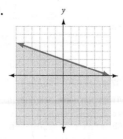

9.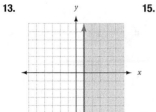

11.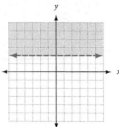

13.

15.

17.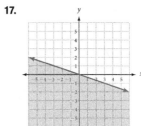

19.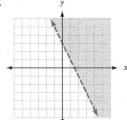

21.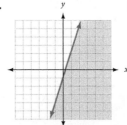

23.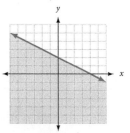

25. a. $y < \frac{8}{3}$ **b.** $y > -\frac{8}{3}$ **c.** $y = -\frac{4}{3}x + 4$
d.

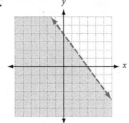

27. a. $y = \frac{2}{5}x + 2$ **b.** $y < \frac{2}{5}x + 2$ **c.** $y > \frac{2}{5}x + 2$
29. b   **31.** $-6x + 11$ **33.** -8 **35.** -4
37. $w = \frac{P - 2l}{2}$ **39.** $\{x \mid x < -1\}$

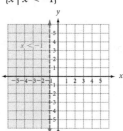

41. $y \geq \frac{3}{2}x - 6$ **43.** Width 2 inches, length 11 inches

CHAPTER 3 TEST

1.-4.

5. $(0, -3), (2, 0), (4, 3), (-2, -6)$
6. $(0, 7), (4, -5)$

7.

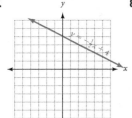

8.

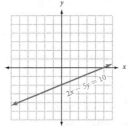

5. $\{(2, 1)\}$

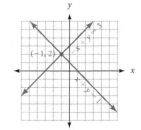

7. $\{(-1, 2)\}$

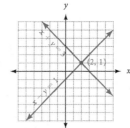

9.

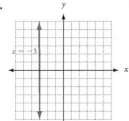

10.

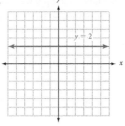

9. $\{(3, 5)\}$

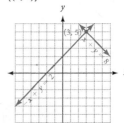

11. $\{(4, 3)\}$

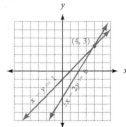

11. x-intercept = 2, y-intercept = -4
12. x-intercept = -4, y-intercept = 6
13. No x-intercept, y-intercept = 3
14. x-intercept = -2, no y-intercept
15. $-\frac{1}{2}$ **16.** $-\frac{8}{7}$ **17.** -3 **18.** Undefined slope   **19.** 0
20. $m = -\frac{1}{2}$, y-intercept = 6   **21.** $m = 3$, y-intercept = 0
22. $m = \frac{3}{7}$ **23.** $m = \frac{1}{4}$ **24.** $y = 3x - 5$
25. $y = -\frac{1}{2}x + 3$ **26.** $y = -\frac{2}{3}x - 2$
27. $y = -\frac{6}{5}x + \frac{18}{5}$ **28.** $3x - 2y = 7$
29. $2x - 3y = -17$ **30.** $y = -5$ **31.** $x = -2$

13. $\{(0, -6)\}$

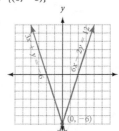

15. $\{(1, 0)\}$

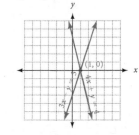

32.

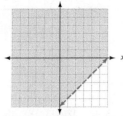

33.

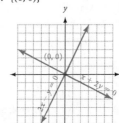

17. $\{(0, 0)\}$

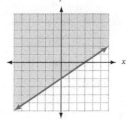

19. $\{(-5, -6)\}$

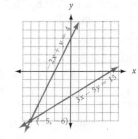

34.

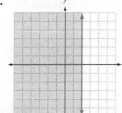

21. $\{(-1, -1)\}$

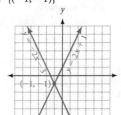

23. $\{(-3, 2)\}$

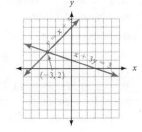

Chapter 4

PROBLEM SET 4.1

1. a. No   **b.** Yes   **c.** No   **3. a.** Yes   **b.** No   **c.** Yes
4. a. No   **b.** Yes   **c.** Yes

25. $\{(-3, 5)\}$

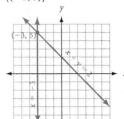

27. $\{(-4, 6)\}$

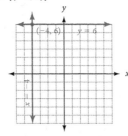

29. $\varnothing$

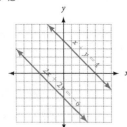

31. $\{(x, y) \mid 2x - y = 4\}$

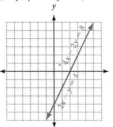

33.

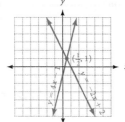

35.

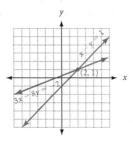

37. $a = 5, b = -5$

39. a. $a = 3, b = 1$ **b.** $a = 3, b \neq 1$ **c.** $x \neq 3$

41. a. 25 hours **b.** Gigi's **c.** Marcy's

43. a **45.** b **47.** $2x$ **49.** $7x$ **51.** $13x$

53. $3x - 2y$ **55.** 1 **57.** 0 **59.** -5

PROBLEM SET 4.2

1. $(2, 1)$ **3.** $(3, 7)$ **5.** $(2, -5)$ **7.** $(-1, 0)$

9. $\{(x, y) \mid 3x + 2y = 1\}$ **11.** $(4, 8)$ **13.** $\left(\frac{1}{5}, 1\right)$

15. $(1, 0)$ **17.** $(-1, -2)$ **19.** $\left(-5, \frac{3}{4}\right)$ **21.** $(-4, 5)$

23. $(-3, -10)$ **25.** $(3, 2)$ **27.** $\left(5, \frac{1}{3}\right)$ **29.** $\left(-2, \frac{2}{3}\right)$

31. $(2, 2)$ **33.** $\varnothing$ **35.** $(1, 1)$ **37.** $\varnothing$ **39.** $(10, 12)$

41. c **43.** 1 **45.** 2 **47.** All real numbers

49. $x = 3y - 1$ **51.** 1 **53.** 5 **55.** 34.5 **57.** 33.95

PROBLEM SET 4.3

1. $(4, 7)$ **3.** $(3, 17)$ **5.** $\left(\frac{3}{2}, 2\right)$ **7.** $(2, 4)$ **9.** $(0, 4)$

11. $(-1, 3)$ **13.** $(1, 1)$ **15.** $(2, -3)$ **17.** $\left(-2, \frac{3}{5}\right)$

19. $(-3, 5)$ **21.** $\varnothing$ **23.** $(10, 12)$ **25.** $\left(\frac{2}{7}, -\frac{12}{7}\right)$

27. $(3, 1)$ **29.** $(4, 4)$ **31.** $\left(\frac{1}{3}, \frac{5}{6}\right)$ **33.** $(2, 6)$

35. $(5, -2)$ **37.** $(18, 10)$ **39.** $\{(x, y) \mid x - y = 2\}$

41. $\left(-\frac{1}{2}, \frac{1}{2}\right)$

43. a. 1,000 miles **b.** Car **c.** Truck

d. We are only working with positive numbers.

45. b **47.** 3 and 23 **49.** 15 and 24

51. Length = 23 in.; width = 6 in.

53. 14 nickels and 10 dimes

PROBLEM SET 4.4

1. 10 and 15 **3.** 3 and 12 **5.** 4 and 9 **7.** 6 and 29

9. $9,000 at 8%, $11,000 at 6%

11. $2,000 at 6%, $8,000 at 5% **13.** 6 nickels, 8 quarters

15. 12 dimes, 9 quarters **17.** 6L of 50%, 12L of 20%

19. 10 gallons of 10% solution, 20 gallons of 7% solution

21. Boat: 9 mph; current: 3 mph

23. Plane: 270 mph; wind 30 mph

25. 20 adults, 50 kids **27.** 16 feet wide, 32 feet long

29. 33 $5 chips, 12 $25 chips **31.** 50 at $11, 100 at $20

33. a **35.** c **37.** 47 **39.** 14 **41.** 70 **43.** 35

45. 5 **47.** 6,540 **49.** 1,760 **51.** 20 **53.** 63 **55.** 53

CHAPTER 4 TEST

1. $(0, 6)$ **2.**

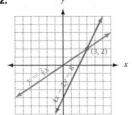

3. **4.**

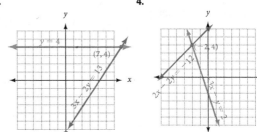

5. $(-4, 5)$ **6.** $(1, 2)$ **7.** $(-6, 3)$

8. Lines coincide, $\{(x, y) \mid 2x + 3y = 4\}$

9. $(4, 0)$ **10.** $(19, 9)$ **11.** $(-3, 4)$ **12.** $(11, 3)$ **13.** 4, 14

14. $1,520 at 7%, $480 at 6% **15.** 8 dimes, 11 nickels

16. 20 gallons of 40% and 10 gallons of 70% **17.** 71 ft × 28 ft

Chapter 5

PROBLEM SET 5.1

1. 4, 2, 16 **3.** 0.3, 2, 0.09 **5.** 4, 3, 64 **7.** $-5, 2, 25$

9. 2, 3, -8 **11.** 3, 4, 81 **13.** $\frac{2}{3}, 2, \frac{4}{9}$ **15.** $\frac{1}{2}, 4, \frac{1}{16}$

17. a.

Number x	1	2	3	4	5	6	7
Square x^2	1	4	9	16	25	36	49

b. larger **19.** x^9 **21.** y^{30} **23.** 2^{12} **25.** x^{28}

27. x^{10} **29.** 5^{12} **31.** y^9 **33.** 2^{50} **35.** a^{3x}

37. b^{xy} **39.** $16x^2$ **41.** $32y^5$ **43.** $81x^4$
45. $0.25a^2b^2$ **47.** $64x^3y^3z^3$ **49.** $8x^{12}$ **51.** $16a^6$
53. x^{14} **55.** a^{11} **57.** $16x^4y^6$ **59.** $\frac{8}{27}a^{12}b^{15}$
61.

Number x	-3	-2	-1	0	1	2	3
Square x^2	9	4	1	0	1	4	9

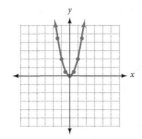

63.

Number x	-2.5	-1.5	-0.5	0	0.5	1.5	2.5
Square x^2	6.25	2.25	0.25	0	0.25	2.25	6.25

65. 4.32×10^4 **67.** -5.7×10^2 **69.** 2.38×10^5
71. 2,490 **73.** -352 **75.** 28,000 **77.** 27 inches^3
79. 15.6 inches^3 **81.** 36 inches^3 **83.** Answers will vary
85. 6.5×10^8 seconds **87.** \$740,000 **89.** \$180,000
91. 219 inches^3 **93.** 182 inches^3 **95.** a **97.** a
99. -3 **101.** 11 **103.** -5 **105.** 5 **107.** 2
109. 6 **111.** 4 **113.** 3

PROBLEM SET 5.2

1. $\frac{1}{5}$ **3.** $\frac{1}{x}$ **5.** $\frac{1}{9}$ **7.** $\frac{1}{36}$ **9.** $\frac{1}{64}$ **11.** $\frac{1}{125}$
13. $\frac{1}{a^4}$ **15.** $-\frac{1}{16}$ **17.** $-\frac{1}{x}$ **19.** $-\frac{1}{125}$ **21.** $\frac{1}{16}$
23. $\frac{2}{x^3}$ **25.** $\frac{1}{8x^3}$ **27.** $\frac{1}{25y^2}$ **29.** $\frac{1}{100}$

31.

Number x	Square x^2	Power of 2 2^x
-3	9	$\frac{1}{8}$
-2	4	$\frac{1}{4}$
-1	1	$\frac{1}{2}$
0	0	1
1	1	2
2	4	4
3	9	8

33. $\frac{1}{25}$ **35.** x^6 **37.** 64 **39.** $8x^3$ **41.** 6^{10}
43. $\frac{1}{6^{10}}$ **45.** $\frac{1}{2^8}=\frac{1}{256}$ **47.** $2^8=256$ **49.** $27x^3$

51. $81x^4y^4$ **53.** 1 **55.** $2a^2b$ **57.** $\frac{1}{49y^6}$
59. $\frac{1}{x^8}$ **61.** $\frac{1}{y^3}$ **63.** x^2 **65.** a^6 **67.** $\frac{1}{y^9}$
69. y^{40} **71.** $\frac{1}{x}$ **73.** x^9 **75.** a^{16} **77.** $\frac{1}{a^4}$
79.

Number x	-3	-2	-1	0	1	2	3
Power of 2 2^x	$\frac{1}{8}$	$\frac{1}{4}$	$\frac{1}{2}$	1	2	4	8

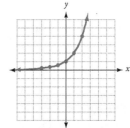

81. 4.8×10^{-3} **83.** 2.5×10^1 **85.** 2.5×10^{-1}
87. 9×10^{-6}
89.

Expanded Form	Scientific Notation $n \times 10^r$
0.000357	3.57×10^{-4}
0.00357	3.57×10^{-3}
0.0357	3.57×10^{-2}
0.357	3.57×10^{-1}
3.57	3.57×10^0
35.7	3.57×10^1
357	3.57×10^2
3,570	3.57×10^3
35,700	3.57×10^4

91. 0.00423 **93.** 0.00008 **95.** 4.2 **97.** 0.24
99. 0.002
101. Craven/Busch 2×10^{-3}; Earnhardt/Irvan 5×10^{-3}; Harvick/Gordon 6×10^{-3}; Kahne/Kenseth 1×10^{-2}; Kenseth/Kahne 1×10^{-2}
103. 2.5×10^4 **105.** 2.35×10^5 **107.** 8.2×10^{-4}
109. 100 inches^2; 400 inches^2; 4 **111.** x^2; $4x^2$; 4
113. 216 inches^3; 1,728 inches^3; 8 **115.** x^3; $8x^3$; 8
117. b **119.** a **121.** d **123.** $\frac{5}{14}$ **125.** 3.2
127. -11 **129.** x^3 **131.** y^3 **133.** x **35.** $\frac{1}{x^3}$
137. 0.0006

PROBLEM SET 5.3

1. Coefficient = 7, degree = 3
3. Coefficient = -1, degree = 1
5. Coefficient = $\frac{1}{2}$, degree = 2
7. Coefficient = -4, degree = 11
9. Coefficient = 8, degree = 0
11. $12x^7$ **13.** $-16y^{11}$ **15.** $32x^2$ **17.** $200a^6$
19. $-24a^3b^3$ **21.** $24x^6y^8$ **23.** $3x$ **25.** $\frac{6}{y^3}$

27. $\frac{1}{2a}$ **29.** $-\frac{3a}{b^2}$ **31.** $\frac{x^2}{9z^2}$

33.

a	b	ab	$\frac{a}{b}$	$\frac{b}{a}$
10	5x	50x	$\frac{2}{x}$	$\frac{x}{2}$
$20x^3$	$6x^2$	$120x^5$	$\frac{10x}{3}$	$\frac{3}{10x}$
$25x^5$	$5x^4$	$125x^9$	$5x$	$\frac{1}{5x}$
$3x^{-2}$	$3x^2$	9	$\frac{1}{x^4}$	x^4
$-2y^4$	$8y^7$	$-16y^{11}$	$-\frac{1}{4y^3}$	$-4y^3$

35. 6×10^8 **37.** 1.75×10^{-1} **39.** 1.21×10^{-6}
41. 4.2×10^3 **43.** 3×10^{10} **45.** 5×10^{-3} **47.** $8x^2$
49. $-11x^5$ **51.** 0 **53.** $4x^3$ **55.** $31ab^2$
57.

a	b	ab	a + b
$5x$	$3x$	$15x^2$	$8x$
$4x^2$	$2x^2$	$8x^4$	$6x^2$
$3x^3$	$6x^3$	$18x^6$	$9x^3$
$2x^4$	$-3x^4$	$-6x^8$	$-x^4$
x^5	$7x^5$	$7x^{10}$	$8x^5$

59. $128x^7$ **61.** $432x^{10}$ **63.** $128x^{17}y^9$ **65.** $4x^2$
67. $\frac{27x^2}{16}$ **69.** $\frac{4x^6}{9y^4}$ **71.** $4x^3$ **73.** $\frac{1}{b^2}$ **75.** $\frac{6y^{10}}{x^4}$
77. 2×10^6 **79.** 1×10^1 **81.** 4.2×10^{-6} **83.** $9x^3$
85. $-20a^2$ **87.** $6x^5y^2$ **89.** b   **91.** d   **93.** -5
95. 6 **97.** 76 **99.** $6x^2$ **101.** $2x$ **103.** $-2x - 9$
105. 11

PROBLEM SET 5.4

1. Trinomial, 3   **3.** Trinomial, 3   **5.** Binomial, 1
7. Binomial, 2   **9.** Monomial, 2   **11.** Monomial, 0
13. $5x^2 + 2$; 2, 5   **15.** $-x^3 + 3x^2 - 6x$; 3, -1
17. $6x^2 + x - 1$; 2, 6   **19.** 14   **21.** -8 **23.** 12
25. 4   **27.** $5x^2 + 5x + 9$ **29.** $5a^2 - 9a + 7$
31. $x^2 + 6x + 8$ **33.** $x^2 - 9$ **35.** $-10x + 5$
37. $-5x^2 - x + 2$ **39.** $x^2 - 2x - 3$
41. $6x^3 - 13x^2 + 8x - 3$ **43.** $2a^2 - 2a - 2$
45. $6x^2 - 13x + 5$ **47.** $3y^2 - 11y + 10$
49. $2x^2 - x + 1$ **51.** $-\frac{1}{9}x^3 - \frac{2}{3}x^2 - \frac{5}{2}x + \frac{7}{4}$
53. $-4y^2 + 15y - 22$ **55.** $x^2 - 33x + 63$
57. $8y^2 + 4y + 26$ **59.** $75x^2 - 150x - 75$
61. $12x + 2$ **63.** 56.52 inches^3 **65.** d   **67.** b
69. 5   **71.** -6 **73.** $-20x^2$ **75.** $-21x$ **77.** $2x$
79. $6x - 18$

PROBLEM SET 5.5

1. $6x^2 + 2x$ **3.** $6x^4 - 4x^3 + 2x^2$
5. $2a^3b - 2a^2b^2 + 2ab$ **7.** $3y^4 + 9y^3 + 12y^2$
9. $8x^5y^2 + 12x^4y^3 + 32x^2y^4$ **11.** $x^2 + 7x + 12$
13. $x^2 + 7x + 6$ **15.** $x^2 + 2x + \frac{3}{4}$ **17.** $a^2 + 2a - 15$
19. $xy + xb - ay - ab$ **21.** $x^2 - 36$ **23.** $y^2 - \frac{25}{36}$

25. $2x^2 - 11x + 12$ **27.** $2a^2 + 3a - 2$
29. $6x^2 - 19x + 10$ **31.** $2ax + 8x + 3a + 12$
33. $25x^2 - 16$ **35.** $2x^2 + \frac{5}{2}x - \frac{3}{4}$ **37.** $3 - 10a + 8a^2$
39. $a^3 - 6a^2 + 11a - 6$ **41.** $x^3 + 8$
43. $2x^3 + 17x^2 + 26x + 9$
45. $5x^4 - 13x^3 + 20x^2 + 7x + 5$
47. $6x^4 - 7x^3 - 12x^2 + 3x + 2$
49. $a^5 - 3a^4 + 5a^3 - a^2 - 2a + 8$
51. $2x^4 + x^2 - 15$ **53.** $6a^6 + 15a^4 + 4a^2 + 10$
55. $x^3 + 12x^2 + 47x + 60$ **57.** $x^2 - 5x + 8$
59. $8x^2 - 6x - 5$ **61.** $x^2 - x - 30$ **63.** $x^2 + 4x - 6$
65. $x^2 + 13x$ **67.** $x^2 + 2x - 3$ **69.** $a^2 - 3a + 6$
71. $(x + 2)(x + 3) = x^2 + 2x + 3x + 6 = x^2 + 5x + 6$
73. $(x + 1)(2x + 2) = 2x^2 + 4x + 2$
75. a. $5x + 1$ **b.** $x - 9$ **c.** $x = 9$ **d.** $6x^2 + 7x - 20$
77. $A = x(2x + 5) = 2x^2 + 5x$ **79.** $A = x(x + 1) = x^2 + x$
81. $R = 100p - 10p^2$ **83.** d   **85.** c   **87.** 169
89. $-10x$ **91.** 0   **93.** 0   **95.** $-12x + 16$
97. $x^2 + x - 2$ **99.** $x^2 + 6x + 9$

PROBLEM SET 5.6

1. $x^2 - 4x + 4$ **3.** $a^2 + 6a + 9$ **5.** $x^2 - 10x + 25$
7. $a^2 - a + \frac{1}{4}$ **9.** $x^2 + 20x + 100$
11. $a^2 + 1.6a + 0.64$ **13.** $4x^2 - 4x + 1$
15. $16a^2 + 40a + 25$ **17.** $9x^2 - 12x + 4$
19. $9a^2 + 30ab + 25b^2$ **21.** $16x^2 - 40xy + 25y^2$
23. $x^4 + 10x^2 + 25$ **25.** $a^6 + 2a^3 + 1$
27. $49m^4 + 28m^2n + 4n^2$ **29.** $36x^4 - 120x^2y^2 + 100y^4$
31.

x	$(x + 3)^2$	$x^2 + 9$	$x^2 + 6x + 9$
1	16	10	16
2	25	13	25
3	36	18	36
4	49	25	49

33.

a	1	3	3	4
b	1	5	4	5
$(a + b)^2$	4	64	49	81
$a^2 + b^2$	2	34	25	41
$a^2 + ab + b^2$	3	49	37	61
$a^2 + 2ab + b^2$	4	64	49	81

35. $a^2 - 25$ **37.** $y^2 - 1$ **39.** $81 - x^2$ **41.** $4x^2 - 25$
43. $16x^2 - \frac{1}{9}$ **45.** $4a^2 - 49b^2$ **47.** $36 - 49x^2$
49. $x^4 - 9$ **51.** $a^4 - 16b^4$ **53.** $25y^8 - 64$
55. $2x^2 - 34$ **57.** $-12x^2 + 20x + 8$ **59.** $a^2 + 4a + 6$
61. $8x^3 + 36x^2 + 54x + 27$
63. $(50 - 1)(50 + 1) = 2,500 - 1 = 2,499$
65. Both equal 25.   **67.** $x^2 + (x + 1)^2 = 2x^2 + 2x + 1$
69. $x^2 + (x + 1)^2 + (x + 2)^2 = 3x^2 + 6x + 5$
71. $a^2 + ab + ba + b^2 = a^2 + 2ab + b^2$ **73.** b   **75.** $2x^2$
77. x^2 **79.** $3x$ **81.** $3xy$ **83.** $146\frac{20}{27}$

85. $x^2 - 3x$ **87.** $2x^3 - 10x^2$ **89.** $-2x$ **91.** 2

PROBLEM SET 5.7

1. $x - 2$ **3.** $5xy - 2y$ **5.** $7x^4 - 6x^3 + 5x^2$
7. $-4a + 2$ **9.** $-6a^2b + 3ab^2 - 7b^3$
11. $-\frac{a}{2} - b - \frac{b^2}{2a}$ **13.** $3x + 4y$ **15.** $-y + 3$
17. $5y - 4$ **19.** $xy - x^2y^2$ **21.** $-a + 1$
23. $x^2 - 3xy + y^2$ **25.** $2 - 3b + 5b^2$ **27.** $-2xy + 1$
29. $\frac{1}{4x} - \frac{1}{2a} + \frac{3}{4}$ **31.** $\frac{4x^2}{3} + \frac{2}{3x} + \frac{1}{x^2}$ **33.** $3a^{3m} - 9a^m$
35. $2x^{4m} - 5x^{2m} + 7$ **37.** $3x^2 - x + 6$ **39.** 4
41. $x + 5$ **43.** $x - 2$ **45.** $a + 4$ **47.** $x + 3$
49. $x - 3$ **51.** $x^2 - x - 3$ **53.** $1 + \frac{5}{x-2}$
55. $3 + \frac{-2}{x+2}$ **57.** $x + 2 + \frac{2}{x+3}$ **59.** $x + 4 + \frac{9}{x-2}$
61. $x + 4 + \frac{-10}{x+1}$ **63.** $x - 3 + \frac{17}{2x+4}$
65. $3a - 2 + \frac{7}{2a+3}$ **67.** $2a^2 - a - 3$
69. $1 + \frac{-3x+11}{x^2-3x-2}$ **71.** $a - 5 + \frac{-3a+19}{2a^2+a+3}$
73. $x^2 - x + 5$ **75.** $x^2 + x + 1$ **77.** $x^2 + 2x + 4$
79. $1 + \frac{3a+1}{a^2+1}$ **81.** $a + 3 + \frac{2a+7}{a^2-2}$
83. $2a^2 + 3 + \frac{1}{2a^2-1}$ **85.** Both equal 7.
87. $\frac{3(10)+8}{2} = 19; 3(10) + 4 = 34$ **89.** \$491.17
91. \$331.42 **93.** d **95.** $200x^{24}$ **97.** x^7
99. 8×10^1 **101.** $10ab^2$ **103.** $6x^4 + 6x^3 - 2x^2$
105. $9y^2 - 30y + 25$ **107.** $4a^4 - 49$

CHAPTER 5 TEST

1. -32 **2.** -16 **3.** x^{23} **4.** $16x^4y^6$ **5.** $\frac{1}{16}$
6. 1 **7.** x^3 **8.** $\frac{x^3}{27}$ **9.** $\frac{1}{x^3}$ **10.** 4.307×10^{-2}
11. 7,630,000 **12.** $-24a^3b^4$ **13.** $\frac{y^3z^2}{3x^2}$ **14.** $\frac{a^3b^2}{2}$
15. $12x^3$ **16.** 7.5×10^7 **17.** $9x^2 + 5x + 4$
18. $2x^2 + 6x - 2$ **19.** $5x - 4$ **20.** 21
21. $15x^4 - 6x^3 + 12x^2$ **22.** $x^2 - \frac{1}{12}x - \frac{1}{12}$
23. $10x^2 - 3x - 18$ **24.** $x^3 + 64$ **25.** $x^2 - 12x + 36$
26. $4a^2 + 16ab + 16b^2$ **27.** $9x^2 - 36$ **28.** $x^4 - 16$
29. $3x^2 - 6x + 1$ **30.** $3x - 1 + \frac{-5}{3x-1}$
31. $4x + 3 + \frac{-8x-5}{x^2+2}$ **32.** 32.77 in^3 **33.** $V = w^3$

Chapter 6

PROBLEM SET 6.1

1. 3 **3.** $2x$ **5.** $4a^2b$ **7.** $2x + 1$ **9.** $5(3x + 5)$
11. $3(2a + 3)$ **13.** $4(x - 2y)$ **15.** $3(x^2 - 2x - 3)$
17. $3(a^2 - a - 20)$ **19.** $4(6y^2 - 13y + 6)$
21. $x^2(9 - 8x)$ **23.** $13a^2(1 - 2a)$ **25.** $7xy(3x - 4y)$
27. $11ab^2(2a - 1)$ **29.** $7x(x^2 + 3x - 4)$
31. $11(11y^4 - x^4)$ **33.** $25x^2(4x^2 - 2x + 1)$
35. $8(a^2 + 2b^2 + 4c^2)$ **37.** $4ab(a - 4b + 8ab)$
39. $11a^2b^2(11a - 2b + 3ab)$ **41.** $12x^2y^3(1 - 6x^3 - 3x^2y)$
43. $(x + 3)(y + 5)$ **45.** $(x + 2)(y + 6)$
47. $(a - 3)(b + 7)$ **49.** $(a - b)(x + y)$
51. $(2x + 5)(a - 1)$ **53.** $(9b - 2)(3y + 1)$
55. $(b - 2)(3x - 4)$ **57.** $(x + 2)(x + a)$
59. $(x - b)(x - a)$ **61.** $(x + y)(a + b + c)$
63. $(3x + 2)(2x + 3)$ **65.** $(10x - 1)(2x + 5)$

67. $(4x + 5)(5x + 1)$ **69.** $(x + 2)(x^2 + 3)$
71. $(3x - 2)(2x^2 + 5)$ **73.** 6 **75.** $3(4x^2 + 2x + 1)$
77. $A = 1,000(1 + r)$; \$1,120.00
79. a. $A = 1,000,000 (1 + r)$ **b.** 1,300,000
81. a **83.** c **85.** $x^2 - 9x + 14$ **87.** $x^2 + x - 6$
89. $x^3 - 8$ **91.** $3x^3 - 4x^2 - 16x - 8$
93. $10x^7 + 8x^6 - 6x^5$ **95.** $x^2 + x + \frac{3}{16}$
97. $32a^2 - 52ab + 15b^2$ **99.** $49b^2 + 14b + 1$
101. $x^2 - 16x + 64$ **103.** $x^3 - 27$

PROBLEM SET 6.2

1. $(x + 3)(x + 4)$ **3.** $(x + 1)(x + 2)$
5. $(a + 3)(a + 7)$ **7.** $(x - 2)(x - 5)$
9. $(y - 3)(y - 7)$ **11.** $(x - 4)(x + 3)$
13. $(y + 4)(y - 3)$ **15.** $(x + 7)(x - 2)$
17. $(r - 9)(r + 1)$ **19.** $(x - 6)(x + 5)$
21. $(a + 7)(a + 8)$ **23.** $(y + 6)(y - 7)$
25. $(x + 6)(x + 7)$ **27.** $(x + 2y)(x + 3y)$
29. $(x - 4y)(x - 5y)$ **31.** $(a + 4b)(a - 2b)$
33. $(a - 5b)^2$ **35.** $(a + 5b)^2$ **37.** $(x - 6a)(x + 8a)$
39. $(x + 4b)(x - 9b)$ **41.** $2(x + 1)(x + 2)$
43. $3(a + 4)(a - 5)$ **45.** $100(x - 2)(x - 3)$
47. $100(p - 5)(p - 8)$ **49.** $x^2(x + 3)(x - 4)$
51. $2r(r + 5)(r - 3)$ **53.** $2y^2(y + 1)(y - 4)$
55. $x^3(x + 2)^2$ **57.** $3y^2(y + 1)(y - 5)$
59. $4x^2(x - 4)(x - 9)$ **61.** $-1(a + 5)(a + 6)$
63. $-1(x + 8)(x - 7)$ **65.** $(x^2 - 3)(x^2 - 2)$
67. $(x - 100)(x + 20)$ **69.** $\left(x - \frac{1}{2}\right)^2$
71. $(x + 0.2)(x + 0.4)$ **73.** $x + 16$ **75.** $4x^2 - x - 3$
77. b **79.** c **81.** $6a^2 + 13a + 2$
83. $6a^2 + 7a + 2$ **85.** $6a^2 + 8a + 2$

PROBLEM SET 6.3

1. $(2x + 1)(x + 3)$ **3.** $(2a - 3)(a + 1)$
5. $(3x + 5)(x - 1)$ **7.** $(3y + 1)(y - 5)$
9. $(2x + 3)(3x + 2)$ **11.** $(2x - 3y)^2$
13. $(4y + 1)(y - 3)$ **15.** $(4x - 5)(5x - 4)$
17. $(10a - b)(2a + 5b)$ **19.** $(4x - 5)(5x + 1)$
21. $(6m - 1)(2m + 3)$ **23.** $(4x + 5)(5x + 3)$
25. $(3a - 4b)(4a - 3b)$ **27.** $(3x - 7y)(x + 2y)$
29. $(2x + 5)(7x - 3)$ **31.** $(3x - 5)(2x - 11)$
33. $(5t - 19)(3t - 2)$ **35.** $2(2x + 3)(x - 1)$
37. $2(4a - 3)(3a - 4)$ **39.** $-1(3x + 2)(x - 5)$
41. $-2(2x + 1)(3x - 4)$ **43.** $x(5x - 4)(2x - 3)$
45. $x^2(3x + 2)(2x - 5)$ **47.** $2a(5a + 2)(a - 1)$
49. $3x(5x + 1)(x - 7)$ **51.** $5y(7y + 2)(y - 2)$
53. $a^2(5a + 1)(3a - 1)$ **55.** $3y(2x - 3)(4x + 5)$
57. $2y(2x - y)(3x - 7y)$ **59.** Both equal 25.
61. $4x^2 - 9$ **63.** $x^4 - 81$
65. $h = -2(t - 4)(8t + 1)$

Time t (seconds)	0	1	2	3	4
Height h (feet)	8	54	68	50	0

67. a. $V = x(11 - 2x)(9 - 2x)$ **b.** 11 inches $\times$ 9 inches
69. d **71.** b **73.** $x^2 - 16$ **75.** $25x^2 - 36y^2$
77. $x^4 - 81$ **79.** $x^2 - 8x + 16$ **81.** $9x^2 - 6xy + y^2$

83. $25x^2 - 60xy + 36y^2$
85. a. -1 **b.** -8 **c.** -27 **d.** -64 **e.** -125
87. a. $x^3 + 2x^2 + 4x$ **b.** $-2x^2 - 4x - 8$ **c.** $x^3 - 8$
89. a. $x^3 + 3x^2 + 9x$ **b.** $-3x^2 - 9x - 27$ **c.** $x^3 - 27$

PROBLEM SET 6.4

1. $(x - 1)^2$ **3.** $(x + 1)^2$ **5.** $(a - 5)^2$ **7.** $(y + 2)^2$
9. $(x - 2)^2$ **11.** $(m - 6)^2$ **13.** $(2a + 3)^2$ **15.** $(7x - 1)^2$
17. $(3y - 5)^2$ **19.** $(x + 5y)^2$ **21.** $(3a + b)^2$
23. $3(a + 3)^2$ **25.** $2(x + 5y)^2$ **27.** $5x(x + 3y)^2$
29. $(x + 3)(x - 3)$ **31.** $(a + 6)(a - 6)$
33. $(x + 7)(x - 7)$ **35.** $4(a + 2)(a - 2)$
37. Cannot be factored.   **39.** $(5x + 13)(5x - 13)$
41. $(3a + 4b)(3a - 4b)$ **43.** $(3 + m)(3 - m)$
45. $(5 + 2x)(5 - 2x)$ **47.** $2(x + 3)(x - 3)$
49. $(x - y)(x^2 + xy + y^2)$ **51.** $(a + 2)(a^2 - 2a + 4)$
53. $(3 + x)(9 - 3x + x^2)$ **55.** $(y - 1)(y^2 + y + 1)$
57. $(4 - y)(16 + 4y + y^2)$ **59.** $(5h - t)(25h^2 + 5ht + t^2)$
61. $(x - 6)(x^2 + 6x + 36)$ **63.** $2(y - 3)(y^2 + 3y + 9)$
65. $(4 + 3a)(16 - 12a + 9a^2)$
67. $(2x - 3y)(4x^2 + 6xy + 9y^2)$
69. $32(a + 2)(a - 2)$ **71.** $2y(2x + 3)(2x - 3)$
73. $2(a - 4b)(a^2 + 4ab + 16b^2)$
75. $2(x + 6y)(x^2 - 6xy + 36y^2)$
77. $10(a - 4b)(a^2 + 4ab + 16b^2)$
79. $10(r - 5)(r^2 + 5r + 25)$ **81.** $\left(t + \frac{1}{3}\right)\left(t^2 - \frac{1}{3}t + \frac{1}{9}\right)$
83. $\left(3x - \frac{1}{3}\right)\left(9x^2 + x + \frac{1}{9}\right)$
85. $(4a + 5b)(16a^2 - 20ab + 25b^2)$
87. $\left(\frac{1}{2}x - \frac{1}{3}y\right)\left(\frac{1}{4}x^2 + \frac{1}{6}xy + \frac{1}{9}y^2\right)$
89. $(a^2 + b^2)(a + b)(a - b)$
91. $(4m^2 + 9)(2m + 3)(2m - 3)$
93. $3xy\,(x + 5y)(x - 5y)$
95. $(a - b)(a^2 + ab + b^2)(a + b)(a^2 - ab + b^2)$
97. $(2x - y)(4x^2 + 2xy + y^2)(2x + y)(4x^2 - 2xy + y^2)$
99. $(x - 5y)(x^2 + 5xy + 25y^2)(x + 5y)(x^2 - 5xy + 25y^2)$
101. $(x + 3 + y)(x + 3 - y)$ **103.** $(x + y + 3)(x + y - 3)$
105. 14   **107.** 25
109. a. $x^2 - 16$ **b.** $(x + 4)(x - 4)$
c.

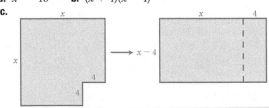

111. $a^2 - b^2 = (a + b)(a - b)$ **113.** c   **115.** b
117. $2x^5 - 8x^3$ **119.** $3x^4 - 18x^3 + 27x^2$
121. $y^3 + 25y$ **123.** $15a^2 - a - 2$
125. $4x^4 - 12x^3 - 40x^2$ **127.** $2ab^5 - 8ab^4 + 2ab^3$

PROBLEM SET 6.5

1. $(x + 9)(x - 9)$ **3.** $(x + 5)(x - 3)$ **5.** $(x + 3)^2$
7. $(y - 5)^2$ **9.** $2ab(a^2 + 3a + 1)$
11. Cannot be factored.   **13.** $3(2a + 5)(2a - 5)$
15. $(3x - 2y)^2$ **17.** $4x(x^2 + 4y^2)$ **19.** $2y(y + 5)^2$
21. $a^4(a^2 + 4b^2)$ **23.** $(x + 4)(y + 3)$
25. $(x^2 + 4)(x + 2)(x - 2)$ **27.** $(x + 2)(y - 5)$
29. $5(a + b)^2$ **31.** $(4 + x)(16 - 4x + x^2)$

33. $3(x + 2y)(x + 3y)$ **35.** $(2x + 19)(x - 2)$
37. $100(x - 2)(x - 1)$ **39.** $(x + 8)(x - 8)$
41. $(x + a)(x + 3)$ **43.** $a^5(7a + 3)(7a - 3)$
45. Cannot be factored.   **47.** $a(5a + 1)(5a + 3)$
49. $(x + y)(a - b)$ **51.** $3a^2b(4a + 1)(4a - 1)$
53. $5x^2(x - 2)(x^2 + 2x + 4)$ **55.** $(3x + 41y)(x - 2y)$
57. $2x^3(2x - 3)(4x - 5)$ **59.** $(2x + 3)(x + a)$
61. $(y^2 + 1)(y + 1)(y - 1)$ **63.** $3x^2y^2(2x + 3y)^2$
65. c   **67.** a   **69.** 5   **71.** $-\frac{3}{2}$ **73.** $-\frac{3}{4}$

PROBLEM SET 6.6

1. $-2, 1$ **3.** $4, 5$ **5.** $0, -1, 3$ **7.** $-\frac{2}{3}, -\frac{3}{2}$
9. $0, -\frac{4}{3}, \frac{4}{3}$ **11.** $0, -\frac{1}{3}, -\frac{3}{5}$ **13.** $-1, -2$ **15.** $4, 5$
17. $6, -4$ **19.** $2, 3$ **21.** -3 **23.** $4, -4$ **25.** $\frac{3}{2}, -4$
27. $-\frac{2}{3}$ **29.** 5 **31.** $4, -\frac{5}{2}$ **33.** $\frac{5}{3}, -4$ **35.** $\frac{7}{2}, -\frac{7}{2}$
37. $0, -6$ **39.** $0, 3$ **41.** $0, 4$ **43.** $0, 5$ **45.** $2, 5$
47. $\frac{1}{2}, -\frac{4}{3}$ **49.** $4, -\frac{5}{2}$ **51.** $8, -10$ **53.** $5, 8$
55. $6, 8$ **57.** -4 **59.** $5, 8$ **61.** $6, -8$
63. $0, -\frac{3}{2}, -4$ **65.** $0, 3, -\frac{5}{2}$ **67.** $0, \frac{1}{2}, -\frac{5}{2}$
69. $0, \frac{3}{5}, -\frac{3}{2}$ **71.** $\frac{1}{2}, \frac{3}{2}$ **73.** $-5, 4$ **75.** $-7, -6$
77. $-3, -1$ **79.** $2, 3$ **81.** $-15, 10$ **83.** $-5, 3$
85. $-3, -2, 2$ **87.** $-4, -1, 4$
89. a. $-4, \frac{1}{2}$ **b.** $(x + 4)(2x - 1)$ **c.** $-3, -\frac{1}{2}$ **d.** $\frac{4}{9}$
91. b   **93.** $x(x + 1) = 72$ **95.** $x(x + 2) = 99$
97. $x(x + 2) = 5[x + (x + 2)] - 10$
99. Bicycle $75, suit $15   **101.** House $2,400, lot $600

PROBLEM SET 6.7

1. 8, 10 and $-10, -8$ **3.** 9, 11 and $-11, -9$
5. 8, 10 and 0, 2   **9.** 2, 12 and $-\frac{12}{5}, -10$
11. 5, 20 and 0, 0   **13.** Width 3 inches, length 4 inches
15. Base 3 inches   **17.** 6 inches and 8 inches
19. 12 meters   **21.** 2 hundred items or 5 hundred items
23. $7 or $10   **25. a.** 5 feet   **b.** 12 feet
27. a. 25 seconds later
b.

t	h
0	100
5	1680
10	2460
15	2440
20	1620
25	0

29. a   **31.** d   **33.** $(-2, 2), (0, 3), (2, 4)$
35.

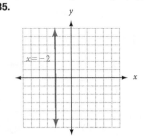

37. 2   **39.** $y = \frac{1}{2}x + 2$ **41.** $y = 2x + 1$

CHAPTER 6 TEST

1. $6(x + 3)$ **2.** $4ab(3a - 6 + 2b)$
3. $(x - 2b)(x + 3a)$ **4.** $(5y - 4)(3 - x)$
5. $(x + 4)(x - 3)$ **6.** $(x - 7)(x + 3)$
7. $(x + 5)(x - 5)$ **8.** $(x^2 + 4)(x + 2)(x - 2)$
9. Cannot be factored.   **10.** $2(3x + 4y)(3x - 4y)$
11. $(x^2 - 3)(x + 4)$ **12.** $(x - 3)(x + b)$
13. $2(2x - 5)(x + 1)$ **14.** $(4n - 3)(n + 4)$
15. $(3c - 2)(4c + 3)$ **16.** $3x(2x - 1)(2x + 3)$
17. $(x + 5y)(x^2 - 5xy + 25y^2)$
18. $2(3b - 4)(9b^2 + 12b + 16)$ **19.** $5, -3$ **20.** $3, 4$
21. $5, -5$ **22.** $-2, 7$ **23.** $5, -6$ **24.** $0, 3, -3$
25. $\frac{3}{2}, -4$ **26.** $0, -\frac{5}{3}, 6$ **27.** $6, 12$
28. $4, 6$ or $-4, -2$ **29.** 4 ft, 13 ft   **30.** 6 ft, 8 ft
31. 200 items, 300 items   **32.** $\$3, \$5$

Chapter 7

PROBLEM SET 7.1

1. $-\frac{1}{6}, 0,$ undefined   **3.** $-\frac{5}{4}, -\frac{1}{2},$ undefined   **5.** 0
7. $-2, 3$ **9.** $-\frac{1}{3}, 1$ **11.** Defined for all real numbers
13. $\frac{1}{x - 2}, x \neq 2$ **15.** $\frac{1}{a + 3}, a \neq -3, 3$
17. $\frac{1}{x - 5}, x \neq -5, 5$ **19.** $\frac{(x + 2)(x - 2)}{2}$
21. $\frac{2(x - 5)}{3(x - 2)}, x \neq 2$ **23.** $2, a \neq -2$ **25.** $\frac{5(x - 1)}{4}$
27. $\frac{1}{x - 3}$ **29.** $\frac{1}{x + 3}$ **31.** $\frac{1}{a - 5}$ **33.** $\frac{1}{3x + 2}$
35. $\frac{x + 5}{x + 2}$ **37.** $\frac{2m(m + 2)}{m - 2}$ **39.** $\frac{x - 1}{x - 4}$
41. $\frac{2(2x - 3)}{2x + 3}$ **43.** $\frac{2x - 3}{2x + 3}$ **45.** $\frac{1}{(x^2 + 9)(x - 3)}$
47. $\frac{3x - 5}{(x^2 + 4)(x - 2)}$ **49.** $\frac{2x(7x + 6)}{2x + 1}$ **51.** $\frac{x^2 + xy + y^2}{x + y}$
53. $\frac{x^2 - 2x + 4}{x - 2}$ **55.** $\frac{x^2 - 2x + 4}{x - 1}$ **57.** $\frac{x + 2}{x + 5}$
59. $\frac{x + a}{x + b}$ **61. a.** $x^2 - 16$ **b.** $x^2 - 8x + 16$
c. $4x^3 - 32x^2 + 64x$ **d.** $\frac{x}{4}$ **63.** $\frac{4}{3}$ **65.** $\frac{4}{5}$ **67.** $\frac{8}{1}$
69.

Checks Written	Total Cost	Cost per Check
x	$2.00 + 0.15x$	$\frac{2.00 + 0.15x}{x}$
0	2.00	undefined
5	2.75	0.55
10	3.50	0.35
15	4.25	0.28
20	5	0.25

71. 40.7 miles/hour
73. Sale, 1.31; Kershaw, 1.29; Scherzer, 1.21; Archer, 1.19
75. 0.125 miles/minute   **77.** d   **79.** b
81. $\frac{5}{14}$ **83.** $\frac{9}{10}$ **85.** $(x + 3)(x - 3)$ **87.** $3(x - 3)$
89. $(x - 5)(x + 4)$ **91.** $a(a + 5)$ **93.** $(a - 5)(a + 4)$
95. 11.8

PROBLEM SET 7.2

1. 2 **3.** $\frac{x}{2}$ **5.** $\frac{3}{2}$ **7.** $\frac{1}{2(x - 3)}$ **9.** $\frac{4a(a + 5)}{7(a + 4)}$
11. $\frac{y - 2}{4}$ **13.** $\frac{2(x + 4)}{x - 2}$ **15.** $-\frac{x + 3}{(x - 3)(x + 1)}$
17. 1 **19.** $\frac{y - 5}{(y + 2)(y - 2)}$ **21.** $-\frac{x + 5}{x - 5}$ **23.** 1

25. $\frac{a + 3}{a + 4}$ **27.** $-\frac{2y - 3}{y - 6}$ **29.** $\frac{(x - 1)(x + 5)}{(x + 1)(x - 2)}$
31. $\frac{3}{2}$ **33. a.** $\frac{4}{13}$ **b.** $\frac{x + 1}{x^2 + x + 1}$ **c.** $\frac{x - 2}{x^2 + x + 1}$
d. $\frac{x + 1}{x - 1}$ **35.** $2(x - 3)$ **37.** $(x + 2)(x + 1)$
39. $-2x(x - 5)$ **41.** $\frac{2(x + 5)}{x(y + 5)}$ **43.** $\frac{2x}{x - y}$
45. $\frac{1}{x - 2}$ **47.** $\frac{1}{5}$ **49.** $\frac{1}{100}$ **51.** 2.7 miles
53. 742 miles per hour   **55.** 0.45 miles per hour
57. 8.8 miles per hour   **59.** b   **61.** b   **63.** $\frac{6}{7}$
65. $\frac{11}{35}$ **67.** $-\frac{23}{105}$ **69.** $x^2 + 2x$ **71.** $x^2 - x - 12$
73. $\frac{1}{x - 7}$ **75.** $-\frac{x - 5}{2(x - 4)}$ **77.** $x^2 - x - 20$

PROBLEM SET 7.3

1. $\frac{7}{x}$ **3.** $\frac{4}{a}$ **5.** 1 **7.** $y + 1$ **9.** $x + 2$
11. $x - 2$ **13.** $\frac{6}{x + 6}$ **15.** $5x$ **17.** $x(x - 3)$
19. $2y^2(y + 4)$ **21.** $(a - 2)(a - 4)(a + 3)$
23. $(x + 2)(x + 3)^2$ **25.** $\frac{(y + 2)(y - 2)}{2y}$ **27.** $\frac{2a + 3}{6}$
29. $\frac{7x + 3}{4(x + 1)}$ **31.** $\frac{1}{5}$ **33.** $\frac{1}{3}$ **35.** $\frac{3}{x - 2}$
37. $\frac{4}{a + 3}$ **39.** $\frac{2(x - 10)}{(x + 5)(x - 5)}$ **41.** $\frac{x + 2}{x + 3}$ **43.** $\frac{a + 1}{a + 2}$
45. $\frac{1}{(x + 3)(x + 4)}$ **47.** $\frac{y}{(y + 5)(y + 4)}$ **49.** $\frac{3(x - 1)}{(x + 4)(x + 1)}$
51. $-\frac{4(2x - 1)}{(x - 2)(x + 2)^2}$ **53.** $\frac{1}{3}$ **55. a.** $\frac{2}{27}$ **b.** $\frac{8}{3}$
c. $\frac{11}{18}$ **d.** $\frac{3x + 10}{(x - 2)^2}$ **e.** $\frac{(x + 2)^2}{3x + 10}$ **f.** $\frac{x + 3}{x + 2}$
57.

Number	Reciprocal	Sum	Quotient
x	$\frac{1}{x}$	$1 + \frac{1}{x}$	$\frac{x + 1}{x}$
1	1	2	2
2	$\frac{1}{2}$	$\frac{3}{2}$	$\frac{3}{2}$
3	$\frac{1}{3}$	$\frac{4}{3}$	$\frac{4}{3}$
4	$\frac{1}{4}$	$\frac{5}{4}$	$\frac{5}{4}$

59. $\frac{x + 3}{x + 2}$ **61.** $\frac{x + 2}{x + 3}$ **63.** $\frac{x - 1}{x + 2}$ **65.** $\frac{x + 4}{x + 1}$
67. $x + \frac{2}{x} = \frac{x^2 + 2}{x}$ **69.** $\frac{1}{x} + \frac{1}{2x} = \frac{3}{2x}$ **71.** c
73. c   **75.** $\frac{3}{4}$ **77.** $\frac{3}{2}$ **79.** $2x^3y^3$ **81.** $\frac{x^2y^3}{2}$
83. $x(xy + 1)$ **85.** $\frac{x^2y^2}{2}$ **87.** $\frac{x - 2}{x - 3}$

PROBLEM SET 7.4

1. 6 **3.** $\frac{1}{6}$ **5.** xy^2 **7.** $\frac{xy}{2}$ **9.** $\frac{y}{x}$ **11.** $\frac{a + 1}{a - 1}$
13. $\frac{x + 1}{2(x - 3)}$ **15.** $a - 3$ **17.** $\frac{y + 3}{y + 2}$ **19.** $x + y$
21. $\frac{a + 1}{a}$ **23.** $\frac{1}{x}$ **25.** $\frac{2a + 3}{3a + 4}$ **27.** $\frac{7}{3}, \frac{17}{7}, \frac{41}{17}$
29.

Number	Reciprocal	Quotient	Square
x	$\frac{1}{x}$	$\frac{x}{\frac{1}{x}}$	x^2
1	1	1	1
2	$\frac{1}{2}$	4	4
3	$\frac{1}{3}$	9	9
4	$\frac{1}{4}$	16	16

31.

Number	Reciprocal	Sum	Quotient
x	$\dfrac{1}{x}$	$1 + \dfrac{1}{x}$	$\dfrac{1 + \dfrac{1}{x}}{\dfrac{1}{x}}$
1	1	2	2
2	$\dfrac{1}{2}$	$\dfrac{3}{2}$	3
3	$\dfrac{1}{3}$	$\dfrac{4}{3}$	4
4	$\dfrac{1}{4}$	$\dfrac{5}{4}$	5

33. d **35.** 3 **37.** 0 **39.** Undefined **41.** $-\dfrac{3}{2}$
43. $2x + 15$ **45.** $x^2 - 5x$ **47.** -6 **49.** -2

PROBLEM SET 7.5
1. -3 **3.** 20 **5.** -1 **7.** 5 **9.** -2 **11.** 4
13. 3, 5 **15.** $-8, 1$ **17.** 2 **19.** 1 **21.** 8 **23.** 5
25. $\varnothing$; 2 does not check **27.** 3
29. $\varnothing$; -3 does not check **31.** 0
33. 2; 3 does not check **35.** -4 **37.** -1
39. $-6, -7$ **41.** -1; -3 does not check
43. a. $\dfrac{1}{5}$ **b.** 5 **c.** $\dfrac{25}{3}$ **d.** 3 **e.** $\dfrac{1}{5}, 5$

45. a. $\dfrac{7}{(a - 6)(a + 2)}$ **b.** $\dfrac{a - 5}{a - 6}$ **c.** 7; -1 does not check

47. a **49.** $\dfrac{7}{2}$ **51.** $-3, 2$

PROBLEM SET 7.6
1. 1 **3.** 10 **5.** 40 **7.** $\dfrac{5}{4}$ **9.** $\dfrac{7}{3}$ **11.** 3, -4
13. 4, -4 **15.** 2, -4 **17.** 6, -1 **19.** 16
21. 15 hits **23.** 21 milliliters **25.** 45.5 grams
27. 14.7 inches **29.** 343 miles **31.** d **33.** $\dfrac{1}{3}$
35. 30 **37.** 1 **39.** -3

PROBLEM SET 7.7
1. $\dfrac{1}{4}, \dfrac{3}{4}$ **3.** $\dfrac{2}{3}$ and $\dfrac{3}{2}$ **5.** -2 **7.** 4, 6
9. 16 miles per hour **11.** 300 miles per hour
13. 170 miles per hour; 190 miles per hour
15. 9 miles per hour **17.** 8 miles per hour
19. 36 minutes **21.** 90 minutes **23.** 60 hours
25. $5\dfrac{5}{11}$ minutes **27.** 12 minutes **29.** c **31.** d
33. $y = 15$ **35.** $y = 4$ **37.** $x = \pm 6$ **39.** $K = 18$
41. $K = 5$

PROBLEM SET 7.8
1. Direct, $K = 10$ **3.** Inverse, $K = 40$
5. Direct, $K = \dfrac{4}{3}\pi$ **7.** Inverse, $K = \dfrac{1}{9}$ **9.** $C = Kr^2$
11. $P = \dfrac{K}{V}$ **13.** $R = K\sqrt{n}$ **15.** 8 **17.** -4
19. 2 **21.** 1 **23.** 3 **25.** $\dfrac{5}{9}$ **27.** 60
29. 84 pounds **31.** $\dfrac{735}{2}$ or 367.5 **33.** \$277.50
35. 96 lbs **37.** 12 amperes **39.** c **41.** a
43. $\dfrac{x + 2}{x + 3}$ **45.** $\dfrac{2(x + 5)}{x - 4}$ **47.** $\dfrac{1}{x - 4}$
49. $\dfrac{x + 5}{x - 3}$ **51.** -2 **53.** 24 hours **55.** 24

CHAPTER 7 TEST
1. $\dfrac{1}{15}$ **2.** 0 **3.** 5 **4.** $-4, 3$ **5.** $\dfrac{x + 3}{x - 3}$
6. $\dfrac{3}{a - 4}$ **7.** $\dfrac{3}{2}$ **8.** $(x - 3)(x + 4)$ **9.** $\dfrac{2x - 3}{x + 4}$

10. $(x + 4)(x - 1)$ **11.** $\dfrac{-2}{x - 8}$ **12.** $\dfrac{2(x + 2)}{(x + 4)(x - 4)}$
13. $\dfrac{2}{(x + 3)(x - 1)}$ **14.** $\dfrac{x + 2}{x - 2}$ **15.** $\dfrac{x + 3}{x + 2}$ **16.** $\dfrac{6}{5}$
17. $-\dfrac{7}{6}$ **18.** -14 **19.** $\dfrac{1}{3}, \dfrac{1}{4}$ **20.** 102 **21.** 15 mph
22. 24 hours **23.** 54 **24.** 2

Chapter 8

PROBLEM SET 8.1
1. 3 **3.** $-\dfrac{4}{3}$ **5.** 7,000 **7.** -3 **9.** $-1, 6$
11. $-\dfrac{4}{3}, 0, \dfrac{4}{3}$ **13.** $-5, 1$ **15.** $0, -3, \dfrac{3}{2}$ **17.** $-3, -\dfrac{3}{2}, \dfrac{3}{2}$
19. a. $\dfrac{5}{8}$ **b.** $10x - 8$ **c.** $16x^2 - 34x + 15$ **d.** $\dfrac{3}{2}, \dfrac{5}{8}$
21. a. $\dfrac{25}{9}$ **b.** $-\dfrac{5}{3}, \dfrac{5}{3}$ **c.** $-3, 3$ **d.** $\dfrac{5}{3}$ **23.** $-\dfrac{9}{2}$
25. 0, 2, 3 **27.** $-\dfrac{7}{640}$ **29.** $\dfrac{7}{10}$ **31.** 24 **33.** $\dfrac{46}{15}$
35. $-2, \dfrac{5}{3}$ **37.** $-3, 0$ **39.** 5 **41.** 4 **43.** 6,000
45. $-4, -2$ **47.** No solution **49.** No solution
51. All real numbers **53.** 30,000 **55.** d **57.** a
59. -3 **61.** 15 **63.** No solution **65.** 6
67. 3 **69.** -3
71. The distance between x and 0 on the number line.
73. -5 **75.** 5 **77.** 7 **79.** 9 **81.** 6
83. $2x - 3$ **85.** $-3, 0, 2$

PROBLEM SET 8.2
1. $-4, 4$ **3.** $-2, 2$ **5.** $\varnothing$ **7.** $-1, 1$ **9.** $\varnothing$
11. $\dfrac{17}{3}, \dfrac{7}{3}$ **13.** $-\dfrac{5}{2}, \dfrac{5}{6}$ **15.** $-1, 5$ **17.** $\varnothing$
19. $-4, 20$ **21.** $-4, 8$ **23.** 1, 4 **25.** $-\dfrac{1}{7}, \dfrac{9}{7}$
27. $-3, 12$ **29.** -4 **31.** $\dfrac{2}{3}, -\dfrac{10}{3}$ **33.** $\varnothing$
35. $\dfrac{3}{2}, -1$ **37.** $-\dfrac{2}{3}$ **39.** 5, 25 **41.** $-30, 26$
43. $-12, 28$ **45.** $-2, 0$ **47.** $-\dfrac{1}{2}, \dfrac{7}{6}$ **49.** 0, 15
51. $-\dfrac{23}{7}, -\dfrac{11}{7}$ **53.** $-5, \dfrac{3}{5}$ **55.** $1, \dfrac{1}{9}$ **57.** $-\dfrac{1}{2}$
59. 0 **61.** $-\dfrac{1}{6}, -\dfrac{7}{4}$ **63.** All real numbers
65. All real numbers **67.** $-\dfrac{3}{10}, \dfrac{3}{2}$ **69.** $-\dfrac{1}{10}, -\dfrac{3}{5}$
71. a. $\dfrac{5}{4} = 1.25$ **b.** $\dfrac{5}{4} = 1.25$ **c.** 2 **d.** $\dfrac{1}{2}, 2$ **e.** $\dfrac{1}{3}, 4$
73. 1987 and 1995 **75.** b **77.** c
79.
81.
83.
85.
87. $x > 4$ **89.** $x \le -\dfrac{11}{3}$ **91.** $x \le 4$ **93.** x^{10}
95. $\dfrac{4b^8}{a^6}$ **97.** $1125x^{17}y^{14}$ **99.** 3.59×10^{-2}
101. 0.025 **103.** 4×10^{13}

PROBLEM SET 8.3

1. $\{x \mid x < 6\}, (-\infty, 6)$

3. $\{x \mid x \geq -1\}, [-1, \infty)$

5. $\left\{x \mid x > \frac{3}{2}\right\}, \left(\frac{3}{2}, \infty\right)$

7. $\left\{x \mid x \leq -\frac{5}{4}\right\}, \left(-\infty, -\frac{5}{4}\right]$

9. $(-\infty, -3]$ **11.** $(20, \infty)$ **13.** $\left(-\infty, \frac{1}{2}\right)$ **15.** $\left[-\frac{17}{4}, \infty\right)$

17. $\{1, 2, 3, 4, 5, 6\}$ **19.** $\{2, 4, 5, 6, 7, 8\}$ **21.** $(1, \infty)$

23. $(-\infty, -3]$ **25.** $(-\infty, -7) \cup (7, \infty)$ **27.** $(-\infty, \infty)$

29. $\varnothing$ **31.** $\{6, 8\}$ **32.** $\varnothing$ **33.** $(6, \infty)$

35. $(-\infty, -4)$ **37.** $\varnothing$ **39.** $\left(-2, \frac{3}{5}\right]$

41. $(-\infty, \infty)$

43. $[-9, \infty)$

45. $(-\infty, 7)$

47. $[-5, \infty)$

49. $(-\infty, -7] \cup [-3, \infty)$

51. $(-\infty, -1] \cup \left[\frac{3}{5}, \infty\right)$

53. $(-\infty, \infty)$

55. $(-10, \infty)$

57. $\left[-\frac{25}{2}, \infty\right)$

59. $[-3, \infty)$

61. $(1, 3)$

63. $[-3, \infty)$

65. $(2, \infty)$

67. $\varnothing$ **69.** $[-4, -2]$

71. $\left(-\frac{1}{4}, \frac{3}{4}\right)$

73. $\left[\frac{4}{3}, \infty\right)$

75. $\left(-\frac{27}{5}, 16\right)$

77. $[-1, 40)$

79. $[3, 7]$ **81.** $(-4, 2)$ **83.** $[4, 6]$ **85.** $(-4, 2)$

87. $(-3, 3)$ **89.** $-2 < x \leq 4$ **91.** $x < -4$ or $x \geq 1$

93. a. $35° \leq C \leq 45°$ **b.** $20° \leq C \leq 30°$
c. $-25° \leq C \leq -10°$ **d.** $-20° \leq C \leq -5°$

95. Eggs to hatching: $0.7 \leq r \leq 0.8$; Hatching to fledgling: $0.5 \leq r \leq 0.7$; Fledglings to first breeding: $r < 0.5$

97. c   **99.** d   **101.** $1 < x$ **103.** $a \leq \frac{2}{3}$ **105.** $t \geq 3$

107. x-intercept $= -\frac{8}{3}$; y-intercept $= 4$; slope $= \frac{3}{2}$

109. $y = 2x + 5$ **111.** $y = \frac{2}{5}x - 5$

PROBLEM SET 8.4

1. $(-3, 3)$ **3.** $(-\infty, -2] \cup [2, \infty)$ **5.** $(-3, 3)$

7. $(-\infty, -7) \cup (7, \infty)$ **9.** $\varnothing$

11. All real numbers, $(-\infty, \infty)$ **13.** $(-4, 10)$

15. $(-\infty, -9] \cup [-1, \infty)$ **17.** $\varnothing$

19. All real numbers, $(-\infty, \infty)$ **21.** $\varnothing$

23. $-1 < x < 5$

25. $y \leq -5$ or $y \geq -1$

27. $k \leq -5$ or $k \geq 2$

29. $-1 < x < 7$

31. $a \leq -2$ or $a \geq 1$

33. $-6 < x < \frac{8}{3}$

35. $\varnothing$ **37.** $[-2, 8]$ **39.** $\left(-2, \frac{4}{3}\right)$

41. $(-\infty, -5] \cup [-3, \infty)$ **43.** $\left(-\infty, -\frac{7}{2}\right) \cup \left(-\frac{3}{2}, \infty\right)$

45. $\left[-1, \frac{11}{5}\right]$ **47.** $\left(\frac{5}{3}, 3\right)$

49. $x < 2$ or $x > 8$

51. $x \leq -3$ or $x \geq 12$

53. $x < 2$ or $x > 6$

55. $0.99 < x < 1.01$ **57.** $x \leq -\frac{3}{5}$ or $x \geq -\frac{2}{5}$

59. $\frac{5}{9} \leq x \leq \frac{7}{9}$ **61.** $x < -\frac{2}{3}$ or $x > 0$

63. $x \leq \frac{2}{3}$ or $x \geq 2$ **65.** $-\frac{1}{6} \leq x \leq \frac{3}{2}$

67. $-0.05 < x < 0.25$ **69.** $|x| \leq 4$ **71.** $|x - 5| \leq 1$

73. a. 3 **b.** $\left\{-2, \frac{4}{5}\right\}$ **c.** no **d.** $x < -2$ or $x > \frac{4}{5}$

75. $|x - 65| \le 10$ **77.** d   **79.** a   **81.** $-2x$

83. $x = 2y + 6$ **85.** 2   **87.** $(1, 2)$

89. $-5x^2 - 31x + 28$ **91.** $9a^8 - 42a^4 + 49$

93. $3x^3 - 17x^2 - 28x$ **95.** $6x^2 + 3xy - 4y^2$

97. $(x - 1)(x - 5)$ **99.** $(3x + 2y)(3x - 2y)(9x^2 + 4y^2)$

101. $\left(y - \frac{1}{3}\right)\left(y^2 + \frac{1}{3}y + \frac{1}{9}\right)$

PROBLEM SET 8.5

1.

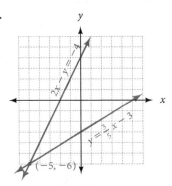

3.

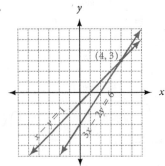

5.

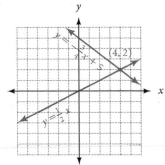

7. Lines are parallel; no solution

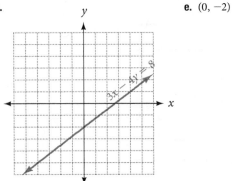

9. $\left(\frac{4}{3}, 1\right)$ **11.** $\left(1, -\frac{1}{2}\right)$ **13.** $\left(\frac{1}{2}, -3\right)$ **15.** $\left(-\frac{8}{3}, 5\right)$

17. $(2, 2)$ **19.** $\varnothing$ **21.** $(10, 24)$ **23.** $\left(-\frac{32}{7}, -\frac{50}{21}\right)$

25. $(3, -3)$ **27.** $\left(\frac{4}{3}, -2\right)$ **29.** $(2, 4)$

31. Lines coincide: $\{(x, y) \mid 2x - y = 5\}$

33. Lines coincide; $\left\{(x, y) \mid x = \frac{3}{2}y\right\}$

35. $\left(-\frac{15}{43}, -\frac{27}{43}\right)$ **37.** $\left(\frac{60}{43}, \frac{46}{43}\right)$ **39.** $\left(\frac{9}{41}, -\frac{11}{41}\right)$

41. $\left(-\frac{11}{7}, -\frac{20}{7}\right)$ **43.** $\left(2, \frac{4}{3}\right)$ **45.** $(-12, -12)$

47. Lines are parallel; $\varnothing$ **49.** $y = 5, z = 2$ **51.** $\left(\frac{3}{2}, \frac{3}{8}\right)$

53. $\left(-4, -\frac{8}{3}\right)$ **55. a.** $-y$ **b.** -2 **c.** -2

d.   **e.** $(0, -2)$

57. $(6{,}000, 4{,}000)$ **59.** $(4, 0)$ **61.** c   **63.** d

65. -10 **67.** $3y + 2z$ **69.** 1   **71.** 3   **73.** $10x - 2z$

75. $9x + 3y - 6z$ **77.** $\frac{2}{3a}$ **79.** $(x - 3)(x + 2)$

81. 1   **83.** $\frac{3 - x}{x + 3}$

PROBLEM SET 8.6

1. a. No **b.** Yes   **3.** $(1, 2, 1)$ **5.** $(2, 1, 3)$ **7.** $(2, 0, 1)$

9. $\left(\frac{1}{2}, \frac{2}{3}, -\frac{1}{2}\right)$ **11.** No solution, inconsistent system

13. $(4, -3, -5)$ **15.** No unique solution

17. $(4, -5, -3)$ **19.** No unique solution   **21.** $\left(\frac{1}{2}, 1, 2\right)$

23. $\left(\frac{1}{2}, \frac{1}{3}, \frac{1}{4}\right)$ **25.** $\left(\frac{10}{3}, -\frac{5}{3}, -\frac{1}{3}\right)$ **27.** $\left(\frac{1}{4}, -\frac{1}{3}, \frac{1}{8}\right)$

29. $(6, 8, 12)$ **31.** $(-141, -210, -104)$

33. 4 amp, 3 amp, 1 amp   **35.** c   **37.** b   **39.** $2 + 3x$

41. $-\frac{160}{9}$ **43.** 320   **45.** $2x + 5y$ **47.** 6

49. $y = -1, z = 5$ **51.** $-\frac{3}{2}$ **53.** $-3, \frac{1}{2}$ **55.** $\frac{5}{4}$ or $\frac{4}{5}$

PROBLEM SET 8.7

1. 5, 13   **3.** 1, 3, 4

5. 225 adult and 700 children's tickets

7. $12,000 at 6%, $8,000 at 7%

9. $200 at 6%, $1,400 at 8%, $600 at 9%

11. 6 ounces of 30%, 4 ounces of 80%

13. 6 liters of 20% acid; 18 liters of 40% acid, 36 liters of 60% acid

15. 10 pounds of $8 beans, 20 pounds of $9 beans, and 20 pounds of $12 beans

17. 12 nickels, 8 dimes   **19.** 3 of each

21. 110 nickels   **23.** $h = -16t^2 + 64t + 80$

25. c   **27.** No   **29.** $(4, 0)$ **31.** $x > 435$

33. $-\frac{1}{2}x + 1$ **35.** $4 + 3x$ **37.** 8   **39.** $-12x - 35$

41. $\frac{25}{4}$ **43.** $0.06x + 48$

PROBLEM SET 8.8

1. 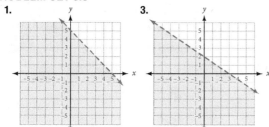   **3.**

5. 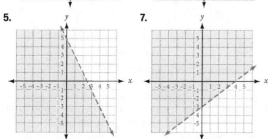   **7.**

9. 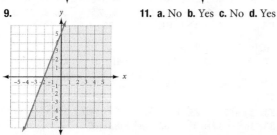   **11. a.** No **b.** Yes **c.** No **d.** Yes

13. 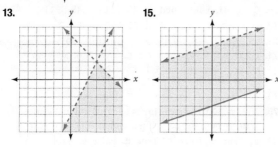   **15.**

17. 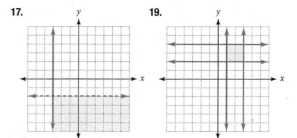   **19.**

21. 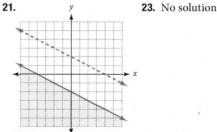   **23.** No solution

25. 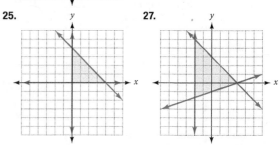   **27.**

29.   **31.**

33. 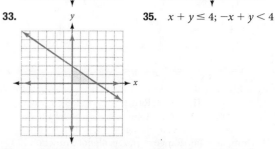   **35.** $x + y \leq 4; -x + y < 4$

37. $x + y \geq 4; -x + y < 4$ **39.** $x \geq -4; x \leq -2$

41. a. $0.55x + 0.65y \leq 40; x \geq 2y; x > 15; y \geq 0$

    b. 10 65-cent stamps

43. d   **45.** c   **47.** -3 **49.** 2   **51.** $(-\infty, 4)$

53. $[-52, \infty)$ **55.** 3, -15 **57.** $-5, 1$

CHAPTER 8 TEST

1. 28   **2.** -3 **3.** $-\frac{7}{4}$ **4.** 2   **5.** $-10, -\frac{1}{2}$

6. 0, 3   **7.** $-6, 3$ **8.** $-5, -3, 3$ **9.** $\{-10, -2\}$

10. $\{2, 6\}$ **11.** $\emptyset$ **12.** $\left\{-\frac{3}{4}, -\frac{1}{6}\right\}$

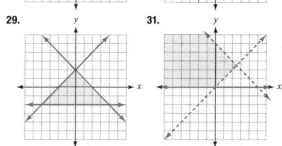

13. {1, 2, 3, 4, 6}   **14.** (−∞, 4]   **15.** {2}   **16.** (−∞, −1)
17. All real numbers   **18.** (−∞, −3)
19. $x < -1$ or $x > \frac{4}{3}$

20. $-\frac{2}{3} \le x \le 4$

21. All real numbers

22. ∅   **23.** lines coincide: {(x, y) | 2x + 4y = 3}

24. (3, 2)   **25.** (1, 2)
26. No solution, inconsistent system   **27.** (3, −2, 1)
28. $\left(\frac{5}{11}, -\frac{15}{11}, -\frac{1}{11}\right)$ **29.** No solution, inconsistent system
30. $4,000 at 5%; $8,000 at 6%
31. 4 gallons of 30%, 12 gallons of 70%
32. 11 nickels, 3 dimes, 1 quarter
33.   **34.**

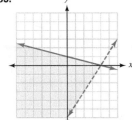
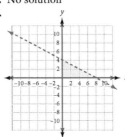

35.   **36.** No solution
37.

Chapter 9

PROBLEM SET 9.1

1. Domain = {1, 3, 5, 7}; Range = {2, 4, 6, 8}, a function
3. Domain = {0, 1, 2, 3}; Range = {4, 5, 6}; a function
5. Domain = {a, b, c, d}; Range = {3, 4, 5}; a function
7. Domain = {a}; Range = {1, 2, 3, 4}; not a function
9. Yes   **11.** No   **13.** No   **15.** Yes   **17.** Yes   **19.** Yes
21. Domain = {x | −3 ≤ x ≤ 1}; Range = {y | −2 ≤ y ≤ 4}
23. Domain = {x | −5 ≤ x ≤ 3}, Range = {y | y = 3}
25. Domain = {x | −5 ≤ x ≤ 5}, Range = {y | 0 ≤ y ≤ 5}
27. Domain = {−4, −3, −1, 0, 2, 5}, Range = {−4, −1, 1, 3, 4}
29. Domain = All real numbers, Range = All real numbers,
A function
31. Domain = {4}, Range = All real numbers,
Not a function

33. Domain = All real numbers, Range = {y | y ≤ 0},
A function
35. Domain = All real numbers, Range = {y | y ≥ −1},
A function
37. Domain = {x | x ≤ 3}, Range = All real numbers;
Not a function
39. a. $y = 8.5x$ for   10 ≤ x ≤ 40
b.

TABLE 7 Weekly Wages		
Hours Worked	Function Rule	Gross Pay ($)
x	y = 8.5x	y
10	y = 8.5(10)	85
20	y = 8.5(20)	170
30	y = 8.5(30)	255
40	y = 8.5(40)	340

c.

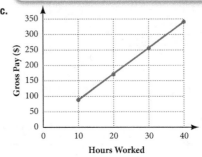

d. Domain = {x | 10 ≤ x ≤ 40};
Range = {y | 85 ≤ y ≤ 340}
e. Minimum = $85; Maximum = $340
41. Domain = {2004, 2005, 2006, 2007, 2008, 2009, 2010};
Range = {680, 730, 800, 900, 920, 990, 1030}
43. a. III **b.** I **c.** II **d.** IV   **45.** b and c   **47.** b
49. 113   **51.** −9   **53. a.** 6 **b.** 7.5   **55. a.** 27 **b.** 6
57. 1   **59.** −3   **61.** $-\frac{6}{5}$ **63.** $-\frac{35}{32}$

PROBLEM SET 9.2

1. (3, 8)   **3.** (−1, 5)   **5.** $f(4) = 0$ **7.** $f(-1) = 9$
9. $f(10) = 0.1$ **11.** $f\left(-\frac{1}{5}\right) = -\frac{1}{10}$ **13.** −1
15. −11   **17.** 2   **19.** 4   **21.** $a^2 + 3a + 4$
23. $2a + 7$ **25.** 1   **27.** −9   **29.** 8   **31.** 0
33. $3a^2 - 4a + 1$ **35.** $3a^2 + 8a + 5$ **37.** $\frac{3}{10}$
39. $\frac{2}{5}$ **41.** Undefined   **43.** −1   **45.** −11   **47.** 99
49. 4   **51.** 0   **53.** 2   **55.** −2   **57.** 2   **59.** 1
61. 15   **63.** −1   **65.** 2   **67.** 0   **69.** −1
71. a. $a^2 - 7$ **b.** $a^2 - 6a + 5$ **c.** $x^2 - 2$ **d.** $x^2 + 4x$
e. $a^2 + 2ab + b^2 - 4$ **f.** $x^2 + 2xh + h^2 - 4$
g. $9x^2 - 4$ **h.** $3x^2 - 12$
73. 1, 4, 9
75. $V(3) = 300$, the painting is worth $300 in 3 years;
$V(6) = 600$, the painting is worth $600 in 6 years.
77. a. True **b.** False **c.** True **d.** False **e.** True

79. a. 3.5 cm **b.** 4 lbs **c.**

81. c **83.** a **85.** $-.1x^2 + 35x$ **87.** $4x^2 - 7x + 3$
89. $-0.1x^2 + 27x - 500$ **91.** $2x^2 + 8x + 8$ **93.** 10

PROBLEM SET 9.3

1. 15 **3.** 98 **5.** $\frac{3}{2}$ **7.** 1 **9.** 40 **11.** 147
13. $6x + 2$ **15.** $-2x + 8$ **17.** $8x^2 + 14x - 15$
19. $\frac{2x + 5}{4x - 3}$ **21.** $4x - 7$ **23.** $3x^2 - 10x + 8$
25. $-2x + 3$ **27.** $3x^2 - 11x + 10$
29. $9x^3 - 48x^2 + 85x - 50$ **31.** $x - 2$
33. $\frac{1}{x - 2}$ **35.** $3x^2 - 7x + 3$ **37.** $6x^2 - 22x + 20$
39. a. 17 **b.** $x^2 + 7x - 1$ **c.** 17
41. a. 48 **b.** $15x^2 + 2x - 8$ **c.** 48
43. -3 **45.** 38 **47.** 81 **49.** 6
51. a. 81 **b.** 29 **c.** $(x + 4)^2$ **d.** $x^2 + 4$
53. a. -2 **b.** -1 **c.** $16x^2 + 4x - 2$ **d.** $4x^2 + 12x - 1$
55. $(f \circ g)(x) = 5\left[\frac{x + 4}{5}\right] - 4$
$$= x + 4 - 4$$
$$= x$$
$$(g \circ f)(x) = \frac{(5x - 4) + 4}{5}$$
$$= \frac{5x}{5}$$
$$= x$$
57. -6 **59.** -5 **61.** 12 **63.** $-\frac{1}{2}$ **65.** 0
67. -4 **69.** 5 **71.** 3 **73.** -3 **75.** 0
77. $\frac{1}{4}$ **79.** 4 **81.** 1 **83.** 3
85. a. $R(x) = 11.5x - 0.05x^2$ **b.** $C(x) = 2x + 200$
 c. $P(x) = -0.05x^2 + 9.5x - 200$ **d.** $\overline{C}(x) = 2 + \frac{200}{x}$
87. a. $M(x) = 220 - x$ **b.** $M(24) = 196$ **c.** 142
 d. 135 **e.** 128
89. c **91.** d **93.** -1 **95.** 2 **97.** $y = mx + b$
99. $y = -2x - 5$ **101.** 5

PROBLEM SET 9.4

1. $\frac{2}{3}$ **3.** Undefined slope **5.** Slope $= \frac{3}{2}$ **7.** Slope $= -\frac{3}{2}$
9. Slope $= 0$ **11.** $a = 5$
13. $m = -\frac{2}{3}$

x	y
0	2
3	0

15. $m = \frac{2}{3}$

x	y
0	-5
3	-3

17. $m = \frac{2}{3}$ **19.** Undefined **21.** $\frac{1}{5}$ **23.** $-\frac{3}{2}$
25. a. Yes **b.** No **27.** $y = -4x - 3$ **29.** $y = \frac{3}{4}$

31. a. 3 **b.** $-\frac{1}{3}$ **33. a.** $-\frac{2}{5}$ **b.** $\frac{5}{2}$
35. Slope $= 3$, y-intercept $= -2$, perpendicular slope $= -\frac{1}{3}$
37. Slope $= \frac{2}{3}$, y-intercept $= -4$, perpendicular slope $= -\frac{3}{2}$
39. Slope $= \frac{1}{2}$, y-intercept $= -4$, $y = \frac{1}{2}x - 4$
41. $y = 2x - 1$ **43.** $y = -3x + 3$ **45.** $y = 6$
47. $3x + 5y = -1$ **49.** $x - 12y = -8$ **51.** $y = 2$
53. $(0, -4), (2, 0); y = 2x - 4$
55. $(-2, 0), (0, 4); y = 2x + 4$
57. a. $x:\frac{10}{3}, y: -5$ **b.** (4, 1), answers may vary
 c. $y = \frac{3}{2}x - 5$ **d.** no
59. a. Slope $= \frac{1}{2}$; x-intercept $= 0$; y-intercept $= 0$
 b. Undefined slope; x-intercept $= 3$; y-intercept $=$ none
 c. Slope $= 0$; x-intercept $=$ none; y-intercept $= -2$
61. $3x - y = -7$ **63.** $x - 4y = -1$ **65.** $2x + 3y = 6$
67. a. 2 **b.** $\frac{3}{2}$ **c.** -3
 d.

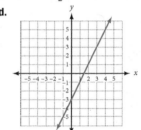

 e. $y = 2x - 3$
69. 4 **71.** $f(x) = -\frac{1}{3}x + 2$
73. 17.5 mph **75. a.** 10 minutes
 b. 20 minutes **c.** 20°C per minute **d.** 10°C per minute
 e. 1st minute
77. a. 0.05 watts/lumen gained. For every additional lumen, the incandescent light bulb needs to use on average an extra .05 watts.
 b. .014 watts/lumen gained. For every additional lumen, the energy effcient light bulb needs to use on average an extra .014 watts.
 c. Energy efficient light bulb. Answers may vary.
79. a. Answers will vary **b.** 86°
81. a. 12 cm **b.** 18 cm **c.** 400 g
 d.

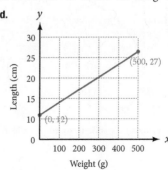

83. a. $s = 1.4w$ **b.** 15.4 cm

85. a. $190,000 **b.** $19 **c.** $6.50

87. b **89.** d **91.** 196 **93.** 4 **95.** 1.6 **97.** 3

99. 2,400

PROBLEM SET 9.5

1. Inverse, $K = 3$ **3.** Direct, $K = 2\pi$ **5.** Joint, $K = \frac{1}{2}$

7. Direct, $K = 0.5$ **9.** $z = K\sqrt{x}$ **11.** $F = \frac{Km^2}{d}$

13. $A = Kh(a + b)$ **15.** 30 **17.** -6 **19.** 40

21. $\frac{81}{5}$ **23.** 64 **25.** 108 **27.** 300 **29.** ± 2

31. 1600 **33.** ± 8 **35.** $\frac{50}{7}$ pounds

37. a. $T = 4P$ **b.**

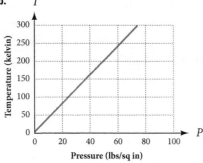

c. 70 pounds per square inch

39. 12 pounds per square inch

41. a. $f = \frac{80}{d}$ **b.**

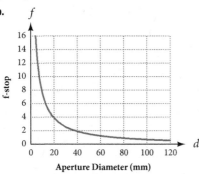

c. An f-stop of 8

43. $\frac{1504}{15}$ square inches **45.** 1.5 ohms

47. a. $P = 0.21\sqrt{L}$ **b.**

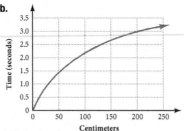

c. 3.15 seconds

49. d **51.** a **53.** 12 **55.** 28 **57.** $-\frac{7}{4}$

59. $w = \frac{P - 2\ell}{2}$ **61.** $[-6, \infty)$ **63.** $(-\infty, 6)$ **65.** 6, 2

67. $\varnothing$

CHAPTER 9 TEST

1. domain $= \{-3, -2\}$, range $= \{0, 1\}$, not a function

2. domain $=$ all real numbers, range $= \{y | y \geq -9\}$, is a function

3. 11 **4.** $3x^2 - 5x - 12$ **5.** 8 **6.** $9x^2 - 6x - 20$

7. x-intercept $= 3$, **8.** x-intercept $= -\frac{3}{2}$,
y-intercept $= 6$, y-intercept $= -3$,
slope $= -2$ slope $= -2$

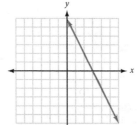
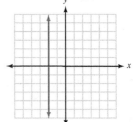

9. x-intercept $= -\frac{8}{3}$, **10.** x-intercept $= -2$,
y-intercept $= 4$, no y-intercept,
slope $= \frac{3}{2}$ Undefined slope

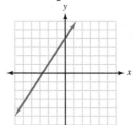

11. $y = -\frac{3}{7}x + \frac{5}{7}$ **12.** $x = 4$ **13.** $y = \frac{2}{5}x - 5$

14. $y = -\frac{1}{3}x - \frac{7}{3}$ **15.** $y = 2x + 5$ **16.** 18 **17.** $\frac{81}{4}$

18. $\frac{2000}{3}$ pounds

Chapter 10

PROBLEM SET 10.1

1. 12 **3.** Not a real number **5.** -7 **7.** -3

9. 3 **11.** -2 **13.** 0.2 **15.** 0.2 **17.** $\frac{1}{6}$

19. $\frac{1}{2}$ **21.** 5 **23.** 2 **25.** 10 **27.** $7x$

29. $6a^4$ **31.** $3a^4$ **33.** xy^2 **35.** $2x^2y$ **37.** $2a^3b^5$

39. a. 5 **b.** 0.5 **c.** 50 **d.** 0.05 **41. a.** $4a^2b^4$ **b.** $2ab^2$

43.

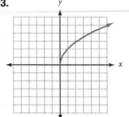

45.

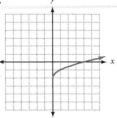

47. 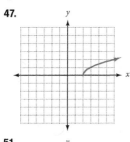   **49.**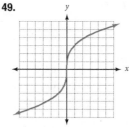

51. 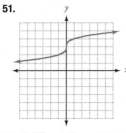   **53.**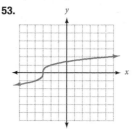

55. $\{x \mid x \ge -3\}$ **57.** $\{x \mid x \ge 0\}$ **59.** $\{x \mid x \ge 5\}$
61. $\{x \mid x \le 5\}$ **63., 65.** $\{x \mid x \text{ is any real number}\}$
67. a. 420 picometers **b.** 594.0 picometers
   c. 5.94×10^{-10} meters
71. b   **73.** c   **75.** 5   **77.** $4x^2y$ **79.** 3
81. $2ab$ **83.** -25 **85.** $\frac{1}{25}$ **87.** x^7 **89.** x^3

PROBLEM SET 10.2

1. 6   **3.** -3 **5.** 2   **7.** -2 **9.** 2   **11.** $\frac{9}{5}$
13. $\frac{4}{5}$ **15.** $5^{1/2}$ **17.** $(3x)^{1/2}$ **19.** $9^{1/3}$ **21.** $(4x^2)^{1/3}$
23. 9   **25.** 125   **27.** 8   **29.** $\frac{1}{3}$ **31.** $\frac{1}{27}$
33. $\frac{6}{5}$ **35.** $\frac{8}{27}$ **37.** 7   **39.** $\frac{3}{4}$ **41.** $x^{4/5}$ **43.** $y^{3/4}$
45. a **47.** $\frac{1}{x^{2/5}}$ **49.** $x^{1/6}$ **51.** $x^{9/25}y^{1/2}z^{1/5}$
53. $\frac{b^{7/4}}{a^{1/8}}$ **55.** $y^{3/10}$ **57.** $\frac{1}{x^{5/6}}$ **59.** $\frac{1}{a^2b^4}$ **61.** $5a^3$
63. xy^5 **65.** $3b^3$ **67.** x^2y^7 **69.** $3a^2b^5$
75. 25 mph   **77.** a   **79.** b   **81.** 6   **83.** $5y$
85. 2   **87.** 25   **89.** $48x^4y^2$ **91.** $4x^6y^6$

PROBLEM SET 10.3

1. $2\sqrt{2}$ **3.** $7\sqrt{2}$ **5.** $12\sqrt{2}$ **7.** $4\sqrt{5}$ **9.** $4\sqrt{3}$
11. $15\sqrt{3}$ **13.** $3\sqrt[3]{2}$ **15.** $4\sqrt[3]{2}$ **17.** $6\sqrt[3]{2}$
19. $2\sqrt[5]{2}$ **21.** $3x\sqrt{2x}$ **23.** $2y\sqrt[4]{2y^3}$
25. $2xy^2\sqrt[3]{5xy}$ **27.** $4abc^2\sqrt{3b}$ **29.** $2bc\sqrt[3]{6a^2c}$
31. $2xy^2\sqrt[5]{2x^3y^2}$ **33.** $3xy^2z\sqrt[5]{x^2}$ **35.** $2\sqrt{3}$
37. $\sqrt{-20}$; not real number   **39.** $\frac{\sqrt{11}}{2}$ **41.** $\frac{\sqrt{5}}{2}$
43. $\frac{\sqrt{3}}{2}$ **45.** $2+\sqrt{3}$ **47.** $3+\sqrt{3}$ **49.** $2+\sqrt{3}$
51. $\frac{-2-3\sqrt{3}}{6}$ **53.** $-2-\sqrt{2}$ **55.** $\frac{\sqrt{7}}{5}$ **57.** $\frac{\sqrt{5x}}{6}$
59. $\frac{\sqrt[3]{3}}{4}$ **61.** $\frac{\sqrt[3]{2a}}{b}$ **63.** $\frac{\sqrt[4]{9}}{2}$ **65.** $\sqrt{5}$ **67.** $\sqrt[3]{3}$
69. $\frac{2x\sqrt{3}}{5}$ **71.** $\frac{x\sqrt{3x}}{2y^3}$ **73.** $\frac{b\sqrt[3]{15b}}{2a}$ **75.** $\frac{xy^2\sqrt[4]{9x^2y^2}}{2z^2}$
77. $5|x|$ **79.** $3|xy|\sqrt{3x}$ **81.** $|x-5|$ **83.** $|2x+3|$
85. $2|a(a+2)|$ **87.** $2|x|\sqrt{x-2}$
89. $\sqrt{9+16} \overset{?}{=} \sqrt{9}+\sqrt{16}$
    $\sqrt{25} \overset{?}{=} 3+4$
     $5 \ne 7$
91. $5\sqrt{13}$ feet   **93.** $\sqrt{2}$
95. a. $\sqrt{2}:1 \approx 1.414:1$ **b.** $5:\sqrt{2}$ **c.** $5:4$ **97.** 1.618
103. b   **105.** a   **107.** $7x$ **109.** $27xy^2$ **111.** $\frac{5}{6}x$

113. $3\sqrt{2}$ **115.** $5|y|\sqrt{3xy}$ **117.** $2a\sqrt[3]{ab^2}$

PROBLEM SET 10.4

1. $7\sqrt{5}$ **3.** $-x\sqrt{7}$ **5.** $\sqrt[3]{10}$ **7.** $9\sqrt[5]{6}$ **9.** 0
11. $7\sqrt{2}+3\sqrt{3}$ **13.** $2\sqrt{x}-12\sqrt{y}$
15. $6\sqrt{3}+\sqrt[3]{3}$ **17.** $\sqrt{5}$ **19.** $-32\sqrt{2}$ **21.** $-3x\sqrt{2}$
23. $-2\sqrt[3]{2}$ **25.** $8x\sqrt[3]{xy^2}$ **27.** $3a^2b\sqrt{3ab}$
29. $11ab\sqrt[3]{3a^2b}$ **31.** $10xy\sqrt[4]{3y}$ **33.** $2\sqrt{3}$ **35.** $\frac{2\sqrt{5}}{3}$
37. $-\frac{\sqrt{x}}{6}$ **39.** $\frac{5\sqrt{2}}{6}$ **41.** $(4x+15y)\sqrt{2}$
43. $(4x-3)\sqrt[3]{2}$ **45.** $\sqrt{2}+\sqrt{3} \approx 3.146$; $\sqrt{5} \approx 2.236$
47. $\sqrt{8}+\sqrt{18} \approx 2.828 + 4.243 = 7.071$;
    $\sqrt{50} \approx 7.071$; $\sqrt{26} \approx 5.099$
49. $8\sqrt{2x}$ **51.** 5   **53.** a   **55.** 6
57. $4x^2+3xy-y^2$ **59.** x^2+6x+9
61. x^2-4 **63.** $6\sqrt{2}$ **65.** 6   **67.** $9x$

PROBLEM SET 10.5

1. $3\sqrt{2}$ **3.** $10\sqrt{21}$ **5.** 720   **7.** 54   **9.** $\sqrt{6}-9$
11. $24+6\sqrt[3]{4}$ **13.** $7+2\sqrt{6}$ **15.** $x+2\sqrt{x}-15$
17. $34+20\sqrt{3}$ **19.** $19+8\sqrt{3}$ **21.** $x-6\sqrt{x}+9$
23. $4a-12\sqrt{ab}+9b$ **25.** $x+4\sqrt{x-4}$
27. $x-6\sqrt{x-5}+4$ **29.** 1   **31.** $a-49$
33. $25-x$ **35.** $x-8$ **37.** $10+6\sqrt{3}$
39. $\sqrt{5}$ **41.** $2\sqrt{5}$ **43.** $\sqrt[3]{4}$ **45.** $\frac{\sqrt{2}}{6}$ **47.** $\frac{2x\sqrt{3}}{3}$
49. $11b\sqrt{2}$ **51.** $\frac{2\sqrt{3}}{3}$ **53.** $\frac{5\sqrt{6}}{6}$ **55.** $\frac{\sqrt{2}}{2}$
57. $\frac{\sqrt{5}}{5}$ **59.** $2\sqrt[3]{4}$ **61.** $\frac{2\sqrt{3}}{3}$ **63.** $\frac{\sqrt[3]{24x^2}}{2x}$
65. $\frac{\sqrt[4]{8y^3}}{y}$ **67.** $\frac{\sqrt[3]{36xy^2}}{3y}$ **69.** $\frac{\sqrt[3]{6xy^2}}{3y}$ **71.** $\frac{3x\sqrt{15xy}}{5y}$
73. $\frac{5xy\sqrt{6xz}}{2z}$ **75. a.** $\frac{\sqrt{2}}{2}$ **b.** $\frac{\sqrt[4]{4}}{2}$ **c.** $\frac{\sqrt[4]{8}}{2}$
77. $\sqrt{2}$ **79.** $\frac{8\sqrt{5}}{15}$ **81.** $\frac{(x-1)\sqrt{x}}{x}$ **83.** $\frac{3\sqrt{2}}{2}$
85. $\frac{5\sqrt{6}}{6}$ **87.** $\frac{8\sqrt[3]{25}}{5}$ **89.** $\frac{\sqrt{3}+1}{2}$ **91.** $\frac{5-\sqrt{5}}{4}$
93. $\frac{x+3\sqrt{x}}{x-9}$ **95.** $\frac{10+3\sqrt{5}}{11}$ **97.** $\frac{3\sqrt{x}+3\sqrt{y}}{x-y}$
99. $2+\sqrt{3}$ **101.** $\frac{11-4\sqrt{7}}{3}$

103. a. $2\sqrt{x}$ **b.** $x-4$ **c.** $x+4\sqrt{x}+4$ **d.** $\frac{x+4\sqrt{x}+4}{x-4}$
105. a. $\sqrt{6}+2\sqrt{2}$ **b.** $2+2\sqrt{3}$ **c.** $1+\sqrt{3}$ **d.** $\frac{-1+\sqrt{3}}{2}$
107. $(\sqrt[3]{2}+\sqrt[3]{3})(\sqrt[3]{4}-\sqrt[3]{6}+\sqrt[3]{9}) =$
   $\sqrt[3]{8}-\sqrt[3]{12}+\sqrt[3]{18}+\sqrt[3]{12}-\sqrt[3]{18}+\sqrt[3]{27}$
   $= 2+3 = 5$
109. $10\sqrt{3}$ **111.** $x+6\sqrt{x}+9$ **113.** 75
115. $\frac{5\sqrt{2}}{4}$ second; $\frac{5}{2}$ second   **117.** Answers will vary
119. Answers will vary   **121.** a   **123.** a
125. $t^2+10t+25$ **127.** x **129.** 7   **131.** $-4, -3$
133. $-6, -3$ **135.** $-5, -2$ **137.** Yes   **139.** No

PROBLEM SET 10.6

1. 4   **3.** $\varnothing$ **5.** 5   **7.** $\varnothing$ **9.** $\frac{39}{2}$ **11.** $\varnothing$
13. 5   **15.** 3   **17.** $-\frac{32}{3}$ **19.** 3, 4   **21.** $-1, -2$
23. -1 **25.** $\varnothing$ **27.** 7   **29.** 0, 3   **31.** -4 **33.** 8
35. 0   **37.** 9   **39.** 0   **41.** 8
43. Possible solution 9, which does not check; $\varnothing$
45. a. 100 **b.** 40 **c.** $\varnothing$
   d. Possible solutions 5, 8; only 8 checks
47. a. 3 b. 9 **c.** 3 **d.** $\varnothing$ **e.** 4 **f.** $\varnothing$
   g. Possible solutions 1, 4; only 4 checks
49. 2   **51.** $\frac{7}{4}$ **53.** $-3, -1$ **55.** $h = 100 - 16t^2$

57. $\frac{392}{121} \approx 3.24$ feet
59. d **61.** d **63.** 5 **65.** $2\sqrt{3}$ **67.** -1 **69.** 1
71. 4 **73.** 2 **75.** $10 - 2x$ **77.** $2 - 3x$
79. $6 + 7x - 20x^2$ **81.** $8x - 12x^2$ **83.** $4 + 12x + 9x^2$
85. $4 - 9x^2$

PROBLEM SET 10.7

1. $6i$ **3.** $-5i$ **5.** $6i\sqrt{2}$ **7.** $-2i\sqrt{3}$ **9.** 1
11. -1 **13.** $-i$ **15.** $x = 3, y = -1$
17. $x = -2, y = -\frac{1}{2}$ **19.** $x = -8, y = -5$
21. $x = 7, y = \frac{1}{2}$ **23.** $x = \frac{3}{7}, y = \frac{2}{5}$ **25.** $5 + 9i$
27. $5 - i$ **29.** $2 - 4i$ **31.** $1 - 6i$ **33.** $2 + 2i$
35. $-1 - 7i$ **37.** $6 + 8i$ **39.** $2 - 24i$
41. $-15 + 12i$ **43.** $18 + 24i$ **45.** $10 + 11i$
47. $21 + 23i$ **49.** $4 + 17i$ **51.** $2 - 11i$
53. $-21 + 20i$ **55.** $-2i$ **57.** $-7 - 24i$
59. 5 **61.** 40 **63.** 13 **65.** 164
67. $-13 - 14i$ **69.** $20 - 4i$ **71.** $-3 - 2i$
73. $-\frac{2}{3} + \frac{5}{3}i$ **75.** $\frac{8}{13} + \frac{12}{13}i$ **77.** $-\frac{18}{13} - \frac{12}{13}i$
79. $-\frac{5}{13} + \frac{12}{13}i$ **81.** $\frac{13}{15} - \frac{2}{5}i$ **83.** $R = -11 - 7i$ ohms
85. c **87.** a **89.** $-\frac{3}{2}$ **91.** $-3, \frac{1}{2}$ **93.** $\frac{5}{4}$ or $\frac{4}{5}$

CHAPTER 10 TEST

1. -9 **2.** -5 **3.** 7 **4.** -15 **5.** $7x^4$
6. $2x^2y^4$
7.

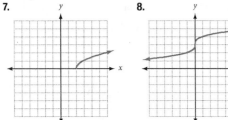

9. $\{x \mid x \leq 9\}$ **10.** $\{x \mid x \text{ is any real number}\}$
11. $\frac{1}{9}$ **12.** $\frac{7}{5}$ **13.** $a^{5/12}$ **14.** $x^{1/2}$ **15.** $\frac{1}{x^{1/12}y^{7/2}}$
16. $2a$ **17.** $(2a)^{1/3}$ **18.** $6x^3y^9$ **19.** $5xy^2\sqrt{5xy}$
20. $2x^2y^2\sqrt[3]{5xy^2}$ **21.** $\frac{\sqrt{2}}{3}$ **22.** $\frac{2a^2b\sqrt{3b}}{5c^3}$
23. $-6\sqrt{3}$ **24.** $-3ab\sqrt[3]{3}$ **25.** $x + 3\sqrt{x} - 28$
26. $21 - 6\sqrt{6}$ **27.** $\frac{\sqrt{30}}{6}$ **28.** $\frac{\sqrt[3]{6xy^2}}{2y}$
29. $\frac{5 + 5\sqrt{3}}{2}$ **30.** $\frac{x - 2\sqrt{2x} + 2}{x - 2}$
31. 8 (1 does not check) **32.** -4 **33.** -3
34. $x = \frac{1}{2}, y = 7$ **35.** $6i$ **36.** $17 - 6i$ **37.** $9 - 40i$
38. $-\frac{5}{13} - \frac{12}{13}i$ **39.** $i^{38} = (i^2)^{19} = (-1)^{19} = -1$

Chapter 11

PROBLEM SET 11.1

1. ± 5 **3.** $\pm 3i$ **5.** $\pm \frac{\sqrt{3}}{2}$ **7.** $\pm 2i\sqrt{3}$ **9.** $\pm \frac{3\sqrt{5}}{2}$
11. $\pm \frac{2\sqrt{21}}{3}i$ **13.** $-2, 3$ **15.** $-\frac{3}{2} \pm \frac{3}{2}i$
17. $-\frac{2}{5} \pm \frac{2\sqrt{2}}{5}i$ **19.** $-4 \pm 3\sqrt{3}$ **21.** $\frac{3}{2} \pm i$
23. $36, 6$ **25.** $4, 2$ **27.** $25, 5$ **29.** $\frac{25}{4}, \frac{5}{2}$

31. $\frac{49}{4}, \frac{7}{2}$ **33.** $\frac{1}{16}, \frac{1}{4}$ **35.** $\frac{1}{9}, \frac{1}{3}$ **37.** $-6, 2$
39. $-3, -9$ **41.** $1 \pm 2i$ **43.** $4 \pm \sqrt{15}$
45. $\frac{5 \pm \sqrt{37}}{2}$ **47.** $1 \pm \sqrt{5}$ **49.** $\frac{4 \pm \sqrt{13}}{3}$
51. $\frac{3}{8} \pm \frac{\sqrt{71}}{8}i$ **53.** $\frac{-2 \pm \sqrt{7}}{3}$ **55.** $\frac{5 \pm \sqrt{47}}{2}$
57. $\frac{5}{4} \pm \frac{\sqrt{19}}{4}i$ **59. a.** No **b.** $\pm 3i$
61. a. $0, 6$ **b.** $0, 6$ **63. a.** $-7, 5$ **b.** $-7, 5$ **65.** No
67. a. $\frac{7}{5}$ **b.** 3 **c.** $\frac{7 \pm 2\sqrt{2}}{5}$ **d.** $\frac{71}{5}$ **e.** 3
69. a. $(2x + 1)(2x - 7)$ **b.** $4x^2 - 12x - 7$ **c.** $-\frac{1}{2}, \frac{7}{2}$
  d. $\frac{3}{2} \pm 2i$
71. $\sqrt{2}$ inches **73.** 781 feet
75. 7.3% to the nearest tenth **77.** 24 ft **79.** 2.8 hours
81. $\frac{-3 + \sqrt{209}}{4} \approx 2.9$ ft **83.** a **85.** d **87.** 1
89. 185 **91.** $-\frac{253}{12}$ **93.** $(5t + 1)(25t^2 - 5t + 1)$

PROBLEM SET 11.2

1. $2 \pm \sqrt{3}$ **3.** $\frac{1 \pm \sqrt{41}}{4}$ **5.** $-\frac{2}{3}, \frac{5}{4}$
7. $-\frac{1}{2} \pm \frac{\sqrt{5}}{2}i$ **9.** $\frac{7}{2}$ **11.** $-3 \pm \sqrt{17}$ **13.** $1, 2$
15. $\frac{2}{3} \pm \frac{\sqrt{14}}{3}i$ **17.** $\frac{3 \pm \sqrt{5}}{4}$ **19.** $\frac{1}{6} \pm \frac{\sqrt{47}}{6}i$
21. $4 \pm \sqrt{2}$ **23.** $-\frac{1}{2} \pm \frac{\sqrt{7}}{2}i$ **25.** $1 \pm \sqrt{2}$
27. $\frac{-3 \pm \sqrt{5}}{2}$ **29.** $3, -5$ **31.** $2, -1 \pm i\sqrt{3}$
33. $-\frac{3}{2}, \frac{3}{4} \pm \frac{3\sqrt{3}}{4}i$ **35.** $\frac{1}{5}, -\frac{1}{10} \pm \frac{\sqrt{3}}{10}i$
37. $0, -\frac{1}{2} \pm \frac{\sqrt{5}}{2}i$ **39.** $0, 1 \pm i$ **41.** $0, -\frac{1}{3} \pm \frac{\sqrt{2}}{3}i$
43. a and b **45. a.** $\frac{5}{3}, 0$ **b.** $\frac{5}{3}, 0$ **47.** No, $2 \pm i\sqrt{3}$
49. Yes **51.** $-3, -2$ **53.** $0, -5$ **55.** $\pm \frac{3\sqrt{3}}{2}$
57. $0, 5$ **59.** $\frac{-5 \pm \sqrt{73}}{4}$ **61.** 1 **63.** $\frac{1}{2}, 1$
65. $-\frac{1}{2}, 3$ **67.** $\frac{20}{19}, \frac{42}{19}$
69. a. $\pm \frac{3}{2}$ **b.** ± 2 **c.** $\frac{-3 \pm \sqrt{7}}{2}$ **d.** $\frac{1 \pm \sqrt{22}}{7}$
71. 7.4 m, 9.4 m **73.** 4.5 cm, 13 cm **75.** $\frac{3120}{121}$
77. a **79.** 169 **81.** 0 **83.** ± 12 **85.** $x^2 - x - 6$
87. $x^2 - 6x + 9$

PROBLEM SET 11.3

1. $D = 16$, two rational **3.** $D = 0$, one rational
5. $D = 5$, two irrational **7.** $D = 17$, two irrational
9. $D = 36$, two rational **11.** $D = 116$, two irrational
13. ± 10 **15.** ± 12 **17.** 9 **19.** -16 **21.** $\pm 2\sqrt{6}$
23. $x^2 - 7x + 10 = 0$ **25.** $t^2 - 3t - 18 = 0$
27. $y^2 - 4 = 0$ **29.** $2x^2 - 7x + 3 = 0$
31. $4t^2 - 9t - 9 = 0$ **33.** $x^2 - 9 = 0$
35. $10a^2 - a - 3 = 0$ **37.** $9x^2 - 4 = 0$
39. $x^2 - 7 = 0$ **41.** $x^2 + 25 = 0$ **43.** $y^2 - 6y - 2 = 0$
45. $t^2 + 12t + 34 = 0$ **47.** $x^2 - 2x + 2 = 0$
49. $x^2 + 4x + 13 = 0$ **51.** $x^2 - 14x + 52 = 0$
53. $x^2 + 6x + 59 = 0$ **55.** $x^2 - 2x - 9 = 0$
57. $x^2 + 4x + 6 = 0$ **59.** d **61.** a
63. $x^2 + 4x - 5$ **65.** $4a^2 - 30a + 56$
67. $32a^2 + 20a - 18$ **69.** $\pm \frac{1}{2}$ **71.** $\frac{1}{2}, -\frac{1}{4} \pm \frac{\sqrt{3}}{4}i$
73. No solution **75.** -64 **77.** 1 **79.** $-2, 4$
81. $-2, \frac{1}{4}$

PROBLEM SET 11.4

1. $1, 2$ **3.** $\frac{7}{2}, 4$ **5.** $\pm 3, \pm i\sqrt{3}$ **7.** $\pm 2i, \pm i\sqrt{5}$

9. $\pm \frac{\sqrt{30}}{6}, \pm i$ **11.** $\pm \frac{\sqrt{21}}{3}, \pm \frac{\sqrt{21}}{3} i$

13. $-1, \frac{1}{2}, -\frac{1}{4} \pm \frac{\sqrt{3}}{4} i, \frac{1}{2} \pm \frac{\sqrt{3}}{2} i$

15. $3, -\frac{3}{2} \pm \frac{3\sqrt{3}}{2} i, 1, -\frac{1}{2} \pm \frac{\sqrt{3}}{2} i$

17. $\pm 1, \pm 3, \pm i, \pm 3i$ **19.** $-\frac{1}{3}, \frac{1}{5}$ **21.** $\pm \frac{1}{3}, \pm \frac{\sqrt{5}}{5}$

23. $-\frac{10}{3}, -\frac{17}{4}$ **25.** $-\frac{3}{5}, -\frac{7}{16}$ **27.** $4, 25$

29. only 25 checks   **31.** $27, 38$ **33.** $4, 12$

35. only $\frac{25}{9}$ checks   **37.** $-\frac{1}{125}, \frac{27}{64}$ **39.** $\pm \frac{1}{8}, \pm 27$

41. $\frac{4}{9}, -\frac{1}{2} \pm \frac{\sqrt{3}}{2} i$ **43.** $4, 36$ **45.** $\pm \sqrt{4 \pm \sqrt{15}}$

47. $\pm \sqrt{-5 \pm \sqrt{3}}$ **49.** only $3 + 2\sqrt{2}$ checks

51. $t = \frac{v \pm \sqrt{v^2 + 64h}}{32}$ **53.** $x = \frac{-4 \pm 2\sqrt{4 - k}}{k}$

55. $x = -y$ **57.** $t = \frac{1 \pm \sqrt{1 + h}}{4}$ **59.** a

61. $4, 1, 0, 1, 4$ **63.** $8, 2, 0, 2, 8$ **65.** $-1, -\frac{1}{4}, 0, -\frac{1}{4}, -1$

67. $0, 1, 4, 9, 16$ **69.** $6, 3, 2, 3, 6$

PROBLEM SET 11.5

1. $27, 12, 3, 0, 3, 12, 27$

3. $-\frac{27}{4}, -3, -\frac{3}{4}, 0, -\frac{3}{4}, -3, -\frac{27}{4}$

5. $36, 25, 16, 9, 4, 1, 0$ **7.** $12, 7, 4, 3, 4, 7, 12$

9. Vertical expansion by 4, upward, narrower

11. Vertical contraction by $\frac{2}{3}$, x-axis reflection, downward, wider

13. Vertical translation upward 4 units

15. Horizontal translation 1 unit right

17. Horizontal translation 2 units right, vertical translation upward 5 units

19. Vertical translation upward 3 units, horizontal translation 6 units left

21. Vertical expansion by 3, horizontal translation 5 units left, vertical translation downward 2 units

23. Vertical translation upward 1 unit, x-axis reflection, vertical expansion by 4, horizontal translation 3 units right

25.
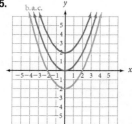

27.
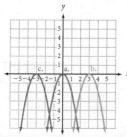

29.
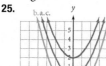
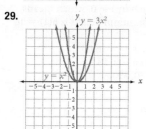

31.
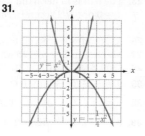

33.
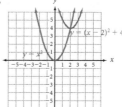

35.
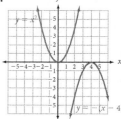

37.
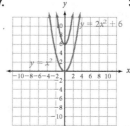

39.
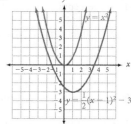

41.
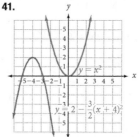

43. $(1, 3)$, lowest, $[3, \infty)$ **45.** $(-2, 4)$, highest, $(-\infty, 4]$

47. $(2, -4)$, lowest, $[-4, \infty)$ **49.** $(4, -1)$, highest, $(-\infty, -1]$

51. $f(x) = (x - 2)^2 - 1$ **53.** $f(x) = -(x - 2)^2 + 4$

55. c   **57.** c   **59.** -2 **61.** $1,322.5$ **63.** $-\frac{7}{640}$

65. $1, 5$ **67.** $-3, 1$ **69.** $\frac{3}{2} \pm \frac{1}{2} i$ **71.** $9, 3$ **73.** $1, 1$

PROBLEM SET 11.6

1. $(3, -4)$, lowest, $[-4, \infty)$ **3.** $(1, 9)$, highest, $(-\infty, 9]$

5. $(2, 16)$, highest, $(-\infty, 16]$

7. $(-4, 16)$, highest, $(-\infty, 16]$ **9.** $(0, -4)$, lowest, $[-4, \infty)$

11. $(1, 11)$, lowest, $[11, \infty)$ **13.** $(-2, -1)$, highest, $(-\infty, -1]$

15. $\left(\frac{1}{2}, 18\right)$, lowest, $[18, \infty)$

17. x-intercepts $= -3, 1$; y-intercept $= -3$; vertex $= (-1, -4)$

19. x-intercepts $= -5, 1$; y-intercept $= 5$; vertex $= (-2, 9)$

21. x-intercepts $= -1, 1$; y-intercept $= -1$; vertex $= (0, -1)$

23. x-intercepts $= -3, 3$; y-intercept $= 9$; vertex $= (0, 9)$

25. x-intercepts $= -3, 1$; y-intercept $= -3$; vertex $= (-1, -4)$

27. x-intercepts $= -1, 3$; y-intercept $= -6$; vertex $= (1, -8)$

29. x-intercepts $= 1 \pm \sqrt{5}$; y-intercept $= -4$; vertex $= (1, -5)$

31. x-intercepts $= 3 \pm \sqrt{2}$; y-intercept $= -7$; vertex $= (3, 2)$

33. x-intercepts $= 2 \pm 2\sqrt{2}$; y-intercept $= -4$;
vertex $= (2, -8)$

35. No x-intercepts; y-intercept $= -5$;
vertex $= (1, -4)$

37. No x-intercepts; y-intercept $= 1$;
vertex $= (0, 1)$

39. No x-intercepts; y-intercept $= -3$;
vertex $= (0, -3)$

41. x-intercepts $= -1, -\frac{1}{3}$; y-intercept $= 1$;
vertex $= \left(-\frac{2}{3}, -\frac{1}{3}\right)$

43. x-intercepts $= 1 \pm \sqrt{3}$; y-intercept $= -4$;
vertex $= (1, -6)$

45. No x-intercepts; y-intercept $= -28$;
vertex $= (-3, -1)$

47. x-intercepts $= -3, 0$; y-intercept $= 0$;
vertex $= \left(-\frac{3}{2}, -\frac{9}{4}\right)$

49. x-intercepts $= 0, 4$; y-intercept $= 0$; vertex $= (2, 8)$

51. x-intercepts $= -\frac{1}{3}, \frac{3}{2}$; y-intercept $= -3$;
vertex $= \left(\frac{7}{12}, -\frac{121}{24}\right)$

53. x-intercepts $= \frac{-1 \pm \sqrt{41}}{4}$; y-intercept $= 5$;
vertex $= \left(-\frac{1}{4}, \frac{41}{8}\right)$

55. No x-intercepts; y-intercept $= 3$; vertex $= \left(\frac{1}{3}, \frac{8}{3}\right)$

57. $f(x) = (x + 2)^2 - 4$, $(-2, -4)$

59. $f(x) = -(x - 1)^2 + 1$, $(1, 1)$

61. $f(x) = 2(x - 2)^2 + 5$, $(2, 5)$

63. $f(x) = -3\left(x + \frac{1}{2}\right)^2 - \frac{5}{4}$, $\left(-\frac{1}{2}, -\frac{5}{4}\right)$

65. $f(x) = 4(x + 1)^2$, $(-1, 0)$ **67.** $x = h \pm \sqrt{-\dfrac{k}{a}}$

69.

t	0	$\frac{1}{2}$	1	$\frac{3}{2}$	2
$h(t)$	0	12	16	12	0

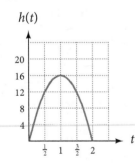

$h(t)$

71.

Time (seconds)	Height (feet)
0	0
0.5	28
1	48
1.5	60
2	64
2.5	60
3	48
3.5	28
4	0

$h(t)$

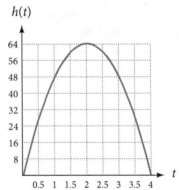

73. c   **75.** d   **77.** 96; 192   **79.** 0, 7   **81.** 2, 5
83. 1, 4   **85.** (1.5, 675)

PROBLEM SET 11.7

1. 675   **3. a.** 3,400 **b.** 3,400   **5. a.** 23 **b.** 23
7. a. y **b.** 630 ft

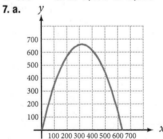

9. 2, 3 seconds   **11.** 0, 2 seconds
13. Yes, at $t = 1$ second   **15.** $7 or $10
17. 100 or 130 DVDs   **19.** 20 or 60 items
21. 875 patterns; maximum profit $731.25
23. The ball is in her hand when $h(t) = 0$, which means
$t = 0$ or $t = 2$ seconds. Maximum height is $h(1) = 16$
feet.
25. Maximum $R = \$3,600$ when $p = \$6.00$
27. Maximum $R = \$7,225$ when $p = \$8.50$
29. $300, $1,800,000   **31.** $30, $900
33. $y = -\frac{1}{135}(x - 90)^2 + 60$
35. $y = -\frac{2}{315}(x - 315)^2 + 630$ **37.** $f(x) = x^2 + 4x - 5$
39. b   **41.** a   **43.** $-2, 4$ **45.** $-\frac{1}{2}, \frac{2}{3}$ **47.** 3

PROBLEM SET 11.8

1. $x < -3$ or $x > 2$ **3.** $-3 \le x \le 4$
5. $x \le -3$ or $x \ge -2$ **7.** $\frac{1}{3} < x < \frac{1}{2}$
9. $-3 < x < 3$ **11.** $x \le -\frac{3}{2}$ or $x \ge \frac{3}{2}$
13. $-1 < x < \frac{3}{2}$ **15.** All real numbers **17.** $\varnothing$
19. $2 < x < 3$ or $x > 4$ **21.** $x \le -3$ or $-2 \le x \le -1$
23. $-4 < x \le 1$ **25.** $-6 < x < \frac{8}{3}$ **27.** $x < 2$ or $x > 6$
29. $x < -3$ or $2 < x < 4$ **30.** $x < -2$ or $1 < x < 5$
31. $x > 4$ or $2 < x < 3$ **32.** $-3 < x < -2$ or $x > 1$
33. $5 \le x < 6$
35. a. $-2 < x < 2$ **b.** $x < -2$ or $x > 2$ **c.** $x = -2$ or $x = 2$
37. a. $-2 < x < 5$ **b.** $x < -2$ or $x > 5$ **c.** $x = -2$ or $x = 5$
39. a. $x < -1$ or $1 < x < 3$ **b.** $-1 < x < 1$ or $x > 3$
　　c. $x = -1$ or $x = 1$ or $x = 3$
41. $x \ge 4$; the width is at least 4 inches
43. $5 \le p \le 8$; charge at least \$5 but no more than \$8 for
　　each radio
45. d **47.** 1.5625 **49.** 0.6549 **51.** $\frac{2}{3}$
53. Possible solutions 1 and 6; only 6 checks; 6
55.

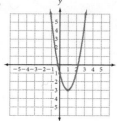

19.

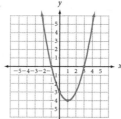

x-intercepts $= -1, 3$
y-intercept $= -3$
vertex $= (1, -4)$

20.

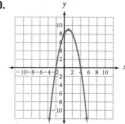

x-intercepts $= -2, 4$
y-intercept $= 8$
vertex $= (1, 9)$

21. $\frac{1}{2}$ or $\frac{3}{2}$ sec
22. 15 or 100 cups

23. profit $= \$900$

24. $-2 \le x \le 3$

25. $x < -3$ or $x > \frac{1}{2}$

Chapter 12

PROBLEM SET 12.1

1. 1 **3.** 2 **5.** $\frac{1}{27}$ **7.** 13 **9.** $\frac{7}{12}$ **11.** $\frac{3}{16}$
13. 1.26 **15.** 0.16 **17.** 20.09 **19.** 0.61 **21.** 1.22
23. 23.14
25.

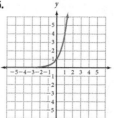

27.

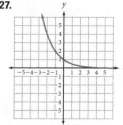

29.

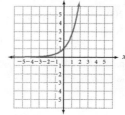

31. $y = 0, \{y \mid y > 0\}$

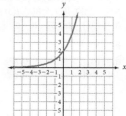

CHAPTER 11 TEST

1. $-\frac{9}{2}, \frac{1}{2}$ **2.** $3 \pm i\sqrt{2}$ **3.** $5 \pm 2i$ **4.** $1 \pm i\sqrt{2}$
5. $\frac{5}{2}, -\frac{5}{4} \pm \frac{5i\sqrt{3}}{4}$ **6.** $-1 \pm i\sqrt{5}$ **7.** $r = \pm\frac{\sqrt{A}}{8} - 1$
8. $2 \pm \sqrt{2}$ **9.** 9 **10.** $D = 81$; two rational solutions
11. $3x^2 - 13x - 10 = 0$ **12.** $x^2 + 4 = 0$
13. $\pm\sqrt{2}, \pm\frac{1}{2}i$ **14.** $\frac{1}{2}, 1$ **15.** $\frac{1}{4}, 9$
16. $t = \dfrac{7 + \sqrt{49 + 16h}}{16}$
17.

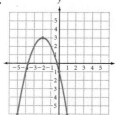

x-intercepts $= -2 \pm \sqrt{3}$;
y-intercept $= -1$;
vertex $= (-2, 3)$

18.

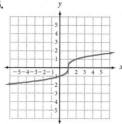

x-intercepts $= 1 \pm \dfrac{\sqrt{6}}{2}$;
y-intercept $= -1$
vertex $= (1, -3)$

33. $y = 2, \{y \mid y > 2\}$

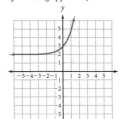

35. $y = 0, \{y \mid y < 0\}$

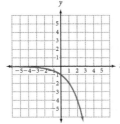

37. $y = 0, \{y \mid y > 0\}$

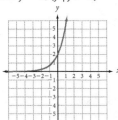

39. $y = 4, \{y \mid y < 4\}$

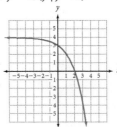

41. $y = 2, \{y \mid y > 2\}$

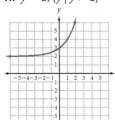

43.

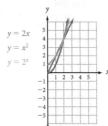

$y = 2x$
$y = x^2$
$y = 2^x$

45.

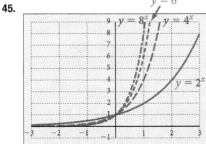

$y = 6^x$
$y = 8^x$ $y = 4^x$
$y = 2^x$

47. $h = 6 \cdot \left(\frac{2}{3}\right)^n$; 5th bounce: $6\left(\frac{2}{3}\right)^5 \approx 0.79$ feet
49. In 2000, \$17.60 per pound; in 2010, \$163.91 per pound; in 2025, \$4,658.68 per pound
51. $f(1) = 200, f(2) = 800, f(3) = 3,200$
53. a. \$1.00   **b.** \$2.38   **c.** \$17.84
55. a. $A(t) = 1,200\left(1 + \frac{.06}{4}\right)^{4t}$ **b.** \$1,932.39   **c.** \$1,939.29
57. a. \$10,777.33   **b.** \$10,778.34   **c.** \$10,778.84
59. 1.4% interest compounded quarterly is a better deal
61. $V(t)$

63. a. 188,934,028   **b.** $B(t)$

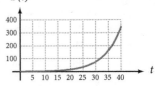

65. a. \$129,138.48   **b.** $\{t \mid 0 \leq t \leq 6\}$
c.

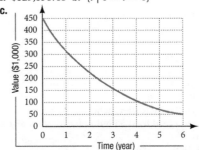

d. $\{V(t) \mid 52,942.05 \leq V(t) \leq 450,000\}$
e. After approximately 4 years and 8 months
67. It approaches e.

x	$(1 + x)^{1/x}$
1	2
0.5	2.25
0.1	2.5937
0.01	2.7048
0.001	2.7169
0.0001	2.7181
0.00001	2.7183

69. c **71.** d **73.** $y = \frac{x + 3}{2}$ **75.** $y = \pm\sqrt{x + 3}$
77. $y = \frac{2x - 4}{x - 1}$ **79.** $y = x^2 + 3$

PROBLEM SET 12.2
1. $\{(0, 1), (1, 2), (2, 3), (3, 4)\}$; function
3. $\{(3, -4), (-1, -2), (3, 1), (-2, 3)\}$; not a function
5. $\{(4, -3), (4, 0), (4, 3)\}$; not a function
7. $y = \frac{x + 1}{2}$ **9.** $y = \pm\sqrt{x + 3}$ **11.** $y = 1 \pm \sqrt{x + 4}$
13. $x = 3^y$ **15.** $x = 4$ **17.** $y = \sqrt[3]{2x}$
19. $y = 2(x - 2)$ **21.** $y = x^2 - 2$ **23.** Yes
25. Yes   **27.** No   **29.** Yes   **31.** No   **33.** No
35. Yes   **37.** $f^{-1}(x) = \frac{x + 1}{3}$ **39.** $f^{-1}(x) = \sqrt[3]{x}$
41. $f^{-1}(x) = \frac{x - 3}{x - 1}$ **43.** $f^{-1}(x) = 4x + 3$
45. $f^{-1}(x) = 2(x + 3) = 2x + 6$
47. $f^{-1}(x) = \frac{3}{2}(x + 3) = \frac{3}{2}x + \frac{9}{2}$
49. $f^{-1}(x) = \sqrt[3]{x + 4}$ **51.** $f^{-1}(x) = \frac{x + 3}{4 - 2x}$
53. $f^{-1}(x) = \frac{1 - x}{3x - 2}$
55. a. 4   **b.** $\frac{4}{3}$ **c.** 2   **d.** 2   **e.** x **f.** x
57. $f^{-1}(x) = \frac{1}{x}$

59.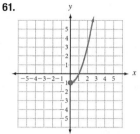

61.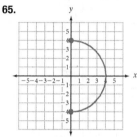

63.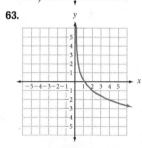

65.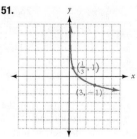

67. $(f \circ g)(x) = 3\left(\frac{x-4}{3}\right)+4 = x$

$(g \circ f)(x) = \frac{3x+4-4}{3} = x$

69. $(f \circ g)(x) = \sqrt{x^2 - 4 + 4} = x$

$(g \circ f)(x) = (\sqrt{x+4})^2 - 4 = x$

71. $(f \circ g)(x) = \dfrac{1}{\frac{1-x}{x}+1} = x$

$(g \circ f)(x) = \dfrac{1 - \frac{1}{x+1}}{\frac{1}{x+1}} = x$

73. $f^{-1}(x) = 7(x+2) = 7x + 14$

75. a. -3 **b.** -6 **c.** 2 **d.** 3 **e.** -2 **f.** 3 **g.** inverses

77. a. \$729.4 billion **b.** $s^{-1}(t) = \frac{t - 249.4}{16}$ **c.** 2036

79. a. 6629.33 ft/s **b.** $f^{-1}(m) = \frac{15m}{22}$ **c.** 1.36 mph **81. b**

83. a **85.** a **87.** 8 **89.** $\frac{3}{5}$ **91.** $\pm 2\sqrt{3}$

93. 3 **95.** 3 **97.** 2 **99.** 0

PROBLEM SET 12.3

1. $\log_2 16 = 4$ **3.** $\log_5 125 = 3$ **5.** $\log_{10} 0.01 = -2$

7. $\log_2 \frac{1}{32} = -5$ **9.** $\log_{1/2} 8 = -3$ **11.** $\log_3 27 = 3$

13. $10^2 = 100$ **15.** $2^6 = 64$ **17.** $8^0 = 1$

19. $10^{-3} = 0.001$ **21.** $6^2 = 36$ **23.** $5^{-2} = \frac{1}{25}$

25. 4 **27.** 3 **29.** 1 **31.** 0 **33.** -1

35. -2 **37.** -2 **39.** $\frac{1}{2}$ **41.** $\frac{1}{3}$ **43.** $\frac{3}{2}$ **45.** $\frac{3}{2}$

47. $\frac{4}{5}$

49.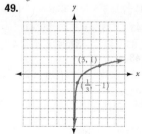

51.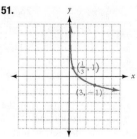

53.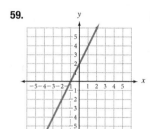

55.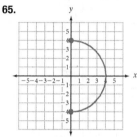

57. $f^{-1}(x) = 4^x$ **59.** $f^{-1}(x) = \log_{1/8} x$

61. $\{x \mid x > 0\}$ **63.** $\{x \mid x > -6\}$ **65.** $\{x \mid x < 1\}$

67. $\left\{ x \mid x > -\frac{3}{2} \right\}$ **69.** $x = 3$ **71.** $x = 0$

73. $x = 0$ **75.** $y = 3^x$ **77.** $y = \log_{1/3} x$

79.

Prefix	Multiplying Factor	$\log_{10}$ (Multiplying Factor)
Nano	0.000 000 001	-9
Micro	0.000 001	-6
Deci	0.1	-1
Giga	1,000,000,000	9
Peta	1,000,000,000,000,000	15

81. 2 **83.** 10^8 times as large **85.** 120 **87.** a

89. a **91.** 4 **93.** $-4, 2$ **95.** $-\frac{11}{8}$

97. $2^3 = (x+2)(x)$ **99.** $3^4 = \frac{x-2}{x+1}$

PROBLEM SET 12.4

1. 0 **3.** 4 **5.** 3 **7.** $\sqrt{2}$ **9.** 12 **11.** 81

13. 4 **15.** 1 **17.** -2 **19.** 0 **21.** $\frac{1}{2}$

23. $\log_3 4 + \log_3 x$ **25.** $\log_6 5 - \log_6 x$

27. $5 \log_2 y$ **29.** $\frac{1}{3}\log_9 z$ **31.** $2\log_6 x + 4\log_6 y$

33. $\frac{1}{2}\log_5 x + 4\log_5 y$ **35.** $\log_b x + \log_b y - \log_b z$

37. $\log_{10} 4 - \log_{10} x - \log_{10} y$

39. $2\log_{10} x + \log_{10} y - \frac{1}{2}\log_{10} z$

41. $3\log_{10} x + \frac{1}{2}\log_{10} y - 4\log_{10} z$

43. $\frac{2}{3}\log_b x + \frac{1}{3}\log_b y - \frac{4}{3}\log_b z$

45. $\frac{2}{3}\log_3 x + \frac{1}{3}\log_3 y - 2\log_3 z$

47. $2\log_a 2 + 5\log_a x - 2\log_a 3 = 2$

49. $2\log_4 x + \log_4 (x+2)$ **51.** $\log_b 5 + 7$

53. $1 + 9\log_8 x$ **55.** $3 + 5\log_2 (x-1)$

57. $2\log_6 x + 3\log_6 z - \frac{1}{2}\log_6 (x+z)$

59. $\frac{1}{2}\log_9 (x+3) - \frac{1}{2}\log_9 (x-3)$ **61.** 2

63. 2 **65.** 1 **67.** $\log_b xz$ **69.** $\log_3 \frac{x^2}{y^3}$

71. $\log_{10} \sqrt{x}\sqrt[3]{y}$ **73.** $\log_2 \frac{x^3\sqrt{y}}{z}$ **75.** $\log_2 \frac{\sqrt{x}}{y^3 z^4}$

77. $\log_{10} \frac{x^{3/2}}{y^{3/4} z^{4/5}}$ **79.** $\log_5 \frac{\sqrt{x} \cdot \sqrt[3]{y^2}}{z^4}$

81. $\log_b x^2(x-10)^3$ **83.** $\log_6 \frac{x^4 z^5}{(y+z)^2}$ **85.** $\log_3 \frac{x-4}{x+4}$

87. Use Property 6 **89. a.** 1.602 **b.** 2.505 **c.** 3.204

90. a. iii **b.** iv **c.** vi **d.** v **e.** i **f.** ii

91. pH $= 6.1 + \log_{10} x - \log_{10} y$ **93.** 2 **95.** a

97. 1 **99.** 1 **101.** 4

PROBLEM SET 12.5

1. 0 **3.** 1 **5.** 4 **7.** 5 **9.** $\frac{3}{2}$ **11.** -3

13. 2.5775 **15.** 5.8435 **17.** -0.3706 **19.** -1.0642

21. x **23.** x **25.** $3x$ **27.** x^4 **29.** $\ln 10 + 3t$

31. $\ln A - 2t$ **33.** $2 + 3t\log 1.01$ **35.** $rt + \ln P$

37. $3 - \log 4.2$ **39.** $\log x(x - 2)$ **41.** $\ln \frac{x+1}{x+4}$

43. $\log \frac{x^2}{y^5}$ **45.** 2.7080 **47.** -1.0986 **49.** 2.1972

51. 2.7724

53.

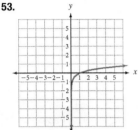

55. 1.3333 **57.** 0.7500 **59.** 1.3917 **61.** 0.7186
63. 2.6356 **65.** 4.1632 **67.** 5.0
69.

Location	Date	Magnitude M	Shockwave T
Moresby Island	Jan. 23	4.0	1.00×10^4
Vancouver Island	Apr. 30	5.3	1.99×10^5
Quebec City	June 29	3.2	1.58×10^3
Mould Bay	Nov. 13	5.2	1.58×10^5
St. Lawrence	Dec. 14	3.7	5.01×10^3

Source: National Resources Canada, National Earthquake Hazards Program

71. 3.19 **73.** d **75.** a **77.** $\frac{7}{10}$
79. 3.1250 **81.** 1.2575 **83.** $t\log 1.05$ **85.** $.05t$
87. 2.5×10^{-6} **89.** 51

PROBLEM SET 12.6

1. 1.4650 **3.** 0.6826 **5.** -1.5440 **7.** -0.6477
9. -0.3333 **11.** 2.000 **13.** -0.1845 **15.** 0.1845
17. 1.6168 **19.** 2.1131 **21.** -1.0000 **23.** 1.2275
25. 0.3054 **27.** 42.5528 **29.** 6.0147 **31.** 9
33. $\frac{1}{125}$ **35.** 2 **37.** $\sqrt[3]{5}$ **39.** 6 **41.** $\frac{1}{64}$
43. 10 **45.** $\frac{1}{100}$ **47.** $\frac{1}{e}$ **49.** 10^{10} **51.** 10^{-20}
53. 1,000 **55.** 758.93 **57.** 0.0075893 **59.** 23.460
61. 0.0047496 **63.** $\frac{2}{3}$ **65.** 18 **67.** 3 **69.** 3
71. 4 **73.** 4 **75.** 1 **77.** 0 **79.** $\frac{3}{2}$ **81.** 27
83. $\frac{5}{3}$ **85.** 25 **87.** $\frac{1}{8}$ **89.** 11.72 years
91. 9.25 years **93.** 8.75 years **95.** 18.58 years
97. 11.55 years **99.** 18.31 years **101.** 11.45 years
103. 4.27 days **105.** 2043 **107.** 3.16×10^5
109. 2.00×10^8 **111.** 1.78×10^{-5} **113.** 2023
115. 2030 **117.** 2029
119. It has been approximately 4,127 years. **121.** 12.9%
123. 5.3% **125.** a **127.** d **129.** $\left(\frac{3}{2}, -\frac{67}{4}\right)$, lowest
131. $\left(\frac{3}{2}, \frac{27}{2}\right)$, highest **133.** 2 seconds, 104 feet

CHAPTER 12 TEST

1.

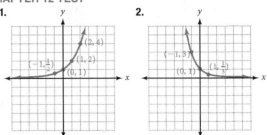

2.

3.

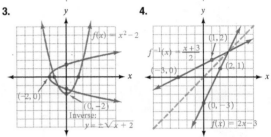

4.

5.

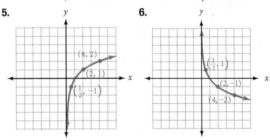

6.

7. -2 **8.** $\frac{2}{3}$ **9.** 4.3692 **10.** -3.0748
11. $3 + 2\log_2 x - \log_2 y$ **12.** $\frac{1}{2}\log x - 4\log y - \frac{1}{5}\log z$
13. $\log_3 \frac{x^2}{\sqrt{y}}$ **14.** $\log \frac{\sqrt[3]{x}}{yz^2}$ **15.** 2.0959
16. -0.0229 **17.** 70,404 **18.** 0.00225 **19.** 64
20. $\sqrt{5}$ **21.** 1.4650 **22.** $\frac{5}{4}$ **23.** 15
24. 8 (-1 does not check) **25.** 6.18 **26.** \$651.56
27. \$7,373 **28.** 13.87 years

Chapter 13

PROBLEM SET 13.1

1. 4, 7, 10, 13, 16 **3.** 3, 7, 11, 15, 19 **5.** 1, 2, 3, 4, 5
7. 4, 7, 12, 19, 28 **9.** $\frac{1}{4}, \frac{2}{5}, \frac{3}{6}, \frac{4}{7}, \frac{5}{8}$ **11.** 1, $\frac{1}{4}, \frac{1}{9}, \frac{1}{16}, \frac{1}{25}$
13. 2, 4, 8, 16, 32 **15.** 2, $\frac{3}{2}, \frac{4}{3}, \frac{5}{4}, \frac{6}{5}$
17. $-2, 4, -8, 16, -32$ **19.** 3, 5, 3, 5, 3
21. 1, $-\frac{2}{3}, \frac{3}{5}, -\frac{4}{7}, \frac{5}{9}$ **23.** $\frac{1}{2}, 1, \frac{9}{8}, 1, \frac{25}{32}$ **25.** 80
27. $\frac{1}{203}$ **29.** 3, $-9, 27, -81, 243$ **31.** 1, 5, 13, 29, 61
33. 2, 3, 5, 9, 17 **35.** 5, 11, 29, 83, 245 **37.** 4, 4, 4, 4, 4
39. $a_n = 4n$ **41.** $a_n = n^2$ **43.** $a_n = 2^{n+1}$
45. $a_n = \frac{1}{2^{n+1}}$ **47.** $a_n = 3n + 2$ **49.** $a_n = -4n + 2$
51. $a_n = (-2)^{n-1}$ **53.** $a_n = \log_{n+1}(n + 2)$
55. a. \$28,000, \$29,120, \$30,284.80, \$31,496.19, \$32,756.04
b. $a_n = 28,000(1.04)^{n-1}$
57. a. 16 feet, 48 feet, 80 feet, 112 feet, 144 feet
b. 400 feet **c.** No

59. a. $10, 8, \frac{32}{5}$ **b.** $a_n = 10\left(\frac{4}{5}\right)^{n-1}$ **c.** 1.34 ft **61.** c
63. 30 **65.** 40 **67.** 18 **69.** $-\frac{20}{81}$ **71.** $\frac{21}{10}$

PROBLEM SET 13.2
1. 36 **3.** 11 **5.** 18 **7.** $\frac{163}{60}$ **9.** 60 **11.** 40
13. 44 **15.** $-\frac{11}{32}$ **17.** $\frac{21}{10}$
19. $(x + 1) + (x + 2) + (x + 3) + (x + 4) + (x + 5)$
21. $(x - 2) + (x - 2)^2 + (x - 2)^3 + (x - 2)^4$
23. $\frac{x+1}{x-1} + \frac{x+2}{x-1} + \frac{x+3}{x-1} + \frac{x+4}{x-1} + \frac{x+5}{x-1}$
25. $(x + 3)^3 + (x + 4)^4 + (x + 5)^5 + (x + 6)^6 + (x + 7)^7 + (x + 8)^8$
27. $(x - 6)^6 + (x - 8)^7 + (x - 10)^8 + (x - 12)^9$
29. $\sum_{i=1}^{4} 2^i$ **31.** $\sum_{i=2}^{6} 2^i$ **33.** $\sum_{i=1}^{5} (4i + 1)$ **35.** $\sum_{i=2}^{5} -(-2)^i$
37. $\sum_{i=3}^{7} \frac{i}{i + 1}$ **39.** $\sum_{i=1}^{4} \frac{i}{2i + 1}$ **41.** $\sum_{i=6}^{9} (x - 2)^i$
43. $\sum_{i=1}^{4} \left(1 + \frac{i}{x}\right)^{i + 1}$ **45.** $\sum_{i=3}^{5} \frac{x}{x + i}$ **47.** $\sum_{i=2}^{4} x^i(x + i)$
49. a. $0.3 + 0.03 + 0.003 + 0.0003 + \ldots$
b. $0.2 + 0.02 + 0.002 + 0.0002 + \ldots$
c. $0.27 + 0.0027 + 0.000027 + \ldots$
51. seventh second: 208 feet; total: 784 feet
53. a. $16 + 48 + 80 + 112 + 144$ **b.** $\sum_{i=1}^{5} (32i - 16)$
55. b **57.** 74 **59.** $\frac{55}{2}$ **61.** $2n + 1$ **63.** $(3, 2)$

PROBLEM SET 13.3
1. Arithmetic, $d = 1$ **3.** Not arithmetic
5. Arithmetic, $d = -5$ **7.** Not arithmetic
9. Arithmetic, $d = \frac{2}{3}$ **11.** $a_n = 4n - 1; a_{24} = 95$
13. $a_{10} = -12; S_{10} = -30$ **15.** $a_1 = 7; d = 2; a_{30} = 65$
17. $a_1 = 12; d = 2; a_{20} = 50; S_{20} = 620$
19. $a_{20} = 79, S_{20} = 820$ **21.** $a_{40} = 122, S_{40} = 2540$
23. $a_1 = 13, d = -6$ **25.** $a_{85} = -238$
27. $d = \frac{16}{19}, a_{39} = 28$ **29.** 20,300 **31.** -158
33. $a_{10} = 5; S_{10} = \frac{55}{2}$
35. a. $18,000, \$14,700, \$11,400, \$8,100, \$4,800$ **b.** $-\$3,300$
c. $V(t)$ **d.** $9,750$
e. $a_0 = 18,000,$
$a_n = a_{n-1} - 3,300$ for $n \geq 1$

37. a. $1,500, 1,460, 1,420, 1,380, 1,340, 1,300$
b. It is arithmetic because the same amount is subtracted from each succeeding term.
c. $a_n = 1,500 - (n - 1)40 = 1,540 - 40n$
39. a. $1, 3, 6, 10, 15, 21, 28, 36, 45, 55, 66, 78, 91, 105, 120$
b. $a_1 = 1; a_n = n + a_{n-1}$ for $n \geq 2$
c. No, it is not arithmetic because the same amount is not added to each term.
41. a. $a_n = 32n - 16$ **b.** $a_{10} = 304$ feet **c.** 1,600 feet
43. a **45.** d **47.** $\frac{1}{16}$ **49.** $\sqrt{3}$ **51.** 2^n
53. r^3 **55.** $\frac{2}{5}$ **57.** -255

PROBLEM SET 13.4
1. 5 **3.** $\frac{1}{3}$ **5.** Not geometric **7.** -2
9. Not geometric **11.** $a_n = 4 \cdot 3^{n-1}$
13. $a_6 = -2\left(-\frac{1}{2}\right)^5 = \frac{1}{16}$ **15.** $a_{20} = 3(-1)^{19} = -3$
17. 10,230 **19.** $S_{20} = \frac{1((-1)^{20} - 1)}{-1 - 1} = 0$
21. $a_8 = \frac{1}{5}\left(\frac{1}{2}\right)^7 = \frac{1}{640}$ **23.** $-\frac{31}{32}$ **25.** $32, 62 + 31\sqrt{2}$
27. $\frac{1}{1000}, 111.111$ **29.** $r = \pm 2$ **31.** $a_8 = 384, S_8 = 255$
33. $r = 2$ **35.** $S = \frac{\frac{1}{2}}{1 - \frac{1}{2}} = 1$ **37.** 8 **39.** 4
41. $\frac{8}{9}$ **43.** $S = \frac{\frac{2}{5}}{1 - \frac{2}{5}} = \frac{2}{3}$ **45.** $S = \frac{\frac{3}{4}}{1 - \frac{1}{3}} = \frac{9}{8}$
51. a. $450,000, \$315,000, \$220,500, \$154,350, \$108,045$
b. 0.7 **c.** $V(t)$
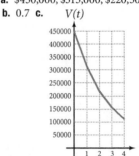
d. $130,000 **e.** $a_0 = 450,000, a_n = 0.7a_{n-1}$
53. a. $\frac{1}{2}$ **b.** $\frac{364}{729}$ **c.** $\frac{1}{1,458}$
55. a. 0.004 inches **b.** 0.064 inches **c.** 67,108.864 inches
57. a. $60,000; \$64,200; \$68,694; \$73,503; \$78,648;$
b. $a_n = 60,000(1.07)^{n-1}$ **c.** $828,987
59. a **61.** d **63.** $x + y$ **65.** $x^3 + 3x^2y + 3xy^2 + y^3$
67. 21

PROBLEM SET 13.5
1. $x^4 + 8x^3 + 24x^2 + 32x + 16$
3. $x^6 + 6x^5y + 15x^4y^2 + 20x^3y^3 + 15x^2y^4 + 6xy^5 + y^6$
5. $32x^5 + 80x^4 + 80x^3 + 40x^2 + 10x + 1$
7. $x^5 - 10x^4y + 40x^3y^2 - 80x^2y^3 + 80xy^4 - 32y^5$
9. $81x^4 - 216x^3 + 216x^2 - 96x + 16$
11. $64x^3 - 144x^2y + 108xy^2 - 27y^3$
13. $x^8 + 8x^6 + 24x^4 + 32x^2 + 16$
15. $x^6 + 3x^4y^2 + 3x^2y^4 + y^6$
17. $16x^4 + 96x^3y + 216x^2y^2 + 216xy^3 + 81y^4$
19. $\frac{x^3}{8} + \frac{x^2y}{4} + \frac{xy^2}{6} + \frac{y^3}{27}$ **21.** $\frac{x^3}{8} - 3x^2 + 24x - 64$
23. $\frac{x^4}{81} + \frac{2x^3y}{27} + \frac{x^2y^2}{6} + \frac{xy^3}{6} + \frac{y^4}{16}$ **25.** 720
27. 3,628,800 **29.** 1 **31.** 8 **33.** 1,365
35. 77,520 **37.** $x^9 + 18x^8 + 144x^7 + 672x^6$
39. $x^{10} - 10x^9y + 45x^8y^2 - 120x^7y^3$
41. $x^{25} + 75x^{24} + 2,700x^{23} + 62,100x^{22}$
43. $x^{60} - 120x^{59} + 7,080x^{58} - 273,760x^{57}$
45. $x^{18} - 18x^{17}y + 153x^{16}y^2 - 816x^{15}y^3$
47. $x^{15} + 15x^{14} + 105x^{13}$ **49.** $x^{12} - 12x^{11}y + 66x^{10}y^2$
51. $x^{20} + 40x^{19} + 760x^{18}$ **53.** $x^{100} + 200x^{99}$
55. $x^{50} + 50x^{49}y$ **57.** $51,963,120x^4y^8$ **59.** $3,360x^6$
61. $-25,344x^7$ **63.** $2,700x^{23}y^2$
65. $\binom{20}{11}(2x)^9(5y)^{11}$

67. $x^{20}y^{10} - 30x^{18}y^9 + 405x^{16}y^8$ **69.** $\frac{21}{128}$ **71.** b

73. a   **75.** $x \approx 1.18$ **77.** $x = \frac{5}{6}$ **79.** ≈ 17.5 years

81. 1.56   **83.** 8.66   **85.** $t = -\frac{1}{5} \ln\left(\frac{A}{P}\right)$

CHAPTER 13 TEST

1. $-2, 1, 4, 7, 10$ **2.** $3, 7, 11, 15, 19$ **3.** $2, 5, 10, 17, 26$

4. $2, 16, 54, 128, 250$ **5.** $2, \frac{3}{4}, \frac{4}{9}, \frac{5}{16}, \frac{6}{25}$

6. $4, -8, 16, -32, 64$ **7.** $a_n = 4n + 2$

8. $a_n = 2^{n-1}$ **9.** $a_n = \frac{1}{2^n}$

10. $a_n = (-3)^n$ **11. a.** 90 **b.** 53 **c.** 130
12. 3   **13.** ± 6 **14.** 320   **15.** 25

16. $S_{50} = \frac{3(2^{50} - 1)}{2 - 1} = 3(2^{50} - 1)$ **17.** $\frac{3}{4}$

18. $x^4 - 12x^3 + 54x^2 - 108x + 81$
19. $32x^5 - 80x^4 + 80x^3 - 40x^2 + 10x - 1$
20. 220   **21.** 3003   **22.** $x^{20} - 20x^{19} + 190x^{18}$
23. $-108{,}864x^3y^5$

Chapter 14

PROBLEM SET 14.1

1. 5   **3.** $\sqrt{106}$ **5.** $\sqrt{61}$ **7.** $\sqrt{130}$ **9.** 3 or -1
11. 0 or 6   **13.** $x = -1 \pm 4\sqrt{2}$
15. $(x - 3)^2 + (y + 2)^2 = 9$ **17.** $(x + 5)^2 + (y + 1)^2 = 5$
19. $x^2 + (y + 5)^2 = 1$ **21.** $x^2 + y^2 = 4$
23. center = $(0, 0)$; radius = 2

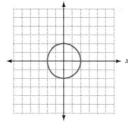

25. center = $(1, 3)$; radius = 5

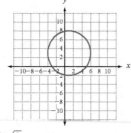

27. center = $(-2, 4)$; radius = $2\sqrt{2}$

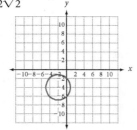

29. center = $(-2, 4)$; radius = $\sqrt{17}$

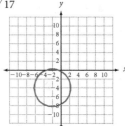

31. center = $(-1, 2)$; radius = 3

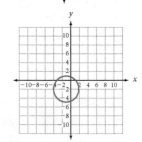

33. center = $(0, 3)$; radius = 4

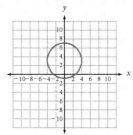

35. center = $(-1, 0)$; radius = $\sqrt{2}$

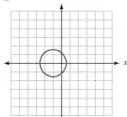

37. center = $(2, 3)$; radius = 3

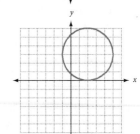

39. center = $\left(-1, -\frac{1}{2}\right)$; radius = 2

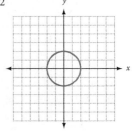

41. center = $\left(\frac{1}{2}, -1\right)$; radius = 2

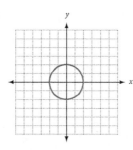

43. $(x - 3)^2 + (y - 4)^2 = 25$

45. **a.** $\left(x - \frac{1}{2}\right)^2 + (y - 1)^2 = \frac{1}{4}$;

b. $(x - 1)^2 + (y - 1)^2 = 1$;

c. $(x - 2)^2 + (y - 1)^2 = 4$

47. $x^2 + y^2 = 25$ **49.** $x^2 + y^2 = 9$

51. $(x + 1)^2 + (y - 3)^2 = 25$ **53.** $(x + 2)^2 + (y - 5)^2 = 73$

55. $x^2 + (y - 2)^2 = 16$ **57.** $C = 6\pi\sqrt{2}, A = 18\pi$

59. $C = 10\pi, A = 25\pi$ **61.** yes

63. $(x - 500)^2 + (y - 132)^2 = 120^2$

65. d   **67.** a   **69.** 3   **71.** $-\frac{1}{4}$ **73.** (4, 1)

75.

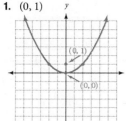

77.

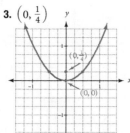

PROBLEM SET 14.2

1. (0, 1)

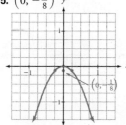

3. $\left(0, \frac{1}{4}\right)$

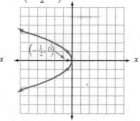

5. $\left(0, -\frac{1}{8}\right)$

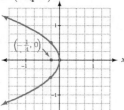

7. $\left(-\frac{1}{2}, 0\right)$

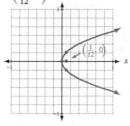

9. $\left(-\frac{1}{4}, 0\right)$

11. $\left(\frac{1}{12}, 0\right)$

13. Vertex: $(-1, -3)$, focus: $\left(-1, -\frac{5}{2}\right)$

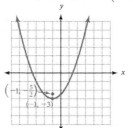

15. Vertex: $(4, 2)$, focus: $\left(4, \frac{7}{4}\right)$

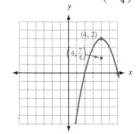

17. Vertex: $(-2, 1)$, focus: $\left(-2, \frac{11}{12}\right)$

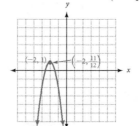

19. Vertex: $(2, 1)$, focus: $\left(\frac{11}{4}, 1\right)$

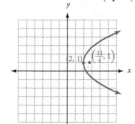

21. Vertex: $(3, -3)$, focus: $\left(\frac{13}{4}, -3\right)$

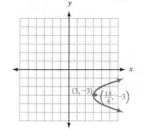

23. Vertex: $(5, 2)$, focus: $\left(\frac{59}{12}, 2\right)$

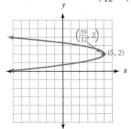

25. Vertex: $(2, -3)$, focus: $\left(2, -\frac{11}{4}\right)$

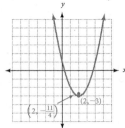

27. Vertex: $(-1, 3)$, focus: $(-1, 1)$

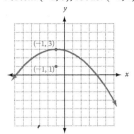

29. Vertex: $(3, -2)$, focus: $\left(\frac{13}{4}, -2\right)$

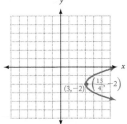

31. Vertex: $(-1, 1)$, focus: $\left(-\frac{5}{2}, 1\right)$

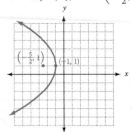

33. 6.25 inches   **35.** 3 inches   **37.** d   **39.** d
41. $x = \pm 5$ **43.** $x = \pm 4i$ **45.** $y = \pm 10$
47. $\frac{x^2}{4} + \frac{y^2}{25}$ **49.** x-intercepts $\frac{1}{3}, -2$; y-intercept -2
51. $\pm \frac{9}{5}$

PROBLEM SET 14.3

1.

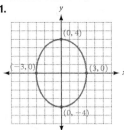

3.

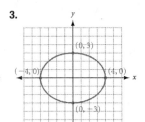

5.

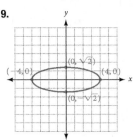

7.

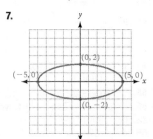

9.

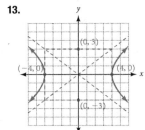

11.

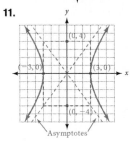

13.

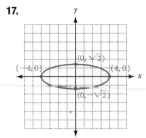

15.

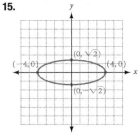

17.

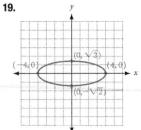

19.

21.

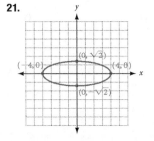

23. x-intercepts $= \pm 3$, y-intercepts $= \pm 2$

25. x-intercepts $= \pm 0.2$, no y-intercepts

27. x-intercepts $= \pm\frac{3}{5}$, y-intercepts $= \pm\frac{2}{5}$

29.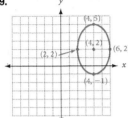

31.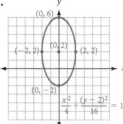
$$\frac{x^2}{4} + \frac{(y-2)^2}{16} = 1$$

33.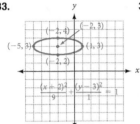
$$\frac{(x+2)^2}{9} + \frac{(y-3)^2}{1} = 1$$

35.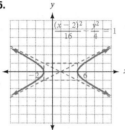
$$\frac{(x-2)^2}{16} - \frac{y^2}{4} = 1$$

37.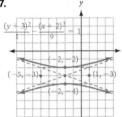
$$\frac{(y+3)^2}{1} - \frac{(x-2)^2}{9} = 1$$

39.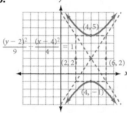
$$\frac{(y-2)^2}{9} - \frac{(x+4)^2}{4} = 1$$

41. $x = 0$ **43.** $y = 0$ **45.** 8 **47.** $\dfrac{x^2}{307.5^2} + \dfrac{y^2}{255^2} = 1$

49. The equation is $\dfrac{x^2}{229^2} + \dfrac{y^2}{195^2} = 1$. **51.** 5.3 feet

53. a **55.** b **57.** $(0, 0)$ **59.** $4y^2 + 16y + 16$

61. $x = 2y + 4$ **63.** $-x^2 + 6$ **65.** $(5y + 6)(y + 2)$

67. $y = \pm 2$ **69.** $x = \pm 2$

PROBLEM SET 14.4

1.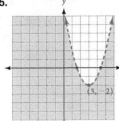

3.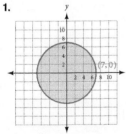

5.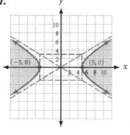

7.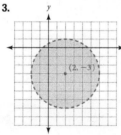

9.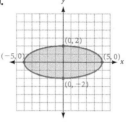

11.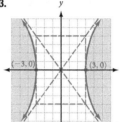

13.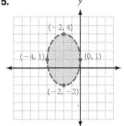

15.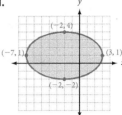

17.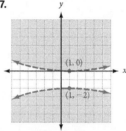

19. $(0, 3)$, $\left(\frac{12}{5}, -\frac{9}{5}\right)$ **21.** $(0, 4)$, $\left(\frac{16}{5}, \frac{12}{5}\right)$

23. $(5, 0)$, $(-5, 0)$ **25.** $(0, -3)$, $(\sqrt{5}, 2)$, $(-\sqrt{5}, 2)$

27. $(-4, 0)$, $(3, \sqrt{7})$, $(3, -\sqrt{7})$ **29.** $(-4, 11)$, $\left(\frac{5}{2}, \frac{5}{4}\right)$

31. $(-4, 5)$, $(1, 0)$ **33.** $(-3, 2)$, $(0, 5)$

35. $(3, 0)$, $(-3, 0)$ **37.** $(4, 0)$, $(0, -4)$

39. $\left(\frac{2\sqrt{6}}{3}, \frac{13}{3}\right)$, $\left(-\frac{2\sqrt{6}}{3}, \frac{13}{3}\right)$ **41.** $(1, -2)$

43. $(\sqrt{10}, 0)$, $(-\sqrt{10}, 0)$

45.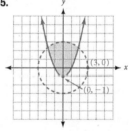

47.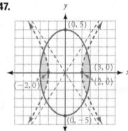

49.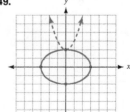

51.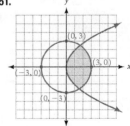

53.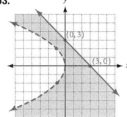

55.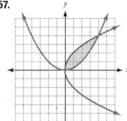

9.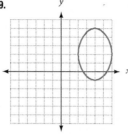

10.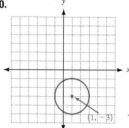

57.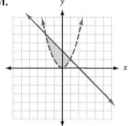

59.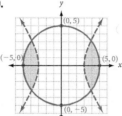

11.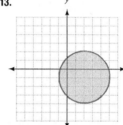

12.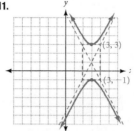

61.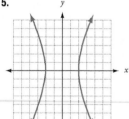

13.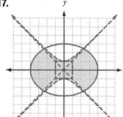

14.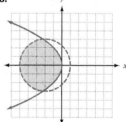

63. 8, 5 or −8, −5 or 8, −5 or −8, 5
65. a. $(-4, 4\sqrt{3})$ and $(-4, -4\sqrt{3})$
   b. $(4, 4\sqrt{3})$ and $(4, -4\sqrt{3})$
67. b   **69.** d   **71.** $x^4 + 8x^3 + 24x^2 + 32x + 16$
73. $8x^3 + 12x^2y + 6xy^2 + y^3$ **75.** $x^{50} + 150x^{49}$

CHAPTER 14 TEST
1. −5, 3   **2.** $(x + 2)^2 + (y - 4)^2 = 9$ **3.** $x^2 + y^2 = 25$
4. $(5, -3), \sqrt{39}$

5.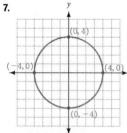

6.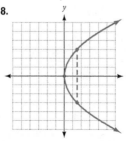

7.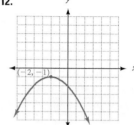

8.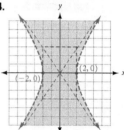

15. $(0, 5), (4, -3)$ **16.** $(0,-4), (-\sqrt{7}, 3), (\sqrt{7}, 3)$

17.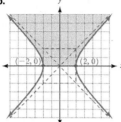

18.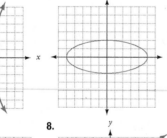

APPENDIX
1. $x - 7 + \dfrac{7}{x + 2}$ **3.** $2x^2 - 5x + 1 + \dfrac{4}{x + 1}$
5. $a^3 + 2a^2 + 4a + 6 + \dfrac{17}{a - 2}$
7. $y^3 + 2y^2 + 4y + 8$ **9.** $x - 7 + \dfrac{20}{x + 2}$
11. $3x - 1$ **13.** $x^2 + 4x + 11 + \dfrac{26}{x - 2}$
15. $3x^2 + 8x + 26 + \dfrac{83}{x - 3}$ **17.** $2x^2 + 2x + 3$
19. $x^3 - 4x^2 + 18x - 72 + \dfrac{289}{x + 4}$
21. $x^4 + x^2 - x - 3 - \dfrac{5}{x - 2}$ **23.** $x + 2 + \dfrac{3}{x - 1}$
25. $x^3 - x^2 + x - 1$ **27.** $x^2 + x + 1$ **29.** Same
31. b